LIBRARY (partly torn): R?RY
ULTURAL (LEGE
D0119537
WITHDRAWN

Dara Kulka
VIII. 51

BACTERIAL CHEMISTRY and PHYSIOLOGY

Bacterial Chemistry and Physiology

BY

JOHN ROGER PORTER

Professor of Bacteriology,
College of Medicine, State University of Iowa

New York: JOHN WILEY & SONS, Inc.
London: CHAPMAN & HALL, Limited

C

Copyright, 1946
BY
John Wiley & Sons, Inc.

All Rights Reserved

This book or any part thereof must not be reproduced in any form without the written permission of the publisher.

Fifth Printing, November, 1950

PRINTED IN THE UNITED STATES OF AMERICA

PREFACE

This book is the outgrowth of lecture material which has been used for the past few years in a bacterial physiology course at the State University of Iowa. Since developments in this branch of science have recently been extremely rapid, it has become almost impossible to condense lectures and discussions to fit into one semester or even two semesters of classes. In the past some degree of success in meeting this problem has been achieved by supplying students with mimeographed tables, charts, and pertinent references for further reading. It has been thought, however, that if a book were available which outlined some of the past developments and other information concerning this science, more attention could be given in the classroom to general discussion of the more recent advances in the field. This material is thus compiled as a guide for a course which is being transformed from the lecture to the seminar type.

The students who are admitted to bacterial physiology at Iowa, as in most other universities, have diversified interests, but they all have had courses in biology and chemistry. For the most part they are advanced students majoring in chemistry, pharmacy, and the biological sciences. Although the subject matter in this book has been chosen and arranged primarily to fit the requirements and interests of these students, some thought has also been given to the needs of persons doing research in microbial chemistry.

An attempt has been made to restrict the discussion to the field of bacteriology, but mention is made from time to time of organisms which belong in other branches of science. Such references have been made in order to stress the fact that the physiological behavior of living matter is much the same in both the plant and the animal kingdoms. For example, we now know that the ability of plants and some bacteria to synthesize organic compounds from carbon dioxide is also a property of certain more fastidious forms of life. Likewise, some of the yeast enzymes responsible for alcoholic fermentation and those concerned with muscle glycolysis have much in common. Furthermore, the external supply of vitamins required by man is needed also by many insects, protozoa, and lower fungi. Since many other examples such as these can be cited, biologists are now beginning to appreciate the fact that certain vital processes can be studied more easily by using microorganisms, and that the information obtained often has direct application to the more complex conditions in higher forms of life.

In citing references to the literature, I have endeavored to give the students a bibliography upon which they can build and also a means of following up for themselves any point in which they are interested. Much of the work from the early period of bacteriology has been omitted, because it has been adequately covered in Buchanan and Fulmer's three volumes, *Physiology and Biochemistry of Bacteria* (1928–1930), in Rahn's *Physiology of Bacteria* (1932), in Stephenson's *Bacterial Metabolism* (1939), and in other books and reviews. Among the great mass of recent publications many important reports have undoubtedly been omitted or overlooked, and others have been included which future events will show to be of no significance. In the absence of historical perspective, however, such errors in judgment are unavoidable.

Details of laboratory techniques are not included in the discussion of this book. For such information the student is referred to the original articles, and to such monographs as *Manometric Techniques and Related Methods for the Study of Tissue Metabolism* (1945) by W. W. Umbreit, R. H. Burris, and J. F. Stauffer, and *Laboratory Manual of Physiological Bacteriology* (1945) by F. W. Fabian.

In so far as possible, the nomenclature used for the bacteria mentioned in this book is that proposed in the Fifth Edition of *Bergey's Manual of Determinative Bacteriology* (1939). The names of genera and species of yeasts, molds, and other fungi are those that were used in the original articles.

The information on the pages that follow is the result of years of research by a large number of investigators, and much of it is widely scattered in the literature. My chief role has been that of a compiler and an editor.

An attempt has been made in the text to give credit for all illustrations and other materials used, and failure to acknowledge indebtedness to any writer or publisher is unintentional. I wish to thank specifically the following publishers, publications, and manufacturers for the use of copyrighted material: Academic Press, Inc., *American Journal of Hygiene*, *American Review of Tuberculosis*, American Sterilizer Co., *Biochemical Journal*, Biotech Publications, Cambridge University Press, Cornell University Press, Eastman Kodak Co., *Handbuch der Virusforschung*, His Majesty's Stationery Office, *Industrial and Engineering Chemistry*, Iowa Engineering Experiment Station, *Iowa State College Journal of Science*, *Journal of Bacteriology*, *Journal of Biological*

Chemistry, Journal of Cellular and Comparative Physiology, Journal of Experimental Medicine, Journal of General Physiology, Journal of Hygiene, Journal of Infectious Diseases, Journal of Laboratory and Clinical Medicine, Julius Springer, The Lancet, Ltd., London County Council, *Manual of Methods for Pure Culture Study of Bacteria,* McGraw-Hill Book Co., *Proceedings of the Royal Society of London,* W. B. Saunders Co., D. Van Nostrand Co., Inc., Westinghouse Electric and Mfg. Co., John Wiley & Sons, Inc., and Williams & Wilkins Co.

For help in the preparation of the manuscript I wish to express my indebtedness to my associates. Thanks are due to Dr. William M. Hale for his encouragement and for permitting me to take time from departmental duties to finish this book. I also wish to express my appreciation to Miss Marion Jones for helping with the reading and checking of the manuscript and proof. Dr. Albert P. McKee, Mrs. John Brooks, and Mrs. W. A. Stephenson are among the others in the department who helped to make the book possible. Finally, I am most sincerely grateful to those who reviewed the manuscript and offered constructive suggestions for its improvement.

J. R. P.

Medical Laboratories
Iowa City, Iowa
December, 1945

CONTENTS

1

SOME PHYSICO-CHEMICAL PROPERTIES OF BACTERIA AND THEIR ENVIRONMENT

THE COLLOIDAL STATE OF MATTER

In a study of bacterial chemistry and physiology it seems pertinent to consider first of all the colloidal state of matter, since basically many of the reactions of bacterial systems are dependent upon the colloidal phenomena that operate within these systems. We shall not attempt to present in this brief treatise an inclusive or mathematical description of colloids. For such information the books by Buchanan and Fulmer (1928), Kruyt (1930), Alexander (1926–1944), Gortner (1937), Weiser (1939), Bull (1943), and other books dealing with colloid chemistry should be consulted.

In 1861 Thomas Graham classified all substances into two groups, *crystalloids* and *colloids* (from the Greek *kolla*, gelatin or glue; *eidos*, like or semblance), depending upon their rate and ability to diffuse through water and parchment membranes. According to Graham, crystalloids passed readily through parchment membranes, whereas colloids did not. We now realize that this distinction between crystalloids and colloids is not tenable because many typical colloids, such as certain proteins, are crystallizable, and under proper conditions practically all crystalloids may be brought into the colloidal state. Thus, according to more modern conceptions, the term colloid is used to define substances with a characteristic kind of physical structure rather than to classify a particular type of matter.

Matter is said to be in the *colloidal state* when it is dispersed permanently and so finely that the individual particles, though larger than molecules, cannot be seen with the ordinary microscope. The medium in which the particles of a colloidal system are scattered is termed the *dispersion medium*, or *continuous phase;* and the scattered particles are called the *dispersed* or *discontinuous phase.* In studying colloidal systems, therefore, it should be emphasized that a heterogeneous system composed of at least two components (dispersed phase and dispersion medium) is under consideration.

Particle size is one characteristic of the colloidal state, and colloidal state may be defined (somewhat arbitrarily) in terms of particle size. The maximum size of colloidal particles is conveniently placed just below the lower limit of ordinary microscopic visibility, using the oil immersion objective. The minimum size of the particles is arbitrarily set above that of the average molecule. This means that the largest colloidal particles are below about 0.1 μ or 0.0001 mm. in diameter and thus invisible with the ordinary microscope, but are above 1.0 mμ or 0.000001 mm. The following diagram shows the relationship which exists between coarse suspensions, colloids, and molecular solutions:

	Suspensions	*Colloids*	*True Solutions*
	Molecular aggregates (matter in mass)	Molecular aggregates	Molecules and ions
Size or diameter:	>0.1 μ	0.1 μ — 1.0 mμ	<1.0 mμ

It is generally believed that there is a continuous gradation of properties from coarse suspensions through the colloidal state to true solutions. There are, however, certain characteristic properties of matter in the colloidal state which are not exhibited by true solutions and which are shown in a negligible degree by gross suspensions. Certain of these properties will be briefly discussed later in this chapter.

Although all our known bacteria are larger than the upper limits of the colloidal system, many of the smaller organisms studied by the bacteriologist fall in this region and exhibit several properties of true colloids. It should be emphasized, however, that the properties of colloidal systems do not coincide strictly with the arbitrary boundaries described above. For this reason bacterial cells in various media behave in many respects like colloidal systems [Kendall (1925), Silbereisen (1939), McCalla (1940)].

Bacterial protoplasm, like that of all other living cells, is an intimate association of salts, carbohydrates, fats, and proteins. It is generally believed that the salts and carbohydrates of living protoplasm are, in part, in true solution and, in part, absorbed or otherwise bound to organic matter. The proteins exist as jellies, and the fats as emulsions. Water is the dispersion medium of all. Other substances, such as organic acids, not included in the above groups, can probably be regarded as minor constituents in most cases.

Although the living system includes all the component parts just enumerated, certain of these may be looked upon as representing the ultimate living substance itself with the other constituents functioning as nutrient material. But the importance of regarding protoplasm as a highly organized and coordinated heterogeneous system, all parts of which are necessary to life, cannot be overemphasized. One of the most remarkable powers of protoplasm, which is due to its organization, is its ability to carry on simultaneously in the same cell a number of chemical reactions without one interfering with the other and without any evident boundaries of separation. Only a highly complex "organized" colloidal system with continuity of structure could be the site of such intricate and closely confined chemical reactions [Seifriz (1928)].

CLASSIFICATION OF COLLOIDAL SYSTEMS (LYOPHOBIC AND LYOPHILIC)

The broadest classification of colloidal systems is that devised in 1907 by Ostwald, who separated them on the basis of the physical state (gaseous, liquid, or solid) of the subdivided substance (dispersed phase) and the medium in which the particles of the subdivided substance were distributed. Thus the following nine systems are possible:

Dispersed Phase	*Dispersion Medium*	*Example*
1. Gas	Gas	Hypothetical case, since gases occur in a molecular state
2. Gas	Liquid	Foam, air in beaten egg white
3. Gas	Solid	Gaseous inclusions in minerals (meerschaum)
4. Liquid	Gas	Clouds, fog
5. Liquid	Liquid	Oil in water, cream
6. Liquid	Solid	Opal, pearl, water in paraffin wax
7. Solid	Gas	Smoke
8. Solid	Liquid	Colloidal gold
9. Solid	Solid	Ruby glass, black diamond

From a biological standpoint this classification is of little true value because it is too general and does not include the gels.

Another classification of certain colloidal systems is based on the attraction or affinity of the dispersed phase and the dispersion medium for each other. If the mutual affinity is small, the system is said to be *lyophobic;* whereas, if the mutual affinity is great, the system is called *lyophilic.* If water is the dispersion medium, the system is usually termed *hydrophobic* or *hydrophilic,* as the case may be; if benzene is the dispersion medium, *benzophobic* or *benzophilic;* etc. Gold neither dissolves nor swells in water, hence gold dispersed in water is a hydrophobic system. Gelatin and agar, on the other hand, take up water and swell to a marked degree; thus such colloidal systems are hydrophilic. A given dispersed phase may be lyophobic in one medium and lyophilic in another. For example, starch forms a lyophobic system in alcohol and a lyophilic one in water.

In many of their physical properties, such as viscosity, lyophobic colloids differ only slightly from the pure dispersion medium. The particles carry a definite electric charge which can be changed only by special methods. Such colloids are flocculated by very small quantities of electrolytes and, when so precipitated, cannot ordinarily be brought back into the colloid state. The precipitation is therefore *irreversible*. Since the proteins and the higher carbohydrates form lyophilic systems, such systems are of much greater biological importance and interest than the lyophobic colloids. The viscosity of lyophilic systems is usually much higher than that of the pure dispersion medium. The particles carry an electric charge which may be changed by such simple measures as altering the pH of the solution. They require large amounts of electrolytes for their precipitation and, when precipitated, usually may be brought back into the colloidal state by the addition of fresh solvent. The precipitation is therefore *reversible*.

Colloidal systems possessing a high degree of fluidity are defined as *sols*. Lyophilic sols, under changing conditions of temperature and concentrations of disperse phase, of pH and of electrolytes, possess the property of imbibing large quantities of water and forming semi-rigid *gels*. These gels probably have a rather definite structure consisting in some cases of a network of disperse phase, or hydrated material, enclosing some of the dispersion medium. These properties of *imbibition* and *gel* formation exhibited by lyophilic colloids are probably responsible for the characteristic physical structure of protoplasm.

It can thus be seen that lyophilic and lyophobic colloids exhibit essential differences in their behavior toward the solvent and in their sensitivity to electrolytes. According to Kruyt (1930), the stability of lyophobic colloids depends entirely upon the charges on particles, which permit them to repel each other and thus prevent aggregation into coarser particles. If the charges on the particles are neutralized, or reduced below a certain critical value by an electrolyte, the particles coalesce and precipitate. Lyophilic colloids, on the other hand, possess two stability factors, charge and hydration, either of which is capable of preventing the aggregation and flocculation of colloidal particles. Neutralization of the charges on the particles of a lyophilic colloidal solution converts it into a neutral, or *isoelectric*, colloid which is stable as long as the particles remain hydrated. Dehydration of a charged, electrolyte-free lyophilic colloid by the addition of a dehydrating agent, such as alcohol, converts it into a lyophobic colloid exhibiting the characteristic sensitivity to electrolytes. The precipitating action of large amounts of salts on lyophilic colloids is due to the fact that saturated solutions of the common salts act as dehydrating agents, thereby discharging and dehydrating the system at the same time. For further discussion of this subject see the section on the effect of electrolytes on colloids, pp. 19 to 22.

An additional system which should be considered in a study of colloidal systems is the *emulsions*. Emulsions are not necessarily true colloidal systems, if we limit our definition to the size of the particle concerned. Emulsions are drops of one liquid dispersed in the bulk of a second liquid. They usually consist of systems of oil dispersed in water or of systems of water dispersed in oil. Frequently the dispersion medium contains a lyophilic colloid which assists in stabilizing the emulsion. Very dilute emulsions could be classified as liquid-liquid colloidal systems, providing all the particles fell within the range of size characteristic of such systems. Most emulsions, however, contain oil or water droplets much larger than the upper limit of the truly colloidal field. Latex, milk, and mayonnaise are typical examples of emulsions. In each of these examples we are dealing not only with oil droplets suspended in an aqueous medium, but we have present at the same time lyophilic colloids in the form of proteins which stabilize the system. Therefore, a study of emulsions involves an investigation of not only the dispersion medium and the disperse phrase but also the nature and properties of the lyophilic colloid which acts as the stabilizer.

When viewed through the microscope, protoplasm (of cells larger than most bacteria) presents the appearance of an emulsion. Certainly there are droplets of fats and oils in all living protoplasm which are stabilized by the lyophilic colloids which are present. It is also true that there are solid particles in all protoplasm, so that protoplasm can be looked upon, in part, as a complex colloidal system, the dispersion medium being water and the disperse phase consisting of lyophilic (hydrophilic) colloids, lyophobic (hydrophobic) colloids, and fat droplets in the form of an emulsion.

CERTAIN CHARACTERISTICS OF COLLOIDAL SYSTEMS AND THEIR RELATIONSHIP TO BACTERIOLOGY

At this point it may be well to consider briefly several of the general properties of colloidal solutions and to point out their application to bacteriology.

1. Brownian Movement. In 1828 the English botanist, Robert Brown, announced that he had observed microscopically a continuous trembling motion when pollen grains were suspended in a liquid.

We now know that what Brown saw was the process which bears his name, the Brownian movement of particles, caused by the bombardment of the particles of the disperse phase by the molecules of the dispersion medium.

Particles exhibit Brownian movement only when below a definite size and in a medium of sufficiently low viscosity. Particles larger than about 4.0 μ exhibit no motion in water, and the viscosity of the surrounding medium determines the amplitude of motion for a particle of given size. For example, glycerin is about 800 times as viscous as water and, therefore, particles suspended in it do not move as freely as those suspended in water. In fact, particles larger than 1.0 μ to 2.0 μ do not exhibit Brownian movement in glycerin. In truly colloidal systems, where the dispersed phase cannot be seen with the ordinary microscope, dark-field illumination or the ultramicroscope must be used to demonstrate Brownian movement.

If the cells of many nonmotile bacteria are suspended in various media, they show Brownian movement when examined under the microscope, and particles in the protoplasm of the larger microorganisms are often in an active state of motion. However, Brownian movement may be inhibited or abolished in bacteria, as in certain typical colloids, by the addition of electrolytes.

For details of the historical phases and the theoretical significance of studies dealing with Brownian movement, the books of Kruyt (1930), Gortner (1937), and other authors on colloid chemistry should be consulted.

2. Sedimentation and Particle Weights. A particle suspended in a liquid medium tends to settle out under the influence of gravitational force. With particles in the colloidal realm the rate of sedimentation under gravity is negligibly slow because back diffusion acts in opposition to the gravitational force. However, if the force of gravity is increased by means of a centrifuge, the rate of settling is greatly increased. Ordinary laboratory centrifuges, which run up to 3,000 to 5,000 r.p.m., are usually sufficient to settle most bacteria. So-called supercentrifuges, which run at 40,000 r.p.m. and generate a force in excess of 42,000 times that of gravity, have been constructed. Such an instrument is useful for washing precipitates that settle very slowly, for sedimentation of certain particles, and for the preparation of certain sols; but it cannot be employed in the estimation of the size of colloidally dispersed particles because vibration in the apparatus sets up convection currents which modify the effect of the centrifugal force. To overcome this difficulty, Svedberg and coworkers [see Svedberg and Pedersen (1940)] have devised an apparatus called an ultracentrifuge, which may be defined as "a centrifuge of low or high power in which convection does not occur and in which it is possible to measure any redistribution of the contents." In Svedberg's apparatus this redistribution is followed either by determination of the light absorption or the refractive index, and fields of 400,000 times that of gravity have been obtained.

Svedberg's ultracentrifuge has been used extensively to determine the "particle" or molecular weights of proteins, celluloses, other biochemical compounds, dyes, soaps, etc. For the technical details of the method the book by Svedberg and Pedersen (1940) should be consulted. In Table 1 are given the particle or molecular weights of a number of substances as obtained or quoted by Svedberg and associates from data on sedimentary velocity and diffusion.

TABLE 1

MOLECULAR OR PARTICLE WEIGHTS (*M*) OF VARIOUS SUBSTANCES

[From Svedberg and Pedersen (1940) and Others]

Substance	*M* *	Substance	*M* *
Tuberculin polysaccharide	9,000	Diphtheria antitoxin [2]	113,000
Scarlet fever toxin [1]	4,000–13,000	Serum globulin (man)	176,000
Cytochrome c	15,600	Antipneumococcus serum globulin: rabbit	158,000
Mycobacterium phlei protein	17,000	Antipneumococcus serum globulin: man	195,000
Lactalbumin	17,400	Antipneumococcus serum globulin: horse	910,000
Gliadin	27,500	Antipneumococcus serum globulin: cow	910,000
Mycobacterium tuberculosis (human) protein	32,000	Antipneumococcus serum globulin: pig	930,000
Pepsin	35,500	Thymonucleic acid	200,000
Pectins: Apple, pear, plum	25,000–35,000	Catalase	250,000
Pectins: Orange	40,000–50,000	Edestin	310,000
Zein	40,000	Rubber sols	400,000–435,000
Insulin	41,000	Urease	480,000
Cellulose acetate in acetone	50,000–250,000	Hemocyanin from different sources	400,000–6,700,000
Hemoglobin (man)	63,000	Bushy stunt virus	7,600,000
Diphtheria toxin [2]	74,000	Bacterial glycogen from the avian tubercle bacillus [3]	12,100,000–13,200,000
Yellow enzyme	82,000	Tobacco mosaic virus protein	17,000,000–42,500,000

* Some of these values are only apparent molecular or particle weights.

[1] Barron, Dick, and Lyman (1941).

[2] Petermann and Pappenheimer (1941).

[3] Chargaff and Moore (1944).

The initial cost of the Svedberg ultracentrifuge is so great that its use is greatly restricted. In recent years, however, relatively inexpensive qualitative ultracentrifuges have been constructed by Beams and others [see review by Beams (1938)] based on the principle of a rotor driven by compressed air and spinning on a thin cushion of air—the spinning top of Henriot and Huguenard (1925). Beams has also developed "suspended rotor" types of ultracentrifuges driven by air, steam, or electricity, which have been adapted and improved by various workers to suit their special problems. With such instruments centrifugal forces up to 4,000,000 times that of gravity have been obtained, the maximum value being limited only by the tensile strength of the material from which the rotor is made.

By means of the ultracentrifuge the size and distribution of particles in sols may be determined. Considerable use is also being made of the ultracentrifuge to purify and study viruses, enzymes, and certain components of the bacterial cell.

3. Diffusion, Osmotic Pressure, and Imbibition. The kinetic energy of molecules causes them to diffuse in all directions. Thus, when a gas is set free in a chamber, it will in time be distributed equally throughout; and, when a crystal of ordinary salt is placed in a glass of water, it soon becomes uniformly dissolved in the water. Such movement of gases and dissolved substances from a region of high concentration to one of low concentration is called *diffusion*. When diffusion takes place through a membrane or through a gel, the process is called *dialysis*. Dialysis is frequently used to purify colloidal sols, the membrane restraining the movement of the colloidal particles while permitting crystalloids and ions to pass through into the external solvent phase. By the introduction of electrodes into the dialysate and the external water, and the passage of a suitable electric current, the removal of diffusible matter may be hastened. This process is known as *electrodialysis* or *electro-osmosis*.

It has already been mentioned that Graham in 1861 used the phenomenon of diffusion as a basis for differentiating between crystalloids and colloids. Crystalloids readily diffused through parchment membranes, whereas colloids did not. It should be emphasized again, however, that this distinction is not sharp. It is only a question of degree, since ions migrate at different speeds, and even some typical colloids, such as egg albumin, diffuse very slowly through certain membranes. However, membranes can be prepared which are sufficiently dense to retain the egg albumin molecules.

The diffusion constant (D, the specific diffusion rate) of an ion or molecule may be defined as the amount of solute which will diffuse unit distance across unit area under a concentration gradient of unity in unit time. The following diffusion constants of several crystalloidal and colloidal substances are old values but are widely quoted in the literature:

DIFFUSION CONSTANTS

(D = cm.^{2}/sec. $\times 10^5$)

Substance	D	Substance	D
Hydrogen ion	32.5	Rennin	0.066
Sodium ion	4.51	Egg albumin	0.059
Urea	1.01	Emulsin	0.036
Glucose	0.57	Diphtheria toxin	0.014–0.06
Cane sugar (sucrose)	0.31	Diphtheria antitoxin	0.0015–0.05
Svedberg's nuclear gold sol	0.27	Tetanolysin	0.037
Pepsin	0.07	Antitetanolysin	0.0021

From the foregoing data it will be seen that the diffusion constant of Svedberg's nuclear gold sol, which has a particle size just within the lower limits of the colloidal realm, is only slightly less than that of sucrose, which is ordinarily regarded as a true crystalloid. Accordingly, we should expect some of the gold sol to pass through a membrane, and this is what actually happens. On the other hand, the extremely low value for the antitetanolysin would indicate that practically none of this substance will diffuse, and this is actually the case.

Osmotic pressure is defined several different ways in the literature [Eyster (1943)]. In general, it may be defined as the diffusion pressure of a solvent diffusing through a semipermeable membrane. Solutions of equal osmotic pressure are said to be *isotonic;* those having a greater osmotic pressure than the standard are said to be *hypertonic;* and those with less osmotic pressure are called *hypotonic* solutions.

When a sugar solution is enclosed in a parchment bag and immersed in water, a hydrostatic pressure is set up in the bag because of the entrance of water. The incoming water is in excess of the outgoing water because of the inability of the sugar to diffuse out and set up an equilibrium. The greater the number of sugar molecules, the greater will be the difference between the incoming and the outgoing water, and therefore the greater will be the hydrostatic pressure developed within the bag. The amount of this hydrostatic unbalance is termed the osmotic pressure. It may be measured simply by observing the rise of sugar solution (because of increase in its volume by the incoming water) in a tube or manometer into which the solution is allowed to expand directly. Protein molecules and colloidal particles in general are large and occupy considerable space compared to crystalloids. Consequently, in equimolecular concentrations of crystalloids and colloids, there will be fewer colloids per unit volume in the parchment bag.

This also means that the difference between incoming and outgoing water, and therefore the hydrostatic pressure, will be less.

Colloidal solutions possess a definite, though slightly osmotic, pressure. For example, Gortner (1937) recorded an observation made by Sørensen on the osmotic pressure of an aqueous egg albumin solution (22.66 g. per 100 ml.), using a water manometer. A rise of water pressure as high as 86 cm. was observed. A 4.0 per cent solution of cane sugar at 15°C., on the other hand, has an osmotic pressure of approximately 208.2 cm. For most lyophilic systems much smaller values are encountered than the one given above for egg albumin. As a matter of fact, in most instances the osmotic pressure is only 1.0 to 2.0 cm. For many lyophobic systems the pressure is too low to be measured. Therefore, the amount of osmotic pressure exerted by colloidal solutions is usually so slight that it is customary to disregard it as a fundamental characteristic of the colloidal state. This does not mean, though, that osmotic phenomena are not important in biological systems because, for example, the process responsible for the turgor of bacteria and other cells is osmosis.

Very few quantitative data have been recorded on osmotic phenomena in bacteria. In general, a bacterial cell may be regarded as a colloidal protoplasmic mass contained in a semipermeable envelope, the ectoplasm (cytoplasmic membrane), and surrounded by a cell wall [see Lewis (1941)]. Although some organisms may contain cellulose or hemicellulose, or chitin or pectin-like substances, the ectoplasm is probably not made up of these substances. Because of the minute size of bacteria, differential analyses of cell walls and contents are not simple. In some organisms, such as *Bacterium cyanogenes*, it has been reported that the cell wall is sharply distinguished from the cytoplasm, whereas in others, such as spirilla, the cell wall is so slightly differentiated that it is difficult to tell whether one actually exists. Future studies using the electron microscope will help a great deal to settle such points. In this respect the study by Mudd, Polevitzky, Anderson, and Chambers (1941) on the bacterial cell wall in the genus *Bacillus* is very interesting.

The permeability of the cell wall and the semipermeable cytoplasmic membrane of the cell probably varies according to the species of organism, the age of the cell, the composition of the cell, the nature and amount of surface tension reducing substances in the medium, the temperature, the *p*H, and many other factors. The characteristics of these outer cell membranes influence morphology, growth, composition, and distribution of cell substances, osmotic phenomena, and important electrical properties of the cells. At this point it should be emphasized that the cell wall may not always act as the only part of the cell which determines what substances may enter and what materials may leave the cell. Some differential action is usually attributed also to the ectoplasmic layer (cytoplasmic membrane) just inside the cell wall. That such ectoplasmic layers actually exist has been shown by Knaysi (1941) and others. That such structures behave as semipermeable membranes is deduced from the fact that there is normally an osmotic or turgor pressure of the cell contents when bacteria are immersed in water. According to Rideal (1930), the turgor pressure of cells is very low, being about 1.0 to 10 atmospheres. Insertion of many bacteria in hypertonic solutions effects plasmolysis. If the hypertonicity of the solution is not too great, the cells gradually adjust themselves to the new conditions, regain turgor, and continue to grow. If the hypertonicity is great, the cells remain permanently plasmolyzed and are finally killed. The phenomenon of swelling, or plasmoptysis, has been reported for bacteria, but it is not so easy to demonstrate as plasmolysis. Cases of negative osmosis in cylindrical but not spherical bacteria have also been recorded. In 1895 Fischer noted that cholera vibrios, immersed in a 2.0 per cent solution of salt after treatment with 0.75 per cent NaCl, underwent swelling instead of the anticipated shrinking. Some organisms, such as those in sea water and brines or on salted hides, can withstand considerable changes in environment (up to 28 per cent NaCl) without serious harm [see Stuart *et al.* (1933, 1934)], whereas others are peculiarly sensitive to osmotic changes. In some species there appears to exist an optimum tonicity for growth.

Imbibition is used to designate the taking in of water by protoplasm and other gels. There has been considerable controversy in the past among biologists as to whether this process is different from osmosis. We shall not attempt to discuss the controversy, since sufficient evidence has accumulated to show that imbibition is quite independent of osmotic pressure, as far as the respective physiological roles of the two are concerned. Since this point will be discussed more fully in the section on hydrophilic sols and gels, pp. 22 to 30 of this chapter, only one example will be given here to demonstrate that imbibition is a characteristic of certain types of colloidal matter (protoplasm). Gortner (1937) quotes an example in which dry seeds will, by imbibition, withdraw water from a saturated lithium chloride solution (osmotic pressure = 1,000 atmospheres), although their salt content is sufficient to account for only a few atmospheres of osmotic pressure. It is probably by this phenomenon that bacterial spores take up water and germinate and that certain bacteria are able to take up water and live in concentrated brine solutions.

4. Ultrafiltration. For the most part colloidal sols pass unchanged through filter paper (pores approximately 2 to 5 μ in diameter) or through the common porcelain filters (pores approximately 0.2 to 0.6 μ) used in the bacteriological laboratory. Ultrafilters have been devised, however, with pores sufficiently small to retain the dispersed phase of a colloidal system but large enough to allow the dispersion medium and its crystalloidal solutes to pass through. This process of separation is known as *ultrafiltration*. Ultrafilters are invariably colloidal gels, so that ultrafiltration may be defined as filtration of a sol through a gel. Such filters have been largely used to determine particle size in colloidal systems. For further discussion on this subject see the section on filtration, pp. 208 to 216 of Chapter 3.

5. Viscosity, Plasticity, and Elasticity. Viscosity and plasticity measurements are extremely useful in the study of colloids. In fact Gortner (1937) states that "viscometric technique is of importance second to none in the study of lyophilic colloid systems." *Viscosity* is that property of liquids which causes them to resist flow. It is practically synonymous with consistency. The standard or unit of viscosity is the *poise* (named after Poiseuille, the French physicist), which is represented by the Greek letter eta (η). It is the tangential force required to maintain a velocity of 1.0 cm. per second between two parallel planes each 1.0 sq. cm. in area and 1.0 cm. apart. The *centipoise* is 0.01 of a poise. *Fluidity* measures the tendency to flow and is therefore the reciprocal of the viscosity. *Plasticity* is somewhat different from viscosity and requires a little more explanation. Fluids flow under the smallest conceivable shearing stress, for example, by virtue of their own weight. On the other hand, there are many substances to which external pressure must be applied before flow begins. Such substances are said to be *plastic*, and their flow is designated as *plastic flow*. The force, f, required to start *plastic flow* (as distinguished from viscous flow) is termed the *yield value* (see Fig. 1). The yield value represents the force required to convert a static system into a moving or dynamic system. Plasticity, therefore, differs from viscosity in that, when plastic materials are dealt with, a determination must be made of the yield value as well as the rate of flow per unit of force applied.

Viscosity values may be expressed as *relative* to a standard or as *absolute*. In the first case, water is the customary standard and has an absolute viscosity of 1.005 centipoises (0.01 poise) at 20°C. In the second, the value is expressed in dyne seconds per square centimeter, or poises, and is known as the coefficient of viscosity. For example, at 20°C. water has an absolute viscosity of 0.01 poise, olive oil 0.84 poise, and glycerin 8.30 poises. The relative viscosity value (water as standard) for glycerin is therefore 830, which means that glycerin is 830 times as viscous as water at 20°C.

Various types of instruments, called viscosimeters, are available for measuring the viscosity of fluids. The most commonly used type is the Ostwald viscosimeter, with which the time of flow through a capillary orifice under a fixed head or pressure is determined. Other instruments, such as the MacMichael and the falling-ball viscosimeters, are frequently used in industry [see Gortner (1937)].

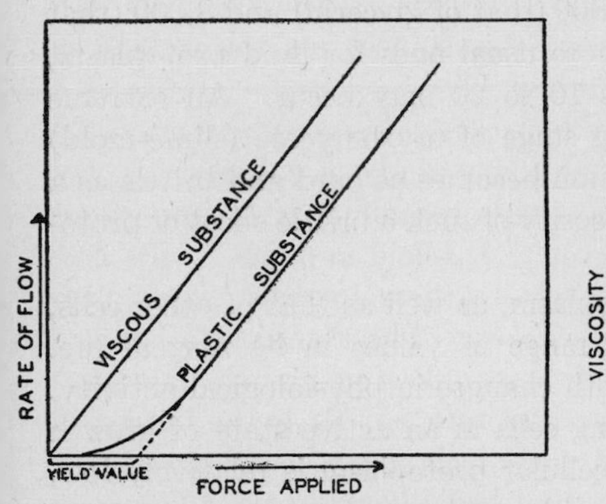

FIG. 1. Diagrammatic Representation of the Relationship between Viscosity and Plasticity.

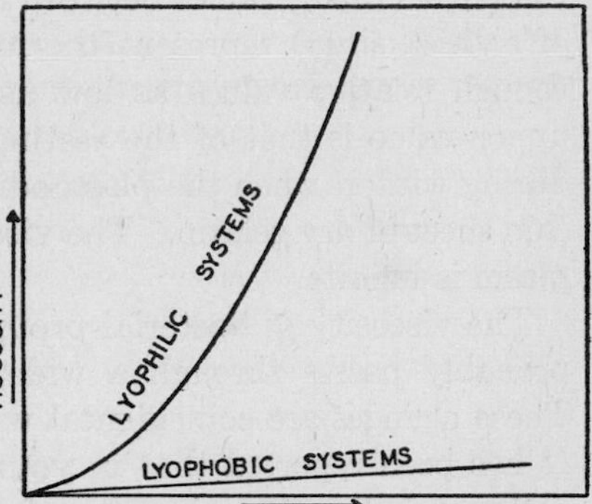

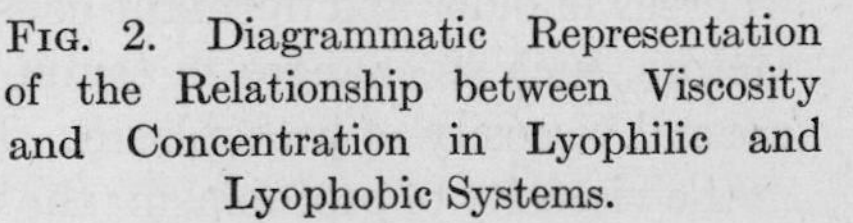

FIG. 2. Diagrammatic Representation of the Relationship between Viscosity and Concentration in Lyophilic and Lyophobic Systems.

Colloidal systems show a wide range in viscosity or plasticity. Usually the lyophobic sols exhibit a viscosity only slightly higher than that of the pure dispersion medium, and this viscosity increases very slightly when the concentration of the dispersed material is increased (Fig. 2). On the other hand, lyophilic systems (sols and gels) may reach very high values for viscosity, and since some are truly plastic they may have relatively high yield values. With lyophilic colloids we do not have a linear relationship between viscosity and the concentration of dispersed phase, but rather a parabola (Fig. 2). This is thought to be due, in part at least, to the fact that lyophilic systems are solvated, and accordingly the dispersed phase has associated with it a large or small amount of the dispersion medium. Thus the actual amount of the dispersion medium is decreased with each added increment of the dispersed phase. This intimate relationship between the solvent and the solute has led Ostwald, Gortner, and others to believe that there are at least eleven factors which must be considered and controlled when viscosity studies are being made on lyophilic systems. These factors are: (1) degree of dispersion, (2) solvation, (3) electrical charge, (4) previous thermal treatment, (5) previous mechanical treatment, (6) presence or absence of other lyophilic colloids, (7) presence or absence of electrolytes, including changes in hydrogen-ion concentration, (8) age of the sol, (9) rate of shear, (10) temperature, and (11) concentration.

Protoplasm in general shows a wide range in viscosity values. It may have a relative viscosity from above a minimum of 10 to 20 times that of water to the practically infinite value of a firm jelly. According to Seifriz (1936), values between 800 (that of glycerin) and 8,000 (that of a thick sirup) represent the more usual ones for fluid protoplasm, though relative values as low as 10 to 20 may occur. An extreme upper value is that of the resting stage of myxomycete (slime-mold) during winter, when the plasmodium becomes as hard and brittle as a thin sheet of dry gelatin. The viscosity of such a brittle sheet of protoplasm is infinite.

The viscosity of bacterial protoplasm, as well as that of other cells, probably passes through a wide range of values in its normal life. These changes are coincidental with changes in physiological activity. It has been reported that in young cells in an active state of growth and metabolism the viscosity of cellular protoplasm is relatively low, whereas in older and dormant cells it becomes greater. Environmental factors, such as changes in temperature, salts, and *p*H, may alter the normal viscosity of protoplasm. Death brings about a marked change in the viscosity of protoplasm; the usual change is coagulation, although this is often replaced or followed by complete disintegration.

Falk and Harrison [see Falk (1928)] have reported on the influence of *p*H upon the viscosity of washed and unwashed suspensions of *Escherichia coli*. In Fig. 3 the effects of *p*H on the viscosity of suspensions containing 8.3, 10, 17, and 50 billions of bacteria per millimeter are presented. It appears from the curves in Fig. 3 that viscosity increases slightly with increasing concentrations of bacteria and that the effect of *p*H is significant only in zones near *p*H 3.8 and 13.0. It is interesting to note that in these zones of *p*H the suspensions show agglutination. For further interesting data on this study the original article by Falk (1928) should be consulted.

Variations in the viscosity of gelatin media have been used by Levine and Shaw (1924), Werkman and Stahly (1933), and others to follow the proteolytic changes brought about by bacterial action. Such a method seems to be much more quantitative than one in which proteolysis is determined merely by gelatin liquefaction in a "gelatin stab" tube.

Elasticity, in general, implies "springiness" or resilience. It may be defined as that property of a substance which causes it to resist deformation and thereby to recover its original shape and size once it has been deformed. Although elasticity is not a property of all colloidal systems, it is a characteristic of many lyophilic systems, especially certain gels.

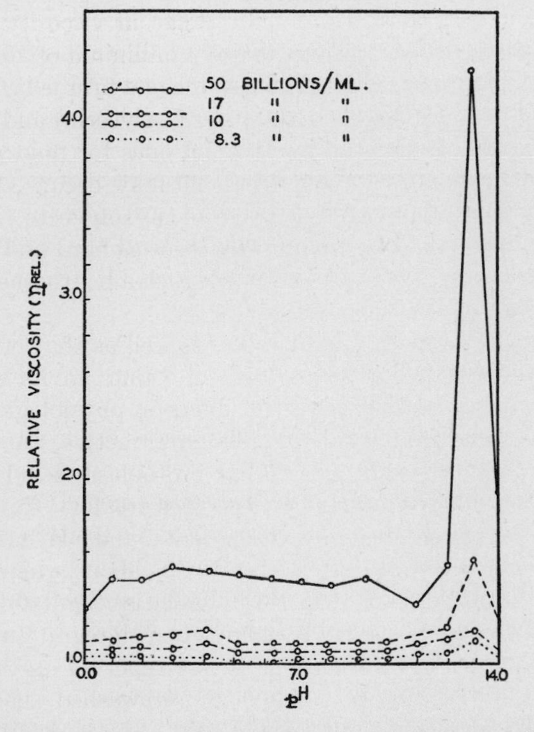

FIG. 3. The Influence of the Hydrogen-Ion Concentration on the Viscosity of Bacterial Suspensions (*Escherichia coli*) of Several Concentrations. (Redrawn from Falk's chapter in *Colloid Chemistry*, edited by J. Alexander, Chemical Catalog Company, New York, 1928.)

Our chief interest in elasticity is that protoplasm is elastic. It is the best indication that we have of the structure of living matter. Although the elastic qualities of higher plant and animal protoplasm have been studied by several workers, very few investigations have been made using bacteria. Wámoscher (1930), by microdissection of bacteria under direct microscopic observation, noted that the cell membrane has enormous elasticity against pulling, stretching, and torsion. This important study should be consulted for details of the technique employed and for many interesting data and photomicrographs. The elasticity of the protoplasmic strands of the myxomycetes has been studied in detail by several workers. For example, Norris (1940) observed that the modulus of elasticity for strands of *Physarum polycephalum* was about 9×10^4 dynes per square centimeter at room temperature (23° to 24°C.) for increases in length up to 40 per cent; the value of the modulus was lower at 30°C. and higher at 10°C. Most of the material responsible for the elasticity did not appear to be concentrated at the surface, because saponin had no effect on the elastic properties. Chloretone (2 : 1,000 aqueous) anesthesia had no effect on the elasticity of *Physarum* strands, although protoplasmic streaming was reversibly stopped.

6. Optical Properties. The optical properties of colloidal systems help to distinguish them from true solutions, although it is not an easy task to make solutions that do not exhibit the Tyndall phenomenon in any degree. So-called optically void distilled water even requires a special preparation.

If a concentrated beam of light is passed through a colloidal solution in which the dispersed phase has a different refractive index from that of the dispersion medium, its path or "cone" through the solution is plainly visible as a milky turbidity when viewed at right angles. This phenomenon, known as the *Tyndall effect*, is due to the reflection and scattering of the light by particles in the medium. It is similar to the commonplace event of the rays of a projection lantern or a beam of sunlight passing through the dust-laden atmosphere of a dark room. The true nature of the Tyndall phenomenon becomes apparent when colloidal systems are viewed by dark-field illumination or under the ultramicroscope (not to be confused with the electron microscope). With the ultramicroscope a very fine, intense beam of light is focused in a colloidal system and its path observed with a microscope placed at right angles to the beam.

Although considerable qualitative information in regard to colloid systems can be obtained by use of the Tyndall beam, it is not directly applicable to a careful study of colloids. Lyophobic colloids, as a rule, show intense Tyndall cones, whereas lyophilic systems may show a faint cone or almost none at all. The degree to which a cone is shown depends upon the difference between the refractive index of the dispersion medium and the dispersed phase. The greater the difference in refractive index between the two phases, the stronger will be the Tyndall cone. Since the human eye is sensitive to only a narrow band of the electromagnetic spectrum, the Tyndall cones ordinarily seen are derived from only a small portion of the spectrum. When ultraviolet light is used as a source of illumination, we are usually unable to see the resulting cones. Thus many systems which normally are optically empty to the eye may show a marked Tyndall beam when photographed under ultraviolet light.

Few studies have been conducted on biological material with the ultramicroscope, although for many years the bacteriologist has used dark-field illumination to facilitate the observation of certain structural features of bacteria.

The *refractive index* of bacteria, as determined by sodium light in media at 15°C., probably lies between 1.33 and 1.44. Von Angerer (1923) observed that bacteria are just visible in a 1.0 per cent NaCl solution and invisible in amyl alcohol. The refractive index of spores has been reported to be somewhat greater than 1.55. Bacteria in general are translucent and transmit 60 to 70 per cent of visible light. As the cells grow older or produce pigment, they become less translucent. Radiations in the region of the spectrum between the wavelengths 400 mμ and 180 mμ are almost completely absorbed by bacteria. This absorption of rays of short wavelength is directly related to the germicidal action of ultraviolet light. Amann (1893) discovered that the cell wall of bacteria shows double refraction (birefringence) in polarized light.

Bacteria in suspension scatter light rays and exhibit the Tyndall cone. Advantage is taken of this property to measure densities of bacterial suspensions and to enumerate the cells in them by means of scales for comparison of densities or by calibrated nephelometers.

7. Electrical Properties. A very important property of colloidal particles is the fact that they are generally electrically charged with respect to their surroundings. Certain colloidal particles are negatively charged, whereas others carry a positive charge. Thus, when an electric current is passed through a colloidal system, it will be found that, if the particles are positively charged, they will move toward the cathode and, if negatively charged, they will migrate to the anode. One of the most active fields of research in colloidal physics in recent years has had for its object the determination of the magnitude and nature of the charge on colloidal particles. Much of the experimental work has dealt with electrophoretic phenomena (cataphoresis and anaphoresis). These studies will not be reviewed here. For a general discussion on the electrical properties of colloids the exhaustive review by Abramson (1934) and the very readable treatise by Weiser (1939) should be consulted.

The importance of studies of the electrical properties of colloids and their application to biological research should not be regarded too casually, for in such studies probably lies an explanation to many fundamental biological processes. Later in the chapter, on pp. 41 to 57 on electrophysiology, this subject will be discussed more fully, and several examples pertaining to bacteriology will be listed.

8. Specific Gravity. Measurements of specific gravity usually are not discussed under colloids. But, since a few data with relation to bacteria are available, the subject should be considered here.

The *specific gravity* of any substance is the ratio of the weight of a given volume of the material to the weight of an equal volume of a standard substance. The *density* of a substance is defined as the weight of a unit volume. When the metric system is employed, the weight of 1 ml. of water at 4°C. is taken as the standard. Thus at this temperature, but not at others, the specific gravity and density of water are numerically equal.

Specific gravity values are usually expressed on scales, such as with the well-known Twadell and Baumé hydrometers. With the Twadell system the degrees registered on the hydrometer scale are multiplied by 5 and added to 1.000 to give specific gravity. The scale on a Baumé heavier-than-water hydrometer is wholly arbitrary. At 17.5°C. zero degree (0°) is the point to which the hydrometer sinks in pure water, and 10° the point to which it sinks in a 10 per cent solution of NaCl. The portion of the scale between 0° and 10° is marked off into 10 equal parts and used as the ruler to mark the entire scale. For use with liquids lighter than water the scale is reversed. Tables for the conversion of specific gravity or degrees Baumé into concentrations have been prepared for many substances used commercially, especially alcohols, sugars, salts, and acids.

On account of a number of variables, determinations of the specific gravity of bacteria are somewhat unsatisfactory. Differences in the specific gravity may be caused, for example, by the water-content; the relative proportion of light substances, such as fats, to substances such as proteins and carbohydrates, which have a specific weight greater than that of water; the age of the cells; and the conditions of cultivation. Older studies, such as the one by Stigell (1908), are of little value today. Stigell studied the specific gravity of 27 different bacteria by centrifuging them in various concentrations of NaI, and found that they ranged in specific gravity from 1.118 (*Staphylococcus citreus*) to 1.321 (*Staphylococcus aureus*). More recently Ruffilli (1933) used a better technique and reported the following values: 1.094 for *Escherichia coli*, 1.129 for an air coccus, 1.105 for *Bacillus subtilis*, and 1.115 for the spores of *B. subtilis*. Values for the specific gravity of yeasts, bacteriophage, and viruses have been published and are essentially the same as those given above for bacteria.

THE EFFECT OF ELECTROLYTES ON COLLOIDAL SYSTEMS

The effect of electrolytes on lyophobic and lyophilic colloids has been the subject of many studies. Only a few general remarks will be made here with respect to *flocculation*, *protective colloids*, and the *lyotropic series* of Hofmeister. For further details on the action of electrolytes on colloids the references and books on colloid chemistry should be consulted.

Flocculation (Precipitation). It has been mentioned already that colloid particles are stabilized by an electric double layer, and, if the charge is neutralized, the particle becomes isoelectric and flocculation results. It thus becomes evident that, if electrolytes are added to colloidal solutions, they will have a marked effect upon the properties of the colloidal system. In general, those colloids which are *negatively charged* become *isoelectric* and are precipitated by the *cations* of an added electrolyte, whereas positively charged particles are sensitive to added *anions*. However, as an electrolyte is usually added to a colloidal solution, the charge on the particles is progressively decreased to zero and then increased with further addition, thereby forming a new system with a charge opposite that of the original. Although not a hard and fast law, the flocculating power of an ion follows the rule that *the precipitating power of an electrolyte depends upon the valency of the ion whose charge is opposite to that on the colloid particle.* The influence of valence is not an arithmetical (1 : 2 : 3) ratio but more closely resembles geometrical progression ($1 : x : x^2$), which in some cases (x) has a value somewhere between 16 and 32. Thus, for example, colloidal particles with a negative charge are coagulated by the cations, Na^+, Ca^{++}, and Al^{+++}, but are not affected to any degree by the anions, Cl^-, $SO_4^=$, and $PO_4^{\equiv}$. On the other hand, the reverse is true for colloidal systems with a positive charge. If (x) had a value of 20, it would mean that Ca^{++} is 20 times as efficient a precipitating agent as Na^+ and that Al^{+++} is 400 times better than Na^+.

It is generally believed that the precipitating action of electrolytes upon lyophobic sols (suspensoids) is due almost entirely to the effect on the stabilizing electric potential (Fig. 4). Kruyt and his coworkers [see Kruyt (1930)] have shown that the potential does not have to drop to zero before the system becomes unstable; rather there is a *critical zone* in the vicinity of the isoelectric point where the magnitude of the electric charge is not sufficient to insure indefinite stability of the lyophobic system. On the other hand, lyophilic sols (emulsoids) are stabilized by the electric charge plus solvation (Fig. 4). Therefore, if small amounts of electrolytes are added to a lyophilic sol, they influence only the electric charge on the particles; but the addition of larger quantities of electrolytes influences the degree of solvation and brings about precipitation. Since the liquid of solvation influences the stability of lyophilic sols, the apparent effect of electrolytes on such systems is much less marked than on lyophobic sols.

Another phenomenon which should be mentioned here is that a quantity of electrolytes which is capable of producing complete precipitation when added all at once to lyophobic sols (suspensoids) is

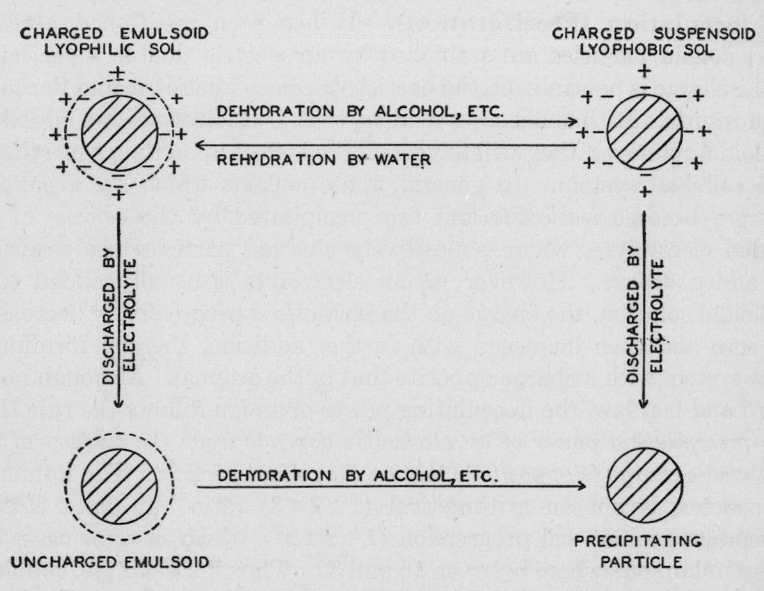

FIG. 4. Factors Involved in the Precipitation of Colloids. (Reprinted, by permission, from *Colloids* by Kruyt and Van Klooster, John Wiley & Sons, New York, 1930.)

ineffective when added in small quantities. This phenomenon, which is exhibited also when toxins and antitoxins are mixed together, is thought to be due to the fact that precipitation depends on inequality and irregular distribution of electric charges, a condition which becomes established when the electrolyte is suddenly added, but not when it is gradually added.

Two hydrophilic sols of opposite signs of charge may coagulate each other under proper conditions. The mutual precipitation of colloids is of considerable importance in certain industries, such as the dyeing of fabrics and the coagulation of the collagen of hides by tannin in the tanning process.

The phenomena which have been discussed are of considerable importance in several reactions used by the bacteriologist and immunologist.

Protective Colloids. From the foregoing discussion it can be seen that lyophilic colloid sols are much more resistant to the precipitating action of electrolytes than are lyophobic sols. Thus, if a certain concentration of a lyophilic colloid, such as gelatin, is placed in a lyophobic sol, such as a nuclear gold sol, it is usually sufficient to "protect" the lyophobe from the precipitating action of electrolytes. This phenomenon is known as *protective colloid action.* The protective action on a given sol varies widely with different substances, and in 1903 Zsigmondy and his associates devised what they called the *gold number* as a means of measuring the relative protective power of a given substance. The gold number is defined as the number of milligrams of protecting colloid added to 10 ml. of Zsigmondy's red gold sol which just fails to prevent the change in color from red to blue on the addition of 1.0 ml. of 10 per cent NaCl solution. Several gold numbers are:

Gelatin	0.005–0.01
Casein	0.01
Gum arabic	0.15–0.5
Sodium oleate	0.4–1.0
Dextrin	6.2
Potato starch	25.0

Gelatin is the most efficient among the protective colloids, that is, less is needed, since it is most resistant to electrolytes. It should be emphasized that the gold number gives only a rough indication of the protective action, because it is influenced by a number of factors, such as the size of the particles in the gold sol, the *p*H of the system, and the degree of dispersion of the protecting colloid.

The protective action of organic matter plays an important part in many physiological processes. For example, the curdling of milk is due to the action of electrolytes on the casein. However, in the presence of lactalbumin, which is more resistant to electrolytes than casein, coagulation is much more difficult. The resistance of many bacteria in nature to the harmful rays of the sun, such as ultraviolet rays, is thought to be due in part to the protective action of organic matter. In the past the gold number (Lange's gold sol reaction) has been used somewhat in medicine for the diagnosis of certain diseases. The gold number of the spinal fluid of a normal person is a fairly definite value. Certain pathological fluids, on the other hand, have been reported as deviating markedly from the normal value.

Several theories of the protective action of colloids have been proposed. The action is probably due to the adsorption of a thin film of the lyophilic colloid on the surface of each particle of the lyophobic colloid. This adsorption in turn alters the properties of the lyophobic system.

The Lyotropic Series (Hofmeister Series). From the preceding discussion of flocculation it might be assumed that valency is the only factor involved in the behavior of ions toward a colloidal system. This however, is not the case, since, for example, a group of monovalent ions possesses within itself varying degrees of ability to precipitate colloidal systems. In a series of papers from 1888 to 1891, Hofmeister reported on the effects of various anions and cations on the coagulation of proteins (egg albumin). He found the following order of increase in coagulating power:

a. For the anions:

$$\text{Citrate} > \text{Tartrate} > SO_4 > \text{Acetate} > Cl > NO_3 > ClO_3 > I > CNS$$

b. For the cations:

$$Li > K > Na > NH_4 > Mg$$

Similar lyotropic series have since been obtained and studied in detail by others. Also several theories have been advanced to account for the observed differences in behavior of the various salts on colloid systems, but they will not be discussed here.

The behavior of the lyotropic series of ions is not limited to its effect on colloidal systems, since it has been demonstrated many times in other connections. Weiser (1939) reports that among the physico-chemical phenomena by which the lyotropic series manifest themselves are their effects on: (1) the surface tension of water; (2) the displacement of the maximum density of water; (3) the rate of inversion of cane sugar; and (4) the solubility in water of nonelectrolytes, such as the amino acids, urea, quinone, and hydroquinone. To this list we might add a bacteriological example, namely, the toxic effects of cations and anions for bacteria. This point will be discussed later in more detail in Chapter 4, The Effects of Chemical Agents on Bacteria.

HYDROPHILIC SOLS AND GELS

The preceding discussion has been concerned mainly with colloidal sols, although it has been mentioned that certain sols may be transformed into semisolid or rigid gels by increasing the content of the disperse phase or may pass spontaneously into such gels by an aggregation of the particles. In certain cases, especially with lyophilic colloids, the sol $\rightleftarrows$ gel transformation is a reversible reaction. Thus, for example, with ordinary bacteriological gelatin or agar media, temperature and hydrogen-ion concentration in a large measure determine whether the system will be a sol or a gel. Some of the properties of gels are retained in their sols; a firm gelatin jelly is elastic, and so also is liquid gelatin under certain conditions.

Attempts have been made to state arbitrarily when a sol ceases to be a sol and becomes a gel. All such attempts have led to confusion. It may be said, however, that a gel firm enough to maintain its shape unsupported is a true gel, but if it collapses and flows freely, it is a sol. A more important point to realize is that certain lyophilic colloidal systems exist in a state that is not truly solid or liquid and retain some of the properties of each state.

HYDROPHILIC SOLS

A hydrophobic or hydrophilic sol may be defined as a colloid system in which the dispersion medium is water. In the hydrophilic sols there is a closer attraction or affinity between the dispersed phase and water than is found in hydrophobic sols, with the result that the particles in hydrophilic sols are surrounded by a so-called hydration shell. This

TABLE 2

CERTAIN CHARACTERISTIC PROPERTIES OF HYDROPHOBIC AND HYDROPHILIC SOLS

(Reprinted, by permission, from *Colloid Chemistry* by Weiser, published by John Wiley & Sons, Inc.)

	Type of Sol	
Property	*Hydrophobic* *	*Hydrophilic* †
Presence of electrolyte	Small amount essential for stability	Not essential for stability
Stability toward electrolyte	Coagulated by small amounts	Not coagulated by small amounts
Reversibility of coagulation	Irreversible as a rule	Reversible as a rule
Ultramicroscopic image	Bright particles in motion	Diffuse light cone
Electrical charge	Definite sign, not readily changed	Sign changed readily by suitable change in *p*H
Electric field	Particles migrate	Particles may or may not migrate
Viscosity	About the same as for H_2O, if the temperature is the same	Viscosity greater than H_2O and rises rapidly with decreasing temperature and increasing concentration of dispersed phase

* Examples: sols of elements, oxides, and salts.

† Examples: sols of proteins, higher carbohydrates, and soaps.

accounts for part of the differences between the two classes of sol systems that are given in Table 2. It should be mentioned, however, that no classification of this type is perfect. It is true that typical hydrophobic and hydrophilic sols show the characteristic differences given in the table, but there are exceptions and borderline cases.

Although the chemist may be interested in all types of hydrophobic and hydrophilic sols, the biologist is concerned mainly with the hydrophilic sols, because this group contains such substances as the proteins and higher carbohydrates.

Before proceeding to a discussion of gels, it may be well to mention briefly a few of the factors which affect the stability of hydrophilic sols.

Coagulation of Hydrophilic Sols. The coagulation of hydrophilic sols may be conveniently discussed under these headings: (1) coagulation by electrolytes, (2) coagulation by heat, (3) mutual coagulation, and (4) mechanical coagulation.

1. Coagulation by Electrolytes. It has already been mentioned that hydrophilic sols may be coagulated by electrolytes. In general, however, much larger amounts of electrolytes are necessary than with hydrophobic sols. Because of the high concentrations that are required for coagulation, the process is often spoken of as "salting out."

In a negatively charged sol the cations favor coagulation and the anions oppose it, whereas in a positively charged sol the situation is reversed. The order of coagulating power of anions and cations for an albumin sol has already been given in the discussion of the lyotropic series of Hofmeister. Gelatin sols are like albumin sols in that they require relatively high concentrations of alkali salts for coagulation. According to Weiser (1939), 4 N KCl and 0.75 N Na_2SO_4 are needed to coagulate a gelatin sol. Sols of agar, gum arabic, and starch are similar to gelatin in their behavior toward neutral electrolytes.

None of the hydrophilic sols is precipitated simply by bringing the charge on the particles to zero (isoelectric point). The system also has to be dehydrated.

2. Coagulation by Heat. Certain protein sols, such as albumins and globulins, coagulate at a definite temperature which is relatively constant for each protein. A familiar example is the coagulation of egg white when eggs are cooked. The destruction of bacteria by heat is another important bacteriological example.

It is generally believed that the phenomenon of heat coagulation involves at least three distinct processes:

Denaturation, which is apparently an intramolecular rearrangement whereby certain chemical groups that are not detectable in the native protein appear in the modified product. The modified protein is called *denatured protein.* Although denaturation is necessary, it is not sufficient to produce the final coagulated material.

Flocculation of the denatured molecules is the second process. Studies indicate that this process closely resembles the flocculation of certain hydrophobic colloids where the electric charge is the predominating stability factor.

Irreversible coagulation consists in the formation of an insoluble coagulum from the flocculated mass.

3. Mutual Coagulation. Two hydrophilic sols of opposite charge may at times coagulate each other.

4. Mechanical Coagulation. Certain hydrophilic sols may be coagulated by shaking or by other means of agitation. It is thought that under certain conditions bacteria may be destroyed in a similar fashion.

The Isoelectric Point of Certain Hydrophilic Sols (Proteins). The stability of protein sols, such as gelatin, is at a minimum at the isoelectric point. The *isoelectric point* of colloidally dispersed material is the *p*H value or hydrogen-ion activity of the dispersion medium at which the dispersed phase does not migrate in an electric field. Table 3 gives the exact isoelectric point or range of isoelectric points for a few proteins and other amphoteric substances, as reported by several investigators [Weiser (1939), Svedberg and Pedersen (1940)].

TABLE 3

Isoelectric Points of Several Substances as Reported by Various Investigators

Substance	Isoelectric Point, *p*H	Substance	Isoelectric Point, *p*H
Lactalbumin	5.12	Cytochrome c	9.7
Casein	4.6–4.9	Yellow enzyme	5.22
Gelatins	4.4–5.6	*Mycobacterium tuberculosis* protein	4.3
Pepsins	2.5–3.3	Antipneumococcus serum globulin (horse)	4.4
Trypsin	7.0–8.0	Bushy-stunt virus protein	4.11
Protamins	10.0–12.4		

Several other properties of such sols which are usually at a minimum at or very close to the isoelectric point are viscosity, osmotic pressure, precipitation by alcohol, and conductivity.

HYDROPHILIC GELS

Gels are usually defined as rigid or semisolid colloidal systems. They are usually classified into two groups: (a) *nonelastic* or *nonswelling gels,* and (b) *elastic* or *swelling gels.* Examples of the first group are gels of such inorganic substances as chromic oxide and silica; ordinary bacteriological gelatin and agar media are the best examples of the second group. The elastic gels are of greater importance to the bacteriologist and will be given more attention here. The nonelastic gels, other than silica gel, are of little importance to the biologist. [For a review and an easy method of preparing silica gel for bacteriological use see the paper by Moore (1940)]. Compared with certain other media, silica gel offers larger pore size, lower pouring temperatures, and the possible presence of more free water to carry nutrients to the cells.

The ability of a given system to gel is in direct proportion to the affinities which exist between the dispersed phase and the dispersion medium. If the dispersion medium is strongly attracted by the dispersed phase, the dispersed particles becomes highly solvated and surrounded by "shells" of the dispersion medium. The viscosity of the system increases during the solvation process until a semisolid or rigid jelly is formed. Another way to visualize the process of gelatinizing of hydrophilic sols is as an *agglomeration of hydrated particles which retain the remaining water inside the capillary spaces between them.* For sols of the silica type this agglomeration occurs simply by electrolyte flocculation and is irreversible. In sols of agar or gelatin, the agglomeration is controlled mainly by temperature and is reversible. In regard to the reversibility, however, it must be remembered that the temperatures of initial gelatinizing and of "melting" are never quite the same. For example, a gelatin sol solidifies at around 26° to 28°C., and the resulting gel melts at around 31°C. For agar sols these limits are much farther apart: gelatinizing takes place at about 35° to 40°C., and melting starts around 85° to 95°C., with complete liquefaction occurring at 100°C.

Undoubtedly gels have a structure, but little is actually known about their internal configuration. The two most important theories which have been postulated for gel structure are: (a) a *honey-comb structure,* in which the dispersed phase forms a fairly uniform network of cell-like walls, the interior being filled with the dispersion medium; and (b) a *brush-heap* or *sponge structure,* in which ultramicroscopic fibrils are interlaced into a mass throughout the system, and the dispersion medium is held within the mass by capillary forces. Most workers favor the brush-heap structure or a modification of it, since both the liquid and solid phases in a gel appear to be continuous, and the fibrils frequently appear to be symmetrically arranged, overlapped, and concentrated at regular intervals [Seifriz (1942)].

Some knowledge of gels is very important to the bacteriologist for various reasons. Many of the media used in bacteriological studies are simply agar or gelatin gels. The jelly-like nature of bacterial protoplasm undoubtedly gives it that continuity in structure, or organization, so necessary as a background for the multiplicity of reactions which take place in such a living cell.

Formation of Gels. Gels may be formed by several methods, although only two are of importance to the bacteriologist. Briefly they are: (a) by allowing a sol to "set-up" by a change in temperature (cooling); melted agar and gelatin media are examples of this method; (b) by altering the *p*H or electrolyte content of a sol; the formation of a silicic acid gel by the addition of an acid to sodium silicate is the best example of this method.

General Properties of Gels. Several of the more important properties of gels may be briefly mentioned here. Since some of the general characteristics of colloids, which also may at times apply to gels, have already been enumerated, these properties will not be repeated.

1. Syneresis. This phenomenon, which was first observed by Graham in 1861 with silica gels, occurs to a greater or lesser extent in all gels. The word itself means a "drawing together." Thus *syneresis* is contraction of gels, which results in the giving off of water. The gel "sweats," so to speak. Since the jelly-forming process consists in the coagulation of the hydrous particles into an enmeshing network, the syneresis which follows the initial set is the visible manifestation of further slow agglomeration and coagulation, accompanied by the squeezing out of some of the dispersion medium. The more rapid the "set," the sooner the gel starts to synerize.

The separations of water from fresh agar slants, of serum from clotted blood, and of whey from curds in sour milk are phenomena of syneresis which are of interest to the bacteriologist. The exudation of water and other fluids from protoplasm and cells may, in certain cases, be due to syneresis.

2. Thrixotropy. If a suitable amount of electrolyte is added to a fairly strong sol, such as ferric oxide, and the mixture is allowed to stand, it will set to a jelly which is no more cloudy than the original sol. If the resulting gel is then shaken, a sol is again formed which sets once more when allowed to stand. This phenomenon may be repeated many times with the same system. Such a reversible sol–gel

transformation has been termed *thrixotropy*. The word thrixotropy is derived from the Greek and means literally "to change by touching." Gelatin and agar sols will also liquefy reversibly at constant temperature if shaken before the structure has set too firmly.

According to Seifriz (1936), thrixotropic phenomena occur in protoplasm, since slight agitation of highly viscous protoplasm will often reduce its consistency. Such changes also occur under certain conditions with tobacco mosaic virus, myosin, and other biological materials [Freundlich (1942)].

3. Swelling, Imbibition, and Water Relationships. Almost all the substances which form the so-called elastic gels swell in a suitable liquid or in the vapors of such liquid. The taking up of water, when accompanied by swelling, is *imbibition*. Thus dry gelatin, agar, fibrin, and starch swell in water at ordinary temperatures to form thin jellies but are transformed into sols at higher temperatures. Albumin swells in water but not in alcohol, benzene, or ether.

The swelling of gels may exert a very high pressure. For example, it has been reported that starch swells against a pressure of 2,500 atmospheres (approximately 37,000 lb. per square inch), and dried seaweeds will take up water against a pressure of 41 atmospheres. Gels on shrinking also exert a pull. The dehydration of gelatin pulls with sufficient force to bend or chip the glass to which it is attached.

The effect of *p*H and salts on swelling has been studied extensively with gelatin and other elastic gels. Concerning such effects, Weiser (1939) pointed out that the swelling of gelatin, for example, approaches a minimum value at the isoelectric point, increasing on either side of *p*H 4.7. Salts influence the swelling of gelatin, some increasing and some decreasing it. For sodium salts the swelling follows the order of the lyotropic series:

a. For anions:

$$CNS > I > Br > NO_3 > ClO_3 > Cl > \text{Acetate} > \text{Citrate} > \text{Tartrate} > SO_4$$

b. For cations:

$$Cs > Li > Rb > K > Na > NH_4$$

Fibrin behaves much like gelatin in the presence of salts, but agar swells less in any salt solution than in water.

The elastic organic hydrogels lose water continuously in dry air, just as do the inorganic hydrogels. The two differ, however, in that the dehydration of inorganic gels is not reversible, whereas dry flakes or sheets of the elastic gels take up water and swell again in the presence of water. The state of water in hydrophilic gels has been the subject of many investigations. Gortner and associates at Minnesota have come to the conclusion that part of the water in such systems differs in certain physical properties from water in bulk. Such water is said to be "bound" in the sense that the molecules have been so reduced in activity that they may be exposed to low temperatures without being oriented into the crystalline lattice characteristic in ice. For instance, Jones and Gortner (1932) found that the free water in gelatin freezes at approximately −6°C., whereas the bound water does not freeze even at −50°C. They reported also that the amount of bound water varied with the concentration of gelatin in the gel; 0.70 g. of water per gram of dry gelatin being bound in a 32 per cent gel and 4.675 g. in a 2.0 per cent gel. Gortner has emphasized this parallelism between bound water in protoplasmic material and biological behavior, and he suggests that the water relationships in biocolloids may determine, to a large degree, the vital activities of an organism. The bound ⇄ free water equilibrium is of primary importance for winter hardiness and drought resistance in plants, for winter resistance of insects, and for the regulation of cellular activities in general in both plants and animals. Possibly the resistance of bacterial spores to heat and cold and the ability of thermophilic bacteria to grow at high temperatures and of psycrophilic forms to grow at low temperatures are directly related to their bound ⇄ free water equilibrium.

4. Hysteresis. *Hysteresis* is a characteristic phenomenon of gels and has been spoken of as the "memory of a colloid system." The word comes from the Greek and means literally "coming after" or a lagging of one process behind another. Although lyophobic sols show hysteresis to a certain degree, the property is most marked in the case of lyophilic gels. As used by workers in the field of colloids, hysteresis refers to the effect of past mechanical and thermal treatment on the present behavior of a colloid system. Thus, for example, when gelatin media are repeatedly melted and allowed to resolidify, the temperature of the melting point and also of the solidifying point becomes progressively lower. This behavior is known as hysteresis.

5. Elasticity. Another property of hydrophilic gels is elasticity. For instance, it has been reported that a 10 per cent gelatin gel can support a weight of 2.42 g. per square millimeter, and a 45 per cent gel, 29.4 g. per square millimeter for a short time and then resume their normal shape. This property is influenced by the presence of various substances, such as salts, glycerol, and cane sugar in the gel. The volume of a jelly does not change when it undergoes extension.

It will be seen from this brief discussion of gels that those properties of protoplasm which characterize it fundamentally, such as swelling, imbibition, and elasticity, are also properties of gels.

SPECIFIC SURFACE, SURFACE ENERGY, SURFACE TENSION AND INTERFACIAL TENSION, AND ADSORPTION

The subdivision of a substance increases the area of its effective surface very greatly. Consequently surface forces, such as surface tension and interfacial tension, adsorption, and capillarity, are magnified and of fundamental importance.

SPECIFIC SURFACE

The enormous increase in extent of surface and in specific surface (area/volume) on progressively subdividing a hypothetical cube of 1.0-cm. diameter into smaller and smaller particles is shown in Table 4. It will be seen that the surface area increases from 6 sq. cm. to 60 sq. m. as the upper limit of the colloidal realm is reached, and the specific surface increases from 6 to 600,000. The area and specific surface of colloidal material are even greater if the mass possesses a porous structure.

From Table 4 it will be seen that a micrococcus with a diameter of 1.0 μ may have a surface area of approximately 6.0 sq. m. (64.5 sq. ft.) per gram of mass. Thus such an organism may be expected to show many of the properties of matter in the colloid state.

TABLE 4

INCREASE IN SURFACE BY DECIMALLY DIVIDING ONE CUBIC CENTIMETER OF SOLID

(From *Colloid Chemistry* by J. Alexander, courtesy of D. Van Nostrand Company)

Number of Cubes	Length of Edge	Total Surface Area		Specific Surface, Surface area / Volume	Typical Object *
		Metric units	U.S. units		
1	1.0 cm.	6.0 sq. cm.	0.93 sq. in.	6	Small pea
10^3	1.0 mm.	60.0 sq. cm.	9.30 sq. in.	60	Fine shot
10^6	0.1 mm.	600.0 sq. cm.	93.00 sq. in.	600	Talcum powder
10^9	0.01 mm.	6,000.0 sq. cm.	6.46 sq. ft.	6,000	Ameba
10^{12}	1.0 μ	6.0 sq. m.	64.58 sq. ft.	60,000	Small bacteria
10^{15}	0.1 μ	60.0 sq. m.	645.83 sq. ft.	600,000	Large colloids
10^{18}	0.01 μ	600.0 sq. m.	6,458.33 sq. ft.	6,000,000	{ Small colloids Large molecules
10^{21}	1.0 mμ	6,000.0 sq. m.	7,176.00 sq. yd.	60,000,000	Molecules

* Most of these objects are merely examples of approximate size, since they are not necessarily cubes.

SURFACE ENERGY

If we define surface tension as the force that operates in each square centimeter of cross section of the surface to hold it together, then surface energy is the work required to increase the surface by 1.0 sq. cm. (at constant temperatures). Surface energy is the product of two quantities, the *intensity factor* (surface tension or interfacial tension in ergs per square centimeter) and the *capacity factor* (surface area in square centimeters). Surface energy is a very active form of energy and is readily converted into work or other forms of energy. The free surface energy of a given system is decreased under many conditions, such as (1) a reduction in area (capacity factor), or (2) a reduction of surface tension or interfacial tension (intensity factor).

If a 1.0-cm. cube of water is dispersed into droplets 1.0 mμ on each edge (see Table 4), Gortner at Minnesota has calculated that the total surface energy (surface tension × extent of surface) increases from 438 ergs to 4,380,000,000 ergs (105 cal.).

SURFACE TENSION AND INTERFACIAL TENSION

As a general rule liquids differ from gases in that their molecules are closer together and they are capable of assuming a definite form with a boundary. For instance, a gas always completely fills the container in which it is placed, whereas a liquid may occupy only a certain more or less fixed volume. Like gases, liquids possess kinetic energy, but because they have a surface they also exhibit surface energy. It is this surface energy which gives liquids many of the properties which are not possessed by gases.

The boundary surface of a liquid differs essentially from the body of the liquid in that the molecules at the surface are, in general, arranged in an orderly fashion and oriented in some particular direction, whereas the molecules in the bulk of the liquid are apparently distributed at random. Usually the concentration of molecules per unit area in the surface layer is greater than it is in a similar volume within the body of the liquid. The layer of molecules on the surface behaves as if there were a "membrane" drawn over the bulk of the liquid and is responsible for the phenomenon known as surface tension. This apparent membrane is not identical with a rubber membrane, however, because the tension of rubber increases with stretching, whereas surface tension is independent of the enlargement of the surface. Space does not permit a discussion of the molecular orientation of various compounds, types of surface films, and similar subjects, although the bacteriologist is finding more need for such information. The book by Weiser (1939) is a very readable treatment of monomolecular films or monolayers.

Willard Gibbs in 1876 first deduced thermodynamically the relation between the change of concentration in the boundary layer and the effect of the dissolved substance on the surface tension of the liquid. He found that, if a substance lowers the surface tension, the boundary layer is richer in this substance than the body of the liquid; and, conversely, if the substance raises the surface tension, the boundary layer is poorer. Variations in the concentration of the boundary layer are commonly called adsorption. Positive adsorption is that which occurs when there is an increase in concentration in the boundary layer, and negative adsorption is that which takes place when there is a decrease in concentration. As we shall point out shortly, positive adsorption is much more important than negative adsorption.

Since a small drop of a liquid tends to form a sphere in a gas (air) and thus assumes a minimum surface area, it follows that in order to enlarge the surface, work will have to be done. The downward and lateral pull of molecules which are in the surface film or are entering the surface film as the surface is enlarged is the tension which is measured and called surface tension. Therefore, *surface tension is simply defined as the amount of work required to produce a new surface of unit area at constant temperature.* The term surface tension applies only to the tension of a liquid against a gas (air).

There are a number of ways of measuring surface tension, but they will not be discussed here, since everyone is familiar with the du Noüy tensiometer, the most commonly used instrument for making such measurements. With the du Noüy tensiometer direct readings in dynes per centimeter can be made. Some surface tension values in dynes per centimeter for certain liquid-air interfaces are:

Chloroform	= 26.20 at 25°C.	Glycerol	= 63.4 at 20°C.
Methyl alcohol	= 22.61 at 20°C.	Mercury	= 480.3 at 0°C.
Ethyl alcohol	= 22.27 at 20°C.	Mercury	= 436.0 at 15°C.
Ethyl ether	= 17.10 at 20°C.	Water	= 75.64 at 0°C.
Benzene	= 28.86 at 20°C.	Water	= 72.75 at 20°C.
Aniline	= 42.58 at 20°C.	Water	= 71.18 at 30°C.

A great many factors influence the surface tension of a solution. For example, surface tension decreases with an increase in temperature and becomes zero at the critical temperature. Solutes may either increase or decrease the surface tension of a solution. The surface tension of most salts in solution is greater than water. The strong bases also increase surface tension, but ammonia and nitric and hydrochloric acids lower it. The surface tension of water is lowered most strongly by organic compounds with long chains of carbon atoms or with one or more benzene rings. Such compounds are said to be *surface active* or *capillary active.* Good examples of strong capillary-active compounds are the fatty acids, alcohols, and urethanes. Many colloidally dispersed substances, such as proteins, soaps, and certain dyes, likewise exhibit high surface activity. On the other hand, the salts of the lower fatty acids and hydroxy acids have little effect on the surface tension of water.

Interfacial tension differs from surface tension only in that surface tension refers to a liquid-vapor interface, whereas interfacial tension refers to a liquid-solid or liquid-liquid interface. As yet no satisfactory technique has been developed for accurately measuring the interfacial tension of liquid-solid systems. However, the interfacial tension of liquid-liquid interfaces can be determined by techniques similar to those used for measuring surface tension. The following data, taken from Pound (1926), show certain values of the interfacial tension of pure organic liquids against a water surface:

	Interfacial Tension at 30°C.		*Interfacial Tension at 30°C.*
Cresol	4.28	Ether	11.13
Amyl alcohol	4.89	Chloroform	31.41
Aniline	6.00	Benzene	32.5
Ethyl acetate	6.27	Carbon tetrachloride	42.75
Amyl acetate	10.88	Carbon disulfide	46.31

Pound has pointed out that the greater the mutual solubility between two liquids, the lower will be the interfacial tension between them.

Undoubtedly surface tension and interfacial tension are responsible for many of the phenomena which are characteristic of both lyophobic and lyophilic colloid systems. Likewise, many vital reactions are thought to be due to such phenomena. Cell division, ameboid movement, and protoplasmic streaming are only a few of the reactions in which changes in interfacial or surface tension are thought to be involved. That fission or cellular division of organisms, such as blue-green algae and bacteria, is due in part to surface activities may be seen from the following hypothetical example. First imagine a cell with a membrane of relatively uniform tension throughout. Now suppose that, because of certain specific chemical reactions within the cell, the surface tension of the membrane increases along a narrow band, encircling the cell like a belt until it is pinched into two cells, just as if a heavy rubber band were placed around the imaginary equator of a toy balloon. Although several investigators think that a process similar to this may happen in simple cell division, there is no proof. Thus it is with almost all our surface-tension theories of vital processes.

Surface tension (air-medium interface) may be an important factor in the growth of a microorganism, since those organisms (*Bacillus subtilis*, molds, etc.) which grow in a surface pellicle will find an environment considerably different from that in the bulk of the liquid. Surface tension may also be significant in determining the type of growth in the bulk-of-liquid media. It has been reported by Larson at Minnesota, for example, that organisms may grow as a membrane on the surface of a broth medium with relatively high surface tension but may not form a pellicle if the surface tension is sufficiently depressed by appropriate solutes.

The nature and concentrations of substances in the surface boundary of a liquid medium may modify the rate of gaseous diffusion and evaporation. For instance, the oxygen concentration in a medium will necessarily depend upon the rate at which the gas is removed because of cell metabolism and the rate at which it will diffuse into the medium from the air. If the surface film has in it a higher concentration of solutes than the bulk of the medium, it may act as a membrane and modify the rate of diffusion of the oxygen. It is conceivable that such a situation might constitute a limiting factor for growth. The effect of surface tension upon the rate of diffusion of gases through the surface of liquids has apparently not been studied.

It cannot be assumed that a material which affects the surface tension will affect the interfacial tension (microorganism-medium interface) in the same way, although this assumption has been made many times. It has been reported, for instance, that certain salts which increase surface tension decrease the interfacial tension between a hydrocarbon and water. In general, substances which lower the interfacial tension between a microorganism and its medium will tend to concentrate (be positively adsorbed) at the interface; the opposite tendency exists for materials raising the interfacial tension. This statement applies, of course, to the metabolic products as well as to the original constituents in the medium. Thus the addition to the medium of materials which are more strongly adsorbed than the metabolic products will tend to replace them and thus nullify their action on growth.

An interesting application of interfacial tension in bacteriology is the work by Mudd and his associates (1930). In a series of studies these investigators have developed a technique, involving an interfacial film, for the study of the passage of bacteria and blood cells through various films. Briefly their technique is as follows: Water and oil are brought into contact on a microscope slide; the cells to be studied are suspended in the water. It was found that red blood cells pass from the water into the oil through the interfacial film. Because of the tension exerted by this film, however, the red blood cells are stretched into the shape of a lens. Normal acid-fast bacteria readily pass into the oil and hence behave like lyophobic colloids because of their fatty or waxy coat. After the fatty material is removed from the bacteria, they no longer pass from the water into the oil, since their surface is presumably protein in nature.

According to Holmes (1940), surface-tension depressants, such as alcohols, soaps, and esters, have little effect on certain serological systems. She concluded that the influence of such agents on immunological reactions can be correlated with their action on the charge of the antigen particles, but not with their effect on interfacial tension.

ADSORPTION

The phenomenon of adsorption plays a very important role in many types of vital and nonvital systems. Adsorption is a surface affair and, since it is at or on surfaces that chemical reactions take place, adsorption is in many instances the precursor, if not the determiner, of these reactions. Because bacteria and other microorganisms offer many surfaces, adsorption must be a very important factor in initiating surface chemical reactions and controlling other cellular activities.

Most colloid chemistry books allocate at least one hundred pages to a discussion of adsorption by various types of colloid systems. Certain of these systems can probably be directly applied to bacteria and their environment. Since several books dealing with colloidal phenomena are readily available for reference, we will not attempt to present more than a brief outline of some of the fundamental principles dealing with adsorption and then to cite a few examples pertaining to bacteriology.

It is not easy to give a clear and precise definition of adsorption. It is best to use the word simply to mean the concentration of one substance at or on the surface of another. The origin of the word is obscure, but it is thought to have arisen from absorption. *Adsorption* is usually distinguished from *absorption* by the fact that adsorption has to do with purely surface forces, whereas absorption is concerned with capillary forces. Thus, for example, a dye is adsorbed to the surface of charcoal, whereas water is absorbed by (in the capillaries) a blotter or sponge. This differentiation is weak and arbitrary, however, because the ultimate forces in both are thought to be similar. A further complication of the distinction given above is the fact that the chemist uses adsorption to indicate the taking up of gases by liquids, which involves essentially a going into solution. Still it seems permissible to distinguish between the adsorption of a gas by charcoal, through condensation of it on the surface where it is held by *ad*hesion and, on the other hand, the absorption of water by capillaries where it is held in the pores by capillary action or *co*hesion. The root *sorption* implies the taking on of substance without indicating the mechanism involved, although usually it suggests that no new compound has been formed.

Adsorption constants are mathematical measurements of the degree to which a substance is taken up by an adsorbent. Thus if meerschaum, a hard, porous substance, is placed in a chamber with ammonia gas, it will take up a definite amount of gas per gram of adsorbent (meerschaum). Van Bemmelen, Freundlich [see vol. I, Alexander (1926)], and others have pointed out that the adsorption of substances is not stoichiometric but follows the empirical formula, $a = \alpha c \frac{1}{n}$, where a is the amount adsorbed per gram of the adsorbent; c is the final concentration of the substance in solution or in equilibrium; and α (the adsorption constant) and n are constants. Freundlich applied this formula extensively and found that it holds in a great number of systems within a certain concentration range. When the effect of pressure on the amount of substance adsorbed by a solid at constant temperature is plotted, a curve known as Freundlich's *adsorption isotherm* is obtained.

Adsorption may be either positive or negative. Positive adsorption from solution is the concentration of the solute in the interfacial film, whereas negative adsorption is the concentration of the solvent in the surface film. Positive adsorption is a much more important phenomenon than negative adsorption for the following reason. Suppose there is a certain concentration of a substance in aqueous solution. By adding more of the same solute or a second substance, the concentration in the boundary layer may be greatly increased but may not be considerably decreased because the surface layer can never contain less dissolved matter than is present in pure water. The nature of the solvent is of very great importance in determining not only in many cases whether adsorption will take place, but also the extent of the adsorption reaction. As a general rule, adsorption is greatest from solvents which have a high surface tension and least from solvents which have a low surface tension. For the most part the bacteriologist is interested in aqueous solutions which give a relatively high surface tension reading.

A simple example or two of adsorption may give a better understanding of the phenomenon and the mechanism involved than do terms and definitions. The following experiments work very well to demonstrate that adsorption is a surface event. Color dilute soapy water with methyl violet or a similar dye, shake vigorously, and then pipette off the foam. Repeat the shaking and the collecting of foam ten or twelve times and then compare the color of the liquid which has settled from the collected foam with that of the original solution. It will be seen that the foam solution is much darker in color because the dye was concentrated on the surface of the membranes of the soap bubbles each time the original solution was shaken. Another similar experiment is to shake a dilute solution of albumin and draw off the foam. After repeating the process a number of times, the foam portion drawn off will be found to be richer in albumin than the remaining aqueous solution. Not only do such simple experiments illustrate that adsorption is a surface phenomenon, but they also prove the rule of J. Willard Gibbs that substances which lower surface tension tend to accumulate at the liquid-vapor interface, whereas substances which decrease interfacial tension tend to concentrate in a liquid-solid or a liquid-liquid interface.

At this point the studies of McCalla (1940–1941) on cation and dye adsorption by bacteria should be discussed. These important studies help to elucidate some of the laws governing the physiological activities of bacteria and give us an understanding of the probable mechanism by which a bacterial cell adsorbs ions from its environment and concentrates them in a limited area around and possibly inside the cell, with an electrical force sufficient to limit their freedom of movement. For the details of the techniques employed and for many interesting data the original papers by McCalla should be consulted. His results are briefly summarized on the next few pages.

Since in general the bacterial cell carries a negative charge and is also known to form acids (carbon dioxide and water), the following theoretical equations may be written to demonstrate cation adsorption by bacteria:

$$(\text{Bacterial cell}^{n-}) + n\text{H}^+ \leftrightarrows (\text{Bacterial cell}^{n-})(n\text{H}^+)$$

$$(\text{Bacterial cell}^{n-})(n\text{H}^+) + \begin{pmatrix} n\text{NaOH} \\ n\text{KOH} \\ \frac{1}{2}n\text{Ca(OH)}_2 \\ \frac{1}{2}n\text{Mg(OH)}_2 \end{pmatrix} \leftrightarrows (\text{Bacterial cell}^{n-}) \begin{pmatrix} n\text{Na}^+ \\ n\text{K}^+ \\ \frac{1}{2}n\text{Ca}^{++} \\ \frac{1}{2}n\text{Mg}^{++} \end{pmatrix} + n\text{HOH}$$

From these equations it might be expected that bacteria growing in a well-balanced mineral-medium would adsorb Na^+, K^+, Ca^{++}, Mg^{++}, etc., from the medium. Then, if an excess of hydrogen ions was added to these cells as HCl, it might be expected that the cations (Na^+, K^+, Ca^{++}, Mg^{++}, etc.) would be replaced by the H^+. The basic ions released from the adsorption-complex would unite with the Cl^- ions to form the respective water-soluble chlorides, which could be removed by washing as indicated in the following equation:

$$(\text{Bacterial cell}^{n-})\begin{pmatrix} n\text{Na}^+ \\ n\text{K}^+ \\ \tfrac{1}{2}n\text{Mg}^{++} \\ \tfrac{1}{2}n\text{Ca}^{++} \\ \text{etc.} \end{pmatrix} + n\text{HCl} \rightleftarrows (\text{Bacterial cell}^{n-})(n\text{H}^+) + \begin{pmatrix} n\text{NaCl} \\ n\text{KCl} \\ \tfrac{1}{2}n\text{MgCl}_2 \\ \tfrac{1}{2}n\text{CaCl}_2 \\ \text{etc.} \end{pmatrix}$$

The H-bacteria complex thus formed should be titratable with $Ca(OH)_2$, and the amount of $Ca(OH)_2$ used should be a measure of the H^+ ions adsorbed, or the cation-adsorption capacity of the bacterial cells. This may be illustrated by the equation:

$$(\text{Bacterial cell}^{n-})(n\text{H}^+) + \tfrac{1}{2}n\text{Ca(OH)}_2 \rightleftarrows (\text{Bacterial cell}^{n-})(\tfrac{1}{2}n\text{Ca}^{++}) + n\text{HOH}$$

By drying an aliquot of the suspension of bacteria at 105°C. and weighing, values obtained by the above method could be expressed as m.e. (milligram equivalents) of cations per 100 g. of bacteria.

Theoretically it should be possible to substitute other chlorides, such as methylene blue chloride (MBCl) and mercuric chloride, for the hydrogen chloride, and since the methylene blue ion can be measured colorimetrically and the mercury ion functions as a lethal agent, they afford two additional tools for testing the adsorption hypothesis. Such theoretical reactions are indicated in the following equations:

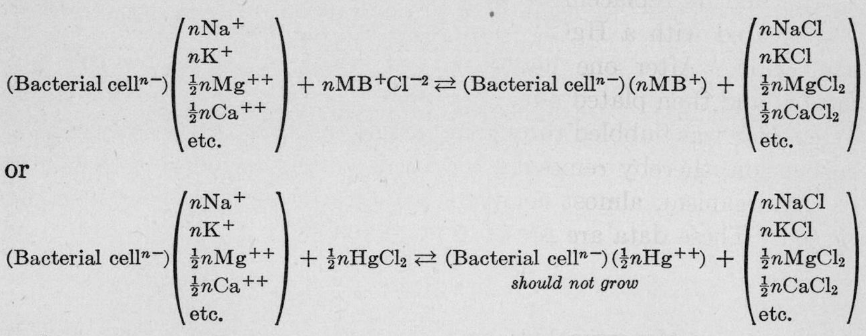

$$(\text{Bacterial cell}^{n-})\begin{pmatrix} n\text{Na}^+ \\ n\text{K}^+ \\ \tfrac{1}{2}n\text{Mg}^{++} \\ \tfrac{1}{2}n\text{Ca}^{++} \\ \text{etc.} \end{pmatrix} + n\text{MB}^+\text{Cl}^{-2} \rightleftarrows (\text{Bacterial cell}^{n-})(n\text{MB}^+) + \begin{pmatrix} n\text{NaCl} \\ n\text{KCl} \\ \tfrac{1}{2}n\text{MgCl}_2 \\ \tfrac{1}{2}n\text{CaCl}_2 \\ \text{etc.} \end{pmatrix}$$

or

$$(\text{Bacterial cell}^{n-})\begin{pmatrix} n\text{Na}^+ \\ n\text{K}^+ \\ \tfrac{1}{2}n\text{Mg}^{++} \\ \tfrac{1}{2}n\text{Ca}^{++} \\ \text{etc.} \end{pmatrix} + \tfrac{1}{2}n\text{HgCl}_2 \rightleftarrows \underset{\textit{should not grow}}{(\text{Bacterial cell}^{n-})(\tfrac{1}{2}n\text{Hg}^{++})} + \begin{pmatrix} n\text{NaCl} \\ n\text{KCl} \\ \tfrac{1}{2}n\text{MgCl}_2 \\ \tfrac{1}{2}n\text{CaCl}_2 \\ \text{etc.} \end{pmatrix}$$

and

$$(\text{Bacterial cell}^{n-})(\tfrac{1}{2}n\text{Hg}^{++}) + \tfrac{1}{2}n\text{H}_2\text{S} \rightleftarrows \underset{\textit{should grow}}{(\text{Bacterial cell}^{n-})(n\text{H}^+)} + \tfrac{1}{2}n\text{HgS}$$

On the basis of this hypothetical consideration, McCalla measured the adsorption capacity of *Escherichia coli*, *Bacillus subtilis*, and other bacteria by four methods. Several of his experiments may be reviewed briefly.

The adsorption capacity of *E. coli* ranged from 35 to 57 m.e. of hydrogen ions per 100 g. of bacteria, as is shown in Table 5. Cells treated in such a manner are 88 to 100 per cent viable. That this adsorption is purely a physico-chemical phenomenon, in no way depending upon the existence of living cells, was demonstrated by the fact that bacteria killed by heating at 100°C. exhibited, within the limits of error, the same adsorption capacity. McCalla also demonstrated that methylene blue and magnesium ions, as well as other ions, were adsorbed by bacteria. Such ions as Na^+ and K^+ appear to be only weakly adsorbed and are not toxic in dilute solutions, whereas Ag^+ and Hg^{++} are strongly adsorbed and are toxic in dilute solutions. One other interesting experiment was the adsorption of $HgCl_2$ by *E. coli* and its replacement by H_2S. A washed suspension of *E. coli* was treated with a $HgCl_2$ solution of approximately 0.0004 M concentration. After one hour's contact some of the suspension was diluted and then plated out. Less than 1.0 per cent of the cells grew. When H_2S was bubbled through a portion of the same Hg-cell-complex suspension, thereby removing the Hg ion from the adsorption sphere of the organism, almost complete viability of the organisms was observed. These data are presented in Table 6.

TABLE 5

HYDROGEN-ADSORPTION CAPACITY OF *Escherichia coli* AND VIABILITY OF THE H-BACTERIA COMPLEX

[From McCalla (1940)]

Trials	Adsorption Capacity, m.e./100 g. bacteria	H-Bacteria Complex, per cent viable
1	54	100
2	35	88
3	57	100
4	38	89
5	53	100

TABLE 6

ADSORPTION OF MERCURIC IONS BY *Escherichia coli* AND THEIR REPLACEMENT

[From McCalla (1940)]

Trials	Viable Cells after 60 Minutes, per cent	
	Hg	Hg Removed with H_2S
1	1.0	99
2	0.0	90
3	1.0	97

Since antigen and antibody solutions may be regarded as colloidal systems, it is quite probable that adsorption phenomena have a great deal to do with the union of these substances. In fact, before 1909 Bordet suggested that immunological reactions are fundamentally physico-chemical in nature and that many of the laws governing adsorption reactions in colloid systems could be directly applied to antigen-antibody unions. Space does not permit a detailed discussion of this subject. For further reading the book by Wells (1929), the monograph by Marrack (1938), and the paper by Heidelberger (1939) should be consulted.

The first reaction between an enzyme and its substrate is apparently an adsorption of the catalyst by the substrate. This adsorption is followed by the chemical action of the enzyme. The initial adsorption reaction may be readily demonstrated by the following simple experiment. If pepsin is added to a suspension of fibrin in 0.2 per cent hydrochloric acid and the mixture is vigorously shaken and immediately filtered, the pepsin will be almost completely removed from solution with the fibrin. This fact can be proved by the addition of fresh fibrin to the acid filtrate, under which conditions no appreciable digestion of fibrin will occur. If, on the other hand, fresh acid is added to the fibrin particles which were removed by filtration, hydrolysis proceeds, and the substrate will become completely digested. Quastel (1930) emphasizes adsorption as an essential feature of enzyme action and accounts for specificity on this basis. He studied the oxidation ⇄ reduction reactions of bacteria on 108 organic compounds. Of these, 56 were "activated" so that they acted as hydrogen donators; that is, the hydrogen atoms in the molecule were transferable to a suitable "acceptor," such as oxygen or methylene blue. Strict specificity of enzyme action would require 56 dehydrogenases. Quastel found, however, that the 56 compounds could be grouped into classes, for example, a formic acid class, a lactic acid class, and a succinic acid class. The rate of oxidation ⇄ reduction of any compound in a given class was altered (lessened) by the presence in the system of any other compound of the same class grouping but was unchanged in the presence of a compound belonging to another class. Quastel assumes adsorption at "active centers" on the bacterial membrane surface, these centers being specific for certain molecular groupings. Thus the "lactic acid center" adsorbs the grouping, —CO·COH* or —CHOH·COH*, where H* is mobile. Glycollic, oxalic, hydroxymalonic, glyceric, α-hydroxybutyric, and pyruvic acids are all "adsorbed" and activated at the lactic acid center, and in a mixture of two or more of these compounds there is competition for the area available for adsorption. The "succinic acid center" is apparently specific for the grouping, —C·CH_2·COOH or —C·CH·COOH, and in addition to succinic acid is the locus for adsorption of such acids as malonic, glutaric, and phenylpropionic acid. All these compete with one another for adsorption and for "activation," but none interferes noticeably with the lactic acid group of compounds. The "formic acid center" appears to be specific for formic acid, since not even acetic acid interferes with reactions occurring at this center. An interesting demonstration of the specificity of adsorption as determined by chemical configuration is afforded by the fact that malonic acid is adsorbed and activated at the succinic acid center and hydroxymalonic acid at the lactic acid center, but ethyl malonic acid is not adsorbed at any of the centers.

ELECTROPHYSIOLOGY

One of the most active fields of research in biology in recent years has had for its object the determination of the nature and magnitude of electrical phenomena exhibited by cells and their environment. Many of the studies have dealt with the migration of cells when they are freely suspended in a fluid through which an electric current is flowing (electrophoresis), although several other types of studies have also been undertaken with animal and plant cells and tissues.

Electrical phenomena in living systems are of two more or less distinct kinds. One includes electromotive forces which give rise to electric currents in nerve tissues, to oxidation-reduction potentials, to injurious potentials, and the like. The other involves what Freundlich [see Abramson (1934)] has grouped under the term electrokinetic phenomena and includes electrophoresis, electro-osmosis, agglutination, and related processes. Relatively little is known of the exact part played by electric forces in vital systems, but it has been possible to determine their presence there, to measure some of them, and to correlate them with certain physiological processes. In such phenomena probably lies an explanation of many fundamental biological reactions.

The brief discussion on the next few pages should be considered only an introduction to the subject of electrophysiology, since it is impossible within the space at our disposal to cover the theoretical background and all the techniques involved in the various methods used for measuring such processes. For such details the student is referred to articles and several excellent monographs under the individual subject headings.

ELECTROLYTIC CONDUCTION

The flow of an electric current through a solution is spoken of as *electrolytic* (or *ionic*) conduction to distinguish it from *metallic* (or *electronic*) conduction in a wire.

The measurement of electrolytic conduction can be made quite easily and with considerable accuracy by placing the solution to be tested in a specially constructed conductivity vessel and measuring its resistance with a Wheatstone bridge apparatus (Fig. 5). Usually the values are expressed in terms of specific electrical conductivity (C), conductivity being the reciprocal of resistance (R); that is, $C = 1/R$. Resistance is measured in ohms, while conductivity is expressed in mhos. In determining the resistance of an electrolyte solution an alternating current must be employed because a direct current produces electrolysis and after a few minutes a variation in results will be obtained. When alternating current is used, the galvanometer usually employed in a Wheatstone bridge set-up is replaced by a telephone receiver, and minimum buzzing in the receiver indicates the point on the slide wire where the resistance of the bridge is equal to that of the solution. In other words, when the detector (T or G) indicates that no current is passing between C and S, the following relation holds: $V : SB = R : AS$.

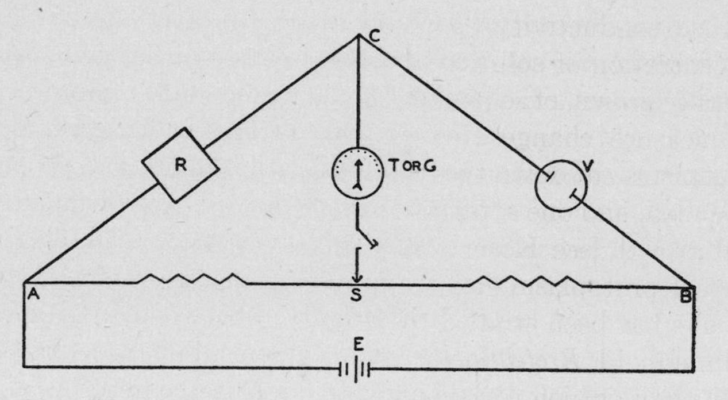

FIG. 5. Diagram of a Wheatstone Bridge Set-up.

The *specific conductivity* of a solution is the conductivity of a cube (1.0 cm. on an edge) of the solution between two platinized electrodes each having an area of 1.0 sq. cm. and placed exactly 1.0 cm. apart. The construction of a conductivity vessel having these specifications is extremely difficult and is seldom attempted. Usually to get around this difficulty the *vessel constant* of an electrode vessel is determined by measuring in it the conductivity of an electrolyte solution which has already been determined. From such information the vessel constant is calculated, using the equation:

$$\frac{BS}{AS} R_k = \text{Vessel constant}$$

where AS = length of slide wire between A and S (Fig. 5).
BS = length of slide wire between B and S.
R = resistance in ohms, as measured by the resistance box (R).
k = specific electrical conductivity of the known solution.

Solutions of potassium and sodium chloride are commonly used as a standard for measuring vessel constants. Several specific conductible (k) values for potassium chloride at various temperatures are:

	k Values of KCl Solutions		
Temperature	*N*	0.1 *N*	0.01 *N*
0°C.	0.06517	0.00713	0.00077
18°C.	0.09783	0.01116	0.00122
25°C.	0.11134	0.01285	0.00140

When biological systems are studied, it is not correct to translate a specific electrical conductivity value into a concentration figure, because conductivity is dependent upon the nature of both the solute and the solvent.

Electrical conductivity has been used extensively to determine the salt concentration of solutions (water culture) in which plants are experimentally grown, of sea water, and of the fluids of plants and animals and to measure changes in cell permeability. Bacteria and other microorganisms cut down the conductance of the solution in which they are suspended, and one attempt has been made to use this fact to follow bacterial growth [see Koser and Saunders (1938)]. The electrical conductivity of protoplasm free from interference by cell walls, vacuoles, and the like has been studied by Brooks (1925), using the plasmodium of the slime-mold, *Brefeldia maxima*. The protoplasm had a resistance of 19,000 ohms, which corresponds to a conductivity of approximately 0.00005 mho. This is about equal to that of 0.00145 N NaCl. The conductivity of saliva is about 50×10^{-4} mho, horse blood has been found to give a value of 0.01216 (or 12×10^{-3}) mho, and the extracted juice from plants, such as the onion, gives a somewhat higher value. For a review on the electric conductance of biological systems the paper by Cole (1933) should be consulted.

GENERAL CONSIDERATION OF ELECTRICAL POTENTIALS

Several types of electrical potentials are known. Certain of these, such as the ones studied by the physicist, are quite simple, well understood, and definite in character. On the other hand, the potentials studied in biological systems are not so simple, since they are usually due to a combination of electrical forces. The following potentials are of interest to the bacteriologist.

1. Electrode Potential (metal/solution). When certain metal electrodes are immersed in a solution, the metal goes very slightly into solution, gives off ions, and creates a charge on the electrode. An example of this type is the copper and zinc electrodes of a simple galvanic cell. Between these electrodes there exists a potential difference which is called the electromotive force (e.m.f.) of the cell. In such a cell the cations move in one direction and carry with them a definite quantity of positive electricity, whereas the anions migrate in the opposite direction and carry negative electricity. Although electrode potentials do not normally enter into biological systems, they often cause considerable trouble due to polarization occurring when measurements of other potentials are being made by employing metal electrodes.

2. Concentration Potential (solution/solution). In the galvanic cell which has just been mentioned, the electrodes consist of two different metals in a common solution. Now suppose that two electrodes of the same metal are immersed in separate solutions of the same salt but of different concentrations. Because of the difference in concentration of the two solutions a flow of current will take place if the two electrodes are joined by a conductor. Such a potential is known as a concentration potential.

3. Diffusion Potential (liquid/liquid; miscible). When two miscible liquids come in contact, a diffusion potential is often produced at the surface of the contact, because of the unequal diffusion of ions across the boundary from one liquid to another. Such potentials are usually very weak and of short duration.

4. Liquid Junction Potential (liquid/liquid; immiscible). When two immiscible solutions come in contact, a permanent interface is formed, and a liquid junction potential is set up. The potential results because of different degrees of solubility of ions in the two phases and is not due to the rate of diffusion. For example, water and amyl alcohol are quite immiscible, and H^+ and Cl^- ions are not equally soluble in both of them. Thus, if the two immiscible liquids are shaken with hydrochloric acid and then allowed to stand, they separate and form a sharp boundary where a potential is set up, because of the unequal solubility of the H^+ and Cl^- ions.

5. Injury Potential (normal tissue/injured tissue). It is well known that the surfaces of injured muscle, and of animal tissues in general, are electronegative to the relatively uninjured surface; that is, electrons, or negatively charged particles of any sort, tend to flow from the relatively normal to the injured zone. Although a measurable potential is set up between normal and injured tissues, the actual physical basis for such a potential is unknown. For further discussion on this subject the review by Abramson (1933) should be consulted.

6. Membrane Potential (solution/membrane/solution). Certain membranes, such as the protoplasmic membrane of cells, parchment, and collodion, have the property of permitting only certain ions to pass through or of allowing different ions to penetrate more rapidly than others. Membranes such as these are spoken of as being

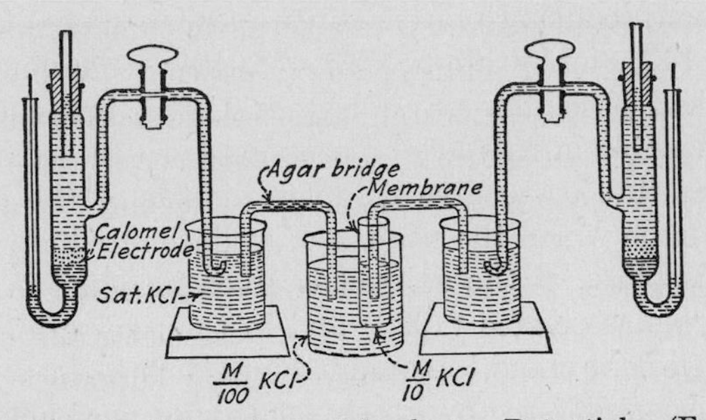

FIG. 6. Connections for Measuring a Membrane Potential. (From *Protoplasm* by Seifriz, courtesy of McGraw-Hill Book Company, New York, 1936.)

semipermeable, selective, or differential in character. Many nonliving and all living membranes are semipermeable.

When a selectively permeable membrane separates two electrolyte solutions (see Fig. 6) of different concentration, an unequal distribution of ions soon occurs on the two sides of the membrane, and a so-called membrane potential results. In certain cases the potential can be measured with the aid of electrodes and a potentiometer. Potential values of 40 to 50 mv. (0.040 to 0.050 volts) have been reported for collodion membranes, apple skins, and other membranes [Seifriz (1936)].

Figure 6 shows two calomel electrodes. In this case they are not used for reference electrodes, as in *p*H measurements, but are merely employed to connect the electrolytic conductors with metallic conductors. Before inserting a membrane and performing an experiment, however, the investigator must always check the calomel electrodes against each other to be sure that there is not a flow of current between them. If there is no current flowing, then any potential recorded in the system after the membrane and different solutions have been inserted must be due to the electrical stresses across the membrane.

Membrane potentials are usually classified into two groups: (1) those resulting from ionic (a Donnan) equilibrium, and (2) those formed as a result of the unequal diffusion of ions through the membrane. The first type may be permanent, but the second undergoes constant change in order to maintain itself and is, therefore, a likely condition of living systems. Undoubtedly membrane potentials play a very important role in many vital phenomena. However, the measurement of such a potential on the protoplasmic membrane of a cell as small as a bacterium would be impossible.

7. Oxidation-Reduction Potential (oxidizing system/reducing system). Since the introduction of accurate methods of measuring the oxidizing and reducing powers of various substances by Clark and coworkers in 1923, many applications of their techniques have been made in the field of cellular physiology and other branches of science. It will be impossible in this brief discussion even to begin a review of the recent literature or to give complete details or the derivation of the equations upon which the subject of oxidation-reduction potentials is based. This phase of the subject is given in detail in the bulletin by Clark and his associates (1928) and in the monograph by Hewitt (1936). The student should acquaint himself with these two reports, which are indispensable to the library of anyone working in this field. Recent information on biological oxidations and reductions is reviewed by Dixon (1939), Barron (1941), and Lardy and Elvehjem (1945).

In the next few pages we will express a few fundamental concepts, accept without question the derivation of certain equations, and then give a few examples of how this subject has been applied to the science of bacteriology.

When the term oxidation is mentioned, it immediately suggests the addition of oxygen to some oxidizable substance. The combustion of methane to form carbon dioxide and water, the oxidation of acetaldehyde to acetic acid, the transformation of ferrous to ferric oxide, and the oxidation of glucose to water and carbon dioxide are all simple examples.

$$CH_4 + 2O_2 \rightarrow CO_2 + 2H_2O$$

$$CH_3CHO + \tfrac{1}{2}O_2 \rightarrow CH_3COOH$$

$$2FeO + \tfrac{1}{2}O_2 \rightarrow Fe_2O_3$$

$$C_6H_{12}O_6 + 6O_2 \rightarrow 6H_2O + 6CO_2$$

It should be kept in mind, however, that an important distinction exists between the oxidation of ferrous iron and the oxidation of sugar in metabolism; the former is reversible but the latter is not. By a perfectly reversible chemical reaction is meant one that requires the application of the same amount of energy to reverse it as is yielded by the original reaction. Oxidation-reduction systems may be completely reversible, partially reversible, or irreversible, with the fact kept in mind that a system may be completely reversible under one set of conditions but partially reversible or irreversible under another.

The term oxidation, as now generally used, is not restricted to the simple combustion of oxygen with some substance but includes also certain other reactions. For example, the conversion of hydroquinone to quinone can be classified as an oxidation even though the oxidant and reductant contain the same amount of oxygen.

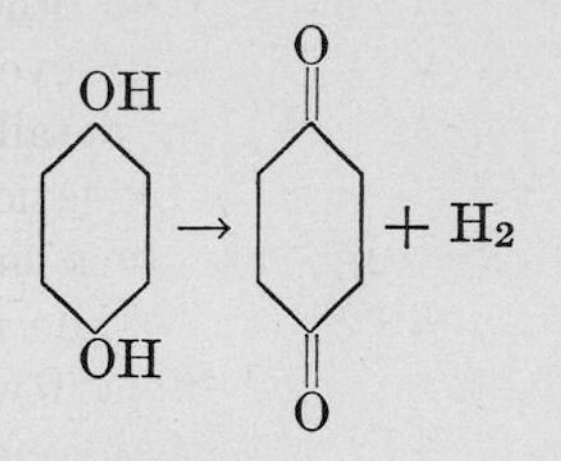

Thus we can now expand our definition of oxidation to cover the removal of hydrogen from a substance. Even this expansion, however, is not sufficient to cover all cases, since the transformation of ferrous chloride to ferric chloride must be regarded as an oxidation, although neither oxygen nor hydrogen is involved in the reaction:

$$FeCl_2 + Cl \rightarrow FeCl_3$$

The examples just mentioned, like other chemical reactions, involve the transfer of electrons from one atom to another, and to gain a general view of oxidation-reduction processes we must now briefly consider the electronic concept of atomic constitution. For the moment let us consider the ionization of ferrous chloride and ferric chloride in solution. The two salts ionize as indicated by the downward arrows shown below; the effect of chlorine is indicated by the horizontal arrow. The symbol (+) signifies the possession of a single positive charge of electricity, and (−) a unit negative charge, or an electron:

$$\begin{array}{ccc} FeCl_2 & & FeCl_3 \\ \downarrow & & \downarrow \\ Fe^{++} + 2Cl^- & \xrightarrow{+\,Cl} & Fe^{+++} + 3Cl^- \end{array}$$

If we confine ourselves to the principal reactants, the equation may be written:

$$Fe^{++} + Cl \rightleftarrows Fe^{+++} + Cl^-$$

In this equation it will be seen that there is an exchange of one electron between ferrous iron and chlorine; the ferrous iron loses an electron which is taken up by chlorine. Furthermore, if we confine our attention to the two states of iron, the transformation may be written:

$$Fe^{++} \underset{\text{Reduction}}{\overset{\text{Oxidation}}{\rightleftarrows}} Fe^{+++} + e,$$

where *e* represents an electron.

When a reaction of this nature proceeds from left to right, an oxidation is said to be taking place, and conversely, when the reaction goes from right to left, a reduction is said to be taking place. Oxidation and reduction reactions are, therefore, essentially electrical in nature, and we can make the following statement: *Oxidation is a process involving the loss of electrons, and reduction is a process involving the gain of electrons.*

Oxidation cannot take place unless there is a corresponding reductant to take up the electrons liberated, and likewise a substance cannot be reduced unless there is a corresponding oxidation to liberate the necessary electrons. Thus, in the preceding ferrous-ferric chloride oxidation-reduction system, the ferrous ion gives up an electron and becomes *oxidized* to the ferric ion:

$$Fe^{++} \xrightarrow{\text{Oxidation}} Fe^{+++} + e$$

However, at the same time the chlorine atom takes up the electron and in so doing becomes reduced to a chloride ion:

$$Cl + e \xrightarrow{\text{Reduction}} Cl^-$$

According to our definition, a metal in the presence of its ions is an oxidation-reduction system:

$$Ag \underset{\text{Reduction}}{\overset{\text{Oxidation}}{\rightleftarrows}} Ag^+ + e$$

and considerable use is made of this fact in preparing "standard" half-cells. Also, hydrogen gas and hydrogen ions form an oxidation-reduction system (hydrogen electrode).

$$\underset{\text{(gas)}}{H_2^{2e}} \underset{\text{Reduction}}{\overset{\text{Oxidation}}{\rightleftarrows}} \underset{\text{(ion)}}{2H^+} + 2e$$

From this brief discussion it becomes apparent that oxidizing agents are substances capable of taking up electrons and reducing agents are those capable of parting with electrons. The oxidation-reduction potential is a measure of the tendency for a substance to give up or take up electrons. In other words, it is a quantitative measure of the free energy of the reaction which is involved in the electronic transfer.

It is now possible to measure the potential of an oxidation-reduction system with considerable accuracy. If an inert metal such as platinum is immersed in an "unknown" reversible oxidation-reduction system and this electrode is connected to a potentiometer set-up, together with a "reference half-cell" (calomel or quinhydrone), a potential difference will be observed. Although the hydrogen electrode is used as the theoretical reference half-cell for all oxidation-reduction potential studies, it is never used for practical measurements. Instead some half-cell such as the calomel half-cell, whose potential has been compared or standardized against the hydrogen half-cell, is employed. It has been demonstrated theoretically and experimentally that the potential value which results when electrodes are immersed in a solution depends largely on the ratio: $\frac{\text{Oxidized form}}{\text{Reduced form}}$. When the oxidized component is predominant in the solution, the potential is higher (more positive) than when the reduced form prevails.

When the hydrogen half-cell is used as a reference cell to complete the system in measuring the oxidation-reduction potential of any solution, the potential (E) of the solution is expressed in volts with reference to the normal hydrogen electrode (H), which is taken as zero, and is called E_h (the subletter of which refers to the system of standardization, namely, the hydrogen electrode).

$$E_h = E_{\text{reference}} - E_{\text{measured}}$$

It has been demonstrated that the E_h of any oxidation-reduction system is directly affected by the hydrogen-ion concentration, the temperature, and the gas constant, as well as by the ratio: $\frac{\text{Oxidant}}{\text{Reductant}}$. The relationship of these factors has been computed on a thermodynamical basis, verified experimentally, and expressed in the *general electrode equation:*

$$E_h = E_0 + \frac{RT}{nF} \ln \frac{(\text{Ox.})}{(\text{Red.})}$$

where E_h = a difference in volts between the oxidation-reduction electrode and a normal hydrogen electrode (or an electrode which has been compared to a hydrogen half-cell).

E_0 = a constant characteristic of the system in question when the pH is zero; when the oxidant and reductant are equal, then $\frac{(\text{Ox.})}{(\text{Red.})} = 1.0$, since $\ln 1 = 0$, and then $E_h = E_0$.

R = gas constant (8.315 volt coulombs).

T = degrees temperature above absolute zero (−273°C.).

n = number of electrons transferred in the reaction formula.

F = the faraday (96,500 coulombs).

ln = symbol for Naperian logarithms or logarithms to the base e.

$\ln x = 2.302 \log x$.

(Ox.) and (Red.) = concentrations of oxidant and reductant, respectively.

To simplify this equation let us use common logarithms and consider a system at 30°C., at constant pH (zero), and involving one electron transfer. Then the above equation may be written:

$$E_h = E_0 + 0.06 \log \frac{(\text{Ox.})}{(\text{Red.})}$$

since at 30°C. $= 2.302 \frac{RT}{F} = 0.0601$.

For a reduction involving two electrons at 30°C., the equation becomes:

$$E_h = E_0 + 0.03 \log \frac{(\text{Ox.})}{(\text{Red.})}$$

These equations show that the potential, E_h, is dependent upon E_0, a constant for the system in question, the proportion of oxidized and reduced forms of the substance studied, and the other factors just mentioned. With an increase in the proportion of oxidized substance the potential will be higher, and with a reduction of the substance the potential will be lower or more negative. E_0 in the above equations has considerable significance. It has been stated that when (Ox.) = (Red.), that is, when the system is 50 per cent oxidized, $E_h = E_0$. In other words, E_0 is the value of the electrode potential of the 50 per cent oxidized (or reduced) system at pH zero. Since many biological systems cannot be studied at pH zero, the application of E_0 becomes somewhat limited. For this reason another term, E'_0, is often used.

The E'_0 of a system at a certain definite pH is the potential value of the half-reduced system at this pH. When E'_0 is given, the pH must also be stated; otherwise, the term has no meaning.

When the E_0 of a system is known, it is possible to calculate the electrode potential at any degree of oxidation or reduction of the system; and, vice versa, the degree of oxidation can be calculated from the value of the electrode potential. Furthermore, E_0 is a measure of the oxidation or reduction intensity level of the system and permits oxidizing and reducing agents to be graded on the basis of their oxidizing or reducing effects. For example, a system of $E_0 = +0.1$ volt will oxidize a system of $E_0 = -0.1$ volt or one of -0.05 volt but, on the other hand, will itself be oxidized by a system of $E_0 = +0.3$ volt. Usually, however, the sign and magnitude of the oxidation-reduction potential tells us nothing concerning the relative speeds of oxidation and reduction. Nevertheless the measurement of various oxidation-reduction potentials allows one to study the oxidation-reduction conditions of a system and to grade them in order of their oxidizing or reducing tendencies.

It should be emphasized that the oxidation-reduction potential is an *intensity factor* and not a *capacity factor*. In this way E_h resembles temperature and pH. Since temperature and pH give us no information as to heat capacity and buffering power, respectively, so also is E_h independent of "poising effect," the capacity term in oxidation-reduction systems. This is evident from the derivation of E_h, which depends upon the ratio of oxidized and reduced forms of the substance being studied and not on their absolute quantities. Thus an 80 per cent oxidized system will have the same electrode potential whether the total concentration is 10 per cent or 0.1 per cent, but the poising effect of the 10 per cent concentration will be 100 times greater than that of the 0.1 per cent concentration. These points are quite important to remember when biological systems, many of which have definite electrode potentials but are not well poised, are dealt with.

The hydrogen-ion concentration must be taken into consideration when dealing with oxidation-reduction systems because frequently the reduced form is an anion which can accept hydrogen ions and thus become inoperative in contributing to the potential. Therefore, if the hydrogen-ion concentration of a system, such as quinhydrone, is allowed to vary, the potential will be greatly influenced. In most bacterial culture systems buffers are added to maintain a stable pH.

To summarize this theoretical discussion we may say that the oxidation-reduction potential of a system depends principally on three factors: (1) the innate tendency of the system to take up or give off electrons, (2) the ratio of the oxidant to the reductant, and (3) the hydrogen-ion concentration.

Measurement of Oxidation-Reduction Potentials. Two methods are in general use for the measurement of oxidation-reduction potentials: (1) the dye indicator method, and (2) the direct electrometric determination of the potential. For various reasons the electrometric method is the most reliable. These two methods will be briefly discussed.

1. Dye Indicator Method. Clark, Cohen, and their associates (1928, 1933) have studied a number of dyes which behave as oxidation-reduction systems. Such dyes show full color when in their highest state of oxidation and are colorless when completely reduced. Between these extremes various degrees of color are exhibited. Most of the dyes employed in oxidation-reduction potential studies cover a range of approximately 0.1 volt between the colored and the colorless form. Thus by using a series of dyes that change color at different ranges of E_h it is possible to make approximate E_h measurements in a manner comparable to *p*H determinations.

The use of dyes for measuring E_h is based on the following: Let D_o represent the oxidized form and D_r the reduced form of a reversible oxidation-reduction dye system where the exchange of two electrons is involved:

$$D_r \underset{\text{Reduction}}{\overset{\text{Oxidation}}{\rightleftarrows}} D_o + 2 \text{ electrons}$$

If the temperature (30°C.) and the *p*H (7.0) are kept constant and the general electrode equation is applied, then

$$E_h = E'_0 + 0.03 \log \frac{(D_o)}{(D_r)}$$

Now suppose that the potential of a given dye when 50 per cent reduced or oxidized ($D_o = D_r$) is +0.1 volt, then $E'_0 = +0.1$ volt, and

$$E_h = +0.1 + 0.03 \log \frac{(D_o)}{(D_r)}$$

By using this equation it is possible to calculate the potential at different stages of oxidation or reduction of the dye (D). For example, when 95 per cent oxidized (5 per cent reduced), the potential in volts will be:

$$E_h = +0.1 + 0.03 \log \tfrac{95}{5} = +0.138 \text{ volt}$$

In a similar manner the following E_h values may be calculated:

Percentage Oxidation	Percentage Reduction	E_h in Volts	
2	98	+0.051	Approximately colorless
5	95	+0.062	
10	90	+0.071	
25	75	+0.086	
50	50	+0.100 (E'_0)	50 per cent colored
75	25	+0.114	
90	10	+0.129	
95	5	+0.138	
98	2	+0.151	Approximately full color

It can also be seen from this list that the oxidation-reduction state of the dye system can be read off by determining the potential. For example, if the E_h is +0.062 volt, the system is 95 per cent in the reduced form and 5 per cent in the oxidized form. The E'_0 values for several oxidation-reduction indicator dyes are given in Table 7. For more complete details about the effect of *p*H, etc., on these indicators

TABLE 7

OXIDATION-REDUCTION INDICATOR DYES (THE E'_0 VALUES—POTENTIALS OF 50 PER CENT REDUCED DYES—ARE AT *p*H 7.0)

[From Hewitt (1936)]

Dye	E'_0, volts	Dye	E'_0, volts
Oxygen electrode (1 atm. pressure)	+0.81	*m*-Toluylenediamine indophenol	+0.125
Phenol-*m*-sulfonate-indo-2:6-dibromophenol	+0.273	Toluylene blue	+0.115
m-Chlorophenol-indo-2:6-dichlorophenol	+0.254	Thionine (Lauth's violet)	+0.063
m-Bromophenol indophenol	+0.248	Cresyl blue	+0.047
Phenol-*o*-sulfonate-indo-2:6-dibromophenol	+0.242	Gallocyanine	+0.021
o-Chlorophenol indophenol	+0.233	Methylene blue	+0.011
o-Bromophenol indophenol	+0.230	Ciba scarlet sulfonate	−0.036
Phenol indophenol	+0.227	Indigo tetrasulfonate	−0.046
Phenol blue	+0.224	Methyl capri blue	−0.060
2:6-Dibromophenol indophenol	+0.218	Indigo trisulfonate	−0.081
m-Cresol indophenol	+0.208	Indigo disulfonate	−0.125
o-Cresol indophenol	+0.191	Brilliant alizarine blue	−0.173
Thymol indophenol	+0.174	Phenosafranine	−0.252
		Safranine-T	−0.289
		Neutral red	−0.325
		Viologens	−0.400
		Hydrogen electrode (1 atm. pressure)	−0.421

the student should consult the bulletin by Clark and associates (1928) or the monograph by Hewitt (1936). The choice of one of these dyes for practical use depends on several important factors. For instance, the indicator must not act as a hydrogen-ion indicator at the *p*H of the system under investigation; the normal oxidation-reduction potential of the indicator must be close to that of the system under study; the indicator should have an intense and distinctive color and should come to equilibrium in a short time; the indicator should not be toxic or enter into the reactions of the system under investigation.

The indicator method has proved useful in the study of living cells and tissues, since it has not as yet been possible to devise an electrode for intracellular measurements. Where attempts at electrode measurement have been made, the cell after a very short time apparently forms a vacuole around the electrode, and as a result the measured potential is not that of the cell proper. In determining the reducing intensity of cells with indicators two techniques are used: the dye is injected into the cell by microinjection methods, or the dye is allowed to diffuse into the cell. In either case the indicator dyes are taken in sequence and their reactions observed in the cell.

A number of living cells normally contain oxidation-reduction potential indicators, and important respiratory functions have been attributed to some of these pigments. The cytochrome components, flavins, and pyocyanine are just a few examples.

2. Direct Electrometric Method. Since the use of various indicator dyes in oxidation-reduction potential studies is limited, the electrometric method should be used whenever possible.

Although a number of factors must be carefully controlled when making direct potentiometric determinations of E_h, the measuring apparatus is relatively simple. To measure the potential of an "unknown" half-cell [unattackable electrode/oxidation-reduction system (x)] it must be coupled to another half-cell (standard) by an agar-saturated salt bridge (S.B.), which permits electrical contact without introducing errors due to liquid/liquid potentials or other factors. The two half-cells are then connected to a potentiometer set-up. According to definition, the E_h is the potential referred to the normal hydrogen electrode, which is taken as zero. However, since the normal hydrogen electrode is not a practical possibility, any convenient standard half-cell may be employed, providing its potential with reference to the hydrogen electrode is known. The two standard half-cells frequently used are the calomel electrode and the quinhydrone electrode. By means of the potentiometer (P) the electromotive force (E_1) is varied until the galvanometer (G) shows no deflection. At this point the electromotive force (E_1) of the potentiometer just balances the electromotive force of the complete cell, $E_h - E_{\text{standard}}$ (the negative sign is given because the two half-cells are in opposition). Therefore, when the potentiometer is balanced:

$$E_1 = E_h - E_{\text{standard}}, \quad \text{or} \quad E_h = E_1 + E_{\text{standard}}$$

The theoretical circuit employed is represented diagrammatically in Fig. 7.

For complete details on methods and standard techniques for use with bacteria and other microorganisms the monograph by Hewitt (1936) and the papers by McAlister (1938), Ward (1938), Gillespie and Rettger (1938), Klobusitzky (1940), Johnstone (1940), Kanel (1941), and Wynd and Varney (1941) should be consulted. Wynd and Varney have developed a very convenient vessel for measuring the E_h of bacterial cultures.

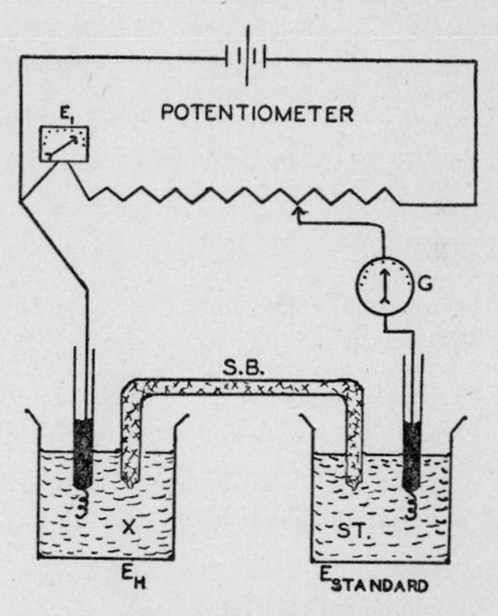

FIG. 7. Theoretical Circuit for the Measurement of E_h. G = galvanometer; E_1 = e.m.f. on potentiometer where the unknown half-cell (x) and the standard half-cell (*st.*) are equal; *S.B.* = salt bridge. (From Hewitt, 1936.)

Biological Oxidation-Reduction Systems. It is now a well-established fact that oxidation-reduction systems play an important role in the respiratory and metabolic processes of the living organism. In fact, Hewitt (1936) has stated, "[Such] systems play so intimate and so essential a part in living organisms that life itself might be defined as a continuous oxidation-reduction reaction."

Several biological oxidation-reduction systems have been studied, and some of them are quite well characterized. They include systems containing sulfhydryl groups, hemoglobin, the cytochromes, certain respiratory pigments, ascorbic acid, various sugar systems, succinate-fumarate, and adrenaline, as well as cell and tissue suspensions (Table 8). A classification of known reversible oxidation-reduction systems found in the living cell has been presented by Barron (1941). Many direct electrometric oxidation-reduction potential studies have been made on bacteria, yeasts, and other microorganisms, though obviously not of the interior of the cells themselves but rather of the surrounding medium. It is necessary, therefore, to distinguish between potentials obtained within cells or with cellular components

TABLE 8

Approximate Oxidation-Reduction Potentials * of Certain Biological Systems

[From Allyn and Baldwin (1932), Hewitt (1936), McAlister (1938), Gillespie *et al.* (1938), Axelrod and Johnson (1939), Burrows (1941), and others]

System	E_h, volts
Oxygen electrode (1 atm. pressure)	+0.81
Cultures containing peroxide	+0.42
Adrenaline	+0.38
Aerobic culture broth	+0.30
Cytochrome a (pH 7.4, 20°C.)	+0.29
Cytochrome c (pH 7.4, 20°C.)	+0.262
Saccharomyces cerevisiae cultures	+0.22
Ascorbic acid (vitamin C) (pH 4.6)	+0.14
Aspergillus niger culture	+0.20
Chlororaphin (pH 3.09)	+0.119
Phenicin	+0.05
Salmonella cultures (range for 31 species)	+0.035 to −0.160
Hallochrome	+0.022
Juglone (pH 7.31)	+0.023
Succinate-fumarate	+0.01
Penicillium granulatum cultures	−0.024
Hermidine	−0.03
Cytochrome b (pH 7.4, 20°C.)	−0.04
Pyocyanine	−0.04
Toxoflavin	−0.05
Yellow enzyme	−0.059
Ameba in air	−0.07
Brucella species cultures	+0.09 to +0.15
Rhizobium cultures (range of 4 species)	+0.10 to −0.20
Alcohol-acetaldehyde (pH 7.4)	−0.09
Succinate-maleate	−0.094
Hemin	−0.114
Oral lactobacilli cultures	−0.130 ±0.02
Pneumococcus cultures	−0.15
Phthiocol	−0.18
Lactate-pyruvate	−0.186
Corynebacterium diphtheriae cultures	−0.20
Bacillus polymyxa cultures	−0.20
Riboflavin	−0.208
Glutathione (pH 7.15)	−0.233
Lactobacillus acidophilus cultures	−0.24 ±0.02
Ameba in N_2	−0.25
Bacillus macerans cultures	−0.27
Coenzyme I (pH 7.4, 20°C.)	−0.325
Escherichia coli cultures	−0.40
Clostridium botulinum cultures; *Clostridium tetani* cultures	−0.3 to −0.41
Hypoxanthine-uric acid (pH 7.2)	−0.41
Hydrogen electrode (1 atm. pressure, pH 7.0)	−0.42

* For pigments, the potential of the half-reduced system, E'_0, at pH 7.0 is given; determinations at other pH values are so listed. The values for mold, yeast, and bacterial cultures are minimum values.

and those obtained in cell suspensions. In cell suspensions the changes of potentials are probably due largely to cellular products. In Table 8 are listed the approximate oxidation-reduction potentials of several biological systems.

It should be emphasized that the derivation of the oxidation-reduction equations rests on the assumption that the system is in equilibrium. It is questionable that any living cell can be said to be in a state of true equilibrium; the best that can be achieved is a steady state. For this reason, as well as others, time : potential (E_h) curves are usually plotted in studies of bacterial cultures. In general, the curves follow those plotted for a hypothetical aerobe and anaerobe in Fig. 8, adopted from Hewitt (1936). A significant result of oxidation-reduction potential measurements on both cells and cell suspensions is that more negative potentials are found under anaerobic, as contrasted with aerobic, conditions. Bacterial cultures develop reducing conditions, not so much because of the liberation of reducing substances by the cells as on account of the exertion of reducing activities.

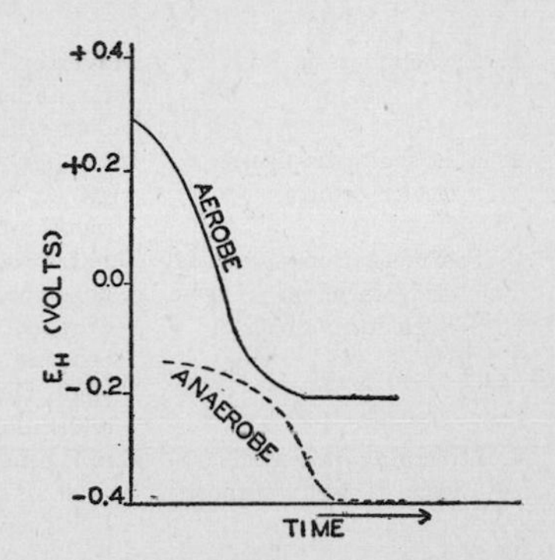

FIG. 8. Potential: Time Curves Exhibited by a Hypothetical Aerobe and Anaerobe. (From Hewitt, 1936.)

Probably the most promising field for further investigation in oxidation-reduction potentials is the isolation and study of oxidation-reduction systems occurring in cells and tissues. When various culture media and intact cells are dealt with, the situation is too complicated to analyze with any degree of clarity. About all that can be said of the work done on oxidation-reduction potentials in living systems (bacterial cultures) is that the potential value obtained is at least an indication or measure of relative physiological activity. Burrows (1941) has also observed a rather close association between the oxidation-reduction potentials of certain *Salmonella* species and the immunological character (type of agglutination) of the bacterial species.

ELECTROKINETIC PHENOMENA

Colloidal particles and most cells, including bacteria, when freely suspended in an aqueous medium, will migrate toward the anode or the cathode if they are subjected to the influence of an electric field. Therefore they must possess an electric charge. The electric charge on the surface of nonliving colloidal particles and on living cells is an important property of colloidal systems; the nature of this charge has been the subject of a great many studies in colloidal chemistry and biology. Usually four electrical phenomena are grouped under the term electrokinetics. They are briefly summarized in Table 9. The apparatus employed and the important factors which must be carefully controlled in studying these phenomena cannot be discussed here. For such technical details the books by Abramson (1934) and Gortner (1937) and the papers by Moyer (1936, 1940), Abramson and Moyer (1937), and Tiselius (1940) should be consulted.

Of the four phenomena mentioned above, the techniques for measuring electrophoresis seem to be the most useful for the investigation of

TABLE 9

ELECTROKINETIC PHENOMENA

Name	Phenomenon	Produced by
1. Electrophoresis	Movement of colloidal particles, bacteria, and other cells with respect to the dispersion liquid.	Applied e.m.f.
2. Electroendosmosis or electro-osmosis	Movement or flow of a liquid through a gel or capillaries (tubes, pores of membranes, etc.).	Applied e.m.f.
3. Sedimentation potential or Dorn effect (reverse of electrophoresis)	E.m.f. produced. May be positive or negative. For example, lead shot dropped through water, alcohol, or benzene carry down a (+) charge, while through turpentine or carbon tetrachloride a (−) charge.	Movement of particles with respect to liquid
4. Streaming potential (reverse of electro-osmosis)	E.m.f. produced.	Movement of liquid through pores of a diaphragm or a capillary tube due to restraining action of capillaries

bacteria, blood cells, proteins, and other organic surfaces of especial interest to the biologist. The techniques of electro-osmosis and streaming potential serve best to develop our knowledge of the electrokinetic properties of certain chemical systems, especially those involving small pores and those complicated by surface conductance [Abramson and Moyer (1937)]. However, the one-way protoplasmic streaming in the filaments of some of the common molds and the passage of fluids under certain conditions through the common bacteriological filters are probably examples of electro-osmosis [see Mudd and Mudd (1924)]. Since very few bacteriological data are available on the electrokinetic phenomena other than electrophoresis, no attention will be given to them here.

ELECTROPHORESIS

The phenomenon of electrophoresis has been known and studied by physical chemists for the past hundred years. However, it did not become of significance in biochemistry until 1899, when Sir William Hardy observed that proteins show this phenomenon in a highly characteristic way. Later Michaelis and his associates demonstrated the value of electrophoretic methods for the characterization of enzymes and proteins. As early as 1904 Bechhold noted that bacteria suspended in an aqueous medium carry an electrical charge. Since that time a great number of studies have appeared on the electrophoresis of bacteria and other microorganisms [see Falk (1928), Abramson (1934), Moyer (1936), Stearns and Roepke (1941)].

When a potential difference is set up between two electrodes in a colloidal system, the particles move toward the anode or cathode, depending upon their charge. The movement of such particles, or cells, under the influence of an electric current is called *electrophoresis.* The words *anaphoresis* and *cataphoresis* are used to designate migration to the anode and cathode, respectively. The most direct method of studying electrophoresis, and the one most commonly used by the bacteriologist, is observing with the microscope or ultramicroscope the migration of individual particles (bacteria) in a solution through which an electric current is flowing. Unfortunately this method is very limited in its application, since many of the substances, such as proteins and viruses, which are of interest have such a small molecular or particle size that they are beyond the resolving power of ordinary microscopes.

The observation of electrophoretic migration of these substances must, therefore, depend upon measurements of the movement of a layer of the solution of the substances in an electrophoresis tube. For this purpose two different methods have been employed: (1) the *transference* method, which depends upon the determination by chemical or biological analysis of the increase or decrease of the amount of substance above a fixed level in the tube, when a known amount of electricity is allowed to flow through; and (2) the *moving boundary* method, which measures the distance traveled by the boundary between the solution and a supernatant medium of the same electrolytic composition. The transference method has been used particularly for studying certain enzymes; the moving boundary method is especially convenient for colored materials. Both methods are, of course, identical in principle with those used by the physical chemist for measuring migration velocities of ordinary ions. The moving boundary method has been developed largely by Tiselius in Sweden and is now used extensively for studies on native fluids and other substances of interest to the chemist and biologist. Since the excellent review by Tiselius (1940) is readily available to the student, further details on the application of the moving boundary method will not be given here. Let us now return to a brief discussion of the direct method of studying electrophoresis and its application in the field of bacteriology.

Bacteria in general carry a negative charge when suspended in a natural solution of low salt content and thus migrate to the anode when observed in a microelectrophoretic cell. When various cations are added to the fluid in which the bacteria are suspended or when the hydrogen-ion concentration is increased, this negative charge is reduced or is sometimes even replaced by a positive charge, so that the movement in a microelectrophoretic cell is decreased in velocity or reversed in direction. So far as the hydrogen-ion concentration is concerned, the majority of the bacteria have an *isoelectric point* in the range *p*H 3.0 to 4.0, and at this point migration in an electric field ceases. Even though most bacteria possess a negative charge, a few observations have been made using certain bacterial species suspended in neutral buffer solutions in which the cells have shown no definite electrophoretic mobility at any field strength. Apparently the charge on the surface of such organisms is so low that it is impossible to assign them a mobility value.

Most of the viruses so far examined migrate to the anode in neutral solutions; thus they carry a negative charge [McFarlane (1940)]. The same statement holds true for yeast. The spirochetes and protozoa appear to be divided between species or strains which bear positive and those which carry negative charges; however, it should be kept in mind that erroneous results may account for this difference. Failure to observe the level at which cellular movement takes place in the microelectrophoretic cell and failure to measure *p*H are two very common faults in electrophoresis research work. The strong electro-osmotic flow of the medium in a microelectrophoretic chamber may cause a weakly charged negative particle to move toward the negative pole against its own attraction for the positive pole; and, if acid is added to a suspension of electronegative cells, they may reverse the charge at reactions on the alkaline side of their isoelectric points.

Direct measurements of the velocity with which particles or cells move in an electrophoretic apparatus have been made by many workers. The proper apparatus and a standard technique for bacterial electrophoretic studies have been discussed at some length in two papers by Moyer (1936). He has shown that, when experiments of this type are carefully performed, results are no more variable than with nonliving systems. Similar findings have been reported by Stearns and Roepke (1941). These papers should be consulted by those interested in this subject. In a general way, the technique consists of suspending particles or cells in a buffer solution placed in a special apparatus known as a microelectrophoretic cell and observing with a microscope the time required for a single particle to move a certain distance under a definite potential gradient. The flow of current through the microelectrophoretic cell is then reversed, and the velocity of another particle is determined. This process is repeated several times. If certain factors are carefully controlled, uniform results will be obtained each time.

When electric migration studies are carried out with bacteria, it is found that the cells, like the particles of colloidal sols, migrate to the pole in the microelectrophoretic cell possessing the opposite sign from that on the cell. The formula for the velocity of migration is:

$$V = \frac{\zeta ED}{4\pi\eta}$$

where V = the velocity of the particles or cells in centimeters (or micra) per second.

ζ = the electrokinetic potential (zeta potential), the potential at the surface of the cell (or particle) and the medium.

E = the drop in applied e.m.f. per centimeter between the electrodes of the microelectrophoretic cell, that is, the potential gradient or the field strength in electrostatic units per centimeter.

D = the dielectric constant of the medium (approximately 80 for water).

η = the viscosity of the medium (0.01 poise for water at 20°C.).

From this equation we can also solve for the electrokinetic potential (Helmholtz potential, ζ):

$$\zeta = \frac{4\pi\eta V}{ED}$$

Thus, by knowing the rate of migration (V) of a particle or bacterial cell and by making use of the theories pertaining to the electrical double layer at the surface of a particle suspended in a liquid, it is possible to measure indirectly the potential difference or the electrokinetic potential (ζ, zeta potential), between the bacterial cell and its medium.

We now know that the concept of Helmholtz, visioning a rigid electrical double layer of ions at the surface of a particle suspended in a fluid, has been replaced by the idea of a diffuse double layer, the so-called Gouy cloud of ions. In other words, instead of having two rigid layers opposite in sign at a molecular distance, the outer layer is free to move and exists as an ionic cloud. Over a time average, the outer layer has a net charge opposite in sign to the ions held by the particle. The thickness of the ionic atmosphere around colloidal particles or cells varies from the unimolecular dimension of the compact Helmholtz double layer (from 1 to 20 Å., or about 1 $\mu\mu$) to the hundred or more molecules in the depth of an ionic cloud. The depth of the ionic cloud has been calculated to be 0.96 mμ for a 0.1 N solution of salt, 9.6 mμ for a 0.01 N solution of salt, and 1,010 mμ for pure water. It can thus be seen that, if the ionic cloud is diffuse and free to move, it is not a fundamental characteristic of the surface particle. For this reason recent studies on electrophoresis have been concerned more with the *net charge density* (σ) per square centimeter of cell surface. Charge and potential should always be clearly distinguished; charge is often carelessly used to indicate potential. Potential is pressure, whereas charge is quantity. Potential is always expressed in volts; charge is expressed in coulombs, or electrostatic units. Between charge and potential there is a definite relationship and interdependence, which can be calculated [see derivation of formula in the paper by Moyer (1936)] if the rate of mobility (V), the zeta potential (ζ), and several other factors are known:

$$\zeta = \frac{4\pi\sigma\lambda}{D}$$

where σ = the surface charge per unit area.
λ = the thickness of the ionic cloud, and the other symbols have their usual meaning.

Thus, by determining the mobility in a microelectrophoretic cell, by experimentally measuring the thickness of the double layer, by knowing the area of the bacterial cell and the above constants, the value for σ can be determined.

The literature on bacterial electrophoresis is very large [see Falk (1928), Abramson (1934), Moyer (1936), and Stearns and Roepke (1941)], and space does not permit a discussion here of all the results. Thus only a few general remarks will be made.

Many and varied bacterial phenomena have been associated with electrophoretic values. In fact, it can be said that electrophoresis is one of the most powerful tools at the disposal of the biologist for the investigation of the surface phenomena which are so intimately linked to biological processes. Falk and his associates studied at some length the relationship between electrokinetic potential and bacterial virulence for experimental animals. Although they noted a direct parallelism between these two characteristics with diphtheria bacilli and pneumococci, their facts have not been used for practical purposes. Others have correlated electrophoretic values with the ability of bacteria to fix nitrogen, with the agglutination of organisms, with the bacterial population cycle, with cultural and biological characteristics [Verwey and Frobisher (1940)], and with bacterial variation. Abramson (1934) observed that the mobility and zeta potential of living cells and proteins was lowered by the addition of salts, whereas the net charge density per square centimeter of surface actually increased. This fact can be seen very well in Table 10, which shows the influence of salt on the

TABLE 10

THE INFLUENCE OF SALT ON THE MOBILITY, ZETA POTENTIAL, AND NET CHARGE DENSITY OF UNSENSITIZED "ROUGH" TYPHOID BACILLI

[From Abramson (1934)]

NaCl Concentration	Agglutination	Mobility, V, μ/sec.	Zeta Potential, ζ, volts	Net Charge Density, σ, e.s.u.*
0.001 *M*	+	3.9	0.053	1,420
0.004	++	3.6	0.049	2,590
0.01	++	3.2	0.043	3,390
0.02	++	2.4	0.033	3,600
0.04	+++	1.6	0.022	3,150

* The electrostatic unit is the charge which will repel with a force of one dyne an equal charge placed at a distance of one centimeter in air.

agglutination of "rough" typhoid bacilli. These data demonstrate that, during coagulation by simple salts, particles in general do not have their net surface charge decreased. Rather it is the surface potential (zeta potential) which is lowered. When staphylococci, colon bacilli, and dysentery bacilli were sensitized by decreasing dilutions ($\frac{1}{800}$ to $\frac{1}{100}$) of specific immune sera, the net charge density, σ, of the staphylococci hardly changed, that of the colon bacilli was lowered, and that of dysentery bacilli actually increased as agglutination took place. From these results Abramson concluded that such agglutinations were not connected with the zeta potential but were connected with the reaction of the bacterial surface with the specific antibody.

Moyer (1936) studied the electrophoresis of *Escherichia coli* during various phases of the population cycle. His data show that definite changes in the surface of the cell occur during the cycle, and that "smooth" and "rough" strains exhibit different mobilities. These changes are intimately linked with the growth process and especially with the periods of lag and physiological youth. Moyer believes that the cells may possibly show an increase in permeability during the early phases of growth and that all these changes are due to actual changes in the physical or chemical constitution of the bacterial surface during the population cycle. In the discussion of the period of physiological youth in Chapter 2 this phase of the subject is briefly mentioned. Only one other example dealing with electric mobility will be given here. From the time of inoculation of fresh media with *E. coli* until about one hour later, a sharp decrease in the electric mobility of the cells was observed (Fig. 9). This decrease in mobility persists from about the first hour until the third or fourth hour, whereupon there occurs an increase in mobility up to the original value observed for the cells in the culture used as the inoculum. Although it will be seen that the mobility of cells from rough cultures was about 600 per cent higher than that of those from smooth cultures, both types passed

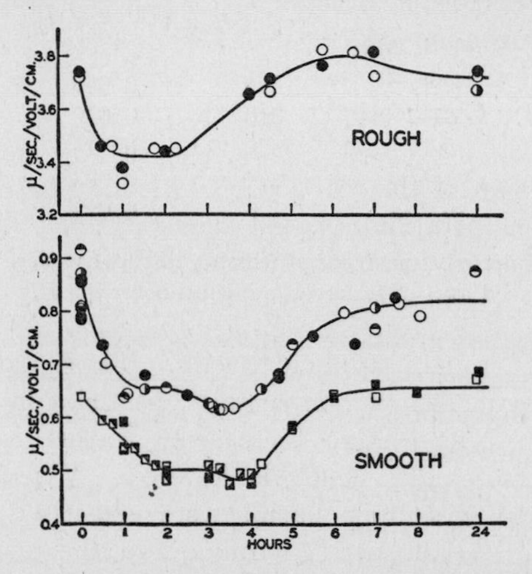

Fig. 9. The Effect of the Age of the Culture on the Electrophoretic Mobility of Rough and Smooth Forms of *Escherichia coli* Grown in Peptone Media and Suspended in Buffers. *Upper curve:* Rough form in 0.02 M acetate buffer, pH 5.5. *Lower curves:* Smooth form measured in 0.0066 M phosphate (*circles*) and 0.02 M acetate (*squares*) buffers at pH 6.9 and 5.5, respectively. Different markings represent experiments done on different days. (From Moyer, 1936.)

through a minimum in electric mobility in the early stages of their culture cycle. Calculation of σ, the net charge density, showed a similar decrease during the early phase of the population cycle (see Fig. 5, Chapter 2). Similar interesting data have been presented by Stearns and Roepke (1941), working with *Brucella* species.

HYDROGEN-ION CONCENTRATION AND ACTIVITY, TITRATABLE ACIDITY, AND BUFFER ACTION

A few years ago the conception of hydrogen-ion concentration and activity as a more exact expression of acidity, or rather "reaction," than titratable acidity or alkalinity was only of academic interest. Soon it was realized, however, that the extension of this conception to science and industry provided not only a solution to many problems but also, in certain processes, a valuable means of control. The measurement of hydrogen-ion concentration and activity probably owes its origin to biochemical research; in fact, it is no exaggeration to say that the requirements of biochemical problems have led, more than any other factor, to improvements in technique and a realization of the importance of the subject. No attempt will be made here to cover the theoretical aspects or to discuss the technical details involved in measuring hydrogen-ion concentration and activity. For those interested in such phases of the subject the books by Michaelis and Perlzweig (1926), Clark (1928), and Buchanan and Fulmer (1928) are recommended.

The measurement of the reaction of a medium by determining the hydrogen-ion concentration is based principally on the theory of the dissociation of electrolytes, formulated as early as 1887 by the Swedish chemist, Svante Arrhenius. According to his theory, substances such as acids, alkalies, and salts (known as electrolytes), whose aqueous solutions conduct electricity, are in part split up or dissociated in solution into two portions or *ions*. One (the *cation*) carries a positive charge and is therefore attracted to a negatively charged plate or electrode (*cathode*) placed in solution; the other (the *anion*) is negatively charged and migrates through the solution to the *anode* or positively charged electrode. Arrhenius also observed that electrolytic conductance in an aqueous solution is not entirely proportional to the amount of electrolyte which is dissolved. This fact led him to believe that at infinite dilution complete dissociation of electrolytes takes place, whereas in more concentrated solutions the breakdown is not entirely complete and part of the original electrolyte remains in solution in an undissociated state. Thus, according to his conception, an aqueous solution of sodium chloride or hydrochloric acid would have the following equilibria:

$$NaCl \rightleftarrows Na^+ + Cl^-$$

and

$$HCl \rightleftarrows H^+ + Cl^-$$

For dilute solutions the equilibrium of either equation would shift toward the right, whereas in more concentrated solutions the equilibrium would shift farther and farther to the left. As a result we have so-called *dissociation constants* of electrolytes, which are expressions of the ratio between the product of the concentrations of the dissociated ions and the concentration of the undissociated molecules. We shall point out two facts shortly: (1) dissociation constants apparently do not indicate degree of dissociation, as was originally thought, but rather the degree of interionic friction and therefore the extent to which the electrolyte will diverge from the theoretically perfect behavior of solutions; and (2) the reaction or acidity of an aqueous solution should be expressed by the hydronium-ion (H_3O^+) concentration and its activity rather than by the hydrogen-ion concentration, because free protons (H^+ is a proton) do not occur to any measurable extent in solution.

Although Arrhenius laid the foundation upon which is built the theory of hydrogen-ion concentration and hydrogen-ion activity, his views in respect to the incomplete dissociation of electrolytes in a concentrated solution have been altered as a result of more recent research. As we know, chemists and physicists have presented data which discredit the existence of individual molecules as represented by KCl, NaCl, and similar formulas. Studies on the crystalline structure of salts such as sodium chloride have shown that there are no molecules of NaCl in crystalline matter, but rather atoms of sodium and chlorine spaced at equal distances from each other throughout the salt. Thus, if the atoms all exist as ions in the solid salt, why should they not remain so when in solution, regardless of the concentration? This question cannot be answered here, but for our purposes it will probably be sufficient to say that the difference is due to ion pairs or the electrolytic friction of the ions. This view seems reasonable, because the higher the concentration, the closer together are the ions and the greater is the interionic electrical friction. On the other hand, in very dilute solutions the ions are farther apart, their mutual electrostatic attractions are negligible, and the ions can exercise their full kinetic energy and activity.

The hydrogen-ion activity of a solution is an intensity factor and is related to the hydrogen-ion concentration in the following way:

H-ion activity = (H-ion concentration) × (f, the mean ion-activity coefficient)

At infinite dilution or in a very low concentration of hydrogen ions, the mean ion-activity coefficient is considered to be equal to 1.00 (a 0.0005 M solution of HCl has an activity coefficient of 1.00). Therefore, under such conditions, hydrogen-ion activity equals hydrogen-ion concentration. Although for practical purposes it is convenient to regard the two values as identical, it must be kept in mind that the methods which are employed for the measurement of hydrogen-ion concentration, or pH, are in reality measuring hydrogen-ion activity.

Several other points concerning the hydrogen ion should be mentioned because they are rather disturbing in connection with certain accepted theories. Although it is natural to indicate the hydrogen ion by the symbol H^+, Brönsted, Lowry, and others [see Kolthoff (1930)] say that there is no such thing as a hydrogen ion in an aqueous solution because no good reason exists why one and not both of the two hydrogen atoms of water should become detached. Furthermore, since H^+ is a naked proton and extremely small, it is able to penetrate the structure of any other molecule with which it comes in contact. In an aqueous solution this would probably be an undissociated water molecule (H_2O), and the structure might be written as $(H_3O)^+$, the so-called *hydronium ion.* Other recent studies indicate that the hydronium ion must not only be regarded as OH_3^+, but also some of the higher polymers, such as $O_2H_5^+$ and $O_3H_7^+$, must be considered, since water exists in an indefinite number of polymers of H_2O. If we do accept the fact that hydronium ions exist, then the following reaction takes place when hydrochloric acid is added to water:

$$H_2O + H^+ + Cl^- \rightleftharpoons H_3O^+ + Cl^-$$

From this reaction it can be seen that it is necessary to define an acid as a compound which can split off protons rather than one which dissociates, yielding a preponderance of hydrogen ions. Furthermore the requirement that an acid should combine with a metal hydroxide to form a salt is also discarded. Thus it can be stated very simply:

$$\text{Acid} \rightleftharpoons \text{Base} + \text{Proton}$$

If these facts are accepted for an acid, then the older definition of a base—that it must give off hydroxyl ions—must also be discarded. By this new concept a base would be defined as a substance that can take up protons. Since the hydrogen ion is a proton, we can illustrate this definition by the equation $H_2O + HCl \rightleftharpoons H_3O^+ + Cl^-$, which shows water to be a base, and by the equation $H_2O \rightleftharpoons OH^- + H^+$, which shows water to be an acid. In accepting these points, we do not necessarily have to discard all the older theories which attribute acidity to the hydrogen ion. In this discussion we shall continue to use the older terminology and write the hydrogen ion by the symbol H^+, keeping in mind, however, that it is only a symbol and may not represent the true condition in a solution.

The reactions with which we are mostly concerned in bacteriology take place in aqueous solutions. Since pure water undergoes a very slight dissociation into positively charged hydrogen ions, characteristic of acids, and negatively charged hydroxyl ions, characteristic of bases, the dissociation constant of water becomes a very important value in the calculation of hydrogen-ion activity or hydrogen-ion concentration. The equation for the dissociation may be written as:

$$\frac{(H^+) \times (OH^-)}{(HOH)} = K$$

where (H^+) = the molecular concentration of hydrogen ions.
(OH^-) = the molecular concentration of hydroxyl ions.
(HOH) = the molecular concentration of the undissociated water.
K = the dissociation or ionization constant.

If this equation is stated in words, we say that the product of the concentration of hydrogen ions and hydroxyl ions divided by the concentration of the undissociated water is equal to a constant. Since the dissociation of water is so slight (only about one molecule in every 555,000,000 molecules is dissociated into H^+ and OH^- ions), the concentration of undissociated water will always remain extremely large in relation to the dissociated products $(H^+) \times (OH^-)$. Therefore no significant change will occur in the denominator of the dissociation equation with an ordinary alteration in the degree of dissociation, and (HOH) may be disregarded. Thus we can now rewrite the above equation:

$$(H^+) \times (OH^-) = K_w$$

where K_w is the dissociation constant of water.

This equilibrium holds for any aqueous solution and thus for all biological reactions, since water is essential in all living systems. If, for example, the hydrogen-ion concentration in a system is doubled by the addition of an acid, then the hydroxyl-ion concentration will simultaneously be halved so that the above reaction will remain in equilibrium and the product of the concentrations will remain constant at the value of K_w. On the other hand, if the hydroxyl-ion concentration is increased by the addition of an alkali, then the hydrogen-ion concentration will correspondingly decrease in proportion to maintain the equilibrium.

The value of K_w, the dissociation constant of water, has been determined by conductivity measurements and has been shown to vary with temperature. For example, Burns (1929) gives the following values:

$$1.\ \text{At } 0°\text{C.}, K_w = \frac{1}{10{,}000{,}000{,}000{,}000{,}000}.$$

$$2.\ \text{At } 22°\text{C.}, K_w = \frac{1}{100{,}000{,}000{,}000{,}000}.$$

$$3.\ \text{At } 40°\text{C.}, K_w = \frac{3.5}{100{,}000{,}000{,}000{,}000}.$$

$$4.\ \text{At } 100°\text{C.}, K_w = \frac{48}{100{,}000{,}000{,}000{,}000}.$$

Since such fractions are very cumbersome to write, the index notation may be used, and the above fractions become:

1. $0.01 \times 10^{-14} = K_w$ at 0°C.
2. $1 \times 10^{-14} = K_w$ at 22°C.
3. $3.5 \times 10^{-14} = K_w$ at 40°C.
4. $48 \times 10^{-14} = K_w$ at 100°C.

Since $(H^+) \times (OH^-) = K_w$, and H^+ and OH^- are produced in equal amounts when pure water dissociates, $(H^+) = (OH^-) = \sqrt{K_w}$. Between 22° and 23°C. water has a dissociation constant convenient to work with, and measurements of hydrogen-ion concentrations (activities) are frequently made at this temperature. Thus at 22° to 23°C.:

$$K_w = 10^{-14}$$

$$(H^+) \times (OH^-) = 10^{-14}$$

$$(H^+) \text{ is therefore equal to } \sqrt{10^{-14}} = 10^{-7}$$

and

$$(OH^-) \text{ is likewise equal to } \sqrt{10^{-14}} = 10^{-7}$$

According to these figures, pure water at 22°C. has a concentration of 10^{-7} g. (0.0000001 g.) of hydrogen ions per liter.

It can be seen from the preceding discussion that it is rather inconvenient to use either numerical terms with decimal figures or an expression such as 1.3×10^{-3}, which is the hydrogen-ion concentration of 0.1 N acetic acid. To get around these difficulties, Sørensen in 1909 suggested that *hydrogen-ion concentration be expressed as the logarithm of the reciprocal of the hydrogen-ion concentration.* This he called the pH value, in which p stands for *Potzen* (German, power), that is, the index or logarithm; and C_{H^+} stands for hydrogen-ion concentration. This important definition is expressed by the equations:

$$pH = \log \frac{1}{C_{H^+}} = -\log C_{H^+}, \quad \text{or} \quad C_{H^+} = 10^{-pH}$$

In reality, the C_{H^+} in this equation should be replaced by the symbol (aH^+), representing the hydrogen-ion activity. However, as we stated before, we are assuming that for ordinary purposes H-ion activity = H-ion concentration.

Pure water at 22°C. has a hydrogen-ion concentration of 10^{-7}, or a pH = 7.0:

$$pH = \log \frac{1}{10^{-7}} = -\log 10^{-7} = 7$$

and 0.1 N hydrochloric acid, which contains approximately 9.1×10^{-2} g. of hydrogen ions per liter, has:

$$pH = \log \frac{1}{9.1 \times 10^{-2}} = 2 - \log 9.1 = 2 - 0.959 = 1.041$$

Likewise for 0.1 N acetic acid containing 1.3×10^{-3} g. of hydrogen ions per liter:

$$pH = \log \frac{1}{1.3 \times 10^{-3}} = 3 - \log 1.3 = 3 - 0.114 = 2.886$$

The concentration of hydrogen ions in any aqueous solution may be obtained by transposing the general formula for dissociation as follows:

$$H^+ = K \frac{(HOH)}{(OH^-)}$$

When the acidity of an aqueous solution decreases, the alkalinity increases, so that with a decrease in H^+ there is a corresponding increase in OH^-. A convenient limit is reached in normal acid and alkaline solutions, respectively. These limits constitute the ends of the hydrogen-ion scale and are expressed by the values 1.0 to 10^{-14}. Table 11

TABLE 11

HYDROGEN-ION CONCENTRATIONS EXPRESSED IN DIFFERENT WAYS

Reaction	Normality *	H^+, grams/ liter	OH^-, grams/ liter	pH
Acid	1.0 N	1	10^{-14}	0.0
Acid	0.1 N	10^{-1}	10^{-13}	1.0
Acid	0.01 N	10^{-2}	10^{-12}	2.0
Acid	0.001 N	10^{-3}	10^{-11}	3.0
Acid	0.0001 N	10^{-4}	10^{-10}	4.0
Acid	0.00001 N	10^{-5}	10^{-9}	5.0
Acid	0.000001 N	10^{-6}	10^{-8}	6.0
Neutral	Pure water	10^{-7}	10^{-7}	7.0
Alkaline	0.000001 N	10^{-8}	10^{-6}	8.0
Alkaline	0.00001 N	10^{-9}	10^{-5}	9.0
Alkaline	0.0001 N	10^{-10}	10^{-4}	10.0
Alkaline	0.001 N	10^{-11}	10^{-3}	11.0
Alkaline	0.01 N	10^{-12}	10^{-2}	12.0
Alkaline	0.1 N	10^{-13}	10^{-1}	13.0
Alkaline	1.0 N	10^{-14}	1	14.0

* In respect to H^+ or OH^- ions.

shows the relationship between pH values and the corresponding (H^+) and (OH^-) concentrations in grams per liter.

Although pure water has a pH of 7.0 (or a pOH = 7.0 and pHOH = 14.0) at 22° to 23°C., it will not have the same value at different temperatures because of the effect of temperature on the dissociation. This fact is shown by the following data:

Temperature	*p*H	*p*OH	*p*HOH
0°C.	7.43	7.43	14.86
8°C.	7.30	7.30	14.6
16°C.	7.10	7.10	14.2
18°C.	7.07	7.07	14.14
20°C.	7.03	7.03	14.06
22°C.	7.0	7.0	14.0
25°C.	6.95	6.95	13.9
30°C.	6.88	6.88	13.76
37°C.	6.75	6.75	13.5
50°C.	6.52	6.52	13.04
70°C.	6.33	6.33	12.66
99°C.	6.07	6.07	12.14

Such data as these are fairly important in bacteriology. For example, when a medium is adjusted to *p*H 7.0 at 22°C. and then is used at this temperature, it is neutral with respect to (H^+)-ion and (OH^-)-ion concentration. However, if this same medium is adjusted to *p*H = 7.0 at 99°C., it will be distinctly alkaline; likewise, if the adjustment is made at 0° to 5°C., it will actually be on the acid side of neutrality when it is used at 22°C. Therefore, it should be kept in mind that a neutral solution at any given temperature is one which has the same *p*H as pure water at the corresponding temperature. These data explain also why it is that, when sugar broth tubes containing Andrade's indicator are taken fresh from the autoclave, they are more acid than when they were made or after they have been allowed to cool to room temperature. With Sørensen's method it is rather difficult to appreciate the relative concentrations of ions at two temperatures. As the temperature increases, dissociation increases, but the negative exponent or *p*HOH decreases. At 8°C., for example, the *p*H is 7.3 and at 22°C. it is 7.0. Put in this way, the fact is not readily grasped that the H-ion concentration at 22°C. is double that at 8°C. If, however, the negative exponent is kept a whole number and the fraction is written as a multiplier, the relationship is seen at once:

$$\text{At } 8°\text{C., } p\text{H} = 7.3 = 0.5 \times 10^{-7} = C_{H^+}$$

and

$$\text{at } 22°\text{C., } p\text{H} = 7.0 = 1.0 \times 10^{-7} = C_{H^+}$$

The symbol *p*H is very convenient because it can be used to designate either acidity or alkalinity, and it is possible to express in 14 units of a scale acidities of solutions which range from one-tenth normal to one-hundred trillionth normal (10^{-14}) in terms of hydrogen ions. In the use of the *p*H scale there are two important facts to keep in mind.

First, we are dealing with reciprocals, and therefore the *p*H will decrease as the hydrogen-ion concentration increases. Second, we are using a logarithmic scale with 10 as a base; therefore each change of one in our *p*H scale corresponds to a tenfold change in the hydrogen-ion concentration. For example, at 22°C. a solution that has ten times the hydrogen-ion concentration of pure water (*p*H = 7.0) will have a *p*H of 6.0, one with 100 times the concentration a *p*H of 5.0, and one with one-tenth the concentration a *p*H value of 8.0. Also, since the scale represents logarithmic values, the difference in acidity between *p*H 5.0 and 5.1 is greater than between *p*H 7.0 and 7.1.

The strength of an acid (or base) in an aqueous solution may be apprehended in two ways. (1) The potential acidity or the quantity of hydrogen ions which can be made to combine with a base can be measured. This is usually referred to as the *titratable acidity* (or alkalinity) or the *capacity factor* of an acid. For example, a normal solution of an acid, irrespective of its molecular constitution, contains 1 g. per liter of hydrogen replaceable by metallic ions. A normal solution of hydrochloric acid, therefore, contains the same amount of replaceable hydrogen as a normal solution of acetic acid. The two solutions have the same total acidity and require the same amount of alkali to neutralize them. They are thus equimolecular with regard to their acidity. (2) The concentration of the free or active hydrogen ions (or hydroxyl ions) can be determined. This is sometimes called the *intensity factor* of an acid and is usually represented by the symbol *p*H. Two acids which are equimolecular may not contain the same number of active hydrogen ions because they dissociate differently in aqueous solutions. The extent to which acids dissociate depends not only on the concentration but also on the nature of the electrolyte. For example, a 0.1 *N* solution of hydrochloric acid is dissociated to the extent of approximately 91 per cent, whereas a 0.1 *N* solution of acetic acid is dissociated only to the extent of about 1.3 per cent. This fact means that of the 100 mg. of replaceable hydrogen which 1 liter of a 0.1 *N* solution of HCl contains, 91 mg. exists as ions of hydrogen and can be expressed as:

$$\frac{0.1 \times 91}{100} = 0.091 = 0.91 \times 10^{-1} = 9.1 \times 10^{-2} = 10^{0.96} \times 10^{-2}$$

(0.96 being the log of 9.1), and finally by $10^{-1.04}$ g. per liter; whereas in acetic acid there is only 1.3 mg. of hydrogen, and this fact can likewise be expressed as:

$$\frac{0.1 \times 1.3}{100} = 0.0013 = 1.3 \times 10^{-3} = 10^{0.11} \times 10^{-3} = 10^{-2.89} \text{ g. per liter}$$

It can thus be seen that the quantity of active hydrogen ions in 0.1 N HCl is 70 times as great as that in 0.1 N acetic acid and also that the strength of an acid is a function of its dissociation. It follows logically that the real strength of an acid is not determined by the total quantity of hydrogen replaceable by a metal but only by the dissociated portion. Thus the "real acidity" of 0.1 N HCl is 0.091 N and that of 0.1 N acetic acid is 0.0013 N, or, simply, the hydrochloric acid solution contains 91 mg. of hydrogen in the ionic state per liter and acetic acid 1.3 mg.

What has just been stated concerning the dissociation of acids applies also to the alkalies whose active group, so far as reaction is concerned, is characterized by the negatively charged hydroxyl ion (OH^-). Just as we can have equimolecular acids, so can we have strong and weak alkalies which have equimolecular concentration but which likewise undergo different degrees of dissociation. For example, the strong alkali, sodium hydroxide, is dissociated to the extent of about 84 per cent in a 0.1 N solution, whereas a 0.1 N solution of ammonia, a relatively weak alkali, is dissociated only to the extent of 1.4 per cent in a 0.1 N solution. Thus the same calculations hold for sodium hydroxide:

$$\frac{0.1 \times 8.4}{100} = 0.084 = 8.4 \times 10^{-2} = 10^{0.92} \times 10^{-2} = 10^{-1.08} \text{ g. per liter}$$

and for ammonia:

$$\frac{0.1 \times 1.4}{100} = 0.0014 = 1.4 \times 10^{-3} = 10^{0.15} \times 10^{-3}$$
$$= 10^{-2.85} \text{ g. per liter of active } (OH^-) \text{ ions.}$$

A number of substances, however, are able to dissociate in various ways, so that under one set of conditions they yield hydrogen ions and under others hydroxyl ions, and sometimes even both ions simultaneously. These are called *amphoteric substances*, and they have a very important function in all biological processes. The best examples are the proteins and their degradation products. Their dissociation takes place by either of these formulas:

$$H \cdot R \cdot OH \rightleftarrows H \cdot R + OH^- \text{ (Basic dissociation)}$$
$$H \cdot R \cdot OH \rightleftarrows R \cdot OH + H^+ \text{ (Acidic dissociation)}$$

The way in which amphoteric substances dissociate depends upon the reaction of the medium. Alkaline dissociation predominates when the medium is acid, and acidic dissociation when the medium is alkaline. The hydrogen-ion concentration at which this type of dissociation is at a minimum is the *isoelectric point* of the amphoteric substance.

THE MEASUREMENT OF *p*H

One of two methods of measuring the hydrogen-ion activity of a solution is now generally used. The two methods of measurement are: (1) *the colorimetric method*, and (2) *the electrometric method.* The electrometric is by far the more accurate of the two, although the colorimetric method is convenient and acceptable for most bacteriological work. It is beyond the scope of this discussion to do more than mention the techniques by which hydrogen-ion activity (or concentration) can be measured. Several excellent manuals [Clark (1928), LaMotte, Kenny, and Reed (1932), and *Manual of Methods for Pure Culture Study of Bacteria*, Leaflet IX (1938)] are available, and they should be consulted for all details.

The Colorimetric Method. Various indicators are used extensively in bacteriology to determine *p*H. The method depends upon the use of various organic compounds which show color changes over certain characteristic ranges of *p*H when they are introduced into aqueous solutions. The color change may be due to the conversion of an almost undissociated weak acid or base of a certain color to a salt, which is almost completely dissociated and whose ion has a particular color. An example is methyl orange, which exists in an acid solution as the yellow undissociated acid, but, when present in an alkaline solution, dissociates to give the characteristic red basic ion. At other times the change in color is associated with a change in the internal structure of molecules which exhibit tautomerism. In such cases the tautomers are of different color. Phenolphthalein, which is colorless below *p*H 8.2 but pink above this value, is a good example. This color change has been attributed to the tautomeric rearrangement:

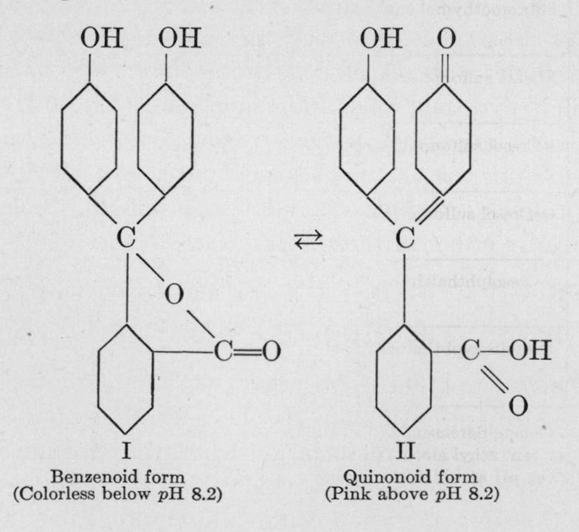

I
Benzenoid form
(Colorless below *p*H 8.2)

II
Quinonoid form
(Pink above *p*H 8.2)

TABLE 12

INDICATORS * FOR *p*H DETERMINATIONS

[From Clark (1928) and others]

Indicator		Molecular Weight	Concentration to Use,† per cent	Sensitive *p*H Range and Color	*pK* ‡
Common Name	Chemical Name				
meta-Cresol purple (acid range)	*m*-Cresol sulfonphthalein	382	0.04	1.2–2.8 red to yellow	1.5
Thymol blue (acid range)	Thymol sulfonphthalein	466	0.04	1.2–2.8 red to yellow	1.5
Bromophenol blue	Tetrabromophenol sulfonphthalein	670	0.04	3.0–4.6 yellow to blue	4.1
Bromochlorophenol blue	Dibromodichlorophenol sulfonphthalein	581	0.04	3.0–4.6 yellow to blue	4.0
Bromocresol green	Tetrabromo-*m*-cresol sulfonphthalein	698	0.04	3.8–5.4 yellow to blue	4.7
Chlorocresol green	Tetrachloro-*m*-cresol sulfonphthalein	520	0.04	4.0–5.6 yellow to blue	4.8
Methyl red	Dimethylaminoazobenzene-*o*-carboxylic acid	269	0.02	4.4–6.0 red to yellow	5.1
Chlorophenol red	Dichlorophenol sulfonphthalein	423	0.04	4.8–6.4 yellow to red	6.0
Bromocresol purple	Dibromo-*o*-cresol sulfonphthalein	540	0.04	5.2–6.8 yellow to red	6.3
Bromothymol blue	Dibromothymol sulfonphthalein	624	0.04	6.0–7.6 yellow to blue	7.0
Phenol red	Phenol sulfonphthalein	354	0.02	6.8–8.4 yellow to red	7.9
Cresol red	*o*-Cresol sulfonphthalein	382	0.02	7.8–8.8 yellow to red	8.3
meta-Cresol purple (alkaline range)	*m*-Cresol sulfonphthalein	382	0.04	7.4–9.0 yellow to purple	8.3
Cresolphthalein	*o*-Cresolphthalein	346	0.04	8.2–9.8 colorless to red	9.4
Phenolphthalein	Dihydroxyphthalophenone	318	0.04	8.3–10.0 colorless to red	9.7

* Clark and Lubs, Cohen, Sørensen, and Eastman indicators.
† Dissolve in 95 per cent ethyl alcohol or the solvent recommended by Eastman.
‡ The *pK* value is the *p*H at which the indicator is 50 per cent dissociated.

Phenolphthalein in the benzenoid form (I) is colorless, whereas the tautomer (II), because of its quinonoid double bond, is pink. Since form II has a carboxyl group, it is also strongly acidic. We know, of course, that phenolphthalein, Congo red, and litmus rapidly change color over a narrow range of *p*H and thus lend themselves well to the determination of the end-point when titrating acids and alkalies. These end-points, however, occur at different *p*H values, that is, about *p*H 8.2 to 9.0 for phenolphthalein, *p*H $\pm$ 4.4 for Congo red, and *p*H $\pm$ 7.0 for litmus. Although these indicators are widely used, the ones employed mostly in bacteriological work for colorimetric *p*H determinations are those which change color only gradually over a range of two to three units on the *p*H scale.

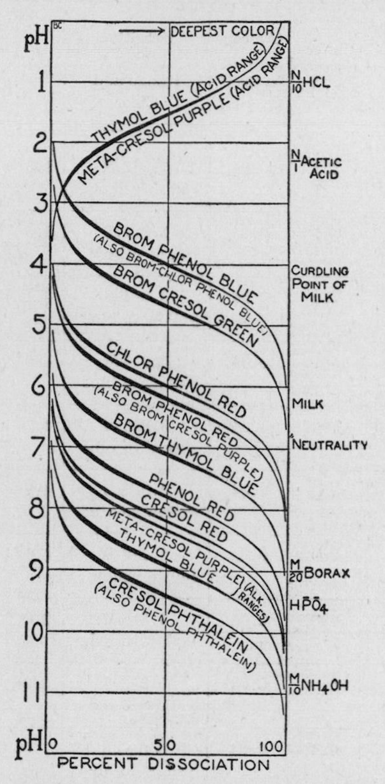

CHART 1. The Relative Positions of the Sensitive Ranges of the Indicators of Clark and Lubs, and of Cohen on the *p*H Scale in Comparison with the *p*H Values of Certain Solutions. (From Cohen in *Manual of Methods*, 1938.)

By comparing the color of a suitable indicator in a solution of unknown *p*H with the range of colors which the particular indicator gives in a buffer solution of known *p*H value, the apparent hydrogen-ion activity can be determined. Indicators ranging in *p*H values from 1.0 to 13 are available. Many of these indicators are put up commercially in a series of small tubes of buffer mixtures of known *p*H values covering the range of the indicator's colors. Such tubes serve as standards for comparison. If the commercially prepared standards are not available, buffer mixtures can be easily prepared. Comparator discs of the LaMotte roulette-wheel type, in which the indicator tubes just mentioned are replaced by tinted glass, are also available. Usually the tinted glass is so prepared that the changes in color are at intervals of 0.2 *p*H units. The tinted glass standards are convenient and do not fade, as the buffer-solution indicators may, especially when they are exposed to light for any period of time. Some of the most useful

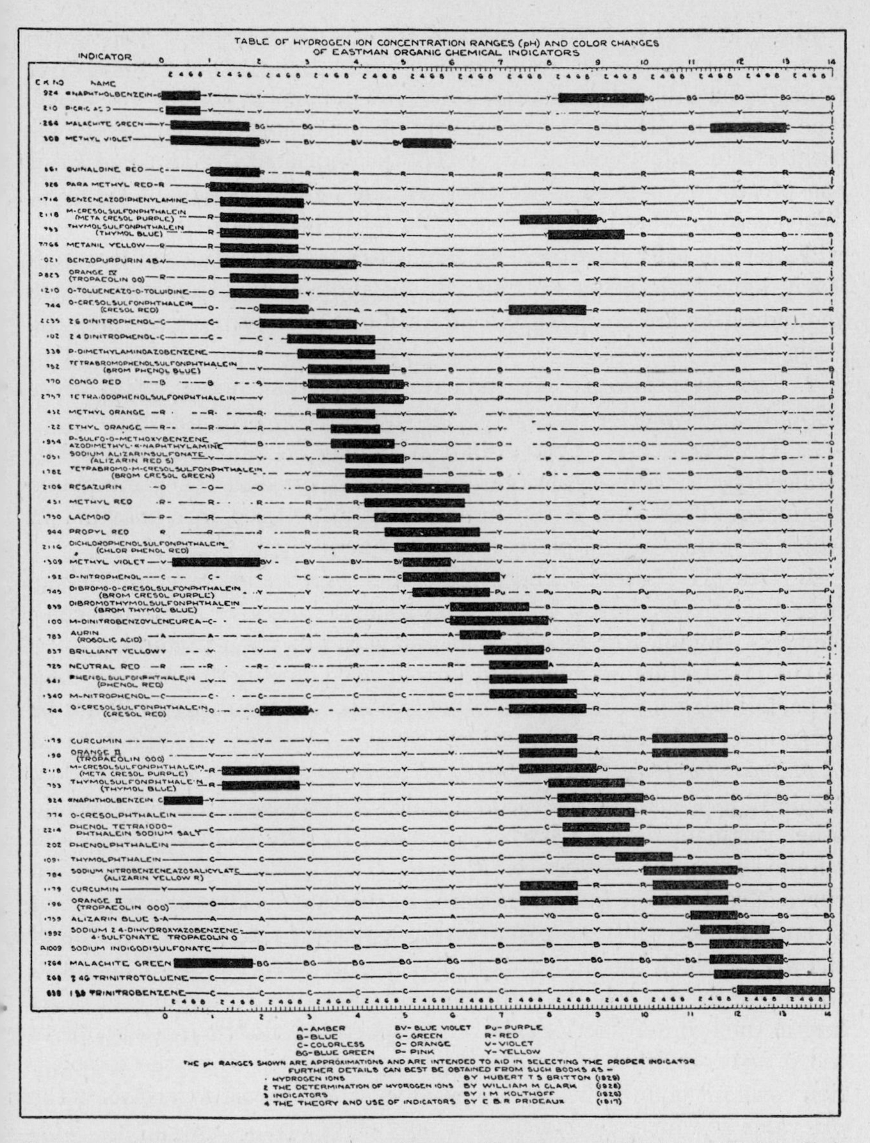

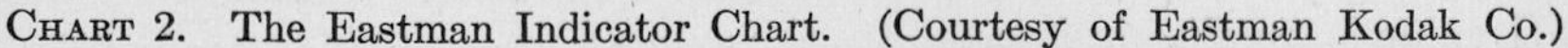

CHART 2. The Eastman Indicator Chart. (Courtesy of Eastman Kodak Co.)

color indicators are given in Table 12 and Charts 1 and 2. In making a choice of one of these indicators several factors must be kept in mind. The more important of these factors are:

1. THE PROTEIN AND SALT ERRORS. Since most of the indicators are dyes, the presence of colloids, precipitates, etc., in the solution being

tested may tend to remove some of the dye from solution by adsorption. The effect of the proteins is more or less specific and depends upon the nature and concentration of the particular protein substance. The change in *p*H due to the adsorption (or change) of part of the indicator is usually referred to as the "protein error." In some cases the protein error is so great that certain indicators cannot be used. When certain other ions are present in fairly high concentrations, they will alter the *p*H indicators. As a rule, salt concentrations of less than 0.2 *N* have little effect on the various indicators. However, where the indicators are changed, the alteration is usually referred to as the "salt error."

2. The Brilliance. An indicator should be chosen which gives not only a sharp color change but also a relatively brilliant one.

3. The Stability. Certain indicators may be attacked (oxidized or reduced) by the growth of organisms, their enzymes, or their metabolic products. Therefore, if the indicator is to be used in a medium in which growth is taking place, it should be relatively stable.

4. The *p*H Range. Those indicators which show a color change over a relatively narrow range, as a general rule, give a sharper color change. An indicator should be chosen with this point in mind.

The preparation of stock solutions of *p*H indicators commonly used in bacteriological work is not a difficult task, and the details will not be given here. For such information Leaflet IX by Cohen in the *Manual of Methods for Pure Culture Study of Bacteria* (1938) is recommended. Table 12 lists some of the recommended indicators, along with certain other pertinent data. Chart 1, prepared by Dr. Barnett Cohen and adopted from the *Manual of Methods* (1938), shows the dissociation curve of some of the indicators noted in the table. The change in color of an indicator will take place within a narrow range on each side of the *p*H at which the indicator is 50 per cent dissociated. This point, where half the dye is in the form of undissociated indicator and the other half in the form of free ions, is very important, since it corresponds to the invert logarithm of its dissociation constant. Thus the dissociation constant of an indicator is a number whose invert logarithm is the *p*H value at which the indicator is only 50 per cent dissociated. This *p*H value is usually designated by the symbol *pK*. Several *pK* values, taken from the *Manual of Methods,* are given in Table 12. A very convenient chart for colorimetric *p*H work has been prepared by the Eastman Kodak Company. It is reproduced as Chart 2.

The Electrometric Method. The electrometric method of measuring *p*H is generally more accurate and reliable than the colorimetric method and must always be considered the final appeal in doubtful cases. Such a method also lends itself very well to the measurement of *p*H in highly colored, or protein-containing solutions, whereas indicators are almost useless under such conditions. So many laboratories are now equipped with *p*H electrometers that the measurement of hydrogen-ion activity has become as routine and simple as taking temperature readings with a thermometer.

The principle of the electrometric method depends on the measurement of the voltage of a cell made up of two half-cells, the potential or voltage of one of the half-cells being a constant whose value is known with great precision. The potential of the other is dependent on the *p*H value of the unknown solution in which it is placed. Therefore, if the voltage of the combination is measured, the *p*H value of the unknown can be obtained by subtracting the potential of the known half-cell from that of the whole. Four of the most important half-cells or electrodes used in *p*H determinations will now be discussed.

1. The Hydrogen Electrode. The arbitrary standard for all *p*H determinations is the hydrogen electrode, although, as will be pointed out shortly, it is not generally used for practical purposes.

All electrometric determinations of *p*H are based on the assumption that ions in solution obey the gas laws. Therefore, when a metal electrode is placed in a solution containing ions of the same metal, the partial pressure of the ions in solution will be proportional to their ionic concentration. Since the metal will slowly dissolve and increase the partial pressure of the solution, a difference in electromotive force, or potential, between the electrode and the solution may be observed. This electromotive force can be measured, and by means of the proper formula the ionic concentration of the metal in solution can be determined.

The so-called *hydrogen electrode* is the arbitrary standard for all *p*H measurements and is nothing more than a noble metal, such as platinum, which has been coated with a thin layer of spongy platinum black and then completely saturated with hydrogen. To keep the electrode saturated, a stream of hydrogen gas must constantly flow through the solution (the gas, however, does not affect the *p*H of the solution). Platinum is known to have the property of holding hydrogen; the minute pores of the spongy coating greatly increase the surface and therefore the adsorption of hydrogen ions. When the hydrogen electrode is placed in a solution containing hydrogen ions, it rapidly comes to an equilibrium with the solution, but its potential varies with the activity of the hydrogen ions in solution. It behaves as though it were an electrode composed of metallic hydrogen and is therefore sensitive to hydrogen ions. Figure 10, taken from the paper by Klopsteg (1922), shows how the potential of the hydrogen electrode varies in respect to the negative logarithm of the hydrogen-ion concentration (pH) of the solution.

It is not possible to measure a single metal electrode in a solution. Two electrodes, in the form of half-cells, are necessary to give a poten-

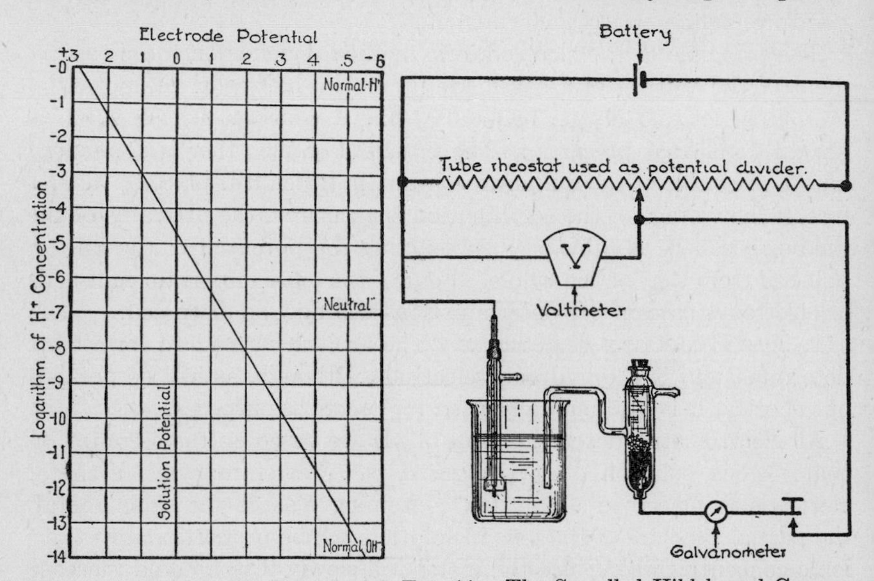

FIG. 10. The Electrode Potential of the Hydrogen Electrode with Reference to the Hydrogen-Ion Concentration of the Solution in Which It Is Immersed. (From Klopsteg, 1922.)

FIG. 11. The So-called Hildebrand Connections for Measuring Gas-Chain Voltage. The e.m.f. from the gas chain is balanced by adjustment of the potential divider until the galvanometer shows zero. The voltmeter, permanently connected as shown, then gives the potential difference which is required to balance the unknown e.m.f. (From Klopsteg, 1922.)

tial which can be measured. If the potential of one is known, such as a hydrogen electrode in a buffer solution of known pH or a calomel half-cell whose potential value is known with great precision, then that of the other can be calculated by the formula of Nernst after the potential difference is measured with a potentiometer. The electrode whose potential is known is termed the *reference electrode* or the *standard half-cell.* A simple set-up for making such measurements is shown in Fig. 11.

The following equation (based on the Nernst formula) gives the relationship between a hydrogen electrode immersed in a solution containing a normal concentration of hydrogen ions (reference electrode) and a similar electrode immersed in a solution to be measured which contains an unknown concentration of hydrogen ions ($C_{H_x^+}$) less than normal.

$$E = 0.0001983T \log \frac{1}{C_{H_x^+}}$$

where E = the potential difference between the half cells.
T = degrees temperature above absolute zero (−273°C.).

2. The Calomel Electrode. Since it is extremely difficult to prepare a solution which is exactly normal in respect to hydrogen ions, the so-called calomel electrode or half-cell is generally used as the standard reference electrode for measuring *p*H. Space does not permit a description of the preparation and standardization of the calomel electrode. It will probably be sufficient to say that the calomel electrode is a glass tube containing potassium chloride solution saturated with and resting on mercurous chloride (calomel) and mercury. Calomel electrodes are quite easily prepared, but their potential must always be standardized against that of the normal hydrogen electrode. The potentials of calomel electrodes at various temperatures are given in Table 13.

TABLE 13

Potentials in Volts of Calomel and Quinhydrone Electrodes at Various Temperatures in Relation to the Normal Hydrogen Electrode

Temperature, °C.	0.0001983× (t°C. + 273)	Calomel Electrode, $E_{cal.}$			Quinhydrone Electrode, E_q.
		Saturated	1.0 *N*	0.1 *N*	
15	0.03728	0.2525	......	0.3406	0.7064
18	0.05774	0.2506	0.2864	0.3380	0.7044
20	0.05813	0.2490	0.2860	0.3378	0.7029
22	0.05853	0.2475	......	......	0.7012
25	0.05912	0.2462	0.2848	0.3376	0.6991
30	0.06011	0.2437	0.2836	0.3372	0.6954
38	0.06168	0.2350	......	0.3355	0.6896
40	0.06207	0.2340	......	......	0.6881

By using one of the calomel electrodes as a reference half-cell and substituting its potential value in the preceding equation, the hydrogen-ion concentration (*p*H) or activity of an unknown solution in contact with a hydrogen electrode can be measured directly by the following formula:

$$\frac{\text{e.m.f.}_{\text{observed}} - E_{\text{calomel electrode}}}{0.00019837T} = \log \frac{1}{(\mathrm{H}^+)} = p\mathrm{H}$$

3. THE QUINHYDRONE ELECTRODE. The *p*H of a solution may be determined by combining the quinhydrone electrode, instead of the hydrogen electrode, with the calomel electrode. The quinhydrone electrode gives excellent results in solutions which have a *p*H of less than 8.0 to 8.5, providing no other oxidation-reduction system is present. In more alkaline solutions two factors come into play which make the quinhydrone electrode unreliable. One is the dissociation of the hydroquinone as an acid, and the other is the decomposition and oxidation of the components of the system. Since no gas phase is involved as it is in the hydrogen electrode, the quinhydrone electrode is particularly suited for certain types of biological and commercial work.

Quinhydrone is a slightly soluble equimolecular complex of quinone and hydroquinone which dissociates into its two component parts in aqueous solutions and gives definite and stable electrode potentials, providing the temperature and *p*H are constant. In reality it is an oxidation-reduction system where quinone is the oxidant and hydroquinone the reductant. Therefore what is actually measured in the quinhydrone method of *p*H determination is the electromotive force produced in this oxidation-reduction system as modified by changes in hydrogen-ion concentration or activity. If a metal electrode is placed in an acid solution (or one below *p*H 8.0) saturated with hydroquinone, a potential difference is set up as a result of the reduction of quinone to hydroquinone by the hydrogen ions. The potential produced varies in a linear fashion with the hydrogen-ion activity of the solution and may be used as a *p*H number of the solution. A possible interpretation of the complete reaction is:

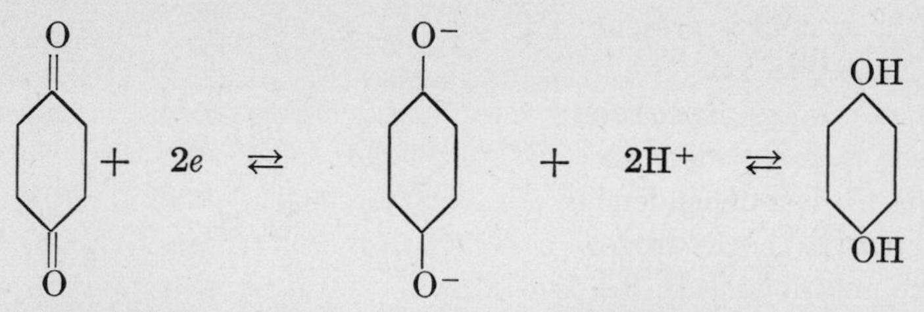

Quinone + Electrons ⇄ Anion of hydroquinone + Hydrogen ions ⇄ Hydroquinone

The potential ($E_{q.}$) of the saturated quinhydrone electrode is constant at any given temperature and *p*H. If the *p*H of an unknown solution is to be determined by using the quinhydrone electrode, instead of the hydrogen electrode, in combination with the calomel electrode, the following equation is used for the calculation:

$$pH = \frac{E_{q.} - E_{cal.} - E_{obs.}}{0.00019837T}$$

where $E_{q.}$ = the potential in volts of the quinhydrone electrode at the given temperature (T).

$E_{cal.}$ = the potential in volts of the calomel electrode used at the given temperature (T).

$E_{obs.}$ = the observed e.m.f. required to balance the half-cells, using a potentiometer.

Table 13 shows the potential of the saturated quinhydrone electrode and several calomel electrodes at different temperatures. To determine the *p*H of an unknown aqueous solution at a given temperature, the potential values of the calomel electrode and quinhydrone electrode used are substituted in the equation just given, and the observed e.m.f. is obtained directly from the potentiometer. For example, if a determination at 25°C. is desired, a saturated calomel electrode being employed as the reference half-cell, then the unknown solution is saturated with quinhydrone and a platinum wire is immersed in it. The platinum wire and calomel electrode are then attached to a potentiometer set-up, and the two half-cells are connected by a liquid junction or agar-salt bridge. By adjusting the potentiometer until the galvanometer stands at zero, the voltage required to balance the two half-cells can be read directly from the voltmeter. If these values are substituted in the equation, the *p*H of the unknown can be determined at once:

$$pH = \frac{0.4530\ (= 0.6992 - 0.2462) - E_{obs.}}{0.05912}$$

It must be kept in mind that the quinhydrone electrode gives accurate results for hydrogen-ion activity only when no other oxidation-reduction system is present and when the *p*H values to be determined are below 8.0 to 8.5.

4. THE GLASS ELECTRODE AND OTHER ELECTRODES. The glass electrode is now widely used for routine *p*H determinations. For the most part it is independent of salt and protein errors and of substances which poison the hydrogen or quinhydrone electrodes. In strongly alkaline solutions (*p*H 9.4 and above) the glass electrode responds more and more to cations other than hydrogen ions, and its potential is influenced by the activity and kind of these foreign cations. Sodium and lithium ions produce the most marked effects, although potassium and the bivalent cations produce slight changes. Another advantage of such an electrode in biological and chemical work is that the fluids being tested are not contaminated with quinhydrone or other chemicals and therefore can be used for other studies after their *p*H has been determined. In the physiological range, determinations with an accu-

racy of 0.05 *p*H may be made rapidly in unbuffered, colored, or turbid solutions.

The glass electrode consists of a bulb of special glass, usually containing a chloride buffer with a silver chloride contact that is electrically connected with the amplifier-potentiometer system. Because of the relatively high resistance of the glass the measurement of the potential of a glass electrode requires the use of a sensitive amplifying circuit.

When the glass electrode is immersed in the sample to be tested, it constitutes a half-cell, which is opposed by a calomel half-cell in the usual manner. This arrangement may be represented by the following electrochemical notation of the complete cell:

(*a*) Ag | AgCl | Chloride buffer | Glass | Unknown solution || Saturated KCl solution | HgCl | Hg

However, since the potential established within the glass electrode is constant, the complete cell (*a*) can be simply expressed as:

(*b*) Glass electrode | Unknown solution || Saturated KCl solution | Calomel electrode or half-cell

In the cells (*a*) and (*b*) the electrode on the right is positive. The double vertical lines indicate the liquid junction or bridge; the single vertical lines represent junctions of various phases.

Most of the *p*H electrometers on the market today are equipped with glass electrodes of various types. For more details on the theory and general construction of the glass electrode Dole (1935), MacInnes (1939), and the instructions furnished by several commercial houses should be consulted.

Numerous other metal and gas electrodes have been described in the literature. They are mainly of theoretical importance or have been devised for special purposes.

THE EFFECT OF *p*H ON BACTERIAL ACTIVITIES

Pasteur was one of the first persons to observe that microorganisms can develop only in media of determined reaction. "A feeble acidity," he said, "hinders the development of bacteria and infusoria and favors, on the contrary, the growth of molds. Neutrality or slight alkalinity acts in a precisely contrary manner."

In the study of enzymes the influence of the reaction of the substrate was recognized very early. In fact, in 1879 Kjeldahl published his ob-

TABLE 14

MINIMUM, OPTIMUM, AND MAXIMUM REACTION (*p*H) FOR THE GROWTH OF SEVERAL BACTERIA

Organism	Reaction (*p*H) Minimum	Optimum	Maximum	Reference
Mycobacterium tuberculosis	6.0	6.8–7.2	7.6	Dernby (1921)
M. tuberculosis	4.0–5.0	7.3–7.7	7.9–8.6	Gieszczykiewicz and Wroblewski (1927)
Corynebacterium diphtheriae	6.0	7.3–7.6	8.3	Dernby (1921)
C. diphtheriae	6.3	6.5–7.5	8.2	Bunker (1917)
Nitrosomonas, species	7.0–7.6	8.0–8.8	9.4	Nelson (1931)
Nitrobacter, species	6.6	7.6–8.6	10.0	Nelson (1931)
Rhizobium leguminosarum	4.9		11.0	Fred and Davenport (1918)
Rhizobium japonicum	3.4		11.0	Fred and Davenport (1918)
Bacterium radiobacter	4.5–5.0		11.5–12.0	Hofer (1941)
Azotobacter chroococcum	5.8	7.4–7.6		Yamagata and Itano (1923)
Azotobacter agile	5.9	7.5–7.7		Yamagata and Itano (1923)
Thiobacillus thiooxidans	±1.0	2.0–2.8	4.0–6.0	Waksman and Joffe (1922)
Thiobacillus, species	5.88	7.9–8.5	10.7	Trautwein (1921)
Clostridium tetani	5.5	7.0–7.6	8.3	Dernby (1921)
Clostridium sporogenes, *Clostridium histolyticum*, *Clostridium perfringens*, *Clostridium lentoputrescens*	5.0–5.8	6.0–7.6	8.5–9.0	Dernby (1921), Dernby and Blanc (1921)
Clostridium botulinum	5.0	6.6–7.2	9.0	Dozier (1924)
Bacteroides halosmophilus	5.5	7.4–7.6	8.5	Baumgartner (1937)
Lactobacillus bifidus	3.8–4.4	5.4–6.4	7.2	Weiss and Rettger (1934)
Lactobacillus acidophilus	4.0–4.6	5.8–6.6	6.8	Weiss and Rettger (1934)
Pseudomonas aeruginosa	5.6	6.6–7.0	8.0	Dernby (1921)
Erwinia carotovora	5.6	7.1	9.3	Quirk and Fawcett (1923)
Erwinia aroideae	5.3	7.2	9.2	Quirk and Fawcett (1923)
Phytomonas campestris	6.1	7.4	8.8	Quirk and Fawcett (1923)
Phytomonas solanacearum	5.6	6.7	8.4	Quirk and Fawcett (1923)
Phytomonas tumefaciens	5.7	7.3	9.2	Quirk and Fawcett (1923)
Serratia marcescens	5.0	6.0–7.0	8.0	Dernby (1921)
Aerobacter aerogenes	4.4	6.0–7.0	9.0	Cohen and Clark (1919)
Escherichia coli	4.4	6.0–7.0	9.0	Dernby and Näslund (1923)
Proteus vulgaris	4.4	6.0–7.0	8.4	Dernby (1921)
Eberthella typhosa	4.5	6.5–7.2	8.0	Dernby and Näslund (1923)
Salmonella paratyphi	4.5	6.5–7.5	8.5	Dernby and Näslund (1923)
S. paratyphi	4.0	6.2–7.2	9.6	Fennel and Fisher (1919)
Salmonella schottmuelleri	4.5	6.5–7.5	8.5	Dernby and Näslund (1923)
Salmonella enteritidis	5.0	7.0–8.0	8.5	Dernby and Näslund (1923)
Shigella dysenteriae	4.5	6.0–7.2	8.2	Dernby and Näslund (1923)
Shigella paradysenteriae	4.5	6.0–7.2	8.2	Dernby and Näslund (1923)
Brucella melitensis	6.3	6.6–8.0	8.4	Fennel and Fisher (1919)
Alcaligenes fecalis	6.4	8.5	9.7	Cohen and Clark (1919)
Pasteurella pestis	5.0	7.2–7.6	9.6	D'Aunoy (1923), Sokhey and Habbu (1943)
Noguchia granulosis	6.8	7.8	8.8	Noguchi (1928)
Vibrio comma	5.6	6.2–8.0	9.6	Fennel and Fisher (1919)
V. comma	6.4	7.0–7.4	7.9	Dernby (1921)
Staphylococcus albus	5.6	7.2–7.6	8.1	Dernby (1921)
Diplococcus pneumoniae, types I, II, III	7.0	7.8	8.3	Dernby (1921)
D. pneumoniae, types I, II, III, IV	7.2	7.8	8.2	Fennel and Fisher (1919)
Streptococcus pyogenes	6.35	6.4–8.5	9.2	Foster (1921)
Neisseria intracellularis	7.4	7.6	7.8	Fennel and Fisher (1919)
N. intracellularis	6.1	7.4	7.8–8.0	Gates (1919)
Neisseria gonorrhoeae	6.0	7.3	8.3	Dernby (1921)
N. gonorrhoeae	5.8	6.8–7.4	8.2	Torrey and Buckell (1922)
Yeasts	Range 2.5 to 8.0; optimum usually between *p*H 4.0 and 5.8.			
Molds	Range 1.5 to 8.5; optimum usually between *p*H 3.8 and 6.0.			

servations of the function of the acidity of the medium in the action of the enzyme of malt. He demonstrated that, up to a definite concentration, acids favored the action of the amylase enzyme on starch and alkalies hindered it. The classical studies on sucrase by Fernbach about 1890 revealed facts of the same order. At the time when the investigations just mentioned and many others were carried out, the theory of neutrality, acidity, and alkalinity was still very vague. However, investigators used certain indicators to show different degrees of acidity; methyl violet, Congo red, and others were used to distinguish between "strong" mineral acids and "weak" organic acids. To Fernbach is due the credit for introducing into biological studies a method which allowed an evaluation of the degree of acidity of a particular substrate and for demonstrating that it was necessary to determine the neutrality of the indicators being used to test the acidity or alkalinity.

We now know it is not sufficient to say that molds and yeasts prefer acid media, whereas bacteria grow best in slightly alkaline substrates. Some knowledge of the hydrogen-ion activity of the particular medium is necessary. With modern methods of measuring *p*H it is possible to determine the effect of the hydrogen-ion concentration or activity of a given medium on many activities of bacteria. Growth (see Table 14) and the production of enzymes, toxins, and other immune substances are all closely associated with or dependent upon the *p*H of the medium in which bacteria are seeded. Studies have also been made which indicate that *p*H plays an important part in the ability of an organism to take up stain [Stearn and Stearn (1933)] or to be killed by disinfectants. The phenomenon of acid agglutination, bacterial agglutination by sera, hemolysin, and precipitin reactions are all governed to a certain extent by the *p*H of the substrate. In many applied fields, such as the food industries and the purification of water and sewage, where microorganisms play an important role, the proper control of *p*H is often of great importance.

BUFFER ACTION

The buffering action of a solution means its ability to resist marked changes in *p*H through the addition or loss of acid or alkali. Thus, buffers may be defined as substances which by their presence in solution increase the amount of acid or alkali that must be added to cause unit change in *p*H. The word buffer is the English rendering of *Puffer*, the German translation of the term tampon (plug or bung), suggested by Fernbach in 1900. For a general discussion of buffers and buffer action the book by Clark (1928) and for additional data on the measurement of buffer values of various substances the paper by Van Slyke (1922) should be consulted.

If 1.0 ml. of 0.1 *N* HCl is added to a liter of pure water of *p*H 7.0, the resulting solution will have a *p*H of about 4.0. Such a solution will be toxic to certain bacteria. However, if the same amount of acid is added to a liter of meat infusion broth of *p*H 7.0, the medium will change little, if any, in *p*H. We can, therefore, say that pure water has no resistance (buffering action) to changes in *p*H, whereas the meat infusion broth does because of the salts and the amphoteric nature of the substances, such as peptones and amino acids, present.

The most efficient buffers are mixtures of weak acids or weak bases, in combination with their salts, and certain other amphoteric substances. Primary and secondary phosphates are quite commonly used in bacteriological media, and it may be well to discuss how they buffer media. If a strong acid is added to a solution containing secondary phosphates, the phosphates are changed into primary phosphates and thus diminish the hydrogen-ion concentration of the solution to which the acid is added. This may be illustrated by the reaction:

$$K_2HPO_4 + \underset{\text{Highly dissociated}}{HCl} \rightarrow \underset{\text{Slightly dissociated}}{KH_2PO_4} + KCl$$

The reverse occurs when an alkali is added to a solution containing primary phosphates:

$$KH_2PO_4 + \underset{\text{Highly dissociated}}{KOH} \rightarrow \underset{\text{Slightly dissociated}}{K_2HPO_4} + H_2O$$

It can thus be seen that a mixture of these two phosphates will oppose, until their transformation is complete, a marked change in the *p*H of a medium and will tend to keep it in equilibrium. Phosphates, carbonates, and bicarbonates are the principal buffer salts encountered in biological processes, and they are of great importance in maintaining the correct hydrogen-ion concentration in cells and tissue fluids. All reactions of living protoplasm take place in buffered media.

A buffering action takes place in a similar way in solutions containing the salts of other weak acids. A salt such as sodium acetate is a good example; it is almost completely dissociated in dilute aqueous solutions:

$$CH_3COONa \rightleftarrows Na^+ + CH_3COO^-$$

TABLE 15

COMPOSITION OF MIXTURES GIVING *p*H VALUES AT 20°C. AT INTERVALS OF 0.2

[From Clark (1928)]

KCl-HCl Mixtures

*p*H	0.2 *M* KCl	0.2 *M* HCl	Dilute to
1.2	50 ml.	64.5 ml.	200 ml.
1.4	50 ml.	41.5 ml.	200 ml.
1.6	50 ml.	26.3 ml.	200 ml.
1.8	50 ml.	16.6 ml.	200 ml.
2.0	50 ml.	10.6 ml.	200 ml.
2.2	50 ml.	6.7 ml.	200 ml.

Phthalate-HCl Mixtures

*p*H	0.2 *M* KH Phthalate	0.2 *M* HCl	Dilute to
2.2	50 ml.	46.70 ml.	200 ml.
2.4	50 ml.	39.60 ml.	200 ml.
2.6	50 ml.	32.95 ml.	200 ml.
2.8	50 ml.	26.42 ml.	200 ml.
3.0	50 ml.	20.32 ml.	200 ml.
3.2	50 ml.	14.70 ml.	200 ml.
3.4	50 ml.	9.90 ml.	200 ml.
3.6	50 ml.	5.97 ml.	200 ml.
3.8	50 ml.	2.63 ml.	200 ml.

Phthalate-NaOH Mixtures

*p*H	0.2 *M* KH Phthalate	0.2 *M* NaOH	Dilute to
4.0	50 ml.	0.40 ml.	200 ml.
4.2	50 ml.	3.70 ml.	200 ml.
4.4	50 ml.	7.50 ml.	200 ml.
4.6	50 ml.	12.15 ml.	200 ml.
4.8	50 ml.	17.70 ml.	200 ml.
5.0	50 ml.	23.85 ml.	200 ml.
5.2	50 ml.	29.95 ml.	200 ml.
5.4	50 ml.	35.45 ml.	200 ml.
5.6	50 ml.	39.85 ml.	200 ml.
5.8	50 ml.	43.00 ml.	200 ml.
6.0	50 ml.	45.54 ml.	200 ml.
6.2	50 ml.	47.00 ml.	200 ml.

KH_2PO_4-NaOH Mixtures

*p*H	0.2 *M* KH_2PO_4	0.2 *M* NaOH	Dilute to
5.8	50 ml.	3.72 ml.	200 ml.
6.0	50 ml.	5.70 ml.	200 ml.
6.2	50 ml.	8.60 ml.	200 ml.
6.4	50 ml.	12.60 ml.	200 ml.
6.6	50 ml.	17.80 ml.	200 ml.
6.8	50 ml.	23.65 ml.	200 ml.
7.0	50 ml.	29.63 ml.	200 ml.
7.2	50 ml.	35.00 ml.	200 ml.
7.4	50 ml.	39.50 ml.	200 ml.
7.6	50 ml.	42.80 ml.	200 ml.
7.8	50 ml.	45.20 ml.	200 ml.
8.0	50 ml.	46.80 ml.	200 ml.

Boric Acid-KCl–NaOH Mixtures

*p*H	0.2 *M* H_3BO_3– 0.2 *M* KCl	0.2 *M* NaOH	Dilute to
7.8	50 ml.	2.61 ml.	200 ml.
8.0	50 ml.	3.97 ml.	200 ml.
8.2	50 ml.	5.90 ml.	200 ml.
8.4	50 ml.	8.50 ml.	200 ml.
8.6	50 ml.	12.00 ml.	200 ml.
8.8	50 ml.	16.30 ml.	200 ml.
9.0	50 ml.	21.30 ml.	200 ml.
9.2	50 ml.	26.70 ml.	200 ml.
9.4	50 ml.	32.00 ml.	200 ml.
9.6	50 ml.	36.85 ml.	200 ml.
9.8	50 ml.	40.80 ml.	200 ml.
10.0	50 ml.	43.90 ml.	200 ml.

If a weak acid like acetic acid is added to this solution, there will be a momentary increase in the hydrogen-ion concentration because of the slight dissociation of acetic acid:

$$CH_3COOH \rightleftarrows H^+ + CH_3COO^-$$

The presence, however, of the secondary supply of negative acetate ions disturbs the equilibrium which exists when acetic acid dissociates. Thus some of the free hydrogen ions will combine at once with the acetate ions to form undissociated acetic acid. This reaction continues until a definite equilibrium is again established. Since the acid, as opposed to the salt, is very slightly dissociated, the hydrogen ions remaining active in the solution will not be sufficient to bring about a marked change in the *p*H, with the result that the acetic acid is less dissociated than it would be if the sodium acetate were not present, or, in other words, the sodium acetate simply depresses the dissociation of acetic acid. If a strong acid like hydrochloric acid is added to the above solution, the equilibrium will again be disturbed as a result of the dissociation of the acid and the presence of active hydrogen ions. Here again the acetate ions and the active hydrogen ions will react to form relatively undissociated acetic acid. This reaction will continue until all the acetate ions have combined with the free hydrogen ions liberated by the dissociation of the hydrochloric acid. If there is an excess of hydrochloric acid, there will not be enough acetate ions to take care of the free hydrogen ions liberated, and as a result the hydrogen-ion concentration will increase and the *p*H will be lowered. When an alkali, such as sodium hydroxide, is added to the sodium acetate-acetic acid solution, a very similar change takes place. Since sodium hydroxide is almost completely dissociated in weak solutions:

$$NaOH \rightleftarrows Na^+ + OH^-$$

there will be a momentary excess of hydroxyl ions, but they will combine at once with the hydrogen ions liberated from acetic acid to form water. As we know, water is relatively undissociated in comparison to sodium hydroxide.

Although buffers play a very important role in maintaining equilibria in cellular reactions, space does not permit further details of the theories which are involved. Brief mention should be made, however, of the use of buffer solutions in the laboratory for accurate colorimetric *p*H work. Buffer mixtures of various types, giving definite *p*H values, have been devised by several workers [see Clark (1928)]. Table 15 lists the composition of the Clark and Lubs mixtures which can be used for reference purposes. Anyone preparing these solutions for the first time should carefully read the discussion in the book by Clark (1928), since there are several important details which must be considered.

REFERENCES

Abramson, H. A. 1933. *Cold Spring Harbor Symposia Quant. Biol.*, **1**:92–106.

Abramson, H. A. 1934. *Electrokinetic Phenomena and Their Application to Biology and Medicine.* Chemical Catalog Co., New York.

Abramson, H. A. 1934. *Trans. Electrochem. Soc.* **66**:153–161.

Abramson, H. A., and L. S. Moyer. 1937. *Trans. Electrochem. Soc.*, **71**:115–131.

Alexander, J. (ed.) 1926–1944. *Colloid Chemistry*, Vols. I–V. Chemical Catalog Co., New York, and Reinhold Publishing Corp., New York.

Alexander, J. 1937. *Colloid Chemistry*, 4th Ed. D. Van Nostrand Co., New York.

Allyn, W. P., and I. L. Baldwin. 1932. *J. Bact.*, **23**:369–398.

Amann, J. 1893. *Centr. Bakt., I Abt. Orig.*, **13**:775–780.

Angerer, K. von. 1923. *Arch. Hyg.*, **93**:14–25.

Axelrod, A. E., and M. J. Johnson. 1939. *Respiratory Enzymes*, Chapter IX. Burgess Publishing Co., Minneapolis, Minn.

Barron, E. S. G. 1941. *Ann. Rev. Biochem.*, **10**:1–30.

Barron, E. S. G., G. F. Dick, and C. M. Lyman. 1941. *J. Biol. Chem.*, **137**:267–282.

Baumgartner, J. G. 1937. *Food Research*, **2**:321–329.

Beams, J. W. 1938. *Rev. Modern Phys.*, **10**:245–263.

Brooks, S. C. 1925. *J. Gen. Physiol.*, **7**:327–330.

Buchanan, R. E., and E. I. Fulmer. 1928. *Physiology and Biochemistry of Bacteria*, Vol. I. Williams and Wilkins Co., Baltimore.

Bull, H. B. 1943. *Physical Biochemistry.* John Wiley & Sons, Inc., New York.

Bunker, J. W. M. 1917. *Abstracts Bact.*, **1**:31–32.

Burns, D. 1929. *An Introduction to Biophysics.* The Macmillan Co., New York.

Burrows, W. 1941. *J. Infectious Diseases*, **69**:141–147.

Chargaff, E., and D. H. Moore. 1944. *J. Biol. Chem.*, **155**:493–501.

Clark, W. M. 1928. *The Determination of Hydrogen-Ions*, 3rd Ed. Williams and Wilkins Co., Baltimore.

Clark, W. M., B. Cohen, H. E. Gibbs, and R. K. Cannon. 1928. *U. S. Pub. Health Service Hyg. Lab. Bull.* 151. 363 pp. Washington, D. C.

Cohen, B., and W. M. Clark. 1919. *J. Bact.*, **4**:409–427.

Cohen, B. 1933. *Cold Spring Harbor Symposia Quant. Biol.*, **1**:214–223.

Cole, K. S. 1933. *Cold Spring Harbor Symposia Quant. Biol.*, **1**:107–116.

D'Aunoy, R. 1923. *J. Infectious Diseases*, **33**:391–415.

Dernby, K. G. 1921. *Ann. inst. Pasteur*, **35**:277–290.

Dernby, K. G., and J. Blanc. 1921. *J. Bact.*, **6**:419–430.

Dernby, K. G., and C. Näslund. 1923. *Z. Immunitäts.* **35**:450–454.

Dixon, M. 1939. *Ann. Rev. Biochem.*, **8**:1–36.

Dole, M. 1935. *Principles of Experimental and Theoretical Electrochemistry.* McGraw-Hill Book Co., New York.

Dozier, C. C. 1924. *J. Infectious Diseases*, **35**:105–133.

Eyster, H. C. 1943. *Botan. Rev.*, **9**:311–324.

Falk, I. S. 1928. *Colloid Chemistry*, ed. by J. Alexander, Vol. II, Chapters 29 and 41. Chemical Catalog Co., New York.

Fennel, E. A., and M. B. Fisher. 1919. *J. Infectious Diseases*, **25**:444–451.

Foster, L. F. 1921. *J. Bact.*, **6**:161–209.

Fred, E. B., and A. Davenport. 1918. *J. Agr. Research*, **14**:317–336.

Freundlich, H. 1942. *The Structure of Protoplasm*, ed. by Wm. Seifriz. Iowa State College Press, Ames, Iowa.

Gates, F. L. 1919. *J. Exptl. Med.*, **29**:321–328.

Gieszczykiewicz, M., and V. Wroblewski. 1927. *Compt. rend. soc. biol.*, **96**: 337–339.

Gillespie, R. W. H., and J. R. Porter. 1938. *J. Bact.*, **36**:633–637.

Gillespie, R. W. H., and L. F. Rettger. 1938. *J. Bact.*, **36**:605–620, 621–631.

Gortner, R. A. 1937. *Selected Topics in Colloid Chemistry.* Cornell University Press, Ithaca, N. Y.

Heidelberger, M. 1939. *Bact. Rev.*, **3**:49–95.

Henriot, E., and E. Huguenard. 1925. *Compt. rend. acad. sci.*, **180**:1389–1392.

Hewitt, L. F. 1936. *Oxidation-Reduction Potentials in Bacteriology and Biochemistry*, 4th Ed. 101 pp. London County Council, London.

Hofer, A. W. 1941. *J. Bact.*, **41**:193–224.

Hofmeister, F. 1888–1891. *Arch. exp. Path. Pharmakol.*, **24**:247–260; **28**:210–238.

Holmes, L. F. 1940. *J. Bact.*, **40**:466.

Johnstone, K. I. 1940. *J. Path. Bact.*, **51**:59–74.

Jones, I. D., and R. A. Gortner. 1932. *J. Phys. Chem.*, **36**:387–436.

Kanel, E. S. 1941. *Microbiology (U.S.S.R.)*, **10**:595–620.

Kendall, A. I. 1925. *Colloid Symposium Monograph*, Vol. II, Paper 18. Chemical Catalog Co., New York.

Klobusitzky, D. von. 1940. *Brasil-Medico*, **54**:847–852.

Klopsteg, P. E. 1922. *Ind. Eng. Chem.*, **14**:399–406.

Knaysi, G. 1941. *J. Bact.*, **41**:141–153.

Kolthoff, I. M. 1930. *Rec. trav. chim.*, **49**:401–414.

Koser, S. A., and F. Saunders. 1938. *Bact. Rev.*, **2**:99–160.

Kruyt, H. R., and H. S. van Klooster. 1930. *Colloids.* John Wiley & Sons, New York.

LaMotte, F. L., W. R. Kenny, and A. B. Reed. 1932. *pH and Its Practical Application.* Williams & Wilkins Co., Baltimore.

Lardy, H. A., and C. A. Elvehjem. 1945. *Ann. Rev. Biochem.*, **14**:1–30.

Levine, M., and F. W. Shaw. 1924. *J. Bact.*, **9**:225–234.

Lewis, I. M. 1941. *Bact. Rev.*, **5**:181–230.

Lowry, T. M. 1930. *Trans. Faraday Soc.*, **26**:45–46.

MacInnes, D. A. 1939. *The Principles of Electrochemistry.* Reinhold Publishing Corp., New York.

Manual of Methods for Pure Culture Study of Bacteria. 1938. Leaflet IX, 7th Ed. 19 pp. By B. Cohen. Biotech Publications, Geneva, N. Y.

Marrack, J. R. 1938. "The Chemistry of Antigens and Antibodies." *Med. Res. Council (Brit.) Rept.* 230. London.

McAlister, D. F. 1938. *Am. J. Botany*, **25**:286–295.

McCalla, T. M. 1940. *J. Bact.*, **40**:23–32, 33–43, 333.

McCalla, T. M. 1941. *Stain Tech.*, **16**:27–32.

McCalla, T. M. 1941. *J. Bact.*, **41**:775–784.

McFarlane, A. S. 1940. *Trans. Faraday Soc.*, **36**:257–264.

Meek, C. S., and C. B. Lipman. 1922. *J. Gen. Physiol.*, **5**:195–204.

Michaelis, L., and W. A. Perlzweig. 1926. *Hydrogen-Ion Concentration.* Williams & Wilkins Co., Baltimore.

Moore, H. N. 1940. *J. Bact.*, **40**:409–413.

Moyer, L. S. 1936. *J. Bact.*, **31**:531–546; **32**:433–464.

Moyer, L. S. 1940. *Trans. Faraday Soc.*, **36**:248–256.

Mudd, S., and E. B. H. Mudd. 1924. *J. Bact.*, **9**:151–167.

Mudd, S., B. Lucké, M. McCutcheon, and M. Strumia. 1930. *J. Exptl. Med.*, **52**:313–329.

Mudd, S., K. Polevitzky, T. F. Anderson, and L. A. Chambers. 1941. *J. Bact.*, **42**:251–264.

Nelson, D. H. 1931. *Centr. Bakt., II Abt.*, **83**:280–311.

Noguchi, H. 1928. *J. Exptl. Med.*, **48**:(Suppl. 2) 1–53.

Norris, C. H. 1940. *J. Cellular Comp. Physiol.*, **16**:313–322.

Petermann, M. L., and A. M. Pappenheimer, Jr. 1941. *J. Phys. Chem.*, **45**:1–9.

Pound, J. R. 1926. *J. Phys. Chem.*, **30**:791–817.

Quastel, J. H. 1930. *Trans. Faraday Soc.*, **26**:853–864.

Quirk, A. J., and E. H. Fawcett. 1923. *J. Infectious Diseases*, **33**:1–59.

Rideal, E. K. 1930. *A System of Bacteriology in Relation to Medicine*, Vol. I, Chapter III. Medical Research Council, London.

Ruffilli, D. 1933. *Biochem. Z.*, **263**:63–74.

Seifriz, W. 1928. *Colloid Chemistry*, ed. by J. Alexander. Vol. II, Chapter 21. Chemical Catalog Co., New York.

Seifriz, W. 1936. *Protoplasm.* McGraw-Hill Book Co., New York.

Seifriz, W., and Others. 1942. *The Structure of Protoplasm.* 283 pp. Iowa State College Press, Ames, Iowa.

Silbereisen, K. 1939. *Wochschr. Brau.*, **56**:193–198.

Sokhey, S. S., and M. K. Habbu. 1943. *J. Bact.*, **46**:33–37.

Stearn, E. W., and A. E. Stearn. 1933. *J. Bact.*, **26**:9–75.

Stearns, T. W., and M. H. Roepke. 1941. *J. Bact.*, **42**:411–430.

Stigell, R. 1908. *Centr. Bakt., I. Abt. Orig.*, **45**:487–491.

Stuart, L. S., R. W. Frey, and L. H. James. 1933. *U. S. Dept. Agr. Tech. Bull.* 383. 24 pp.

Stuart, L. S., and T. L. Swenson. 1934. *J. Am. Leather Chem. Assoc.*, **29**:142–158.

Svedberg, T., and K. O. Pedersen. 1940. *The Ultracentrifuge.* Oxford University Press, London and New York.

Tiselius, A. 1940. *Bull. N. Y. Acad. Med.*, **16**:751–780.

Torrey, J. C., and G. T. Buckell. 1922. *J. Infectious Diseases*, **31**:125–147.

Trautwein, K. 1921. *Centr. Bakt., II Abt.*, **53**:513–548.

Van Slyke, D. D. 1922. *J. Biol. Chem.*, **52**:525–570.

Verwey, W. F., and M. Frobisher, Jr. 1940. *Am. J. Hyg.* (Sect. B.), **32**:55–62, 63–68.

Waksman, S. A., and J. S. Joffe. 1922. *J. Bact.*, **7**:239–256.

Wámoscher, L. 1930. *Z. Hyg. Infektionskr.*, **111**:422–460.

Ward, W. E. 1938. *J. Bact.*, **36**:337–355.

Weiser, H. B. 1939. *Colloid Chemistry.* John Wiley & Sons, New York.

Weiss, J. E., and L. F. Rettger. 1934. *J. Bact.*, **28**:501–521.

Wells, H. G. 1929. *The Chemical Aspects of Immunity.* Chemical Catalog Co., New York.

Werkman, C. H., and G. L. Stahly. 1933. *Iowa State Coll. J. Sci.*, **7**:93–108.

Wynd, F. L., and P. L. Varney. 1941. *J. Lab. Clin. Med.*, **26**:1513–1516.

Yamagata, U., and A. Itano. 1923. *J. Bact.*, **8**:521–531.

2

THE GROWTH AND DEATH OF BACTERIA

The material in this chapter is concerned principally with the dynamic phases of growth and death of bacteria or, simply, the rate of change in a bacterial population. Some of the other important aspects accompanying this change, such as respiration and metabolism, are also considered here.

In spite of the fact that many complicated changes occur during the course of bacterial growth under favorable conditions, cellular development and reproduction seem to take place quite regularly and in a rather orderly fashion. In fact, it is possible to observe definite phases of growth, and with a reasonable degree of accuracy the rate of change can be determined as well. It is apparent, however, that in order to study the bacterial population cycle or to evaluate the effect of the physical or chemical environment on bacterial cells some method of estimating changes in growth must be considered.

THE TECHNIQUE OF COUNTING BACTERIA

Bacteria are so small that it is almost impossible to study the activity of a single bacterial cell, although it has been done. For the most part, however, bacteria are studied in masses.

Bacteria may be counted in such a way as to determine either the total number of living and dead cells or the number of living cells alone. The first method is usually referred to as the *total count* and the second as the *living* or *viable count*. The choice of one of these methods will depend upon the particular information desired. The use of both methods, which are discussed on the following pages, is usually recommended for making a quantitative study of bacterial metabolism or calculating the growth phases of a bacterial culture.

TOTAL COUNT

The several methods which can be used to evaluate the total number of bacterial cells present in a given medium may be classified as follows:

A. Direct count with the microscope.
   1. A stained preparation on a slide.
   2. Wright's proportional count method.
   3. Counting chamber method.

B. Indirect count.
   1. The opacity method.
   2. Total nitrogen content.
   3. The centrifuge method.
   4. Miscellaneous methods.

Direct Count. The technique of counting bacteria in various materials by means of a microscope has been employed since the early days of bacteriology. This is essentially the basis of the Breed (1911) or Breed and Brew (1916) method for counting bacteria in milk. The merits of this technique have been discussed in detail by Hanks and James (1940) and by Wang (1941).

1. A Stained Preparation on a Slide. This method consists of spreading a known volume (usually 0.01 ml. for milk) over a specific area (usually 1 sq. cm.) on a slide, then drying, fixing, staining, and examining the resulting film under the microscope. The organisms are counted in a given number of fields, and, by knowing the area of a field, it is possible to determine with considerable accuracy the total number of bacteria present in the original sample. This method is valuable, since the results are obtained quickly, little work and apparatus are required, and some idea is obtained of the types of organisms that are present. On the other hand, it has certain disadvantages, one of which is that a true picture of existing conditions may not be given if only a few bacteria are observed on the preparation, for not all organisms, especially when dead, take up sufficient stain to be distinctly visible under the microscope. Several other disadvantages of this method are discussed by Hanks and James (1940). They suggest the preparation of circular films and microscopic sampling along two diameters at right angles. Such a modification takes into account the concentric distribution of bacteria and minimizes the effect of abnormal distribution. To reduce the error or variation between counts in the circular film technique, Olson and Warren (1944) have developed two unique mechanical devices (glass circle marker and notched knobs with spring stops on the mechanical stage).

2. Wright's Proportional Count Method. The essentials of this method were first worked out by Wright (1902). It consists of mixing a known volume of the bacterial suspension with a known volume of normal human blood. The mixture is spread uniformly on a slide,

then dried, fixed, stained, and examined under the microscope. The average number of bacteria and red cells in a given number of fields is then counted. In the blood of the normal adult male there are about 5 million red cells per cu. mm., and, by knowing the numerical proportion of the red cells to the bacteria, the number of bacteria in the original suspension can be estimated. The error connected with this technique results mainly from not being able to obtain a uniform distribution of the bacteria and the red cells on the slide.

3. Counting Chamber Method. The ordinary hemacytometer can be employed for the direct counting of bacterial cells and is especially applicable for the enumeration of yeast cells. Much better results have been obtained, however, by using the Petroff-Hausser bacteria counter or the Helber chamber as adapted by Wilson (1922). As a rule, the organisms are examined unstained, using dark-field illumination, with the high-power or oil-immersion lens. But Jennison (1937) and others have obtained good results by examining a formalized suspension of bacteria in a light field by staining with methylene blue. With ordinary precaution the counts should not vary by more than ± 10 per cent from the true value. In fact, Wilson (1922) estimated an error of about 3 per cent when dealing with a suspension of 15 billion bacteria per milliliter.

Indirect Count. Several methods have been proposed for the enumeration of bacteria by indirect methods.

1. The Opacity Method. The opacity of the bacterial suspension to be estimated by this method is compared with a control suspension of standard opacity, such as a barium sulfate solution or a bacterial suspension which has been previously counted. The comparison is made by the unaided eye or by the use of a nephelometer [Liese (1926), Strauss (1930)], photoelectric cell [Pulvertaft and Lemon (1933), Alper and Sterne (1933)], precision photometer as described by Mestre (1935), or a photoelectric densitometer [Longsworth (1936)]. For the theory underlying this technique the reader should consult the references in this brief discussion.

Figure 1, taken from the paper by Alper and Sterne (1933), shows that the method can be used with a considerable degree of accuracy if a number of technical points are kept in mind.

Possibly the advantage of such a method was pointed out by Henrici in 1926 when he stated, "Since the cells change in size while growing, the number of cells is not a true measure of growth, which could only be obtained by computing the volume of the protoplasm." If the opacity curve is, in a certain degree, a measure of protoplasmic mass, possibly it does represent a truer measure of growth than is obtained by some of the actual count methods. However, Wilson (1926) pointed out that this method is not too well suited for accurate counting, since different strains of the same species and even cells of the same strain vary in size at different ages. Since the cells from young cultures are larger than those from old ones, it was found that the number of organisms required to bring about a given opacity was five times as great in a 26-hour as in a 4-hour culture. Liese (1926), working with spherical organisms, observed that the opacity is determined

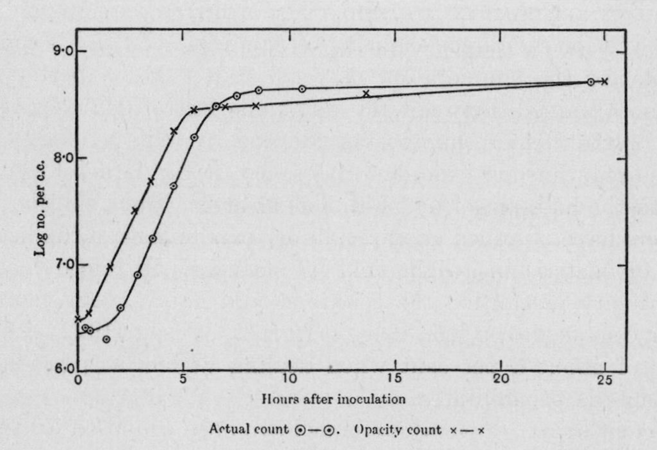

FIG. 1. The Growth of *Shigella gallinarum* as Measured by Different Methods. (From Alper and Sterne, 1933.)

by the surface area of the cells ($4\pi r^2$) and thus varies with the square of the radius, but Strauss (1930) doubts that the relationship is this simple. Undoubtedly other factors, such as volume and density, are also important.

Although the method has disadvantages for enumerating bacteria, it is of value in standardizing bacterial vaccines, where the total amount of bacterial protoplasm, but not necessarily the actual number of cells, is of importance.

2. TOTAL NITROGEN CONTENT. Rubner (1906) first employed this method to determine the total mass of bacteria in a culture. More recently Mueller (1935) has made indirect determinations of the mass of bacterial growth by means of a micro-Kjeldahl technique. This technique has certain advantages but may be subject to some error because of the possibility that nitrogenous material from the medium may be included with the organisms or that some nitrogen may be lost if the cells are washed too thoroughly.

This procedure for estimating the growth of bacteria and yeasts has also been used in other studies [Hottle, Lampen, and Pappenheimer (1941), Porter and Pelczar (1941), and Williams (1941)].

3. Centrifuge Method. The details of this technique, as worked out by Schmidt (1926) and Schmidt and Fischer (1930), consist of centrifuging the bacterial suspension in a capillary tube and measuring the height of the column of sedimented bacteria. The number of cells is then estimated by calculations based on their average diameter or their specific gravity. This method may have some value when the suspension shows a tendency to clump but is undoubtedly subject to some serious errors.

4. Miscellaneous Methods. The titratable acidity produced by bacteria, the amount of dye adsorbed, and the direct weighing [Coombs and Stephenson (1926)] of the mass of organisms formed have also been used as an index of growth by certain investigators. Others [see Koser and Saunders (1938)] have attempted to determine growth by physical means, such as conductivity and refractive index measurements.

The use of vital stains for making differential counts between dead and living bacteria has been employed, but the technique has been questioned by several investigators, especially Bickert (1930) and Knaysi (1935).

LIVING OR VIABLE COUNT

The Dilution Method (Most Probable Number). This method was one of the first used in bacteriology to enumerate the approximate number of living cells in various fluids and sometimes to obtain pure cultures from a mixed suspension.

The theory of the technique is based on diluting the suspension to a point beyond which no growth occurs. Usually several successive dilutions are made in saline or broth, and from each of them a number of tubes of liquid media are inoculated with equal quantities. After incubation the tubes showing growth are noted, and the probable number of bacteria in the original solution is calculated by formulas developed by McCrady (1915), Greenwood and Yule (1917), and others. Several modifications of the original methods have been made to suit individual needs, especially in routine water, sewage, and milk analyses and in filtrable virus work.

In using this technique a uniform procedure should be followed, as suggested by Buchanan and Fulmer (1928). The dilutions should be prepared in a suitable nutrient liquid medium and extended so that most of the tubes containing the highest dilution remain sterile after incubation.

The findings are obtained by observing the number of positive results secured in each set of dilutions and looking up the significant number in probable numbers tables. Let us explain this further by taking a hypothetical example, using an extended series of dilutions with five tubes in each, as shown in Table 1.

TABLE 1

ESTIMATION OF BACTERIA BY THE DILUTION METHOD

Number of Tubes for Each Dilution	Amount of Sample Used or Dilution				
	10 ml.	1.0 ml.	0.1 ml.	0.01 ml.	0.001 ml.
1	+	+	+	−	−
2	+	+	+	−	−
3	+	+	−	−	−
4	+	+	−	−	−
5	+	−	−	−	−
Total positives	5	4	2	0	0

\+ = growth after incubation.
− = no growth after incubation.

By studying Table 1, it can be seen that all five tubes inoculated with a 10-ml. portion showed growth and that four of the tubes with a 1.0-ml. and two of the tubes with a 0.1-ml. sample were positive; the dilutions with a 0.01-ml. and 0.001-ml. portion were negative throughout. We next determine the *significant number* for our example. The *significant number* is defined as that series of figures representing the number of tubes in the lowest dilution in which all tubes are positive, and the number of positive tubes in the next two higher dilutions. Thus it can be seen in our example that 542 is the significant number. By searching for this number in Table 2 under the heading Significant Number and reading directly across under the Most Probable Number column, the most probable number of bacteria is found to be 220 per 100 ml. of the original sample.

If all the tubes in the lowest dilution are not positive, then the figures from the first three dilutions make up the significant number.

For example, a set of results may be obtained like 02200, and the significant number will be 022. Sometimes the significant number will contain four figures, as 5,432. If such is the case, the last figure is added to the one preceding it and the significant number becomes 545 (543 + 2), and the most probable number of bacteria per 100 ml. of sample will be 430.

When all the tubes in the dilutions used show no growth or when all show growth, the result is indeterminate and no probable number can be computed. All that can be said is that the most probable number of bacteria is greater or less than it is possible to determine in the range of dilutions used; possibly a set of dilutions higher or lower will give a value which can be computed.

Probable numbers tables suitable for use with several dilution combinations were first prepared by McCrady (1918) and since then by several investigators. Table 2 is an adaptation from the tables prepared by Hoskins (1934) and serves to illustrate the dilution method. For a more detailed account of the subject the original article should be consulted. The basic tables of most probable numbers, as prepared by McCrady (1918), Hoskins (1934), and others, may be expanded to suit a wide variety of dilution combinations.

The experimental error connected with the dilution method has been studied by Allen (1932), Halvorson and Ziegler (1933), Gordon (1938), Gordon and ZoBell (1938), Dalla Valle (1941), and others. Using Fisher's method of statistical analysis, Allen pointed out that, if the probable relative error is to be reduced to about 5 per cent, at least 1,000 tubes must be used for the dilutions. Halvorson and Ziegler found that with 40 tubes in each dilution the count may vary between 47 per cent above and 38 per cent below the true count, and with only five tubes for each dilution, the figures are 260 per cent above and 70 per cent below. Gordon and ZoBell have evaluated the data of Halvorson and Ziegler and give formulas and figures which indicate that their tables must be replaced by tables of geometric mean estimates. For further interesting information on the dilution method of determining bacterial populations see the papers by Savage and Halvorson (1941) and Dalla Valle (1941). Dalla Valle has developed a very usable nomograph for determining most probable numbers per 100 ml. of sample portions, using three dilutions.

The Plating Method. This technique consists essentially in preliminary dilution of the material, if necessary, and adding unit quantities of suitable dilutions to a liquefied solid medium such as nutrient agar. The sample is pipetted aseptically into sterile Petri dishes and liquefied solid media are added, or Esmarch roll-tubes are prepared

TABLE 2

Most Probable Number of Organisms per 100 ml. of Sample, Using Five Tubes in Each of Three Dilutions in Geometric Series

[From Hoskins (1934)]

Significant Number *Positive tubes with*			Most Probable Number *	Significant Number *Positive tubes with*			Most Probable Number	Significant Number *Positive tubes with*			Most Probable Number
10 ml.	1.0 ml.	0.1 ml.		10 ml.	1.0 ml.	0.1 ml.		10 ml.	1.0 ml.	0.1 ml.	
0	0	0	0.0	1	0	0	2.0	2	0	0	4.5
0	0	1	1.8	1	0	1	4.0	2	0	1	6.8
0	0	2	3.6	1	0	2	6.0	2	0	2	9.1
0	0	3	5.4	1	0	3	8.0	2	0	3	12
0	0	4	7.2	1	0	4	10	2	0	4	14
0	0	5	9.0	1	0	5	12	2	0	5	16
0	1	0	1.8	1	1	0	4.0	2	1	0	6.8
0	1	1	3.6	1	1	1	6.1	2	1	1	9.2
0	1	2	5.5	1	1	2	8.1	2	1	2	12
0	1	3	7.3	1	1	3	10	2	1	3	14
0	1	4	9.1	1	1	4	12	2	1	4	17
0	1	5	11	1	1	5	14	2	1	5	19
0	2	0	3.7	1	2	0	6.1	2	2	0	9.3
0	2	1	5.5	1	2	1	8.2	2	2	1	12
0	2	2	7.4	1	2	2	10	2	2	2	14
0	2	3	9.2	1	2	3	12	2	2	3	17
0	2	4	11	1	2	4	15	2	2	4	19
0	2	5	13	1	2	5	17	2	2	5	22
0	3	0	5.6	1	3	0	8.3	2	3	0	12
0	3	1	7.4	1	3	1	10	2	3	1	14
0	3	2	9.3	1	3	2	13	2	3	2	17
0	3	3	11	1	3	3	15	2	3	3	20
0	3	4	13	1	3	4	17	2	3	4	22
0	3	5	15	1	3	5	19	2	3	5	25
0	4	0	7.5	1	4	0	11	2	4	0	15
0	4	1	9.4	1	4	1	13	2	4	1	17
0	4	2	11	1	4	2	15	2	4	2	20
0	4	3	13	1	4	3	17	2	4	3	23
0	4	4	15	1	4	4	19	2	4	4	25
0	4	5	17	1	4	5	22	2	4	5	28
0	5	0	9.4	1	5	0	13	2	5	0	17
0	5	1	11	1	5	1	15	2	5	1	20
0	5	2	13	1	5	2	17	2	5	2	23
0	5	3	15	1	5	3	19	2	5	3	26
0	5	4	17	1	5	4	22	2	5	4	29
0	5	5	19	1	5	5	24	2	5	5	32

* Values correct to two significant figures.

TABLE 2 (*Continued*)

MOST PROBABLE NUMBER OF ORGANISMS PER 100 ML. OF SAMPLE, USING FIVE TUBES IN EACH OF THREE DILUTIONS IN GEOMETRIC SERIES

[From Hoskins (1934)]

Significant Number *Positive tubes with* 10 ml.	1.0 ml.	0.1 ml.	Most Probable Number	Significant Number *Positive tubes with* 10 ml.	1.0 ml.	0.1 ml.	Most Probable Number	Significant Number *Positive tubes with* 10 ml.	1.0 ml.	0.1 ml.	Most Probable Number
3	0	0	7.8	4	0	0	13	5	0	0	23
3	0	1	11	4	0	1	17	5	0	1	31
3	0	2	13	4	0	2	21	5	0	2	43
3	0	3	16	4	0	3	25	5	0	3	58
3	0	4	20	4	0	4	30	5	0	4	76
3	0	5	23	4	0	5	36	5	0	5	95
3	1	0	11	4	1	0	17	5	1	0	33
3	1	1	14	4	1	1	21	5	1	1	46
3	1	2	17	4	1	2	26	5	1	2	64
3	1	3	20	4	1	3	31	5	1	3	84
3	1	4	23	4	1	4	36	5	1	4	110
3	1	5	27	4	1	5	42	5	1	5	130
3	2	0	14	4	2	0	22	5	2	0	49
3	2	1	17	4	2	1	26	5	2	1	70
3	2	2	20	4	2	2	32	5	2	2	95
3	2	3	24	4	2	3	38	5	2	3	120
3	2	4	27	4	2	4	44	5	2	4	150
3	2	5	31	4	2	5	50	5	2	5	180
3	3	0	17	4	3	0	27	5	3	0	79
3	3	1	21	4	3	1	33	5	3	1	110
3	3	2	24	4	3	2	39	5	3	2	140
3	3	3	28	4	3	3	45	5	3	3	180
3	3	4	31	4	3	4	52	5	3	4	210
3	3	5	35	4	3	5	59	5	3	5	250
3	4	0	21	4	4	0	34	5	4	0	130
3	4	1	24	4	4	1	40	5	4	1	170
3	4	2	28	4	4	2	47	5	4	2	220
3	4	3	32	4	4	3	54	5	4	3	280
3	4	4	36	4	4	4	62	5	4	4	350
3	4	5	40	4	4	5	69	5	4	5	430
3	5	0	25	4	5	0	41	5	5	0	240
3	5	1	29	4	5	1	48	5	5	1	350
3	5	2	32	4	5	2	56	5	5	2	540
3	5	3	37	4	5	3	64	5	5	3	920
3	5	4	41	4	5	4	72	5	5	4	1600
3	5	5	45	4	5	5	81	5	5	5	....

[Gee (1932)]. After the medium has solidified, it is incubated under favorable conditions, and the number of colonies which develop are counted. By counting the average number of colonies per plate and multiplying by the reciprocal of the dilution, an estimate of the number of viable organisms in the original suspension can be reached with a fair degree of accuracy.

Several technical points must be carefully controlled when this method is used. If it is necessary to make preliminary dilutions before plating, some attention should be given to the type of diluent used, since Winslow and Falk (1918, 1923), Winslow and Brooke (1927), and Butterfield (1932) have demonstrated that different bacterial species, when exposed to different diluents, often only for a period of a few minutes, show a marked variation in viability. The clumping of cells and the counting of plates which are overcrowded with colonies are especially important factors which must be taken into consideration. For the source and measurement of errors of this method, Ziegler and Halvorson (1935), Wilson *et al.* (1935), or the article by Jennison and Wadsworth (1940) should be consulted. The *dilution error* and the *distribution error* are the main sources of variation that account for the total error.

THE BACTERIAL CULTURE CYCLE

When a given viable bacterium is inoculated into a suitable nutrient medium and incubated under favorable conditions, the resulting growth will follow a rather definite course. As a rule, it takes some little time before the cells, especially the older ones, begin to divide in a fresh medium, but once this period of adjustment is over, the rate of multiplication increases until a maximum speed of growth is attained. Retarding influences, such as the lack of food or the accumulation of metabolic products, then soon come into play, and the cells begin to divide more and more slowly until growth ceases entirely. After a period when the number of bacteria remains almost constant the viable cells begin to decrease. The rate of death of the bacteria then becomes more rapid until it reaches a maximum, after which it slows down and eventually all the organisms die. If we plot the number of living cells in a known quantity of liquid medium against time, a characteristic growth curve or population cycle is obtained.

The bacterial culture cycle or growth curve was first divided into four distinct parts by Rahn (1906) and Lane-Claypon (1909), but Buchanan (1918) believed that the life phases of bacteria were more complicated and further subdivided the curve, describing seven phases as seen in the continuous line of Fig. 2.

1. *The latent or initial stationary phase, a* to *b*, is characterized by a period during which there is no increase in the number of cells. In fact, there may even be a decrease in number. Later in the discussion we will refer to this phase and the lag phase as the phase of adjustment in a bacterial culture cycle. According to Winslow and Walker (1939), this term is preferable because it includes the change in numbers as well as all the metabolic changes which take place during the adjustment of the inoculated cells to a new medium.

2. *The lag phase, b* to *c*, is a period when multiplication is slow but there is an increased acceleration in the growth rate.

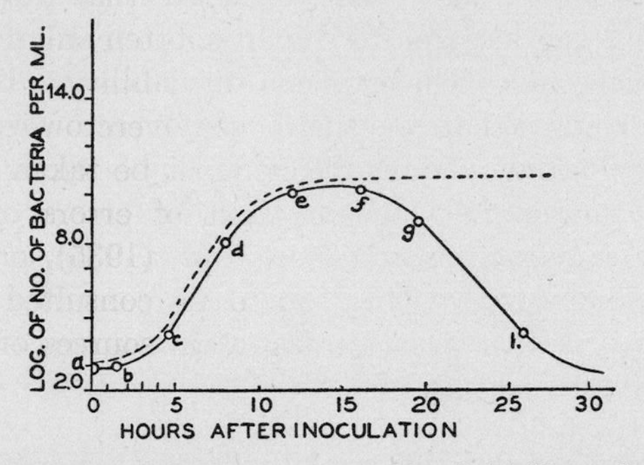

FIG. 2. Bacterial Growth Curves. ------ = Total (viable and dead) number of bacteria; —— = number of viable bacteria.

3. *The logarithmic phase, c* to *d*, is a period when the cells are dividing regularly and at maximum speed. If the logarithms of the numbers of organisms are plotted against time, they will fall on an ascending straight line, since the increase in cells is in geometric progression.

4. *The negative acceleration phase, d* to *e*, is a time when the bacteria cease to multiply at a maximum rate and the number of cell divisions becomes less and less.

5. *The stationary phase, e* to *f*, is a period during which the bacterial population remains almost constant and there is a theoretical equilibrium between the dying cells and those that are being newly formed.

6. *The accelerated death phase, f* to *g*, is a period when the equilibrium of the stationary phase is disrupted and the cells start to die more rapidly and pass into the next phase.

7. *The logarithmic death phase, g* to *h*, is a period during which the cells are dying at a constant rate. If the logarithms of the numbers of organisms are plotted against time, they will fall on a descending straight line. Certain investigators have suggested that a better term for this phase would be the phase of decline, since there is some indication that it is not truly logarithmic. Also, such a term would include

the final phase of death, when cells are found alive in a culture after a long period of time. This subject is discussed in more detail on pp. 136 to 139.

If conditions are favorable, all these phases of growth may be observed, but certain environmental factors may alter the conditions and one stage of growth or another may be absent. For example, if young, actively growing cells are used as the inoculum, the initial stationary phase and lag phase may be so short that they are not observed, or they may not exist at all. For this reason the term phase of adjustment probably better explains these two phases of a bacterial population cycle.

Also, in Fig. 2, we have plotted a hypothetical curve representing the total bacterial count. The total count has been considered generally to be somewhat higher than the viable count obtained by plating in a suitable nutrient medium. This difference has been studied very little in the past. Jennison (1937) listed three explanations for this discrepancy: "(1) counting errors (due to chance) involved in the two methods; (2) clumping; (3) variation in resistance of cells, in which case some cells die either in culture, during the process of plating, or on an unsatisfactory plating medium." After a careful study of the subject Jennison came to the same conclusion as did Ziegler and Halvorson (1935) and showed that, if the clumps of cells could all be broken up, the plate count would be within limits of experimental error, identical with the total count. Part of the discrepancy may be due to other factors, especially the tendency for some bacteria to die during the diluting and plating-out processes and the failure of certain cells to survive once they have been formed.

Each of the growth phases will now be considered briefly. For a more thorough discussion on this subject, the references, especially the books by Buchanan and Fulmer (1928) and Rahn (1932) and the review by Winslow and Walker (1939), should be consulted.

THE PHASE OF ADJUSTMENT AND PHYSIOLOGICAL YOUTH

The terms period of adjustment, latent or initial stationary phase, lag period, and period of physiological youth have been used rather loosely in the literature. In the brief discussion which follows, the use of any of these terms, except the period of physiological youth, will refer to that period from the time when the inoculation is made to the time when the cells start to divide at a maximum rate of speed (logarithmic growth phase). The term physiological youth will refer to that relatively short span of the population cycle when the cells are in the so-called late lag phase and/or the very early logarithmic phase of growth.

It is quite generally accepted that, when a bacterium is inoculated into a fresh medium, a period of time elapses before there is any decided increase in the total number of cells present. Therefore, the first portion of the population cycle may be characterized by a stationary or, in some cases, by a slightly decreasing population. This period is most apparent when a suspension of spores is used as the inoculum. In fact, Esty and Meyer (1922), Burke (1923), and Burke, Sprague, and Barnes (1925) found that, when heated cultures of several spore-forming organisms were planted in a favorable medium, they may lie dormant for weeks before germination. This phase is not restricted to spore-forming bacteria, however, since it has been brought out by several workers [Lane-Claypon (1909), Penfold (1914), Chesney (1916), and others] that old cells may be at times in a relatively dormant stage.

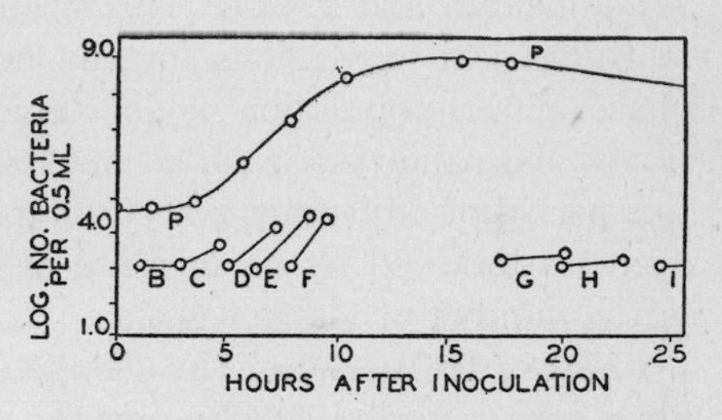

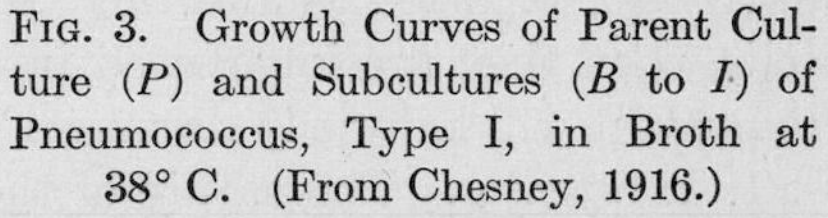

FIG. 3. Growth Curves of Parent Culture (*P*) and Subcultures (*B* to *I*) of Pneumococcus, Type I, in Broth at 38° C. (From Chesney, 1916.)

The effect of the age of the parent culture on the phase of adjustment can be seen very clearly in Fig. 3, adopted from the work of Chesney (1916). His work shows the growth curve of a parent culture (*P*) of pneumococcus and subcultures at different intervals during growth. The subculture (*B*) made during the early phase of the population cycle showed no immediate growth when transferred to a suitable medium. The subculture (*C*) made during the so-called lag phase (later stage of the phase of adjustment) showed a slight growth in 2 hours, whereas the subcultures (*D*, *E*, and *F*) taken during the so-called logarithmic phase showed no lag but grew at once in the fresh medium and at a rate parallel to that of the parent culture. Later on in the population cycle the subcultures (*G*, *H*, and *I*) from the older cells exhibited the phenomenon of lag but did show a slight growth.

The separation of the initial stationary phase and the lag phase was first suggested by Buchanan (1918). Although the division of the two phases is not made by many investigators, it is probably warranted when the first is prolonged over a long period of time, as it may be when dormant cells or spores are used as an inoculum.

The first description of the lag phase in a favorable medium was made by Müller (1895), who made calculations using the formula introduced by Buchner, Longard, and Riedlin in 1887. Müller showed that the time required for one cell to divide into two (generation time) increased with the age of the primary culture used for inoculating the medium in which the generation time was measured. For example, when he inoculated typhoid bacilli from a $2\frac{1}{2}$- to 3-hour parent culture into a fresh medium, the cells completed one generation in 40 minutes, whereas those from a $6\frac{1}{4}$-hour culture gave a generation time of 85 minutes, and those from a 14- to 16-hour culture required over 160 minutes for one complete generation. This early work by Müller was the stimulus for extensive studies on the so-called lag phase by Rahn (1906), Penfold (1914), Chesney (1916), Buchanan (1918), Sherman and Albus (1924), Lodge and Hinshelwood (1943), and others.

Ledingham and Penfold (1914) and Slator (1917) have formulated mathematical expressions for the multiplication rate during the lag phase of the population cycle. Some workers, however, have questioned the validity of such an analysis because of the fact that during this period of adjustment, according to circumstances, there may be a decrease followed by an increase or a gradually accelerating increase in the number of viable cells.

Factors Influencing the Phase of Adjustment. Several factors have been reported as affecting the period of adjustment of bacterial cells when they are introduced into a fresh medium. The four most important will be briefly discussed below.

1. INOCULUM. The nature of the inoculum used has a considerable influence on the earlier phases of the bacterial culture cycle.

a. Number of Organisms in the Inoculum. The quantity of the inoculum, as stated by Rahn (1906), has an influence on the period of adjustment of an organism when it is transferred to a fresh medium. In brief, Rahn believed that a larger quantity of inoculum shortened the period of adjustment. In 1914 Penfold made a complete study of bacterial lag and could not confirm in whole the findings of Rahn. More recently, however, Herrington (1934) has expressed by an equation the relationship between the inoculum and the time for turbidity to develop in a liquid culture medium. From this work it seems that the lag phase is a linear function of the logarithm of the inoculum.

If the nutrients and gaseous tension in a medium are optimum for development of the cells, the quantity of the inoculum may be of less importance than has been previously believed. This subject is discussed in more detail on pp. 108 to 109.

b. Stage of Growth and Age of the Inoculum. The age of the parent culture has considerable bearing on the adjustment of an organism to a fresh medium. For non-spore-forming bacteria the age of the inoculum follows, as a general rule, the curves of the subcultures in Fig. 3. It will be observed that those subcultures prepared during the various changes in the population cycle follow the growth of the parent culture. It is of special interest to note that those subcultures (*D*, *E*, and *F*) made during the most rapid period of growth showed no observable delay in rate of multiplication. Similar observations have been made by Coplans (1910), Penfold (1914), and others. As we have stated, spores may show an extended lag period if they are in a dormant stage, but do not always do so.

Graham-Smith (1920) demonstrated that the adjustment phase was shorter when the inoculum was from bacteria which had been frequently subcultured than from those in which few previous subcultures had been made.

c. Nature of the Organism Used as the Inoculum. Various bacteria show an inherent difference in their ability to initiate active growth and to develop at a maximum rate of speed in a favorable medium. The members of the coliform group and some of the thermophilic bacilli require a relatively short period of time to make the adjustment and develop very rapidly, whereas organisms of the genera *Corynebacterium* and *Mycobacterium* develop more slowly. The genus *Nitrobacter* and related organisms are probably the slowest of all to divide, according to Mason (1935).

2. Nature of the Medium. With a favorable medium a bacterium, as a rule, will quickly adapt itself to the new environment, and consequently the phase of adjustment will be shortened. The lag period may be prolonged for some time in a medium which is not optimum for growth, but in a number of such cases the organisms are able eventually to bring about the proper adjustment, either in the medium or in their cells, and to initiate some growth.

Sometimes the period is different in two or more media, even though the parent culture is growing favorably in each. To illustrate this point we can take the experiments of Coplans (1910) and Penfold (1914), in which they have shown that a subculture of a dulcitol-peptone broth culture of *Escherichia coli* onto dulcitol-peptone broth gives a longer lag than a subculture of a peptone broth culture of the same species onto a peptone broth, even though the parent cultures were the same age. Winslow, Walker, and Sutermeister (1932) have noted in *E. coli* a difference of 6 hours in the lag phase between peptone broth and a synthetic medium, the synthetic medium showing the longer lag. It is of interest to note, however, that the lag phase of certain bacteria in synthetic media may be reduced by the addition of small amounts of such nutrients as glucose and asparagine [see Lodge and Hinshelwood (1943)].

3. Temperature of Incubation. Very few data seem to be available on the effect of temperature on the initial period of adjustment. It can probably be assumed that, if a medium is incubated at the optimum temperature for the growth of the particular organism, the lag period will be greatly shortened.

The data presented by Müller (1903) for several bacterial species indicate that lowering the temperature of incubation lengthens the period of adjustment, and similar results have been observed by Penfold (1914), working with *E. coli*. A study by Anderson and Meanwell (1936), using a streptococcus cultured in milk, showed a lag of one-half hour at 42°C., 1 hour at 37°C., 2 hours at 30° and 26°C., and 3 hours at 20°C.

Sudden changes in the temperature have an interesting influence on bacterial growth and may be mentioned here. During the period between lag and the very early part of logarithmic growth sudden cold shock has but slight initial effect upon the cells, whereas a marked sensitivity to cold shock extends throughout the entire logarithmic phase of growth. Mature cells are not appreciably affected by either an initial cold shock or prolonged holding at 0°C.

4. Effect of Carbon Dioxide. The effect of carbon dioxide on the growth of bacteria has been fully reviewed by Valley and Rettger (1927), Valley (1928), and Hes (1938). Valley and Rettger studied the effect of carbon dioxide on one hundred different organisms representing different families and genera of bacteria. The removal of carbon dioxide from an environment which was otherwise favorable for the development of bacteria resulted in the complete cessation of growth. When small amounts of carbon dioxide were added to the natural atmospheric environment, bacterial action and growth were often increased, especially with *Brucella abortus* and *Lactobacillus acidophilus*. Valley and Rettger came to the conclusion that carbon dioxide is necessary for the growth and development of both aerobic and anaerobic bacteria. Since that time several reports [see Walker (1932), Gladstone, Fildes, and Richardson (1935), Levine (1936), and Rahn (1941)] have appeared which cannot be covered in detail here. The data accumulated on this subject indicate that bacteria cannot divide until the concentration of carbon dioxide, either in the medium or in the cells, reaches a certain level. Walker (1932) regarded the lag phase as the time necessary for this level to be reached. The production of an optimum concentration is determined by the rate of respiration of the organisms, balanced by the rate of removal of the carbon dioxide, which normally occurs by diffusion and chemical combination. Any factor affecting either of these processes will in turn affect growth.

Rahn (1941) has demonstrated that bacteria need carbon dioxide not only during the lag phase for purposes of rejuvenation but also during the period of active growth.

The role played by carbon dioxide in stimulating the growth of bacteria is at present not clearly understood. Whether it acts as a stimulant to cell division as a process apart from growth, whether it is a factor in protoplasmic synthesis, or whether it has some other function awaits further study. However, according to the classical studies by Wood and Werkman (1936 to 1940), certain organisms actually use the carbon dioxide in their metabolism. For example, a four-carbon chained acid, such as succinic, may be synthesized from carbon dioxide and a three-carbon compound.

Theories Advanced to Explain the Phase of Adjustment. The phenomenon of bacterial lag or adjustment has been the subject of much study, and several workers have suggested theories to explain this period at the beginning of the growth curve. Several of the more important of these theories may be briefly mentioned.

1. Theory of Cell Secretion. Rahn (1906) suggested that the optimum growth of a bacterium could be attained only when some heat-stable, nonfilterable substance formed by the cells themselves had been secreted into the medium. This theory has been pretty much disregarded in the past because of the fact that actively growing cells show no lag, whereas cells taken from a culture which has stopped growing have a lag phase. This information led Chesney (1916) and others to conclude that the cause of the lag is in the cell itself, not in the medium. Lodge and Hinshelwood (1943), however, have demonstrated that during the early lag phase a diffusible substance appears in the solution; it may be transferred with inocula or with sterile filtrates and reduce lag in fresh media.

2. Theory of Essential Intermediate Cell Constituents. The hypothesis put forward by Penfold (1914) suggests that some of the constituents of bacterial protoplasm are synthesized in steps. Thus, when an organism is transferred to a fresh medium, these intermediate compounds diffuse out of the cells into the medium. Before growth can occur, these bodies again have to be synthesized and accumulate in optimum proportion within the bacterial cells. Rettger (1918) suggests that lag in culture media may be decreased or eliminated by supplying "satisfactory substitutes for the intermediate bodies in the form of amino acids and perhaps amines of simple composition, and also certain growth-accessory substances."

3. Theory of Biological Selection. This theory was put forward by Ledingham and Penfold in 1914. Their hypothesis was based on

the supposition that a given inoculum consists of cells which have "individually different powers of growth." Thus during the lag phase the more rapidly growing cells would predominate, and the phenomenon of selection would be taking place, since those cells endowed with the power of rapid multiplication would increase more rapidly than the weaker cells. Kelly and Rahn (1932) and others have attempted to prove this theory with experimental data, but they have not been too successful. The studies of Kelly and Rahn consisted of direct microscopic observations of more than seventeen hundred individual cells of bacteria and yeasts inoculated on a solid medium. The "family tree" of individual cells was studied for four generations. They observed considerable variation in the rate of growth of individual cells, but it was not inherent. Cells which divide rapidly for one generation tend to slow up during the next generation, whereas those which divide slowly for one generation separate quickly the next. Thus, once cells start to divide, it seems as though they continue to do so at a rather average rate, and one strain does not supersede another.

4. Theory of Cellular Injury or Shock. Chesney (1916) regarded the occurrence of bacterial lag as "an expression of injury which the bacterial cell has sustained from its previous environment." His work was done with the pneumococcus, and he noted that a toxic substance was formed during growth which tended to poison some of the cells. The greatest concentration of this noxious substance was present at the end of the logarithmic phase but decreased when cultures were incubated for a longer period of time. Thus some of the cells were being poisoned by their own metabolic products. When a fresh subculture was prepared, some time was required for the cells to recover entirely from the poisonous effects encountered in their previous environment. This time of recovery was considered the period of lag.

The work of Chesney is very interesting in the light of our present knowledge of the respiratory mechanism of the pneumococcus. To illustrate this point we may mention the work by McLeod and Gordon (1922, 1923) and Avery and his coworkers [Avery and Morgan (1924), Neill and Avery (1925)]. They have shown that pneumococci produce hydrogen peroxide in sufficient amounts to exert a toxic action when other bacteria are added to the culture medium of these hydrogen peroxide-producing cells. Besides being toxic to pneumococci, hydrogen peroxide is also volatile, a fact which would tend to account for the diminution of the toxic action on prolonged incubation which Chesney noted. That the shock theory cannot be of general application to other bacteria is made clear by the studies of Broom (1929) and Barnes (1931). These investigators tried to demonstrate growth-inhibiting substances in cultures previously inoculated with staphylococci and coliform bacilli, hoping to prove or disprove the toxic-cellular theory of Chesney. Since they failed to confirm this theory with bacteria other than pneumococci, the inference is that Chesney's work is of value only in explaining the lag phase of the pneumococcus and a few other bacterial species.

5. THEORY OF STIMULATION BY CARBON DIOXIDE. A more recent explanation of the occurrence of bacterial lag is that offered by Walker (1932). He wrote, "The phenomenon of lag under certain conditions can be explained very simply as the period needed to build up the concentration of CO_2 in the environment—or in the cell—to a value essential for growth." For further information on the role played by carbon dioxide in bacterial metabolism the interesting papers by Wood and Werkman (1940) and Werkman and Wood (1942) should be consulted.

None of these five theories is supported by sufficient experimental data to allow its acceptance without reservations. Probably the true explanation of the phenomenon of lag or adjustment which a bacterial culture undergoes when transferred to a fresh medium will consist of parts of several of these theories.

During the early stages of the phase of adjustment cells have the following general properties: (1) low multiplication rate [Rahn (1906), Lane-Claypon (1909), Coplans (1910), Penfold (1914)]; (2) relatively small size [Clark and Ruehl (1919), Bayne-Jones and Sandholzer (1933)]; (3) low biochemical activity [Martin (1931–1932), Mooney and Winslow (1935), Huntington and Winslow (1937)]; (4) rather high resistance to unfavorable conditions [Sherman and Albus (1924), Elliker and Frazier (1938)]; and (5) relatively high electrophoretic mobility [Moyer (1936)]. Near the end of the lag phase, however, the process of adjustment is completed, and the cells pass into a phase of physiological youth characterized by active metabolism, ready adaption of certain enzymes to new substrates, lowered resistance to unfavorable agents, and rapid increase in cell mass, with, however, delayed cell division at first. Sufficient data are now available on these points which characterize the phase of physiological youth so that a brief discussion of them is warranted.

Biochemical Changes during the Phase of Physiological Youth. Several older studies indicated that cell metabolic activity was high during the early phases of the culture cycle, but these results were not computed on the basis of cell numbers.

Bayne-Jones and Rhees (1929) were probably the first investigators to present actual data on metabolic activity per cell per hour at different periods of the culture cycle. They studied heat production in cultures of *Escherichia coli* and *Staphylococcus aureus*. Their most interesting results were obtained when *E. coli* was cultivated in peptone broth. The gram-calories of heat produced per cell in this case were 60×10^{-11} at 1 hour, 198 at 2 hours, 130 at 3 hours, and 75 at 7 hours. Their other results indicated the same general relationship.

Similar interesting data for oxygen consumption are also available. Burk and Lineweaver (1930), working with *Azotobacter*, showed that the rate of oxygen consumption per unit rate of increase in cell numbers

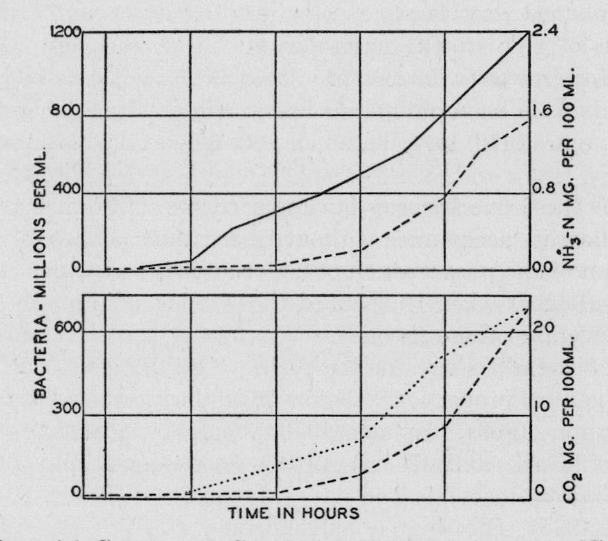

Fig. 4. Bacterial Counts and Cumulative Yields of Ammonia Nitrogen and Carbon Dioxide in Aerated Peptone Broth. ----- = Bacterial count; —— = cumulative $NH_3 - N$; · · · · = cumulative CO_2. (From Walker, Winslow, Huntington, and Mooney, 1934.)

was greater during the first 9 hours of the culture than it was during the ninth to twelfth hours. Eaton (1931), using staphylococcus cultures, reported the highest respiration rate occurred during the first $2\frac{1}{2}$ hours of the culture cycle. Gerard and Falk (1931) presented quantitative data for *Sarcina lutea*. They computed a consumption of 6.5 cu. mm. of oxygen per milligram of dry weight of culture for the early stages of the population cycle, as compared with 2.6 cu. mm. during the phase of stable maximal population. Although Martin (1931–1932) did not compute rates per cell, he did note that the rate of oxygen consumption by *Escherichia coli* reached a peak between 30 and 90 minutes, whereas cell size was greatest at 60 to 120 minutes. Similar data on the oxygen consumption by several bacterial species have been computed by Greig and Hoogerheide (1941).

More complete information on biochemical activity during the phase of physiological youth is available in regard to carbon dioxide production. Several examples may be cited to illustrate this point. Walker and Winslow (1932), working with *E. coli*, reported 41 to 185 mg. $\times 10^{-11}$ CO_2 per cell per hour formed in the late lag period, against less than 2 mg. $\times 10^{-11}$ for the close of the logarithmic phase. Walker, Winslow, Huntington, and Mooney (1934), using the same organism and various media, found maximal production of CO_2 (117 to 123 mg. $\times 10^{-11}$ per cell per hour) during the second hour of the population cycle (late lag and early logarithmic phase), falling to 16 to 22 mg. $\times 10^{-11}$ after 5 hours (beyond the close of the logarithmic phase). Some of their data on the cumulative yields of NH_3 and CO_2 in relation to the bacterial count are shown in Fig. 4. Mooney and Winslow (1935) included *Salmonella gallinarum* and *Salmonella pullorum* in their study and likewise noted a high peak of metabolic activity during the late lag and early logarithmic period. This high point is shown very well in one example taken from their paper. A relatively long period of adjustment was characteristic for *S. pullorum* in glucose-peptone broth (Table 3). However, the CO_2 production increased gradually until a peak was reached during the period of physiological youth and then gradually declined.

Since these high rates of CO_2 production during the period of physiological youth might be due in part to the larger size of the cells, Huntington and Winslow (1937) computed their data in terms of CO_2 pro-

TABLE 3

RELATIONSHIP BETWEEN AGE, NUMBER, AND CARBON DIOXIDE PRODUCTION BY *Salmonella pullorum*

[From Mooney and Winslow (1935)]

Age of Culture, hours	Bacteria in Glucose-Peptone Broth, millions/ml.	CO_2 Production per Cell per Hour in Glucose-Peptone Broth, mg. $\times 10^{-11}$
1	11.7	6
2	10.0	30
3	13.0	33
4	16.2	99
5	38.9	114
6	70.3	96
7	320.2	57
8	603.4	26
9	705.8	17
25	331.7	8

duction per cubic micron of bacterial cell substance, using *Escherichia coli*, *Salmonella gallinarum*, and *Salmonella pullorum* in their study. They found that maximum values for the late lag and early logarithmic phases ranged from 86 to 216 $\times 10^{-11}$ mg. of CO_2 per cubic micron of cell substance, whereas for the phase of stationary maximum population the corresponding figures varied from 5 to 19.

The liberation of ammonia-nitrogen is another type of metabolic activity associated with the period of physiological youth. Here the question may be raised whether the lower values reported for NH_3-nitrogen liberation in the later growth phases may not be due to more rapid utilization rather than to a lessened rate of production. This question cannot be categorically answered, but the close parallelism between NH_3 liberation and CO_2 liberation suggests that both are examples of the same phenomenon. Two examples may be cited of this parallelism. Walker and Winslow (1932) determined the rate of NH_3 production for *E. coli*, in the lag phase in different media, as 6 to 36 mg. $\times 10^{-11}$ per cell per hour; the corresponding figure for the phase of maximum population was 0.2 mg. $\times 10^{-11}$ or less. Walker, Winslow, Huntington, and Mooney (1934) reported that at $1\frac{1}{2}$ hours (late lag phase) the NH_3-nitrogen yield varied in different media from 26 to 50 mg. $\times 10^{-11}$ per cell per hour, whereas after 5 hours (post-logarithmic phase) the values fell to 3 mg. $\times 10^{-11}$ or less.

A fifth measure of biochemical activity, for which a little similar evidence is available, is acid production. Stark and Stark (1929) found the rate of fermentation of *E. coli* to be 4.6 $\times 10^{-11}$ mg. per cell per hour for young cells and 0.9 for old cells. A somewhat similar relationship for fermentation by *Streptococcus lactis* was reported by Rahn, Hegarty, and Deuel (1938).

A sixth interesting point which can be mentioned under the metabolic activities of bacteria in relation to growth phases is the elaboration of soluble capsular polysaccharides. For example, Bukantz, Cooper, and Bullowa (1941) found that pneumococcus, type III, produced 174 $\times 10^{-11}$ mg. of soluble capsular polysaccharide per cell per hour during the phase of physiological youth; later, during the phase of maximal stable population, only 1.0 to 8.4 $\times 10^{-11}$ mg. was produced.

The metabolic activity of bacterial cells during the various phases of growth has been fully reviewed by Winslow, Walker, and Sutermeister (1932), Walker, Winslow, Huntington, and Mooney (1934), Clifton (1937), Winslow and Walker (1939), and Bukantz, Cooper, and Bullowa (1941).

Adaptive Enzyme Formation during the Phase of Physiological Youth. For some time it has been known that old cells adapt themselves very slowly, if at all, to certain substrates, while young, growing cultures seem to produce specific new enzymes quite easily.

In 1930 Karström differentiated bacterial enzymes into two main groups: (1) the "constitutive" enzymes, those which are always formed by the cells of a given species, irrespective of the composition of the medium; (2) the "adaptive" enzymes, those which are produced as a specific response to the presence of the homologous substrate in the culture medium.

Hegarty (1939) tested cells of *Streptococcus lactis* of various ages to determine the stage of growth during which new "adaptive" enzymes are most easily manufactured. One of his experiments may be cited (Table 4) to show that the most rapid adaption to a new sugar is always observed with cells from cultures just coming out of the lag phase, during the so-called period of physiological youth. The data in Table 4 show that, when cells are taken from a glucose broth culture 1 hour after being inoculated (late lag phase) and placed in galactose, lactose, and sucrose, they will begin to form lactic acid after 1.5, 8.0, and 0.5 hours, respectively. During the logarithmic phase (2 to 5 hours) adaptibility decreased rapidly and continuously. Also of interest is the fact that adaption seems to vary with the kind of sugar, since the formation of lactase requires more time than that of galactozymase. However, this difference may be related to the susceptibility of the cell to harmful agents.

For further interesting information on the nature and production of adaptive enzymes by bacteria consult the papers by Karström (1937–1938), Rahn (1938), Dubos (1940), and the references listed by these authors.

TABLE 4

DELAY (HOURS) BEFORE ADAPTION OCCURS BY *Streptococcus lactis* CELLS OF VARIOUS AGES GROWN IN GLUCOSE BROTH

[From Hegarty (1939)]

Age of Cells, hours	Time Required for Adaption When Placed in			
	Glucose, hours	Galactose, hours	Lactose, hours	Sucrose, hours
1	0	1.5	8.0	0.5
2	0	3.0	9.0	0.0
3	0	7.0	15.0	0.0
4	0	9.0	16.0	1.5
6	0	13.0	20.0	3.0
8	0	13.0	20.0	4.0
10	0	13.0	20.0	4.0
36	0	18.0	29.0	8.0

Morphological Changes during the Phase of Physiological Youth. Experimental studies on the morphology of bacteria have provided convincing evidence that the cells of early generations developing in a fresh, favorable medium are quite different from those of generations developing after the period of maximum multiplication.

Measurements of bacterial cells indicate that individuals of a large number of species increase in size during the early hours of culture growth but soon decrease to approximately their original size. This change in morphology almost parallels the increase in metabolic activity which characterizes the phase of physiological youth.

Clark and Ruehl (1919) were among the first to study the change in size of bacteria at different times during the culture cycle. Using a micrometer, they measured 70 strains of organisms, representing 37 different species, at intervals during their growth. In all instances, with the exception of members of the diphtheria group and *Malleomyces mallei*, they found that the cells in cultures from 4 to 9 hours old were much larger than those in cultures 24 hours old. They stated that the change in size of the cells was sometimes so great "as to render the organisms unrecognizable when viewed by the ordinary standards of the 24-hour culture."

Extensive studies of this phenomenon were made by Henrici between 1921 and 1928. For many interesting data and the details of his technique, his book, *Morphologic Variation and the Rate of Growth of Bacteria*, should be consulted. Briefly, however, he noted that cells of *Escherichia coli* grown on agar increased in length from 1.5 μ to 4.0 μ in the first 3 hours after inoculation and subsequently declined in size. *Bacillus megatherium* increased in length from 3.4 μ to 9.1 μ in the first $3\frac{1}{2}$ hours and to 19.8 μ in $5\frac{1}{2}$ hours after seeding. The organism at $3\frac{1}{2}$ hours had not yet entered the logarithmic phase of growth.

Adolph and Bayne-Jones (1932) and Bayne-Jones and Adolph (1933) obtained very accurate records with motion photomicrography of changes in the size and rate of growth of individual cells of *E. coli* and *B. megatherium* cultivated on agar. With *E. coli* it was found that the mean rate of growth in volume of individual cells reached a maximum 60 minutes after inoculation of the medium and then declined rapidly, whereas the mean rate of reproduction did not reach a peak until 2 hours after the inoculation. Maximum cell volume was greatest at 90 minutes and thereafter diminished progressively; the cells observed at the end of the experiment were only one-fifth the size of those seen at first.

Huntington and Winslow (1937) have reported data which give additional support to the conclusion that increase in cell size precedes the logarithmic phase of multiplication. They studied three of the characteristics of physiological youth, using cultures of *E. coli*, *Salmonella gallinarum*, and *Salmonella pullorum*, and found them to exhibit a definite and orderly relationship. First the metabolic activity started to increase, followed by an increase in cell volume and then by cell division rate. Once the peak had been reached, cell volume and metabolic activity decreased, but the rate of cell division continued high for a period of several hours. The greatest reproductive activity came 1 to 5 hours after the peak of cell size (Table 5).

TABLE 5

RELATIONSHIP BETWEEN CELL SIZE, METABOLIC ACTIVITY, AND RATE OF CELL MULTIPLICATION

[From Huntington and Winslow (1937)]

Organism and Medium	Time of Maximum Activity, hours after inoculation		
	Size of Cells	*Metabolic Activity*	*Rate of Cell Multiplication*
Escherichia coli			
Peptone	2	2	4
Peptone-glucose	2	2	3
Salmonella gallinarum			
Peptone	3	4	5
Peptone-glucose	3	4	6
Peptone-lactose	3	5	7
Salmonella pullorum			
Peptone	4	2	9
Peptone-glucose	4	5	7
Peptone-lactose	3	3	7

In regard to changes in cell size and the period of adjustment the work of Hershey and Bronfenbrenner (1938) and Hershey (1939) is very interesting and sheds further light on this subject. They have reported results for *E. coli* which indicate that the age or phase of growth of the cells is not one of the factors influencing their rate of growth. Calculations of growth rates were deduced from measurements of turbidity, bacterial nitrogen, and oxygen uptake of broth transplants of *E. coli*, and in all cases identical values were observed, irrespective of the age of the inoculum. The same relationship does not exist, however, for the rate of multiplication. In explanation of this difference Hershey states:

The paradox that old and young bacteria may exhibit identical growth rates, while differing markedly in rate of multiplication, is to be explained only by consideration of average cell-size. Growing at the same rate, the smaller bacteria from old cultures require a longer time ("lag") to reach the size at which fission occurs in freshly seeded broth, than do young bacteria of greater initial size.

Thus the lag in rate of multiplication must be attributed to changes in the environmental factors limiting the size at which fission occurs during the period of growth, and not to any peculiarity inherent in the bacterial cells.

Change in Resistance of Cells to Unfavorable Agents during the Phase of Physiological Youth. Another important characteristic of the large, actively metabolic cells of the phase of physiological youth is their reduced resistance to certain harmful physical and chemical agents.

The biological importance of this characteristic was first emphasized by Sherman and Albus (1923, 1924), who studied the effect of heat, cold, and weak disinfectants on bacteria at different ages. Their work indicates that bacterial cells during the early part of the lag period are less sensitive to slightly toxic salts and other inimical agents than are the organisms of the late lag and early logarithmic phase of growth. For example, they cultivated a strain of *Escherichia coli* in 1 per cent peptone broth for 1 week at room temperature to obtain old cells and then made a transfer to a fresh flask of the same medium, which was incubated at 37°C. Plate counts were made at frequent intervals. At the same time 1-ml. portions of the culture were transferred to 100 ml. of 5 per cent sodium chloride solution and held at 20°C. for 1 hour, after which a plate count was made on the salt solution and the number of cells calculated in terms of the 1 ml. of the broth culture added. The results of two of their experiments, using 5 per cent NaCl solution, are given in Table 6.

From the data in Table 6 it can be seen that, immediately after inoculation from an old culture and for a period of about 1 hour thereafter, the bacterial cells were not very susceptible to the action of the 5 per cent NaCl solution. However, once the cells of *E. coli* entered the phase of physiological youth ($1\frac{1}{2}$ to 2 hours), destruction of the organisms increased to a marked degree when they were subjected to the same treatment. The mortality in Experiment A was 14.06 per cent at the beginning and 92.94 per cent at the end of $2\frac{1}{2}$ hours of growth, and in Experiment B 0 per cent, as against 68.37 per cent after $2\frac{1}{4}$ hours. Sherman and Albus interpret this result as indicating that during the period of lag the old bacteria which have been used as an inoculum are undergoing a process of "biologic rejuvenescence" which fits them for reproduction.

TABLE 6

EFFECT OF 5 PER CENT NaCl SOLUTION ON *Escherichia coli* DURING THE EARLY PHASES OF GROWTH

[From Sherman and Albus (1924)]

Time, hours after inoculation	Experiment A			Experiment B		
	Original Culture	*After 1 Hour in 5% NaCl*	*Mortality, %*	*Original Culture*	*After 1 Hour in 5% NaCl*	*Mortality, %*
0	96,000	82,500	14.06	70,500	70,000	0
1	80,500	60,500	24.72	75,500	62,000	17.88
1½	90,500	41,000	53.59	72,000	42,000	41.66
1¾	......	.....	....	89,000	37,000	58.42
2	143,000	33,000	76.22	108,000	40,500	62.50
2¼	......	.....	....	158,000	50,500	68.37
2½	225,000	16,500	92.94	......	.....	....

The effect of heat on bacteria at different ages has been studied by a great many workers [see Winslow and Walker (1939)]. The early study by Schultz and Ritz (1910) is particularly interesting and illustrates this subject very well. These investigators, using coliform bacilli, exposed cultures of various ages to heat treatment at 53°C. for 25 minutes. In a 20-minute culture approximately 5 per cent survived such treatment. In a 50-minute culture (still in late lag phase) 1 per cent survived. In a 4-hour culture (early logarithmic phase) 100 per cent were killed, and in cultures from 7 to 13 hours old (late logarithmic phase) the same treatment produced little or no reduction at all. Quite similar results have been reported by Elliker and Frazier (1938), who worked with *E. coli* grown at 28°C. and 38°C. and then heat-shocked at 53°C. for 30 minutes. One very interesting point should be mentioned in connection with this study. The usual fall in resistance was observed for the late lag and early logarithmic phase, but more interesting was a temporary, brief, fivefold increase in resistance in the very early lag phase, which suggests a new characteristic of the early lag phase.

The lowered resistance of cells in the period of physiological youth has been demonstrated also with other chemical and physical agents. For example, Gates (1929) reported that a 4-hour culture of *Staphylococcus aureus* was more readily killed by a given intensity of ultraviolet light than a 28-hour culture.

Change in Electrophoretic Mobility and Agglutination during the Phase of Physiological Youth. Closely related to the low resistance of cells to harmful chemical and physical agents during the period of physiological youth is the property of low susceptibility to certain types of agglutination, coupled with a low electrophoretic charge.

In 1914 Gillespie observed that very young cultures of pneumococci require a longer agglutination period than older cells. Sherman and Albus (1923) reported that 4-hour cultures of *E. coli* were not agglutinated by an acidity of *p*H 3.0, whereas a 24-hour culture was agglutinated at a *p*H of 3.8. Similar results with different organisms have been reported by other workers.

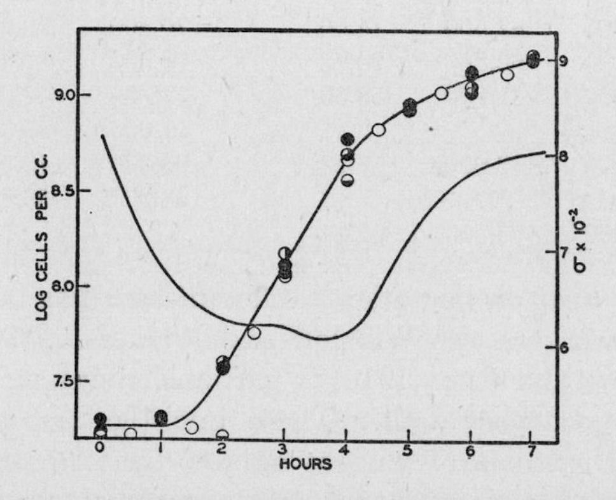

Fig. 5. Growth Curve (circles) of a Smooth Strain of *Escherichia coli,* and the Mean Charge Density-Age Curve of the Same Organism Plotted for Comparison. (From Moyer, 1936.)

Although a number of early studies have appeared on the electrophoretic charge of bacteria, the most complete report dealing with this phenomenon in relation to the culture cycle is that by Moyer (1936). He worked with smooth and rough strains of *E. coli* in an aerated medium and drew the following principal conclusions. Rough and smooth strains exhibit distinctly different charges, but within each strain results are highly consistent. Mobility is high at the start and falls during the first hour for the rough strain, remaining low for the second and part of the third hour and then rising again. The mobility of the smooth strain drops during the first and second hours and remains low during the third and fourth hours (Fig. 9, Chapter 1). The low mobilities correspond to the lag and the beginning of the logarithmic phases, and the subsequent rise in mobility comes near the end of the logarithmic phase. When these same data were computed on the basis of the net charge density (σ) of the cell surface, a similar relationship was noted (Fig. 5).

Two other experiments which Moyer made may be mentioned. He mixed large cells from a 90-minute culture with the small cells from a 16- to 24-hour culture and determined the mobility of the morphological types under the microscope. The large young cells moved at a mean rate of about 0.7 μ/sec./volt/cm., whereas the mean rate for the small old cells was 0.87. Heating cultures at 56°C. for three-fourths of an hour did not alter the mobility of 24-hour cells but greatly reduced the mobility of 3-hour cells.

A careful analysis of the causative factors involved showed that the low mobility of young cells was not due to the irreversible changes in surface caused by the buffer, nor to the adsorption of dissolved or gaseous metabolites, nor to the presence of flagella, but, probably, to a change in the physical or chemical nature of the surface of the cells, perhaps associated with expansion of the surface and increased permeability.

THE LOGARITHMIC PHASE

The logarithmic phase is that period of growth in a bacterial culture during which regular and maximum multiplication per cell is taking place.[1] We have just pointed out that the final characteristic of physiological youth is a rapid rate of cell multiplication. This characteristic, however, is initiated slightly later than the increase in metabolic activity and cell size, the lowered resistance to unfavorable physical and chemical agents, and the decreased electrophoretic charge which are so characteristic of the youth phase. By the time the maximum rate of cell multiplication is reached, most of the other characteristics of youth are on the decline. For actual data on these changes, the tables and figures already mentioned and the references given by Winslow and Walker (1939) should be consulted.

The logarithmic phase can also be defined as that period during which the generation time has been reduced to a minimum. As we have mentioned, the generation time is that interval during which one bacterium develops and completely divides into two cells. Since bacteria divide by binary fission, the increase in the number of cells is by geometric progression; that is, at the end of the first generation a single cell will divide into two (2^1), at the end of the second generation the two bacteria will separate to form four (2^2), the four will then divide into eight (2^3), etc., until at the end of the nth generation period the number will be 2^n. It can be seen that this phase of growth is the one most susceptible to simple mathematical analysis. Furthermore it is of major importance in the study of the effect of environment upon bacteria.

[1] This definition is widely quoted for the logarithmic phase; however, work by several investigators [see Rogers and Greenbank (1930) and Hirsch (1933)] indicates that growth in a bacterial culture may, under some conditions, be intermittent.

In studying bacterial growth during its various phases, the progeny from more than one cell are usually encountered. Thus it is necessary to consider this problem in terms of several organisms rather than one bacterium.

In such a study it is convenient to use certain abbreviations, and those of Buchanan and Fulmer (1928) will be followed in this brief discussion. They are:

t = time.
B = number of bacteria at the beginning of a given time, taken as $t = 0$.
b = number of bacteria at the end of a given time (t).
g = generation time, or the time for one complete cellular division to take place.
n = number of generations occurring in time (t).
log = logarithms to the base 10 (common logs).
ln = logarithms to the base e (natural logs).

If counts are made at intervals by one of the methods already discussed, the number of generations, n, during the growth period and the length of each of the generations, g, can easily be calculated. It can now be seen that, if we are dealing with more than one cell, at the end of the first generation:

$$b = B \times 2$$

At the end of the second generation:

$$b = B \times 2 \times 2$$

And at the end of the nth generation:

$$b = B \times 2^n$$

If this equation is solved for the number of generations, (n), it becomes:

$$\log b = \log B + n \log 2$$

or

$$n = \frac{\log b - \log B}{\log 2} \tag{1}$$

Since the log of 2 is 0.30103, equation 1 may also be written:

$$n = 3.3 \log \frac{b}{B} \tag{2}$$

that is, if the number of bacteria at the end of a given time, t, is divided by the number at the beginning, $t = 0$, and the logarithm of this quotient is multiplied by 3.3, the resulting figure gives the number of generations occurring in time, t.

It is further evident that the number of generations, n, which will develop in a given time, t, will be equal to the total time divided by the generation time, g, thus:

$$n = \frac{t}{g} \tag{3}$$

or

$$g = \frac{t}{n} \tag{4}$$

and

$$g = \frac{t \log 2}{\log b - \log B} \tag{5}$$

or

$$g = \frac{t}{3.3 \log \frac{b}{B}} \tag{6}$$

It is apparent that the more rapid the growth of a bacterial cell, the smaller will be the value of g. Thus, if a comparison of the effect of different environmental factors on the growth of a bacterium is desired, it can be made by comparing the values of g obtained under different conditions.

It is often more desirable in such studies, however, to determine the *growth rate constant* of Slator (1916) or, as it is usually called, the *velocity coefficient*. This is simply the *rate of increase per cell during the period of growth or the rate of decrease during the phase of death*. In other words, the number of new cells produced by 1 given bacterial cell in a certain period of time is the increase for that particular cell. For example, if 1 cell divides to form 2, the 2 divide to form 4, and the 4 separate into 8 during 1 hour, then there are 7 more bacteria at the end of 1 hour than at the beginning. Thus, the velocity coefficient or rate of increase is 7 per hour. Also, the shorter the generation time, the faster will be bacterial cell division and the greater will be the numerical value of the velocity coefficient or rate of increase.

The velocity coefficient is usually designated by the constant k, and, when solved by calculus, the following formulas are obtained:

$$\ln b = kt + \ln B$$

or

$$k = \frac{\ln b - \ln B}{t} = \frac{1}{t} \ln \frac{b}{B} \tag{7}$$

By comparing the above expression with the formula for the generation time, we see that the growth rate constant of Slator or the velocity constant, k, is nothing but the reciprocal of the generation time multiplied with a constant factor, as:

$$k = \frac{1}{g}\frac{\log 2}{\ln 2} = \frac{0.692}{g} \tag{8}$$

If equation 7 is changed to logarithms to the base 10, it becomes

$$k = \frac{\log b - \log B}{0.434t} = \frac{2.3}{t} \log \frac{b}{B}$$

or

$$0.434k = \frac{1}{t} \log \frac{b}{B} \tag{9}$$

It must be kept in mind that the constant, k, is just a number which indicates the relative growth rate and cannot be defined descriptively.

Slator (1916) made use of this constant to measure by a nephelometric method the rate of growth of *Lactobacillus delbrückii* in malt-wort broth at 45°C. The following results were obtained:

t, hours	$\frac{b}{B}$	$0.434k$
2.53	119	0.82
3.48	800	0.83
4.00	2,260	0.84
4.73	9,060	0.84
5.02	18,100	0.85
	Average:	0.84

Since the generation time is inversely proportional to the rate of growth per cell, this rate (k) can be evaluated in terms of generation time, g, by the following expression from equation 8:

$$g = \frac{\ln 2}{k} = \frac{0.692}{k}$$

because $\ln 2 = 2.307 \log_{10} 2 = 0.692$.

In the data from Slator $k = 1.93$ ($0.434k = 0.84$); therefore the generation time becomes:

$$g = \frac{\ln 2}{1.93} = \frac{0.692}{1.93} = 0.358 \text{ hour} = 21.5 \text{ minutes.}$$

The influence of environment can be easily measured by comparing values of k obtained by cultivating organisms under different sets of

TABLE 7

EFFECT OF TEMPERATURE ON THE RATE OF GROWTH OF *Lactobacillus delbrückii*

[From Slator (1916)]

Temperature, °C.	Time, t, hours	$\frac{b}{B}$	$0.434k$
58°	No growth	...	....
55°	Slight growth	...	....
52.5°	5.5	614	0.51
	6.5	5,220	0.57
	10.3	317,000	0.54
			Mean: 0.54
50°	3.1	614	0.90
	3.9	5,220	0.95
	4.2	31,500	1.07
	5.4	270,000	1.01
			Mean: 0.98
45°	*See data on p. 124.*		Mean: 0.84
40°	4.0	305	0.62
	5.25	1,550	0.61
	6.0	5,530	0.62
	6.8	23,400	0.64
			Mean: 0.62
35°	6.5	195	0.35
	8.5	830	0.345
	9.6	4,180	0.38
	11.6	29,800	0.385
			Mean: 0.365
30°	18.0	1,840	0.181
	21.0	7,800	0.185
	25.0	46,800	0.187
			Mean: 0.184
25°	29.0	277	0.084
	43.0	3,310	0.082
	49.5	19,900	0.087
			Mean: 0.084
22°	90.0	126	0.02
20°	No growth	...	....

conditions. Table 7 shows the effect of temperature on the growth of *Lactobacillus delbrückii.*

As has been stated, when the logarithms of the numbers of bacterial cells in this phase are plotted against time, they fall on an ascending straight line. Equation 7, $\ln b = kt + \ln B$, is in the form of an equation of a straight line, and the slope of this line is represented by the numerical value of k.

It is generally assumed that during the period of logarithmic growth all the bacteria are alive and all are actively dividing at regular intervals. If such is the case, then the total count should be equal to the viable count. It is upon this basis that the preceding equations have been developed. There seems to be some disagreement among workers, however, as to whether all the cells are taking an active part in the process of division during the logarithmic phase. Kelly and Rahn (1932) observed that, once bacteria germinated and started to grow, there was no such thing as "infant mortality," at least during the first few generations. Jennison (1937) found that, if certain technical points were carefully controlled, the viable and total counts were almost identical. On the other hand, Wilson (1922, 1926), Régnier, David, and Kaplan (1932), and others have noted that in broth cultures the total count is usually higher than the viable count, even during the period of logarithmic growth.

Wilson (1922) thought that the most likely explanation for the discrepancy between the total and viable counts during the logarithmic phase was the fact that some of the organisms generated fail to survive their first generation. The actual percentage of the viable cells to the total is not constant for any one organism and probably varies even more for different species. Using a single bacterial species, Wilson obtained figures varying between 57.86 per cent and 122.8 per cent in 16 experiments, with an average of approximately 80 per cent between the two counts at the end of the logarithmic phase of growth. These results mean that about 200 organisms in every 1,000 produced die during each generation. If, for example, we assume that 80 per cent of the bacteria produced during a given generation continue to live and divide while 20 per cent dies, then at the end of the logarithmic phase of growth the total number of organisms alive and dead will exceed the number living. The increase in the living bacteria would still occur in geometrical progression, and the curve obtained by plotting the logarithms of the numbers against time would still fall along an ascending straight line. The only difference would be that, instead of the number of bacteria being doubled in each generation, they would increase by only 1.6 times. This factor of increase is sometimes called the *generation index.*

Let us explain further by assuming that we have inoculated a favorable medium with a bacterium and that at the beginning of the logarithmic phase of growth there are 1,000 living bacteria per milliliter and 1,000 nonviable cells per milliliter which do not germinate. At the end of the first generation 2,000 new organisms would theoreti-

TABLE 8

INCREASE IN VIABLE, DEAD, AND TOTAL BACTERIA WITH A 20 PER CENT MORTALITY PER GENERATION

Generations	Number of Viable Cells per Milliliter	Number of Dead Cells per Milliliter	Total Number of Cells per Milliliter	Ratio of $\frac{\text{Viable}}{\text{Total}}$
0	1,000	1,000	2,000	0.500
1	1,600	1,400	3,000	0.533
2	2,560	2,040	4,600	0.556
3	4,096	3,064	7,160	0.571
4	6,554	4,702	11,256	0.581
5	10,486	7,323	17,809	0.589
6	16,777	11,517	28,294	0.592
7	26,843	18,227	45,070	0.595
10	109,232	73,452	182,684	0.597

cally have been produced, of which 80 per cent or 1,600, would be alive and capable of further division, whereas 20 per cent, or 400, would fail to survive. In the second generation these 1,600 cells would divide to produce 3,200, of which 2,560 would be viable and 20 per cent, or 640, would become inactive. This situation can be seen more clearly in Table 8, which has been adopted from the work of Wilson (1922).

The data in Table 8 show that the ratio of viable to total organisms, $\frac{V}{T}$, increases with each generation until it approaches a value of 0.6. The *generation index* can be obtained with some degree of accuracy near the end of the logarithmic phase of growth by calculating the ratio of the viable to the total count and adding 1; thus in the preceding example it is approximately 1.6, rather than the usual value of 2.

The *generation index* can also be determined [Topley and Wilson (1936)] at any time during the logarithmic phase of growth if the viable and total counts are known both at the beginning and at the end of the nth generation, since:

$$\frac{V_n - V_o}{T_n - T_o} = i - 1 \tag{10}$$

or

$$i = \frac{V_n - V_o}{T_n - T_o} + 1 \tag{11}$$

where i = the *generation index.*

V_o and T_o = the number of viable and total bacteria, respectively, at the beginning of the experiment.

V_n and T_n = the number of viable and total organisms, respectively, at the end of the nth generation.

If it is granted that there is a normal death rate even during the logarithmic period of growth, then the above equations must be calculated on a new basis. If, for example, a generation index of 1.6 is used, equation 1 for calculating the number of generations, and in turn the generation time, will then have to be altered to:

$$n = \frac{\log b - \log B}{\log 1.6}$$

In using this new equation, Wilson (1922) pointed out, the calculations for generation time will be smaller and the number of generations will be greater than are obtained with the formula in which the usual generation index of two is used.

Factors Influencing Growth during the Logarithmic Phase. Several factors have been studied which influence the growth or the generation time of bacteria during the logarithmic phase of growth. The following may be briefly mentioned:

1. Nature of the Bacterium. Because of the inherent nature of some bacteria they seem to grow more rapidly than others. The growth rates, computed as generation times, of several bacteria growing under optimum conditions have been studied and reviewed by Mason (1935). The data listed in Table 9, adapted partly from Mason, show the shortest recorded generation times for some of the common species of bacteria. The members of the coli-aerogenes group are probably the most rapidly growing bacteria, with an average generation time of less than 20 minutes. Some of the spore-forming bacilli grow at about the same rate, the fastest of all being the thermophilic species, although Henrici has observed that *Bacillus megatherium* may divide in 9 minutes under some conditions. Bacteria belonging to the genera *Eberthella, Salmonella,* and *Proteus* have a generation time of 20 to 30 minutes. The staphylococci, streptococci, and diplococci have an average generation time of 25 to 30 minutes. Much slower are the polar flagellates of the genus *Pseudomonas,* which separate every 30 to 40 minutes during maximum growth. Slower still is the growth of the plant pathogenic group [see Hildebrand (1938)], and slowest of all are species of the genera *Rhizobium* and *Azotobacter.*

2. Nature of the Medium. As a general rule, the more favorable the concentration of nutrients in the medium, the more rapid is the

TABLE 9

GROWTH RATES (GENERATION TIMES) OF SEVERAL COMMON BACTERIA

[From Walker, Anderson, and Brown (1932), Mason (1935), Cameron and Sherman (1935), and Hildebrand (1938)]

Organism	Medium	Generation Time, minutes
Azotobacter chroococcum	Sugar-mineral	240
A. chroococcum	Sugar-urea	74
A. chroococcum	Glucose broth	27–39
Rhizobium trifolii	Mannitol-mineral yeast extract	101–174
Rhizobium leguminosarum (six strains)	Mannitol-mineral yeast extract	78.6–150.6
R. trifolii (five strains)	Mannitol-mineral yeast extract	140.4–218.4
Rhizobium meliloti (six strains)	Mannitol-mineral yeast extract	75.0–193.8
Rhizobium japonicum	Mannitol-mineral yeast extract or dextrose	343.8–460.8
Diplococcus pneumoniae, type I	Broth	24.5–31.0
D. pneumoniae, type I	Serum broth	20.5
D. pneumoniae, type II	Broth	33–38
D. pneumoniae, type II	Serum broth	23
Streptococcus lactis	Milk	23.5–26
Streptococcus fecalis	Milk	23–26.5
Streptococcus pyogenes	Beef-heart broth	32
Staphylococcus aureus	Broth	27–30
Vibrio comma	Broth	21.2–38
Pseudomonas fluorescens	Broth	40
Ps. fluorescens	Glucose broth	34–34.5
Pseudomonas aeruginosa	Broth	34
Erwinia amylovora	Broth	71–94
Erwinia carotovora	Broth	57
Phytomonas campestris	Broth	74–165
Phytomonas, range for 11 species	Broth	55–155
Lactobacillus acidophilus	Milk	66–87
Lactobacillus bulgaricus	Milk	39–74
Escherichia coli	Broth	16.5–17
Aerobacter aerogenes	Broth	18.0–30
A. aerogenes	Glucose broth	17.2–17.4
Proteus vulgaris	Broth	21.5
Eberthella typhosa	Broth	23.5
E. typhosa	Glucose broth	29
Shigella dysenteriae	Peptone-phosphate	37
Bacillus mycoides	Broth	28
Bacillus megatherium	Broth	31
Bacillus cereus	Broth	18.8
Bacillus subtilis	Glucose broth	26–32
Bacillus thermophilus	Glucose broth	16
Clostridium botulinum	Glucose broth	35
Clostridium welchii	Milk	35
Clostridium butyricum	Corn mash	51
Corynebacterium diphtheriae	Glucose-serum broth	34

growth. Penfold and Norris (1912) observed the effect on the rate of growth of bacteria of varying the concentration of peptone in the medium, taking care to eliminate the lag phase from their data. When the peptone concentration was increased from 0.125 per cent to 1 per cent, the generation time of *Eberthella typhosa* was reduced from about 800 minutes to approximately 40 minutes.

Graham-Smith (1920) studied the relationship between the concentration of food material and the growth of bacteria, but his observations were confined to the stages of growth occurring after 20 hours and are therefore of little value in determining the relative effects upon the logarithmic phase.

The addition of special substances, such as glucose, to a medium sometimes reduces the generation time and may increase the total yield of organisms.

3. Temperature of Incubation. Since different bacteria have varying optimum temperatures, it can be assumed that the nearer the incubation temperature is to the optimum for growth of any given organism, the shorter will be the generation time.

One investigator, Barber (1908), isolated single cells of *Escherichia coli* and placed them in hanging drops under the microscope, where he could watch them for a considerable time, in order to determine the actual rate of division, or generation time. He found that the generation time gradually decreased up to about 42°C., after which it again increased. The following generation-time figures were obtained with the *E. coli* organism and are widely quoted:

5.5°–8.5°C.	Very slight growth in 5 days
9.0°–11.0°C.	750 minutes for one generation
15.4°–15.8°C.	161 " " " "
21.5°–21.8°C.	62.2 " " " "
30.0°C.	29.7 " " " "
32.0°C.	25.0 " " " "
37°C.	20.0 " " " "
37.5°C.	17.2 " " " "
42°C.	19–20 " " " "
44.6°–44.8°C.	20.8 " " " "
46.8°C.	45.7 " " " "
47°–48.5°C.	Growth slight and irregular
50°C.	No growth

The maximum rate of growth of *E. coli* is at about 37.5°C., but there is little change in the generation time between 37° and 44°C.

More recently Jennison (1935) has studied the effect of temperature on the rate of growth of several species of bacteria. In the third column of Table 10, adapted from his work, the mean generation time for four species at five different incubation temperatures is given.

Length of the Logarithmic Phase. The period of logarithmic growth varies somewhat for different bacteria and is dependent upon several factors, of which only three will be mentioned here.

1. NUMBER OF ORGANISMS IN THE INOCULUM. Lane-Claypon (1909) and Graham-Smith (1920) stated that the length of the logarithmic phase for a given volume of culture fluid was dependent upon the number of bacteria contained in the inoculum and thus varied inversely with the size of the inoculum.

2. VOLUME OF THE CULTURE MEDIUM. The work of Lane-Claypon (1909) and others indicates that the duration of the logarithmic phase varies directly with the volume of culture medium.

TABLE 10

MEAN GENERATION TIME AND LENGTH OF LOGARITHMIC PHASE AT THE SAME TEMPERATURE

[From Jennison (1935)]

Organism	Temperature, °C.	Mean Generation Time (G), minutes	Approximate Length of Logarithmic Phase (L), hours	Ratio (G/L)
Escherichia coli (two strains)	22°	73 65	12 14	6.0 4.6
	27°	46 39	10 8	4.6 4.9
	32°	33 26	8 4	4.1 6.5
	37°	25 20	6 6	4.2 3.3
	42°	26 26	6 4	4.3 6.5
Aerobacter aerogenes	22°	62	10	6.2
	27°	33	6	5.5
	32°	21	6	3.5
	37°	21	4	5.2
	42°	29	4	7.2
Serratia marcescens	22°	52	10	5.2
	27°	37	6	6.1
	32°	26	4	6.5
	37°	22	4	5.5
Chromobacterium violaceum	22°	55	14	4.0
	27°	34	6	5.5
	32°	23	4	5.7
	37°	25	4	6.2

3. Temperature of Incubation. Lane-Claypon (1909) and Jennison (1935) have fully reviewed the effect of temperature on the length of the logarithmic phase, and their work indicates that it varies inversely with the temperature. If the period of lag was discounted, the length of time over which *Escherichia coli* maintained the maximum rate of multiplication was, according to Lane-Claypon, approximately

$7\frac{1}{2}$ hours at 37°C.	12–15 hours at 25°C.
8–$8\frac{1}{2}$ hours at 30°C.	20–24 hours at 20°C.

Eberthella typhosa grew more slowly and the logarithmic increase persisted longer at all temperatures.

Jennison (1935) showed that at any temperature up to the optimum, the ratio of the generation time (in minutes) to the length of logarithmic phase (in hours) is fairly constant (5 : 1), both for the same organism at different temperatures and for various organisms at the same temperature. This ratio seems to change above the optimum temperature for growth as shown in Table 10. The data further indicate the inverse relationship between the incubation temperature and the length of the logarithmic phase, as well as the ratio between the generation time and the period of maximum multiplication.

THE NEGATIVE ACCELERATION PHASE

After the period of rapid multiplication during the logarithmic phase, which varies with the medium, the temperature of incubation, and the nature of the organism, the bacterial cells become less active and division occurs at less frequent intervals. The factors which bring about this slowing-down process in a bacterial culture are not well understood at this time.

One of the most frequent explanations of this phenomenon is that the available food supply in the medium in which the bacteria are growing becomes exhausted. This theory was doubted by Penfold (1914) who demonstrated that, if a 24-hour peptone-broth culture of *Escherichia coli* was centrifuged, the few bacteria remaining in the supernatant fluid again showed a rapid growth when reincubated, but not without a period of lag. Graham-Smith (1920) observed that, if an organism such as *Staphylococcus aureus* or *E. coli* was allowed to grow in meat-extract broth at 37°C. until near the end of the population cycle, and the tubes were then inoculated with the species originally present, little or no growth took place. However, if one of several other organisms was inoculated, multiplication of the added cells took place. If the cultures were sterilized by boiling before inoculation with fresh organisms, the original bacterium and other species, when added, showed an increase. From this experiment he concluded that boiling liberated some food for added organisms of the strain which was originally present. From these experiments and others it seems that factors other than mere exhaustion of food supply are important in the slowing down of growth in a bacterial culture.

Another natural explanation which has been suggested for this phenomenon is the accumulation of toxic metabolic products formed during the period of most active growth and multiplication. This hypothesis can be used to explain the results in certain cases, such as the retardation of growth in a pneumococcus culture resulting from the production of hydrogen peroxide by the organisms, but, as has been mentioned previously, it probably does not account for the decreased rate of growth in all bacterial cultures. In poorly buffered carbohydrate media certain bacteria may produce sufficient acid to retard their growth, but often growth continues if the acid is neutralized by a sterile solution of a weak alkali.

As was suggested by Buchanan and Fulmer (1928), certain bacteria may pass into a morphological and physiological resting stage at the end of the logarithmic phase and no longer take part with those cells which are dividing rapidly, or perhaps some of the cells die.

Undoubtedly other important factors also come into play during this period, or possibly a series of several different factors may be responsible for the retardation of growth. For example, it has been shown in some cases that the slowing-down process is due to a deficiency of oxygen supply in the culture medium, since a readily available supply of oxygen allows the growth of certain aerobic and facultative bacteria to continue for some time after it has ceased in a medium incubated under ordinary aerobic conditions or anaerobically.

THE STATIONARY PHASE

The rate of cellular division, which was at a maximum during the logarithmic phase, decreases more or less gradually during the negative acceleration period until there is an apparent equilibrium between the cells which are passing into the resting stage, or dying, and those which are being newly formed. This equilibrium may last for some time, or it may be disrupted quickly and pass directly into a period of decline. Since there is theoretically no change in the number of bacteria during this phase, the growth curve will be represented by a straight line parallel to the abscissa.

The factors determining the limitation of bacterial growth have not been studied as extensively as have certain controlling influences of the other phases of growth. Brief mention may be made here of several recent experiments along this line.

Some workers believe that the maximum number of bacteria present per unit volume of culture media will reach a rather constant value. Bail (1929) studied this problem in some detail and decided that for each individual bacterial species there was a maximum population which could not be surpassed no matter what factors were controlled. To this maximum in the population cycle he applied the term "M-concentration" and gave the following proof for his claims:

1. Any given bacterial species attains a characteristic M-concentration level when cultivated in a liquid medium, the value of which differs with different species. For example, the M-concentration of cells reached by the dysentery organism is not so great as that of the coliform bacteria or staphylococci.

2. With a large inoculum the M-concentration is reached much sooner than with a small inoculum.

3. Viable bacteria which have reached the M-concentration are not able to multiply at once when inoculated into a fresh medium; and, when the number of cells introduced into a given volume of medium is above the characteristic M-concentration, the cells die until the characteristic level is reached.

4. When cultures that have reached their M-concentrations are centrifuged and reincubated, fresh growth again takes place in the supernatant fluid until the characteristic maximum for the particular species is reached. If, however, after centrifuging, the sedimented cells are again uniformly resuspended in the same medium by shaking, no new growth takes place. From this fact Bail concluded that only the biological space was important for bacterial growth in a medium, and not the available physical space.

5. When a broth culture of dysentery bacilli which had reached the M-concentration was heated to 55°C. for a period of time sufficient to kill most but not all of the viable bacteria, growth again took place upon reincubation until the M-concentration was attained. This fact, according to Bail, indicates that bacteria destroyed by heat do not consume the available biological space.

6. The M-concentration is not due to the exhaustion of the available foodstuffs, since meat-infusion broth can be diluted as much as 25 times without affecting the maximum level of growth. Adding an enriching substance, such as serum or glucose, to the broth never caused the viable organisms to exceed their characteristic M-concentration, although the total number of bacteria increased.

7. Once the M-concentration level has been reached for a given species, growth does not stop at once, but rather an equilibrium is established between the newly formed cells and the number of bacteria which are dying.

Fukuda (1929) investigated this same problem and gave some support to the claims of Bail. He believed, however, that some of the controlling factors of the M-concentration could only be applied to certain bacterial species. To prove his theory he demonstrated that, if broth cultures of *Pseudomonas aeruginosa* were centrifuged, sterilized by heat, and reinoculated with a fresh culture, growth again took place until the previous level was reached. This experiment could be repeated two or three times with the same results, using a culture of *Ps. aeruginosa;* however, only about one-third of the original M-concentration was attained after treating a culture of *Shigella gallinarum* in the same manner.

Von Wikullil (1932) observed that, if two organisms such as *Escherichia coli* and *Salmonella schottmuelleri* (*Bact. paratyphosum* B), which have approximately the same M-concentration of 1,600 million per milliliter, were inoculated together in the same numbers into a tube of fresh broth, the mixed culture had the same final M-concentration of 1,600 million per milliliter. Analysis showed that the two species were present in the approximate proportion of 800 million to 800 million. From this fact it was concluded that the total biological space was divided between the two species. When two organisms having extremely different M-concentration, such as 1,600 million and 300 million per milliliter, were inoculated together into a tube of fresh broth, the M-concentration again reached 1,600 million per milliliter. However, in this experiment the final population was made up almost entirely of the species with the largest M-concentration, the explanation being that the one grew more rapidly than the other and utilized a greater proportion of the available space.

Still further support was given to some of Bail's claims by the work of Koláčný [see Kořínek (1939)]; however, he stated that the M-concentration was directly proportional to the food. The following data were presented to show that, when the foodstuffs were diluted, the final M-concentration was lower.

Broth, per cent	Addition of Water, per cent	M-concentration of *Escherichia coli* per Milliliter
100	0	$2{,}100 \times 10^6$
75	25	$1{,}566 \times 10^6$
50	50	$1{,}033 \times 10^6$
25	75	555×10^6

Dagley and Hinshelwood (1938) demonstrated that, when *Aerobacter aerogenes* was cultivated in a synthetic medium, the final concentration varied with the final food in such a way that exhaustion of the food, rather than the accumulation of toxic products, was the factor limiting growth.

The data presented by Koblmüller (1936) are not in accord with the so-called space theory of Bail. However, his work differed from that of Bail in that he used solid media rather than broth, and this fact may have accounted for some of the difference in results.

This subject was fully reviewed by Kořínek (1939), who believed that it could be explained by the help of Langmuir's adsorption-isotherm theory. Most investigators believe that, if a fermentable carbohydrate such as glucose is added to a medium, it serves as a food material and thus allows the M-concentration to reach a slightly higher level than it would in ordinary broth. Kořínek was of the opinion, however, that the sugar changed the lyophilic properties of the protein and did not serve entirely as a food.

There is considerable evidence in favor of some of Bail's claims concerning space theory and M-concentration, but many of his points are not accepted at this time. Further work will have to be done on this subject—why bacteria stop dividing at a maximum speed when a certain population is reached—before any definite conclusions can be reached.

THE ACCELERATED DEATH PHASE

The equilibrium between newly formed organisms and dying cells which was noted in the preceding phase may last for about an hour or be prolonged for several days. Once this equilibrium has been disrupted and the cells start to die more rapidly than new ones are generated, the number of viable bacteria will begin to decrease, and the stationary phase will pass gradually into a period of decline. This interval of slow decline may represent a sort of lag or adjustment to the unfavorable environment in the medium.

Like the lag phase and the negative acceleration phase, this period is subject to considerable variability, depending upon the particular organism and the environment. Thus an accurate mathematical analysis is difficult to formulate.

THE LOGARITHMIC DEATH PHASE AND THE FINAL PHASE OF DECLINE

The rate at which bacteria die when subjected to unfavorable environmental conditions has interested bacteriologists since the early days of this science. Most workers have reported that the decrease in bacterial numbers under such influences follows a gradual and rather orderly course throughout most of the phase, with some tendency to slow up during the later stages, as is shown in Fig. 2, p. 103.[2] The period of decline may be relatively short for some organisms, such as the gonococcus or meningococcus, where the culture may be sterile in a few days, or it may be prolonged for several months or years with some other bacteria.

The proper interpretation of this phase is of importance, since it is upon the rate of death of bacteria that the dynamics of sterilization and disinfection are based. This subject, however, will be discussed more in detail in Chapters 3 and 4. In the present discussion, then, only some of the more general aspects of the problem of bacterial death will be mentioned.

In the study of death rates of bacteria several different theories have been formulated to explain the general curve obtained by plotting the number of surviving organisms against time. The two main theories which have been advanced are:

1. Theory of Natural Selection. Some investigators [see Buchanan and Fulmer (1928) and Knaysi (1930) for a review of the subject] have attributed the phenomenon of death to a process of natural selection and impute the form of the mortality curve to biological differences in the resistance of the individual bacterial cells. It is assumed in this case that the surviving organisms are of a more resistant character. These workers believe also that any true resemblance between the "survivors' curve" and that of a monomolecular chemical reaction, which will be discussed shortly, is purely an accident. Further support is given to this viewpoint by the work of Fulmer and Buchanan (1923), in which it was shown that the slopes assumed by the rate curves and survivors' curves of yeasts under unfavorable environment were not always logarithmic in nature. Similar observations were noted by Levine, Buchanan, and Lease (1927) in studies on disinfection by sodium hydroxide. In this case the rate increased progressively with the time of exposure to the disinfectant and, as a result, straight-line curves were not always obtained.

2. Theory of Logarithmic Death. Other workers [see Madsen and Nyman (1907), Chick (1908, 1910), Cohen (1922), Falk and Winslow (1926), Beamer and Tanner (1939), and Rahn and Schroeder (1941)], studying the action of heat, chemical disinfectants, and other unfavorable influences on the death of bacteria, have given a somewhat different interpretation to the mortality curve. These investigators presented data which, when plotted in logarithmic form, showed a

[2] Some evidence is available which would indicate that growth and multiplication are not entirely stopped during this period, for, if counts are performed at short intervals, transitory rises in the bacterial population are sometimes noticed.

close agreement to the curve of a monomolecular chemical reaction. "These researches and others," Phelps (1911) summarized, "have shown that the rate of dying, whether under the influence of heat, cold, or chemical poison, is unfailingly found to follow the logarithmic curve of the velocity law, if the temperature be constant. This curve never reaches a zero value, although approaching it indefinitely."

If under some conditions bacteria die at a constant rate, then the general slope of the mortality curve during the period of rapid decline will be similar to that of the curve for the increase of a bacterial population during its period of rapid multiplication. In the phase of increase the logarithms of the number of new cells formed from a single initial cell in a given time are proportional to the lapse of time; in the phase of decrease the logarithms of the proportion of the cells present which die in a given interval of time are proportional to the length of that interval. In other words, increase and decrease alike bear a direct relation to the number of cells present at the beginning of a unit period and a logarithmic relation to any time period of greater duration.

Thus, according to this theory, if the logarithms of the number of surviving bacteria after various lengths of time are plotted against time, the points will be found to lie on a straight line. The slope of the line will be a negative value and is termed the velocity coefficient of the reaction. The formula for the rate of decrease is, in the form used by Phelps (1911) and Buchanan (1918), as follows:

$$\log \frac{B}{b} = kt$$

or

$$-k = \frac{1}{t} \log \frac{b}{B}$$

and

$$k = \frac{1}{t} \log \frac{B}{b} \qquad (12)$$

where k = the velocity constant.
t = the interval of time between successive observations.
B = the number of bacteria initially present.
b = the number present at the end of time t.

It will be noted that this is in the form of the equation for a monomolecular reaction.

Where the rate of death does not follow the monomolecular reaction, Falk and Winslow (1926) have pointed out that it is much simpler to assume that the lethal reactions which go on in the bacterial cells dying in an unfavorable environment proceed in accordance with a bimolecular reaction, or reactions of higher order, than to postulate biological variations in the resistance of the bacteria. They further state that there is no reason to assume that the decomposition of a single chemical compound is always the determining factor of death.

In summary, it can be said that most investigators believe that there is no true evidence that the cells which die near the end of the bacterial population cycle are intrinsically more resistant than those which perish earlier. Furthermore, their work leads to a belief that the curve for such a cycle is governed by a series of simple reactions which follow the laws of the more simple chemical processes. It must be kept in mind, however, that not all workers are in agreement with this viewpoint, and, until more data are available concerning protoplasmic death, no one theory should be hastily accepted as the final explanation.

If it can be proved definitely that bacterial death under unfavorable environmental conditions does follow the so-called logarithmic curve, then many problems can be correctly solved.

RELATIONSHIP OF GROWTH CURVES TO A CURVE OF AUTOCATALYSIS

A study of the typical growth curve (Figs. 1 and 2, pp. 96 and 103) shows that it is more or less sigmoid or S-shaped. The exact form in any given case will depend upon the type of organism, its previous history, and the various environmental influences which come into play during its multiplication. One explanation or interpretation of this curve has been developed in the preceding discussion as a succession of growth phases. Another interesting explanation has been given by several investigators [see McKendrick and Pai (1911) and Lotka (1925)], who have explained the growth curve on the basis that it shows a marked resemblance to a curve of autocatalysis. For further reading on this subject the books by Lotka (1925) and Buchanan and Fulmer (1928) should be consulted.

INTERPRETATION OF GROWTH CURVES BY LEMON'S FORMULA

Lemon (1933) pointed out that the usual method of expressing the increase of bacterial growth in a medium by graphical methods in which the numbers of bacteria are plotted against time has certain disadvantages. He states:

> The maximum growth rate cannot be accurately determined, nor the period of optimum propagation. . . . A perfect growth-rate curve indicating bacterial increase in numbers per time of incubation usually involves a sigmoid logarithmic curve, neglecting precipitation, death of bacterial organisms, etc.

This curve, while indicating the total number of organisms at any given time, fails in not accurately indicating the period of incubation at which the organisms are most rapidly propagating.

To solve these difficulties Lemon estimated the actual rate of growth in unit intervals of time by a special formula which he developed. This point is of interest to the bacteriologist, since it indicates at what period the optimum propagating rate is reached. For an application of the details of this method the paper by Lemon (1933) should be consulted.

REFERENCES

Adolph, E. F., and S. Bayne-Jones. 1932. *J. Cellular Comp. Physiol.*, **1**:409–427.
Allen, E. S. 1932. *Iowa State Coll. J. Sci.*, **6**:251–262.
Alper, T., and M. Sterne. 1933. *J. Hyg.*, **33**:497–509.
Anderson, E. B., and L. J. Meanwell. 1936. *J. Dairy Research*, **7**:182–191.
Avery, O. T., and H. J. Morgan. 1924. *J. Exptl. Med.*, **39**:275–287.
Bail, O. 1929. *Z. Immunitäts.*, **60**:1–22.
Barber, M. A. 1908. *J. Infectious Diseases*, **5**:379–400.
Barnes, L. A. 1931. *J. Bact.*, **21**:395–406.
Bayne–Jones, S., and H. S. Rhees. 1929. *J. Bact.*, **17**:123–140.
Bayne–Jones, S., and E. F. Adolph. 1933. *J. Cellular Comp. Physiol.*, **2**:329–348.
Bayne–Jones, S., and L. A. Sandholzer. 1933. *J. Exptl. Med.*, **57**:279–304.
Beamer, P. R., and F. W. Tanner. 1939. *Centr. Bakt., IIAbt.*, **100**:81–98.
Bickert, F. W. 1930. *Centr. Bakt., I Abt. Orig.*, **117**:548–551.
Breed, R. S. 1911. *Centr. Bakt., II Abt.*, **30**:337–340.
Breed, R. S., and J. D. Brew. 1916. *N. Y. Agr. Exp. Sta. Bull.* **49**:1–31. Geneva, N. Y.
Broom, J. C. 1929. *Brit. J. Exptl. Path.*, **10**:71–83.
Buchanan, R. E. 1918. *J. Infectious Diseases*, **23**:109–125.
Buchanan, R. E., and E. I. Fulmer. 1928. *Physiology and Biochemistry of Bacteria*, Vol. I. Williams & Wilkins Co., Baltimore.
Buchner, H., K. Longard, and G. Riedlin. 1887. *Centr. Bakt.*, **2**:1–7.
Bukantz, S. C., A. Cooper, and J. G. M. Bullowa. 1941. *J. Bact.*, **42**:29–49.
Burk, D., and H. Lineweaver. 1930. *J. Bact.*, **19**:389–414.
Burke, G. S. 1923. *J. Infectious Diseases*, **33**:274–284.
Burke, V., A. Sprague, and La V. Barnes. 1925. *J. Infectious Diseases*, **36**:555–560.
Butterfield, C. T. 1932. *J. Bact.*, **23**:355–368.
Cameron, G. M., and J. M. Sherman. 1935. *J. Bact.*, **30**:647–650.
Chesney, A. M. 1916. *J. Exptl. Med.*, **24**:387–418.
Chick, H. 1908. *J. Hyg.*, **8**:92–158.
Chick, H. 1910. *J. Hyg.* **10**:237–286.
Clark, P. F., and W. H. Ruehl. 1919. *J. Bact.*, **4**:615–629.
Clifton, C. E. 1937. *J. Bact.*, **33**:145–162.
Cohen, B. 1922. *J. Bact.*, **7**:183–230.
Coombs, H. I., and M. Stephenson. 1926. *Biochem. J.*, **20**:998–1002.
Coplans, M. 1910. *J. Path. Bact.*, **14**:1–27.
Dagley, S., and C. N. Hinshelwood. 1938. *J. Chem. Soc.*, **1938**: 1930–1948.
Dalla Valle, J. M. 1941. *Pub. Health Repts.*, **56**:229–234.

Dubos, R. J. 1940. *Bact. Rev.*, **4**:1–16.
Eaton, M. D., Jr. 1931. *J. Bact.*, **21**:143–156.
Elliker, P. R., and W. C. Frazier. 1938. *J. Bact.*, **35**:63–64; **36**:83–98.
Esty, J. R., and K. F. Meyer. 1922. *J. Infectious Diseases*, **31**:650–663.
Falk, I. S., and C.-E. A. Winslow. 1926. *J. Bact.*, **11**:1–25.
Fukuda, Y. 1929. *Z. Immunitäts.*, **60**:88–104.
Fulmer, E. I., and R. E. Buchanan. 1923. *J. Gen. Physiol.*, **6**:77–89.
Gates, F. L. 1929–1930. *J. Gen. Physiol.*, **13**:231–248.
Gee, H. 1932. *J. Bact.*, **24**:35–41.
Gerard, R. W., and I. S. Falk. 1931. *Biol. Bull.*, **60**:213–226.
Gladstone, G. P., P. Fildes, and G. M. Richardson. 1935. *Brit. J. Exptl. Path.*, **16**:335–348.
Gordon, R. D. 1938. *Proc. Nat. Acad. Sci. U. S.*, **24**:212–215.
Gordon, R. D., and C. E. ZoBell. 1938. *Centr. Bakt., IIAbt.*, **99**:318–320.
Graham-Smith, G. S. 1920. *J. Hyg.*, **19**:133–204.
Greenwood, M., Jr., and G. U. Yule. 1917. *J. Hyg.*, **16**:36–54.
Greig, M. E., and J. C. Hoogerheide. 1941. *J. Bact.*, **41**:549–556.
Halvorson, H. O., and N. R. Ziegler. 1933. *J. Bact.*, **25**:101–121.
Halvorson, H. O., and N. R. Ziegler. 1933. *J. Bact.*, **26**:331–339.
Halvorson, H. O., and N. R. Ziegler. 1933. *J. Bact.*, **26**:559–567.
Halvorson, H. O., and N. R. Ziegler. 1933. *Quantitative Bacteriology.* Burgess Publishing Co., Minneapolis, Minn.
Hanks, J. H., and D. F. James. 1940. *J. Bact.*, **39**:297–305.
Hegarty, C. P. 1939. *J. Bact.*, **37**:145–152.
Hegarty, C. P., and O. B. Weeks. 1940. *J. Bact.*, **39**:475–484.
Henrici, A. T. 1926. *J. Infectious Diseases*, **38**:54–65.
Henrici, A. T. 1928. *Morphologic Variation and the Rate of Growth of Bacteria.* Charles C. Thomas, Springfield, Ill.
Herrington, B. L. 1934. *J. Bact.*, **28**:177–179.
Hershey, A. D., and J. Bronfenbrenner. 1938. *J. Gen. Physiol.*, **21**:721–728.
Hershey, A. D. 1939. *J. Bact.*, **37**:285–299.
Hes, J. W. 1938. *Ann. fermentations*, **4**:547–558.
Hess, E. 1934. *J. Biol. Board Can.*, **1**:109–119.
Hildebrand, E. M. 1938. *J. Bact.*, **35**:487–492.
Hirsch, J. 1933. *Klin. Wochschrift.*, **12**:191–192.
Hoskins, J. K. 1934. *Pub. Health Repts.*, **49**:393–405.
Hottle, G. A., J. O. Lampen, and A. M. Pappenheimer, Jr. 1941. *J. Biol. Chem.*, **137**:457–458.
Huntington, E., and C.-E. A. Winslow. 1937. *J. Bact.*, **33**:123–144.
Jennison, M. W. 1935. *J. Bact.*, **30**:603–623.
Jennison, M. W. 1937. *J. Bact.*, **33**:461–477.
Jennison, M. W., and G. P. Wadsworth. 1940. *J. Bact.*, **39**:389–397.
Karström, H. 1937–1938. *Ergeb. Enzymforsch.*, **7**:350–376.
Kelly, C. D., and O. Rahn. 1932. *J. Bact.*, **23**:147–153.
Knaysi, G. 1930. *J. Infectious Diseases*, **47**:322–327.
Knaysi, G. 1935. *J. Bact.*, **30**:193–206.
Koblmüller, L. O. 1936. *Z. Hyg. Infektionskr.*, **118**:687–696.
Kořínek, J. 1939. *Centr. Bakt., IIAbt.*, **100**:16–25.
Koser, S. A., and F. Saunders. 1938. *Bact. Rev.*, **2**:99–160.
Lane-Claypon, J. E. 1909. *J. Hyg.*, **9**:239–248.

Ledingham, J. C. G., and W. J. Penfold. 1914. *J. Hyg.*, **14**:242–260.
Lemon, C. G. 1933. *J. Hyg.*, **33**:495–496.
Levine, M., J. H. Buchanan, and G. Lease. 1927. *Iowa State Coll. J. Sci.*, **1**:379–394.
Levine, P. P. 1936. *J. Bact.*, **31**:151–160.
Liese, W. 1926. *Z. Hyg. Infektionskr.*, **105**:483–487.
Lodge, R. M., and C. N. Hinshelwood. 1939, 1943. *J. Chem. Soc.*, **1939**:1683–1692, 1692–1697; **1943**:208–221.
Longsworth, L. G. 1936. *J. Bact.*, **32**:307–328.
Lotka, A. J. 1925. *Elements of Physical Biology.* Williams & Wilkins Co., Baltimore.
Madsen, T., and M. Nyman. 1907. *Z. Hyg. Infektionskr.*, **57**:388–404.
Martin, D. S. 1931–1932. *J. Gen. Physiol.*, **15**:691–708.
Mason, M. M. 1935. *J. Bact.*, **29**:103–110.
McCrady, M. H. 1915. *J. Infectious Diseases*, **17**:183–212.
McCrady, M. H. 1918. *Can. Pub. Health J.*, **9**:201–220.
McKendrick, A. G., and M. K. Pai. 1911. *Proc. Roy. Soc. Edinburgh*, **31**:649–655.
McLeod, J. W., and J. Gordon. 1922. *Biochem. J.*, **16**:499–506.
McLeod, J. W., and J. Gordon. 1923. *J. Path. Bact.*, **26**:326–331.
Mestre, H. 1935. *J. Bact.*, **30**:335–358.
Mooney, G., and C.-E. A. Winslow. 1935. *J. Bact.*, **30**:427–440.
Moyer, L. S. 1936. *J. Bact.*, **32**:433–464.
Mueller, J. H. 1935. *J. Bact.*, **29**:383–387.
Müller, M. 1895. *Z. Hyg. Infektionskr.*, **20**:245–280.
Müller, M. 1903. *Arch. Hyg.*, **47**:127–193.
Neill, J. M., and O. T. Avery. 1925. *J. Exptl. Med.*, **41**:285–298.
Olson, C., Jr., and F. G. Warren. 1944. *J. Bact.*, **47**:495–497.
Penfold, W. J., and D. Norris. 1912. *J. Hyg.*, **12**:527–531.
Penfold, W. J. 1914. *J. Hyg.*, **14**:215–241.
Phelps, E. B. 1911. *J. Infectious Diseases*, **8**:27–38.
Porter, J. R., and M. J. Pelczar, Jr. 1941. *J. Bact.*, **41**:173–192.
Pulvertaft, R. J. V., and C. G. Lemon. 1933. *J. Hyg.*, **33**:245–251.
Rahn, O. 1906. *Centr. Bakt., II Abt.*, **16**:417–429.
Rahn, O. 1932. *Physiology of Bacteria.* P. Blakiston's Son & Co., Inc., Philadelphia.
Rahn, O., C. P. Hegarty, and R. E. Deuel. 1938. *J. Bact.*, **35**:547–558.
Rahn, O. 1938. *Growth*, **2**:363–367.
Rahn, O. 1941. *Growth*, **5**:113–118, 197–199.
Rahn, O., and W. R. Schroeder. 1941. *Biodynamica*, **3**:199–208.
Régnier, J., R. David, and A. Kaplan. 1932. *Compt. rend. acad. sci.*, **194**:323–325
Rettger, L. F. 1918. *J. Bact.*, **3**:103–113.
Rogers, L. A., and G. R. Greenbank. 1930. *J. Bact.*, **19**:181–190.
Rubner, M. 1906. *Arch. Hyg.*, **57**:161–192.
Savage, G. M., and H. O. Halvorson. 1941. *J. Bact.*, **41**:355–362.
Schmidt, H. 1926. *Z. Hyg. Infektionskr.*, **106**:314–326.
Schmidt, H., and E. Fischer. 1930. *Z. Hyg. Infektionskr.*, **111**:542–553.
Schultz, J. H., and H. Ritz. 1910. *Centr. Bakt., I Abt. Orig.*, **54**:283–288.
Sherman, J. M., and W. R. Albus. 1923. *J. Bact.*, **8**:127–139.
Sherman, J. M., and W. R. Albus. 1924. *J. Bact.*, **9**:303–305.
Slator, A. 1916. *J. Chem. Soc.*, **109**:2T–10T.

Slator, A. 1917. *J. Hyg.*, **16**:100–108.
Stark, C. N., and P. Stark. 1929. *J. Bact.*, **17**:2–3.
Strauss, W. 1930. *Centr. Bakt., I Abt. Orig.*, **115**:228–235.
Topley, W. W. C., and G. S. Wilson. 1936. *The Principles of Bacteriology and Immunity.* William Wood & Co., Baltimore.
Valley, G., and L. F. Rettger. 1927. *J. Bact.*, **14**:101–137.
Valley, G. 1928. *Quart. Rev. Biol.*, **3**:209–224.
Walker, H. H., and C.-E. A. Winslow. 1932. *J. Bact.*, **24**:209–241.
Walker, H. H. 1932. *Science*, **76**:602–604.
Walker, H. H., C.-E. A. Winslow, E. Huntington, and M. G. Mooney. 1934. *J. Bact.*, **27**:303–324.
Walker, H. H., C.-E. A. Winslow, and M. G. Mooney. 1934. *J. Gen. Physiol.*, **17**:349–357.
Walker, R. H., D. A. Anderson, and P. E. Brown. 1932. *Centr. Bakt. II Abt.*, **87**:27–44.
Wang, S.-H. 1941. *J. Bact.*, **42**:297–319.
Werkman, C. H., and H. G. Wood. 1942. *Advances in Enzymology*, **2**:135–182.
Wikullil, L. von. 1932. *Centr. Bakt., I Abt. Orig.*, **126**:488–508.
Williams, R. J. 1941. *Biol. Rev. Cambridge Phil. Soc.*, **16**:49–80.
Wilson, G. S. 1922. *J. Bact.*, **7**:405–446.
Wilson, G. S. 1926. *J. Hyg.*, **25**:150–159.
Wilson, G. S., R. S. Twigg, R. C. Wright, C. B. Hendry, M. P. Cowell, and I. Maier. 1935. *Med. Res. Council (Brit.) Spec. Rept.* 206. London.
Winslow, C.-E. A., and I. S. Falk. 1918. *Proc. Soc. Exptl. Biol. Med.*, **15**:67–69.
Winslow, C.-E. A., and I. S. Falk. 1923. *J. Bact.*, **8**:215–236.
Winslow, C.-E. A., and O. R. Brooke. 1927. *J. Bact.*, **13**:235–243.
Winslow, C.-E. A., H. H. Walker, and M. Sutermeister. 1932. *J. Bact.*, **24**:185–208.
Winslow, C.-E. A., and H. H. Walker. 1939. *Bact. Rev.*, **3**:147–186.
Wood, H. G., and C. H. Werkman. 1940. *Biochem. J.*, **34**:7–14, 129–138.
Wooldridge, W. R., R. Knox, and V. Glass. 1936. *Biochem. J.*, **30**:926–931.
Wright, A. E. 1902. *Lancet*, **80**(2):11–17.
Ziegler, N. R., and H. O. Halvorson. 1935. *J. Bact.*, **29**:609–634.

3

THE EFFECTS OF PHYSICAL AGENTS ON BACTERIA

Since living bacterial cells consist largely of the substance in delicate equilibrium known as protoplasm, their normal life processes may be easily disrupted by certain changes in the environment. Physical forces may bring about changes in the environment which tend to stimulate, attenuate, produce variants of, or completely destroy bacteria and their products. Whether these agents affect chemical changes, bring about mechanical disorganization of the cells, or produce a combination of reactions is not always well understood. As more studies appear on the colloidal chemistry of protoplasm, however, the more apparent it becomes that the protoplasmic complex is so constituted as to be sensitive to various types of external agents and to respond to many diverse treatments in much the same manner.

The physical forces which we shall briefly consider here are electromagnetic waves, temperature, desiccation, electricity and magnetism, pressure (mechanical, osmotic, gaseous), surface tension, sound waves, filtration, and agitation. Buchanan and Fulmer (1930) have summarized in a systematic treatise a large amount of information on these subjects. Their book should be consulted for more details than are given here.

ELECTROMAGNETIC WAVES

Many experiments have been carried out on the effect of the rays of the electromagnetic spectrum on microorganisms. This discussion, however, will be restricted entirely to the field of bacteriology, with only brief mention from time to time of the action of radiation on allied substances such as viruses, serological phenomena, and other bodies which bacteriologists study. Although the so-called alpha- and beta-rays emitted from the radioactive elements are not truly part of the electromagnetic spectrum, they will be given some consideration.

For the most part radiation of this type tends to be detrimental to bacteria and their products rather than beneficial. Whether the rays bring about their harmful effect by producing secondary toxic chemical substances such as ozone and hydrogen peroxide in the medium, alter the cell permeability, or act on the protoplasm of the cell in some other way to bring about protein coagulation and dehydration has not been definitely proved.

Before discussing the bactericidal effect of the various regions of the electromagnetic spectrum, it may be well to discuss briefly the terms used in classifying such rays and list the various regions of the spectrum.

CLASSIFICATION AND REGIONS OF THE ELECTROMAGNETIC SPECTRUM

Units of Wavelengths, Wave Number, Frequency, and Photon Energy. The electromagnetic waves may be classified by one of several methods. The definition of terms as used by Darrow (1936) will be reviewed briefly:

1. The ultimate *unit of wavelength* is the centimeter, but various submultiples of this universal unit are usually employed in various parts of the spectrum. They include:

The *micron* (μ), equal to 10^{-4} cm., sometimes employed in the extreme infrared.

The *millimicron* (mμ), equal to 10^{-7} cm., occasionally employed in the infrared, the visible, and the ultraviolet, but not so commonly as the unit next mentioned.

The *angstrom* (Å.), equal to 10^{-8} cm., usually employed in the near infrared, the visible, and the ultraviolet.

The *X-unit* (X), equal to 10^{-11} cm., employed in the X-ray and gamma-ray regions.

2. The *wave number* is by definition the reciprocal of wavelength. When a wave number is to be calculated from a wavelength, the latter is generally expressed in centimeters, so that the customary unit of wave number is the reciprocal centimeter (cm.$^{-1}$).

3. The *frequency* (ν) is by definition the product of wave number by c, the speed of light *in vacuo*. The first factor is commonly expressed in cm.$^{-1}$, the second in centimeters per second or cm./sec.; the frequency is, therefore, in reciprocal seconds (sec.$^{-1}$).

4. The c.g.s. unit of energy is the *erg*. The energy of a photon of light of frequency ν is computed in *ergs* by multiplying ν expressed in sec.$^{-1}$ by the value of h expressed in c.g.s. units (gm. cm.^{2} sec.$^{-1}$), which is 6.55×10^{-27}. The erg is far too large a unit for convenience in dealing with any portion of the spectrum, and the customary *unit of energy* is the electron volt (e.v.) equal to 1.59×10^{-12} erg. Sometimes this is called the *equivalent volt* and sometimes simply the *volt of energy*. As the name implies, it is the amount of kinetic energy acquired by an electron in passing unimpeded between two points, of which the latter is at a potential one volt higher than the former. In the

gamma-ray region, photon energies are sometimes expressed in millions of electron volts (m.e.v.).

To get photon energy in electron volts from wavelength in angstroms, it is often convenient to remember that photons of one electron volt correspond to waves of 12,337 Å.

The Regions of the Spectrum. Even though the regions of the spectrum have derived their names because of physiological and historical accidents rather than from fundamental reasons, it is important to know their location and approximate range. In Fig. 1, a diagram shows the approximate range of the electromagnetic spectrum with bactericidal action. It will be seen that the *visible spectrum* extends from about 3,900 Å. at the end of the violet to about 8,000 Å. at the end of the red, the exact limits varying with the eye. From the red end of the visible spectrum in the direction of increasing wavelengths extends the *infrared* portion of the spectrum, and beyond lie the *Hertzian* or *radio waves* generated by oscillating electrical circuits. From the violet end of the visible spectrum, in the direction of decreasing wavelengths, lies the *ultraviolet;* beyond this are the *X-ray region*, the *gamma-ray spectrum*, and, still further, the *cosmic rays*. The boundaries imposed between these regions are, at present, more or less arbitrary, but in Fig. 1 they have been given a definite value for the sake of convenience. Attention should be called to the fact that little, if any, bacteriological work has been done on some parts of the spectrum, and for this reason the data listed in the accompanying figure should be considered only as a guide to the possible action of these radiations.

The more important regions of the spectrum, in so far as bacteriology is concerned, will now be taken up separately.

SUNLIGHT (SOLAR RADIATION)

Direct sunlight is quite destructive to bacteria, especially when they are not protected by extraneous organic matter. The observations by Downes and Blunt (1877, 1878) that sunlight had a lethal effect on bacteria and other microorganisms drew the attention of bacteriologists to the importance of this type of radiation. These two investigators also noted that the germicidal effect of sunlight on decomposing organic matter took place only in the presence of air, and they regarded sterilization by light as depending on oxidation. The work of Downes and Blunt was confirmed by Roux (1887), who concluded that oxygen was a factor in the lethal action of sunlight on bacteria. Using anthrax spores suspended in tubes of nutrient media, he found that, when there was plenty of oxygen available, the spores were killed by sunlight in 29 hours. Under anaerobic conditions, however, the spores were not

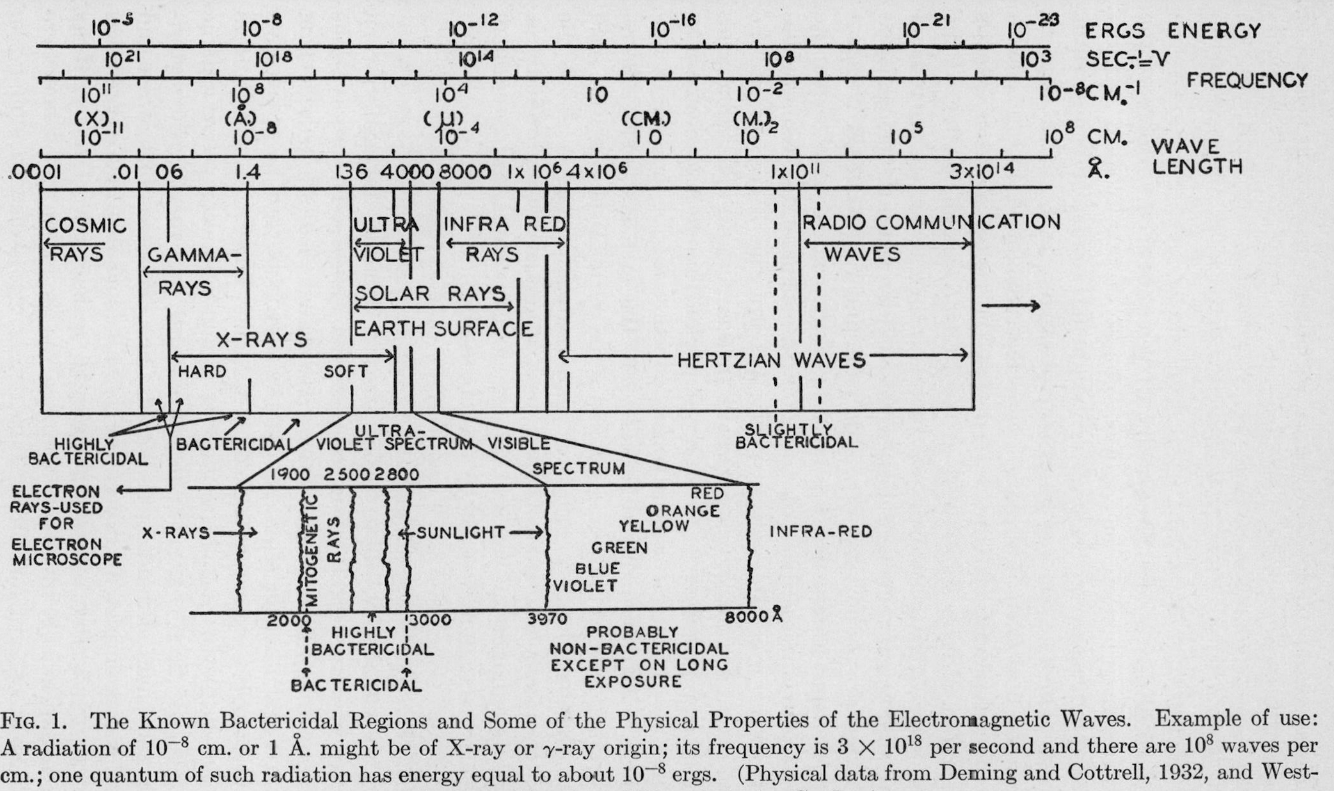

Fig. 1. The Known Bactericidal Regions and Some of the Physical Properties of the Electromagnetic Waves. Example of use: A radiation of 10^{-8} cm. or 1 Å. might be of X-ray or γ-ray origin; its frequency is 3×10^{18} per second and there are 10^{8} waves per cm.; one quantum of such radiation has energy equal to about 10^{-8} ergs. (Physical data from Deming and Cottrell, 1932, and Westinghouse Electric and Manufacturing Co. Inc.)

destroyed even by 83 hours' exposure to the sun. About this same time Tizzoni and Cattani (1891) observed that sunlight had a lethal effect on the vegetative cells and spores of *Clostridium tetani*.

In 1887 Duclaux reviewed his work and that of others on this subject and showed that in sunlight vegetative bacilli were killed and sometimes even spores were destroyed. In the same year Arloing (1887) observed that the spores of *Bacillus anthracis*, known to be resistant to high temperature, were easily destroyed by sunlight. He believed this bactericidal action was due to the entire solar spectrum.

A series of papers was published by Ward (1892–1894) in which he reported some well-controlled experiments. Gelatin and agar plates seeded with anthrax spores were exposed to the autumn sunlight. The destructive action of the sun was demonstrated to be due to a direct action and not to an increase in temperature, because at no time during the exposure did the temperature of the plates rise above 18°C. Furthermore, the lethal action was not due to desiccation or other changes in the substrate, since plates exposed for a reasonable time were suitable for the growth of fresh cultures. Using both glass and liquid filters, Ward found no inhibition of growth behind filters transmitting red, orange, and yellow light rays; however, the destructive action was marked behind filters transmitting blue-violet rays.

The exotoxin from the diphtheria bacillus was the first bacterial toxin whose photolability was studied. Roux and Yersin in 1889 published the significant observation that, although quite stable in the dark, this toxin was almost completely inactivated by a 10-hour exposure to sunlight. When sealed in small tubes without air, the toxin was only partially destroyed by similar irradiation. From this finding the authors concluded that visible light plus oxygen was the active agent. Two years later Tizzoni and Cattani (1891) showed that tetanus toxin was destroyed by 4½ months' exposure to diffuse daylight, providing oxygen was present. Controls in a hydrogen atmosphere or in the dark were not inactivated in the same time. Fermi and coworkers (1892, 1894) studied the effect of sunlight on both dried and dissolved tetanus toxin. If the temperature was much above 40° to 50°C., both toxins were inactivated in 15 hours by direct sunlight; however, if the temperature did not exceed 37°C., the dried toxin showed some activity after 100 hours of irradiation, whereas the dissolved toxin was again completely inactivated in 15 hours.

In his early studies on the germicidal action of light Roux (1887) found that, if a shallow layer of media in the presence of oxygen was exposed to sunlight for 3 to 4 hours, it became altered in such a way that seeded anthrax spores would not germinate. The same media however, allowed the growth of vegetative cells of *Bacillus anthracis*. This phenomenon was reinvestigated by Burnet (1925), who observed that staphylococci would not grow on agar plates which had been previously exposed to sunlight. The inhibitory action was attributed to the production of hydrogen peroxide in the media by the sunlight. This explanation, according to some investigators, does not satisfy the conditions for all experiments.

Other reports [see de Laroquette (1918)] on the effect of sunlight have been published, but many of the investigators have given little or no attention to the measurement of light intensities. Since the intensity of sunlight is influenced by time, place, and local climatic and atmospheric conditions, no special conclusions can be drawn from such experiments.

No further mention will be made of the entire solar spectrum except for its relationship to photodynamic sensitization.

VISIBLE SPECTRUM

It has been quite generally believed in the past that light rays of the visible spectrum have little or no physiological effect on most bacteria, in spite of the fact that many early investigators demonstrated some lethal effects for such rays and all bacteriologists have observed that certain bacterial cultures grow best in the dark. It is also of interest that Duggar (1936) stated, "Further quantitative studies in the visible spectrum may give evidence of lethal effects, or at least of other physiological effects of fundamental interest." Since 1936 this statement has been verified by several workers. For example, Buchbinder, Solowey, and Phelps (1941) and Miller and Schad (1944) have observed that visible light is definitely germicidal to streptococci and meningococci on continued exposure. Hollaender (1943) has also shown that long ultraviolet and short visible radiation (3,500 to 4,900 Å.) is lethal for *Escherichia coli;* however, it requires 10,000 to 100,000 times as much incident energy to produce 50 per cent killing in this region as in the more lethal ultraviolet (2,650 Å.). Kreitlow (1941) studied the effects of visible radiation on pigmentation of *Serratia marcescens*, and found that blue light (3,800 to 5,000 Å.) inhibited pigment formation at 20° and 27°C., whereas the best pigmentation took place in red light (above 6,000 Å.) or in darkness, and green light had no effect at all on color production by this organism.

PHOTODYNAMIC ACTION

It has just been mentioned that experiments concerned with killing bacteria by sunlight are difficult to control and that the visible rays of the spectrum possess little, if any, lethal effect on microorganisms. It has been demonstrated by a number of investigators, however, that, when certain dyes are added to a biological system (protozoa, bacteria, toxins, enzymes, and viruses), they bring about a "sensitization" of the system, so that the physiological effects of the visible spectrum are greatly increased.

The early work on this subject was done principally by von Tappeiner and Jodlbauer (1900, 1904, 1905, 1909). They used several absorptive dyes in the flourescene, anthracine, and quinine groups and obtained some interesting data. Although their early work was concerned with the photodynamic action of dyes on protozoa, they did demonstrate in their later papers that this sensitization phenomenon also manifested itself in the destruction of bacteria and inactivated toxins and antitoxins.

In the last few years the photodynamic action of dyes has been studied more in detail and expanded to include certain immunological reactions. For example, Clifton (1931) found that a staphylococcus bacteriophage suspended in 0.01 to 0.1 per cent methylene blue solution was inactivated by exposure to sunlight for about 5 minutes. The inactivation did not take place *in vacuo,* in an atmosphere of nitrogen, or in the presence of such reducing agents as cysteine hydrochloride. This work was confirmed by Perdrau and Todd (1933), who also showed that the greatest inactivation of the bacteriophage was obtained when a methylene blue solution of 1 : 100,000 was used. Some of the filterable viruses have also been inactivated by photodynamic action without an apparent loss of their antigenicity [Perdrau and Todd (1933), Galloway (1934)]; and three of the toxic properties of staphylococcus toxin were completely removed by the photodynamic action of methylene blue, without destroying the antigenic property of the toxin [Li (1936)]. Table 1 illustrates the effect on the hemolytic property of the staphylococcal toxin. Tuberculin, complement, antigens, and precipitins of various types have also been inactivated by photodynamic action.

The effect of eosin and methylene blue photosensitization on antibodies has recently been studied by Zia, Chow, and T'ung (1938) and Ross (1938). They have observed that such treatment brings about a deleterious effect on the several antibodies tested. Probably of more interest, however, is the fact that such treatment causes a mild chemical change in the antibody protein.

T'ung (1935, 1936, 1940) has reviewed the literature on the effect of photodynamic action on microorganisms and related substances and has presented many of his own experiments. He has shown that

TABLE 1

MAXIMUM DILUTION OF STAPHYLOCOCCUS TOXIN * WHICH COMPLETELY HEMOLYZES 1 PER CENT RABBIT ERYTHROCYTES AFTER ONE HOUR IN A WATER BATH AT 37°C.

[From Li (1936)]

Hours Exposed	Concentration of Methylene Blue 1 : 10,000	1 : 50,000	1 : 500,000
To light			
1	1/1,024+	1/1,024+	1/1,024+
2	1/512	1/1,024	1/1,024
4	1/256	1/256	1/1,024
6	1/32	1/64	1/512
8	None	1/2	1/32
Control (in dark)			
72	1/1,024+	1/1,024+	1/1,024+
240	1/1,024+	1/1,024+	1/1,024+

* Undiluted toxin, *p*H 7.2, exposed to 100-watt Mazda light at 20 cm.

Gram-positive bacteria are more susceptible to photosensitization than are Gram-negative species. In fact, eosin, mercurochrome, and methylene blue photodynamically inactivate only Gram-positive organisms, whereas safranine acts only on Gram-negative species. The explanation for the differential action of dyes is unknown.

The Nature of the Photochemical Process Involved. The actual mechanism involved in this phenomenon has not been worked out. Since photochemical reactions are probably complicated, further quantitative work is needed before accurate interpretations can be made. An explanation of the process involved has been offered in the extensive review by Blum (1932):

> In photosensitized reactions the sensitizing substance acts as the light absorber, which, while remaining unchanged itself, brings about reactions of other components of the system which themselves are not affected by light. In accordance with the Grotthus-Draper absorption law, which states that only light which is absorbed can produce chemical change, the active radiation is limited to those wavelengths which are absorbed by the sensitizer.

That there is some relationship between the sensitization phenomenon and the particular light rays which cause the various dyes to fluoresce has been noted by many investigators. For example, Hertel (1905) found that light of 518 mμ destroyed bacteria and paramecia sensitized with eosin or erthyrosine, whereas 448 mμ did not. The former radiation lies within the absorption spectrum of these dyes, whereas the latter does not. Likewise, Metzner (1924) observed an approximate correspondence of the active wavelengths to the absorption spectrum for a number of dyes. Sometimes minor deviations were noted in the active radiation and the absorption of the dye in an aqueous solution. These differences were attributed to the fact that the absorption spectrum of certain dyes is shifted considerably toward the red by combination of the dye with the protoplasm of the cell. Under these circumstances it would be necessary to consider the absorption spectrum of the dye-protoplasm-complex and not simply that of the dye in aqueous solution. Apparent deviations in some instances may be accounted for by a difference in the hydrogen-ion concentration within the cells and in the surrounding medium, since in certain cases the absorption spectrum is shifted by changes in the hydrogen-ion concentration.

Oxygen is apparently necessary for the photosensitization process to take place. Bayliss (1924) believed the process was due to an activation of oxygen or to an oxidation product of the dye. The failure of the process to take place in a vacuum or in an atmosphere of nitrogen further shows the important role of oxygen in this phenomenon. Additional support to the theory that photodynamic action involves a process of oxidation is presented by T'ung (1940).

At this point it should be mentioned that Burge and Neill (1915) demonstrated that the fluorescent bacteria were less susceptible to certain light rays than the nonfluorescent organisms. They attributed this difference to the ability of the fluorescent organisms to convert the destructive light rays into longer waves, thus dissipating the energy of the absorbed short waves, which would otherwise be spent in coagulating the bacterial protoplasm.

ULTRAVIOLET RAYS

That portion of the spectrum known as the ultraviolet is endowed with exceptional properties, and its physiological effect on bacteria and related substances will be discussed in some detail.

Ward (1894), Strebel (1901), and other early workers in this field came to the conclusion that ultraviolet rays were an important factor in the reported lethal effects of sunlight on microorganisms, as well as light from artificial sources. At about the same time Barnard and Morgan (1903), working with the arc spectrum of carbon and certain metals, were of the opinion that the bactericidal action of light was restricted almost entirely to the region of the ultraviolet. In fact, the rays 3,287 Å. and 2,265 Å., or the range from the near-visible violet to the extreme ultraviolet, were found to be the most lethal for the six species of bacteria studied. General confirmation of these results is seen in the work by Browning and Russ (1917), Bayne-Jones and Van der Lingen (1923), Coblentz and Fulton (1924), Eidinow (1926, 1927), Newcomer (1917), Prudhomme (1938), Whisler (1940), and many others. The general findings reported by all these investigators are quite consistent in showing the most effective wavelengths as beginning at about 3,000 Å. and extending down to about 2,000 Å. The highest efficiency was found in the general region of 2,300 Å. to 2,750 Å., with 2,650 to 2,660 Å. being the most bactericidal of all.

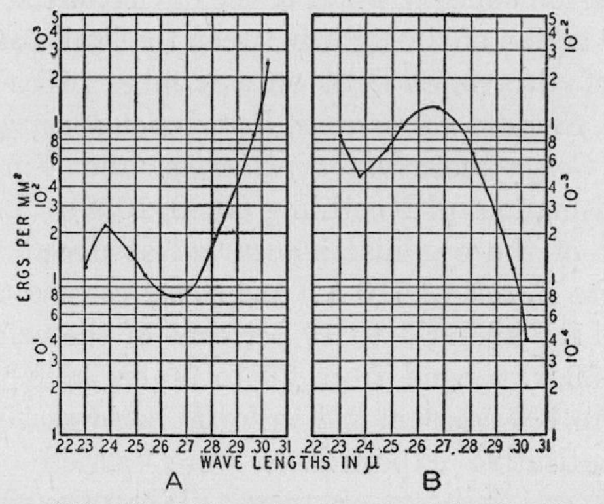

Fig. 2. *A* = Curve of Incident Energies Involved in the Destruction of 50 Per Cent of *Escherichia coli*. *B* = curve of the reciprocals of *A*. (From Gates, 1930.)

The work by Gates (1929, 1930) has added a great deal to our knowledge concerning the bactericidal action of ultraviolet light. He used a quartz-mercury-vapor lamp as a source of radiation and a thermopile and galvanometer for the energy measurement. To separate and focus the specific wavelengths required, he used a large quartz monochromator of special design and a system of quartz lenses. *Staphylococcus aureus* and *Escherichia coli* were employed as the test organisms, being streaked over the surface of hardened agar Petri plates. To prevent the spreading of colonies and to facilitate colony counting, a second thin layer of melted agar was placed over the surface of the plate immediately after exposure and before incubation. The ultraviolet rays chosen for study were chiefly in the range of 2,253 Å. to 3,126Å. The amount of energy required to kill 50 per cent of the organisms was determined for the various wavelengths in this region. The results for *E. coli* are presented in the form of a graph in Fig. 2 from the work of Gates (1930). The incident energy required to kill is less between 2,600 Å. and 2,700 Å. than in any other portion of the spectrum. Some of the actual figures given by Gates are 88 erg/mm.^{2}

at 2,675 Å., 3,150 erg/mm.^{2} at 3,020 Å., and 25,000 erg/mm.^{2} at 3,126Å. Since the curves show a general similarity to those for monomolecular reactions, some mention should be made of their significance. Taking into consideration variations in susceptibility of individual organisms, due especially to age and metabolic activity, Gates believed that the typical curve could best be interpreted "as one of probability." Furthermore, the simple conclusion that the shorter the wavelength of ultraviolet light, the greater is the bactericidal action is in error.

The hydrogen-ion concentration of the environment had no effect on the bactericidal action of the light between the limits of *p*H 4.5 and 7.5.

The action of ultraviolet light on a number of bacteria, including *Escherichia coli, Serratia marcescens, Pseudomonas aeruginosa, Staphylococcus aureus, Corynebacterium diphtheriae,* and *Vibrio comma,* was studied by Ehrismann and Noethling (1930, 1932). The highest sensitivity for most of the organisms occurred at about 2,650 Å.; exceptions to this were *E. coli* (2,510 Å.) and *S. marcescens* (2,801 Å.). The energy required for killing 1 to 10 per cent of the cells of the various bacteria at 2,650 Å. ranged from 29 to 60 erg/mm.^{2}, and the value obtained at 90 to 100 per cent killing for *E. coli* was 174 erg/mm.^{2}

Further quantitative experiments were carried out by Wyckoff (1932), using *E. coli* as a test organism. When the survival ratios for six wavelengths ranging from 3,132 Å. to 2,536 Å. were plotted on semilogarithmic paper, they were found to fall along a straight line. By comparing the results obtained in the ultraviolet region with his previous studies on X-rays, Wyckoff noted that the energy required for killing in the ultraviolet was about 100 times greater than that required for the X-ray region.

Duggar and Hollaender (1934) observed very little difference in resistance between vegetative cells and spores of *Bacillus subtilis* and *Bacillus megatherium* when exposed to ultraviolet light (2,650 Å.). Herčík (1937) in a similar study found that it required about twice as much incident energy to kill the spores as the vegetative cells of *B. megatherium.* These experiments are particularly interesting, since they demonstrate that there is little relation between light resistance and heat resistance of vegetative cells and spores.

Quantitative experiments on the bactericidal effect of ultraviolet light by Dreyer and Campbell-Renton (1936) and Hollaender and Claus (1936) have added further information to this subject.

When bacterial spores are radiated with ultraviolet light, especially in the Schumann region between 1,250 and 1,600 Å., they become sensitized in some way, so that they are more easily destroyed by heat [Curran and Evans (1938)]. According to Rouyer and Servigne (1938), the most bactericidal region of the ultraviolet spectrum is at 2,650 Å.

Sharp (1939) tested ten species of bacteria for their resistance to short ultraviolet rays (85 per cent 2,537 Å.) and the energy necessary to reduce each to a 10 per cent survival ratio. The results summarized in Table 2 indicate that the resistance to 2,537 Å.-rays of the several species of bacteria was not only of the same order of magnitude but that a spore-forming organism (*Bacillus anthracis*) was only about two and three-fourths as resistant as the least-resistant bacterium, *Shigella paradysenteriae.*

The effect of ultraviolet radiation (2,573 Å.) on the viability, staining properties, virulence, and immunizing power of tubercle bacilli has been studied by Smithburn and Lavin (1939). Heavy suspensions of human tubercle bacilli (1 mg. per milliliter) required at least 10 minutes' exposure to render them nonviable. The organisms killed by such light retained their acid-fast property. Cells which had been irradiated for a short time, but not killed, still possessed the capacity of inducing immunity in laboratory animals, whereas those organisms killed by extended exposure no longer retained this power.

The most quantitative study which has appeared to date on the bactericidal effect of ultraviolet radiation is that of Rentschler, Nagy, and Mouromseff (1941). These workers have described a simple method for uniformly seeding the surfaces of Petri plates with bacteria and other microorganisms. This point had not been controlled in

TABLE 2

INCIDENT ENERGY AT 2,537 Å. NECESSARY TO KILL 90 PER CENT OF SEVERAL SPECIES OF BACTERIA

[From Sharp (1939)]

Organism *	Incident Energy, erg/mm.^{2}, for 90 Per Cent Killing
Bacillus anthracis (mixed spores and vegetative forms)	452
Corynebacterium diphtheriae	337
Staphylococcus aureus (hemolytic)	260
Escherichia coli	245
Serratia marcescens	220
Streptococcus pyogenes	216
Eberthella typhosa	214
Streptococcus salivarius	200
Staphylococcus albus	184
Shigella paradysenteriae	168

* Cultivated on plain or blood agar at *p*H 7.4.

many of the earlier reports. An integrating ultraviolet meter, which responds only to the bactericidal wave band, was also devised. With this instrument it is possible to eliminate errors in exposure due to fluctuations in light intensity and likewise to control the nature of the emitted radiation. Although the original paper should be consulted for many interesting experiments, the following points briefly summarize the data. The various bacterial species studied show widely different resistance to ultraviolet radiation at different stages of the population cycle. A sublethal dose of radiation retards the rate of colony development. The relation between the amount of ultraviolet radiation and the percentage of bacteria killed in a given culture is determined by the distribution of bacteria of varying resistance to the radiation and is not due to the probability of hitting a vital spot in a given organism by a photon (see also the discussion of X-rays, pp. 160 to 164).

Bacterial Antigens and Agglutinins. Very little work seems to have been done on the effect of ultraviolet on the antigenic properties of bacteria and their agglutinins.

Baroni and Jonesco-Mihaiesti (1910) found that, when horse anticholera serum was exposed to ultraviolet light, it became inactive after about 20 minutes; and Heuer (1922) studied the rate of titer decrease in typhoid, paratyphoid B, and cholera antisera during irradiation with ultraviolet. Exposure for 1 to 6 minutes seemed to increase the antigenicity of certain strains of meningococci; whereas extended irradiation decreased their ability to produce agglutinins, according to Eberson (1920). Hasskó (1930) found that bacteria of the typhoid-dysentery group lost some of their specific agglutinability when irradiated with ultraviolet rays for a short time. Reference should again be made to Smithburn and Lavin's (1939) study of the tubercle bacillus. Brief exposure did not destroy the antigenic properties of the organism, whereas, if the irradiation was continued until the bacteria were killed, no protective antibodies were produced when the bacteria were injected into laboratory animals.

Bacterial Toxins and Antitoxins. The rapid inactivation of diptheria toxin by ultraviolet light was observed by Baroni and Jonesco-Mihaiesti (1910) and Hartock, Schürmann, and Stiner (1914). The toxic and antigenic properties, as well as the ability to unite with antitoxin, were destroyed by exposure to these rays. More recently Welch (1930) has observed that purified diphtheria toxin is inactivated more quickly than is a crude filtrate when exposed to the rays of a carbon arc. This difference has been attributed to the fact that the crude broth filtrate contains materials which offer some protection to the toxin by screening some of the destructive rays. Repetto (1940) reported that diphtheria toxin, toxoid, and antitoxin were destroyed by irradiation with ultraviolet light.

A number of papers have also appeared on the inactivation of tetanus toxin by ultraviolet. Thus Courmont and Nogier (1909) found tetanolysin to be rapidly inactivated either in the presence or the absence of oxygen. In a later report the same year they showed that undiluted broth containing crude tetanus toxin required about $2\frac{1}{2}$ hours' exposure for inactivation, but, if some of the original material was diluted 1 : 2,000 with distilled water, it became detoxified after exposure for only a few minutes. These observations were confirmed and extended by Cernovodeanu and Henri (1909). Such facts are very interesting, especially since oxygen is essential for the rays of the visible spectrum to bring about their destructive action in the presence of certain dyes. To explain the detoxifying action under anaerobic conditions it has been suggested that the ultraviolet rays may release oxygen from water or other compounds, thus bringing about some indirect oxidative reaction, but this does not seem to be the whole answer. This subject is discussed more in detail on pp. 159 to 160 on the method of action of ultraviolet light. More recently, Schubert (1928) has observed little difference between the lability of dried and dissolved tetanus toxin upon exposure to such radiation.

Other reports have been published [see Miley (1942), Blundell, Erf, Jones, and Hoban (1944)] on the ability of ultraviolet rays to destroy bacterial toxins, but, since the results are somewhat controversial, they will not be discussed further. The original reports should be consulted for details.

The inactivation of antitoxins by ultraviolet light has received little or no attention. Baroni and Jonesco-Mihaiesti (1910) and Scott (1911) observed that diphtheria antitoxin was destroyed by ultraviolet, but no recent experiments seem to have been reported.

Complement or Alexin. The nonspecific substance, complement, present in all normal sera, which is not increased in amount as the result of immunization, has received a great deal of attention from the bacteriologist, the immunologist, and the chemist. Thus the effect of ultraviolet radiation has not gone unnoticed.

By exposing dilute guinea-pig serum (1 per cent in 0.9 per cent saline) in a layer 1.5 mm. deep to the light of a quartz-mercury arc at 16.5 cm., its complement was inactivated in 40 to 60 seconds, whereas it required 17 to 20 minutes to inactivate the complement in the undiluted serum [Baroni and Jonesco-Mihaiesti (1910)]. It would seem from the experiments of Friedberger (1914) that the complement of dried and powdered serum is more stable than complement in solution, since he was unable to bring about an inactivation of the complement of dried and powdered serum even after long exposure to ultraviolet. Many workers have observed that complement partially inactivated by heat may regain its activity. With this in mind Brooks (1920) partially inactivated a number of sera with heat and ultraviolet radiation but found no evidence whatsoever of regeneration in those sera exposed to the ultraviolet. The complementary action of fresh, unheated serum depends on the interaction of a number of separate components rather than a single chemical substance. At least four components are now recognized. The fraction of complement which is precipitated with the globulin is known as "mid-piece," more recently designated as C′1, and the residual fluid containing albumins is called the "end-piece" (C′2). Both these fractions are inactivated by heat. The other two parts are spoken of as the third and fourth components, or C′3 and C′4, respectively; both are heat-stable. The first two fractions have been the subject of much study, from which it seems probable that the mid-piece is more sensitive to light than the end-piece. Schubert (1928, 1931) made a very careful fractionation and observed that the mid-piece retained less than 3 per cent of its activity when given an exposure to ultraviolet which left the end-piece unharmed. The photolability of the third and fourth components apparently has not been studied.

Miscellaneous Substances. The action of ultraviolet light on several other substances has been studied. For example, ultraviolet rays interfere with bacterial luminescence (*Achromobacter fischeri*), the decrease in total luminescence being proportional to dosage [Giese (1941)]. Dilute tuberculin was found to be inactivated by ultraviolet of less than 3,250 Å. in about 2 hours [Hausmann, Neumann, and Schuberth (1926)]. The ability of a substance such as normal serum or antiserum to induce anaphylactic shock in sensitized animals is reduced by treatment with ultraviolet, but it seems to be one of the more resistant substances in serum. Precipitins in the form of rabbit anti-egg-white serum were inactivated in a few hours by such rays of a quartz-mercury arc lamp [Doerr and Moldovan (1911)]. Bacteriophage, antibodies in the form of hemolytic amboceptor and bacteriolysins, the Wassermann antigen, and other immunological substances have been the subject of irradiation studies [see Brooks (1936) for a detailed discussion]. The most effective wavelength for the inactivation of yeast is around 260 mμ, and some 500 ergs/mm.^{2} produces 50 per cent reduction in viable cells [Landen and Uber (1939)]. The spores of *Trichophyton mentagrophytes* are destroyed when exposed to ultraviolet light (253.7 to 265 mμ), according to Hollaender and Emmons (1939). They found that it takes approximately 7×10^{-4} ergs to obtain 50 per cent inactivation of these spores, as compared with 8×10^{-6} ergs for certain bacteria. Certain enzymes and some viruses have also been subjected to ultraviolet radiation. All viruses so far examined in purified or semipurified preparations have been found to be inactivated by this agent. Although sufficient data are not available to draw any definite conclusions, it seems that viruses require about the same energy for inactivation as bacteria. The inactivation seems to be of a rather mild type, however, since some of the physical, chemical, and serological properties are retained after inactivation [see Stanley (1938)]. Hodes, Webster, and Lavin (1940) have used ultraviolet light (2,537 Å.) in preparing nonvirulent antirabies vaccine. Less than 1 hour's exposure to such radiation rendered the vaccine nonvirulent without destroying the immunizing potency for mice. Taylor and his associates (1941) have also studied the effects of ultraviolet light (2,537 Å.) on equine encephalomyelitis virus protein (eastern strain). They observed that the rate of inactivation of infectivity was of the same order of magnitude as the destruction of *Serratia marcescens* under similar conditions. Inactivation by such light did not affect the sedimentation pattern or constant of the virus protein.

The practical use of ultraviolet light for destroying harmful bacteria in milk [Ayers and Johnson (1913)], drinking water [Thresh and Beale (1910), Schroeter (1912)], swimming pool water, and hydrocoolers [Smith and Perry (1941)] has been suggested, but it has not been generally used because of its expense and for several other reasons. Recently interest has been revived in such problems as the sterilization of air by ultraviolet light as a protection against air-borne infections [see Sharp (1939), Wells (1940), and Whisler (1940)] and the destruction of organisms on glassware [Tanner and Appling (1941)].

Mention should be made of the fact that a great many studies have been carried out on the effect of ultraviolet irradiation *in vivo*. Whether irradiation of animals has any direct or indirect consequences upon the immune properties of their blood plasma is a debatable topic which will not be discussed.

Method of Action of Ultraviolet Light. The mode of action of ultraviolet light is not known at the present time, although a number of workers have theorized concerning its mechanism.

For a time it was thought that some oxidizing substance, such as ozone, was produced during irradiation and that this would account for the bactericidal properties of the light. The formation of an oxidizing agent by ultraviolet irradiation would be in partial accord with the action of the visible spectrum in the phenomenon of photosensitization, where oxygen is apparently essential. On the other hand, Thiele and Wolf (1906, 1907), Buchholz and von Jeney (1935), and others have proved definitely that ultraviolet light is lethal under anaerobic conditions, so such oxidizing substances cannot account for the action. The generation of hydrogen peroxide in lethal quantities has been offered as an explanation, but, as brought out by Ehrismann (1930), it would require a concentration of 30 per cent in the medium or cell to account for the lethal action of the light.

The fact that these rays inactivate cellular products, such as enzymes, toxins, and antibodies, as well as organized cells, would tend to indicate that possibly some general physico-chemical change takes place. In support of this theory is the work of Gates (1930), Ehrismann and Noethling (1932), and Hollaender and Claus (1936). Their work shows that the destructive action is due to the alteration of certain molecular groupings in the cell or its products, which have a high specific absorption spectra for ultraviolet light. In this connection we can state that the sensitivity curve of microorganisms to ultraviolet radiation shows a striking similarity to the absorption curve of certain proteins. Since it is a well-known fact that exposure of albumins and globulins, as well as other proteins, to ultraviolet light brings about a change in the solubility or denaturation [see Spiegel-Adolf (1939)], it is possible that some such change takes place in the bacterial cells. Further proof is given by the fact that photographs of microorganisms killed by ultraviolet radiation reveal that cellular coagulation has taken place.

From this brief discussion it would seem that the denaturation of proteins is the most logical explanation for the mode of action of ultraviolet light on bacteria and their products. However, the action has been attributed to changes in the suspending material, to changes in the permeability of the cell wall, to an alteration in the enzymes within the organism, to a disruption of the colloidal structure of the cytoplasm, and to an alteration in the nucleus or material which controls cell division. Probably the mode of action is complex, involving several or all of these factors. For interesting discussions of the nature of the bactericidal action of ultraviolet and other radiations the papers by Henshaw (1940) and Lea, Haines, and Bretscher (1941) should be consulted.

X-RAYS (ROENTGEN RAYS)

Although the literature on this subject is quite extensive, there are but few quantitative studies which permit of any definite conclusions concerning the action of X-rays on bacteria and their products. Most of the early workers believed that X-rays had little effect on bacteria [Minck (1896), Wittlin (1896), Dozois, Titsler, Lisse, and Davey (1932)], the agglutinins for *Eberthella typhosa* [Fiorini and Zironi (1914, 1915)], or *Salmonella pullorum* [Lusztig (1929)], the Wassermann antigen [Brann (1925)], amboceptor [Konrich (1925)], complement [Fiorini and Zironi (1914), Merlini (1929)], rabbit anti-horse-serum precipitins [Lusztig (1929)], diphtheria toxin [Gerhartz (1909)], tetanus antitoxin [Lusztig (1929)], and other related substances. The reasons for these negative results were, possibly, that the dosage was too small, too many bacteria were used, or the various titration techniques were not sensitive enough to detect a slight change in the material.

While these negative results were being reported, data began to accumulate which showed that X-radiation does have some harmful action on microorganisms and their products. Rieder (1898, 1902) exposed *Escherichia coli*, *Bacillus anthracis*, *Staphylococcus aureus*, *Corynebacterium diphtheriae*, and other organisms on agar and gelatin plates to Roentgen rays and observed a definite killing after irradiation intervals of 20 to 30 minutes at a distance of 10 to 12 cm. When the organisms were suspended in broth 5 mm. deep, the results were not so clear-cut. Clark and Boruff (1929) observed that X-rays act like other sterilizing agents on *E. coli* and *Serratia marcescens* in that the death-rate curves were logarithmic with respect to time. The lethal effect of hard Roentgen rays on typhoid bacilli was demonstrated by Forfota and Hámori (1937). Dietz (1935) studied the volume-increase of bacteria during X-radiation and estimated the total volume of coliform cell to be 0.75 cu. μ under normal conditions but increased to 2 cu. μ after a short irradiation. Schubert (1928) reported a slight inactivation of complement in 1 hour by exposure to X-rays, and Lusztig (1929) observed some destruction by doses ranging from 0.5 to 4.0 H.E.D. (Haut-Erythema-Dosis). One H.E.D. was defined as 9 minutes' irradiation at 28 cm. through 0.5 mm. of zinc from a tube operating at 200 kilovolts (kv.) and 4 milliamperes (ma.). Lusztig was able to demonstrate also about two-thirds inactivation of the antibody hemolysin by 3 H.E.D.

Any further review of the early literature on this subject seems superfluous, since it has already been done by Klövekorn (1925), Pugsley, Oddie, and Eddy (1935), Lea, Haines, and Bretscher (1941), and Lorenz and Henshaw (1941). A few results of the more recent studies, however, will be mentioned. Wyckoff exposed freshly inoculated plate cultures of *E. coli* and *Salmonella typhimurium* to X-rays in the range between 4 Å. and 0.5 Å. The radiation was obtained from a tungsten tube operating at about 4 ma. and 34 kv. or by the K-radiation of copper or silver. After 20 seconds' exposure to filtered copper radiation only about 20 to 33 per cent of the organisms were dead, but after 2 minutes 80 to 90 per cent were killed. Destruction occurred in a semilogarithmic fashion but at a slower rate than with cathode rays. Within limits of experimental error there was no difference between the sensitivity of *S. typhimurium* and *E. coli* when exposed to X-radiation. According to Wyckoff, only about one in 15 to 20 of the absorbed quanta of these radiations proved lethal. The course of the curve from these results suggests that the sensitive cell constituents whose destruction leads to the death of the cell have a volume of 0.01 to 0.06 of the bacterium itself. Such reasoning, however, must be accepted with some caution, and no general conclusions as to the biological effectiveness of Roentgen rays can be drawn from a single series of experiments [Mohler and Taylor (1935)].

Pugsley, Oddie, and Eddy presented quantitative results which show that *Sarcina lutea* and *E. coli* are not sensitive to the same degree when exposed to the X-rays of wavelength 0.25 to 2 Å. When freshly inoculated plates were exposed to the X-ray beam, the bacteria died in an exponential manner, providing a correction factor was introduced to account for the lack of uniformity of the radiation. Irradiation of bacterial colonies gave a different type of death-rate curve.

A study on the lethal and dissociative effects of X-rays on *Staphylococcus aureus* and *Serratia marcescens* was conducted by Haberman and Ellsworth (1940). They found that the cells were killed in a logarithmic manner. Lea, Haines, and Bretscher (1941) have reported on the bactericidal action of X-rays, neutrons, and radioactive radiations for *E. coli* and spores of *Bacillus mesentericus*. They showed that the survival curves are exponential and that the lethal dose is independent of the intensity of the radiation and of the temperature during irradiation. They believe the lethal action of radiation is due to the production of lethal mutations and deduce that the number of "genes" in *E. coli* is of the order of 1,000. Lorenz and Henshaw (1941) recorded experiments in which the survival curve for *Achromobacter fischeri*, after treatment with 200-kv. X-rays, was found to be of the exponential type. Another interesting study is that of Whelden, Enzmann, and Haskins (1941). They observed the influence of graded X-ray doses upon nitrogen fixation and respiration by three species of *Azotobacter* by means of the Warburg method. It was found that nitrogen fixation decreases approximately linearly with increasing X-ray doses. Respiration, in contrast, was affected only indirectly through some inhibition of cell multiplication.

Blank and Kersten (1935) have demonstrated that the action of soft X-rays on agar or agar-water gel alters the agar in such a way as to render a medium subsequently made from that agar unsuitable for the growth of *Bacillus subtilis*. Thus investigators who irradiate organisms on the surface of agar media must differentiate between the direct action of the radiation on the organisms and the indirect action of the radiation on the agar.

Certain of the viruses, bacteriophages, and enzymes have also been irradiated with X-rays. For example, Beckwith, Olson, and Rose (1929–1930) found four out of seven strains of coliphage to be unaffected by X-radiation, but it is possible that the purified bacteriophage proteins might be affected. Friedewald and Anderson (1940) studied the factors which influence the inactivation of the rabbit papilloma virus by X-rays and reported that extremely large doses [million roentgen (r.) units] are necessary for complete inactivation. Syverton, Harvey, Berry, and Warren (1941) found that virus-induced papillomas on domestic rabbits permanently disappeared when treated with Roentgen rays (dosage 3,600 r., 200 kv.). Other viruses have also been studied by several workers. Dale (1940) studied the X-ray inactivation of crystalline cocarboxypeptidase and partially purified polyphenol oxidase.

The X-ray incident either passes through a cell without altering it or else gives up one or more quanta whose energy content is connected with the wavelength λ of the rays through the relation

$$E = h\nu = h\frac{\lambda}{c}$$

where h is Planck's constant (6.55×10^{-27} erg sec.), ν is the frequency of the rays, and c is the velocity of light (2.99×10^{10} cm. sec.$^{-1}$). It is known that as a result of such an absorption a high-velocity electron is liberated. This electron gives rise to a chain of ions in the matter through which it passes and to X-rays which, in their turn, liberate more ions of less and less energy. The alterations which X-rays produce in protoplasm are identified with the physico-chemical changes induced by this ionic shower.

Further research will have to be carried out to determine whether the mode of action of X-radiation can be explained by chance (that is, a bacterium has a definite chance of being hit and killed by a single quantum or electron or by two or more consecutive quanta); by the fact that the "genes" of bacteria are altered and lethal mutations are formed; by the "resistance" theory, which assumes that there is a distribution of resistance among bacteria; or by differences in the metabolic rate and an increased water content in the cell. For interesting discussions of the mechanism of the bactericidal action of radiations the papers by Henshaw (1940), Lea, Haines, and Bretscher (1941), and Lorenz and Henshaw (1941) should be consulted.

CATHODE RAYS

In 1925 Coolidge irradiated bacteria with high-voltage cathode rays. An exposure for 0.1 second was sufficient to kill even the highly resistant spores of *Bacillus subtilis.* A study of the rate of killing of *Escherichia coli*, *Salmonella typhimurium*, and *Staphylococcus aureus* by cathode rays was carried out by Wyckoff and Rivers (1930). Freshly inoculated agar plates were bombarded with a known number of cathode rays, and after incubation the number of survivors was determined by counting the colonies of bacteria on the plates. The cathode rays were generated in a Coolidge-type electron tube, and the velocity of the emitted electrons increased with the voltage applied to the tube. For this study approximately 155 kv. was used, and the velocity of the electrons was in the order of 0.8 of the velocity of light. Since the absorption of a 150-kv. electron in inanimate matter is attended by the release of a large number of ions—10^4 ions within less than 0.001 ml.—it is postulated that any changes brought about in the bacterium by cathode rays are caused by the absorption of electrons and the subsequent shower of ions freed by such electrons. Such an ionic shower is lethal for bacteria but may cause only injury in larger cells, such as those of yeast [Wyckoff and Luyet (1931)]. Destruction of the bacteria was semilogarithmic in nature, and after 20 seconds' exposure approximately 90 per cent of the organisms were dead. From the shape of the survival curves it is concluded that the absorption of one electron is sufficient to kill a bacterium.

Buchwald and Whelden (1939) have been able to show that, when spores of *Aspergillus niger* are irradiated with cathode rays of certain energies and densities and subsequently cultured on potato-maltose agar, they are definitely stimulated. Earlier and more rapid swelling and a higher percentage of production of germ tubes have all been found in the irradiated samples, as compared with the controls. These stimulative effects were observed only at relatively low cathode-ray energies of the order from 1.5 to 3.0 kv.

EMANATIONS FROM RADIOACTIVE ELEMENTS

The radiations emitted by radioactive elements, such as uranium, thorium, radium, polonium, and actinium, are complex. Such radiations consist, usually, of three types, known as alpha-, beta-, and gamma-rays. It is not always easy to dissociate the effect of the three types when a radioactive substance is acting upon a bacterial cell or tissue. They do exhibit differences, however, as the following discussion will show.

The *alpha-rays* (α*-particles*) have been shown to consist of positively charged helium atoms ejected at high velocities from radioactive elements. The average velocity of these alpha-particles from various radioactive substances is about 0.1 that of light. Such particles affect a photographic plate, cause many bodies to fluoresce brilliantly, and have a very intense ionizing power. Their penetrating capacity is quite weak; in fact, they are stopped by a thin layer of glass, aluminum, or even paper.

The *beta-rays* (β*-particles*) consist of high-velocity particles with a negative charge emitted by radioactive substances. Compared with alpha-particles, they are less active photographically, their fluorescent action is less brilliant, and their ionizing power is not so great. The beta-particles are capable of penetrating thin glass, aluminum (0.1 mm.), or liquid before being completely absorbed, but they can be screened off by 5 mm. of aluminum or 1 mm. of lead.

The *gamma-rays* (γ*-rays*) are truly electromagnetic waves analogous to X-rays but of shorter wavelengths. Such rays are not so active photographically as the alpha- and beta-particles, and their fluorescent and ionizing powers seem to be less intense. The penetrating ability of the gamma-rays is much greater than that of the alpha- or beta-particles and corresponds to that of the very hard type of X-rays.

Since it is well known from a physical standpoint that only those rays which are absorbed can exert destructive effects, it can be assumed that gamma-rays have only slight destructive action on bacteria and their products. Such has been found to be the case by Chambers and Russ (1912), Bruynoghe and Mund (1925), and others.

In 1899 Pacinotti and Porcelli [see Spencer (1934)] made the first attempt to determine the effect of radiations from a radioactive element upon bacteria. They exposed several different species to preparations of uranium powder and reported that the organisms were killed within 24 hours. Strebel (1900) exposed *Serratia marcescens* on agar to rays from 20 mg. of radium under various conditions of screening. After different periods of irradiation the degree of growth was compared with that of nonirradiated cultures. In general, the preparations exposed to such radiation were inhibited. These observations with radium and its salts received confirmation and extension by the experiments of many workers, especially those of Pfeiffer and Friedberger (1903), Dixon and Wigham (1903), Strassmann (1904), Dorn, Baumann, and Valentiner (1905). On the other hand, Van Beuren and

Zinsser (1903) and Prescott (1904) found radium rays to have little or no effect on several species of bacteria which they studied. The consensus of these early studies indicates that the alpha- and beta-particles from radioactive substances are capable of inhibiting and, if of sufficient intensity, of stopping the growth of cultures of various microorganisms. The gamma-rays have some physiological action, but it is not so great as that of the alpha- and beta-emanations. It is difficult to determine from these experiments, however, the amount of radiation actually required to produce lethal effects.

Most of the early experiments were made with bacteria growing on culture media. Chambers and Russ (1912) suspended their organisms in distilled water and thus avoided any possible action of the rays upon the medium. Such suspensions of *Staphylococcus aureus, Escherichia coli, Pseudomonas aeruginosa,* and *Mycobacterium tuberculosis* were exposed either to a known concentration of radium emanation or a definite intensity of beta-rays. At various time intervals some of the suspension was removed from the influence of the radiation and plated on agar. The gradual bactericidal effect upon these bacteria was then determined.

Lacassagne and Paulin (1925) determined the relative susceptibility of over 20 different bacteria to beta-rays, but their procedure of estimating a sterilized zone around the colonies on agar plates is not an accepted quantitative method. According to Bruynoghe and Mund (1925), gamma-rays have no lethal action on bacteria but the alpha- and beta-rays are distinctly bactericidal. Von Schroetter (1927) studied the action of radium on several microorganisms and observed some interesting morphological changes. Bacilli and cocco-bacilli tended to elongate and became filamentous, whereas cocci increased in size more or less equally in all diameters. Spirochetes did not change in size and remained motile until just before death.

The effects of gamma-rays on *Staphylococcus aureus, Escherichia coli,* and *Bacillus mesentericus* were considered by Klövekorn and Gaertner (1928). For the experiments 15 mg. of radium filtered through 1.0 mm. of brass was hung 5 mm. above the plate cultures. After 4 hours' irradiation there was a decrease of growth, but the bacteria were not killed. Even when the organisms were exposed to 70 mg. of radium for 48 hours, or 3,360 mg.-hr., they were not all killed. Spencer (1934, 1935) introduced metal needles, emitting beta- and gamma-rays, into tubes of broth inoculated with *Eberthella typhosa, Proteus X 19,* and *Streptococcus pyogenes* and then incubated the tubes at 37°C. Growth was retarded for a short time, but by 24 hours it equalled that in the control tubes. Sometimes filamentous forms or long-chained streptococci were observed after continued daily transfers in the presence of such radiation. When the cultures were irradiated at 0°C., they died within a few days.

A quantitative study of the destructive effects of the beta-rays of radium on several bodies was made by Baker (1935). The comparative resistance of bacteria, viruses, and ferments was estimated and compared with the data of other workers. A summary of the findings is presented in Table 3.

TABLE 3

COMPARATIVE RESISTANCE OF VARIOUS BODIES TO BETA-RAYS

[From Baker (1935)]

Body	Time of Exposure, hours
Escherichia coli	1 *
Staphylococcus aureus	2.5
Vaccinia	1–3
Bacteriophage	5
Rous sarcoma No. 1 (filtrate)	5–10
Tetanus toxin	9
Bacillus anthracis (spores)	20
Hemolytic amboceptor	100
Guinea-pig complement	130
Trypsin	250
Lysozyme	250
Pepsin	9,000
Invertase	15,000

* Time of exposure for *Escherichia coli* taken as unity.

Dozois, Ward, and Hachtel (1936) found that gamma-rays of radium with wavelengths of approximately 0.06 to 0.002 Å. reduced the electrophoretic migration velocity of suspensions of *E. coli.* The rays were emitted from 70 mg. of radium at a distance of 1.25 cm. from the surface of the suspension in dosages of from 70 to 2,940 mg.-hr.

Lea, Haines, and Coulson (1936, 1937) made a study of the action of alpha-particles from polonium, beta-particles from radon, and gamma-rays emitted by radium on *E. coli, Staphylococcus aureus,* and the spores of *Bacillus mesentericus.* For exposure to the alpha- and beta-particles, which have shallow penetrating powers, a new technique was devised, whereby the organisms were suspended and held intact by gelatin films approximately 4 μ in thickness. This procedure worked very well for spores but was less efficient for use with vegetative cells. After various periods of exposure to the radiation the films were dropped into 5 or 10 ml. of sterile water at 37°C. and shaken for a short time to dissolve the gelatin. Suitable dilutions were then plated in the usual manner and incubated at 37°C. Counts revealed that the organisms died in an exponential manner. The rate of disinfection by such particles was found to be independent of the temperature but proportional to the intensity of the radiation. No difference was observed between the effects of a divided exposure and a single exposure. There was little difference between the sensitivity of the three organisms to alpha-particles, but toward beta-particles *B. mesentericus* spores differed greatly from the other two bacteria. These workers

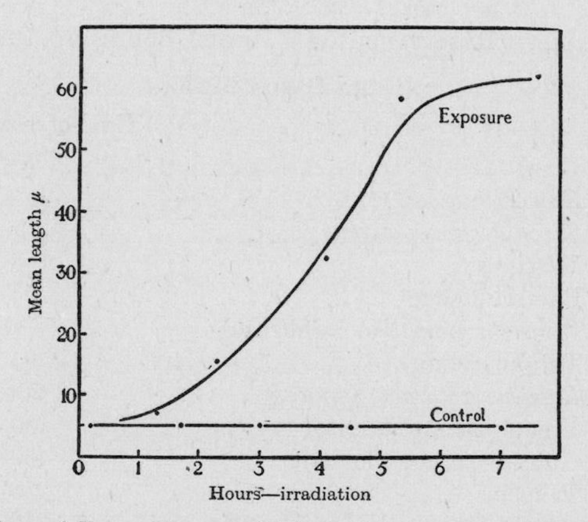

FIG. 3. Production of Long Forms of *Escherichia coli* by γ-Rays from Radium. (From Lea, Haines, and Coulson, 1937.)

concluded that the mode of action of alpha- and beta-particles can be explained best on the "target hypothesis." Such a hypothesis depends simply upon the assumption that there is a sensitive region within which the production of a small amount of ionization leads to death, whereas the production of a similar amount of ionization elsewhere in the organism does not have this effect. Secondary poisoning of the cell by chemical substances liberated in it by the radiation appeared to have no part in the lethal action.

Contrary to some of the earlier studies, Lea, Haines, and Coulson demonstrated that gamma-rays are lethal for bacteria in aqueous suspensions. Death of the organisms occurred exponentially but at a much slower rate than when exposed to beta-radiation. Under certain conditions irradiation with gamma-rays produced abnormal forms similar to those previously noted by other workers. To illustrate this point, the mean lengths of fifty cells of *Escherichia coli* in the logarithmic phase of growth are plotted in Fig. 3. A quantitative analysis of the results led Lea, Haines, and Coulson to conclude that the production of long forms is due to cellular division being inhibited, while growth, in the sense of increase in volume, is unaffected. More recently Lea, Haines, and Bretscher (1941) have studied the lethal effect of alpha-, beta-, and gamma-rays of radium, and neutrons (from a 1,000,000-volt generator) on *E. coli* and spores of *Bacillus mesentericus*. They found the survival curves in all cases to be logarithmic in character.

Miscellaneous Substances. The effect of radioactive emanations on substances related to bacteria has also been studied.

Chambers and Russ (1911) showed that alpha-particles had some action on complement but that the beta- and gamma-rays were inactive. Exposure of serum complement to gamma-rays for 13 hours destroyed only about 8 per cent of its activity, and even after $46\frac{1}{2}$ hours' irradiation 52.9 per cent of its fixing power was still present in the serum. Radium sulfate (1 μg. per liter) inactivated diphtheria toxin in 10 to 43 days but had no effect on tetanus toxin in the same length of time, according to Fabre and Ostrovsky (1911–1912). However, Muttermilch and Ferroux (1925) showed that beta-rays will inactivate tetanus toxin. Brann (1925) reported that radium bromide had no effect on the Wassermann antigen.

Some of the viruses and bacteriophages have been exposed to such radiation by several investigators. Danysz (1906) bombarded the virus of rabies with beta- and gamma-rays from 20 mg. of radium bromide without observing any change in the virus; but Bruynoghe and Le Fèvre de Arric (1925) claimed to have destroyed the virulence of the viruses of rabies, encephalitis, and herpes by radiations emitted by radon in a dose of 5 millicuries for 48 hours. The bacteriophage of typhoid still possessed its lytic action after 3 days' contact with 7 to 8 millicuries of radium emitting only gamma-rays, according to Bruynoghe and Mund (1925).

MISCELLANEOUS RADIATIONS

We are now vaguely familiar with some of the effects obtained in bacteriology by the use of visible light, ultraviolet rays, X-radiation, and the rays emitted by radioactive elements. In general, it will be noted that all these form one continuous spectrum of electromagnetic waves, the various regions of which differ only in wavelength. Although the spectral band is continuous, there are still gaps which have not been investigated because of instrumental difficulties. Such gaps exist between the ultraviolet region and the X-rays and between near infrared and those waves used in wireless and radio. However, with the improvement of the three-electrode vacuum tube, the second of these gaps is now being rapidly filled. What action these regions will have on bacteria and other biological substances will have to await further study. The infrared spectrum supposedly has little or no direct effect upon bacteria, although it is known to have biological effects on other forms of life [Nelson and Brooks (1933)]. The effect of waves just above the infrared is limited because the present vacuum tube is unable to generate in adequate intensity electromagnetic waves of much less than 1 meter. On the other hand, the use of apparatus which generates wavelengths of over 100 meters is not applicable to simple bacteriological procedures. There is a region, however, between 3.5 and 30 meters which shows some bactericidal action and has been used to a certain extent in clinical medicine in the treatment known as diathermy. This topic is given some consideration on pp. 197 to 198, dealing with the effect of high-frequency electrical currents on bacteria.

BACTERIA AS A SOURCE OF RADIATION (HEAT, FLUORESCENCE, PHOSPHORESCENCE, LUMINESCENCE, MITOGENETIC RAYS)

Until now our discussion has centered principally on the harmful effects of electromagnetic waves upon bacteria. Now let us briefly consider living cells and tissues as a source of radiation. *Heat* radiation from organisms of all types is such a common phenomenon that it hardly needs to be mentioned. Although it has long been known that bacteria under special conditions may produce considerable heat, the factors influencing microbial thermogenesis in the decomposition of plant materials have recently been studied in some detail by Norman, Richards, and Carlyle (1941), Carlyle and Norman (1941), and by Wedberg and Rettger (1941). Space does not permit our discussing their results. Anyone who is interested in this subject should consult the original articles. The production of *electricity* by living cells is also quite well known. Although the voltage produced by certain organisms may be so low that it cannot be measured, others, such as the South American electric eel, may produce as much as 500 to 1,000 volts and 200 watts. *Fluorescence,* another type of radiation from organisms (protozoa, green algae, and bacteria), is the transformation of light from that form which illuminates matter into that which radiates from it in such a way that it is of a different (greater) wavelength. *Phosphorescence,* a phenomenon which is practically synonymous with *luminescence* and differs from fluorescence in that it continues after illumination has ceased, is exhibited by many marine organisms.

Luminescence. Light is produced by many organisms. In fact, Harvey (1940) reports that of the 17 phyla in the Animal Kingdom 11 contain luminous forms and 1 is doubtful. Certain bacteria and higher fungi are also luminous, and Harvey very appropriately speaks of luminous bacteria as "the smallest lamps in the world." Luminous bacteria differ from ordinary bacteria only in that they possess ability to luminesce. Many different species of light-producing bacteria have been described. Morphologically they are rods, spheres, or curved rods. They can be easily grown on ordinary culture media under aerobic conditions.

Luminous bacteria are so small that the light from a single bacterium cannot be seen by the naked eye or with the aid of a microscope. It takes a mass of many thousands to produce enough light to affect the retina, and the intensity of the light shows considerable variation. Harvey reports that bacterial colonies may have a light intensity of about 0.7×10^{-10} international candle per square millimeter of colony. He also estimates that a single luminous bacterium has an intensity of approximately 1.9×10^{-14} candles. By comparison, fireflies give values ranging from 1/1,600 to 1/150 candle. The brightness of the luminescence is more important than the intensity in candles. According to Harvey, measurements of the light of the glowworm have been reported as 14.4 millilamberts (mL.) and of the firefly 45 mL., whereas a brightness of 23 to 144 microlamberts (μL.) has been observed for well-aerated bacterial suspensions in a vessel 2.7 cm. thick. To make these figures intelligible we can think of paper properly illuminated for reading as having a brightness of 4 mL. and the luminous paint on watch dials having a brightness of 0.01 to 0.02 mL. Calculations show that the relative efficiency of bacteria to convert food into light is only about 0.16 to 1.0 per cent. However, compared with certain types of chemiluminescences (oxidation of phosphorus, 0.017 per cent efficient and Grignard compounds, 0.0026 per cent efficient), this efficiency is remarkably high.

Luminous organisms, as judged by our eye, produce light of quite different colors. A range of spectral tints has been described which extends from red to violet, but silver-white, yellowish, greenish, and bluish tints are the commonest. Bacteria usually produce silver-white light, although greenish tints have also been observed. Luminescence in most organisms is due to a reaction between the enzyme *luciferase* and its substrate *luciferin*, although this reaction has never been demonstrated positively in bacteria. For further details on this interesting subject the book by Harvey (1940) and the review by the same author (1941) should be consulted.

Several reports [see Harvey (1940)] have appeared in the literature stating that bacteria and other cells produce rays in the X-ray region of the electromagnetic spectrum. These studies, however, have not been confirmed.

Mitogenetic Rays (Gurwitsch Rays). In spite of the prevailing opinion that light rays retard the growth of bacteria rather than act as specific stimuli, considerable data have accumulated which suggest that certain plant and animal tissues, especially meristematic tissues, or cells in a state of active growth, may emit mitogenetic rays which stimulate the growth of other cells placed in a position favorable for their absorption. Since it is a well-known fact that some of the living microorganisms give up light in the visible spectrum, it is not entirely improbable that ultraviolet radiation is emitted by living material, although it is much less likely.

Most of the workers report that mitogenetic rays are ultraviolet radiations of very low intensity with wavelengths of 1,900 to 2,500 Å. These radiations pass through quartz or very thin layers of glass but are absorbed by films of gelatin and glass more than 140 μ thick. Because of the physical characteristics of such rays they are difficult to use experimentally, and their accurate measurement, even with the most sensitive physical instruments, is almost impossible. To overcome this last handicap the rays have been detected mainly by biological means. Onion-root tips were used in the original work by Gurwitsch in 1923, but since that time yeasts, bacteria, and other cells have been used as biological detectors. It has been stated that for bacteria to act as efficient detectors they must be used just prior to the phase of maximum growth, that is, during the late lag phase, but Faguet (1938) found no detection of mitogenetic rays by cultures of *Escherichia coli* or staphylococci during any phase of growth. Although it is difficult to prove the nonexistence of such radiation, the careful work of Hollaender and Claus (1937) and Hollaender (1939) gives no indication that such alleged radiation exists. Thus the claims advanced for such rays must be received with caution until more sensitive measuring methods are available and the results obtained are outside the realm of experimental error. Frenkel and Gurvich (1943), however, are still presenting evidence for the existence of mitogenetic rays.

The more important papers on the detection and emission of mitogenetic rays by yeast and bacteria are those of Magrou and Magrou (1927), Baron (1928), Sewertzova (1931), Ács (1933), Wolff and Ras (1933), and Ferguson and Rahn (1933). The entire subject has been reviewed by Bateman (1935), Hollaender (1936, 1939), and Hollaender and Claus (1937).

TEMPERATURE

Of the physical agents to which bacteria are subjected, temperature has the most varied influence. Depending upon the intensity and period of exposure, temperature may stimulate the growth of microorganisms, alter their morphology, metabolism, or pathogenicity, act as a sterilizing agent, or bring about other changes in the life processes of the organisms [Hampil (1932)]. It is quite generally assumed that all such alterations are accompanied by chemical changes in the cellular material, and for that reason we should give brief consideration to the influence of temperature on chemical reactions.

THE INFLUENCE OF TEMPERATURE ON RATES OF REACTIONS

The influence of temperature on the rates of simple chemical processes is often expressed in terms of the *temperature coefficient* of the reactions, or the ratio between the velocity constants $\left(k = \frac{1}{t} \ln \frac{a}{a - x}\right.$ for a monomolecular reaction) of the reactions at two different temperatures. The symbol $Q_{\Delta t^\circ}$ is usually employed to signify the value of this ratio, as:

$$Q_{\Delta t^\circ} = \frac{k_2}{k_1}$$

where k_1 = velocity constant at any temperature, t°.
k_2 = velocity constant at a temperature higher than t°; that is, $t^\circ + \Delta t^\circ$.
$Q_{\Delta t^\circ}$ = temperature coefficient of reaction rates at two temperatures differing by Δt°.

To indicate the value of this coefficient or ratio for a difference of 10°C., the symbol is generally written as Q_{10}.

In some chemical reactions, especially those taking place at temperatures of optimum biological activity, this equation exhibits a reasonable degree of constancy. Usually the Q_{10} values lie between two and three; that is, the speed of such reactions is increased between twofold and threefold for a 10° rise in temperature. In other chemical processes, however, there is a definite decrease in value with increments of temperature, signifying that such a ratio should be regarded as a rough approximation to the true relation.

For any temperature interval, Δt°, a value can be found for Q_{10} by employing the following formula:

$$Q_{10} = \sqrt[\Delta t^\circ]{\left(\frac{k_2}{k_1}\right)^{10}} = \left(\frac{k_2}{k_1}\right)^{\frac{10}{t^\circ}} = \frac{10}{\Delta t^\circ} \log \frac{k_2}{k_1}$$

This doubling or trebling of the reaction rate for each 10° rise in temperature is commonly called the R.G.T. rule (Reaktionsgeschwindigkeit-Temperatur-Regel).

These formulas are based on reactions in fairly homogeneous chemical systems, and for that reason some investigators are opposed to applying them to complex heterogeneous biological processes. Until some other means of determination is developed, however, this method of evaluating rates of reactions in biological systems as influenced by environment will continue to be used. In spite of the fact that caution should be exercised, it is interesting to note that some of the bacterial activities do fall within this particular range. Table 4 shows the velocity constants and the temperature coefficients of the rates of growth of *Lactobacillus delbrückii* in a special medium. It can be seen that the temperature coefficients do not deviate very far from two to three for each 10° rise in the incubation temperature.

TABLE 4

TEMPERATURE COEFFICIENTS AND VELOCITY CONSTANTS OF GROWTH OF *Lactobacillus delbrückii*

(From Table 7, Chap. 2)

Temperature of Incubation, °C.	Velocity Constant, $0.434k$	Temperature Coefficient, Q_{10}
50	0.98	1.4
40	0.62	
45	0.84	2.3
35	0.365	
40	0.62	3.3
30	0.184	
35	0.365	4.3
25	0.084	

Another example of the use of this coefficient is given in Table 5. In this case the ratios are for the rate of destruction of several organisms and their spores as influenced by temperature. Here it will be noted that some of the Q_{10} values vary considerably from the usual two- to threefold increase, but this deviation is not unusual in biological destruction rates as influenced by heat. According to Crozier (1924) and others, the temperature coefficient, Q_{10}, giving the ratio of velocities for an interval of 10°C., is a rather imperfect means of characterizing a process, since it is not a constant quantity but depends upon the particular temperature range.

In order to have a more adequate expression of the complex relationship between temperature and rates of reactions at different ranges in the temperature scale, van't Hoff and, later, Arrhenius (1915)

TABLE 5

TEMPERATURE COEFFICIENTS OF DEATH BY HEAT FOR DIFFERENT ORGANISMS

[From Sattler (1929) and Chick (1930)]

Organism	Temperature Range, °C.	Average Q_{10}
Micrococcus sulfureus	63–80	5.4
Aerobacter aerogenes	63–80	2.6
Pseudomonas fluorescens	63–80	2.1
Eberthella typhosa	49–54	110–170
Escherichia coli	49–52	12
Staphylococcus, species	49–53	29
Bacillus anthracis, spores	90–103	10
B. anthracis, spores	80–90	40
Foot-and-mouth disease virus	50–60	201
Yeast, rose pigment	63–80	1.2

deduced by calculus the following equation based on thermodynamical grounds:

$$k_2 = k_1 e^{\frac{\mu}{R}\left(\frac{1}{T_1} - \frac{1}{T_2}\right)}$$

where k_1 and k_2 = velocity constants (or figures proportional thereto) at the absolute temperatures T_1 and T_2, respectively.

e = the base of natural logarithms.

R = the gas constant.

μ = a constant, the so-called *temperature characteristic* which characterizes a particular reaction.

R, the gas constant, is 1.986 for gram-calorie units, so the preceding equation becomes approximately:

$$k_2 = k_1 e^{\frac{\mu}{2}\left(\frac{1}{T_1} - \frac{1}{T_2}\right)}$$

Converting this equation to common logarithms and solving for μ gives us the form:

$$\mu = 4.6 \times \frac{(\log k_2 - \log k_1)}{\dfrac{1}{T_1} - \dfrac{1}{T_2}} = 4.6 \frac{(\log k_2 - \log k_1)T_2 T_1}{T_2 - T_1}$$

The quantity μ has been used extensively in biological studies, especially by Crozier, Stier, and others, to test the assumption that each group of reactions having the same *temperature characteristic* (μ) are processes influenced by the same type of catalyst. In other words, it serves as an index of the reproducibility of the relation of rate of change to temperature.

According to Crozier, most biological processes fall well within the range, $\mu = 4{,}000$ to 35,000, which happens to be the limiting values for most simple chemical reactions. He therefore believes μ is a more delicate, as well as theoretically a more significant, index than the Q_{10} ratio for the characterization of a biological process. This hypothesis was offered after analysis of a great deal of data taken from the most

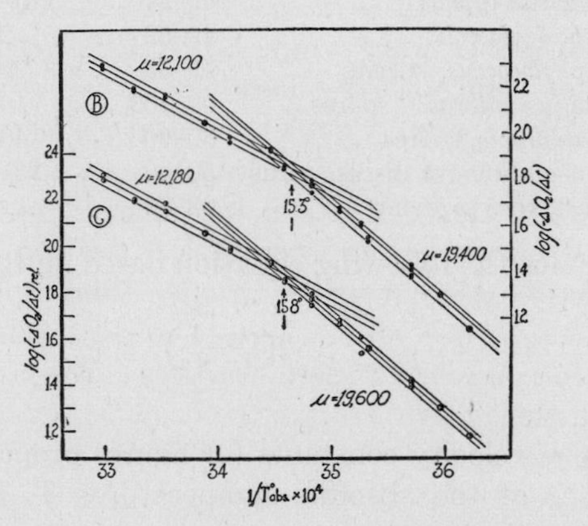

FIG. 4. The Relation of O_2 Uptake to the Reciprocal of the Absolute Temperature. The data plotted on lines *B* and *C* were obtained on different days, a new suspension of *Saccharomyces cerevisiae* being used for each determination. (From Stier, 1933.)

varied phenomena, such as, for example, the rate of forward movement of paramecia, the rate of oxygen utilization by insect eggs, the rate of reduction of methylene blue by anaerobic bacteria, and the rate of carbon dioxide production by yeast at various temperatures.

Unfortunately, in the published accounts of respiratory functions and other phenomena of bacteria and yeasts there are few data on rates of reactions studied carefully enough at an adequate number of temperatures so that the measurements can be used for proper analysis. One example taken from Stier (1933) will be sufficient to show how the constant μ can be used as an index of the reproducibility of the relation of the rate of oxygen consumption by *Saccharomyces cerevisiae* to temperature in the range 3° to 35°C. Line *B* of Fig. 4 shows the data obtained by one method of measuring the oxygen uptake, the logarithms of the rates of oxygen utilization being plotted against the reciprocals of the absolute temperatures, according to the final equation on p. 175. The observed values lie on two straight lines intersecting at 15.3°C. When the value of the temperature coefficient was 30° to

15°C., μ = 12,100; when it was 15° to 3°C., μ = 19,400. When a slightly different technique was used to calculate the ratios of oxygen uptake to temperature, the data in line *C* were obtained. These points fall on two straight lines intersecting at 15.8°C. For the range 30° to 15°C., μ = 12,180, and for 15° to 3°C., μ = 19,600. The variability of μ was not over ±2 per cent in any experiment. The interesting point about these experiments is the fact that a close similarity exists between these thermal characteristics (μ) and values obtained for respiratory activities in organisms other than yeasts and bacteria.

In many of the studies of thermal coefficients the values for μ remain constant through rather wide temperature ranges, whereas in other studies an abrupt change is frequently observed at certain specific temperatures. The location of such a deviation is best determined by graphing, as is shown in Fig. 4, where the points 15.3°C. and 15.8°C. are clearly shown to be "breaks" in the rate of the process. These points are called *critical temperatures.* Such sudden changes in the slope of the reaction-rate curves are usually interpreted as indicating shifts in the basic processes which control the particular reaction under investigation. In considering these sudden changes in μ, Crozier remarks, "In discussion of temperature coefficients the role of the slowest process of a catenary set as the master process of the whole is sometimes insufficiently appreciated." In other words, in such interlocked systems the speed of the whole must depend upon the speed of the slowest reaction of the system.

In spite of the criticism of this method of studying biological processes Cameron (1930) is of the opinion that the determination of μ is a useful method of attack to ascertain the underlying chemical and physico-chemical factors governing certain biological phenomena. He believes the reason for the incompleteness of such work lies mainly in the lack of association of definite values of μ found for living processes with values found for chemical reactions in the laboratory. Considerable interesting data have been obtained by applying this method of study to certain biological problems, especially when it is used in conjunction with other methods of analysis. The entire subject of temperature relationships, however, appears to be so complex that some caution should be used in the interpretation of complex heterogeneous processes by the van't Hoff-Arrhenius equation alone. This equation is based on simple reactions for homogeneous systems and not on the supposedly heterogeneous processes of the cell.

THE CARDINAL TEMPERATURES

Bacteria, like other living cells, have a *minimum*, an *optimum*, and a *maximum* growth temperature and a so-called *growth temperature range.*

These special temperatures are called the *cardinal points.* For a review of the influence of temperature on the life processes of bacteria the paper by Hampil (1932) should be consulted.

Minimum Growth Temperature. The lowest temperature at which detectable growth occurs in a known environment is called the minimum growth temperature of the organism. Some of the pathogenic bacteria and heat-loving forms (thermophiles) are very sensitive to low temperatures and are unable to grow when held a few degrees below their optimum. On the other hand, most bacteria will grow and multiply at temperatures of about 10°C. or even lower. Growth has been observed as low as −7.5°C. for certain marine bacteria. In general, organisms are prevented from growing at low temperatures because of the physical changes, such as desiccation, involved in the freezing of the substrate. Thus it must be kept in mind that the minimum growth temperature for any given bacterium is not a fixed temperature but instead shows some variation, depending upon the environment. Attempts to develop strains of bacteria with lower minimum growth temperatures have been unsuccessful.

Optimum Growth Temperature. The temperature which is most favorable for the rapid growth of an organism is called the optimum growth temperature. At such a temperature the generation time will be at a minimum during the logarithmic phase of the population cycle. Although it is customary to speak of the optimum temperature for bacterial growth, we know that for many species it is necessary to define the process to which this term is applied. For example, the optimum temperature for growth is not necessarily the most favorable for fermentative, proteolytic, and synthetic processes. Recently published data (Table 6) by Dorn and Rahn (1939) explain this point very well. The formation of flagella and spores in some cases requires different temperature optima from those controlling toxin production and

TABLE 6

EFFECT OF TEMPERATURE UPON DIFFERENT LIFE FUNCTIONS OF *Streptococcus lactis* AND *Streptococcus thermophilus*

[From Dorn and Rahn (1939)]

Function	*Streptococcus lactis* °C.	*Streptococcus thermophilus* °C.
Most rapid rate of growth at	34	37
Largest number of cells at	25–30	37
Most rapid rate of fermentation at	40	47
Largest amount of acid at	30	37

virulence. To complicate further a true definition of optimum growth temperature is the fact that this temperature may vary with the composition and reaction of the particular medium in which the organism is cultivated.

Maximum Growth Temperature. The maximum growth temperature is the highest temperature at which growth and multiplication of an organism can take place. Like the minimum and the optimum, the maximum temperature of growth varies with each bacterium and is controlled by the environment. Many of the saprophytic water and soil bacteria have a maximum between 30° and 35°C. Most of the pathogenic microorganisms show little growth above 40° to 45°C. Certain other forms may develop at temperatures of 70° to 75°C. oı even higher. The temperature maxima for several spore-forming bacteria were investigated by Blau (1906). Some of his data are presented in Table 7.

TABLE 7

TEMPERATURE MAXIMA FOR SEVERAL SPORE-FORMING BACTERIA

[From Blau (1906)]

Organisms	Maximum Temperature for *Spore Germination* °C.	*Vegetative Growth* °C.	*Spore Formation* °C.
Bacillus mycoides	30–35	30–35	30–35
Bacillus teres	35–40	35–40	35–40
Bacillus simplex	35–40	40–45	35–40
Bacillus asterosporus	40–45	35–40	35–40
Bacillus alvei	40–45	45–50	45–50
Bacillus sphericus	45–50	40–45	40–45
Bacillus megatherium	45–50	45–50	35–40
Bacillus tumescens	45–50	45–50	40–45
Bacillus subtilis	55–60	55–60	55–57
Bacillus robustus	65–67	65–67	65–67
Bacillus calidus	70–73	70–73	70–73
Bacillus cylindricus	73–74	73–74	70–73
Bacillus tostus	74–75	74–75	73–74

The relation of certain respiratory enzymes to the maximum growth temperatures of bacteria is very interesting. This problem was investigated by Edwards and Rettger (1937), and some of their data are presented in Table 8. Determinations of the minimum temperatures of destruction of the specific bacterial enzymes, indophenol oxidase, catalase, and succinodehydrogenase were made and compared statistically with the maximum growth temperatures of spore-forming bacteria. A high degree of correlation was found for each enzyme individually and for all three collectively, which suggests that to a marked degree the maximum growth temperatures for bacteria may bear a definite relationship to the minimum temperatures of destruction of respiratory enzymes. It has been suggested that spores are more resistant to heat than vegetative cells, because a firmer enzyme-protein union is present in the spores. Thus Edwards and Rettger suggest that the resistance of thermophiles may be explained by a firmer enzyme-protein union in them than is found in mesophilic bacteria. Some doubt has been cast on these interpretations by Rahn and

TABLE 8

THE RELATION OF THE MAXIMUM GROWTH TEMPERATURES OF BACTERIA TO THE MINIMUM TEMPERATURES OF DESTRUCTION OF CERTAIN ENZYMES

[From Edwards and Rettger (1937)]

			Minimum Temperature of Destruction		
Organism	Number of Strains	Maximum Growth Temperature	*Indo-phenol oxidase*	*Catalase*	*Succino-dehydro-genase*
		°C.	°C.	°C.	°C.
Bacillus mycoides	4	40	41	41	40
Bacillus prausnitzii	1	40	44	40	40
Bacillus simplex	3	43	55	52	40
Bacillus cereus	21	45	48	46	50
Bacillus megatherium	8	46	48	50	47
Bacillus tumescens	1	46	55	46	46
Bacillus subtilis	10	54	60	56	51
Bacillus vulgatus	5	55	56	56	50
Bacillus mesentericus-fuscus	12	58	60	63	53
Thermophiles	9	76	65	67	59

Schroeder (1941). Attempts to acclimate bacteria and their spores to higher temperatures have resulted in only a small degree of success [Casman and Rettger (1933), Williams (1936)].

Growth Temperature Range. The difference between the minimum and maximum growth temperatures is called the *growth temperature range*. For most pathogenic bacteria, which normally lead a parasitic existence, this range is rather short. Certain saprophytic forms which are not so highly specialized have a much wider range.

In spite of the difficulty in assigning distinct temperature boundaries to all bacterial activities, it is often convenient to classify such organisms into three large groups based on their relation to temperature.

Such a division is given in Table 9. It must be kept in mind that the boundaries between such groups are indistinct and show considerable overlapping.

TABLE 9

CLASSIFICATION OF BACTERIA BASED ON TEMPERATURE

Group	Temperature, °C. *Minimum*	*Optimum*	*Maximum*	Forms
Psychrophilic	−5–0	10–20	25–30	Water, cold-storage growths, etc.
Mesophilic	10–25	20–40	40–45	Pathogens and many saprophytes
Thermophilic	25–45	50–60	70–80	Soil, manure, hot springs, etc.

Psychrophilic bacteria are those which grow best below 20°C. In nature they are commonly found in deep lakes, cold springs, and ocean waters and undoubtedly play a part in decomposing the organic matter which falls to the bottom of such waters. These organisms sometimes cause considerable trouble in the preservation of foods kept in cold storage. Some bacteriologists object to the use of the term psychrophile on the grounds that bacteria allocated to this group really grow better at higher temperatures. However, the data presented by Rubentschik (1925), Horowitz-Wlassowa and Grinberg (1933), Hess (1934), ZoBell (1934), and others prove beyond all doubt that certain bacteria grow best at temperatures below 20°C. Hess studied the growth of several bacteria of marine origin in buffered nutrient broth at 37°, 20°, 5°, 0°, and −3°C. Quantitative measurements were made by means of plate counts, and data were collected over a period of 60 days. Maximum crops were obtained at 5°C. in all cases and higher total yields at 0°C. and −3°C. than at 37°C. and 20°C. Because of the slow rate of growth of psychrophilic bacteria the crop yield was considered a better criterion for determining the optimum temperature than the growth rate during the logarithmic phase. Practically all cultural characteristics of these organisms were evident at −3°C. A strain of *Pseudomonas fluorescens* did not lose its motility even at −6.5°C.; in fact, the organism actually maintained this ability much longer at the lower temperatures than at the higher ones. Berry and Magoon (1934) in a fine review have recorded growth at −4°C. for *Ps. fluorescens* and species of the genera *Lactobacillus*, *Torula*, *Monilia*, and *Penicillium*.

A number of investigators have observed decided proteolysis of milk, fish, and meat, denitrification, storage diseases of fruits, and other physiological activities by bacteria at 0°C., but few reports have been published on such activities below 0°C. Rubentschik (1925) in his studies of *Urobacteria* at 0°C. to −2.5°C. reported urea fermentation, gelatin liquefaction, and pigment formation at these low temperatures. In a careful study by Hess (1934) practically all the common physiological characteristics were noticed at −3°C. for the bacteria he studied. Fermentation of dextrose, sucrose, and maltose, proteolysis of fish-muscle protein, peptonization of milk, formation of indol from tryptophan broth, reduction of nitrates, liquefaction of gelatin, growth on potato, and fluorescence on fish-extract agar all took place at these low temperatures. No temperatures lower than −6.5°C. were used for unfrozen media, but Hess believes that growth and other characteristic reactions might take place at lower temperatures if the media could be kept from freezing and undue increase of growth-retarding properties such as osmotic pressure could be avoided. Berry and Magoon believe that microbial growth below −10°C. is unlikely, regardless of the physical condition of the substrate.

Mesophilic bacteria are those which show optimum growth between 20° and 40°C. Since the body temperature of most of the higher animals is within this range, all the parasitic bacteria are considered mesophilic. The temperature 37.5°C. is considered the optimum for most pathogenic bacteria. Many of the microorganisms responsible for putrefaction and decay are placed in this group and have an optimum between 20° and 35°C.

Thermophilic bacteria are usually classified as *strict thermophiles*, which show optimum growth above 55°C. and fail to grow below 37°C., and *facultative thermophiles*, with an optimum between 45° and 55°C. Although the maximum growth temperature for bacteria seems to be about 75°C., vegetation has been observed growing in a hot spring in Iceland which had a temperature of 98°C. [Flourens (1846)]. This seems to be the highest recorded temperature at which life exists. Most thermophilic bacteria belong to the spore-forming types, though non-spore-forming bacteria, algae, and related forms have been described. Heat-resistant spores are commonly produced by thermophilic spore-forming bacilli; in fact, some will stand boiling at 100°C. for 20 to 25 hours.

In nature thermophiles are widely distributed. They have been isolated, for example, from thermal springs, manure piles, decaying compost, soil, milk products, canned goods, tobacco, hay, and silage. Because of their wide distribution and ability to withstand high temperatures they are of considerable economic importance, especially in the canning, dairy, and sugar industries, where spoilage is often caused by their growth. None of the thermophilic bacteria, so far as is known, produces disease or has any public health significance [Hansen (1932)]. Excellent reviews on this subject have been published by Robertson (1927), Prickett (1928), and Cameron and Williams (1928).

Thermoduric bacteria are those which survive exposure to ordinary pasteurization temperatures (60° to 63°C.). For the most part they are mesophilic bacilli, streptococci, and sarcinae which possess unusual thermal resistance. They are particularly bothersome at times in the food and dairy industries, although none of them is regarded as dangerous to health.

THERMAL DEATH TIME OF BACTERIA AND RELATED SUBSTANCES

The older bacteriological literature contains records of many determinations of what has been called the *thermal death point* of bacteria. This term is misleading and has been generally discarded and replaced by the more suitable expression *thermal death time*, which merely means the time required to kill an organism at a given temperature in a known environment.

Some knowledge of the heat resistance of microorganisms is desirous for several reasons. The significance of such information in the canning industry is well known, since it is necessary to know the resistance of spoilage bacteria to arrive at satisfactory processes for canned foods. Because of the importance of such facts special apparatus for the determination of spore-destruction rates has been developed by bacteriologists in this industry [Williams, Merrill, and Cameron (1937), Townsend, Esty, and Baselt (1938)]. Preparation of various products, such as certain sutures for surgical work, is based on the destruction of bacteria by heat. In the pasteurization of milk and milk products much work has been done on the heat resistance of organisms at pasteurization temperatures. In addition to these practical problems heat resistance is often desirable as one of the differential characteristics for classifying bacteria.

For a number of years canning technologists and others who have had to study the heat resistance of bacterial cells and spore suspensions have plotted the data on semilogarithmic paper to secure what is called a thermal death-time curve. Space does not permit a discussion of the procedures followed to determine this curve. Briefly, however, it may be stated that, when the number of surviving cells per unit of material is plotted against the time of heating, the resulting thermal death-time curve approximates a straight line on semilogarithmic paper. Two values are now commonly used to describe this curve:

F = the number of minutes required to destroy the cell (in any specific medium) at 121.1°C. (250°F.).

z = the slope of the thermal death-time curve, expressed as °F. This is the range of temperature required for the plotted line to pass through one log cycle on semilogarithmic paper, or a measure of the change in thermal death time with changing temperature.

These two factors (a point and a slope) characterize the thermal death-time curve quite well, and they have been used extensively to determine safe processes for canned foods and milk pasteurization [see Townsend, Esty, and Baselt (1938), Ball (1943)].

In studying the lethal action of heat on bacteria, several factors must be kept in mind to insure uniform and dependable results. Several of these factors will be discussed briefly.

Time. The time of exposure at a given temperature is one of the most important factors involved in studying the lethal action of heat on bacteria. In general, the time necessary for sterilization varies inversely with the temperature, as was shown by Bigelow and Esty (1920) when working with a known suspension of bacterial spores in a medium of a known *p*H. The cells of the gonococcus are destroyed by heat at 50°C. in a few minutes, whereas at 42°C. the time necessary to obtain sterilization is about 5 hours and at 41°C. over 11 hours; death of all the cells is not obtained in 30 hours at 40°C. [Carpenter and coworkers (1933)]. The thermal death time of *Treponema pallidum* in extracts from rabbit testis is 5 hours at 39°C., 3 hours at 40°C., 2 hours at 41°C., and 1 hour at 41.5°C. [Boak, Carpenter, and Warren (1932)]. A temperature of 62°C. to 63°C. for 20 to 30 minutes is usually sufficient to destroy most non-spore-forming organisms, such as the typhoid, diphtheria, and tubercle bacilli. Bacterial spores are

TABLE 10

Time Necessary to Destroy the Most Resistant Spores of *Clostridium botulinum*

[From Esty and Meyer (1922)]

Temperature, °C.	Minimum Killing Time, minutes
100	360
105	120
110	36
115	12
120	5

more resistant and require longer periods of exposure at higher temperatures. An example is shown in the data (Table 10) taken from the paper by Esty and Meyer (1922) for the spores of *Clostridum botulinum.* In their investigations the spores were suspended in a phosphate buffer solution at *p*H 6.98.

Number, Age, and Type of Cells. There is considerable evidence indicating that the larger the initial number of bacteria or spores present to be killed, the longer it will take to attain sterile conditions. It is also possible that the greater the initial number of cells, the greater the probability that a number of very resistant forms, which can endure more heat, are present. The effect of numbers is shown in Table 11, taken from Williams (1929).

TABLE 11

RELATION BETWEEN THE INITIAL NUMBER OF SPORES AND THE SURVIVAL TIME

[From Williams (1929)]

Number of Spores per Milliliter	Survival Time at 100°C., minutes
100,000,000	19
75,000,000	16
50,000,000	14
25,000,000	12
1,000,000	8
100,000	6

The age of the culture is another factor which must be considered when studying the heat resistance of bacteria and their spores. Most investigators have found that young spores and cells are much less resistant to high temperatures than older ones. Heiberg (1932) reported that $1\frac{3}{4}$- and $2\frac{3}{4}$-hour cultures of *Escherichia coli* were reduced 10,000 and 2,000 times, respectively, when heated at 53°C. for 15 minutes, whereas a culture 62 hours old was reduced in number by only twelvefold. Similar results have been observed by other workers for non-spore-forming bacteria. There seems to be considerable variation in the heat resistance of spores at different ages; in fact, Magoon (1926) is of the opinion that the resistance of spores to heat is not a fixed property but, rather, a variable one, the degree of resistance being influenced by several factors, especially age and the temperature and humidity of the environment. In connection with the type of organism it would seem that the inherent nature of the cells is also important. For example, some of the thermophiles have their optimum growth range at temperatures which are lethal in a short time for many bacteria.

Moisture Content. It is well known that moisture hastens the coagulation of proteins by heat, and the destruction of bacteria by this agent may be due to such coagulation. Several workers have found the moisture content of spores of bacteria to be lower than that of the vegetative cells, but others doubt that this difference is sufficient to account for the greater thermostability exhibited by spores. A more likely explanation, in so far as moisture is concerned, seems to lie in the fact that Friedman and Henry (1938) have shown that spores and vegetative forms contain different amounts of bound water (Table 12), which may be inactive so far as its influence on the coagulation of protein material by heat is concerned.

TABLE 12

THE BOUND-WATER CONTENT OF SPORES AND VEGETATIVE CELLS OF THREE BACTERIAL SPECIES

[From Friedman and Henry (1938)]

	Bacillus subtilis		*Bacillus megatherium*		*Bacillus mycoides*	
	Vegetative	Spores	Vegetative	Spores	Vegetative	Spores
Grams bound water per gram solids	0	2.5	0.8	1.9	1.3	2.0
Per cent bound water in bacterial mass	0	69.0	17.7	62.6	28.2	58.7

Substrate. The chemical composition and physical state of the medium on which the organisms have been cultivated, as well as the substrate in which the cells are suspended for heating, may also influence thermal death results. It has been demonstrated that heat resistance is affected by the presence of varying amounts of sodium chloride or other salts, sugar, proteins, and other substances, which may serve in some way as protective materials.

The hydrogen-ion concentration of the substrate often influences the rate of death of bacteria, although Bigelow and Esty (1920), Murray and Headlee (1931), Lang and Dean (1934), and other workers found that within reasonable limits the reaction of the medium may not noticeably reduce the thermal death time. Thus Lang and Dean found that *p*H values between approximately 5.0 and 6.8 gave no correlation with heat resistance of *Clostridium botulinum.* Williams (1929) and Murray and Headlee believe that the heat resistance of organisms is greatest at about *p*H 7.0, but reactions above or below this point cause decreased heat resistance. That acid reactions are more toxic than alkaline reactions is illustrated by the data (Table 13) taken from Murray and Headlee's paper.

TABLE 13

RELATION OF HYDROGEN-ION CONCENTRATION TO KILLING TIME OF SPORES OF *Clostridium tetani* SUSPENDED IN BUFFER SOLUTION

[From Murray and Headlee (1931)]

*p*H	Thermal Death Time, minutes, at			
	105°C.	100°C.	95°C.	90°C.
1.2	5 *	5 *	5 *	5 *
2.0	5 *	5 *	5 *	5 *
3.0	5 *	5 *	5 *	5 *
4.0	5 *	10	15	25
5.0	10	10	20	30
6.0	10	15	40	55
7.0	10	30	55	60
8.0	10	15	45	60
9.0	5 *	10	30	50
10.0	5 *	10	20	35

* Five minutes or less.

The osmotic conditions of the medium may have certain influences. Robertson (1927) demonstrated that an increase in osmotic pressure was accompanied by a rise in the thermal death rate of bacterial cells. Hypotonic solutions decreased the resistance of cells and hypertonic solutions increased, within limits, the heat resistance.

Miscellaneous Factors. In certain instances the size and shape of the container used in the heating experiment, the conduction and convection currents within the container, and several other factors have considerable influence on the killing of bacteria by heat. Several of the papers already mentioned and books on food technology discuss these topics at some length.

Mechanism of Cell Destruction by Heat. Several theories have been advanced to explain the processes involved in the destruction of bacteria and their products by heat or their resistance to it. Chick and Martin (1910) believe that the death of bacteria under the influence of heat is due, possibly, to protein coagulation, and that the higher the temperature to which they are submitted, the more rapidly their cellular protein is coagulated. This explanation seems well founded, but probably other factors are also involved in bringing about the so-called "irreversible changes in the bacterial protoplasm." Some workers believe that death of the cell is invariably due to influences which bring about increased permeability of the cell wall. Undoubtedly the denaturation of the proteins results in a surface change of some type. Other investigators have ascribed the heat resistance of some bacteria and spores to differences in the mineral content of their protein or the nutritive conditions under which cells are formed and to protective substances in the heating medium. That differences in heat resistance are due to the low water content of the protoplasm of certain cells or spores was suggested by Lewith (1890). Workers of that period had already established the fact that bacterial cells contain heat-coagulable proteins, so Lewith undertook to show how cells containing various percentages of moisture might resist heat coagulation. This point is illustrated by the following data taken from Lewith's paper:

Egg Albumin	*Temperature of Coagulation in 30 Minutes,* °C.
Aqueous solution	56
With 25 per cent water	74–80
With 18 per cent water	80–90
With 6 per cent water	145
Water-free	160–170

Since Lewith's time careful studies of the free-water content of bacteria have failed to show any great difference between either various vegetative cells or spores. The work of Friedman and Henry (1938), however, shows that there is considerable difference in the bound-water content of spores and vegetative cells (see Table 12). It will be interesting to see if the thermophilic bacteria also have a higher bound-water content than mesophiles. Another logical explanation for differences in resistance can be deduced from the work of Edwards and Rettger (1937), in which they have shown an almost perfect relationship between the maximum growth temperature of several bacilli and the minimum temperature at which some of their respiratory enzymes are destroyed. Undoubtedly, lethal temperatures for bacteria destroy some of the cellular enzymes, although it is not the primary cause of death, according to Rahn and Schroeder (1941).

At present no one theory can be proposed which will explain the phenomenon of heat resistance or ease of destruction exhibited by certain bacteria. It is probably better to think of the process as a series of both surface and internal changes involving several factors. It has already been shown that increases in temperature stimulate the rate of cellular reactions. Those cells which are easily destroyed by heat apparently do not have the mechanism, enzymatic or otherwise, to carry on their activities at high temperatures. The underlying reactions increase to such a point that catabolism exceeds anabolism, and death results. Resistant forms, such as thermophiles or spores, may continue to be active at higher temperatures, either because of their bound-water content, which does not enter into the heat-coagulation process, or because of a difference in their enzyme-protein union. Such cells seem to be controlled by a "governor" of some type which prevents the rate of catabolism from exceeding that of anabolism until very high temperatures are reached, at which they are also destroyed.

Heat Resistance of Enzymes, Toxins, and Viruses. Many of the viruses are inactivated by heating to a temperature of 75°C., but there is considerable variation in the sensitivity of the different viruses to temperature. Some, such as the cucumber mosaic, tobacco ring spot, and encephalitis, are so unstable that they become inactivated on standing at room temperature for a few hours, but it is not known whether this reaction is due to temperature alone or to the presence of some extraneous material which contains agents such as oxidizing enzymes. Other viruses, such as tobacco mosaic virus, the Shope papilloma virus, and certain bacteriophages, require temperatures above 65°C. for inactivation. Of this group the tobacco mosaic virus seems to be the most thermostable, since the crude infectious juice requires a temperature of 94°C. for 5 minutes and the purified material the same period at 75°C. before being completely inactivated. The viruses of vaccinia, poliomyelitis, dog distemper, foot-and-mouth disease, and the neurotropic strain of horse sickness have all been inactivated on heating at about 60°C. for 30 minutes. Less stable are the viruses of fowl pox and yellow fever, which are destroyed in 30 minutes at a temperature of approximately 55°C. [Stanley (1938)]. High temperatures are destructive to most enzymes. This subject is discussed in greater detail on pp. 460 to 461. Bacterial toxins in general are also destroyed by heat, although they show a wide variation in their thermostability, and some are even peculiarly sensitive to heat. In regard to this supersensitivity to heat Smith (1941) has shown in an experiment that one of the staphylococcus toxins is more sensitive to 60°C. than to 80°C., even though the exposure time was the same in both cases.

METHODS FOR STERILIZATION BY HEAT

The methods for the complete destruction of bacteria by heat are usually discussed at some length in a beginning course in bacteriology, and for that reason only a brief review will be given here. The effects of incineration of animal carcasses, garbage, and other materials, as well as the flaming of inoculating needles and small objects in the laboratory, are well known and need no comment. Sterilization by heat can best be discussed and reviewed under the headings *dry heat* and *moist heat*.

Dry Heat. The first studies concerned with sterilization by dry heat, using a hot-air oven, were carried out by Robert Koch and his associates as early as 1881 to 1882. They came to the conclusion that, unless the exposure was for a considerable period of time, dry heat was not an efficient method of sterilization, especially when bacteria may be protected by some relatively nonconducting material. This fact is due, of course, to the very slow rate of penetration of dry heat. For example, when a bundle of linen measuring 50 by 55 cm. is exposed to dry heat for 3 hours at a temperature of 140° to 150°C., the center will be only about 75°C., a temperature and time interval far too low to kill most bacterial spores. Oag (1940) has studied the effect of dry heat on the spores of *Bacillus anthracis*, *Clostridium perfringens*, and several other spore-forming bacilli. At 400°C. the spores were killed in 20 to 30 seconds, whereas 1 hour was necessary at 120°C. There is apparently an abrupt change in the resistance of spores at 160°C., since they are killed much more rapidly just above this temperature than just below it.

Dry heat is used in laboratories for the sterilization of glassware and other articles which are not injured by high temperatures or which moisture may affect in some way. To insure absolute sterilization of objects in a hot-air oven, the internal temperature should be kept at 160° to 180°C. for 1 hour or longer. When processing glassware plugged with cotton or wrapped in paper, it should be remembered that these materials scorch at a temperature of about 190°C. in a short time.

Moist Heat. The presence of moisture allows sterilization to be accomplished much more easily and at lower temperatures than does dry heat. Moist heat may be applied with boiling water or steam, in which cases the temperature will vary little from 100°C. Live flowing steam, without pressure, may be used where the temperature remains more or less constant at 100°C., but prolonged exposure is required to assure the destruction of resistant spores. A higher efficiency is attained by the use of steam under pressure; then temperatures far exceeding 100°C. may be produced. Some of the temperatures attained at sea level by the application of pure steam under pressure are as follows:

Steam Pressure, gauge	Temperature °C.	°F.
0	100.0	212.0
5	109.0	228.2
10	115.5	239.9
12	118.0	244.4
15	121.5	250.7
18	124.3	255.7
20	126.5	259.7
30	134.6	274.8
40	141.5	286.7

Exposure to steam under 15 to 17 lb. of pressure, providing the temperature is 121° to 123°C., for 15 to 20 minutes is sufficient for the sterilization of most bacteriological media. Sometimes, however, certain materials require a higher temperature and pressure and a longer period of exposure to insure the proper margin of safety. Thus Underwood (1941), using the recommended temperature and pressure, suggests the following times for these materials:

	Minutes
Unwrapped instruments or utensils in trays	10
Instruments or utensils wrapped in muslin	15
Rubber gloves in muslin packs	15
Flasks of solution, never more than two-thirds filled	
One-liter flasks	15
Two- or three-liter flasks	20
Dressings wrapped in thick muslin or drums properly packed	30
Mattresses lying flat or on edge	30

When the autoclave is used, attention must be given to certain technical details to insure complete sterilization and best results. Packages should not be too large nor packed too tightly in the sterilizer. At least a 2-in. air space should be left behind the door when it is closed, and under no circumstances should dressings rest against the door. The reason is that the door remains cooler than the chamber during the sterilization process, so that steam condenses on its surface, and this condensate will wet the dressings if they are touching the door. After the period of exposure the outlet and inlet valves must be closed so that the sterilizer can cool off slowly, otherwise a sudden change in pressure within the chamber may destroy the material being autoclaved.

The most important precaution to be taken in using the autoclave is to permit all air to escape from the apparatus before the vent is closed. If this is not done, air pockets will be left about the objects to be sterilized, and they will not be heated to the temperature indicated by the pressure. Wyatt (1936) and Underwood (1941) discussed at some length the effect of air in the sterilizer on the final temperatures obtainable. Underwood showed that, if steam is applied at 15 lb. of pressure to a completely evacuated sterilizer, a temperature of 250°F.

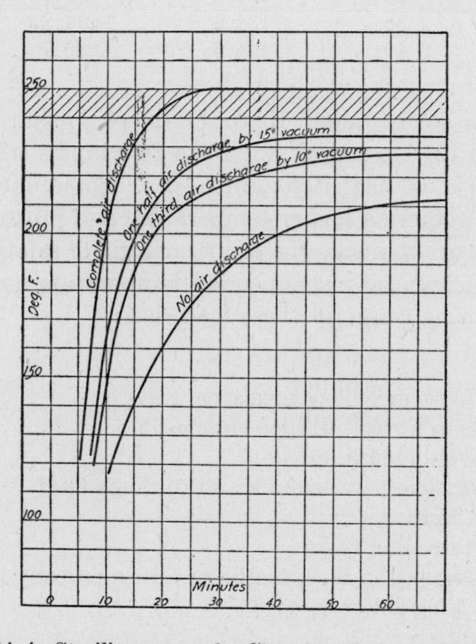

Fig. 5. Effect of Air in Sterilizer upon the Chamber Temperature. (From Underwood, 1941.)

(121°C.) is promptly attained. Evacuating one-half of the air before applying steam gives a final temperature of 234°F. (112°C.); removal of one-third of the air allows a maximum of 228°F. (109°C.); and, when none of the air is removed, the ultimate temperature, with 15 lb. of steam pressure, is only 212°F. (100°C.). Figure 5 is a graph of these values.

PASTEURIZATION

This process was first developed by Louis Pasteur to prevent certain abnormalities in wine, but it now finds its widest application in the dairy industry. The advantages of properly pasteurized milk are a reduction in the spread of pathogenic organisms and an improvement in the keeping qualities of the product. Milk products may not be sterile after treatment by this process, but all the pathogenic organisms should be destroyed and the other forms greatly reduced in number.

Two main types of pasteurization are now generally used in the dairy industry. The *holding method* consists of heating to a comparatively low temperature for a considerable period of time. Usually the exposure for market milk is 61.1°C. (142°F.) to 62.8°C. (145°F.) for 30 minutes.

Sometimes slightly higher temperatures are used for market cream. The *flash* or *short-time holding method* consists of heating to a comparatively high temperature for a short period of time. The minimum exposure accepted for milk is 71.1°C. (160°F.) for 15 seconds, but 71.7°C. (161°F.) for 16 seconds is used quite commonly. Ball (1943) has discussed in some detail the problems involved in the pasteurization of milk, and his paper should be consulted by those interested in this subject. Lower temperatures are usually used for pasteurizing wines and fruit juices to prevent injury to the product.

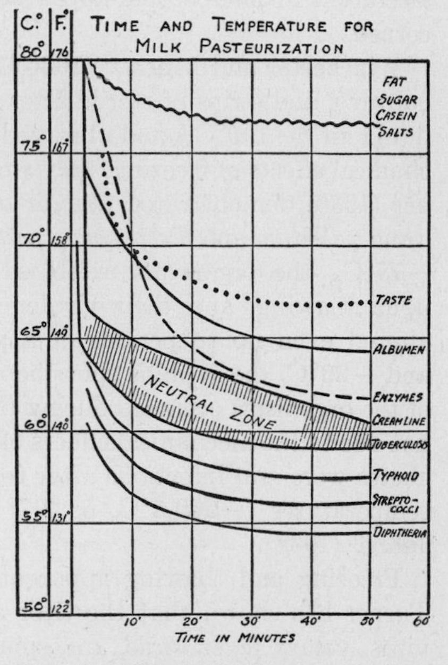

FIG. 6. Time and Temperature for Milk Pasteurization. (From North and Park, 1927.)

The time and temperature used in the pasteurization of milk are based on the heat resistance of *Mycobacterium tuberculosis*. The other pathogenic organisms often present in milk, such as typhoid, diphtheria, and brucella bacilli, are destroyed at lower temperatures, as is shown in Fig. 6 from the paper by North and Park (1927). Other methods of pasteurization have been proposed, but they have not been widely accepted. The technical details and types of apparatus used are readily available from other sources.

LOW TEMPERATURES (COLD)

In the past bacteriologists have given less attention to the effects of low temperatures on bacteria than to the action of high temperatures. This difference has probably been due to the general belief that cold is an excellent means of preventing putrefaction and decay and that frozen products are incapable of transmitting disease.

One of the early studies on this subject was made by MacFadyen (1900), who exposed cultures of ten species, including *Escherichia coli, Eberthella typhosa, Proteus vulgaris, Bacillus anthracis,* and *Staphylococcus aureus,* to liquid air (−190°C.) for a period of 7 days with no appreciable impairment of their vitality when subsequently cultured. At the same time MacFadyen and Rowland (1900) sealed organisms in glass tubes and subjected them to liquid hydrogen (−252°C. or 21° absolute) for 10 hours. The results were entirely negative as far as alteration in microscopic appearance or in vigor of growth was concerned.

Winchester and Murray (1936) immersed agar slant cultures, broth cultures, and strips of sterile filter paper impregnated with bacteria in liquid air (−190°C.) and observed that, when forms survived the mechanical effects of freezing, they were still viable after 19 months. Turner (1938) demonstrated that, if testicular extracts containing *Treponema pallidum* and *Treponema pertenue* were frozen and maintained at −78°C., the organisms exhibited normal morphology and motility upon thawing, and their virulence for rabbits was not appreciably altered even up to periods of a year. At temperatures of −10°C. and −20°C. the syphilis spirochete did not survive 2 months. Death of the organisms occurred during the maintenance period and thus was not due to the mechanical effects of freezing. Trypanosomes and spirochetes were still infectious after freezing 1 to 3 hours at liquid helium temperatures (−269.5°C. or 3.7° from absolute zero), according to Jahnel (1938).

Freezing and thawing apparently only slightly inactivate viruses. Turner has shown that the titer of preparations of human influenza virus, yellow fever virus, and spontaneous encephalomyelitis virus of mice was unchanged after the preparations had been maintained at −78°C. for 6 months. Similar results have been reported by other workers for the viruses of vaccinia, herpes, tobacco mosaic, foot-and-mouth disease, several bacteriophages, and complement.

With the rapid development of commercially frozen foods, especially vegetables, the effect of freezing on the spores and toxins of *Clostridium botulinum* assumes a greater significance. Studies indicate that spores of *Cl. botulinum* will survive freezing at −16°C. or lower for at least a year, and the toxins from this organism show little decrease in potency when held at −79°C. for 2 months or at −16°C. for 14 months. There is little danger from the consumption of frozen foods which are properly prepared. However, when certain of these foods are allowed to thaw and stand at room temperature, they should be consumed within a day. The entire subject of frozen foods has been reviewed extensively by

Wallace and Tanner (1933–1935), and McFarlane (1941) has studied the influence of sucrose and hydrogen-ion concentration on the destruction of microorganisms at subfreezing temperatures.

DESICCATION

The survival of microorganisms subjected to an environment of low moisture content depends on many variable factors, such as the particular species, the number of bacteria present, the rapidity of drying, the nature of the suspending medium, and the gaseous condition of the environment.

Some of the early bacteriologists reported that anthrax spores dried on silk threads were still alive after 20 years, and at the present time there is considerable controversy concerning the isolation of bacteria from coal, rock, adobe brick, and other materials which are relatively dry and supposedly centuries old [Burke and Wiley (1937)]. More recently a number of investigators [see Flosdorf and Mudd (1935, 1938), Swift (1937), Scherp and Hughes (1939), and Polding (1943)] have shown that many sensitive bacteria, viruses, enzymes, and other materials are able to withstand drying almost indefinitely, provided that desiccation is complete and that the preparation is maintained in a high vacuum (0.01 mm. mercury or less). Even the meningococcus is much more resistant to dehydration than is generally supposed. For example, Miller and Schad (1944) found that, when *Neisseria intracellularis* suspensions were dried on glass beads, pieces of wood, and cotton fabrics which were kept at room temperature in the dark and cultured each day, viable meningococci were recovered from the glass beads after 10 days and from wood and cotton cloth after 8 and 7 days, respectively. Survival was shortened at 37°C. and prolonged in the ice box (6° to 10°C.).

Although most workers have assumed that organisms in the desiccated state will remain viable for long periods of time, few or no quantitative data are available on environmental factors involved in the survival and death of organisms under such conditions. Heller (1941) has studied death rates of *Streptococcus pyogenes* and *Escherichia coli* in the desiccated state, and has observed that death proceeds logarithmically. The rate of death for both organisms varied with the nature of the environment in which they were dried. For example, the death rates were highest when the organisms were dried in a simple menstruum, such as distilled water, and lowest when the organisms were dried in the presence of mixtures of dissimilable crystalline substances, such as sucrose and other sugars or tryptophan, and hydrophilic colloids, such as peptones. Future studies on this subject will do much to explain the degree of activity of organisms in the desiccated state.

Desiccation is now being used extensively for the preservation of stock cultures of bacteria, viruses, normal and convalescent human sera, animal antisera, complement, enzymes, and other materials. In carrying out the procedure, 0.5 to 1.0 ml. or larger quantities of a concentrated suspension are distributed in suitable glass containers. The material is first frozen at −78°C. in a bath of solid carbon dioxide and alcohol. When the samples are frozen, the containers are attached to a specially designed apparatus which quickly and efficiently brings about the desired evacuation and desiccation. The term *cryochem-process* has been coined by Flosdorf and Mudd for this technique. After the material has been completely desiccated, the glass containers are sealed in a flame and are then ready for storage. Organisms and other bodies so dried and preserved are supposedly resistant to high temperatures. For example, typhoid bacilli are said to survive an exposure of 115°C. for over 30 minutes, and Remlinger and Bailly (1938) found that the equine encephalomyelitis virus stood 110° to 112°C. for 5 minutes before becoming inactivated. The literature pertaining to the preservation of bacterial cultures by desiccation has been reviewed by Morton and Pulaski (1938).

ELECTRICITY AND MAGNETISM

Two other physical agents which have received some attention in the field of bacteriology are electricity and magnetism. Bacteria are so small that it is difficult to determine any direct effect of electricity on the cells, but there is no reason to assume that they differ from other cellular material in response to an electrical current. So far experiments have been conducted by passing a current of electricity through media in which bacteria were growing or suspended. During such treatment heat and chemical changes are sometimes brought about, which may conceal any direct effect which the electricity has upon the bacteria.

LOW-FREQUENCY ELECTRIC CURRENTS

Many of the early experiments, using electricity of low frequency, were so poorly controlled that little or no attention will be given to them. In passing, though, the conclusions reached by Prochownick and Spaeth (1890) should be mentioned. After subjecting suspensions of *Bacillus subtilis*, *Bacillus anthracis*, and *Staphylococcus aureus* to a current of 60 to 230 ma. for various intervals of time, these investigators observed some lethal action. They concluded, however, that this action was not due to the electricity itself, but rather to chlorine which was evolved at the anode by the electrolytic dissociation of saline. This explanation seems to have some merit, since other workers have reported that the sterilizing action of a constant current is due to electrolysis, with the liberation of acids, alkalies, chlorine, and ozone at the positive pole.

More recently Tracy (1932) has studied the action of alternating current of 60 cycles on yeast cells. Suspensions of *Saccharomyces ellipsoideus* were placed in a small glass chamber fitted with hard carbon and graphite electrodes. The voltage and amperage were varied for experimental purposes by means of rheostats. Table 14 shows a comparison of percentage kills by equal quantities of electricity applied at different amperages. Thus, by passing alternating current through yeast cell suspensions at nonlethal temperatures, pronounced killing effects were obtained, indicating that alternating current of 60 cycles has some destructive action independent of temperature. An increase in the current density or amperage (see the last column in Table 14) was accompanied by an increase in the percentage of yeast cells killed. Tracy has suggested the possibility that the killing effect was due to the formation of temporary toxic substances, such as free chlorine, which were immediately reduced upon cessation of the current.

TABLE 14

Comparison of Percentage Kills by Equal Quantities of Electricity Applied at Different Amperages

[From Tracy (1932)]

Test	Amperes	Volts	Temperature, °C.	Time, minutes	Cells per Milliliter *Before Treatment*	Cells per Milliliter *After Treatment*	Per Cent Killed	Quality of Electricity, coulombs	Current Density per Square Centimeter, amperes
A	0.31	20	35	5	255,000	143,000	44.0	93	0.063
B	0.31	20	37	5	420,000	200,000	52.5	93	0.063
C	0.35	22	44	5	2,350,000	452,000	80.7	105	0.071
D	0.35	27	42	5	1,830,000	673,000	63.4	105	0.071
E	0.35	22	44	5	1,650,000	420,000	74.6	105	0.071
F *	0.10	20–22	43–44	15	480,000	462	99.7	90	0.140

* In F is given the average of four tests at 0.1 ampere and 15 minutes.

HIGH-FREQUENCY ELECTRIC CURRENTS

By making use of vacuum-tube oscillators, high-frequency electromagnetic and electrostatic fields can be produced. The range is probably unlimited, but because of certain technical difficulties wavelengths outside approximately 2 to 30 meters are not generally available for biological work.

In many of the early investigations in which high-frequency electric currents were used the temperature was not controlled; as a result a difference of opinion arose as to whether the biologic effects observed were due to the action of the current which produced disturbances in the chemical equilibrium in the cell or to the action of the heat induced by the current. More recently a number of investigators have carefully controlled the temperature during the exposure period, so that this factor can probably be disregarded in considering their results. Szymanowski and Hicks (1932), Hicks and Szymanowski (1932), Fabian and Graham (1933), Hasché and Loch (1937), and Schenck (1938) have studied the effect of high-frequency radiation on bacteria, toxins, antibodies, and bacteriophage and its use in the treatment of certain diseases and tumors. It is difficult to compare the data, because different exposures were used by the various workers and all of them did not study the same materials. Fabian and Graham reported that in a high-frequency displacement current of 10 megacycles (corresponding to a wavelength of approximately 30 meters per second and an intensity of 0.08 ampere) *Escherichia coli* continued to multiply at a normal rate. However, when the current was increased tenfold to 0.8 ampere, the lethal action of the current became evident. In fact, when the logarithms of the numbers of survivors were plotted against time, a typical straight-line survivor curve resulted, indicating a regular order of death. Frequencies of 7.5 and 15 megacycles were less effective as far as killing action on bacteria was concerned. These results are typical of those reported by other workers.

The use of electricity to pasteurize milk and to sterilize water has been proposed, but because of the expense and certain technical difficulties the procedure has not been able to compete with the other established methods of treatment.

MAGNETISM

When suspensions or plate cultures of bacteria are subjected to magnetic forces, little, if any, appreciable effect is observed. Leusden (1929) found magnetic forces to have no inhibitory action on *Escherichia coli* or *Staphylococcus aureus;* and Jennison (1937) detected no change in morphology, size of colonies, pigment, or spore production when he exposed 25 species of bacteria, yeasts, and molds to an electromagnet with an intensity of approximately 3,000 gauss [1] for 48

[1] A gauss is the unit of magnetic force or intensity which exists at unit distance from a unit pole. It is derived from the absolute system of measurements.

hours at about 25°C. On the other hand, Kimball (1938) reported that the heterogeneous field of a small horseshoe magnet distinctly retarded the budding of yeast cells, and Lenzi (1940) has reported that electromagnetic fields of from 1,500 to 1,700 gauss may affect biological (tumors, *Pseudomonas aeruginosa,* and *Saccharomyces cerevisiae*) and colloidal systems if the exposure is for long periods of time.

PRESSURE

The action of pressure on bacteria and related bodies will be briefly discussed under the headings *mechanical pressure, osmotic pressure,* and *gaseous pressure.* All these can probably be regarded as physical forces, but, since osmotic pressure is so closely related to the cell membrane and is controlled to such a large extent by various chemical agents, some mention will be made of it in other places. Comparatively little is known about the influence of pressure on bacterial processes, although the subject has interested bacteriologists for a number of years and many reports have been published.

MECHANICAL PRESSURE

The mechanical pressures employed by workers before 1900 were so low that they could hardly be expected to have any great effect upon bacteria. An example is shown in the work of Certes (1884), who reported that a pressure of 600 atmospheres (atm.) (approximately 9,000 lb.) for 24 hours had no influence on the pathogenicity of *Bacillus anthracis.* Just after the turn of the century, however, Chlopin and Tammann (1903) were able to employ pressures sufficiently great to note definite influences on bacteria, yeasts, and molds. The maximum pressure used by these workers was approximately 3,000 kg./cm.^{2} [1 kg./cm.^{2} or 14.7 lb./in.^{2} is approximately 1 atm., and 1 lb./in.^{2} may be considered 0.07 kg./cm.^{2} or 0.068 atm.]. None of the organisms employed was killed, but various restrictions were observed, including (1) a partial loss of motility, (2) a decrease in the ability to multiply, (3) various changes in metabolism and pigmentation, and (4) a decrease in virulence. *Vibrio comma* and *Pseudomonas aeruginosa* were the most sensitive to pressure, whereas *B. anthracis* and yeast were found to be particularly resistant.

This work was greatly extended by Hite, Giddings, and Weakley (1914), who applied maximum pressures of approximately 120,000 lb./in.^{2} to a number of bacteria. For cultures of *Serratia marcescens, Aerobacter aerogenes,* and *Streptococcus lactis* the pressure death point was found to be as follows: for an exposure of about 4 to 5 minutes, pressures between 85,000 and 100,000 lb./in.^{2} were required; for a 10-minute exposure, 50,000 to 65,000 lb./in.^{2}; and for an exposure of 1 hour, between 30,000 and 45,000 lb./in.^{2}. *Eberthella typhosa* and *Corynebacterium diphtheriae* were most sensitive to high pressures, being killed by 40,000 to 45,000 lb. The pressure death point of a yeast, *Saccharomyces cerevisiae*, was found to be 85,000 lb./in.^{2} for a 5-minute exposure and 30,000 to 35,000 lb. for 1 hour's exposure. Still higher pressures were used by Larson, Hartzell, and Diehl (1918). Maximum pressures of 12,000 atm. (approximately 175,000 lb./in.^{2}) were reached. *Escherichia coli*, *Proteus vulgaris*, *Eberthella typhosa*, *Bacillus subtilis*, staphylococci, streptococci, and pneumococci were subjected to such pressures with the hope of extracting the antigenic principle from bacteria and thus making better antigens for use in vaccine therapy. It was found that a direct pressure of 6,000 atm. killed the non-spore-forming bacteria in 14 hours but that about twice this pressure for the same time was required to kill spores.

More recently in France Basset, Macheboeuf, and Wollman (1937) employed hydrostatic pressures up to 20,000 atm. (294,000 lb.) in studying their effect on bacteria, viruses, toxins, malignant tumors, and enzymes. Nonsporulating bacteria, such as *Escherichia coli*, *Eberthella typhosa*, pneumococci, and staphylococci, resisted pressures up to 5,000 atm. for 45 minutes but failed to survive when 6,000 atm. was applied for the same time. The sporulating bacteria (*Bacillus subtilis*, *Bacillus megatherium*, and *Clostridium tetani*), on the other hand, survived compression at much higher pressures; in fact, *B. subtilis* spores were not destroyed after 45 minutes at 20,000 atm. The diastases were not completely inactivated until pressures of 12,000 to 13,000 atm. were reached; pancreatic lipase was destroyed at 11,000 atm., but trypsin was not completely inactivated even when compressed at 17,000 atm. The bacterial toxins (diphtheria and tetanus) were attenuated in the range 12,000 to 15,000 atm. and were completely inactivated at 16,000 to 18,000 atm. Several viruses, including those of vaccinia, herpes, rabies, and encephalomyelitis, were studied. For the most part they resisted 1,000 to 2,000 atm. but were generally inactivated by pressure just below 5,000 atm. The encephalomeylitis virus was the most resistant of all, being able to stand compressions of 6,500 atm. Four bacteriophages, a Rous sarcoma filtrate, and a transplantable mouse tumor were all inactivated in the same range as the viruses. Matthews, Dow, and Anderson (1940) found that pressures ranging between 5,000 and 6,000 kg./cm.^{2} completely destroyed the activity of pepsin and rennin. Lauffer and Dow (1941) have observed that the tobacco mosaic virus nucleoprotein is almost completely inactivated in a few minutes at a pressure of about 7,500 kg./cm.^{2}.

Very little is known concerning the mechanics involved in the inactivation of enzymes, viruses, bacteria, and related bodies by high pressures. As brought out by Cattell (1936), the pressures required to destroy some of these substances are very nearly the pressure necessary to produce the first perceptible clouding of pure protein solutions. Since the clouding of protein solutions under pressure is in the nature of an irreversible denaturization, it is possible, even in the absence of any precise knowledge of the structure of bacteria and viruses, to suppose that this type of change plays a part in bringing about their inactivation. Other factors, however, are involved and Cattell believes that changes in function resulting from high pressure must find their final explanation in connection with the physical and chemical properties of liquids, such as, for example, changes in volume, rates of chemical reactions, viscosity, and ionic dissociation. Volume changes seem to be of great significance, since pure water under a pressure of 12,000 atm. at room temperature will show a reduction of almost 20 per cent in volume. The velocity of chemical reactions in the liquid phase is increased by a rise in pressure; in fact, Cattell refers to data which show five- to tenfold increases for a number of organic reactions when subjected to 3,000 atm. Viscosity changes seem to be of the greatest magnitude, since reports indicate that a pressure of 12,000 kg./cm.^{2} may increase the viscosity of certain chemicals many hundred times. On the other hand, water shows a decrease in viscosity when compressed. Pressure, in general, increases the dissociation of electrolytes in a weak solution.

Here again, as with other physical agents, no one factor explains the behavior of protoplasm when subjected to mechanical pressure.

OSMOTIC PRESSURE

In this brief treatment of osmotic pressure and its relation to bacterial processes, only some of the more general effects of the changes in substrate will be discussed. The phenomenon is truly a physical influence, but it is so intimately related to the cell itself and to certain chemical factors that it would be difficult to discuss the subject in full without becoming involved in the action of chemical agents on bacteria and the role played by the semipermeable membrane of the cell. Therefore further mention of osmotic pressure is made elsewhere, especially in Chapter 1, Some Physico-Chemical Properties of Bacteria and Their Environment.

It is a well-known fact that, when two solutions of the same substance, but in different concentrations, are mixed, diffusion will take place. The *solute*, as well as the *solvent*, will tend to diffuse from the region of high concentration to one of less concentration. If these same two solutions are separated by a semipermeable membrane, which will allow the solvent to diffuse but not the solute, a pressure will be exerted on the membrane. The pressure which will produce a condition of equilibrium in this system or will prevent the solvent from flowing in either direction is spoken of as *osmotic pressure.* Osmotic pressure is usually expressed in atmospheres. A number of factors influence this phenomenon, such as the extent of dissociation of the solute, the rates of diffusion of the various substances in solution, and their molecular weights. These topics will not be discussed here because they become too involved and because they are readily available in the literature.

The membrane surrounding bacterial cells and spores is a differential membrane of some type and can thus be placed in the category of semipermeable membranes. This membrane allows water and certain inorganic and organic substances in solution to pass, while other materials are held back. How this permeability is brought about and controlled is not known. In so far as the cell is concerned, three different substrates are possible. Those solutions which are supposedly in osmotic equilibrium with the cellular protoplasm are spoken of as *isotonic solutions.* Solutions having less osmotic pressure than that of the cellular protoplasm are said to be *hypotonic solutions*, and those solutions having a greater osmotic pressure than the cell are known as *hypertonic solutions.* It can be readily seen that, when cells are placed in a hypotonic solution, the water (solvent) will pass into the cell in an effort to bring the system into equilibrium. The cellular protoplasm swells and, if the internal pressure becomes great enough, the cell membrane bursts. This is called *plasmoptysis.* Actually, it is doubtful whether bacteria are ever destroyed by this process in nature. On the other hand, when cells are placed in hypertonic solutions, the water in the cell passes into the surrounding medium, the cell contents shrink, and the cell loses turgor. This is spoken of as *plasmolysis.*

The preservation of many foods by salt and sugar is probably due to the plasmolytic changes which they exert on bacteria. It must be kept in mind, though, that several bacteria can grow in solutions having extremely high osmotic pressures. For example, Stuart, Frey, and James (1933) reported several instances where organisms could be cultivated in media containing 30 per cent sodium chloride. The upper limit of osmotic pressure of liquid media for the germination of spores of *Bacillus mycoides* is in the range of 36 to 46 atm., according to Curran (1931), but the optimum tension for germination is much lower than this range. Usually values below 7 atm. give the best results when the nutritional conditions are at an optimum. The osmotic tension necessary for spore germination is generally lower than that required for maximum vegetative development. Osmotic pressure also has an influence on bacterial luminescence [Schoepfle (1941)].

GASEOUS PRESSURE

Considerable work has been done on the optimum gaseous tension of media in relation to food supply, optimum growth, anaerobic conditions, and effects on the morphology and physiology of the cell. These topics are discussed on pp. 108 and 630 to 635. Little work has been done on the influence of gases under high pressure on bacterial processes.

Some interesting bacteriological data were obtained by Larson, Hartzell, and Diehl (1918), using gases such as carbon dioxide, hydrogen, and nitrogen under pressure. Their results may be briefly summarized as typical findings. The nonsporulating bacteria studied were killed by carbon dioxide of 50-atm. pressure in about $1\frac{1}{2}$ hours, whereas yeast cells withstood the same action for more than 24 hours. They concluded that the lethal action of this gas was not due to changes in *p*H, but rather to sudden changes in the osmotic tension of the fluid in which the bacteria were suspended. Many Gram-negative bacteria could be broken up by the sudden release of the carbon dioxide, whereas the Gram-positive bacteria suffered little or no morphologic change, even though they were killed. A 120-atm. pressure of hydrogen killed 10 to 40 per cent of the cells in a suspension of *Escherichia coli* after 24 hours. The most marked effect of hydrogen gas on bacteria was its tendency to affect their staining reaction. Gram-positive bacteria often became Gram-negative, and even the acid-fast property of the tubercle bacillus was impaired. The pathogenicity of the pneumococcus for white mice was unaltered by treatment with hydrogen gas under pressure. Bacteria were not killed, nor did they show any morphologic change when they were subjected to nitrogen gas under a pressure of 120 atm. All their experiments showed this gas to be inert in its action.

SURFACE TENSION

Surface tension is another physical force which has received considerable attention from the bacteriologist. Cell division and growth, pellicle formation, protoplasmic streaming, and permeability changes have been, at one time or another, regarded as purely surface-tension phenomena. It would be quite extraordinary if surface tension did not play a part in some of these processes. Just how far the laws of physical chemistry can be applied to protoplasm, a system which undoubtedly includes infinitely more variables than the systems for which the laws were proposed, however, is a problem which requires careful consideration by all biologists. Let us explain further by digressing a little to mention the simple law of diffusion.

This law states, in part, that the rate of diffusion of a pure solute in a pure solvent is inversely proportional to the molecular size of the solute. This is not always the case in protoplasm, where salts often enter the cell more slowly than do certain large organic molecules. Many of the fundamental physical laws can be applied with great success to biological problems, but they do not explain the behavior of protoplasm. Surface-tension measurements are no exception. Such applications are interesting and instructive but, for the most part, highly speculative.

Surface tension may be defined simply as a force per unit length tangential to the surface of a liquid at a constant temperature and is expressed in dynes per centimeter [Antonoff (1943)], or it is the force necessary to overcome the tendency of the liquid to maintain a minimum surface area. To measure the force of surface tension several procedures have been proposed. The one used most commonly employs a Du Noüy "tensiometer," which is calibrated to give readings directly in dynes per centimeter.

The foregoing definition refers to the tension exerted by a liquid against air and does not apply to the tension of a bacterium against its medium, which is called *interfacial tension.* The assumption that substances which alter surface tension will exhibit a like change on the interfacial tension lacks proof, since there is no satisfactory method of measuring the interfacial tension between a bacterium and its substrate. Therefore the use of the term surface tension in physico-biological reasoning must be accepted with some reservations, especially in reference to the bacterium-medium relationship. This statement does not imply that surface tension *per se* and its indirect effects, whatever they may be, are not important in bacteriology. It has been shown, for example, that those organisms which normally form a pellicle on liquid media of high surface tension may form no pellicle at all if the tension is lowered below a certain point. Other processes can also be associated with surface-tension values. Distilled water has a surface tension of 74.9 dynes per centimeter at 5°C., 72.8 dynes at 20°C., 70 dynes at 40°C., and 61.5 dynes at 100°C. Ordinary nutrient broth gives readings between 57 and 60 dynes per centimeter, and certain inorganic media may give values as high as 73 dynes per centimeter. Many organic acids and alcohols, soaps, saponins, and other substances have the property of markedly lowering the surface tension of liquids such as culture media, whereas some of the inorganic salts may bring about a slight increase in the surface tension of media. When employing these chemicals to bring about changes in tension, the investigator must be certain that they are not directly the cause of the alteration in the bacterial processes under investigation rather than the surface tension.

Some of the bacterial functions influenced by, or associated with, surface tension are rather interesting, and several of the published reports may be briefly mentioned. For a review of the subject up to 1932 the paper by Lasseur, Vernier, Dupaix, and Georges (1932) should be consulted. Larson, Cantwell, and Hartzell (1919) and Larson (1921) were undoubtedly the first to make a direct study of the effect of lowered surface tension on the growth of bacteria. *Bacillus subtilis* did not form a pellicle in media whose surface tension was reduced to 45 dynes, but grew in the body of the medium. The growth of pneumococci and streptococci was depressed at a surface tension below 50 dynes per centimeter. Certain intestinal bacteria, however, grew well in media of low surface tension. Kopeloff and Beerman (1927) found that, on the average, strains of *Lactobacillus acidophilus* were able to grow at a surface tension of 3 or more dynes below that of the *Lactobacillus bulgaricus* strains employed when sodium ricinoleate was used as the depressant. The average critical point of *L. acidophilus* was 37.9 dynes, whereas the critical point for *L. bulgaricus* strains was 5.2 dynes higher, or 43.1 dynes. Curran (1931) observed that a reduction of the surface tension of the media from 50 to 35.1 dynes had no appreciable effect upon the rate of germination of *Bacillus mycoides* spores. Below 32.8 dynes there was a marked decrease in both the rate and total germination of spores. Thus, it was concluded that surface tension is not a significant factor in the germination of bacterial spores under ordinary environmental conditions. According to Lasseur, Vernier, Dupaix, and Georges (1932), various species of bacteria react differently towards the same surface-tension depressant. *Bacillus subtilis*, *Bacillus mesentericus*, and *Bacillus megatherium* were found to be especially sensitive to the action of sodium glycocholate and sodium taurocholate and failed to develop at all if the tension was reduced from 54.5 dynes per centimeter to 37.2 to 37.5 dynes per centimeter.

SOUND WAVES (SONIC AND ULTRASONIC VIBRATIONS)

Some of the biological effects of sound waves were clearly demonstrated by Wood and Loomis in 1927. Since that time the action of such vibrations at different intensities on biological systems has received considerable attention from biologists working in many fields.

Sound has been defined as a disturbance of such a nature that, when it falls upon the ear, it is capable of exciting the auditory nerve. This definition, of course, applies only to vibrations within the audible range. A sound having a frequency of less than 32 or more than 32,000 vibrations per second is generally inaudible to the average human ear. However, a sharp line cannot be drawn between the audible and inaudible regions. Ultrasonics include any sounds above the audible range, but, since this is indefinite, any frequency above about 10,000 vibrations per second is usually considered to be in the ultrasonic range.

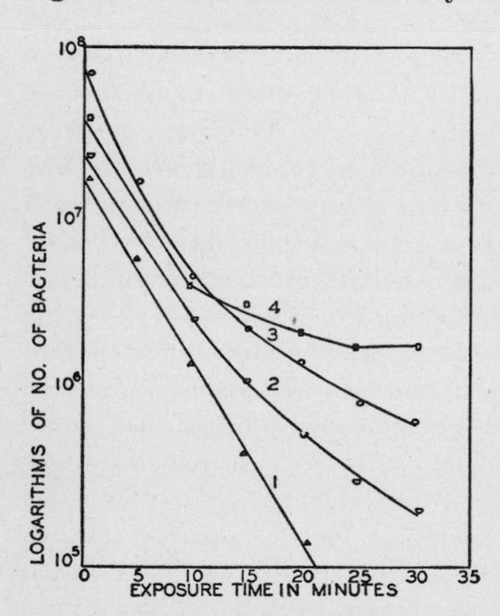

Fig. 7. Survivor-Time Curves of *Escherichia coli* Cultures of Different Ages. (1) 12-hour culture; (2) 5-day culture; (3) 8-day culture; (4) 14-day culture. (From Chambers and Gaines, 1932.)

Chambers and Gaines (1932) studied the effect of sound waves of an audible frequency (8,900 cycles per second), but of very great intensity, on several biological processes. The sonic waves were produced by a cold-drawn nickel tube vibrating in a strong electromagnetic field in resonance with a high-volt oscillating power circuit. The vibrating element was submerged in a water jacket during the operation. This was found necessary, for, if no liquid damper was provided, the vibrations were so intense as to overcome the tensile strength of the nickel tube. Materials to be treated were placed in tubes or flasks and were held about 2 mm. above the end of the vibrator. Isotonic suspensions of red blood cells were lysed completely after about 10 minutes' treatment. The leucocytes present in the suspension had their cytoplasm stripped away, but the nuclei apparently remained uninjured. The rate of death of a 12-hour culture of *Escherichia coli* was found to follow the logarithmic law of death. Quite different results were obtained, however, when old (5- to 14-day) cultures were subjected to the same exposure. During the first few minutes the rate of destruction paralleled that in a young culture, but after about 5 to 10 minutes the rate began to lessen, and the logarithmic curves tended to level off asymptotically (Fig. 7). This change was possibly due to the fact that in the old cultures there were present more resistant forms. Increased resistance has been held accountable for similar results when heat, chemicals, and other bactericidal agents have been used.

Chambers, Flosdorf, Mudd, and their coworkers [see Flosdorf, Kimball, and Chambers (1939)] at the University of Pennsylvania have employed sonic vibrations of a frequency of approximately 8,900 cycles per second to rupture bacterial cells and liberate certain antigenic substances which are normally very labile. LeGalley and Patterson (1940) have also used sound waves of the same frequency in an attempt to sterilize bacterial cultures. They concluded that the method was of little practical value for vaccines, since the investigator could not be certain of sterility.

Rivers, Smadel, and Chambers (1937) partially inactivated the elementary bodies of vaccinia virus in 15 minutes by sonic vibrations with a frequency of about 8,900 cycles per second. The elementary bodies were not disrupted by such treatment, and these workers suggested that oxidation may play some role in the inactivation of the virus particles. Hopwood, Salaman, and McFarlane (1939) irradiated vaccinia virus at 550 kilocycles per second in a thin-walled glass tube containing phosphate buffer. Three successive exposures lasting $1\frac{1}{2}$ minutes were given. Intracutaneous inoculations in the rabbit showed no significant difference between the titers of the original undried virus and that treated with ultrasonic vibrations. The microscopic appearance, the sedimentation rate, and the boundary homogenicity were also unaffected by the ultrasonic treatment. From these findings it seems that further work is necessary before any definite conclusions can be drawn concerning the effect of sonic or ultrasonic vibrations on vaccinia virus.

Ultrasonic waves from 100,000 to 2,250,000 cycles per second are produced as a result of certain crystals, such as quartz, expanding and contracting under the influence of a periodic electric field. This phenomenon is known as the piezo-electric effect or property of crystals. Païc and his coworkers (1935) observed that crystals vibrating at 280,000 cycles per second had no destructive action after 2 hours on diphtheria and tetanus toxin, a *coli* bacteriophage, the herpes virus, complement, or a number of different microorganisms. On the other hand, the work of Takahashi and Christensen (1934), Yen and Liu (1934), Beckwith and Weaver (1936), and Kasahara, Sha-Shi-Nan, and Kakusui (1939) demonstrates that yeast, bacteria, toxins, viruses, and other substances may be destroyed by such waves. Although it has been reported that bacteriophage is unharmed by supersonic waves, recent studies by Krueger, Brown, and Scribner (1941) indicate that staphylococcus phage is inactivated in a logarithmic manner by sonic vibrations of a frequency of 9,000 cycles per second.

The mechanism involved in the destruction of living cells and other bodies by sound waves is not known. It seems that some cells are literally torn apart, while in others inactivation results without visible injury to the cells. Possibly the inactivation is due to "intra- or extracellular ebullition of dissolved gases," or to oxidative changes. It has been demonstrated several times, however, that, when red blood cells or bacteria are placed in a vacuum and then exposed to such vibrations, they are not destroyed.

Sound waves also produce many interesting changes in nonliving colloidal systems. According to Sollner (1944), for example, they cause, on the one hand, disruptive and destructive phenomena such as peptization, dispersion of certain solids in liquids, and formation of fogs; whereas, on the other hand, they bring about orientation, aggregation, and coagulation in some liquid and gaseous colloidal and semicolloidal systems.

FILTRATION

The separation of bacteria from liquids by mechanical means apparently dates back to 1871, when Tiegel, with the aid of a Bunsen air pump, passed anthrax fluids through a crude filter made of porous unburnt clay. In 1884 Chamberland employed cylinders composed of unglazed porcelain for filtration experiments, and later, in 1891, filters of infusorial earth or kieselguhr were made by Nordtmeyer and named Berkefeld filters in honor of the owner of the mines from which the infusorial earth was first obtained. Since that time several other filters have been developed for bacteriological and virus work. The application of the principles of filtration to water and sewage purification and to the removal of bacteria from the air will not be discussed here, since they are treated in detail in other courses.

Filtration methods are used for three main purposes in the bacteriological laboratory: (1) *to clarify media* by removing the gross particles; (2) *to remove bacteria from fluids,* while allowing toxins, viruses, etc., to pass into the filtrate; (3) *to separate selectively bacteria from viruses or one virus from another*—a technique known as *ultrafiltration.* Usually the first procedure is carried out by merely passing the material to be filtered through a glass funnel fitted with filter paper, cotton, or glass wool. The second procedure is generally referred to as *bacterial filtration* and consists of aspirating the material through special filters into sterile glass containers. Several of the filters which can be used are:

1. Diatomaceous earth (kieselguhr) filters. The Berkefeld filters and the Mandler filters belong to this group. Both are widely used in bacteriological laboratories and are manufactured in several different sizes and grades. They are shaped like a hollow candle, closed at one end and usually fitted with a metal collar and nozzle at the other end. Their main disadvantage is the danger of a leak developing at the cemented metal-filter junction. *Berkefeld filters* are molded from a mixture of sifted kieselguhr, organic matter, and asbestos. Three grades, V (coarse), N (normal), and W (dense), are available, the classification being based on the rate at which pure water passes through them under a certain pressure. The Berkefeld V filter is usually employed to remove coarse particles from suspension, since its pores are too large for it to serve efficiently as a bacterial filter. The N grade is the one most commonly used to obtain a bacteria-free filtrate. W-grade Berkefelds are also very efficient, but because of the small diameter of their pores the rate of filtration is very slow. The mean pore diameter of these filters is listed in Table 15.

Mandler filters are similar in appearance, function, and operation to Berkefeld filters. They differ only slightly in composition, being composed of kieselguhr (60 to 80 per cent), asbestos (10 to 30 per cent), and plaster of Paris (10 to 15 per cent). By a slight variation in the proportion of these substances three porosities, based on the air pressure they stand in water, are obtained: Preliminary, 2 to 5 lb.; Regular, 6 to 9 lb.; and Fine, 10 to 16 lb. per sq. in.

2. Porcelain filters. The so-called porcelain filters are usually shaped like a hollow candle and closed at the lower end. The lower portion is unglazed and is the section of the filter concerned with filtration. The upper portion is of glazed porcelain. They are molded from kaolin and mixtures of silica, allowed to dry, and then hardened by heating to a temperature just below the sintering point. The best known of this group is the Chamberland-Pasteur type. Similar ones, known as the Doulton, the Allen, the Maassen, and the Coors filters, are frequently used for certain work. The Chamberland-Pasteur types are available in several grades, depending upon their porosity. Those designated as Ll are the most porous and allow the passage of most bacteria. Under controlled conditions L3 filters will hold back all bacteria, and L5 some of the viruses. Chamberland filters of decreasing porosity are designated as L7, L9, L11, and L13. Porcelain water filters of this type are marked F and B and correspond to the L5 and L7 laboratory filters.

3. Plaster of Paris filters. Filter candles are sometimes made in the laboratory from a mixture of plaster of Paris. Such filters are known as Kramer filters. They differ from other bacterial filters in that they carry a positive electric charge.

4. Asbestos filters (*Seitz*). Specially molded asbestos discs which fit into a metal or glass container known as the Seitz filter are used a great deal. The asbestos discs are manufactured in various sizes and in two grades, K for clarifying media and EK for removing bacteria. The discs can be used only once, then they must be discarded.

5. Sintered (*fritted*) *glass filters*. Filters of this type now enjoy wide popularity in bacteriological work. They are made from Jena 20 glass which has been ground to very fine particles of uniform size, molded in the form of a small disc, and then heated to the sintering

TABLE 15

SOME OF THE COMMON FILTERS USED IN THE BACTERIOLOGY LABORATORY

Filter	Designation	Size	Approximate Mean Pore Diameter	Approximate Amount of Liquid Retained by Filter
Berkefeld	V	$2\frac{1}{2} \times \frac{5}{8}$ in.	8.0–12.0 μ	3.0–4.0 ml.
	N	$2\frac{1}{2} \times \frac{5}{8}$ in.	5.0–7.0 μ	3.5–4.0 ml.
	W	$2\frac{1}{2} \times \frac{5}{8}$ in.	3.0–4.0 μ	3.0–4.0 ml.
Mandler	Preliminary 4 lbs. (205 mm. Hg)	5×1 in.	9.0–9.5 μ	3.5–4.0 ml.
	Regular 6 lbs. (310 mm. Hg)	$2\frac{1}{2} \times \frac{5}{8}$ in.	6.8 μ	
	Regular 9 lbs. (465 mm. Hg)	$1\frac{3}{8} \times \frac{5}{8}$ in.	4.2 μ	
Chamberland	L3	155 × 15 mm.	2.5–2.7 μ	7.0–7.5 ml.
	L3	75 × 15 mm.	2.5–2.7 μ	3.0–4.0 ml.
	L5 (F)	75 × 15 mm.	1.5–1.7 μ	3.0–4.0 ml.
	L7 (B)	75 × 15 mm.	<1.3 μ	3.0–4.0 ml.
Sintered (fritted) glass	3G5 auf 3 Pyrex	30–50-ml. capacity	1.01–1.09 μ	0.4–0.5 ml.
Seitz filter discs	EK	60 mm.		5.0 ml.
		35 mm.		2.0 ml.
Ultrafilters	Collodion (Gradocol) membranes		Can be graded from 3.0 μ to 10.0 mμ	Insignificant

point without the addition of any other substance. The discs are then fused into glass vessels of the desired shape and capacity. Usually one relatively porous disc, of, say, porosity 3, is put in place, and then one that is less porous, perhaps of porosity 5, is superimposed on it. The first layer serves mainly as a support for the thinner, less porous disc. Such filters are now available in this country, being made of Pyrex by Corning [see Morton (1943)].

Morton's discussion (1938) of bacterial filters and filtration techniques is very comprehensive. Some of the data from his paper are incorporated in Table 15.

Because of several disadvantages inherent in the filters just mentioned, an entirely different type has been developed in an effort to reduce the technique of filtration to a process in which the size of the particle largely determines its passage through the filter. This technique is known as *ultrafiltration* and is especially applicable in the separation of one virus from another or the determination of the size of particles which are below the range of the ordinary microscope.

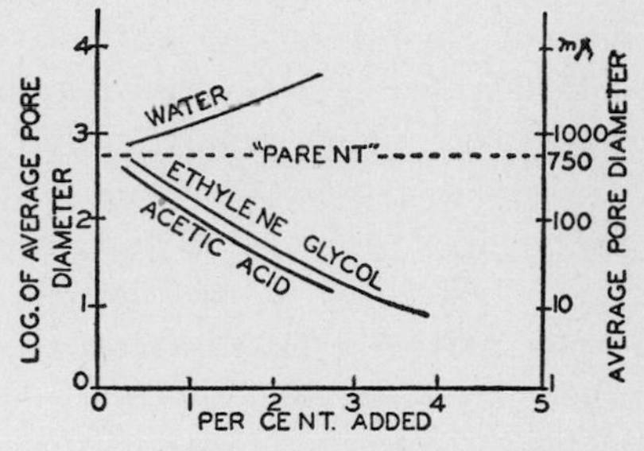

FIG. 8. Influence of the Addition of Solvent and Nonsolvent on the Membrane Porosity of the "Parent" Collodion. (From Elford, 1938.)

Many different jelly ultrafilters have been designed to separate colloids from one another, from their solvents, and from dissolved crystalloids. The types best suited for bacteriological work were introduced by Elford (1931) and are known as "Gradocol membranes." The preparation of such membranes requires not only special apparatus but considerable technical skill if uniform results are to be obtained. A detailed description of the technique to be followed is given in the reports by Elford (1931, 1933, 1938) and Ferry (1936). Briefly, the procedure consists of preparing in the proper proportions a stock solution of collodion, consisting of Parlodion or Celloidin, amyl alcohol, and an alcohol-ether mixture. This is known as the "parent" collodion solution; and, when it is held at a constant temperature and properly poured into a special glass cell, allowed to set, and then carefully washed in distilled water, a membrane from it will have an average pore diameter of about 750 mμ. None of the pores will probably vary by more than 5 to 10 per cent from this mean value. Membranes more porous than this are obtained by adding small percentages of water to the parent; less porous membranes are made by adding to the parent small percentages of a good solvent, such as acetic acid. Figure 8, adopted from the paper by Elford, shows how the membrane porosity can be altered by the addition of a solvent or nonsolvent to the parent solution of collodion. Intermediate grades are obtained by varying the evaporation time. The shorter the period, the more porous will be the membrane.

After the membranes have been prepared, they must be carefully calibrated by special apparatus. This process is usually accomplished by determining the critical air pressure of the membrane, that is, the amount of air pressure which must be exerted against the membrane when it is submerged in water to cause air bubbles to escape from the outer surface, or by measuring the rate of flow of water through the membrane under certain standard conditions. By substituting in standard equations the values obtained in such procedures, the average diameter of the pores in microns may be deduced. The membranes are then stored in sterile distilled water ready for use.

Quantitative Estimation of Particle Sizes by Ultrafiltration. There are several methods for determining particle sizes of various bodies. The most direct method is by optical observation, which is applicable down to diameters of 0.2 to 0.25 μ (200 to 250 mμ) under the very best conditions. By use of ultraviolet photomicrography bodies with diameters as low as 0.10 μ to 0.075 μ (100 to 75 mμ) may be resolved. A more promising method at present is ultracentrifugation. However, at best it requires relatively elaborate apparatus and a means of analyzing the system while in the process of centrifuging.

The estimation of particle sizes by ultrafiltration may be used where

TABLE 16

The Correction Factor to Be Applied to Ultrafiltration Membranes of Different Porosities to Determine the Particle Size

[From Elford (1933)]

Membrane Limiting Pore Diameter	Factor to Employ
10–100 mμ	0.33–0.5
100–500 mμ	0.5–0.75
500–1,000 mμ	0.75–1.0

the other methods are unsuitable or not available. This method does not permit so accurate an analysis of a disperse system as does using the ultracentrifuge, but it has been successfully applied to different viruses and bacteriophages. Briefly, the technique, as developed by Elford, consists of determining what is known as the "filtration end-point" and applying to it an empirical correction factor. The correction factor has been deduced by filtration of systems of known particle size and determination of the ratio between the diameter of the known particle and the average pore diameter which just prevents the particle from passing through the membrane.

TABLE 17

COMPARISON OF THE PARTICLE SIZES OF SEVERAL BODIES AS INDICATED BY ULTRAFILTRATION, ULTRAVIOLET LIGHT PHOTOGRAPHY, AND CENTRIFUGATION

[From Elford (1938)]

Body	Ultrafiltration		Microscopy and Ultraviolet Light	
	Filtration End-point, millimicrons	Particle Size, millimicrons	Photography, millimicrons	Centrifugation, millimicrons
Serratia marcescens	750	750 *	750	750
Psittacosis virus	400	200–300	300	...
Bovine pleuropneumonia organism	250	125–175	200	150
Sewage organisms A, B, and C	250	125–175	...	150
Vaccinia virus	250	125–175	160	180
Canary pox virus	250	125–175	160	120
Herpes virus	200	100–150	...	160
Rabies virus	200	100–150	...	...
Influenza virus †	160	80–120	...	90
Potato virus X	150	75–112	...	...
Vesicular stomatitis virus	120	60–90	90	70
Fowl plague virus	120	60–90	75	88
Bacteriophages:				
Typhoid 105α	120	60–90	...	75
Staphylococcus "K"	110–120	60–90	...	70
Megatherium (De Jong)	80–90	30–45	...	35
Equine encephalomyelitis virus	70	25–35	...	35
Bacteriophages: typhoid III, C36, D13, D20	60	20–30	...	...
Hemocyanin (Helix)	55	18–28	...	24
Tobacco mosaic virus	30	10–15	...	30
Poliomyelitis virus	25	8–12	...	...
Foot-and-mouth disease virus	25	8–12	...	20
Edestin (crystallized)	18	6–9	...	...
Hemoglobin molecule (horse)	...	2.8 × 0.6	...	...
Egg albumin molecule	...	1.8 × 0.6	...	...

* Used as one of the standards to calibrate the membranes.

† According to Stanley (1944), influenza virus activity is associated solely with material having a particle diameter of about 70 mμ.

To determine the filtration end-point a series of membranes having progressively finer porosities (Gradocol membranes) and the other ultrafiltration equipment are essential. A solution of 5 to 10 ml. or more, containing the body whose size is to be estimated, is then passed through the series of graded membranes, starting with the one having the largest porosity and working down through those having progressively finer porosities. This procedure is continued under optimum filtration conditions until a membrane is found which is just able to retain completely all the dispersed particles. If the average pore diameter of the retention membrane in micra is known, the average size of the particle can be determined by simply multiplying the value by Elford's correction factor for the particular membrane range. The Elford correction factors are given in Table 16.

Some estimations using this particular method are given in Table 17, adopted from Elford (1938), which also shows the values obtained by other techniques. It will be noted that the agreement is good. Elford recommends, however, that the estimation of particle sizes from filtration data be checked by other physical methods whenever they are available.

Factors Involved in Filtration. Many of the early workers who used filtration methods were of the opinion that the process was simply one of mechanical sieving; that is, the bacteria were held back because the pores of the filter were too small to allow passage. Such reasoning was partly correct but did not go far enough, for we now know that other factors, both physical and chemical, are involved. Three of the important factors will be briefly described.

1. Surface Adsorption. The importance of surface adsorption in filtration has been recognized for a long time. Most of the bacterial filters carry a negative charge and thus adsorb positively charged substances more strongly than negatively charged bodies. The kieselguhr, porcelain, and asbestos filters are composed of soluble metal cations and insoluble negatively charged silicate anions. Thus, when materials are passed through such filters, there is a tendency for the positively charged substances to combine with the anions of the filter to form an insoluble complex, whereas the negatively charged bodies combine with the soluble cations of the filter and pass on through into the filtrate. This phenomenon can be demonstrated very easily by filtering a basic dye solution, such as methylene blue or safranine. These dyes consist of organic colored cations united to inorganic anions. When filtered, the colored cation will be at first adsorbed on the filter and a clear filtrate will result; however, as soon as the adsorbing surface of the filter has reached a saturation point, the dye will

pass through without hindrance. Proteins in solution exhibit the same type of reaction and show the greatest adsorption at their isoelectric point. The amount of adsorbed protein decreases steadily with increasing alkalinity, whereas with increasing acidity adsorption decreases slowly to a minimum, after which it again increases in strong acid solutions. This fact may account for the greater ease with which enzymes, toxins, and viruses are filtered when they are in solutions on the alkaline side of the isoelectric point than in acid solutions [Mudd (1928)].

2. Nature of the Substrate. The nature of the medium plays an important part in the determination of filtration results. Changes in the salt concentration of the substrate may influence the degree of ionization and the surface charge of colloids; the surface charge may in turn change the stability of the whole colloidal system. The hydrogen-ion concentration of the suspending fluid is of considerable importance, especially when dealing with amphoteric substances, such as bacterial proteins. As we have already mentioned, the adsorption will be at a maximum near the isoelectric point. Certain surface-active substances, such as sodium oleate, or protective colloids possess the property of accumulating at interfaces and lowering the surface or interfacial tension. Thus the presence of such compounds or bodies in the substrate may alter the surface equilibria of the entire system. For example, it has been reported that ultrafilters which are normally impermeable to certain proteins, such as hemoglobin, can be rendered permeable either by first filtering certain surface-active substances like digitonin, peptone, and sodium oleate through the membranes or by adding them directly to the protein solution. Likewise, viruses pass through filter candles much more readily when suspended in broth than in saline or Ringer solutions. These capillary-active substances seem to facilitate filtration by the fact that the surface-active molecules are adsorbed preferentially both on the particles in the suspension being filtered and the wall of the filter pores; thus they exhibit a sort of lubricating action by minimizing the blocking of the pores and adsorption. In other words, they act as an escort for the particles passing through the filter. The more dilute the filtering solution, the greater the volume which must be passed through the filter before the surface adsorption is satisfied and the disperse phase begins to appear in the filtrate.

3. Filtration Pressure and Temperature. When the pores of a filter are large compared with any particles of the disperse phase, the rate at which a liquid filters through is proportional to the applied pressure. This proportionality does not hold, however, when the openings are smaller than the particles contained in the fluid or when the

pores are reduced in size as a result of adsorption or mechanical blocking. Under such circumstances, especially when blocking is the cause, there exists a specific optimum pressure, beyond which the dispersed particles are only packed more tightly into the orifices. Sometimes mechanical blocking can be overcome by stirring or by applying a pulsating pressure. The influence of temperature on filtration manifests itself principally in viscosity changes of the system. Cold liquids should always be warmed to about 25°C. before they are filtered, if the best results are to be obtained.

AGITATION

There are few reports in which the effects of agitation upon bacteria have been studied systematically. It is generally assumed that gentle agitation or aeration is favorable to the growth of the organisms in liquid media, since it aids in breaking up clumps of cells. Vigorous shaking, on the other hand, seems to be detrimental to some of the bacterial processes. Any destructive action which agitation has upon

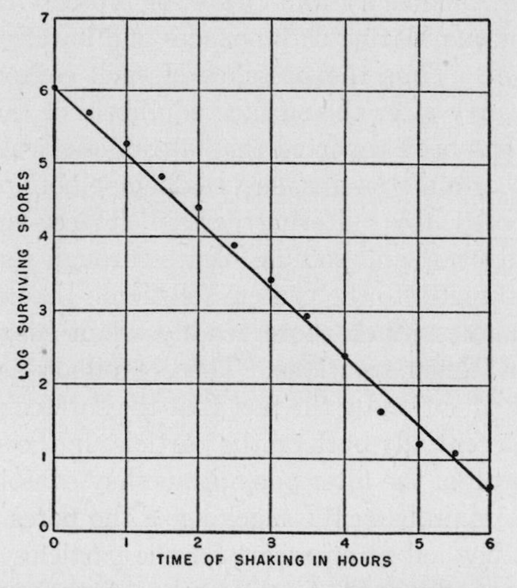

FIG. 9. The Killing of *Bacillus subtilis* Spores in Water When Shaken for Different Periods with Glass Beads (25 ml. of spore suspension, 20 g. of glass beads, 60/80 grade). (From Curran and Evans, 1942.)

the cells themselves is apparently due to a denaturation of their cellular proteins, to a transformation in the colloidal state of their protoplasm, or to complete cellular disintegration. The killing of bacterial spores and vegetative cells in fluids by agitation with small inert particles has been studied in some detail by Curran and Evans (1942). When spore suspensions were agitated vigorously in a mechanical shaker with finely divided abrasives, such as glass beads, Carborundum, Pyrex chips, and boron carbide, they were found to die at a rate which corresponds to the unimolecular law for chemical reactions (Fig. 9). Vegetative cells (*Escherichia coli*) were more rapidly killed by shaking procedures than were spores.

REFERENCES

Ács, L. 1933. *Centr. Bakt., I Abt. Orig.*, **127**:342–350.
Antonoff, G. 1943. *J. Phys. Chem.*, **47**:463–464.
Arloing, S. 1887. *Compt. rend.*, **104**:701–703.
Arrhenius, S. 1915. *Quantitative Laws in Biological Chemistry.* G. Bell and Sons, Ltd., London.
Ayers, S. H., and W. T. Johnson, Jr. 1913. *J. Wash. Acad. Sci.*, **3**:160–164.
Baker, S. L. 1935. *Brit. J. Exptl. Path.*, **16**:148–155.
Ball, C. O. 1943. *Ind. Eng. Chem.*, **35**:71–84.
Barnard, J. E., and H. de R. Morgan. 1903. *Proc. Roy. Soc. London, B*, **72**:126–128.
Baron, M. A. 1928. *Centr. Bakt., II Abt.*, **73**:373–379.
Baroni, V., and C. Jonesco-Mihaiesti. 1910. *Compt. rend. soc. biol.*, **68**:393–395.
Basset, J., M. Macheboeuf, and E. Wollman. 1937. *Ann. inst. Pasteur*, **58**:58–77.
Bateman, J. B. 1935. *Biol. Rev. Cambridge Phil. Soc.*, **10**:42–71.
Bayliss, W. M. 1924. *Principles of General Physiology*, 4th Ed. Longmans, Green and Co., New York.
Bayne-Jones, S., and J. S. Van der Lingen. 1923. *Bull. Johns Hopkins Hosp.*, **34**:11–16.
Beckwith, T. D., A. R. Olson, and E. J. Rose. 1929–1930. *Proc. Soc. Exptl. Biol. Med.*, **27**:285–286.
Beckwith, T. D., and C. E. Weaver. 1936. *J. Bact.*, **32**:361–373.
Berry, J. A., and C. A. Magoon. 1934. *Phytopathology*, **24**:780–796.
Bigelow, W. D., and J. R. Esty. 1920. *J. Infectious Diseases*, **27**:602–617.
Blank, I. H., and H. Kersten. 1935. *J. Bact.*, **30**:21–32.
Blau, O. 1906. *Centr. Bakt., II Abt.*, **15**:97–143.
Blum, H. F. 1932. *Physiol. Rev.*, **12**:23–55.
Blundell, G. P., L. A. Erf, H. W. Jones, and R. T. Hoban. 1944. *J. Bact.*, **47**:85–96.
Boak, R. A., C. M. Carpenter, and S. L. Warren. 1932. *J. Exptl. Med.*, **56**:741–750.
Brann, G. 1925. *Z. Immunitäts.*, **44**:27–32.
Brooks, S. C. 1920. *J. Med. Research*, **41**:411–424.
Brooks, S. C. 1936. *Biological Effects of Radiation*, ed. by B. M. Duggar. Vol. I; Paper X, pp. 341–388. McGraw-Hill Book Co., New York.
Browning, C. H., and S. Russ. 1917. *Proc. Roy. Soc. London, B*, **90**:33–38.
Bruynoghe, R., and M. LeFèvre de Arric. 1925. *Compt. rend. soc. biol.*, **93**:852–854.
Bruynoghe, R., and W. Mund. 1925. *Compt. rend. soc. biol.*, **92**:211–213.

Buchanan, R. E., and E. I. Fulmer. 1930. *Physiology and Biochemistry of Bacteria*, Vol. II. Williams & Wilkins Co., Baltimore.
Buchbinder, L., M. Solowey, and E. B. Phelps. 1941. *J. Bact.*, **42**:353–366.
Buchholz, J., and A. von Jeney. 1935. *Centr. Bakt., I Abt. Orig.*, **133**:299–304.
Buchwald, C. E., and R. M. Whelden. 1939. *Am. J. Botany*, **26**:778–784.
Burge, W. E., and A. J. Neill. 1915. *Am. J. Physiol.*, **38**:399–403.
Burke, V., and A. J. Wiley. 1937. *J. Bact.*, **34**:475–481.
Burnet, F. M. 1925. *Australian J. Exptl. Biol. Med. Sci.*, **2**:65–76.
Cameron, A. T. 1930. *Trans. Roy. Soc. Canada*, 3rd Series, Sec. V., **24**:53–93.
Cameron, E. J., and C. C. Williams. 1928. *Centr. Bakt., II Abt.*, **76**:28–37.
Carlyle, R. E., and A. G. Norman. 1941. *J. Bact.*, **41**:699–724.
Carpenter, C. M., R. A. Boak, L. A. Mucci, and S. L. Warren. 1933. *J. Lab. Clin. Med.*, **18**:981–990.
Casman, E. P., and L. F. Rettger. 1933. *J. Bact.*, **26**:77–123.
Cattell, M. 1936. *Biol. Rev. Cambridge Phil. Soc.*, **11**:441–476.
Cernovodeanu, P., and V. Henri. 1909. *Compt. rend.*, **149**:365–368.
Certes, A. 1884. *Compt. rend.*, **99**:385–388.
Chambers, H., and S. Russ. 1911. *Proc. Roy. Soc. London, B*, **84**:124–136.
Chambers, H., and S. Russ. 1912. *Proc. Roy. Soc. Med., Path. Sec.*, **5**:198–212.
Chambers, L. A., and N. Gaines. 1932. *J. Cellular Comp. Physiol.*, **1**:451–473.
Chick, H., and C. J. Martin. 1910. *J. Physiol.*, **40**:404–430.
Chick, H. 1930. *A System of Bacteriology in Relation in Medicine*, Vol. I, Chapter V, pp. 179–202. Medical Research Council, London.
Chlopin, G. W., and G. Tammann. 1903. *Z. Hyg. Infektionskr.*, **45**:171–204.
Clark, G. L., and C. S. Boruff. 1929. *Science*, **70**:74–75.
Clifton, C. E. 1931. *Proc. Soc. Exptl. Biol. Med.*, **28**:745–746.
Coblentz, W. W., and H. R. Fulton. 1924. *Sci. Papers Bur. Standards* 495, **19**:641–680.
Coolidge, W. D. 1925. *Science*, **62**:441–442.
Courmont, J., and T. Nogier. 1909. *Compt. rend.*, **148**:655; **149**:364–365.
Crozier, W. J. 1924. *J. Gen. Physiol.*, **7**:123–136, 189–216.
Curran, H. R. 1931. *J. Bact.*, **21**:197–209, 211–218.
Curran, H. R., and F. R. Evans. 1938. *J. Bact.*, **36**:455–465.
Curran, H. R., and F. R. Evans. 1942. *J. Bact.*, **43**:125–139.
Dale, W. M. 1940. *Biochem. J.*, **34**:1367–1373.
Danysz, J. 1906. *Ann. inst. Pasteur*, **20**:206–208.
Darrow, K. K. 1936. *Biological Effects of Radiation*, ed. by B. M. Duggar. Vol. I, Paper I, pp. 13–14. McGraw-Hill Book Co., New York.
Deming, W. E., and F. G. Cottrell. 1932. *Rev. Sci. Instruments*, **3**:296–297.
Dietz, T. J. 1935. *Radiology*, **24**:31–38.
Dixon, H. H., and J. T. Wigham. 1903. *Nature*, **69**:81.
Doerr, R., and J. Moldovan. 1911. *Wein. Klin. Wochschr.*, **24**:555–559.
Dorn, E., E. Baumann, and S. Valentiner. 1905. *Z. Hyg. Infektionskr.*, **51**:328–334.
Dorn, F. L., and O. Rahn. 1939. *Arch. Mikrobiol.*, **10**:6–12.
Downes, A., and T. P. Blunt. 1877–1878. *Proc. Roy. Soc. London, B*, **26**:488–500; **28**:199–212.
Dozois, K. P., R. P. Tittsler, M. W. Lisse, and W. P. Davey. 1932. *J. Bact.*, **24**:123–132.

Dozois, K. P., G. E. Ward, and F. W. Hachtel. 1936. *Am. J. Roentgenol. Radium Therapy,* **35**:392–397.

Dreyer, G., and M. L. Campbell-Renton. 1936. *Proc. Roy. Soc. London, B.,* **120**:447–472.

Duclaux, E. 1887. *Ann. inst. Pasteur,* **1**:88–92.

Duggar, B. M. 1936. *Biological Effects of Radiation,* Vols. I, II. McGraw-Hill Book Co., New York.

Duggar, B. M., and A. Hollaender. 1934. *J. Bact.,* **27**:219–239, 241–256.

Eberson, F. 1920. *J. Immunol.,* **5**:345–362.

Edwards, O. F., and L. F. Rettger. 1937. *J. Bact.,* **34**:489–515.

Ehrismann, O. 1930. *Z. Hyg. Infektionskr.,* **111**:618–643.

Ehrismann, O., and W. Noethling. 1932. *Z. Hyg. Infektionskr.,* **113**:597–628.

Eidinow, A. 1926. *Brit. J. Radiol.,* **31**:35–40.

Eidinow, A. 1927. *Brit. Med. J.,* **1927**(2):160–161.

Elford, W. J. 1931. *J. Path. Bact.,* **34**:505–521.

Elford, W. J. 1933. *Proc. Roy. Soc. London, B,* **112**:384–406.

Elford, W. J. 1938. *Handbuch Virusforsch.,* **1**:126–231.

Esty, J. R., and K. F. Meyer. 1922. *J. Infectious Diseases,* **31**:650–663.

Fabian, F. W., and H. T. Graham. 1933. *J. Infectious Diseases,* **53**:76–88.

Fabre, G., and E. Ostrovsky. 1911–1912. *Compt. rend. assoc. Franç avancement sci.,* **40**:122–123; 1004–1006 (cited by S. C. Brooks, 1936).

Faguet, M. 1938. *Compt. rend. soc. biol.,* **128**:969–971.

Ferguson, A. J., and O. Rahn. 1933. *Arch. Mikrobiol.,* **4**:574–582.

Fermi, C., and F. Celli. 1892. *Centr. Bakt.,* **12**:617–619.

Fermi, C., and L. Pernossi. 1894. *Z. Hyg. Infektionskr.,* **16**:385–444.

Ferry, J. D. 1936. *Chem. Rev.,* **18**:373–455.

Fiorini, M., and A. Zironi. 1914. *Arch. eléctr. méd.,* **24**:113–116.

Fiorini, M., and A. Zironi. 1915. *Strahlentherapie,* **6**:457–465.

Flosdorf, E. W., and S. Mudd. 1935, 1938. *J. Immunol.,* **29**:389–425; **34**:469–490.

Flosdorf, E. W., A. C. Kimball, and L. A. Chambers. 1939. *Proc. Soc. Exptl. Biol. Med.,* **41**:122–126.

Flourens. 1846. *Compt. rend.,* **23**:934.

Forfota, E., and A. Hámori. 1937. *Centr. Bakt., I Abt. Orig.,* **139**:163–167.

Frenkel, Y. I., and A. G. Gurvich. 1943. *Trans. Faraday Soc.,* **39**:201–204.

Friedberger, E. 1914. *Berlin Klin. Wochschr.,* **51**:1402–1405.

Friedewald, W. F., and R. S. Anderson. 1940. *Proc. Soc. Exptl. Biol. Med.,* **45**:713–715.

Friedman, C. A., and B. S. Henry. 1938. *J. Bact.,* **36**:99–105.

Galloway, I. A. 1934. *Brit. J. Exptl. Path.,* **15**:97–105.

Gates, F. L. 1929, 1930. *J. Gen. Physiol.,* **13**:231–248, 249–260; **14**:31–42.

Gerhartz, H. 1909. *Berlin klin. Wochschr.,* **46**:1800–1802.

Giese, A. C. 1941. *J. Cellular Comp. Physiol.,* **17**:203–220.

Haberman, S., and L. D. Ellsworth. 1940. *J. Bact.,* **40**:483–503.

Hampil, B. 1932. *Quart. Rev. Biol.,* **7**:172–196.

Hansen, P. A. 1932. *N. Y. Agr. Exp. Sta. Tech. Bull.* 196, Geneva, N. Y.

Hartoch, O., W. Schürmann, and O. Stiner. 1914. *Z. Immunitäts.,* **21**:643–653.

Harvey, E. N. 1940. *Living Light.* Princeton University Press, Princeton, N. J

Harvey, E. N. 1941. *Ann. Rev. Biochem.,* **10**:531–552.

Hasché, E., and P. Loch. 1937. *Z. Hyg. Infektionskr.,* **120**:209–218.

Hasskó, A. 1930. *Biochem. Z.,* **226**:462–481.

Hausmann, W., W. Neumann, and K. Schuberth. 1926. *Z. Tuberk.*, **46**:32–36.
Heiberg, B. 1932. *Z. Hyg. Infektionskr.*, **114**:425–428.
Heller, G. 1941. *J. Bact.*, **41**:109–126.
Henshaw, P. S. 1940. *J. Natl. Cancer Inst.*, **1**:277–290.
Herčík, F. 1937. *J. Gen. Physiol.*, **20**:589–594.
Hertel, E. 1905. *Z. allgem. Physiol.*, **5**:95–122.
Hess, E. 1934. *Contrib. Can. Biol. Fisheries*, Ser. C., **8**:461–474, 491–505.
Heuer, G. 1922. *Centr. Bakt., I Abt. Orig.*, **88**:380–387.
Hicks, R. A., and W. T. Szymanowski. 1932. *J. Infectious Diseases*, **50**:466–472.
Hite, B. H., N. J. Giddings, and C. E. Weakley, Jr. 1914. *West Va. Agr. Exp. Sta. Bull.* 146.
Hodes, H. L., L. T. Webster, and G. I. Lavin. 1940. *J. Exptl. Med.*, **72**:437–444.
Hollaender, A. 1936. *Biological Effects of Radiation*, ed. by B. M. Duggar. Vol. II, Paper XXVIII, pp. 919–959. McGraw-Hill Book Co., New York.
Hollaender, A., and W. D. Claus. 1936. *J. Gen. Physiol.*, **19**:753–765.
Hollaender, A., and W. D. Claus. 1937. *Bull. Natl. Research Council* 100. pp. 96.
Hollaender, A. 1939. *Radiology*, **32**:404–410.
Hollaender, A., and C. W. Emmons. 1939. *J. Cellular Comp. Physiol.*, **13**:391–402.
Hollaender, A. 1943. *J. Bact.*, **46**:531–541.
Hopwood, F. L., M. H. Salaman, and A. S. McFarlane. 1939. *Nature*, **144**:377.
Horowitz-Wlassowa, L. M., and L. D. Grinberg. 1933. *Centr. Bakt., II Abt.*, **89**:54–62.
Jahnel, F. 1938. *Z. Immunitäts.*, **94**:328–341.
Jennison, M. W. 1937. *J. Bact.*, **33**:15–16.
Jodlbauer, A., and H. von Tappeiner. 1904. *Münch. med. Wochschr.*, **51**:1096–1097.
Jodlbauer, A., and H. von Tappeiner. 1905. *Deut. Arch. klin. Med.*, **82**:520–546.
Kasahara, M., Sha-Shi-Nan, and T. Kakusui. 1939. *Monatsschr. Kinderheil.*, **78**:347–348.
Kimball, G. C. 1938. *J. Bact.*, **35**:109–122.
Klövekorn, H. 1925. *Strahlentherapie*, **20**:354–377.
Klövekorn, G. H., and O. Gaertner. 1928. *Strahlentherapie*, **29**:773–778.
Konrich. 1925. *Centr. Bakt., I Abt. Orig.*, **95**:237–244.
Kopeloff, N., and P. Beerman. 1927. *J. Bact.*, **13**:7.
Kreitlow, K. W. 1941. *J. Bact.*, **42**:127–132.
Krueger, A. P., B. B. Brown, and E. J. Scribner. 1941. *J. Gen. Physiol.*, **24**:691–698.
Lacassagne, A., and A. Paulin. 1925. *Compt. rend. soc. biol.*, **92**:61–62.
Landen, E. W., and F. M. Uber. 1939. *Proc. Soc. Exptl. Biol. Med.*, **42**:559–563.
Lang, O. W., and S. J. Dean. 1934. *J. Infectious Diseases*, **55**:39–59.
Laroquette, M. de. 1918. *Ann. inst. Pasteur*, **32**:170–192.
Larson, W. P., T. B. Hartzell, and H. S. Diehl. 1918. *J. Infectious Diseases*, **22**:271–279.
Larson, W. P., W. F. Cantwell, and T. B. Hartzell. 1919. *J. Infectious Diseases*, **25**:41–46.
Larson, W. P. 1921. *Abstracts Bact.*, **5**:2–3.
Lasseur, P., P. Vernier, A. Dupaix, and L. Georges. 1932. *Arch. Mikrobiol.*, **3**:561–579.
Lauffer, M. A., and R. B. Dow. 1941. *J. Biol. Chem.*, **140**:509–518.

Lea, D. E., R. B. Haines, and C. A. Coulson. 1936, 1937. *Proc. Roy. Soc. London, B*, **120**:47–76; **123**:1–21.
Lea, D. E., R. B. Haines, and E. Bretscher. 1941. *J. Hyg.*, **41**:1–16.
LeGalley, D. P., and G. W. Patterson. 1940. *Am. J. Pharm.*, **112**:373–377.
Lenzi, M. 1940. *Radiology*, **35**:307–314.
Leusden, F. P. 1929. *Centr. Bakt., I Abt. Orig.*, **111**:321–325.
Lewith, S. 1890. *Arch. exp. Path. Pharmakol.*, **26**:341–354.
Li, K-H. 1936. *Proc. Soc. Exptl. Biol. Med.*, **34**:659–661.
Lorenz, K. P., and P. S. Henshaw. 1941. *Radiology*, **36**:471–481.
Lusztig, A. 1929. *Centr. Bakt., I Abt. Orig.*, **111**:244–266.
MacFadyen, A. 1900. *Proc. Roy. Soc. London, B*, **66**:180–182, 339–340.
MacFadyen, A., and S. Rowland. 1900. *Proc. Roy. Soc. London, B*, **66**:488–489.
Magoon, C. A. 1926. *J. Bact.*, **11**:253–283.
Magrou, J., and M. Magrou. 1927. *Compt. rend.*, **184**:905–906.
Matthews, J. E., Jr., R. B. Dow, and A. K. Anderson. 1940. *J. Biol. Chem.*, **135**:697–705.
McFarlane, V. H. 1941. *Food Research*, **6**:481–492.
Merlini, A. 1929. *Giorn. batt. immunol.*, **4**:522–535.
Metzner, P. 1924. *Biochem. Z.*, **148**:498–523.
Miley, G. 1942. *Arch. Phys. Therapy*, **23**:536–551.
Miller, C. P., and D. Schad. 1944. *J. Bact.*, **47**:71–77, 79–84.
Minck, F. 1896. *Münch. med. Wochschr.*, **43**:101–102.
Mohler, F. L., and L. S. Taylor. 1935. *Am. J. Roentgenol. Radium Therapy*, **34**:89–91.
Morton, H. E. 1938. *Am. J. Clin. Path., Tech. Suppl.*, **2**:185–205.
Morton, H. E., and E. J. Pulaski. 1938. *J. Bact.*, **35**:163–183.
Morton, H. E. 1943. *J. Bact.*, **46**:312.
Mudd, S. 1928. *Filterable Viruses*, ed. by T. M. Rivers. Chapter II, pp. 55–94. Williams & Wilkins Co., Baltimore.
Murray, T. J., and M. R. Headlee. 1931. *J. Infectious Diseases*, **48**:436–456.
Muttermilch, S., and R. Ferroux. 1925. *Compt. rend. soc. biol.*, **93**:1226–1227.
Nelson, C., and S. C. Brooks. 1933. *Proc. Soc. Exptl. Biol. Med.*, **30**:1007–1009.
Newcomer, H. S. 1917. *J. Exptl. Med.*, **26**:841–848.
Norman, A. G., L. A. Richards, and R. E. Carlyle. 1941. *J. Bact.*, **41**:689–697.
North, C. E., and W. H. Park. 1927. *Am. J. Hyg.*, **7**:147–173.
Oag, R. K. 1940. *J. Path. Bact.*, **51**:137–141.
Païc, M., V. Deutsch, and I. Borcila. 1935. *Compt. rend. soc. biol.*, **119**:1063–1065.
Païc, M., P. Haber, J. Voet, and A. Eliasz. 1935. *Compt. rend. soc. biol.*, **119**:1061–1063.
Perdrau, J. R., and C. Todd. 1933. *Proc. Roy. Soc. London, B*, **112**:277–287, 288–298.
Pfeiffer, R., and E. Friedberger. 1903. *Berlin klin. Wochschr.*, **40**:640–641.
Polding, J. B. 1943. *J. Path. Bact.*, **55**:502–503.
Prescott, S. C. 1904. *Science*, **20**:246–248.
Prickett, P. S. 1928. *N. Y. Agr. Exp. Sta. Tech. Bull.* 147, Geneva, N. Y.
Prochownick, L., and F. Spaeth. 1890. *Deut. med. Wochschr.*, **16**:564–565.
Prudhomme, R.-O. 1938. *Ann. Fermentations*, **4**:103–110.
Pugsley, A. T., T. H. Oddie, and C. E. Eddy. 1935. *Proc. Roy. Soc. London, B*, **118**:276–298.

Rahn, O., and W. R. Schroeder. 1941. *Biodynamica*, **3**:199–208.
Remlinger, P., and J. Bailly. 1938. *Compt. rend. soc. biol.*, **129**:460–462.
Rentschler, H. C., R. Nagy, and G. Mouromseff. 1941. *J. Bact.*, **41**:745–774.
Repetto, O. M. 1940. *Rev. soc. argentinia Biol.*, **16**:567–570.
Rieder, H. 1898, 1902. *Münch. med. Wochschr.*, **45**:101–104, 773–774; **49**:402–406.
Rivers, T. M., J. E. Smadel, and L. A. Chambers. 1937. *J. Exptl. Med.*, **65**:677–685.
Robertson, A. H. 1927. *N. Y. Agr. Exp. Sta. Tech. Bulls.* 130 and 131, Geneva, N. Y.; *Vermont Agr. Exp. Sta. Bulls.* 274 and 275.
Ross, V. 1938. *J. Immunol.*, **35**:351–369, 371–377.
Roux, E. 1887. *Ann. inst. Pasteur*, **1**:445–452.
Roux, E., and A. Yersin. 1889. *Ann. inst. Pasteur*, **3**:273–288.
Rouyer, M., and M. Servigne. 1938. *Ann. inst. Pasteur*, **61**:565–578.
Rubentschik, L. 1925. *Centr. Bakt., II Abt.*, **64**:166–174.
Sattler, W. 1929. *Milchw. Forsch.*, **7**:100–170.
Schenck zu Schweinsberg, H-G. F. 1938. *Strahlentherapie*, **63**:212–224.
Scherp, H. W., and T. P. Hughes. 1939. *J. Immunol.*, **36**:29–36.
Schoepfle, G. M. 1941. *J. Cellular Comp. Physiol.*, **17**:109–116.
Schroeter. 1912. *Z. Hyg. Infektionskr.*, **72**:189–212.
Schroetter, H. von. 1927. *Centr. Bakt., I Abt. Orig.*, **104**:205–210.
Schubert, J. 1928. *Z. Immunitäts.*, **58**:106–122.
Schubert, J. 1931. *Centr. Bakt., I Abt. Orig.*, **122**:82–86.
Scott, W. M. 1911. *Proc. Cambridge Phil. Soc.*, **16**:124–125.
Sewertzova, S. B. 1931. *Ann. inst. Pasteur*, **46**:337–371.
Sharp, D. G. 1939. *J. Bact.*, **37**:447–460.
Smith, F. R., and R. L. Perry. 1941. *Food Research*, **6**:345–360.
Smith, G. H. 1941. *Yale J. Biol. Med.*, **13**:409–422.
Smithburn, K. C., and G. I. Lavin. 1939. *Am. Rev. Tuberc.*, **39**:782–793.
Sollner, K. 1944. *Chem. Rev.*, **34**:371–391.
Spencer, R. R. 1934, 1935. *Pub. Health Repts.*, **49**:183–192; **50**:1642–1655.
Spiegel-Adolf, M. 1939. *Med. Rec.*, **150**:430–433.
Stanley, W. M. 1938. *Handbuch Virusforsch.*, **1**:447–546.
Stanley, W. M. 1944. *J. Exptl. Med.*, **79**:267–283.
Stier, T. J. B. 1933. *J. Gen. Physiol.*, **16**:815–840.
Strassmann, K. 1904. *Arch. Dermatol. Syphilis*, **71**:419–446.
Strebel, H. 1900. *Fortschr. Gebiete Röntgenstrahlen*, **4**:125–132.
Strebel, H. 1901. *Deut. med. Wochschr.*, **27**:69–72.
Stuart, L. S., R. W. Frey, and L. H. James. 1933. *U. S. Dept. Agr. Tech. Bull.* 383.
Swift, H. F. 1937. *J. Bact.*, **33**:411–421.
Syverton, J. T., R. A. Harvey, G. P. Berry, and S. L. Warren. 1941. *J. Exptl. Med.*, **73**:243–248; **74**:223-234.
Szymanowski, W. T., and R. A. Hicks. 1932. *J. Infectious Diseases*, **50**:1–25.
Takahashi, W. N., and R. J. Christensen. 1934. *Science*, **79**:415–416.
Tanner, F. W., and J. W. Appling. 1941. *Proc. Soc. Exptl. Biol. Med.*, **47**:47–51.
Tappeiner, H. von. 1900. *Münch. med. Wochschr.*, **47**:5–7.
Tappeiner, H. von, and A. Jodlbauer. 1904. *Münch. med. Wochschr.*, **51**:737–739.
Tappeiner, H. von. 1909. *Ergeb. Physiol.*, **8**:698–741.

Taylor, A. R., D. G. Sharp, D. Beard, H. Finkelstein, and J. W. Beard. 1941. *J. Infectious Diseases*, **69**:224–231.

Thiele, H., and K. Wolf. 1906, 1907. *Arch. Hyg.*, **57**:29–55; **60**:29–39.

Thresh, J. C., and J. F. Beale. 1910. *Lancet*, **1910**(2):1849–1851.

Tizzoni, G., and G. Cattani. 1891. *Arch. exptl. Path. Pharmakol.*, **28**:41–60.

Townsend, C. T., J. R. Esty, and F. C. Baselt. 1938. *Food Research*, **3**:323–346.

Tracy, R. L., Jr. 1932. *J. Bact.*, **24**:423–438.

T'ung, T. 1935, 1936. *Proc. Soc. Exptl. Biol. Med.*, **33**:328–330; **35**:399–400.

T'ung, T. 1940. *Chinese Med. J., Suppl.*, **3**:304–320.

Turner, T. B. 1938. *J. Exptl. Med.*, **67**:61–78.

Underwood, W. B. 1941. *A Textbook of Sterilization.* American Sterilizer Co., Erie, Penna.

Van Beuren, F., Jr., and H. Zinsser. 1903. *Am. Med.*, **6**:1021–1022.

Wallace, G. I., and F. W. Tanner. 1933–1935. *Fruit Products J.*, **13**:52–54, 109–113; **14**:235–237.

Ward, H. M. 1892, 1894. *Proc. Roy. Soc. London, B*, **52**:393–400; **56**:315–394; *Phil. Trans. Roy. Soc. London, B*, **185**:961–986.

Wedberg, S. E., and L. F. Rettger. 1941. *J. Bact.*, **41**:725–743.

Welch, H. 1930. *J Prev. Med.*, **4**:295–330.

Wells, W. F. 1940. *Science*, **91**:172–174.

Whelden, R. M., E. V. Enzmann, and C. P. Haskins. 1941. *J. Gen. Physiol.*, **24**:789–796.

Whisler, B. A. 1940. *Iowa State Coll. J. Sci.*, **14**:215–231.

Williams, C. C., C. M. Merrill, and E. J. Cameron. 1937. *Food Research*, **2**:369–375.

Williams, F. T. 1936. *J. Bact.*, **32**:589–597.

Williams, O. B. 1929. *J. Infectious Diseases*, **44**:421–465.

Winchester, G., and T. J. Murray. 1936. *Proc. Soc. Exptl. Biol. Med.*, **35**·165–166.

Wittlin, J. 1896. *Centr. Bakt., II Abt.*, **2**:676–677.

Wolff, L. K., and G. Ras. 1933. *Centr. Bakt., I Abt. Orig.*, **128**:314–319.

Wood, R. W., and A. L. Loomis. 1927. *Phil. Mag.* (Ser. 7), **4**:417–436.

Wyatt, H. T. 1936. *Sterilization.* Scanlan-Morris Co., Madison, Wisconsin.

Wyckoff, R. W. G. 1930. *J. Exptl. Med.*, **52**:435–446, 769–780.

Wyckoff, R. W. G., and T. M. Rivers. 1930. *J. Exptl. Med.*, **51**:921–932.

Wyckoff, R. W. G., and B. J. Luyet. 1931. *Radiology*, **17**:1171–1175.

Wyckoff, R. W. G. 1932. *J. Gen. Physiol.*, **15**:351–361.

Yen, A. C. H., and S. C. Liu. 1934. *Proc. Soc. Exptl. Biol. Med.*, **31**:1250–1252.

Zia, S. H., B. F. Chow, and T. T'ung. 1938. *Proc. Soc. Exptl. Biol. Med.*, **38**:688–690.

ZoBell, C. E. 1934. *Quart. Rev. Biol.*, **9**:460–466.

4

THE EFFECTS OF CHEMICAL AGENTS ON BACTERIA

It is a well-known fact that the various vital phenomena of living cells such as bacteria are conditioned by their physical and chemical environment. It is not always easy, however, in biological studies to separate the physical factors affecting the life activities of an organism from the chemical, or vice versa, although for convenience such a division is usually made. Thus in Chapter 3 we discussed the effects of some physical agents on bacteria, and in this chapter we shall take up the more important chemical agents.

The response of microorganisms to the presence of chemical compounds in their environment is sometimes called *chemotaxis* or *chemotropism.* If an organism is attracted or stimulated in its activities, the phenomenon is termed *positive chemotaxis* or *chemotropism;* if the organism is repelled or depressed in its functions, *negative chemotaxis* or *chemotropism.* The ability of chemicals to attract, to serve as nutritional substances, and to stimulate the growth of bacteria will not be discussed here, since they can better be allocated to Chapter 7, Bacterial Nutrition. Thus the material which we shall consider here will be concerned primarily with the nonnutritional or injurious effects of chemicals on bacteria. Chemicals may partially or completely inhibit the growth of bacteria, or they may be so powerful that all the organisms are killed. Apparently there is no true relation between *chemotaxis* and the power of a chemical substance to kill bacteria.

Many terms have been introduced into the literature to explain the injurious effects of chemicals upon microorganisms. The following, as defined by Patterson (1932), are now widely used:

Germicide: Anything that destroys germs (microorganisms); applied especially to agents that kill disease germs.

Bactericide: Anything that destroys bacteria.

Antiseptic: A substance that opposes sepsis, putrefaction, or decay; one that prevents or arrests the growth or action of microorganisms, either by inhibiting their activity or by destroying them; used especially of agents applied to living tissue. Practically synonymous with *bacteriostatic* and *preservative.*

Disinfectant: An agent that frees from infection; usually a chemical agent which destroys disease germs or other harmful microorganisms (but not, ordinarily, bacterial spores); commonly used of substances applied to inanimate objects.

Sterilization: The act or process of sterilizing, or freeing from all living microorganisms.

Deodorant: Anything that destroys or masks offensive odors. It may or may not be an antiseptic or disinfectant.

Prophylactic: Anything that prevents, or that contributes to the prevention of disease; a preventive.

Viricide: Anything that destroys or inactivates viruses.

The ideal disinfectant or viricide has not been discovered, but to qualify as such a substance should possess some of the following characteristics: (1) highly germicidal, (2) stable, (3) homogeneous, (4) readily soluble, (5) nonpoisonous to higher animals and man, (6) noncorrosive, (7) able to penetrate, and (8) moderate in cost.

THE METHODS OF TESTING DISINFECTANTS

Many methods have been proposed for measuring the disinfecting powers of chemical compounds. Most of them are beset with many difficulties. The fundamental researches upon chemical disinfection were carried out by Robert Koch in the latter part of the last century. Some seventy-five disinfectants were in use at that time, many of which had never been tested for their germicidal power. Several were probably nothing more than deodorants. Koch attacked the problem with his usual meticulous care, realizing that chemicals may serve as a useful weapon against disease. His first contribution in this field was the development of a technique for testing such substances. It consisted of impregnating silk threads with cultures of bacteria and then exposing them to the disinfectant under examination. After suitable contact the threads were transferred to nutrient media, where the presence or absence of growth could be observed. Later Krönig and Paul (1897) discarded the thread method and replaced it with one of their own. Garnets were dipped in bacterial cultures, allowed to dry, and then immersed in the test disinfectant. After various intervals the garnets were removed and washed, and agar plates prepared from the washings. The number of colonies which developed was then counted. This procedure rendered the test more quantitative than that proposed by Koch. Most of the methods which have since been devised follow in principle, at least, this method of Krönig and Paul, although they may vary widely in technical details. Further standardization came in 1903, when Rideal and Walker proposed several standard technical steps and chose phenol as a standard reference for the comparison of all disinfectants. By this means it was possible to determine the concentration of the unknown disinfectant and the concentration of phenol which would kill in a given time and to establish a numerical ratio of germicidal efficiency. This ratio became known as the *phenol coefficient.* Other distinct advances were made by Chick and Martin (1908), who listed the essential conditions which must be considered in evaluating disinfectants, and by Anderson and McClintic (1911), whose test became known as the Hygienic Laboratory Method.

The so-called Food and Drug Administration Method (F.D.A. Method), as published by Ruehle and Brewer (1931), is now widely used in the United States. It has combined all the advantages of the older tests but still has several inherent disadvantages. This method requires tests of disinfectant or antiseptic action to be carried out against strains of *Eberthella typhosa* and *Staphylococcus aureus* of known susceptibility to phenol. Stipulations are also made for tests in the presence of organic matter and for a "cup-plate" method applicable to ointments and salves, toothpastes, and other similar products composed of chemicals incorporating inert materials. The differences between the F.D.A., Rideal-Walker, and Hygienic Laboratory Methods are shown in Table 1. The Rideal-Walker Method is used primarily in England; and, although the Hygienic Laboratory Method was developed in this country, it is never used today. However, with few exceptions, such as with certain pine oil preparations [Brewer and Ruehle (1934)], the three methods give almost identical results when compounds chemically related to phenol are tested. For the technical procedures used in these tests the *United States Department of Agriculture Circular* 198 (1931), prepared by Ruehle and Brewer, or McCulloch's book, *Disinfection and Sterilization* (1945), should be consulted.

Many people interested in germicides are of the opinion that a revision of the customary testing methods is urgently needed, because uniform and reproducible results are no longer obtainable in many instances where high-potency materials are used. Several factors are probably responsible for the fluctuating results obtained. For example, Brewer (1943) found that the composition of the peptone used for culturing the test organisms may seriously affect the phenol coefficients obtained with certain germicides; this disturbing phenomenon is attributed to a variation in the phospholipide content of the culture media. In recognition of such discrepancies a committee of the American Public Health Association has been assigned the task of working out the modifications of the older technique.

TABLE 1

DIFFERENCES IN MEDIA AND MANIPULATION OF THE THREE METHODS OF DETERMINING PHENOL COEFFICIENT

[From Ruehle and Brewer (1931)]

	F.D.A. Method	R.-W. Method	H.L. Method
Composition of medium	Peptone,* 10 g. Liebig's beef extract, 5 g. Salt, 5 g. Water, 1,000 ml. Boil 20 minutes.	Peptone,† 20 g. Liebig's beef extract, 10 g. Salt, 10 g. Water, 1,000 ml. Boil 30 minutes.	Peptone,* 10 g. Liebig's beef extract, 3 g. Salt, 5 g. Water, 1,000 ml. Boil 15 minutes.
Acidity of medium	*p*H 6.8	+1.5; no definite *p*H	Unadjusted, but *p*H between 6.0 and 7.0
Amount of culture medium in tube	10 ml.	5 ml.	10 ml.
Amount of culture added to diluted disinfectant	0.5–5.0 ml.	0.5–5.0 ml.	0.1–5.0 ml.
Resistance of test culture to phenol (dilution killing in 10 minutes but not in 5 minutes)	1–90	1–90 to 1–110	No limits stated
Condition of tubes in test	Plugged with cotton	Plugged with cotton	Open tubes
Temperature of test	20°C.	15°–18°C.	20°C.
Time intervals of the test	5, 10, and 15 minutes	2½, 5, 7½, and 10 minutes	5, 7½, 10, 12½, and 15 minutes
Amount of medication mixture transferred (size of loop)	4 mm.-loop (of No. 23 B. and S. gage wire)	4 mm.-loop (of No. 27 Imperial gage wire)	Spiral loop (four spirals wrapped around a No. 13 B. and S. gage wire. Made of No. 23 B. and S. gage wire)
Calculation of phenol coefficient	Highest dilution not killing in 5 minutes but killing in 10 minutes, divided by same for phenol	Highest dilution not killing in 5 minutes but killing in 7½ minutes, divided by same for phenol	Mathematical mean of highest dilutions showing no growth in 5, 10, and 15 minutes, divided by same for phenol

* Armour's special batch set aside for disinfectant testing.
† Allen and Hanbury's.

At this point brief mention should be made of several other techniques which have been developed recently to evaluate germicides, antiseptics, and fungicides. These methods present, in most cases, techniques for determining the germicidal properties of compounds which heretofore could not be tested. However, they should not be regarded as standard.

1. A method whereby the disinfectant is tested for its toxicity to living embryonic tissue, as well as for its ability to kill bacteria, has

been developed by Salle and his coworkers (1939). A number known as the "toxicity index" is determined, which is defined as the ratio of the highest dilution of the disinfectant preventing growth of embryonic tissues in 10 minutes to the highest dilution required to kill the test organism in the same period of time. Tests show that compounds possessing a low toxicity index are quite efficient germicides.

Witlin (1942) has also used the toxicity index as a means of evaluating germicides. However, he uses the developing chick embryo, and defines the toxicity index (ratio) as the amount (in grams) of the germicidal agent contained in each milliliter of the highest dilution which kills *Staphylococcus aureus* in 10 minutes to the amount of the agent required to kill a chick embryo within 24 hours. Theoretically, the smaller is the index, the more practical is the germicide.

A somewhat different technique for determining the toxicity of germicides and antiseptics has been proposed by Welch and Brewer (1942) and by Hirsch and Novak (1942). This technique is based upon a comparison of the ability of an antiseptic to destroy the phagocytic activity of blood with its germicidal power.

2. Another method has been introduced by Bronfenbrenner, Hershey, and Doubly (1939). It consists of measuring manometrically the amount of oxygen consumed by mouse liver and by *Escherichia coli*, respectively, both in the absence and the presence of a given disinfectant. The method is simple and saves time and materials. It is especially useful in making a preliminary survey of new disinfectants. Ely (1939) and Greig and Hoogerheide (1941) have also evaluated germicides by a manometric procedure.

3. A method for testing the germicidal action of chlorine compounds, using the spores of *Bacillus metiens*, has been used by Levine and his associates for a number of years [see Charlton and Levine (1937), Rudolph and Levine (1941)]. Spores of *Bacillus subtilis* may also be employed for the assay of penicillin [Foster and Woodruff (1944)].

4. The phenol coefficients of relatively insoluble compounds (benzylphenols) have been determined by Carswell and Doubly (1936), using sulfonated oils to disperse uniformly the germicide in water.

5. The efficiency of germicides for treating surgical instruments has been studied by Reddish and Burlingame (1938) and by Spaulding (1939).

6. A procedure for testing nonphenolic disinfectants has been worked out by Clark (1938).

7. Brewer (1939) has devised a method for testing antiseptic dusting powders.

8. Techniques for evaluating fungicides are described in papers by Burlingame and Reddish (1939) and Hoffman, Schweitzer, and Dalby (1941).

9. The antiseptic properties of snuffs, including ordinary tobacco snuffs, lycopodium snuff, and several experimental snuffs containing proflavine, penicillin, or sulfathiazole, were determined by a special technique by Delafield, Straker, and Topley (1941).

10. Withell (1942) has suggested a procedure for evaluating bactericides based on calculation of the time required to kill 50 per cent of the cells in a test culture.

11. Heinemann (1943) has recommended that, when mercurial compounds are being tested by the customary method, the organisms be transferred to a thioglycollate medium, which will neutralize the toxicity of any mercury which may be carried over.

12. Various techniques for the assay of penicillin and other microbial antibiotic substances have been developed by several investigators [see Waksman (1941), Abraham and his associates (1941), Rammelkamp (1942), Foster and Woodruff (1943, 1944), Schmidt and Moyer (1944), Dubos (1944), and Schmitt (1944)]. Space does not permit a discussion of these methods; the original articles should be consulted for details.

THE DYNAMICS OF THE DISINFECTION PROCESS

Some of the laws which govern the action of a disinfectant upon bacteria are quite well understood, whereas others are still obscure or poorly defined. There is also considerable controversy as to whether the process is essentially chemical in nature or is controlled entirely by complex biological laws. Believers in the strictly chemical theory of disinfection have shown that the destruction of bacteria by such agencies follows an orderly course quite similar to a monomolecular chemical reaction, where only one substance undergoes change and the velocity of the reverse reaction is unimportant. Many data in opposition to this analogy have been reviewed by Buchanan and Fulmer (1930), Knaysi (1930), and others. The opposition group is convinced that such agreements as have been found between the rate of disinfection and the monomolecular reaction are probably superficial and accidental. Furthermore they believe methods of evaluating disinfectants based on such a concept may prove misleading. This book is no place to discuss such a controversy. All that will be done is to present some of the findings as given in the literature. In general, however, it is agreed that often there is at least a superficial, if not a real, resemblance between the rate of death of bacteria when exposed to a disinfectant and the velocity of some of the simple chemical processes. Whether this resemblance is accidental or real is difficult to prove.

Robert Koch, Krönig and Paul (1897), and other early workers concluded from their studies that the destruction of bacteria by certain chemicals was an orderly process requiring time for completion. The destructive action increased with a higher temperature, and there were differences between the concentrations of chemical compounds required to inhibit the growth of bacteria and those necessary to kill them. After their work many advances were made along several fronts. The chemist produced a host of new compounds, very few of which escaped trial as disinfectants, and considerable progress was made in understanding the principles which underlie the disinfection process.

THE COURSE OF THE PROCESS

Credit for our knowledge concerning the course and rate of reaction of the disinfection process is due chiefly to Krönig and Paul (1897), Madsen and Nyman (1907), Chick (1908, 1910, 1912), Paul and his

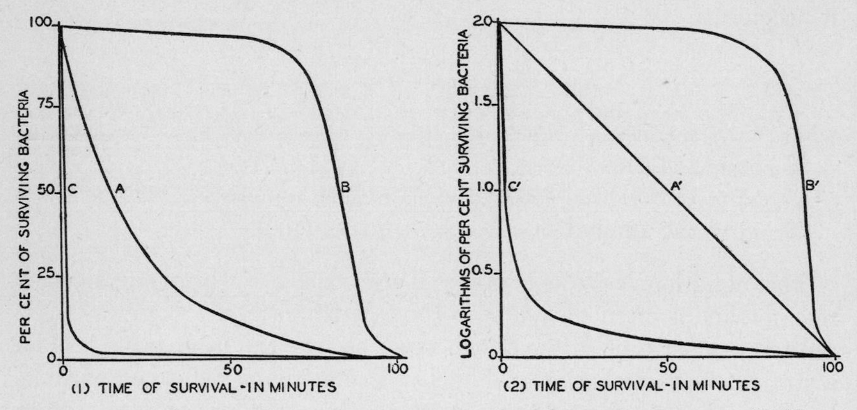

FIG. 1. Time-Survivor Curves Demonstrating the Disinfection Process. (1) Number of survivors per unit volume (percentage of total); (2) the logarithms of the numbers in (1) plotted against time. Curves A, A' = processes in accordance with monomolecular reaction and the law of mass action; curves B, B' = sigmoid curves; curves C, C' = processes in which bacteria are killed more rapidly at first than if the monomolecular reaction and the law of mass action were obeyed.

associates (1909, 1910), Cohen (1922), and Falk and Winslow (1926). A general survey of the results obtained by all these workers will show fairly well that, when the number of surviving bacteria in contact with a unit volume of a disinfectant is plotted against time, the points will lie on a fairly smooth curve of type A shown in Fig. 1. This curve shows an initial rapid reduction in the number of viable organisms followed by a gradual reduction until all are killed; also there is a relationship between the number of bacteria surviving in a unit volume and the time which has elapsed. The form of this curve is rather typical for certain simple chemical reactions where only one substance is regarded as undergoing change (monomolecular reaction), such as, for example, the decomposition of radioactive substances and the inversion of cane sugar by acids. Other workers, however, have plotted their data and find the shape of the curves to be less uniform (curves B and C in Fig. 1 are only two simple possibilities).

If disinfection processes do follow an orderly course resembling that of a monomolecular chemical reaction, then it must be clearly understood that the velocity of the change, according to the law of mass action, will depend upon the nature of the substance and its concentration at any given moment, the temperature and other environmental factors remaining constant. By means of calculus the velocity of a monomolecular reaction may be mathematically expressed. When such an expression is integrated and transposed to common logarithms it becomes:

$$k = \frac{1}{t} \log \frac{a}{(a - x)}$$

where k[1] = a constant depending upon the nature of the substance.
t = the time.
a = the original amount of substance undergoing change.
$(a-x)$ = the amount of substance remaining after time, t.

This equation is the expression of the velocity of a monomolecular reaction and is often spoken of as the logarithmic law. If $\log (a-x)$ is plotted against time in the above equation, the resulting graph will be a straight line (see line A' in Fig. 1). It is perhaps well to emphasize, however, that the formula represents the *course* of events taking place under ideal conditions and makes no pretense of indicating the true *mechanism* involved. When applied to actual experimental observations on monomolecular chemical reactions, it is found that this loga-

[1] When the velocity of a monomolecular reaction is expressed mathematically by calculus and then integrated, the equation $k = \frac{1}{t} \ln \frac{a}{(a - x)}$ is obtained. Thus in the above equation where common logarithms are used, $k = \frac{k}{2.303} = 0.434k$. Usually k is expressed as above when comparative, and not absolute, values are important.

rithmic law holds good only in so far as the ideal conditions can be maintained. Environmental conditions which are not ideal may lead to deflections from the true logarithmic rate at the beginning and at the end of the reaction, so that instead of a straight-line plot of the results, a somewhat sigmoid or s-shaped curve is obtained. Curves B and B', and C and C', in Fig. 1 are only two simple possibilities. If conditions are properly selected, these deflections may be reduced considerably, although in certain cases they are always present.

All that is necessary to apply the monomolecular reaction to the process of disinfection is to assume that at any given time the reaction velocity or rate of death is proportional to the number of bacteria per unit volume. This can be shown best by a hypothetical example. Suppose we subject a bacterial culture containing 10,000 viable organisms per milliliter to a disinfectant, and the death rate is such that 90 per cent of the bacteria are killed every minute. Then the number of organisms remaining alive in each milliliter after each minute will be as follows:

Time	*Number of Surviving Bacteria*
After 0 minutes	10,000 per 1 ml.
After 1 minute	1,000 per 1 ml.
After 2 minutes	100 per 1 ml.
After 3 minutes	10 per 1 ml.
After 4 minutes	1 per 1 ml.
After 5 minutes	1 per 10 ml.
After 6 minutes	1 per 100 ml.

TABLE 2

DISINFECTION OF ANTHRAX SPORES WITH 5 PER CENT PHENOL AT 33.3°C.

[From Chick (1908)]

Time, hours	Mean Number of Bacteria per Drop of Disinfecting Mixture	Value of k (assuming reaction to be in accordance with $k = \frac{1}{t} \log \frac{B}{b}$)
0.0	439.0	....
0.5	275.5	0.40
1.25	137.5	0.40
2.0	46.0	0.49
3.0	15.8	0.48
4.1	5.45	0.46
5.0	3.6	0.41
7.0	0.5	0.42
		Mean value of k = 0.44

If we let B (rather than a, as in the foregoing equation) represent the initial number of viable bacteria and b (rather than $a-x$) the final number, the reaction velocity or rate of death, expressed as a monomolecular reaction, may be written thus:

$$k = \frac{1}{t} \log \frac{B}{b}$$

Now let us turn to some experimental observations in which the investigators have applied the above equation and see how their data fit the logarithmic law. Chick (1908, 1910) carried out experiments on the disinfection of anthrax spores with 5 per cent phenol at 33.3°C.

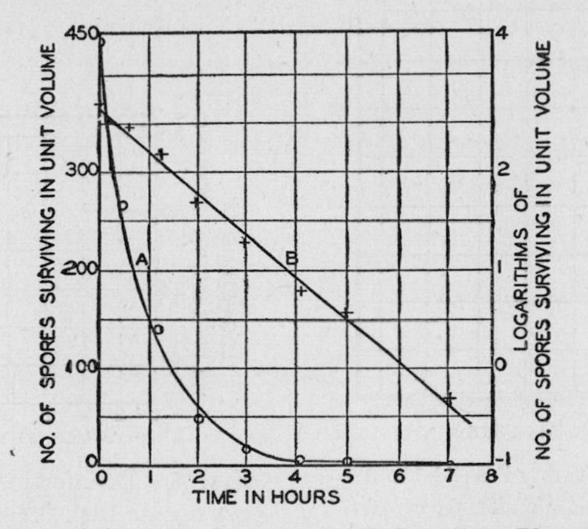

FIG. 2. Disinfection of Anthrax Spores with 5 Per Cent Phenol at 33.3° C. In curve *A* circles represent experimental observations of the number of surviving spores in a unit volume. Line *B* represents a plot of the logarithms of concentration of survivors against time. (From Chick, 1930.)

and found that the logarithm of the number of organisms surviving in a unit volume was proportional to the elapsed time. When one was plotted against the other, the process appeared to obey the law of mass action and to resemble what is known by the chemist as a reaction of the first order or a monomolecular reaction. The results of one of her experiments are shown in Table 2 and Fig. 2.

When vegetative cells of *Eberthella typhosa* and *Escherichia coli* were used as the test organisms in such experiments, the disinfection processes were found to conform to the monomolecular reaction formula. On the other hand, when *Salmonella paratyphi* was exposed to 0.6 per cent phenol and other disinfectants at 20°C. (Fig. 3), there was a rapid period in the rate of destruction which lasted for about 2 minutes.

Thus the rate of disinfection proceeded faster during the early phase than it should have done if the logarithmic law had been obeyed.

A culture of *Staphylococcus aureus* acted entirely the opposite when it was exposed to 0.6 per cent phenol at 20°C. There was always a lag period of about 4 minutes in the rate of death before it became proportional to the number of surviving bacteria. This situation is shown graphically in Fig. 4, where the logarithms of survivors are plotted against time. These data are typical results of a great many studies carried out on bacteria by different investigators, using various disinfectants.

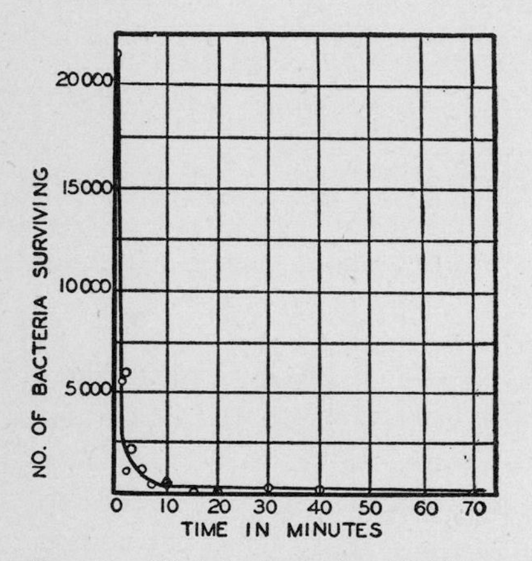

Fig. 3. Disinfection of a 24-Hour-Old Culture of *Salmonella paratyphi* with 0.6 Per Cent Phenol at 20° C. (From Chick, 1908.)

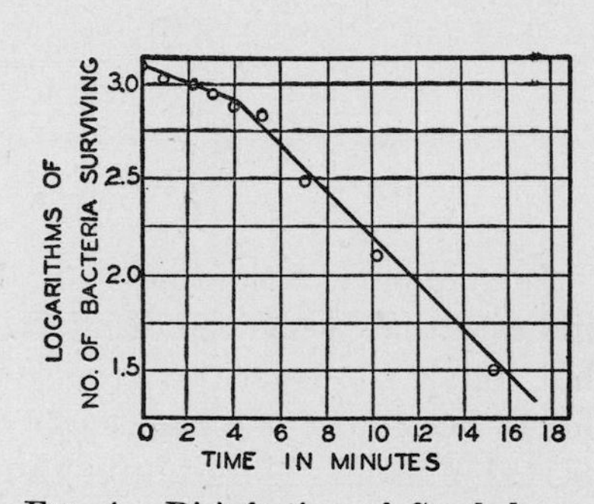

Fig. 4. Disinfection of *Staphylococcus aureus* with 0.6 Per Cent Phenol at 20° C. (From Chick, 1910.)

Falk and Winslow (1926) and others have calculated their disinfection data from equations for uni-, bi-, tri-, and quadrimolecular reactions to determine which reaction the processes most closely resembled. The results of the course of mortality for *Escherichia coli* in dilute solutions of calcium chloride are shown in Table 3. From the second column in this table it is apparent that the disinfection did not follow the logarithmic course because of the inconstancy of k_1. The steadily decreasing values of k_1 indicate that the reaction between disinfectant and bacterium was proceeding at a rate higher than that indicated by the unimolecular equation. But, if the first and last two values of k_2 (third column) are disregarded, the reaction may be considered to have proceeded in accordance with the course of a bimolecular chemical reaction. The almost constant values of k_3 in the fourth column suggest, however, that after the first 3 to 6 hours the reaction took place in the manner of a chemical reaction of the third order (trimolecular). These observations are confirmed by the progressively increasing values of k_4, listed in the last column, which indicate that the course of the disinfection rate was lower than that postulated from the equation of quadrimolecular reaction.

TABLE 3

THE VIABILITY OF *Escherichia coli* IN 0.145 *M* $CaCl_2$ SOLUTION AT 37°C.

[From Falk and Winslow (1926)]

Incubation Period, hours	Velocity Constants			
	k_1	$k_2(\times 10^8)$	$k_3(\times 10^{16})$	$k_4(\times 10^{24})$
1	1.56	2.14	3.39	6.50
3	0.65	1.16	2.59	7.01
6	0.46	1.39	6.48	39.3
9	0.34	1.30	8.23	68.9
12	0.27	1.17	8.50	83.9
24	0.15	0.85	8.92	127.0
125	0.034	0.36	8.00	236.0

In summary, according to Falk and Winslow, the data in Table 3 indicate that, when the disinfection of *E. coli* by 0.145 *M* $CaCl_2$ does not follow the logarithmic course of a unimolecular reaction, it may follow the course of a reaction of a higher order through a considerable period of time. Thus, in this case, during the first 12 hours the course is suggestive of a bimolecular reaction, whereas later the course is similar to that of a third-order chemical reaction.

It would be absurd to say, since the courses of many disinfection processes are found to follow the monomolecular law, that a single molecular species is concerned. No one has definite proof for such a statement. However, whatever the mechanisms are and whatever the number of consecutive reactions may be, they leave still dominant in most cases the effect of bacterial concentration. This change in concentration may be measured. The analogy between the monomolecular reaction and the disinfection process tells us nothing about the mechanisms concerned, but both merely formulate the relation between concentration and the course of the process. The monomolecular reaction is a convenient numerical basis for calculating the rate of disinfection, in spite of the fact that not all data fit the reaction. The mere use of such mathematical formulas does not necessitate the acceptance of a strictly chemical, biological, or physical explanation of the basic forces which control the decrease in numbers of a bacterial population under the influence of a disinfectant. From the analysis of the time curves of disinfection processes it is apparent that the reaction between disinfectant and cell or cellular constituents is highly complex. Although the logarithmic law probably best expresses the rate or course, the correspondence is not always close. This situation is to be expected, however, in complex heterogeneous biological systems.

CONCENTRATION OF DISINFECTANT

It has long been recognized in disinfection procedures that a change in the concentration of disinfectant is accompanied by a corresponding change in the rate of disinfection. Chick (1908) noted that the relationship between the concentration of a disinfectant and the rate at which bacteria were killed was not a simple, but rather an exponential, one. The exponent varied with each disinfectant and expressed the effect that dilution had upon the germicidal efficiency of the substance. For example, doubling the concentration of phenol did not halve the time necessary for the disinfection of *Salmonella paratyphi,* but rather reduced it from 240 minutes to $3\frac{1}{2}$ minutes.

In order to express mathematically the relationship between the concentration of a disinfectant and the time required to kill a bacterial population Watson (1908) introduced the expression:

$$C^n \cdot t = \text{a constant } (A)$$

or, in logarithmic form:

$$n \log C + \log t = \log A$$

where C = the concentration of the disinfectant.

n = the coefficient of dilution, concentration exponent, or simply a constant varying with each disinfectant.

t = the time necessary for the killing process to take place.

When disinfection times are determined for a series of disinfectant concentrations and the results are expressed in the equations, $n \log C_1 = \log A - \log t_1$, $n \log C_2 = \log A - \log t_2$, etc., successive pairs of equations may be combined by subtraction to yield the derived equations:

$$n_1 = \frac{\log t_2 - \log t_1}{\log C_1 - \log C_2}, \quad n_2 = \frac{\log t_3 - \log t_2}{\log C_2 - \log C_3}, \quad \text{etc.,}$$

from which an average value of n may be determined for the series.

The average value of n in such a series may also be determined by the graphical method employed by Watson (1908). When the successive values for $\log C$ and $\log t$ are plotted against each other, the results should lie on an approximately straight line. The value of n may then be calculated by the equation [Tilley (1939)]:

$$n = \frac{y_2 - y_1}{x_1 - x_2}$$

after selection of two suitable points (x_1, y_1) and (x_2, y_2) on the straight line drawn under guidance of the plotted points representing the individual experimental tests. After the average value of n for the series has been obtained either by computation or by the graphical method, values of log A may be obtained by substitution in the equation:

$$n \log C + \log t = \log A$$

and an average value of log A determined for the series.

Experimental results by Tilley (1939), using phenol as the disinfect-

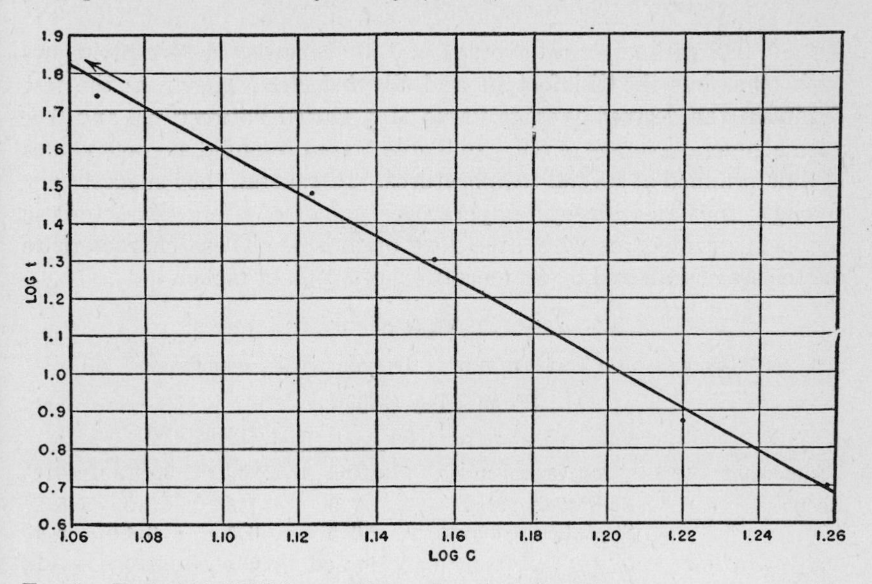

FIG. 5. Bactericidal Efficiency of Phenol against *Staphylococcus aureus*, $n = 5.75$. (From Tilley, 1939.)

ant and *Staphylococcus aureus* as the test organism, are shown in Table 4, together with the derived values of n and log A. All calculations of the value of log A were based upon the average value of $n = 5.7$. The same experimental data are presented in Fig. 5, where the values for log C are plotted against log t.

In 16 similar experiments conducted by Tilley (1939), using phenol and *Eberthella typhosa*, the derived average values of n varied between

TABLE 4

BACTERICIDAL EFFICIENCY OF PHENOL AGAINST *Staphylococcus aureus* AT 20°C.

[From Tilley (1939)]

Dilution	C (parts in 1,000)	t, minutes	Log C	Log t	Log C_1– Log C_2, etc.	Log t_2– Log t_1, etc.	n	Log A
1 : 55	18.1	5	1.25768	0.69897				7.87
1 : 60	16.6	7.5	1.22011	0.87506	0.03757	0.17609	4.69	7.83
1 : 65	15.4	15	1.18752	1.17609	0.03259	0.30103	9.24	7.94
1 : 70	14.3	20	1.15534	1.30103	0.03218	0.12494	3.88	7.88
1 : 75	13.33	30	1.12385	1.47712	0.03149	0.17609	5.59	7.88
1 : 80	12.5	40	1.09691	1.60206	0.02694	0.12494	4.64	7.85
1 : 85	11.7	55	1.06819	1.74036	0.02872	0.13830	4.81	7.83
1 : 90	11.1	80	1.04532	1.90309	0.02287	0.16273	7.11	7.86
Average values							5.7	7.87

6.8 and 9.0, with a general average of 7.3. Likewise in 24 experiments with phenol as the disinfectant and *Staphylococcus aureus* as the test organism the derived average value of n varied between 4.6 and 6.6, with a general average of 5.9. In Table 5 are presented average values of n determined at several temperatures. In general, they suggest very strongly that at ordinary temperatures values of n are characteristic for each disinfectant with each test organism. These characteristic values may be altered by temperatures of 30°C. or higher.

TABLE 5

VALUES OF n DETERMINED AT DIFFERENT TEMPERATURES

[From Tilley (1939)]

Disinfectant	Test Organism	Temperature 10°C.	20°C.	30°C.	40°C.
Phenol	*Eberthella typhosa*	7.9	7.5	5.9	5.2
	Staphylocccus aureus	6.5	6.5	6.4	5.4
o-Cresol	*E. typhosa*	8.3	7.9	5.5	5.1
	S. aureus	7.8	7.6	8.1	6.8
p-Cresol	*E. typhosa*	8.9	8.4	6.4	5.3
	S. aureus	8.2	8.7	9.4	7.0
Resorcinol	*E. typhosa*	4.6	5.1	5.2	...
	S. aureus	4.4	5.0	6.2	...
Ethyl alcohol	*E. typhosa*	12.7	11.4	8.8	...
	S. aureus	11.4	11.1	8.5	...
n-Butyl alcohol	*E. typhosa*	....	11.9	10.3	...
	S. aureus	....	11.8	10.1	...

It is generally assumed that substances which have a large value of n are highly germicidal above a given concentration but lose their efficiency rapidly upon dilution. On the other hand, compounds with a low value of n are not only germicidal in solutions above a given concentration but continue to exercise inhibiting effects on the growth of bacteria even when employed in relatively high dilutions.

Some of the dilution coefficients which have been calculated by several investigators are listed in Table 6.

TABLE 6

DILUTION COEFFICIENT (n) OF SEVERAL DISINFECTANTS

Disinfectant	Value of n in equation $C^n \cdot t$ = a constant (A)	Organism	Reference
Phenol	5.5	*Salmonella paratyphi*	Watson (1908)
	5.5	*Staphylococcus aureus*	Watson (1908)
	5.9	*S. aureus*	Tilley (1939)
	7.3	*Eberthella typhosa*	Tilley (1939)
	4.0	*S. aureus*	Gregersen (1915)
	4.0	*Serratia marcescens*	Gregersen (1915)
Thymol	4.0	*S. aureus*	Gregersen (1915)
Chloral hydrate ($CCl_3 \cdot CH(OH)_2$)	4.0	*S. aureus*	Gregersen (1915)
Sodium hydroxide	1.24	*Brucella abortus*	McCulloch (1936)
	2.7	*Escherichia coli*	Hobbs and Wilson (1942)
	1.75	*Bacillus subtilis*, spores	Hobbs and Wilson (1942)
Hydrochloric acid	1.0	*S. aureus*	Gregersen (1915)
	0.7	*S. aureus*	Cowles (1941)
	1.75	*E. coli*	Cowles (1941)
Lower fatty acids	6.0	*S. aureus*	Cowles (1941)
Mercuric chloride	1.0	*S. aureus* and other bacteria	Gregersen (1915)
	0.5	Staphylococcus and anthrax	Gegenbauer (1922)
Silver nitrate	0.86	*Salmonella paratyphi*	Watson (1908)
Hydrogen peroxide	0.5	*Eberthella typhosa*	Reichel (1908)

We have stated that n is a constant which is characteristic for each disinfectant with each organism. However, the question may be raised as to its actual meaning. Watson (1908) suggested, from analogy with chemical reactions, that the exponent n signifies the average number of molecules of disinfectant which combine with one molecule of the reacting constituent of the bacterium when it becomes incapable of further growth and multiplication. In this case the reaction between phenol and bacterial protoplasm would be a reaction of the fourth, fifth, sixth, or seventh order. This seems rather extraordinary, since the known chemical reactions are rarely above the third order. Cowles (1940) came to some interesting conclusions in his study of the disinfection concentration exponent. He presented evidence, supported by an analogy with the wetting of wool by various germicides, that an important part of the disinfection process may be the wetting of the bacterial cell and that changes in the time of disinfection with changes in the concentration of disinfectant may be due to correlated changes in wetting power. If such is the case, then n in the disinfection formula $C^n \cdot t$ = a constant (A) may be an expression of the effect which changes in concentration have upon the surface activity of the disinfectant solutions, rather than a number indicating a chemical reaction of high order.

The relation between rate of disinfection and change in concentration of disinfectant has been employed several times in the past to standardize disinfectants and to calculate, from the results obtained experimentally with one concentration, the effect which may be expected with a second untested concentration. One example from Watson's paper will illustrate this point.

A solution of phenol containing 10 parts per 1,000 disinfects a given culture in 25 minutes; a second solution takes 35 minutes. What is the strength of the second solution?

Let the strength of the second solution be x. For phenol $n = 5.5$; thus:

$$5.5 \log 10 + \log 25 = 5.5 \log x + \log 35$$

$$5.5 \log x = 5.35$$

$$x = 9.4 \text{ parts per } 1{,}000$$

Just how far such a procedure can be used to test disinfectants is very questionable, since the data in Table 6 show that workers have reported different values of n for the same disinfectant. Until more work has been done on this subject, the only safe way to evaluate germicidal powers is by actual experimentation.

INFLUENCE OF TEMPERATURE

For a long time it has been known that disinfection processes become more rapid at higher temperatures. Mathematically the relation between temperature and rate of disinfection is an arithmo-geometrical one; that is, as the temperature rises in arithmetical units, the rate of the reaction increases in geometrical progression, or there is a linear relation between the logarithm of disinfection rate and the temperature at which the process takes place. The formula relating the velocity constants at two different temperatures is:

$$\frac{k_2}{k_1} = Q_{(T_2 - T_1)}$$

in which k_2 and k_1 are constants of the disinfection reaction at the temperatures T_2 and T_1, respectively, and Q is the temperature coefficient [Phelps (1911)]. Usually the value of a 10-degree rise, Q_{10}, is given, this value being the tenth power of Q. According to the law from which this equation was deduced, the effect of higher temperature is due to an increase in the energy possessed by the reacting molecules and is proportional to the temperature reckoned from absolute zero (−273°C.). To explain this relationship further, let us take a specific example from Cohen (1922), who studied the rate of death of *Escherichia coli* at different *p*H values and temperatures. The data in Table 7 were obtained.

TABLE 7

AVERAGE VELOCITY AND TEMPERATURE COEFFICIENTS OF MORTALITY OF *Escherichia coli* AT DIFFERENT *p*H VALUES AND TEMPERATURES

[From Cohen (1922)]

Temperature,	*p*H 3.5		*p*H 6.1		*p*H 7.1		*p*H 8.0	
°C.	k	Q_{10}	k	Q_{10}	k	Q_{10}	k	Q_{10}
0	0.0176		0.000206		0.000107		0.000260	
		2.12		1.53		1.62		1.22
10	0.0373		0.000315		0.000174		0.000314	
		4.34		1.12		2.99		2.12
20	0.1654		0.000353		0.000520		0.000666	
		3.76		4.56		2.29		3.00
30	0.6214		0.0001611		0.001170		0.001996	

The Q_{10} values are obtained simply by substituting the velocity coefficients at two different temperatures in the preceding formula. For example, the temperature coefficient or the increase in death rate of *Escherichia coli* at *p*H 3.5 between 20°C. and 30°C. is:

$$\frac{k_2}{k_1} = Q_{(T_2 - T_1)}$$

$$\frac{0.6214}{0.1654} = Q_{30-20}$$

$$Q_{10} = 3.76, \quad \text{or} \quad Q = 3.76^{0.1} = 1.142$$

A more simple method for calculating the value of Q is to determine the time of exposure necessary to sterilize completely a suspension of bacteria when exposed to the same agent, but at two different temperatures. Since the time taken for the completion of the process may be considered as inversely proportional to the rate of the disinfection, it is not necessary to calculate the value of k at two different temperatures. Thus, if only the temperature is varied in an experiment and 20 minutes are required to sterilize a culture at 40°C., whereas 44 minutes are necessary at 30°C., then the temperature coefficient can be calculated:

$$Q_{10} = \tfrac{44}{20} = 2.2, \quad \text{or} \quad Q = 2.2^{0.1} = 1.082$$

A summary of the influence of temperature on the action of several chemical disinfectants is given in Table 8. The extent to which the disinfection rate is increased with rise in temperature depends on several

TABLE 8

INFLUENCE OF TEMPERATURE ON THE RATE OF DISINFECTION

Disinfectant	Organism	Q_{10}	Temperature Range, °C.	Reference
Hydrochloric acid	*Staphylococcus*, species	1.5–3.0	1–47	Paul and associates (1910)
Weak acid (buffered at *p*H 3.5)	*Eberthella typhosa*	1.64	0–30	Cohen (1922)
	Escherichia coli	3.41	0–30	
NaOH (0.5%)	*E. coli*	2.15	20–30	Hobbs and Wilson (1942)
	E. coli	3.35	30–40	
NaOH (5.0%)	*Bacillus subtilis*, spores	1.44	30–50	
NaOH (2.0%)	*B. subtilis*, spores	2.89	50–70	
Mercuric chloride	*Salmonella paratyphi*	3.0–4.0	0–42	Chick (1908)
	Anthrax spores	2.5	25–45	Madsen and Nyman (1907)
Silver nitrate	*Salmonella paratyphi*	3.0	15–40	Chick (1908)
Phenol	*S. paratyphi*	7.0–15.0	0–35	
	Anthrax spores	5.5	20–33	
Emulsified tar-acids	Anthrax spores	7.0–8.6	0–25	Chick (1908)
Chloramine-T	*Bacillus metiens*, spores	3.76, 6.11 *	25–35	Charlton and Levine (1937)
Chloramine-T	*B. metiens*, spores	3.09, 5.41 *	35–45	
Chloramine-T	*B. metiens*, spores	3.55, 5.39 *	45–55	
Hypochlorite (B-K), *p*H 10.0	*B. metiens*, spores	1.86	20–30	Rudolph and Levine (1941)
	B. metiens, spores	2.40	30–40	
	B. metiens, spores	2.90	40–50	

* First value observed at *p*H 8.7 and second at *p*H 6.0.

factors. Disinfection with metallic salts, which apparently depends in part upon a union between metal and bacterial protein, is influenced in the same degree as are other chemical reactions which are hastened about two to three times for a 10°C. rise in temperature. On the other hand, disinfection with phenol and other related compounds is increased five to eight times for a similar rise in temperature. Thus, even though it is generally accepted that temperature accelerates the rate of disinfection, several exceptions have been reported. This fact probably indicates that the phenomenon of disinfection is rather complex and that other controlling factors may be involved.

Phelps (1911) is of the opinion that the present tests for determining the potency of disinfectants are rather unsatisfactory. He has suggested that a method of standardization should include the calculation of n and Q for each disinfectant. These values can be determined by experimental trials involving two different dilutions of the disinfectant at the same temperature and two different temperatures at the same concentration. If these data are known, he believes we can better evaluate disinfectants.

EFFECT OF ORGANIC MATTER

It is now generally recognized that the presence of organic matter interferes with the action of all disinfectants. For this reason tests for germicides which are to yield results of practical significance must include organic matter in the test mixture. Some disinfectants, especially those which act by liberating chlorine or oxygen, are considerably weakened in activity by the addition of small amounts of any extraneous material with which these elements can combine. Other disinfectants are more resistant to the presence of organic matter. In fact, some are capable of efficient action in the presence of excreta, blood, dirt, and other organic substances, if used in adequate concentration. What this concentration should be under such conditions must be determined, since the degree of interference is not the same for all disinfectants even in the same class. Furthermore, a constant relationship does not exist between germicidal efficiency under these conditions and in a medium of distilled water.

Chick and Martin (1908) observed that the presence of 10 per cent blood serum reduced the efficiency of 1 per cent phenol about 12 per cent, whereas with mercuric chloride the reduction was much greater.

For example, a 0.5 per cent solution of mercuric chloride was reduced from 0.6 to 0.06 of its original value as the concentration of serum was increased from 5 to 30 per cent. The presence of particulate organic matter, such as a 3 per cent suspension of finely powdered dried feces, reduced the germicidal efficiency of phenol by about 10 per cent; upon commercial cresols a reduction of 30 to 50 per cent was produced, depending upon the completeness with which the preparation dissolved. The freer the sample was from higher and insoluble homologues, the less depreciation occurred in the original value. The so-called Chick-Martin Method of testing disinfectants in the presence of organic matter, such as dried feces, has certain inherent faults which render accurate findings difficult. To make such a test more reliable Garrod (1935) proposed a technique in which a suspension of commercial yeast, killed by heat, is used as the source of organic matter rather than dried feces. Such a suspension causes an equivalent reduction in disinfectant activity and yields constant results. It does not possess any unexpected drawbacks and has certain important advantages, the chief of which is that yeast cells exhibit a degree of regularity in chemical composition not possessed by heterogeneous fecal matter.

A more complete discussion on the effect of organic matter on various disinfectants will be found on pp. 250 to 342 of this chapter, where the various agents are taken up separately.

RELATIONSHIP BETWEEN SURFACE TENSION AND THE ACTION OF DISINFECTANTS

There seem to be some data available in support of the view that surface tension plays a role in certain disinfection processes. Here again, however, the assumption must be made that changes in the liquid-air interface are accompanied by a corresponding change in the bacterium-medium interface. As we have stated before, this analogy has very little definite proof. Therefore, the exact interpretation of the effects of changes in surface tension on disinfection processes must await the development of more accurate methods of measuring the interfacial tension between a bacterium and its medium.

Frobisher (1927) made a complete review and study of this subject. He came to the conclusion that the bactericidal powers of phenol and of hexylresorcinol against *Eberthella typhosa* may be enhanced by slightly reducing the surface tension of their substrate with suitable quantities of sodium oleate or ethyl acetate. When an excess of the surface-tension depressant was added to phenol or hexylresorcinol, its germicidal efficiency was lowered. This result was believed to be due to the adsorption of the soap on the surface of the cells, with the formation of a protective film or coating. The role played by surface-tension depressants in such a case seems to be to increase the penetrative power of the liquid disinfectants.

In a somewhat different type of study Gershenfeld and Milanick (1941) have determined the bactericidal properties of surface-tension depressants. They found that reduced surface tension alone does not explain the bactericidal action of a depressant which possesses germicidal action. Rather the bactericidal action is due to the combination of three factors or agents: (1) the surface-active material—anionic or cationic compounds; (2) the H-ion concentration of the environment—acid or alkaline; and (3) the specific organism or group of organisms—Gram-positive or Gram-negative. The germicidal action of certain anionic compounds (Aerosol and Tergitol-4 and 4T) and cationic compounds (Triton K-12) is markedly influenced by H-ion concentration. The cationic depressant exhibited its greatest efficiency in the alkaline range; the higher the *p*H, the greater was the efficiency. The anionic depressants, on the other hand, exhibited their greatest activity in the acid range; the lower the *p*H, the greater was the activity. The cationic depressant, generally speaking, was slightly more effective against *Eberthella typhosa* (Gram-negative) than against *Staphylococcus aureus* (Gram-positive); the anionic depressants showed the opposite action.

RELATIONSHIP BETWEEN CHEMICAL STRUCTURE AND BACTERICIDAL ACTIVITY

The results of most studies of disinfection are given on a weight, rather than a molecular, basis. However, the relationship between the chemical constitution of chemical compounds and their germicidal activity has been studied by several investigators [see the review by Suter (1941)]. Tilley and Schaffer (1926), for example, determined the phenol coefficients for a series of primary, secondary, and tertiary alcohols and paraphenols, using *Eberthella typhosa* and *Staphylococcus aureus* as test organisms. When the phenol coefficients were converted from the original gram-weight basis to a gram-molecular basis by the formula:

$$\frac{\text{Molecular weight of substance tested}}{\text{Molecular weight of phenol}} \times \text{Phenol coefficient} = \text{Molecular coefficient}$$

Tilley and Schaffer observed that the molecular coefficients of successive members of each series increased almost uniformly, with an average ratio between coefficients of 3.36 for the primary normal alcohols and approximately 3.0, 2.7, and 3.3 for the secondary normal alcohols, tertiary normal alcohols, and paraphenols, respectively.

A more recent study on this subject is that by Klarmann, Shternov, and Gates (1934). They determined the relationship between the chemical structure and the germidical action of aliphatic and aromatic substitution derivatives of *p*-chlorophenol, *o*-chlorophenol, and the halogen-free *p*-alkyl phenol derivatives. One typical example from their work will illustrate the germicidal action of the various derivatives of *o*-chlorophenol on *Eberthella typhosa, Staphylococcus aureus, Mycobacte-*

rium tuberculosis, and *Monilia albicans*. The derivatives of *o*-chlorophenol under consideration may be represented by this general formula:

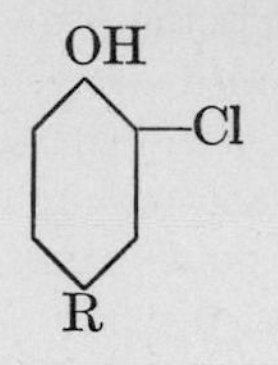

where R is the aliphatic or aromatic substituent. The data obtained with these representative test organisms are presented in Table 9 and

TABLE 9

THE GERMICIDAL ACTION OF HOMOLOGOUS DERIVATIVES OF *o*-CHLOROPHENOL UPON ORGANISMS

[From Klarmann, Shternov, and Gates (1934)]

	Eberthella typhosa		*Staphylococcus aureus*		*Mycobacterium tuberculosis hominis*		*Monilia albicans*	
	I *	II *	I	II	I	II	I	II
o-Chlorophenol	1 : 350	2.5	1 : 200	2.9	1 : 200	2.2	1 : 250	2.2
p-Alkyl Derivatives								
Methyl	1 : 1,000	6.3	1 : 600	7.5	1 : 500	5.6	1 : 750	8.3
Ethyl	1 : 2,750	17.2	1 : 1,100	15.7	1 : 1,600	17.8	1 : 2,000	22.2
n-Propyl	1 : 6,000	40.0	1 : 2,250	32.1	1 : 3,000	33.3	1 : 4,000	44.4
n-Butyl	1 : 13,000	86.7	1 : 7,500	93.8	1 : 7,000	77.8	1 : 8,000	88.9
n-Amyl	1 : 12,000	80.0	1 : 20,000	286.0	1 : 20,000	222.0	1 : 25,000	278.0
tert-Amyl	1 : 4,500	32.1	1 : 10,000	125.0	1 : 10,000	111.0	1 : 10,000	100.0
n-Hexyl	1 : 3,500	23.3	1 : 40,000	500.0	1 : 16,000	178.0	1 : 25,000	278.0
n-Heptyl	1 : 2,500	16.7	1 : 30,000	375.0	1 : 7,000	77.8	1 : 7,000	70.0
Aromatic Derivatives								
4-Benzyl	1 : 5,000	35.7	1 : 10,000	125.0	1 : 13,000	163.0	1 : 14,000	156.0
6-Benzyl	1 : 3,750	25.0	1 : 5,500	68.8	1 : 10,000	125.0	1 : 8,000	88.9
Phenol (control)	1 : 140–150	1.0	1 : 70–80	1.0	1 : 90–100	1.0	1 : 90–110	1.0

* Column I lists the minimum concentrations effective in 10 minutes, and Column II the phenol coefficients.

Fig. 6. These results show clearly the effect of increasing the weight of the substituting side chain on the bactericidal activity of compounds. The maximum germicidal efficiency for *E. typhosa* was reached with the *n*-butyl derivative, for *M. tuberculosis* and the fungus, *Monilia albicans*, with the *n*-amyl derivative, and for *S. aureus* with the *n*-hexyl derivative. Quite similar results were obtained when other derivatives and different organisms were used. In fact, Klarmann, Shternov, and Gates [see also review by Suter (1941) for more details] observed a number of regularities among the various compounds, namely:

1. Halogen substitution intensifies the microbial potency of phenol derivatives, the presence of halogen in the *para*-position to the hydroxyl group being more effective in this respect than in the *ortho*-position. The effect of halogen substitution, in general, increases with increasing atomic weight of the halogen. However, the effect of iodine has been little studied.

2. Introduction of aliphatic or aromatic groups into the nucleus of halogen phenols increases the bactericidal potency (up to certain limits), this increase depending, in the case of alkyl substitution, upon the number of carbon atoms present in the substituting group or groups.

3. As a rule the intensifying effect upon the bactericidal potency of a normal aliphatic chain with a given number of carbon atoms is greater than that of a branched chain, or of two alkyl groups with the same total number of carbon atoms.

4. *Ortho*-alkyl derivatives of *para*-chlorophenol are more actively germicidal than *para*-alkyl derivatives of *ortho*-chlorophenol.

5. In the case of the higher homologues the germicidal action manifests a "quasi-specific" character in that, beginning with a definite point (which is different in the case of the various test organisms), with the further increase in the weight of the substituting groups, the germicidal capacity drops to almost total inactivity with respect to certain microorganisms (*Eberthella typhosa, Shigella paradysenteriae*) while rising to comparatively enormous values with respect to others (*Staphylococcus aureus*, streptococcus, *Mycobacterium smegmatis*).

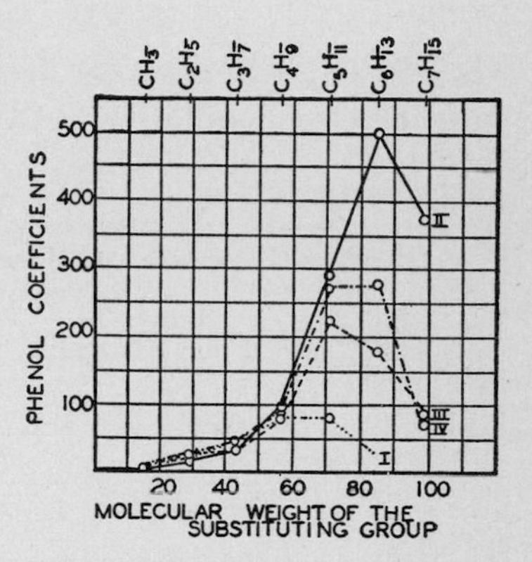

FIG. 6. The Germicidal Action of *para*-Alkyl Derivatives of *ortho*-Chlorophenol. Test organism: I. .... = *Eberthella typhosa*; II. —— = *Staphylococcus aureus*; III. ---- = *Mycobacterium tuberculosis (hominis)*; IV. -·-·- = *Monilia albicans*. (From Klarmann, Shternov, and Gates, 1934.)

6. Separation of an alkyl group from the phenol nucleus by oxygen decreases the germicidal activity, and the presence of oxygen as an alcohol or ether group in the side chain likewise produces this effect. On the other hand, a sulphur atom between the aryl and alkyl group increases the bactericidal action.

7. Increasing the number of hydroxyl groups attached to an aromatic nucleus decreases the germicidal activity, a decrease that cannot effectively be compensated for by alkyl or halogen when more than two hydroxyl groups are present.

Additional data on the relationship between chemical structure and the inhibitory effect of various chemicals for microorganisms will be found on pp. 310 to 315 on sulfonamide compounds and in Chapter 7.

BACTERIOSTASIS

Before the effects of individual chemicals on bacteria are discussed, it should be pointed out that many of the compounds which are commonly referred to as disinfectants or germicides actually exhibit only bacteriostatic or antiseptic action. The inhibition of normal bacterial multiplication by chemical substances, such as dyes and other compounds, is generally spoken of as *bacteriostasis.* However, it has been well established that there is no sharp differentiation between mere inhibition of bacterial multiplication and germicidal action by chemicals. Such a separation is made only for convenience. The general relationship between these categories is shown clearly in a disinfection "spectrum" (Fig. 7), such as the one devised by Marshall and Hrenoff (1937). An analysis of this spectrum reveals a concept of the action of disinfectants as a flexible blending of differentiated modes or degrees of activity. The first band of the spectrum covers a range of dilutions of a chemical agent between zero per cent and the greatest dilution which can be shown to exert any action whatever on bacteria, the *ineffective* band. The second band portrays a range of relatively high dilutions in which there is some slight stimulation of bacterial multiplication, the *stimulative* band. This range is usually narrow and is frequently of no practical significance, although there is no material objection to the application of the spectrum to substances not ordinarily considered as disinfectants, whereupon this band might become broad. The third, or *inhibiting,* and the fourth, or *bactericidal,* bands merge indistinguishably. These bands are those around which interest is primarily centered. The fifth, or *impractical,* band covers a range of concentrations of disinfectant which, for any of various reasons, is too great for reasonable application. The position and width of the bands vary with the disinfectant, the method of testing, the temperature, the organism, and many other factors.

The data presented in Fig. 7, taken from Marshall and Hrenoff (1937), are a condensation of the chief correlations, following in general scheme the idea of the disinfectant spectrum. The twenty disinfectants used are presented vertically, and the pertinent dilutions horizontally. The bars of the chart are constructed from data derived from the growth of six organisms, including *Staphylococcus aureus, Bacillus subtilis, Escherichia coli,* and *Neisseria catarrhalis,* in broth cultures containing various dilutions of the disinfectants indicated. The activity of each disinfectant has been empirically divided into three ranges. One represents concentrations of the chemical agent which, as tested, permitted no apparent multiplication during the period observed. The

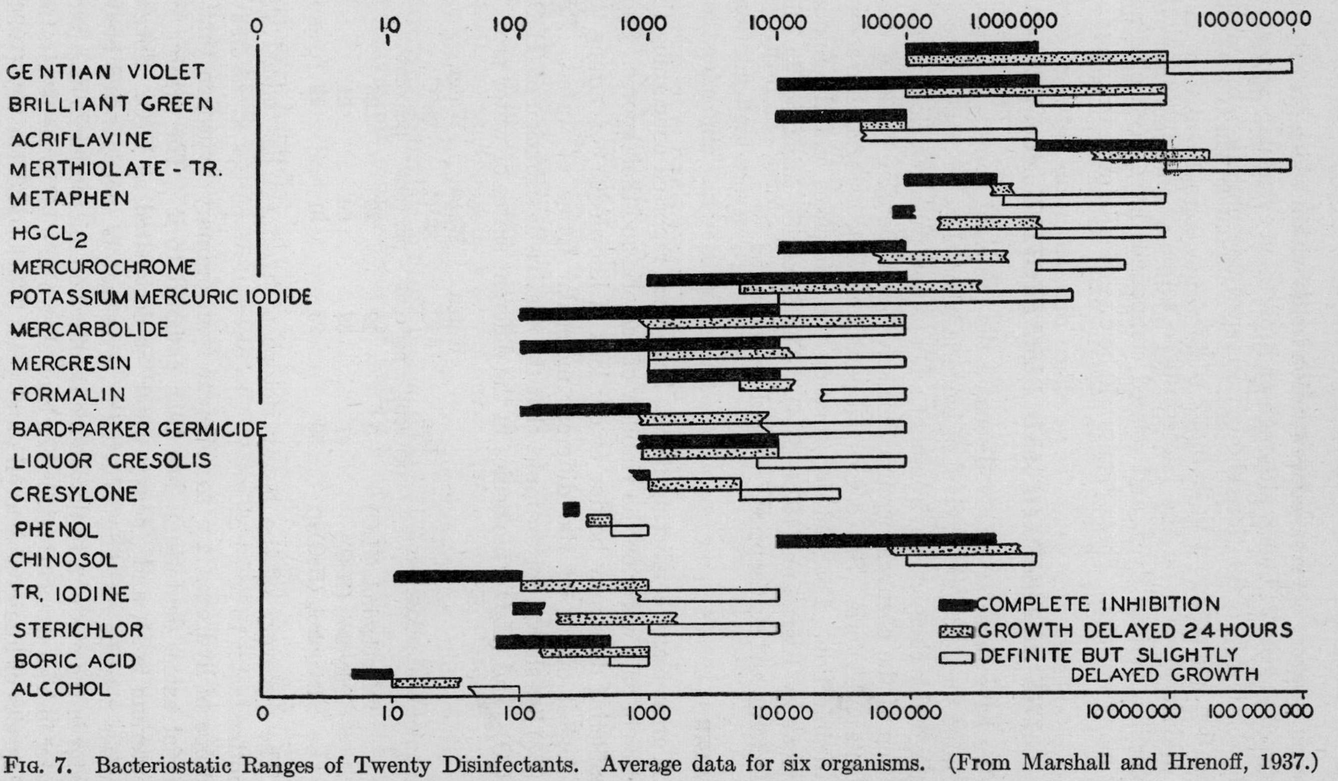

FIG. 7. Bacteriostatic Ranges of Twenty Disinfectants. Average data for six organisms. (From Marshall and Hrenoff, 1937.)

second category covers a concentration range within which growth was delayed at least 24 hours, although multiplication eventually appeared. The third range of dilutions showed demonstrable inhibition, but multiplication was apparent in 24 hours or less.

Additional data on the bacteriostatic action of the sulfonamides, penicillin, various dyes, and related compounds have been obtained by many workers. These results will be discussed later in the chapter.

THE ANTISEPTIC AND DISINFECTING AGENTS

We have thus far briefly discussed the principal factors which determine the death or survival of bacteria when they are exposed to an unfavorable chemical environment. Let us now turn to a closer examination of the chemical agents themselves and mention some of their effects on bacteria. Space does not permit our discussing all the agents of disinfection. For such information the references and the annual reviews by Klarmann (1939–1944), "The Scientific Advances in Disinfectants and Antiseptics," should be consulted.

WATER

A great many conflicting results have been reported concerning the action of pure water on the viability of bacteria and their spores. Such conflicting data may be due to our lack of knowledge concerning the biological effects of the different molecular forms of water. Rao (1933) has shown, for example, that the relative distribution of (H_2O), $(H_2O)_2$, and $(H_2O)_3$ molecules in the different states of water are:

	Ice, per cent	Water, 0°C., per cent	Water, 38°C., per cent	Water, 98°C., per cent
Monohydrol, (H_2O)	0	19	29	36
Dihydrol, $(H_2O)_2$	41	58	50	51
Trihydrol, $(H_2O)_3$	59	23	21	13

The discovery of the heavy isotope of hydrogen has added still another factor to be considered. The physical properties of this heavy isotope of hydrogen are so different from ordinary hydrogen that a special name, deuterium, has been assigned to it. The symbol for deuterium is D, and "heavy water" is designated as D_2O. Several studies may be cited in which the investigators incorporated heavy water in the medium to determine its effect on microorganisms. Such water in high concentrations has been shown to inhibit the respiration of species of luminous bacteria and yeast [Taylor and Harvey (1934)] and to decrease the rate of fermentative deamination of *d*-alanine

[Forjaz and Jacobsohn (1938)]. For example, the respiration of yeast in water containing deuterium oxide in concentrations below 20 per cent was not changed, whereas 45 per cent caused a 5 per cent reduction in respiration, and 97 to 98 per cent heavy water about 50 per cent reduction after 1 hour. Hansen and Blegen's (1935) experiments showed that media containing 92 to 94 per cent D_2O did not inhibit the growth of staphylococci or typhoid bacilli; and Weiser (1937), using concentrations of 0.13, 0.7, and 5.0 per cent deuterium oxide in whey broth, found no appreciable change in the morphology or rate of multiplication of eight strains of *Lactobacillus acidophilus* and *Lactobacillus bulgaricus*.

Many factors influence the action of water on bacterial viability. For instance, Winslow and Falk (1923) found after a great many tests that the rate of death of bacteria in water is increased greatly by increased hydrogen-ion concentration (Table 10). A reaction of about *p*H 6.0 was the most favorable to the viability of *Escherichia coli* in distilled water, the viability decreasing as the solution became more acid or more alkaline.

TABLE 10

VIABILITY OF *Escherichia coli* AFTER 9 HOURS IN DISTILLED WATER AT 37°C.

[From Winslow and Falk (1923)]

	*p*H					
	4.0	5.0	6.0	7.0	7.5	8.0
Percentage of bacteria surviving	1	82	106 *	54	35	12

* A slight increase in cells occurred at this *p*H value.

The amount of carbon dioxide and ammonia absorbed from the air, the quantity of dissolved oxygen, the temperature at which the suspension is maintained, and other factors may influence the action of pure water on the life processes of bacteria. For example, Bigger and Nelson (1943) have observed that coliform bacilli will actually grow in distilled water containing talc, presumably due to their utilization of CO_2 and NH_3 derived from the atmosphere and dissolved in the water.

CATIONS AND ANIONS

A great deal has been written about the physiological antagonistic and stimulative effects of cations and anions, but little is known about the mechanism of their action. Whether they act upon the cell membrane and alter its permeability, change the physical and chemical state of the protoplasm, affect the activities of the cellular enzymes, or bring about a series of changes is not well understood at this time. To complicate the picture at times is the evidence that the toxic action of one ion can be neutralized by different ions and that certain metals exhibit a phenomenon known as oligodynamics.

Ions themselves are not usually classed as antiseptics or disinfectants, at least not in the concentrations used. However, because of their indirect effect on disinfection processes, they must be given some attention. For example, Sprowls and Poe (1943) have found that many inorganic astringents (salts of aluminum, copper, iron, lead, mercury, silver, and zinc) are capable of increasing the germicidal power of such antiseptics as phenol, hexylresorcinol, merthiolate, and metaphen when determined by the F.D.A. method of testing antiseptics. There seems to be a maximum dilution for both astringent and antiseptic, beyond which no enhancement of inhibition is manifested by combining the substances. This point is also clearly illustrated on pp. 268 to 269 on alkalies, where it is mentioned that the addition of electrolytes to a germicide, such as sodium hydroxide, may increase or decrease the action of

TABLE 11

CATIONS IN SERIES OF INCREASING TOXICITY FOR BACTERIA, PARAMECIA, AND FUNDULUS EGGS

[From Falk (1923)]

[Eisenberg (1918)] Bacteria		[Winslow and Hotchkiss (1922)] *Escherichia coli*		[Woodruff and Bunzel (1909)] Paramecium	[Mathews (1904)] Fundulus Eggs
Na		K		K	Sr
K		Na		Ca	Mg
NH_4	Al	NH_4	Al	Zn	Ba
Li	Nd	Li	Ce	Sr	K
Mg	Pb	Sr	Cd	Mg	NH_4
Sr	Cu	Mg	Hg	Mn	Al
Ca	Tl	Ca		Co	Ca
Ba	Zr	Ba		Ni	Na
Mn	Ni	Mn		Cd	Mn
Ce	Cd	Ti^{+++}		Cu	Li
Th	Co	Sn		Ag	Fe^{++}
Fe^{++}	Au	Ni		Pb	Ni
Y	Pt	Ti^{+}		Fe	Co
Cr	Hg	Zn		Hg	Zn
U	Ag	Cu		H	H
Zn		Fe^{++}			Au
Fe^{+++}		Fe^{+++}			Cd
Ti		Co			Cu
Be		Pb			Fe^{+++}

the germicide through an effect upon the dissociation of the germicide, as well as through action upon the bacterial cells.

It is almost impossible to formulate a satisfactory classification of cations and anions based upon their stimulative or toxic effects against bacteria, since they vary considerably in the concentrations which are stimulatory and those which are toxic. Furthermore, since the study of such ions usually depends upon the dissociation of the salts of mineral acids, their action may be due to the undissociated molecule, to the anion, to the cation, or to all three in combination. Several workers [see reviews by Falk (1923) and Seuderling (1933)] have attempted to assess the importance of each of these three factors by making comparative tests with salts of one base combined with different anions, and of one anion combined with different cations. Table 11, adopted from Falk (1923), shows the essential similarities in the toxic action of cations for bacteria, protozoa, and marine eggs. The cations are arranged in series of increasing toxicity for the various cells. In general, the data show that the ionic efficacy increases with the valence. However, there are some exceptions to this general rule.

The actual molar concentrations of salts necessary to cause inhibition of multiplication of *Escherichia coli* were studied by Hotchkiss (1923). Some of her data are summarized in Table 12. The less toxic

TABLE 12

MOLAR CONCENTRATIONS OF SALTS WHICH LIMIT MULTIPLICATION OF *Escherichia coli* IN PEPTONE WATER (INCUBATION PERIOD, 3 DAYS)

[From Hotchkiss (1923)]

Group I			Group II		
Salt	No multiplication	Multiplication	Salt	No multiplication	Multiplication
KCl	2.0	1.0	$TiCl_3$	0.01	0.0025
NaCl	2.0	1.0	TlCl	0.005	0.001
NH_4Cl	1.0	0.75	$SnCl_4$	0.005	0.001
LiCl	0.75	0.5	$NiCl_2$	0.005	0.001
			$ZnCl_2$	0.001	0.0005
$SrCl_2$	1.0	0.25	$CuCl_2$	0.001	0.0005
$MgCl_2$	0.5	0.25	$FeCl_3$	0.001	0.0005
$CaCl_2$	0.5	0.25	$FeCl_2$	0.001	0.0005
			$CoCl_2$	0.0005	0.0001
$BaCl_2$	0.25	0.1	$PbCl_2$	0.0005	0.0001
$MnCl_2$	0.05	0.025	$AlCl_3$	0.0005	0.0001
			$CeCl_3$	0.0005	0.0001
			$CdCl_2$	0.0001	0.00005
			$HgCl_2$	0.00001	0.000005

salts (termed Group I) include the salts of the alkali metals and the alkaline earth metals. The toxic salts (Group II) consist of the salts of the heavy metals. It is known that the salts of Group I give neutral solutions and that, owing to hydrolysis, the salts of Group II yield solutions with an acid reaction, a fact which may account for part of their action. The stimulative action of these salts for *E. coli* was included in the study by Hotchkiss (1923). In 15 of the 23 chlorides studied a concentration was found which stimulated growth, as indicated by the production of a turbidity greater than that in a control solution to which no salt had been added (Table 13). The chlorides of the cations were used in all cases in order to avoid any conflicting results which might arise if different anions were employed. It will be noted that the stimulating salts included not only those of K, Na, NH_4, Li, Sr, Mg, Ca, and Ba but also such toxic salts as those of Sn, Zn, Pb, Ce, and Hg. The stimulating concentrations for the toxic salts were, of course, exceedingly low. This problem has been further investigated by Fabian and Winslow (1929).

TABLE 13

MOLAR CONCENTRATIONS OF SALTS WHICH STIMULATE THE GROWTH OF *Escherichia coli* IN PEPTONE WATER (INCUBATION PERIOD, 3 DAYS)

[From Hotchkiss (1923)]

Salt	Molar Concentration	Salt	Molar Concentration
NaCl	0.25	$TiCl_3$	0.0005
KCl	0.25	$NiCl_2$	0.0001–0.00005
NH_4Cl	0.25	$PbCl_2$	0.00005
LiCl	0.125–0.025 *	$SnCl_4$	0.00005–0.000005
		$ZnCl_2$	0.00005–0.00001
$CaCl_2$	0.05	$CeCl_3$	0.00001 *
$MgCl_2$	0.05	$HgCl_2$	0.000001 *
$SrCl_2$	0.025		
$BaCl_2$	0.05		

* Growth stimulation slight.

Studies of anion effects on bacteria have been less numerous than those of cations, although a considerable literature has grown up around the effect of the hydroxyl ion. For extensive reviews on this subject Eisenberg (1918) and Fabian and Winslow (1929) should be consulted. Some of the anions are known to be toxic for microorganisms, but their use as bactericides is somewhat limited because of their affinity for organic matter.

The most extensive study of the toxicity of anions for bacteria was that reported by Eisenberg in 1918. He used twelve different bacterial species, including *Bacillus anthracis*, *Corynebacterium diphtheriae*, *Escherichia coli*, *Eberthella typhosa*, and *Vibrio comma*, and employed 44 different anions in combination with 11 different cations. Some of his results are indicated in Table 14, where the various anions, in combination with different cations, are arranged in order of increasing toxicity. The results are average findings based on the toxicity for the various bacterial species. It is interesting to note the position of the various anions in the series when they are in combination with different cations. When the various cations were disregarded, the anions followed the following series, based on increasing toxicity: $SO_4 < S_2O_3 <$ tartrate $< H_2PO_2 < MoO_4 < Cl < Br = NO_3 < SO_3 < Fe(CN)_6''''$ < acetate $< ClO_3 <$ citrate $< HPO_3 <$ oxalate < formate < CNS $< ClO_4 < BrO_3 < I < H_2PO_4 <$ benzoate < nitroprusside $< AsO_4 < CrO_4 < P_2O_7 < NO_2 < F < BF_4 < BO_3 < B_4O_7 < Fe(CN)_6'''$ < salicylate $< HSeO_3 < IO_3 < S_2O_8 < S_2O_7 < TeO_4 < SbS_4 < OsO_4 < IO_4 < Cr_2O_7 < TeO_3$. The OH ion has been shown to be more toxic than any of the anions just listed.

TABLE 14

Anions in Series of Increasing Toxicity for Bacteria

[From Eisenberg (1918)]

Various Anions in Combination with										
Na	K	NH_4	Li	Mg	Ca	Sr	Ba	Zn	Cd	Co
SO_4	Tartrate	Tartrate	SO_4	SO_4	Cl	Br	Cl	SO_4	SO_4	F
Tartrate	NO_3	Cl	Cl	Cl	Acetate	Cl	NO_3	NO_3	Cl	NO_3
Acetate	Cl	Br	Br	Br	Br	ClO_3	Br	Cl	NO_3	I
Cl	Br	Oxalate	NO_3	NO_3	ClO_3	NO_3	ClO_3	ClO_3	ClO_3	CNS
ClO_3	Acetate	NO_3	ClO_3	ClO_3	NO_3	I	ClO_4	Br	I	Br
Br	Citrate	ClO_4	Citrate	I	I		I	I	Br	SO_4
NO_3	Oxalate	CNS	CNS		CNS		CNS			Cl
Citrate	BrO_3	I	Oxalate		IO_3					ClO_3
Oxalate	I	F	I							
Formate	CNS	IO_3	IO_3							
CNS	F									
ClO_4	Salicylate									
BrO_3	CN									
I	IO_3									
Benzoate	IO_4									
PO_4										
F										
Salicylate										
IO_3										

Although the foregoing discussion applies quite generally to all bacteria, it must be kept in mind that different bacteria vary in susceptibility to the same salt. For example, Eisenberg (1918) found that *Bacillus anthracis* possessed more than average resistance to fluorides, iodates, oxalates, citrates, chlorates, bromates, cadmium, zinc, and copper; *Corynebacterium diphtheriae* showed a high resistance to tellurites, tellurates, nickel, and copper; and *Vibrio comma* exhibited above-average resistance to chlorates, perchlorates, molybdates, and pyrophosphates.

These general results apply only to the presence of one salt in the solution. When the effect of solutions containing more than one salt is studied, certain other factors must be considered. Of these, "ionic antagonism" has received the greatest attention by students of animal and plant physiology. The classic papers by Ringer in 1880 and 1883 mark the beginning of rational physiological study of the specific influences of inorganic ions. He observed that a solution of NaCl in distilled water did not maintain the beat of a heart which was perfused with it, but that its inadequacy could be remedied by the appropriate addition of calcium or potassium chlorides. As a result of this early work physiologically balanced solutions now known as Ringer's solution, Ringer-Locke solution, and Tyrode solution have been developed. In these solutions the essential ions are provided, and the concurrent toxic or deleterious effects of necessary ions are removed by the addition of other ions. The application of the conception of physiological antagonism of ions was first applied to the study of bacteria by Flexner (1907) and more or less simultaneously by Lipman (1909) and Eisler (1909). Flexner, for example, demonstrated that a solution of NaCl was directly toxic to the meningococcus, but that the toxic effects could be neutralized with calcium or potassium salts, and that Ringer's solution was favorable for the maintenance of viability. Eisler studied the action of NaCl, KCl, K_2SO_4, LiCl, $MgCl_2$, $MgSO_4$, $CaCl_2$, and $BaCl_2$ on vibrios, staphylococci, and *Bacillus subtilis*. The toxic action of LiCl on *B. subtilis* could be neutralized by the addition of a divalent, but not of a monovalent, salt. He was able to inhibit the toxicity of certain divalent salts by both mono- and divalent cations, although with others, such as $HgCl_2$, he could not inhibit or antagonize the toxic action. The extensive studies by Winslow, Falk, and their associates [see reviews by Falk (1923), Winslow and Dolloff (1928), and Winslow and Haywood (1931)] of this subject have done much to clarify the situation. In their early papers they demonstrated that the mere addition of a divalent salt to a toxic monovalent salt was not sufficient to render the solution favorable for bacteria; instead the two salts must be present in definite proportions. For example, a solution containing 0.145 *M* $CaCl_2$ + 0.290 *M* NaCl was highly toxic to *Escherichia coli*, whereas a solution of 0.145 *M*

$CaCl_2$ + 0.680 *M* NaCl was found to be nontoxic. In their more recent studies Winslow, Falk, and their associates have brought forward evidence to show that salts exert a highly characteristic effect upon bacterial viability and that there may be some fallacy in the interpretation of the antagonistic effect of salts. They observed that salts in certain low concentrations stimulated the growth of organisms; in higher concentrations there was a series of "cross-over concentrations," and with further increase in concentration bactericidal action took place. The molal concentrations for nine salts are given in Table 15, where the effects are readily comparable. For the most part these results check fairly well with those obtained in earlier studies. Winslow and Dolloff explain the apparent antagonistic effects of monovalent and divalent salts to the production in the suspension of a more favorable ionic concentration for the survival of bacteria, rather than to a qualitative antagonism between the two cations.

The interesting study by Guest and Salle (1942) may also be mentioned here. They have shown that certain inorganic metallic salts which are not germicidal or are only slightly so may exhibit a pronounced killing effect when mixed in certain combinations ($FeCl_2$ + $FeCl_3$, $SnCl_2$ + $SnCl_4$, etc.), and proportions which produce an oxidation-reduction system. The phenomenon appears to be a function of the metallic ion.

TABLE 15

MOLAL CONCENTRATIONS OF VARIOUS SALTS PRODUCING CERTAIN EFFECTS UPON THE VIABILITY OF *Escherichia coli*

[From Winslow and Haywood (1931)]

Salt	Zone of Increasing Stimulation	Zone of Decreasing Stimulation	Cross-over Concentration	Zone of Toxicity
NaCl	0.009–0.08	0.09–0.17	0.28	0.36–0.44
KCl	0.009–0.05	0.05–0.08	0.29	0.56–0.68
LiCl	0.01–0.02	0.03–0.04	0.06	0.07–0.10
$BaCl_2$	0.001–0.01	0.04–0.05	0.06	0.08–0.13
$MgCl_2$	0.002–0.008	0.008–0.01	0.02	0.07
$CaCl_2$	0.0003–0.008	0.01–0.02	0.02	0.04–0.07
$MnCl_2$	0.00006–0.0002	0.0003	0.0004	0.0006–0.0008
$ZnCl_2$	0.00002–0.00008	0.0001–0.0003	0.0003	0.0004–0.0005
$CdCl_2$	0.000008–0.00002	....	0.0001	....

Mechanism of Salt Action. So much has been written about the action of salts on bacteria and so many theories have been proposed to account for the physiological action of ions that it is almost impossible to review the subject briefly. Several workers believe that ions operate upon the cell by combining with it; others are of the opinion that they operate without combination but at a distance through radio or other activity. Some investigators have suggested highly specific mechanisms whereby the ions unite with components of protoplasm essential to metabolism. Such unions affect the cell because the new compounds cannot operate in the normal protoplasmic economy or because they operate more actively or less actively or in some other abnormal fashion. Unions of protoplasmic components with ions, according to some workers, are purely chemical; according to others, they are physical or physico-chemical. Some authors tell us that the ions combine with proteins; others, with lipoids, electrolytes, enzymes, fluids, etc., in the cell. Such combinations affect the cell's food or its catalysts or its permeability to solids or liquids or to solutes or colloids in the environment. In reviewing this entire subject Falk (1923) stated:

> . . . the development of our understanding of the role which electrolytes play in the economy of metabolizing protoplasm lies in the advancement of colloid chemistry and in the application of these advances to the problem of physiology. If we list certain outstanding phenomena of electrolyte action upon colloidal substances, *i.e.:*
> 1. coagulative powers as determined experimentally by precipitation;
> 2. electrokinetic effects and the phenomena of the isoelectric point;
> 3. parallel action of electrolytes in electro-endosmose phenomena;
> 4. inhibition of Brownian movement;
> 5. effects upon physical properties (color, viscosity, etc.);
> 6. absorption and adsorption of electrolytes upon colloidal coagula;
> 7. mutual precipitation of charged colloids;
> 8. mutual and single protective (stabilizing) action of charged colloids;
>
> we have also listed the outstanding indications towards the line of elucidation of the physiological phenomena in which electrolytes function. This may, at first thought, appear too sanguine. But we are persuaded that the effects of electrolytes on living things are, in the main, the resultants of their effects upon colloids of protoplasm, and in an understanding of the latter lies the elucidation of the former.

For many interesting data on the adsorption of cations by bacteria see the paper by McCalla (1940). Future studies of this nature will probably give us the explanation of the mechanism of salt action. Tarr (1941) has also discussed several possible ways in which sodium nitrite exhibits a bacteriostatic action against various bacteria.

The "Oligodynamic Action" of Elements on Bacteria. In 1893 Carl von Nägeli reported the action of various quantities of metallic salts on different kinds of fresh water algae. He found, for instance, that *Spirogyra* was killed almost at once if metals or metallic salts were present in a high enough concentration. Very little change in cell morphology took place during the killing process. When an extremely weak concentration was employed, however, certain definite morphological changes occurred in the cell before its death. Von Nägeli described these alterations in some detail and assigned the name "oligodynamic action" to the phenomenon. As this term is now used, little attention is given to the morphological changes; instead it is used to designate the zone of inhibition which results when a bright piece of metal is placed on the surface of a fresh agar plate uniformly inoculated with a young bacterial culture.

Since von Nägeli's early work the literature on this subject has grown very large, and no attempt will be made to discuss it here. One example, a study by Seuderling (1933), will be sufficient to explain the phenomenon. He employed forty different microorganisms in his tests, including *Staphylococcus aureus, Brucella abortus, Eberthella typhosa, Escherichia coli, Pseudomonas aeruginosa, Vibrio comma, Bacillus subtilis,* and *Mycobacterium phlei.* The following elements of Group I of the periodic system were used: copper, silver, and gold. Group II was represented by cadmium and mercury. Elements belonging to Groups III and IV were not used, because previous tests had shown that tin and lead have but little effect, and thallium dissolves rapidly in culture media. From Group V were chosen arsenic, antimony, and bismuth. Tellurium alone was selected from Group VI, as selenium had proved itself inactive. Group VII was omitted entirely. In Group VIII cobalt alone proved oligodynamic; a few tests with iron, nickel, palladium, and platinum showed them to be inactive. The total number of elements used was ten: copper, silver, gold, cadmium, mercury, arsenic, antimony, bismuth, tellurium, and cobalt. The technique of the test consisted briefly of spreading the various bacterial cultures uniformly over the surface of agar media and then aseptically placing the clean bright elements on the surface of the inoculated plates. Petri dishes prepared in this way were incubated in a temperature optimum for each microorganism. The cultures were allowed to multiply, and the results were recorded on the following day or later, depending on the time taken by the bacteria to develop. Those elements exhibiting the phenomenon of oligodynamics were accompanied by a so-called "halo," or bacterial-free zone, around the metal. The width of the zone was measured and the appearance of the border line recorded as either sharp or diffuse. Daily transfers, covering a period of 14 days, were taken from this region devoid of visible growth and transplanted into fresh media to determine the presence or absence of viable cells. From his extensive experiments Seuderling was able to draw the following conclusions:

1. Previous statements of several scientists to the effect that bacteria in the region nearest the element, the so-called bacterial-free zone, were actually dead do not hold good. To substantiate this assertion Seuderling demonstrated that the region contained bacteria which were unable to divide because of the deleterious effect of the elements but were able, for a considerable period, to initiate growth when transferred to fresh culture media.

2. A relationship seems to exist between the size of the bacterial-free zone and the length of time it takes for the bacteria to die. A larger bacterial-free region usually means a quicker destruction of bacteria. Of the elements studied cadmium, mercury, arsenic, and antimony were very active, as were copper and tellurium in a considerable number of cases. On the other hand, gold and bismuth showed themselves to be exceedingly weak in this respect, silver and cobalt being slightly more effective.

3. The oligodynamic action of the elements was decreased to a varying extent by the presence of agar, which served as a protective colloid.

4. The effect of the different elements depends chiefly upon their spreading in the culture media. With the exception of gold all the elements used could be shown to exist in the culture media; the existence of copper and cobalt was proved by X-rays.

5. The mycobacteria were the easiest to affect, and they also showed a larger bacterial-free zone than the others. Quite similar results were obtained with the other species tested. In general, death of bacteria was preceded by a weakening and diminishing of colonies. Bacteria which formed pigment lost this property on continued exposure to the various active elements.

Several theories have been advanced to explain the phenomenon of oligodynamics. According to Saxl (1924), for example, such characteristics of metals are nothing but a peculiar form of bactericidal power which cannot be explained in a purely chemical way but which may possibly be due to a physical phenomenon taking place on the surface of metals and may be transferred to other substances, including media. He believes it should be regarded as a far-reaching force originating possibly from the air and still unknown in its nature. He fails, however, to give a satisfactory explanation of oligodynamics. Most scientists embrace the theory of the dissolution of metals. Considerable proof for this viewpoint is given in the work of Seuderling, since he was able to demonstrate the presence of the metals in the media by careful X-ray analyses.

In recent years attempts have been made to apply the oligodynamic action of metals to water purification, especially by using a special form of silver known as katadyn silver. The cost of purification by this method is rather high, even though it is claimed that the katadyn silver will retain its efficiency for 5 years or longer.

ACIDS AND ALKALIES

The disinfectant action of highly dissociated mineral acids, such as hydrochloric and sulfuric, depends upon the number of free hydrogen ions present per unit volume and not upon their normal strength. However, the weak organic acids such as acetic and benzoic, tend to exert a more toxic effect than would be indicated by their degree of dissociation. Here the effect appears to be due in most cases to the whole molecule and is specific for each acid. For example, acetic acid has only 10 to 20 per cent the toxicity of benzoic. These points are more clearly shown in the data (see Table 16) taken from the experiments of Winslow and Lochridge (1906). The hydrogen-ion concentration necessary to bring about a destructive action varies considerably from organism to organism. As was shown by Winslow and Lochridge, water containing 12.80 parts per million (p.p.m.) of dissociated hydrogen sterilized a culture of *Escherichia coli* in 40 minutes, whereas only 4.85 p.p.m. of dissociated hydrogen was necessary to produce the same effect in a suspension of *Eberthella typhosa*. Cowles (1941) has observed that up to a *p*H of about 2.6 (0.0025 *N*) the H ion, as furnished by HCl, is highly germicidal, but above *p*H 2.6 this ion loses its bactericidal power very rapidly.

TABLE 16

PERCENTAGE REDUCTION OF *Escherichia coli* IN 40 MINUTES BY MINERAL AND ORGANIC ACIDS IN TAP WATER

[From Winslow and Lochridge (1906)]

	99 Per Cent Reduction				100 Per Cent Reduction			
	HCl	H_2SO_4	CH_3COOH	C_6H_5COOH	HCl	H_2SO_4	CH_3COOH	C_6H_5COOH
Normality	0.0077	0.0096	0.0812	0.0097	0.0123	0.0166	0.0935	0.0199
Per cent dissociation	97	80	1.50	7.5	96.4	76	1.35	5.4
Parts per million dissociated hydrogen	7.49	7.68	1.21	0.73	12.80	12.60	1.26	1.07

Although strong solutions of mineral acids are quite destructive to most forms of life, it is of interest to note that certain microorganisms possess remarkable tolerance to acidity. For example, the sulfur-oxidizing bacterium *Thiobacillus thiooxidans* will grow well at reactions of *p*H 1.0 or below, and the nitrogen-fixing bacterium *Azotobacter indicum* will grow and fix nitrogen in media with a *p*H as low as 3.0. Probably the most acid-tolerant microorganisms known, however, are two fungi (*Acontium velatum* and a dark-green organism belonging to the *Dematiaceae*) which have been studied by Starkey and Waksman (1943). Both these fungi grow in synthetic media of *p*H 0.1 to 1.0, and the green fungus even develops at *p*H 0.0.

McCalla (1941) is of the opinion that H ion is toxic or impairs the growth of the bacterial cell, not because of any direct lethal effect but by holding the adsorption position and preventing the combination of nutritive ions with the cell. This is a logical assumption, but other factors may also be involved.

The germicidal action of organic acids has been studied by several workers; the most complete investigations have been carried out by Reid (1932), Levine and Fellers (1940), Nunheimer and Fabian (1940), Cowles (1940), Erickson and Fabian (1942), Shillinglaw and Levine (1943), and Rahn and Conn (1944). Reid found that in a given series

TABLE 17

BACTERICIDAL ACTION OF ORGANIC ACIDS AGAINST VARIOUS BACTERIA IN 15 MINUTES AT 20°C.

[From Reid (1932)]

Acids	Bactericidal Dilutions, Normality			
	Pseudomonas aeruginosa	*Eberthella typhosa*	*Escherichia coli*	*Staphylococcus aureus*
Monobasic				
Acetic	0.33	0.5	0.66	1.5
Propionic	0.25	0.25	0.5	1.0
Butyric	0.12	0.125	0.2	0.33
Valeric	0.05	0.05	0.07	0.07
Hydroxy monobasic				
Glycolic	0.02	0.06	0.166	0.5
Lactic	0.03	0.07	0.25	0.083
Dibasic				
Oxalic	0.003	0.011	0.02	0.055
Malonic	0.008	0.03	0.038	0.2
Succinic	0.2	0.33	0.5	1.0^{+}
Tribasic				
Aconitic	0.016	0.02	0.1	0.1
Citric	0.055	1.5	2.5	3.0

of monobasic acids the bactericidal action increased with molecular weight and that the introduction of hydroxyl groups into these acids was found to render them from two to twelve times more effective. He also observed that with the organic acids the undissociated molecule plays a major role. In dibasic acids, however, the activity was found to be proportional to the dissociation, and the bactericidal activity decreased as the series ascended. Of the two tribasic acids tested, aconitic was three to thirty-six times more toxic than citric for bacteria. Some of Reid's data are given in Table 17. The ability of these organic acids to inhibit the growth of *Pseudomonas aeruginosa* in peptone broth was also studied by Reid. The activity of the monobasic series was almost completely reversed from the bactericidal dilutions. Thus acetic and propionic, both of which were comparatively weak when tested in bactericidal dilutions, exerted a much stronger inhibitory action than did butyric and valeric (Table 18). The hydroxy acids of acetic and propionic

TABLE 18

Comparative Bactericidal and Inhibitory Dilutions of Organic Acids for *Pseudomonas aeruginosa*, with *p*H Values

[From Reid (1932)]

	Bactericidal Dilutions		Inhibitory Dilutions	
Acids	Normality	*p*H	Normality	*p*H
Monobasic				
Acetic	0.33	2.7	0.004	5.11
Propionic	0.25	2.8	0.004	5.18
Butyric	0.12	2.9	0.005	5.07
Valeric	0.05	3.1	0.006	5.03
Hydroxy monobasic				
Glycolic	0.02	2.7	0.006	4.60
Lactic	0.03	2.7	0.007	4.65
Dibasic				
Oxalic	0.003	2.9	0.006	4.52
Malonic	0.008	2.8	0.01	4.5
Succinic	0.2	2.65	0.012	4.56
Tribasic				
Aconitic	0.016	2.35	0.011	4.36
Citric	0.055	2.5	0.012	4.43

showed an increase in bactericidal power over the normal acids but exhibited a weakened inhibitory action. An analysis of the bactericidal and inhibitory action of the other acids tested is shown in Table 18. Since organic acids alter the surface tension of solutions, Reid believes that this may be a factor in determining their toxicity. Cowles (1941) has studied the germicidal action of the lower fatty acids (acetic, propionic, butyric, valeric, caproic, and caprylic) against *Staphylococcus aureus* and *Escherichia coli*. He came to the conclusion that the germicidal action of the unbuffered fatty acids for the colon bacillus was due almost entirely to the un-ionized fractions of the acids, whereas for the staphylococcus the action of the lower acids was due to a summation of the H ion and the undissociated molecules, but in the higher members of the series the germicidal action was due to the un-ionized acid.

Nunheimer and Fabian (1940) and Erickson and Fabian (1942) studied the influence of several organic acids upon food-poisoning staphylococci and other bacteria, as well as yeast. The decreasing order of germicidal action of the acids for staphylococci was found to be: acetic > citric > lactic > malic > tartaric; whereas the order of effectiveness for yeast was as follows: acetic > lactic > citric. Shillinglaw and Levine (1943) found from survivor curves for *E. coli* suspended in water and in 0.02 *N* edible acids at 30°C. (86°F.) that the bacteria died considerably faster in all the acid solutions than in water and that the order of effectiveness of the acids was tartaric > glycolic > phosphoric > lactic > acetic > citric. The order of effectiveness of these acids was different at 0.6°C.(33°F.), being phosphoric = lactic > tartaric > citric. Rahn and Conn (1944) have demonstrated that benzoic and salicylic acids are nearly 100 times as efficient antiseptics in strongly acid solutions (*p*H 3.5) as they are in more neutral solutions (*p*H 6.5). In both these acids only the undissociated molecules appear to be antiseptics.

The effect of chlorine, fluorine, and other substituents on the bacteriostatic and fungistatic properties of acetic, propionic, benzoic, cinnamic, mandelic, and phenylacetic acids has been studied by Hoffman, Schweitzer, and Dalby (1940), Feasley, Gwynn, Degering, and Tetrault (1941), and Hager and Grubb (1942). In general, the derivatives are no better antiseptics than the normal acids; in some cases they are even less active.

Several studies have been carried out on the germicidal properties of carbon dioxide [see, for example, Shillinglaw and Levine (1943)]. In low concentrations carbon dioxide is hardly germicidal; in fact, certain organisms are apparently unable to grow in its absence, but in higher concentrations it may be used to some advantage as an antiseptic or preservative. The disinfectant action of carbon dioxide is thought to be due principally to the increased hydrogen-ion concentration produced in the medium, but in high concentrations it does have some direct toxicity for bacterial protoplasm. With respect to the hydrogen-ion concentration it is known that, when neutral water is saturated with carbon dioxide, it has a *p*H of about 3.8, and carbon dioxide pressure reduces the acidity of poorly buffered solutions to a point where many microorganisms are inhibited from growing or are killed.

Tannic acid is not germicidal at low concentrations (1 to 5 per cent) but is active against several organisms when the concentration is increased to 10 to 20 per cent [Martin and Fowler (1934)]. Other acids, especially benzoic, mandelic, salicylic, boric, formic, and sulfurous, have been studied as disinfectants and antiseptics, but for the most part their action is rather weak.

As a rule, the disinfectant action of alkalies is dependent upon the degree of dissociation and, therefore, their concentration of OH ions. This point has been observed by several workers and was especially well demonstrated by Krönig and Paul (1897) in their extensive studies on disinfection. Of the alkalies tested (Table 19) they found potassium hydroxide to be the most active bactericide and likewise the most highly dissociated. On the other hand, ammonium hydroxide was very weakly germicidal and only slightly dissociated. Some hydroxides, such as barium hydroxide, are more active disinfectants than their degree of dissociation would indicate. In such cases the metallic cation exerts a direct toxic action on the bacteria themselves.

TABLE 19

THE EFFECT OF DISSOCIATION ON THE DISINFECTION OF ANTHRAX SPORES BY ALKALIES

[From Krönig and Paul (1897)]

1 *M* Solutions	Per Cent Dissociation	Number of Spores Surviving after 3.3 hours	8.25 hours	18 hours	33.25 hours
KOH	77	585	31	0	0
NaOH	72	619	33	0	0
LiOH	64	778	44	0	0
NH_4OH	0.4	∞	∞	∞	3,500

Factors Influencing the Germicidal Efficiency of Alkalies. In addition to the degree of dissociation of alkalies several other factors influence their germicidal efficiency, such as the period of exposure, the temperature, the composition and concentration of the alkali solution, the number, age, and type of test organism, and the presence of organic matter and salts. These factors will be only briefly mentioned here, since they have been discussed at some length by Levine and Buchanan (1928), Tilley and Schaffer (1931), Watkins and Winslow (1932), and Hobbs and Wilson (1942).

1. EFFECT OF TIME AND TEMPERATURE OF EXPOSURE. The results of numerous experiments with various concentrations of alkalies at different temperatures have invariably shown an increase in the death rate of bacteria with progressive periods of exposure. This fact may be further illustrated by data (Table 20) from the paper by Levine (1938), who calculated the time necessary to sterilize milk bottles with sodium hydroxide solutions of different concentrations. It will be seen that the time required to complete the process decreased as either the concentration or the temperature was increased.

TABLE 20

KILLING TIMES FOR DESIGNATED TEMPERATURES AND CONCENTRATIONS OF SODIUM HYDROXIDE

[From Levine (1938)]

	Per Cent NaOH				
	1.0	1.5	2.0	2.5	3.0
Temperature, °F.	Time to Kill, minutes				
110	432.0	209.0	125.0	83.8	60.4
120	210.0	102.0	60.8	40.7	29.4
130	103.0	49.5	29.6	19.8	14.3
140	49.8	24.1	14.4	9.7	7.0
150	24.2	11.7	7.0	4.7	3.4
160	11.8	5.7	3.4	2.3	1.6
170	5.7	2.8	1.7	1.1	0.8
280	2.8	1.3	0.8	0.5	0.4

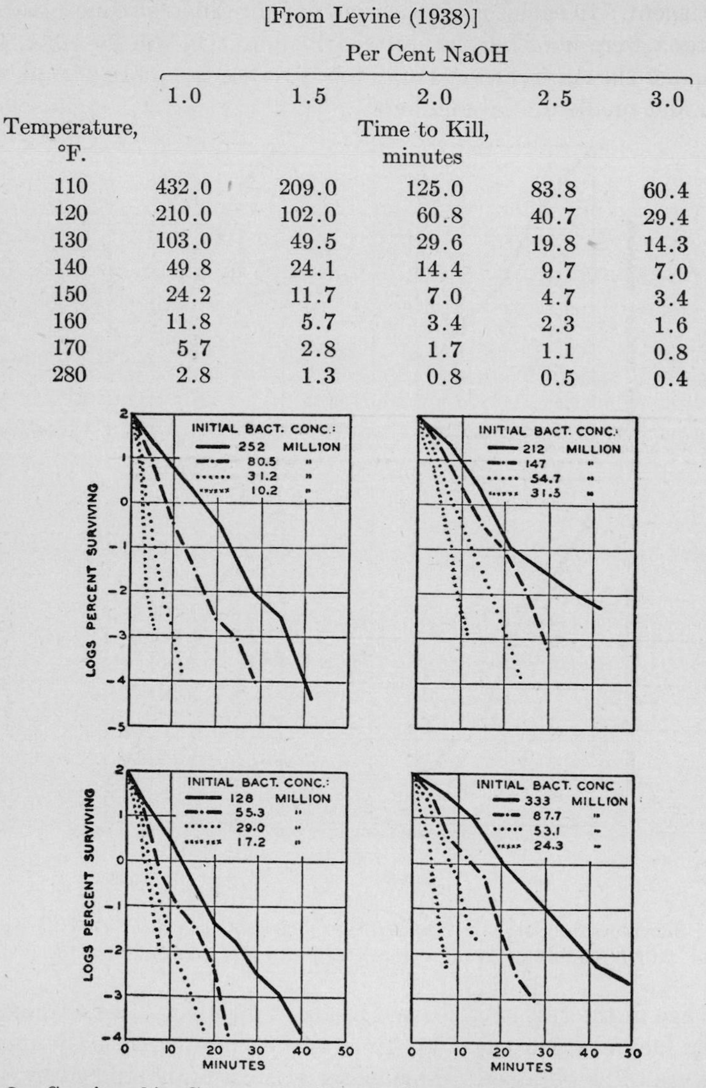

FIG. 8. Survivorship Curves of Different Concentrations of *Escherichia coli* in 0.01 *N* NaOH at 30° C. (culture age, 14 hours). (From Watkins and Winslow, 1932.)

2. EFFECT OF NUMBER, AGE, AND TYPE OF ORGANISMS. The effect of initial cell concentration upon the rate of mortality of bacteria when exposed to an unfavorable environment has been noted or implied by

many workers. This point is well illustrated in Fig. 8, which presents the results of four series of experiments in which cultures of uniform age were used for the inoculum and 0.01 *N* NaOH at 30°C. as the disinfectant agent. In each set of experiments four different concentrations of bacteria were used for the initial inoculum. It will be noted that the slope of the survivorship curve tends to become more abrupt with smaller and smaller initial numbers.

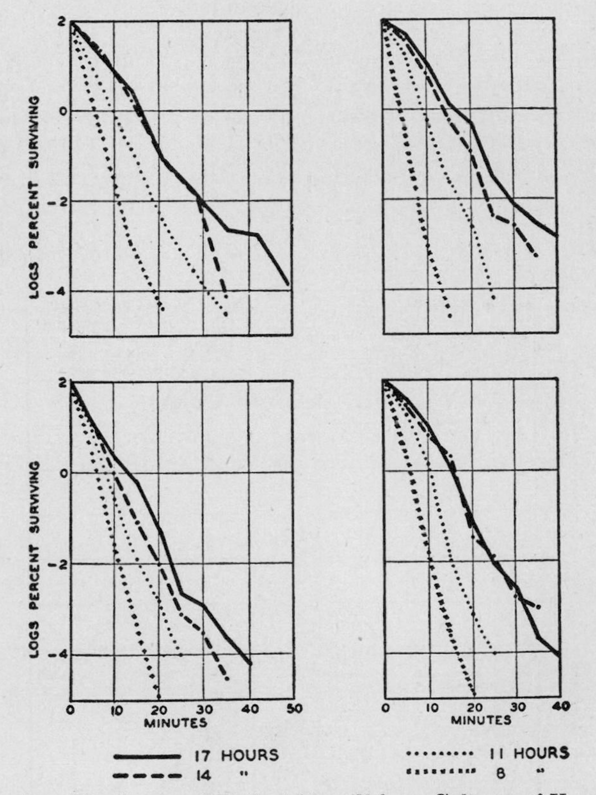

FIG. 9. Survivorship Curves of *Escherichia coli* from Cultures of Varying Ages in 0.01 *N* NaOH at 30° C. (From Watkins and Winslow, 1932.)

The age of the test culture used in alkali disinfection experiments is another factor which must be given some consideration, if uniform results are to be obtained. This factor was carefully studied by Watkins and Winslow (1932), who conducted a special series of sixteen experiments to determine the role played by the age of the culture. In all the experiments the original inoculum was varied between 123 million and 230 million bacteria per milliliter, and the toxic agent was 0.01 *N* NaOH at 30°C. Only the age of the original source culture was varied, it being 8, 11, 14, and 17 hours, respectively. Figure 9 shows that differences in culture age of even as little as 3 hours exert a clear and definite influence upon cell resistance.

Different bacterial species vary considerably in their resistance to the action of alkalies. The vegetative cells of most bacteria are killed within 10 minutes in a 1 per cent solution of sodium or potassium hydroxide, the Gram-negative bacteria being more susceptible than the Gram-positive. Tubercle bacilli are more resistant than other vegetative forms to the action of alkalies, and use is made of this property to free them from sputum and other organic materials contaminated with various bacteria. Bacterial spores, however, are more resistant than any of the vegetative cells.

3. Effect of Organic Matter and Salts. It has been previously mentioned that organic matter influences the action of all disinfectants. The extent of this effect depends upon both the type of organic matter and the particular disinfectant. However, as a general rule, the presence of such material in a germicidal solution lowers its efficiency.

The effect of salts on alkali disinfection has been extensively studied by Levine, Buchanan, and Toulouse (1927), Levine, Peterson, and Buchanan (1927, 1928), Lowman, Buchanan, and Levine (1931), and others. All these workers have observed that the germicidal efficiency of strong alkalies, especially sodium hydroxide, is increased by the addition of weak alkalies, as well as by the addition of neutral and

TABLE 21

Effect of Concentration of Added Salts on the Germicidal Efficiency of Sodium Hydroxide at 60°C.

[From Levine, Buchanan, and Toulouse (1927)]

Added Salt, per cent	1 Per Cent NaOH with		
	NaCl	Na_2CO_3	$Na_3PO_4 \cdot 12H_2O$
	Killing Time, minutes		
0	42.5	42.5	42.5
1	30.6	29.0	34.9
2	23.4	21.9	28.1
3	19.9	20.1	24.7

slightly alkaline salts. The data in Table 21 and Fig. 10 serve to illustrate this point. Both Table 21 and Fig. 10 show that the time necessary to kill bacteria (*Bacillus metiens*) by sodium hydroxide is considerably reduced by the addition of small amounts of different salts.

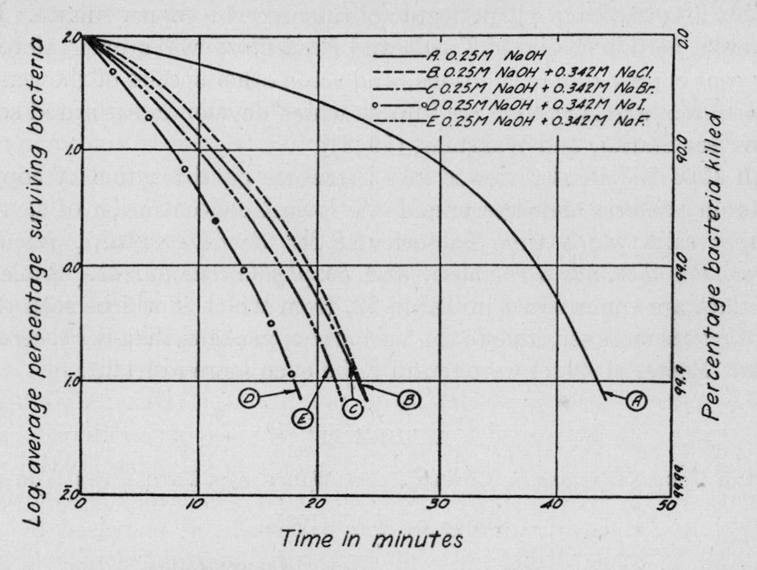

FIG. 10. Effect of Sodium Halides on Germicidal Efficiency of NaOH at 60° C. (From Lowman, Buchanan, and Levine, 1931.)

METALS AND THEIR COMPOUNDS

The toxicity of some of the metallic cations and their salts has already been mentioned. Therefore this discussion will be devoted primarily to a brief statement about the salts of heavy metals and some of the complex metallic compounds which are of importance as germicides or antiseptics.

Copper. The copper salts are not widely used today as bactericides, although they are employed somewhat as fungicides and algicides for the treatment of public water supplies and have been used as sterilizing agents for catgut sutures. Two examples will serve to illustrate the bactericidal properties of copper salts. DeWitt and Sherman (1916) reviewed the published reports on the bactericidal and fungicidal action of copper salts and noted many conflicting testimonies. From their own research, however, they concluded that copper salts were unreliable as general disinfectants. Nevertheless some organisms manifested a certain degree of specificity in their reaction to copper. *Serratia marcescens*, for instance, showed little resistance, since practically all cells were killed by dilutions of copper sulfate up to 1 : 10,000, and of copper chloride up to 1 : 100,000. *Staphylococcus aureus* and certain molds, on the other hand, were relatively resistant; 1 per cent copper as chloride and 5 per cent as sulfate failed to kill every organism. Some higher fungi, however, have a high degree of tolerance for copper sulfate. For example, certain species of *Torula* and *Penicillium* will grow in 10 to 14 per cent copper sulfate solutions, and some other species of the genera *Penicillium* and *Acontium* are known which develop in saturated solutions [see Starkey and Waksman (1943)].

In 1926 Bidzinski reviewed the literature on the action of copper salts on bacteria and determined the lowest concentration of several copper salts which were bactericidal for *Bacillus subtilis, Bacillus niger, Pseudomonas aeruginosa,* and *Staphylococcus aureus.* Some of his data are summarized in Table 22, from which it will be seen that *S. aureus* is more sensitive to the various copper salts than is *Ps. aeruginosa.* Bacterial spores were found to be even more resistant.

TABLE 22

MOLAR CONCENTRATIONS OF COPPER SALTS WHICH ARE LETHAL FOR BACTERIA

[From Bidzinski (1926)]

Copper Salt	Lethal Concentration, grams per liter	
	Pseudomonas aeruginosa	*Staphylococcus aureus*
Nitrate	0.3651	0.2839
Chloride	0.3637	0.2846
Acetate	0.3564	0.2916
Sulfate	0.3500	0.2862
Formate	0.3545	0.2900
Ammoniacal chloride	0.4048	0.3076

More recently Sprowls and Poe (1943) have studied the disinfectant powers of several astringent salts, using the F.D.A. method. The copper salts were not particularly effective against the test organisms, although it was observed that *Eberthella typhosa* was more sensitive to the copper salts than was *S. aureus.*

Copper salts are used rather extensively as fungicides. Bordeaux mixture, which is used as a spray to prevent fungus infections of plants, is simply a mixture of lime (calcium hydroxide) and copper sulfate. Supposedly the copper ions present in such a mixture prevent the infection of plants. A general statement cannot be made concerning the amount of copper which must be used in water to destroy algae. Several different factors, such as species of alga to be destroyed, hardness of water, and temperature, are involved. In regard to the species, for example, the amounts necessary to kill vary from 1 part of copper sulfate in 10,000 for members of the genera *Beggiatoa*, *Pandorina*, and *Endorina* to 1 in 20,000,000 for *Uroglena* and 1 in 25,000,000 for species of *Spirogyra*.

The mode of action of copper salts upon bacteria has been reported as a coagulation of the bacterial colloids [Vignati and Schnabel (1928)]. The process, however, seems to be a reversible reaction, because under certain conditions the copper-bacterium complex can be separated, leaving the bacteria again free to carry on their life processes. Thus it is quite probable that copper salts exhibit their action in a manner similar to that of mercury, that is, by interfering with some essential cellular metabolite or growth factor.

Silver. Of the various simple silver salts, silver nitrate is the most commonly employed as an antiseptic or a germicide. Its main disadvantages are that it is irritating, astringent, and corrosive. The presence of chlorides and organic compounds greatly reduces its

TABLE 23

The Grouping of Silver Compounds According to Their Inhibitory Activity for Yeast in Aqueous Solutions

[From Pilcher and Sollmann (1924)]

Group	Important Members	Inhibiting Quantity, milligrams	Inhibiting Concentration
I. Inorganic salt	Silver nitrate	0.25	1 : 40,000
II. Strong silver-protein preparation	Silver nucleinate Sophol Albargin	0.85–1.2	1 : 13,300–1 : 8,333
III. Silver protein	Protargol Proganol Protargentum Silver proteinate	2.0–3.0 (mean 2.2)	1 : 5,000–1 : 3,300
IV. Stabilized silver protein	Collargol	10–11	1 : 1,000–1 : 900
V. Mild silver-protein preparation	Vargol Argyn Cargentos Argyrol	11–150 (mean 38)	1 : 900–1 : 67
VI. Colloidal silver iodide	Neosilvol	1,000	1 : 10

efficiency, since insoluble precipitates are formed. A silver nitrate solution of 1 : 10,000 will inhibit the growth of most bacteria. It seems to have a somewhat selective action upon gonococci and is therefore instilled routinely in a 1 per cent solution into the eyes of newborn children as a prophylactic against gonococcal infection. Silver nitrate and the salts of other heavy metals in 0.05 to 0.5 *N* solutions will also inactivate purified influenza virus [Knight and Stanley (1944)].

Often ammoniacal silver nitrate [$Ag(NH_3)_2NO_3$], silver citrate [$Ag_3C_6H_5O_7$], silver lactate [$AgC_3H_5O_3 \cdot H_2O$], and numerous protein-silver and colloidal silver preparations are used as antiseptics. The organic and colloidal silver preparations are less antiseptic than silver nitrate, but for the most part they are noncorrosive, relatively non-astringent, and much less irritating. Pilcher and Sollmann (1924) have grouped these compounds according to their dissociation into silver ions and inert material and according to their antiseptic powers against yeast (Table 23). Blood, other proteins, and sodium chloride interfere with the antiseptic action of silver compounds.

Gold. Considerable work has been done on the therapeutic use of simple gold salts and complex organic gold compounds in the treatment of tuberculosis and leprosy. Opinions are still divided concerning the value of gold therapy in these diseases. In primary acute cases gold salts usually fail to produce any effect whatever, and in chronic pulmonary tuberculosis they fail to prevent recurrent relapses. Since observations have shown that the growth of tubercle bacilli *in vitro* is not inhibited by fairly large concentrations of Sanocrysin, the double thiosulfate of gold and sodium [$(AuS_2O_3Na)Na_2S_2O_3 \cdot 2H_2O$], the action of gold salts has been attributed to a stimulation of the defense mechanism of the body. Russu and Sichet (1937), for instance, have shown that under the influence of Sanocrysin the phagocytic activity of the reticulo-endothelial cells is greatly increased. It is claimed that gold in the form of Solganal-B has a definite therapeutic effect in leprosy cases. Sufficiently careful work has not been carried out on the disinfecting powers of gold salts to make a general statement concerning their toxicity or their mode of action. However, as we pointed out on p. 252 on cations and anions, the gold salts show considerable toxicity for bacteria. They may act in a manner similar to that of mercury.

Mercury. Simple mercury salts, especially mercuric chloride [$HgCl_2$], mercury oxycyanide [$Hg(CN)_2 \cdot HgO$], and potassium mercuric iodide [K_2HgI_4], are frequently used as disinfectants. The use of such compounds is limited, however, because of their toxicity to man and animals, their corrosive action on metals, and their tendency to form precipitates with nitrogenous organic matter. A 1 : 1,000 solution of bichloride of mercury is generally used as a practical disinfectant, but it may take many hours to destroy resistant spores, if it does so at all. Reports in the literature state, however, that most spores are killed in 1 to 2 hours by a 1 : 500 solution. This statement should be accepted with some reservations until more work has been carried out. A dilution as high as 1 : 50,000 kills some bacteria, and a 1 : 100,000 solution may be inhibitory for certain species.

The Mode of Action of Mercury. The earlier literature stated that the germicidal efficiency of the simple mercury salts depended upon the concentration of mercury ions in solution and their affinity for the proteins which are present. Since such salts as mercuric chloride, iodide, and nitrate are not highly ionized in solution, their mode of action would thus resemble that of certain nonelectrolytes. We now know more about the mode of action of mercury, and therefore the above statement can be doubted to some extent. Fildes (1940) has clearly demonstrated that the antibacterial action of mercury can best be explained on the basis that it interferes with some essential cellular metabolite, such as certain R-SH compounds. Experimental data in support of this view were presented by Fildes, who came to the following conclusions.

The antibacterial action of Hg is specifically neutralized by —SH compounds, and the reaction is reversible. In glutathione the neutralization takes place approximately in the proportions 1 mol. Hg per 2 mol. —SH, and the formed product is devoid of —SH. If the concentration of —SH in glutathione is about four times that of Hg, growth will occur, whereas in thiolacetic acid 25 times the concentration of —SH is necessary before growth will take place. Mercury combines with —SH groups in the cell to form a similar complex and thus deprives the cell of —SH groups, which are essential for its metabolism. Within limits the action of Hg is merely the inactivation of the —SH group without other demonstrable injury to the cell.

Organic Mercurials. In the past several years a great many organic mercurial compounds have been synthesized and tested for their germicidal action both in septicemia and on localized bacterial lesions. The organic mercurials are less irritating and less toxic than some of the older mercury preparations. Some of these compounds have exceedingly high phenol coefficients, being a thousand or so times as potent as phenol. They show varying results in the presence of organic matter [Rose and Miller (1940)]. The most important of these compounds are Mercurochrome, Metaphen, Merthiolate, Fumerane, phenylmercuric nitrate, Mercarbolide, Mercresin, Mertoxol, and Meroxyl. Although certain of these compounds give relatively high phenol coefficients, they cannot be relied upon as disinfectants when spores are present. Because of their bacteriostatic properties, however, they are of value as first-aid prophylactic antiseptics and as preservatives for certain biologicals for parenteral use. Claims for their ability to penetrate deeply into living tissues and to act as efficient chemotherapeutic agents have yet to be adequately supported.

MERCUROCHROME. This compound was first prepared in 1919 and is chemically known as disodium dibromohydroxymercurifluorescein ($C_{20}H_7O_5Br_2HgOHNa_2$). It has been used extensively as a skin disinfectant and an antidote in cases of septicemia. Unfortunately, as has been pointed out recently by Birkhaug (1933), Salle and Lazarus (1935), Brewer (1939), and others, it has failed to fulfill the hopes which were at first entertained of it as a germicide and antiseptic. Some of Birkhaug's results are indicated in Table 24, where it will be noted that the phenol coefficients obtained for Mercurochrome are very low in comparison to those observed for similar mercurial compounds. Using a slightly different technique to test germicidal efficiency, Salle and Lazarus compared the highest dilutions capable of killing *Staphylococcus aureus* and inhibiting the growth of tissue cultures. Toxicity indexes obtained were for Metaphen 12.7, for phenol 12.9, for Merthiolate 35.3, and for Mercurochrome 262, the smaller the toxicity index the more efficient being the germicide. Recently this technique has been further improved by Salle, McOmie, Shechmeister, and Foord (1939). Brewer (1939) found that a 1 : 50 aqueous solution of Mercurochrome could not be depended upon to kill bacteria spores or to sterilize surgical and dental instruments. The germicidal efficiency of the compound is considerably reduced in the presence of organic matter. A medium more acid than *p*H 5.9 or more alkaline than 7.5 also reduces its efficacy.

METAPHEN. This mercurial is the sodium salt of 4-nitro-5-hydroxymercuri-*o*-cresol ($C_6H_2 \cdot CH_3 \cdot NO_2 \cdot HgOH \cdot ONa$). According to Raiziss and Severac (1927), it is 11 times more germicidal than bichloride of mercury and 615 times more germicidal than Mercurochrome when tested against the spores of *Bacillus anthracis*. Quite similar results were obtained by Birkhaug, whose data are cited in Table 24. Brewer (1939) has observed that a 1 : 2,500 aqueous solution of Metaphen could not be relied upon to kill bacterial spores or to sterilize dental and surgical instruments. Like other mercurials, Metaphen loses much of its germicidal efficacy when it is used in the presence of proteins, such as blood serum [Smith, Czarnetzky, and Mudd (1936)].

MERTHIOLATE. Chemically this compound is sodium ethyl mercurithiosalicylate ($C_2H_5HgSC_6H_4COONa$). It has been reported to be a

TABLE 24

HIGHEST DILUTION OF DISINFECTANTS KILLING MICROORGANISMS AFTER 10 MINUTES' BUT NOT AFTER 5 MINUTES' CONTACT AT 37°C. AND PHENOL COEFFICIENTS

[From Birkhaug (1933)]

Microorganism	Phenylmercuric Nitrate	Merthiolate	Metaphen	Hexylresorcinol	Mercurochrome	Mercuric Chloride	Phenol
			Lethal Dilutions				
Staphylococcus aureus	1 : 192,000	1 : 120,000	1 : 140,000	1 : 14,000	1 : 160	1 : 16,000	1 : 85
Streptococcus pyogenes	1 : 144,000	1 : 112,000	1 : 110,000	1 : 12,000	1 : 320	1 : 32,000	1 : 100
Diplococcus pneumoniae, type I	1 : 96,000	1 : 64,000	1 : 72,000	1 : 9,000	1 : 240	1 : 20,000	1 : 90
Escherichia coli	1 : 48,000	1 : 32,000	1 : 32,000	1 : 6,000	1 : 180	1 : 10,000	1 : 75
Neisseria gonorrhoeae	1 : 80,000	1 : 48,000	1 : 48,000	1 : 8,000	1 : 240	1 : 20,000	1 : 90
Bacillus subtilis	1 : 65,000	1 : 24,000	1 : 36,000	1 : 16,000	1 : 300	1 : 12,000	1 : 80
			Phenol Coefficients				
Staphylococcus aureus	2,259	1,412	1,647	164	1.8	189	
Streptococcus pyogenes	1,440	1,120	1,100	120	3.2	320	
Diplococcus pneumoniae, type I	1,067	701	800	100	2.1	222	
Escherichia coli	640	427	427	80	2.4	133	
Neisseria gonorrhoeae	889	533	533	89	2.1	222	
Bacillus subtilis	801	300	450	200	3.7	150	

rather potent germicide for both vegetative forms and spores of bacteria, but this claim is not entirely true [see Brewer (1939)]. Powell and Jamieson (1931) found that *Eberthella typhosa* and *Staphylococcus aureus* were killed by a 1 : 3,000 solution of Merthiolate in 5 minutes. This would correspond to a phenol coefficient of about 30 to 40. Birkhaug (1933), Brewer (1939), and Salle, Shechmeister, and McOmie (1940) have obtained some interesting data on Merthiolate as a germicide. Birkhaug's results are summarized in Table 24. More recently Powell and Jamieson (1939) have reported on the germicidal activity of *Sulfomerthiolate* (sodium *p*-ethyl mercurithiophenol sulfonate). Its action is very similar to Merthiolate.

PHENYLMERCURIC NITRATE ($C_6H_5HgNO_3$). This compound was first prepared in 1870 but has only recently been suggested as a disinfectant and antiseptic by Weed and Ecker (1931, 1933), Birkhaug (1933), and others. Weed and Ecker found the compound to have a high phenol coefficient, and similar results were observed by Birkhaug (Table 24). The compound is relatively nontoxic, whether given orally, intraperitoneally, or subcutaneously to animals. The presence of phenylmercuric nitrate or chloride did not alter the digestive action of trypsin and pepsin, the lytic action of lysozyme, the minimal skin-reaction dose of diphtheria toxin, or the binding power of complement, according to Weed and Ecker. Some fabrics are now treated with phenylmercuric acetate or other similar salts as a preventive against mildew. Phenylmercuric citrate, borate, and several related compounds have been prepared and tested for their germicidal activity [Klarmann (1939–1944)].

FUMERANE. Chemically this antiseptic is 2-hydroxymercurifuran:

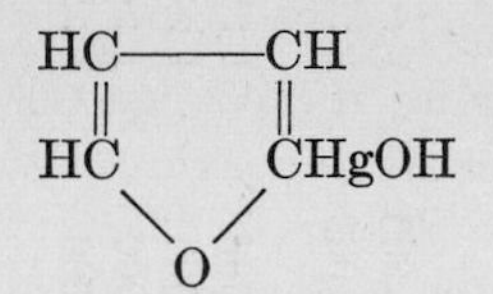

It gives a low toxicity index (1.2) in comparison with other mercurials (2.8 to 35.3), when tested by Salle's technique. In the presence of 50 per cent blood serum Fumerane gives a phenol coefficient of 187 with *Staphylococcus aureus* and 62 with *Escherichia coli;* it is bacteriostatic for these organisms in dilutions of 1 : 7,000,000 to 1 : 9,000,000.

Several other organic mercurials, such as *Mercarbolide* (*o*-hydroxyphenyl mercury bichloride), *Mercresin* (a mixture of Mercarbolide and 5 isomeric amyl *o*-cresols), *Mertoxol* (acetoxymercuri-2-ethylohexylphenol sulfonic acid), and *Meroxyl* (Na salt of 2 : 4-dihydroxy-3 : 5-hydroxymercury benzophenone-2′-sulfonic acid), have been marketed and used as antiseptics and germicides. Although most of these give relatively good phenol coefficients, they cannot be relied upon to kill bacterial spores [see Brewer (1939)]. More recently Heyman and Grubb (1940) have compared the antibacterial activity of several monophenyl and diphenyl mercurials. In general, they possessed a relatively high antibacterial action (up to 1 : 20,000) in aqueous medium, but were markedly affected by serum.

Miscellaneous Metals. Several other metallic compounds have been found to be useful in the treatment of certain bacterial and protozoan infections, but as general disinfectants they are of little or no significance.

ARSENIC COMPOUNDS. According to Friedberger and Joachimoglu (1917) and others, trivalent arsenic (arsenites) is much more toxic for protozoa, bacteria, and yeast cells than is pentavalent arsenic (arsenates). For example, Friedberger and Joachimoglu observed that broth containing 0.01 mg. of trivalent arsenic per milliliter killed a young culture of *Serratia marcescens* in 2 hours, whereas the same concentration of pentavalent arsenic had no apparent effect. Both trivalent and pentavalent arsenic can be readily introduced into a large variety of organic molecules. In this nonionic condition the metal does not produce the ordinary toxic effects on man and higher animals. However, in the course of the oxidation and reduction and other cleavages which these organic molecules undergo in the body, more or less ionic arsenic is gradually split off, thus producing the arsenic actions in a delayed and generally in a milder form. These organic arsenic compounds, on the other hand, are quite toxic to trypanosomes, spirochetes, amebae, and other protozoan parasites which may gain entrance into the body. Such compounds seem to have little or no parasitical action *in vitro;* they require the cooperation of the host to become effective. Probably the most important of these organic arsenic compounds are arsphenamine (Salvarsan, "606," Diarsenol) and its derivatives and neoarsphenamine. Commercial arsphenamine and neoarsphenamine have the following structures:

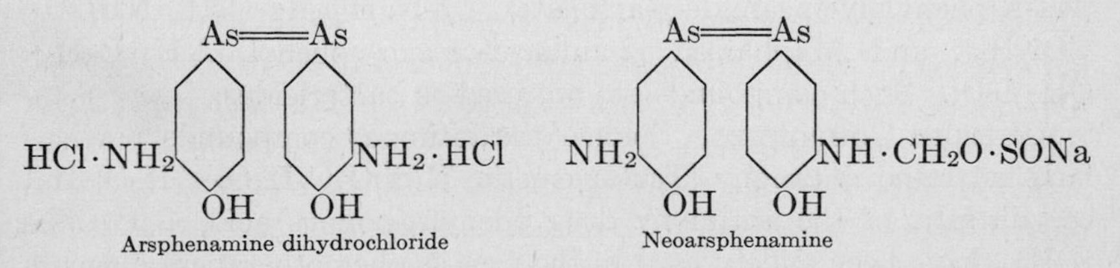

Arsphenamine dihydrochloride

Neoarsphenamine

The introduction of arsphenamine was the direct outcome of the extensive chemotherapeutic studies carried out by Ehrlich around 1910.

He and his associates found that a single injection of a harmless dose freed animals from spirillosis and certain other protozoan infections, including syphilitic spirochetes. Although the use of these drugs has proved remarkably successful in human cases of syphilis, they have not fulfilled the original hope of complete cure by a single injection. Various *in vitro* tests indicate that the compounds possess little direct spirochetal and bactericidal action. The following figures, taken from the paper by Akatsu (1917), show the highest dilution of arsphenamine, neoarsphenamine, and several other antiseptics which will kill the spirochete of syphilis:

Mercuric chloride	1 : 100,000
Arsphenamine	1 : 7,500
Neoarsphenamine	1 : 2,500
Phenol	1 : 2,500
Formalin	1 : 750
Iodine in KI (Lugol's solution)	1 : 75

Although several workers have claimed that neoarsphenamine is directly germicidal to *Bacillus anthracis*, Kurotchkin and Reimann (1930) found it of no value in the treatment of experimentally induced anthrax in rabbits and mice. More recently Rosenthal, Bauer, and Elvove (1939) reported that certain aromatic arsenic compounds possess some bactericidal action, but Gagna (1939) found four compounds to be ineffective against *Staphylococcus aureus*, *Escherichia coli*, and *Serratia marcescens*.

Numerous other arsenic compounds possessing amebicidal, trypanocidal, and spirillicidal properties have been prepared and marketed as chemotherapeutic preparations for treating diseases caused by amebae, trypanosomes, and spirilla. They include such substances as Acetarsone (Stovarsol, Spirozid), which is N-acetyl-4-hydroxy-*m*-arsanilic acid [$HO \cdot CH_3 \cdot CONH \cdot C_6H_3 \cdot AsO(OH)_2$]; Aldarsone [Na-methylenesulfonaminohydroxyphenyl arsonate]; Carbarsone [*p*-ureidobenzenearsonic acid, $(OH)_2OAs \cdot C_6H_4 \cdot NHCONH_2$]; Tryparsamide [Na-N-phenylglycineamide-*p*-arsonate, *p*-$NaHO_3As \cdot C_6H_4 \cdot NHCH \cdot CONH_2$]; and Mapharsen [2-amino-4-arsenosophenol, $NH_2 \cdot C_6H_3 \cdot OH \cdot AsO$]. Such compounds are not used as bactericides.

Antimony Compounds. Some of the antimony compounds, particularly tartrated antimony [Tartar emetic, $K(SbO)C_4H_4O_6 \cdot \frac{1}{2}H_2O$] and certain salts of the antimony drug phenylstibonous acid, $C_6H_5OSb(OH)_2$, have been widely used in the past as chemotherapeutic agents for the treatment of a number of tropical diseases caused by animal parasites. Little or no work has been done on the effects of antimony compounds on bacteria. Excessive doses of these compounds produce in man toxic symptoms resembling those of acute and subacute arsenic poisoning.

Zinc Compounds. Several workers have shown that zinc and some of its simple salts are stimulatory to bacteria in low concentrations, but they do not seem to be entirely essential for the growth of microorganisms. High concentrations of such compounds may show a definite toxicity. In recent years some attention has been given to the use of zinc sulfate, oxide, and peroxide preparations in the chemotherapeutic treatment of several diseases and in ointments for treating local infections.

Bismuth Compounds. Such substances as Dermatol [bismuth subgallate, $C_6H_2(OH)_3 \cdot COOBi(OH)_2$], dihydroxypropyl bismuthate [Wheeler (1943)], and other compounds have been manufactured and sold as powders or ointments to treat certain skin diseases. Little is known concerning their bactericidal properties, although dihydroxypropyl bismuthate [$C_3H_5(OH)_2BiO_3$] works well in the treatment of syphilis.

HALOGENS AND THEIR COMPOUNDS

The free halogens, fluorine, chlorine, bromine, and iodine, and some of their compounds have a marked affinity for living protoplasm and are thus very toxic to bacteria. Such compounds may also inactivate certain viruses, enzymes, and related substances. Chlorine and iodine are probably the most widely used of all chemical disinfectants.

Eisenberg (1918) determined the action of the halogen ions on twelve different bacteria and listed them in the following series, based on increasing toxicity: $Cl < Br < I < F$. More recently Hailer and Bockelberg (1939) have studied the action of the halogens on dried anthrax spores and found the toxic effect to follow the order: $I > Cl > Br$. The disinfecting power of these elements and some of their compounds will now be discussed.

Chlorine Compounds. Several chlorine compounds are extremely efficient germicides. They are used, for example, in the treatment of questionable water supplies, in the purification of swimming-pool water, in the chlorination of sewage and sewage-disposal-plant effluents, for utensil disinfection in many food industries, in the control of slime formation in pulp and paper mills, and in medical practice for general sanitation.

Free Chlorine. Chlorine in the form of a liquid is now widely used in the disinfection of water and sewage. In municipal practice an arbitrary residual chlorine content of 0.1 to 0.2 p.p.m. for $\frac{1}{2}$ to 2 hours has been considered adequate for the production of safe water. To be sure that the vegetative cells of *Escherichia coli* and *Eberthella typhosa*, the viruses, the cysts of *Endameba histolytica*, and certain other related organisms are killed in water, however, concentrations above this level are often employed, especially where the "break-point chlorination" technique is used [see Costigan (1942)]. Very few studies have been made of the effect of chlorination on viruses which may be spread through water. This topic may have considerable public health importance, since the poliomyelitis virus has already been demonstrated in sewage. In this connection the studies by Kempf and Soule (1940) and Kessel, Allison, Moore, and Kaime (1943) are very interesting. They observed that chlorine in a concentration of 0.5 p.p.m., which is an amount in excess of that usually employed in municipal practice, did not inactivate the virus of poliomyelitis after 60 to 90 minutes' exposure. Likewise the virus of cowpox is not killed by several hundred times the chlorine concentration usually considered adequate to protect public drinking water supplies [MacDonald (1940)]. In fact, in certain cases the virus stood a chlorine concentration of 400 p.p.m. for 10 minutes. The addition of ammonia to liquid chlorine greatly increases the germicidal efficiency of the chlorine. Since chlorine readily combines with organic matter, its toxic action is considerably altered by the presence of such material in the water.

HYPOCHLORITES. The best known of the hypochlorites is calcium hypochlorite, CaClOCl, which is also sometimes spoken of as bleaching powder, or simply as bleach. The strength of the various hypochlorites is measured in terms of available chlorine by titrating with potassium iodide and sodium thiosulfate. Such a measurement is misleading, however, because it implies that the disinfecting properties of such compounds depend entirely upon the chlorine. This implication is not entirely justified, because we know that certain oxidative processes also take place. The oxygen, as well as the chlorine, comes from the decomposition of the hypochlorite by the action of acids or even of atmospheric carbon dioxide; for instance:

$$2CaClOCl + 2HCl = 2CaCl_2 + 2HOCl$$

$$2HOCl + 2HCl = 2H_2O + 2Cl_2$$

$$2HOCl = 2HCl + O_2$$

When commercial chlorinated lime is fresh, it may contain approximately 25 to 35 per cent available chlorine, although many commercial preparations may fall far short of this value, especially if they have been stored for a considerable period in a warm, moist place. Several stabilized hypochlorite preparations on the market are for use as disinfectants. Of these, Clorox, Perchloron, and H.T.H. are widely used because of their high percentage of available chlorine. The hypochlorites have had their greatest use in sanitation and have been responsible for great saving of life from water-borne infections since they were first used in about 1850. Although they have been almost entirely replaced in sanitation by liquid chlorine, they still have their place in the home and other places where small-scale disinfection is desired. The most complete study to date on the germicidal action of hypochlorite solutions has been carried out by Rudolph and Levine (1941). The effects of temperature, concentration, and reaction (*p*H) on germicidal efficiency were studied by determining the course of the disinfection process and the time required to effect a reduction of 99 per cent of the viable spores of *Bacillus metiens*.

Dakin's solution is essentially a hypochlorite solution which is suitable for the treatment of wounds. It is prepared so that it contains approximately 0.5 per cent available chlorine, and the alkalinity of the solution is neutralized with boric acid. Manninger (1940) has suggested the use of a modified Dakin's solution for treating wounds, since it kills staphylococci and streptococci in 2 minutes. Baker, Finn, and Twort (1940), Baker (1941), and others have studied the ability of hypochlorites and other disinfectants to serve as aerial germicides. Although such compounds in the form of mists have definite possibilities in combating aerial infections, they are somewhat limited because of several factors.

CHLOROPHENOLS. The germicidal properties of the *o*-, *m*-, and *p*-chlorophenols have been studied by several investigators. In general, their phenol coefficients are rather low. It has been shown by Klarmann and associates (1934), however, that some of the *p*-alkyl and aromatic derivatives of the chlorophenols are efficient germicides. Some of their data are presented in Table 9.

CHLORAMINES. According to Berliner (1931), the chloramines include all amino ($—NH_2$) and imino ($=NH$) groups in which the hydrogen has been partially or completely replaced by chlorine. The medical profession refers to the term chloramine more or less specifically as the mono- and dichloro-substituted toluene sulfonamide derivatives which are sold under several trade names. The first of these was introduced during World War I by Dakin, Cohen, and Kenyon (1916) and was named chloramine-T. Chemically this compound is *p*-toluene-sodium-sulfochloramide ($CH_3C_6H_4SO_2Na:NCl$). Closely related to this compound is dichloramine-T ($CH_3C_6H_4SO_2NCl_2$).

Köser (1926) observed that a 1 : 500 solution of chloramine-T in culture media inhibited the growth of *Escherichia coli* and *Staphylococcus aureus.* A 0.5 per cent solution killed coliform bacilli in 1 minute and *S. aureus* in 30 minutes, whereas a 2 per cent solution was lethal to a suspension of *S. aureus* in 5 minutes. The spores of *Bacillus anthracis* were destroyed in 3 hours by a 5 per cent solution and in 2 hours by a 10 per cent solution. Charlton and Levine (1937) and Weber (1942) have studied the chloramines in detail and have added to our knowledge concerning the action of these chlorine compounds. They determined the effect of the chlorine concentration, the reaction (*p*H), and the temperature on the germicidal efficiency of these compounds. Some of their data are discussed on pp. 283 to 285 on the factors influencing chlorine disinfection.

Azochloramide. In 1935 Schmelkes and Horning reported on the bactericidal action of Azochloramide [N-N′-dichloroazodicarboxamidine, $(NH_2)ClN{:}C\cdot N{:}N\cdot C{:}NCl(NH_2)$]. It possesses the property of killing many organisms in the presence of organic matter, such as serum, and is nonirritating. In this respect it apparently excels all other chlorine compounds. A solution containing 25 p.p.m. available chlorine and 50 per cent serum killed several organisms, including *Staphylococcus aureus*, *Corynebacterium diphtheriae*, *Diplococcus pneumoniae* type II, *Escherichia coli*, and *Pseudomonas aeruginosa* in less than an hour. Salle, Shechmeister, and McOmie (1940) found Azochloramide to be lethal for *S. aureus* at a dilution of 1 : 3,520 and for *Eberthella typhosa* at 1 : 101,000; corresponding phenol coefficients for the two organisms were 32.0 and 543. The effect of Azochloramide on certain physiologically active products of staphylococci has been studied by Heise and Starin (1940). For example, they found that, when staphylococcus filtrates were incubated with Azochloramide at 37°C., their hemolytic and dermonecrotizing activities were greatly reduced. Azochloramide potentiates the action of sulfonamides *in vitro*, whereas other chemotherapeutic substances, such as Optochine, Merthiolate, and actinomycin, do not exhibit such synergism. Several theories have been advanced to explain this phenomenon, but as yet the problem has not been solved [see Henry (1943)].

Chloroform. Trichloromethane ($CHCl_3$) has been used in the past as a preservative, but it possesses little or no direct germicidal action [Bunyea (1927)], since 5 per cent chloroform in a streaming vapor will not kill *Staphylococcus aureus* in 30 minutes.

Factors Influencing the Germicidal Action of Chlorine Compounds. Several factors are important in the determination of the germicidal efficiency of chlorine compounds. Of these factors the concentration of available chlorine, the reaction (*p*H), the temperature, and the presence of organic matter are the most important.

1. Effect of Concentration. It is quite generally assumed that the more available chlorine which is present in a given disinfecting solution, the more efficient will be the killing process. This assumption is not always justified, however, as will be seen in the two examples taken from the study of Charlton and Levine (1937). When solutions of the calcium hypochlorite were employed, the available chlorine was not a measure of the disinfecting power, since the killing times obtained with 1,000 and with 100 p.p.m. available chlorine were not appreciably different. They believed this situation could best be explained by the fact that the more dilute solution was less alkaline (because of a dilution of the stabilizing agent), with resultant increased germicidal power, which was found to be approximately proportional to the calculated amount of hypochlorous acid present. On the other hand, doubling the concentration of available chlorine in the form of chloramine-T resulted in a reduction of the killing time to approximately one-half. For instance, at *p*H 6.2 the spores of *Bacillus metiens* were killed in 27, 12, and 5.4 hours when solutions containing 1,000, 2,000, and 4,000 p.p.m. available chlorine, respectively, were employed.

Costigan (1942) points out:

> Chlorine concentration is certainly important, but, in view of modern chlorination practice, the exact effective concentration more than ever becomes one of individual determination for any given plant. With modern break-point chlorination, considerable variance is found in the finished water chlorine residuals tolerated by the public. For example, results on cysticidal (*Endameba histolytica*) chlorine doses show a 30-minute residual at a *p*H range of 7.0 to 8.2 to be slightly above 3 p.p.m. This may be tolerated in some waters and not in others.

2. Effect of Reaction (*p*H). Several investigators have observed that the hydrogen-ion concentration of the solution greatly influences chlorine disinfection, although this fact has not always been appreciated in practical sterilizing procedures. This factor has been studied in some detail by Charlton and Levine (1937), Rudolph and Levine (1941), and Butterfield and associates (1943). To illustrate this point, two experiments from the study by Charlton and Levine will be cited. A hypochlorite solution with 1,000 p.p.m. available chlorine at a reaction of *p*H 11.3 killed the spores of *Bacillus metiens* in 64 minutes, whereas at pH 7.3 the killing time was less than 20 seconds. Likewise, when a solution containing a concentration of 1,000 p.p.m. available chlorine as chloramine-T was employed, the killing times obtained ranged from 97 to 15 hours for reactions from pH 8.6 to 6.0 (Fig. 11). Quite similar results were obtained with other concentrations of chloramine-T. The hydrogen-ion concentration also has a marked effect on the bactericidal efficiency of free chlorine, the killing power diminishing with increasing pH values [Butterfield *et al.* (1943)].

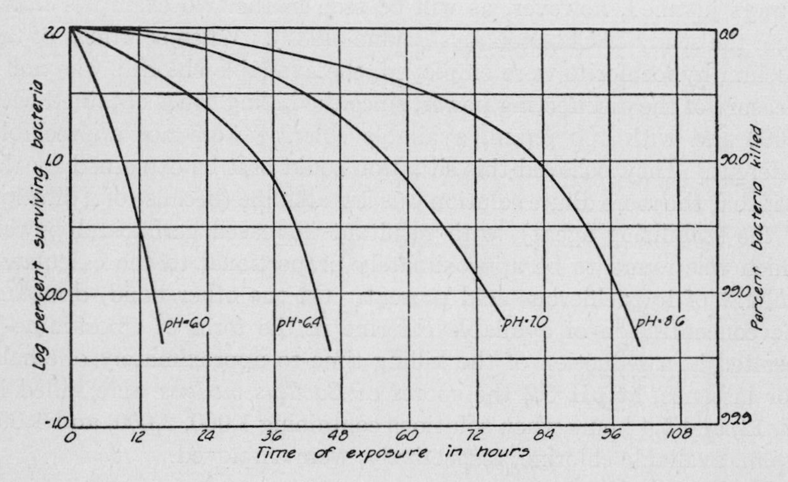

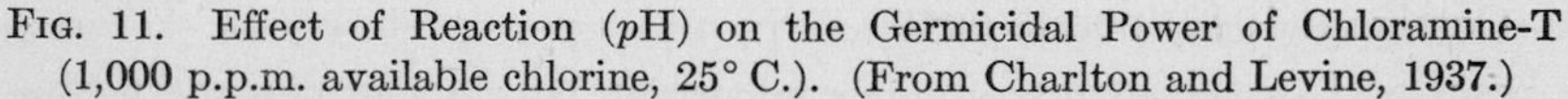
FIG. 11. Effect of Reaction (pH) on the Germicidal Power of Chloramine-T (1,000 p.p.m. available chlorine, 25° C.). (From Charlton and Levine, 1937.)

3. Effect of Temperature. Very few comprehensive studies have been reported of the effect of temperature on the germicidal efficiency of chlorine compounds. Nevertheless temperature is a very important factor, as was clearly demonstrated by Charlton and Levine (1937), who employed a chloramine-T solution containing 2,000 p.p.m. available chlorine at pH 6.0 and four different temperatures (Fig. 12). Actual figures showed that for each 10° rise in temperature the killing time was reduced by 82 per cent. The germicidal efficiency of hypochlorite solutions for certain bacteria seems to be little influenced by temperature [Costigan (1942)], but for others (*Mycobacterium tuberculosis* and spores of *Bacillus metiens*) increasing the temperature decreases the killing time [Costigan (1936), Rudolph and Levine (1941)]. A rise in temperature tends to increase the bactericidal properties of free chlorine [Butterfield *et al.* (1943)].

4. Effect of Organic Matter. The literature reveals several conflicting opinions concerning the effect of organic matter on the disinfecting properties of certain chlorine compounds. However, the present consensus is that the germicidal efficiency of chlorine and chlorine compounds is considerably reduced by the presence of organic matter. Therefore, when disinfection tests are performed, solutions both with and without added organic matter should be employed. Of the chlorine compounds hypochlorites are most affected by the presence of organic matter, chloramine-T and Azochloramide being less affected. This situation is clearly shown in Table 25, where it will be seen, for instance,

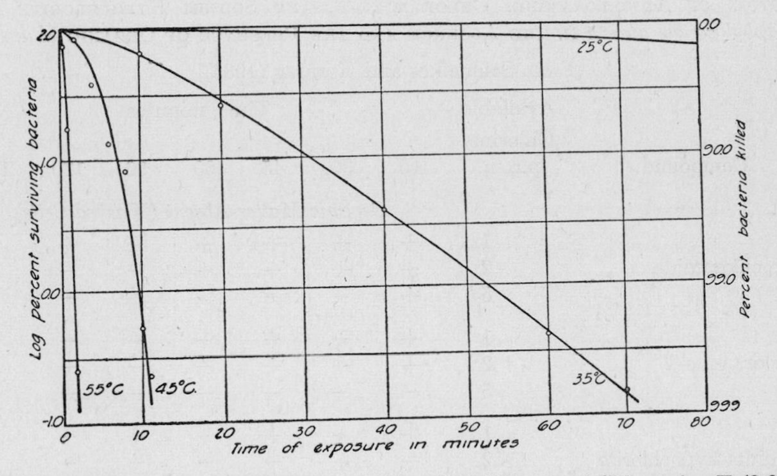

FIG. 12. Effect of Temperature on the Germicidal Power of Chloramine-T (2,000 p.p.m. available chlorine, initial *p*H 6.0, at 25° C.). (From Charlton and Levine, 1937.)

that a solution of chloramine-T containing 300 p.p.m. available chlorine and 50 per cent serum killed *Staphylococcus aureus* in less than 1 hour, while four times that amount of available chlorine (1,200 p.p.m.) was necessary to produce the same effect when sodium hypochlorite was employed as the disinfectant.

MODE OF ACTION OF CHLORINE. Several theories have been advanced to explain the mechanism of disinfection by chlorine, hypochlorites, and chloramine compounds, but we are still uncertain how these compounds destroy microorganisms. The action may be the same for all these substances, although the data available seem to indicate that the various chlorine compounds act in a different manner on specific organisms [see Chang (1944)].

Several early workers were of the opinion that the germicidal action of chlorine was due to oxidative reactions involving nascent oxygen.

It was assumed that nascent oxygen arose in some way by a union of chlorine with the hydrogen of water, thus:

$$Cl_2 + H_2O = 2HCl + [O]$$

This theory has been considered old-fashioned and has been discarded by some workers, who suggest that the toxicity is due to chlorine rather than nascent oxygen. To support their claims they have shown

TABLE 25

ACTION OF AZOCHLORAMIDE, CHLORAMINE-T, AND SODIUM HYPOCHLORITE ON *Staphylococcus aureus* IN THE ABSENCE AND THE PRESENCE OF ORGANIC MATTER

[From Schmelkes and Horning (1935)]

Compound	Available Chlorine, p.p.m.	Time, minutes 15	30	45	60	90	120	180
		Organic Matter Absent (Washed Cells)						
Azochloramide	1	+	+	+	+	+	+	
	2	+	+	+	+	−	−	
	5	+	−	−	−	−	−	
Chloramine-T	1	+	+	+	+	+	−	
	2	+	+	+	−	−	−	
	5	−	−	−	−	−	−	
Sodium hypochlorite	1	+	+	+	+	+	−	
	2	+	+	−	−	−	−	
	5	−	−	−	−	−	−	
		Organic Matter Present (50% Serum)						
Azochloramide	20	+	+		+	+	−	−
	30	+	+		−	−	−	−
	40	+	−		−	−	−	−
Chloramine-T	250	+	+		+	+	+	+
	300	+	+		−	−	−	−
	350	+	−		−	−	−	−
Sodium hypochlorite	800	+	+		+	+	+	−
	1,000	+	+		+	−	−	−
	1,200	+	+		−	−	−	−

(+) = growth; (−) = no growth in 96 hours.

that the nascent-oxygen theory can account for only a part of the reduction in the biochemical oxygen demand of sewage. In a more recent theory the investigators conceive of a process in which the chlorine actually combines chemically with the protoplasm of the bacterial cell, a hydrogen in the amino groups being replaced as:

$$\text{—R—CO—NH—R'— + Cl} \rightarrow \text{—R—CO—NCl—R'— + H}$$

The chloramines thus produced are toxic to bacteria and eventually the cells are killed.

Andrewes and Orton (1903), Charlton and Levine (1937), Rudolph and Levine (1941), and others are of the opinion that hypochlorite solutions and chlorinated water owe their germicidal properties to the same substance, namely, hypochlorous acid (HOCl), which may be formed as follows:

$$Cl_2 + H_2O = HCl + HOCl$$

$$Ca(OCl)_2 + 2HCl = CaCl_2 + 2HOCl$$

If this theory is correct, then the germicidal activity of chlorine and hypochlorites in water will depend upon the concentration of hypochlorous acid. In this respect it was observed by Andrewes and Orton that, when hypochlorite solutions were acidified, hypochlorous acid was liberated, and the germicidal activity was greatly increased. To determine how changes in the *p*H of a hypochlorite solution would affect the amount of hypochlorous acid present, Holwerda (1928, 1930) made the following calculations:

Reaction (*p*H)	Hypochlorite Present in Undissociated HOCl, per cent
4.0	approximately 100.0
5.0	99.6
6.0	95.8
7.0	69.7
8.0	18.7
9.0	2.2
10.0	0.2

These data account for the increase in speed in germicidal reactions by hypochlorites as the solutions are acidified, and they explain some of the discrepancies in the literature where the *p*H factor has not been taken into consideration. However, whether the germicidal activity of hypochlorous acid is due actually to the $(OCl)^-$ ion or to the positive chlorine atom which it contains, or to the liberation of nascent oxygen ($HOCl \rightarrow HCl + O$), is not known.

When we turn to the mechanism of the disinfecting action of the chloramine compounds, we find a difference of opinion among workers. One group believes that chloramine-T and related compounds undergo hydrolysis to yield hypochlorous acid and therefore exert a germicidal action by means of this acid. If this viewpoint is correct, then such compounds act in a manner similar to hypochlorites. On the other hand, Holwerda (1928) was unable to detect any hypochlorous acid in a chloramine solution containing 10 p.p.m. available chlorine. The methyl-orange decolorization test used was sensitive to 0.03 p.p.m.

available chlorine as hypochlorous acid. Similar results have been reported by other scientists. After a careful perusal of the literature and extensive personal researches Charlton and Levine (1937) stated, "The evidence suggests that in solutions of any chloramine with an :N—Cl linkage the germicidal action is not due to hypochlorous acid." Therefore the toxic action of such chloramine compounds seems to be due to the chlorine leaving the compound and attaching itself to a second compound, or to the "undissociated" molecule.

Several other hypotheses have been advanced to explain the mode of action of chlorine compounds, but they lack experimental proof. For instance, they include such suggestions as the precipitation of the bacterial protein by chlorine, the alteration of the cell membrane so that certain solutes present in the cell may rapidly diffuse to the outside, the mechanical disruption of the cell, and the emission of lethal rays when the hypochlorites and the organic matter react. In summary it may be stated that a majority of the investigators believe that bacterial destruction is accomplished by a "poisoning" process, whereby the chlorine atom or atoms, the $(OCl)^-$ ion, or the undissociated chloramine molecules actually combine chemically with the protoplasm of the bacterial cell to produce a toxic organic complex. Modern theories are thus concerned principally with the manner of combination.

Bromine Compounds. Little work has been done on the germicidal action of bromine and its compounds, although they closely resemble the chlorine compounds in their general properties. Beckwith and Moser (1933) found chlorine, bromine, and iodine to be equally effective against *Escherichia coli*. A solution containing 0.2 p.p.m. bromine was 95 to 97 per cent efficient in 60 minutes. More recently the germicidal action of bromine has been studied by Tanner and Pitner (1939). They found the reaction (*p*H) of the solution to be an important factor,

TABLE 26

AMOUNT OF FREE BROMINE REQUIRED TO KILL BACTERIA IN 30 SECONDS AT TWO DIFFERENT REACTIONS

[From Tanner and Pitner (1939)]

Organism	Parts per Million of Bromine *p*H 3.5–4.0	*p*H 6.8–7.2
Proteus vulgaris	40–60	170
Bacillus megatherium	28–35	110
Bacillus mesentericus	180–300	over 450
Bacillus subtilis	170–220	over 450

since at *p*H 3.5 to 4.0 bromine was much more active than at *p*H 6.8 to 7.2 (Table 26). *Staphylococcus aureus* and *E. coli* were killed in 15 to 30 seconds by 15 p.p.m. bromine, while only 0.03 to 0.06 p.p.m. was necessary to destroy *Eberthella typhosa*. *Aspergillus niger* required 28 p.p.m., *Oöspora lactis* 8 p.p.m., and *Monilia albicans* 0.25 p.p.m. When several other organisms were employed, it was found that mold spores were more resistant than yeast or non-spore-forming bacteria.

Several organic bromine compounds have been prepared and tested as disinfectants. For example, Klarmann, Shternov, and von Wowern (1929) found the phenol coefficient of 4-bromothymol to be 12.5 when *E. typhosa* was used as the test organism and 194.5 when *S. aureus* was employed. For the most part such compounds have not been extensively used as disinfectants.

Iodine Compounds. The compounds of iodine are used extensively as disinfectants. Standard tincture of iodine, which consists of 2 to 7 per cent iodine and 5 per cent potassium iodide in alcohol, is the most commonly employed iodine preparation for disinfection of wounds and skin, although many other iodine compounds have been prepared and studied. Gershenfeld and Miller (1932) determined the germicidal efficiency of several iodine preparations, using the Food and Drug Administration technique. Some of their data with *Eberthella typhosa* at 20°C. are shown in Table 27. When the phenol coefficients are calculated on the basis of the iodine itself, values ranging from 135 to 235 are obtained. Salle and his associates (1939) reported phenol coefficients of 32 and 18.1 for *Staphylococcus aureus* and *E. typhosa*, respectively.

TABLE 27

PHENOL COEFFICIENTS OF VARIOUS IODINE PREPARATIONS (F.D.A. TECHNIQUE AND *Eberthella typhosa* AT 20°C.)

[From Gershenfeld and Miller (1932)]

Preparation	Phenol Coefficient	Variation in Phenol Coefficient
2% alcoholic iodine solution (with dilute alcohol)	4.7	4.1–5.2
3% alcoholic iodine solution (with dilute alcohol)	6.6	5.5–7.5
2% alcoholic iodine solution (U.S.P. tincture diluted with alcohol)	3.6	3.2–4.1
3% alcoholic iodine solution (U.S.P. tincture diluted with alcohol)	5.8	5.3–6.1
3% special aqueous iodine solution (Karns' formula)	7.2	6.5–7.5
2% isotonic iodine solution	4.7	4.4–5.5

Iodine has been used somewhat to sterilize water for drinking purposes. Beckwith and Moser (1933) found that a solution containing 0.2 p.p.m. of iodine was 95 to 97 per cent efficient for killing *Escherichia coli* in 60 minutes. However, solutions containing 3 to 5 p.p.m. are more efficient and require less time to disinfect.

Iodine solutions (0.05 to 0.5 *N*) also rapidly inactivate certain viruses, such as the influenza virus [Knight and Stanley (1944)]. *Iodine trichloride* (ICl_3) is an efficient germicide, since it has been reported that a 0.1 per cent solution is lethal for many vegetative bacteria in 1 minute and that a 1 per cent solution kills spores in about 10 minutes. *Iodoform* (CHI_3) is a rather weak germicide which has been employed extensively in the past. When brought in contact with wounds and tissues where active reducing processes are taking place, it supposedly liberates free iodine, which accounts for the germicidal activity of the compound. Several *aromatic iodine* compounds exhibit a bacteriostatic or bactericidal effect on *Mycobacterium tuberculosis*. Concentrations of 3.0 to 5.0 mg. per cent of 2:3:5-triiodobenzoic acid, 3:5-diiodo-2-hydroxybenzoic acid, 2:4:6-triiodophenol, and several other such compounds are quite inhibitory to growth, whereas certain others show little or no inhibition for this organism [Saz, Johnston, Burger, and Bernheim (1943)].

Fluorine Compounds. Chemically, fluorine is the most active of the halogen ions. For this reason it has not been used much as a general disinfectant. The ion is extremely germicidal, however, because it has been stated that hydrofluoric acid is ten to twenty times more inhibitory than hydrochloric acid for yeasts and bacteria. Sodium fluoride is used somewhat to prevent the growth of bacteria and molds and thus to preserve blood and other substances for chemical examination. Field and Field (1932), however, found sodium fluoride to be relatively ineffective in inhibiting the growth of *Lactobacillus casei*. A concentration of 0.08 per cent stimulated the production of acid, and 0.1 per cent allowed the same yield of acid as the control, whereas concentrations of 0.18 to 0.5 per cent produced a sharp decrease in the yield of acid.

In enzyme studies fluorine compounds are extensively used, since they inhibit the activities of many enzymes without interfering with certain other specific cellular catalysts.

The *o*-, *m*-, and *p*-fluoro derivatives of benzoic, phenylacetic, cinnamic, and mandelic acids have been prepared and studied by Hager and Grubb (1942). The introduction of fluorine into the nucleus of these acids caused only a slight increase in their bacteriostatic powers, especially when directed to the *m*- and *p*-positions.

THE PHENOLIC GROUP OF COMPOUNDS

The phenolic group of compounds is extensively used today as disinfectants. Such compounds are relatively cheap and, for the most part, very active bactericides. They differ from some of the other germicides which have so far been considered in that they are only slightly soluble in water. Phenol, for instance, is soluble to the extent of 6.7 g. per 100 ml. of water at 16°C., *p*-cresol to the extent of 2.35 g. at 40°C., and thymol to the extent of 0.083 g. at 15°C. When mixed with water, such compounds form emulsions of varying degrees of fineness.

Phenol (Carbolic Acid). The use of phenol as a disinfectant dates back to Joseph Lister, who introduced it into medicine and surgery in 1865. In sufficient concentration it is effective against the vegetative cells of microorganisms. Most bacteria are killed in 5 to 10 minutes by a dilution of 1 : 80 or 1 : 110 at room temperature. Bacterial spores are more resistant; in fact, the spores of *Bacillus anthracis* may survive 5 per cent phenol for 24 hours or longer. The phenol coefficients of some of the derivatives of phenol are given in the Tables 28 to 33.

Phenol itself plays a minor role today as a disinfectant. It is caustic and irritating when applied to the skin, and its odor is offensive to some people. Several workers have attempted to find a diluent which would exert a protective action on the tissues and still not interfere with the germicidal action of the phenol. Glycerin, alcohol, and various oils have been employed for this purpose, but none of them has been widely accepted. Several factors influence the disinfecting action of phenol and related compounds. Like many other disinfectants, these compounds are more active at high temperatures than at low. They require but little dilution to deprive them completely of their activity. Alkaline reactions usually diminish their germicidal efficiency, whereas low *p*H values increase their efficiency. Salts such as sodium chloride decrease the solubility of phenol and thus influence the activity of its compounds. Reports in the literature state that the presence of organic matter appears to have little effect on compounds with phenol coefficients below five, but substances with high coefficients are affected.

Mode of Action of Phenol. Both physical and chemical theories have been advanced to explain the disinfecting properties of phenol and related compounds. Most workers believe that phenol exerts its action by combining chemically with the bacterial cell to form insoluble proteinates and other compounds. After studying the dispersion phases of phenol between water and other solutions, Reichel (1909) came to the conclusion that the action was a physical phenomenon, as well as a chemical reaction. As proof for this claim he showed that phenol was able to pass into solution in such substances as coagulated albumin and certain lipoids. Hence the germicidal action resulted from the phenol penetrating the bacterial cell in the form of a colloidal solution, where it became a protoplasmic poison by virtue of its ability to form insoluble proteinates. Other workers have suggested that phenol and related compounds act by disrupting the oxidation-reduction potential equilibrium of the cells or by adsorption on to the surface of suspended matter, thus increasing their concentration in the immediate neighborhood of the cells and thereby preventing normal metabolism.

Polyhydroxy Phenols. It is difficult to compare the bactericidal properties of phenol and benzene because of the insolubility of the hydrocarbon in water; however, it is of interest to note the effect of the position of the hydroxyl group, as well as of increasing the number of hydroxyl groups attached to the nucleus (Table 28). Hydroquinone has a highly bacteriostatic action against *Pasteurella pestis*, preventing growth in a dilution of 1 : 432,000, whereas catechol is about one-tenth as active (1 : 48,000), according to Caius, Naidu, and Jang (1927).

TABLE 28

PHENOL COEFFICIENTS OF POLYHYDROXY PHENOLS

[From Suter (1941)]

Compound	Phenol Coefficient at 37°C. *Eberthella typhosa*	*Staphylococcus aureus*
Catechol, $C_6H_4(OH)_2(1,2)$	0.87	0.58
Resorcinol, $C_6H_4(OH)_2(1,3)$	0.4	0.4
Hydroquinone, $C_6H_4(OH)_2(1,4)$	12.0	0.44
Phloroglucinol, $C_6H_3(OH)_3(1,3,5)$	Negligible } slightly bacteriostatic	Negligible } slightly bacteriostatic
Pyrogallol, $C_6H_3(OH)_3(1,2,3)$	Negligible } slightly bacteriostatic	Negligible } slightly bacteriostatic

TABLE 29

PHENOL COEFFICIENTS OF HALOGENATED PHENOLS

[From Suter (1941)]

Compound	Chlorine Derivatives		Bromine Derivatives	
	Eberthella typhosa	*Staphylococcus aureus*	*Eberthella typhosa*	*Staphylococcus aureus*
2-Halophenol	3.6	3.8	3.8	3.7
3-Halophenol	7.4	5.8	...	...
4-Halophenol	3.9	3.9	5.4	4.6
2:4-Dihalophenol	13.0	13.0	19.0	22.0
2:4:6-Trihalophenol	23.0	25.0	...	...
4-Haloresorcinol	0.7	1.0	1.0	1.3
4:6-Dihaloresorcinol	3.2	3.9	4.0	4.5
2:4:6-Trihaloresorcinol	5.0	4.3	6.4	6.4

Halogenated Phenols. It has been shown by Klarmann and his associates (1929, 1934), Heyman and Grubb (1940), and others [see reviews by Klarmann (1939–1944) and Suter (1941)] that the germicidal activity of phenol, cresols, and resorcinol is increased by the substitution of halogens into their molecules. Although fluorophenol differs but little in its germicidal action from phenol, the chloro and bromo derivatives are more effective than the unsubstituted compounds (Table 29). Little is known about the iodinated phenols; they are relatively insoluble in water and possess an unpleasant and persistent odor which prevents their use for practical purposes (see the discussion of iodine compounds, pp. 289 to 290).

Alkylphenols, Alkylresorcinols, Alkylcatechols, Alkylhydroquinones, Alkylphloroglucinols, and Alkylpyrogallols. A great many studies have been published on the effect of alkyl groups on the bactericidal properties of mono-, di-, and trihydroxyphenols, and this literature has been adequately reviewed by Suter (1941). Most of these compounds are only slightly soluble in water, but, when treated with

TABLE 30

PHENOL COEFFICIENTS OF CRESOLS, *p*-ALKYL PHENOLS, AND RELATED COMPOUNDS

[From Schaffer and Tilley (1927) and Tilley and Schaffer (1928)]

Disinfectant	Formula	Phenol Coefficient against *Eberthella typhosa*	Phenol Coefficient against *Staphylococcus aureus*
o-Cresol	$CH_3 \cdot C_6H_4 \cdot OH$	2.20	....
m-Cresol	$CH_3 \cdot C_6H_4 \cdot OH$	2.40	....
p-Cresol	$CH_3 \cdot C_6H_4 \cdot OH$	2.50	2.20
p-Ethyl phenol	$C_2H_5 \cdot C_6H_4 \cdot OH$	7.40	6.00
p-*n*-Propyl phenol	$C_3H_7 \cdot C_6H_4 \cdot OH$	21.60	16.50
p-*n*-Butyl phenol	$C_4H_9 \cdot C_6H_4 \cdot OH$	68.00	50.00
p-*n*-Amyl phenol	$C_5H_{11} \cdot C_6H_4 \cdot OH$	197.00	139.00
p-*n*-Hexyl phenol	$C_6H_{13} \cdot C_6H_4 \cdot OH$	500.00	375.00
p-Xylenol	$(CH_3)_2 \cdot C_6H_3 \cdot OH$	5.50	....
Thymol	$CH_3 \cdot C_6H_3(OH) \cdot C_3H_7$	28.50	....
Carvacrol	$C_3H_7 \cdot C_6H_3(OH) \cdot CH_3$	27.50	....
p-Benzyl phenol	$C_6H_5 \cdot CH_2 \cdot C_6H_4 \cdot OH$	62.00	....

alcohol, alkali, or soap, they yield a homogeneous emulsion. Many of the common disinfectants on the market today are manufactured from crude cresols.

Within experimental error the position of the alkyl group has no effect. For example, the three cresols and the three *n*-butyl phenols are practically identical in their bactericidal action. The *o*- and *p*-*sec*-butyl phenols have phenol coefficients of 28; the branching of the carbon side chain, as in *tert*-butyl phenol, reduces the effectiveness to about 20. The presence of two alkyl groups in the phenol nucleus yields compounds that are fairly effective germicides. However, the six isomeric xylenols do not differ greatly in bactericidal properties, the 2:5-dimethyl phenol being the most active. Carvacrol and thymol both have phenol coefficients of about 28 against *Eberthella typhosa*. Schaffer and Tilley (1927) and Tilley and Schaffer (1928) have tested the germicidal action of many of the phenolic compounds. Some of their results with the cresols and other alkyl phenols are cited in Table 30.

The alkyl resorcinols have been studied by several workers [see Schaffer and Tilley (1927), Rettger, Valley, and Plastridge (1929), and

TABLE 31

PHENOL COEFFICIENTS OF CERTAIN RESORCINOLS

Disinfectant	Formula	Phenol Coefficient against *Eberthella typhosa* *	*Staphylococcus aureus* †
Normal resorcinols			
Resorcinol	$C_6H_4(OH)_2$	0.37	....
Orcinol	$CH_3 \cdot C_6H_3(OH)_2$	0.53	....
Ethyl resorcinol	$C_2H_5 \cdot C_6H_3(OH)_2$	1.60	....
Propyl resorcinol	$C_3H_7 \cdot C_6H_3(OH)_2$	4.80	6.0
Butyl resorcinol	$C_4H_9 \cdot C_6H_3(OH)_2$	15.00	19.0
Amyl resorcinol	$C_5H_{11} \cdot C_6H_3(OH)_2$	47.00	36.0
Hexyl resorcinol	$C_6H_{13} \cdot C_6H_3(OH)_2$	147.00	50.0
Heptyl resorcinol	$C_7H_{15} \cdot C_6H_3(OH)_2$	350.00	60.0
Octyl resorcinol	$C_8H_{17} \cdot C_6H_3(OH)_2$	400.00	16.0
Iso resorcinols			
Isobutyl resorcinol	$(CH_3)_2 \cdot CH \cdot CH_2 \cdot C_6H_3(OH)_2$	12.80	....
Isoamyl resorcinol	$(CH_3)_2 \cdot CH \cdot (CH_2)_2 \cdot C_6H_3(OH)_2$	46.00	24.0
Isohexyl resorcinol	$(CH_3)_2 \cdot CH \cdot (CH_2)_3 \cdot C_6H_3(OH)_2$	105.00	35.0
Normal ketones			
Butylyl resorcinol	$CH_3 \cdot (CH_2)_2 \cdot CO \cdot C_6H_3(OH)_2$	13.50	12.0
Amylyl resorcinol	$CH_3 \cdot (CH_2)_3 \cdot CO \cdot C_6H_3(OH)_2$	37.50	42.0
Hexylyl resorcinol	$CH_3 \cdot (CH_2)_4 \cdot CO \cdot C_6H_3(OH)_2$	106.00	44.0
Heptylyl resorcinol	$CH_3 \cdot (CH_2)_6 \cdot CO \cdot C_6H_3(OH)_2$	280.00	4.0

* Data from Schaffer and Tilley (1927). Modified Rideal-Walker Method.

† Data from Rettger, Valley, and Plastridge (1929). Hygienic Laboratory Method.

Suter (1941)], and the data in Table 31 illustrate the results which have been obtained. In addition to the compounds listed in the table a number of other substitution products, such as several dialkyl resorcinols, have been prepared and tested.

Several alkyl catechols, alkyl hydroquinones, alkyl phloroglucinols, and alkyl pyrogallols have been prepared and tested for their germicidal activity. For the most part they differ little, if any, in activity from the resorcinols, although a number of variations have been noted [Suter (1941)].

Alkylhalophenols and Alkylhaloresorcinols. Since the various alkyl groups and the halogen atoms separately increase the bactericidal activity of a phenol, it is interesting to note the cumulative effect when both types of substituents are present. The literature on this subject has been reviewed by Suter (1941), and only one example (Table 32) will be cited here. Similar data will be found in Table 9. The figures in the tables are self-explanatory and need no further discussion.

TABLE 32

PHENOL COEFFICIENTS OF PHENOL, ALKYL PHENOLS, AND RESORCINOL AND THEIR HALOGEN DERIVATIVES IN THE ABSENCE AND THE PRESENCE OF ORGANIC MATTER

[From Klarmann, Shternov, and von Wowern (1929)]

Disinfectant	Phenol Coefficient against *Eberthella typhosa*		Reduction of Efficiency, per cent	Phenol Coefficient against *Staphylococcus aureus*		Reduction of Efficiency, per cent
	Without Organic Matter	*With Organic Matter*		*Without Organic Matter*	*With Organic Matter*	
Phenol	1.0	0.84	16	1.0	0.81	19
o-Chlorophenol	3.6	3.1	14	3.8	3.0	21
p-Chlorophenol	3.9	3.2	16	4.0	3.3	17
m-Chlorophenol	7.4	5.2	30	5.8	4.2	27
2:4-Dichlorophenol	13.3	9.6	28	12.7	9.9	22
2:4:6-Trichlorophenol	22.6	12.8	44	25.0	10.4	58
o-Bromophenol	3.8	2.8	25	3.7	2.5	32
p-Bromophenol	5.4	4.0	25	4.6	4.1	12
2:4-Dibromophenol	18.8	15.1	20	21.9	14.3	35
m-Cresol	2.5	2.0	20	2.4	1.9	19
4-Chloro-*m*-cresol	30.5	21.9	28	19.5	9.9	49
Xylenol	5.0	4.4	12	5.6	3.2	42
Chloroxylenol	70.9	50.6	29	38.7	9.0	77
Thymol	33.2	27.3	18	23.6	9.3	61
4-Chlorothymol	61.3	21.7	65	158.0	57.3	64
Carvacrol	39.9	25.7	36	17.8	4.7	73
Resorcinol	0.3	0.25	17	0.4	0.24	39
4-Chlororesorcinol	0.7	0.42	40	1.0	0.48	52
4:6-Dichlororesorcinol	3.2	1.7	47	3.9	1.8	54
2:4:6-Trichlororesorcinol	5.0	1.9	61	4.3	1.9	55
4-Bromoresorcinol	1.0	0.84	16	1.25	0.65	48
4:6-Dibromoresorcinol	4.0	2.3	43	4.5	1.6	64
2:4:6-Tribromoresorcinol	6.7	2.4	64	6.4	2.2	66

Nitro-, Amino-, Carboxylic Acid-Phenols and Their Derivatives. A number of nitro, amino, and hydroxycarboxylic acid phenols have been prepared and their bacteriostatic and bactericidal properties determined. Not much is known concerning the germicidal properties of the nitro phenols, although of the three isomers the *p*-compound is the most active [Suter (1941)]. *o*-Aminophenol and various of its *n*-alkyl derivatives have been described in the patent literature as highly active germicidal agents of low toxicity, but they have not been studied extensively. Although esters of salicylic acid ($HO \cdot C_6H_4 \cdot COOH$) have little germicidal or bacteriostatic action, certain alkyl *p*-hydroxy benzoates are highly effective, particularly as preservatives. The presence of halogen in the nucleus increases this effectiveness, as does also the nitro group, whereas the amino group decreases it. The action of numerous dihydroxybenzoic acids and their esters on yeast and bacteria has also been mentioned in the literature [Suter (1941)].

TABLE 33

PHENOL COEFFICIENTS OF HYDROXYDIPHENYLMETHANE

[From Suter (1941)]

Substituted Halogen Compounds on Hydroxydiphenylmethane	Phenol Coefficient		
	Eberthella typhosa	*Staphylococcus aureus*	*Streptococcus pyogenes*
3-Chloro-4-	36	125	165
3-Chloro-2-	24	71	94
4′-Chloro-4-	83	170	165
3-Bromo-4-	19	170	185
5-Bromo-2-	26	295	310
3:4′-Dichloro-4-	41	345	175
5-Chloro-3-methyl-2-	16	245	300
5-Chloro-4-methyl-2-	17	405	455
5-Chloro-4:6-dimethyl-2-	31	920	785

Hydroxy Derivatives of Diphenylmethane. A variety of mono- and di-hydroxydiphenylmethane deviatives has been prepared by Klarmann and his coworkers, Huston, and others [see Suter (1941)]. In general, their results show that a halogen in the *p*-position makes the compound more active than does a halogen in the *o*-position to the hydroxyl group; it makes little difference which ring bears the halogen atom. Also, multiple substitution of methyl and halogen groups produces substances highly active against *Staphylococcus aureus* and *Streptococcus pyogenes*, but slightly less active against *Eberthella ty-*

phosa. These facts may be seen in Table 33. More recently Traub, Newhall, and Fuller (1944) have found that, when a certain derivative of diphenylmethane is incorporated in hand soap, it is very effective in reducing the number of bacteria on the skin. The compound used by these workers is called G-11; chemically it is dihydroxyhexachlorodiphenylmethane (2:2′-dihydroxy-3:5:6-3′:5′:6′-hexachlorodiphenylmethane):

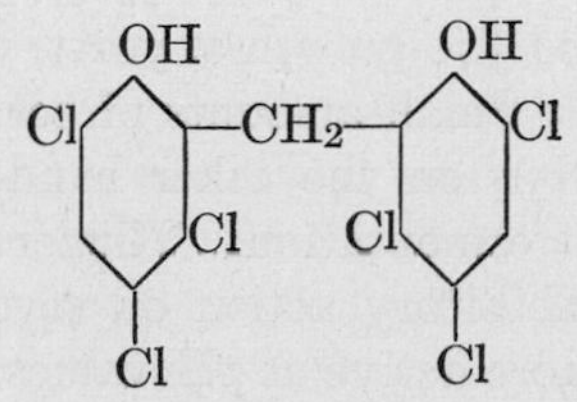

It is nonirritating and more active for Gram-positive than for Gram-negative bacteria. It gives a phenol coefficient of about 125 with *S. aureus*.

THE FURAN (FURFURAN) COMPOUNDS

Several derivatives of furan, which has this formula:

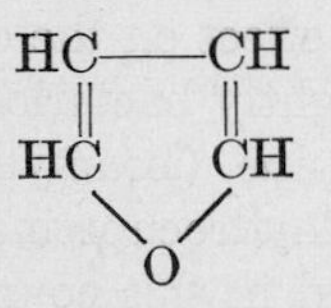

have been shown to possess some germicidal activity. One of these derivatives, Fumarane, has already been mentioned on p. 276 on organic mercurials, and a few other illustrations may be cited here. McGuigan (1923), for example, found that 2-furaldehyde has a phenol coefficient of 0.26 when measured against *Eberthella typhosa*, and that a 2 per cent solution inhibits the fermentation of glucose by yeast. Since this study appeared, nearly fifty furan compounds, including derivatives of 2-furfuryl alcohol and 2-furoic acid, have been studied with respect to their effect on microorganisms [see Calloway, Gilman, and Werkman (1933), Phatak and Leake (1936), Dodd, Stillman, *et al.* (1944)]. In general, the presence of a nitro group in the 5-position of the furan ring increases the activity of these compounds.

ALKALOIDS AND RELATED SUBSTANCES

The term alkaloid is applied to certain nitrogenous bases which occur in various plants. A great many such substances are known, and they differ widely in structure. For example, certain ones, like muscarine, are aliphatic; some, like caffeine, contain a ring of carbon atoms and are related to uric acid; whereas others may be regarded as derivatives of pyridine (for example, nicotine), quinoline (quinine), isoquinoline, and unknown substances.

The effect of alkaloids on microorganisms other than the malarial parasite has not been studied very extensively. Somogyi (1916) found that small amounts of quinine ($C_{20}H_{24}O_2N_2 \cdot 3H_2O$) and atropine ($C_{17}H_{23}O_3N$) accelerated the growth of yeast, whereas larger amounts inhibited development. Small amounts of cocaine ($C_{17}H_{21}O_4N$) and pilocarpine ($C_{11}H_{16}O_2N_2$), on the other hand, inhibited, but larger quantities accelerated, fermentation. Kligler (1918) observed that caffeine had a slight inhibitory action on several intestinal bacteria and that it is slightly more active at *p*H values above 7.4 than it is at 6.2. Williams (1931) tested the soluble forms of ten alkaloids for their ability to inhibit the growth and other activities of several bacteria. Considerable difference in toxicity was observed, and some compounds affected only morphology and pigment formation. More recently, Lawrence (1943) has studied the effects of quinine, atabrine, and other related acridines on coli-aerogenes, typhoid-paratyphoid, and cholera organisms. Some of the acridine compounds were quite bactericidal, but quinine had little or no effect on the organisms other than cholera vibrios, for which it was slightly bacteriostatic.

The organic bases Eucupine (isoamylhydrocupreine, $C_{19}H_{23}ON_2 \cdot OC_5H_{11}$), Vuzine (isooctylhydrocupreine), and Optochine (ethylhydrocupreine) are marketed in this country in the form of powders, oils, or ointments. It is claimed that they possess some bactericidal action for different organisms in dilutions between 1 : 2,000 and 1 : 40,000 [Dernby and Davide (1923)].

ALCOHOLS, ETHERS, ALDEHYDES, KETONES, AMINES, AND QUATERNARY AMMONIUM COMPOUNDS

The germicidal properties of the alcohols, ethers, aldehydes, ketones, and certain amines have been studied, but with a few exceptions they are not as widely used today as disinfectants or germicides as are some other substances.

Alcohols. As early as 1875 Bucholtz found that ethyl alcohol had some inhibitory action on bacteria, but in 1881 Robert Koch demonstrated that pure or dilute ethyl alcohol would not kill anthrax spores even after long exposure. This observation on anthrax spores was soon confirmed by Epstein (1897) and Minervini (1898), who also found that certain less resistant bacteria could not be killed by various concentrations of ethyl alcohol. Using various techniques for testing disinfectants, Minervini (1898), Christensen (1918), Kokko (1939), Witz (1940), Tanner and Wilson (1943), and others have determined the lethal effects of various concentrations of alcohol on several bacterial species (Table 34). The consensus of all investigators is that the maximum efficiency of ethyl alcohol is obtained with a 50 to 70 per cent aqueous solution, concentrations above or below this range being less effective. In this respect the experiments by Price (1939) are very interesting. He has found that alcohol is an efficient germicide on the skin and against vegetative bacteria *in vitro*, providing the concentration is exactly 70 per cent by weight and not by volume. Apparently heating bacteria in the presence of absolute ethyl alcohol has much the same effect as dry heat, because *Staphylococcus aureus* will stand a 1-hour exposure to absolute alcohol under a pressure of 3 atm. at a temperature of 120–130°C.

TABLE 34

TIME REQUIRED TO KILL BACTERIA WITH VARIOUS CONCENTRATIONS OF ETHYL ALCOHOL

[Data from Minervini (1898) and Christensen (1916)]

Organism	Time Required for Various Concentrations of Alcohol to Kill				
	25 Per Cent	*50 Per Cent*	*70 Per Cent*	*80 Per Cent*	*90–100 Per Cent*
Gaffkya tetragena	6 hours	0.5 hour	0.5 hour	6 hours	12 hours
Pseudomonas aeruginosa	1 hour	0.05 hour	0.05 hour	12 hours	24 hours
Serratia marcescens	6 hours	1 hour	0.5 hour	12 hours	24 hours
Staphylococcus aureus	12 hours	0.5 hour	0.5 hour	3 days+	3 days+
Staphylococcus *	....	0.01–0.75 hour	0.008–0.013 hour	0.004–0.3 hour	1–7 days+
Escherichia coli	24 hours	6 hours	6 hours	24 hours+	24 hours
Bacillus subtilis, spores	8 days+	8 days+	8 days+	8 days+	8 days+
Bacillus anthracis, spores	50 days+	50 days+	50 days+	50 days+	50 days +

* The data for this organism were collected from the literature by Christensen, 1916.

It can be seen from the data in Table 34 that ethyl alcohol is not very effective as a germicide, especially against bacterial spores. Tanner and Wilson (1943) also reported that spore-forming organisms were little affected by alcohols; *Bacillus subtilis* and *Bacillus megatherium* were found to be viable after 9 months in contact with 100 per cent primary normal methyl, ethyl, propyl, butyl, amyl, hexyl, heptyl, octyl, nonyl, and undecyl alcohols. The phenol coefficients of several alcohols against *Eberthella typhosa* and *Staphylococcus aureus* are listed in Table 35. Increased germicidal activity of the higher members of the series is prevented by their decreased solubility. Since none of the higher alcohols is used as a disinfectant, these data are of only historical significance. Cowles (1938) studied the germicidal power of certain primary, secondary, and tertiary alcohols for *E. typhosa* and *S. aureus* and observed a close relationship between germicidal action and surface tension. Kokko (1939) and Tanner and Wilson (1943) also studied the germicidal action of some 26 alcohols, containing from 1 to 11 carbon atoms. They found a regular decrease in germicidal action from primary to iso- to secondary to tertiary arrangements of the carbon chain for any given number of carbon atoms.

According to certain investigators, the addition of ethyl alcohol to aqueous solutions of mercuric chloride increases the disinfectant action of the $HgCl_2$, but alcohol reduces the germicidal action of phenol and formaldehyde.

TABLE 35

Phenol Coefficients of Various Alcohols

[From Tilley and Schaffer (1926)]

Disinfectant	Phenol Coefficient against *Eberthella typhosa*	Phenol Coefficient against *Staphylococcus aureus*
Primary normal alcohols		
Methyl	0.026	0.030
Ethyl	0.040	0.039
Propyl	0.102	0.082
Butyl	0.273	0.22
Amyl	0.78	0.63
Hexyl	2.3	.....
Heptyl	6.8	.....
Octyl	21.0	.....
Secondary alcohols		
Propyl	0.064	0.054
Butyl	0.152	0.131
Amyl	0.38	0.32
Hexyl	1.0	.....
Tertiary alcohols		
Butyl	0.081	0.064
Amyl	0.182	0.142
Hexyl	0.45	.....

Ethers. The ethers are supposed to have some germicidal activity, but because of the low boiling point of the dimethyl and diethyl ethers they have little or no significance. Topley (1915) incubated fresh cultures of *Escherichia coli, Staphylococcus aureus, Staphylococcus albus, Pseudomonas aeruginosa,* pneumococci, and streptococci in an atmosphere saturated with diethyl ether. The cultures exhibited no growth, and most of them were killed within 3 hours. The staphylococci were the most resistant; in fact, several strains survived a 24-hour exposure. Shaking the cultures in liquid ether also had a marked effect, and most of the bacteria were killed in 3 to 24 hours.

Formaldehyde and Other Aldehydes. Formaldehyde is a gas and is rather difficult to use as a general disinfectant; however, it has been employed in its gaseous state to fumigate after infectious diseases and to disinfect various contaminated articles, such as books (see pp. 304 to 305 on germicidal gases). The gas is soluble in water and forms a colorless solution with a characteristic acrid odor. It is marketed as formalin, which is an aqueous solution containing 37 to 40 per cent of the gas. Chick (1908) reported that formaldehyde was a moderate disinfectant, since a 5 per cent solution killed the spores of *Bacillus anthracis* in 32 hours at 20°C. and in 90 minutes at 37°C. Similar results have been reported by Scott (1928) and others, who used both aerobic and anaerobic bacteria as test organisms. Tilley and Schaffer (1928) determined the phenol coefficients of several of the aldehydes and observed some interesting results (Table 36). The aldehydes do not exhibit an increase in germicidal activity as the series increases; instead formaldehyde is much more toxic than related compounds.

TABLE 36

PHENOL COEFFICIENTS OF VARIOUS ALDEHYDES

[From Tilley and Schaffer (1928)]

Disinfectant	Formula	Phenol Coefficient against *Eberthella typhosa*
Formaldehyde	$H \cdot CHO$	1.05
Acetaldehyde	$CH_3 \cdot CHO$	0.09
Propionic aldehyde	$C_2H_5 \cdot CHO$	0.15
Butyric aldehyde	$C_3H_7 \cdot CHO$	0.32

The presence of extraneous organic matter does not greatly hinder the germicidal action of formaldehyde, but the presence of methyl and ethyl alcohol markedly reduces its germicidal powers. Formalin possesses the property of converting certain bacterial toxins into nonpoisonous toxoids without destroying their ability to serve as antigens. Likewise it is used to prepare certain bacterial antigens, especially the H antigen of motile organisms, such as *Eberthella typhosa*. Many soil fungi and bacterial plant pathogens are destroyed by formaldehyde gas and various concentrations of formalin. Practical application of this property of formaldehyde and formalin is sometimes made to sterilize soil, seeds, and tubers known to be contaminated.

Ketones. Several workers have shown that acetone and related ketones are only feeble germicides. One example, taken from the paper by Tilley and Schaffer (1928), will make this point clear (Table 37). Most ketones have a phenol coefficient of less than one. Even though acetone has a low phenol coefficient, it is widely used to dehydrate and kill the cells of microorganisms preparatory to the study of their chemical composition, intracellular enzymes, and antigenic structure.

The effect of benzophenone (diphenyl ketone) and allied compounds on human tubercle bacilli has been studied by Freedlander (1942). It was found that benzophenone exhibited bacteriostatic action in a 1 : 10,000 dilution; 2:4′-dichlorobenzophenone was more effective, being bacteriostatic in a dilution of 1 : 100,000. Of the twenty-five other derivatives and related compounds tested, four were more effective than benzophenone but less so than the dichloro derivative; the remaining compounds were much less bacteriostatic than benzophenone.

TABLE 37

PHENOL COEFFICIENTS OF SEVERAL KETONES

[From Tilley and Schaffer (1928)]

Disinfectant	Formula	Phenol Coefficient against *Eberthella typhosa*
Ketones		
Methyl methyl (acetone)	$CH_3 \cdot CO \cdot CH_3$	0.04
Methyl ethyl	$CH_3 \cdot CO \cdot C_2H_5$	0.102
Methyl *n*-propyl	$CH_3 \cdot CO \cdot C_3H_7$	0.275
Methyl *n*-butyl	$CH_3 \cdot CO \cdot C_4H_9$	0.78
Methyl *n*-amyl	$CH_3 \cdot CO \cdot C_5H_{11}$	2.3

Amines and Quaternary Ammonium Compounds. The amines of low molecular weight have weak germicidal powers and apparently have no significance as disinfectants. Tilley and Schaffer (1928) experimented with several amines and found *n*-hexylamine and di-*n*-butylamine to have the highest phenol coefficients (Table 38). In general, bactericidal powers increased as the series ascended. More recently, Ralston (1940) and Fuller (1942) have tested several long-chain mono- and diamines and discovered them to be quite strongly bactericidal. They found that the compounds containing fourteen to sixteen carbon atoms were the most active.

Considerable research is now being conducted on the quaternary ammonium compounds as antibacterial agents. These compounds usually have the general formula $R_1R_2R_3R_4NX$, where the R groups are alkyl, aryl, cycloalkyl, or similar radicals and X is a halogen. Although several of these compounds have been patented, they have not been described to any great extent in scientific journals (see pp. 305 to 310 on soaps and synthetic detergents).

TABLE 38

PHENOL COEFFICIENTS OF CERTAIN AMINES

[From Tilley and Schaffer (1928)]

Compound	Formula	Phenol Coefficient against *Eberthella typhosa*	Phenol Coefficient against *Staphylococcus aureus*
n-Propylamine	$CH_3 \cdot CH_2 \cdot CH_2NH_2$	1.60	0.23
n-Butylamine	$CH_3 \cdot (CH_2)_2 \cdot CH_2NH_2$	2.10	0.62
n-Amylamine	$CH_3 \cdot (CH_2)_3 \cdot CH_2NH_2$	3.00	1.30
n-Hexylamine	$CH_3 \cdot (CH_2)_4 \cdot CH_2NH_2$	4.50	3.10
Diethylamine	$(C_2H_5)_2{:}NH$	2.20	0.21
Di-*n*-propylamine	$(C_3H_7)_2{:}NH$	2.00	....
Di-*n*-butylamine	$(C_4H_9)_2{:}NH$	4.70	....
Triethylamine	$(C_2H_5)_3N$	1.50	0.25
Benzylamine	$C_6H_5 \cdot CH_2NH_2$	1.00	....
Aniline	$C_6H_5 \cdot NH_2$	0.57	0.50
p-Toluidine	$CH_3 \cdot C_6H_4 \cdot NH_2$	1.25	....
Methylaniline	$C_6H_5 \cdot NH \cdot CH_3$	1.80	....
Ethylaniline	$C_6H_5 \cdot NH \cdot C_2H_5$	3.00	....

BILE AND BILE SALTS

Bile and bile salts are used rather extensively in bacteriology for differentiating bacteria by lysis and as ingredients in selective media for separating closely related species. The effect of bile upon certain cocci is particularly striking, since pneumococci are dissolved by solutions of bile or certain bile salts, but streptococci do not undergo lysis in such solutions. This fact has come to be regarded generally as a satisfactory method or test for differentiating these organisms. Certain other organisms also undergo lysis in bile solutions, but they are not usually characterized or differentiated on this basis. The actual mechanism of lysis by bile salts is not well understood. Downie, Stent, and White (1931) have shown that there is no parallelism between lytic activity and the surface tension of solutions, but there seems to be some correlation between chemical structure and power to form addition compounds, and the lytic activity of the various bile salts. Sturdza (1938) has also studied the mechanism of lysis of pneumococci and believes that lysis is actually performed by an autolysin formed by the organisms themselves and that bile salts merely aid this action. Many selective media have been described in which bile or bile salts have been incorporated to inhibit certain organisms. MacConkey's lactose-peptone-bile agar, brilliant-green lactose-bile broth, and sodium desoxycholate agar [Leifson (1935)] are probably the more important examples. Such media have been used mostly in sanitary bacteriology for the differentiation and study of intestinal pathogens.

GERMICIDAL GASES AND VAPORS (AEROSOLS [2])

It has been suggested by several workers that certain gases might be used to good advantage to disinfect various substances. Salle and Korzenovsky (1942), for example, tested formaldehyde, methyl bromide, methyl formate, ethylene oxide, and carbon disulfide gases under various conditions for their ability to sterilize materials contaminated with bacteria. With the exception of formaldehyde, none of the gases was of any value as a germicide under the conditions employed in these experiments. A 28-in. vacuum increased the efficiency of formaldehyde, because it increased the penetration of the gas into the contaminated materials. Under such conditions, an exposure of 25 minutes sterilized all cultures, and even 5 to 10 minutes was effective against organisms other than *Bacillus subtilis*. In the absence of a vacuum an exposure of 2 hours was not sufficient to effect sterilization of all contaminated materials. Other investigators have used a concentration of 100 to 200 g. of ethylene oxide per cubic meter of air to fumigate clothes, potatoes, seeds, and other materials; the gas is probably a better insecticide than it is a bactericide. Ozone is supposed to have an inhibitory or destructive effect on microorganisms, and Ramel and Vulliémoz (1938) concluded that its action is due to the formation of ozonides. Kessel, Allison, Moore, and Kaime (1943) found that ozone in an amount not exceeding 0.45 p.p.m. inactivated a 1 : 1,000 dilution of a strain of poliomyelitis virus in 2 minutes and a 1 : 100 dilution in 45 minutes. However, more concentrated virus suspensions were not inactivated, probably because of the excess amount of organic matter present in these dilutions. Ozone also interferes with other biological systems.

[2] Robertson, Bigg, Puck, and Miller (1943) state: "Liquid aerosols consist of droplets 1 to 2 μ in diameter, dispersed in air. An erroneous use of the term aerosol has been introduced by commercial concerns who have applied it as a trade name to certain wetting and detergent compounds."

In recent years considerable attention has been given to the idea of employing bactericidal mists, vapors, or smokes to control air-borne diseases. The literature on this subject has been reviewed by Twort and Baker (1942), Robertson, Bigg, Puck, and Miller (1943), and Pulvertaft (1944); these references should be consulted for more details than can be given here. In this country mists of such compounds as resorcinol, sodium hypochlorite, and the synthetic detergents have been employed as aerial disinfectants, but they have not proved as satisfactory as triethylene glycol and propylene glycol ($CH_3 \cdot CHOH \cdot CH_2OH$) aerosols or vapors. In England, however, sodium hypochlorite mist is favored, mainly because of its cheapness and deodorizing property.

Most of the work with propylene glycol vapors and mists has been conducted by Robertson and his associates [see Robertson, Bigg, Puck, and Miller (1943), Puck, Robertson, and Lemon (1943), and Bigg (1943)], and their work may be briefly summarized. Concentrations of 1 g. of propylene glycol vapor in 2,000,000 to 4,000,000 cu. cm. of air have been shown to produce immediate sterilization of air into which pneumococci, streptococci, staphylococci, or the influenza virus had been sprayed. The spores of *Bacillus subtilis*, on the other hand, were little affected by such an environment. A temperature below 80°F. (26.6°C.), and an atmospheric relative humidity between 45 and 70 per cent have been found to constitute the most favorable conditions for the lethal action of the vapor. The vapor is just as efficient when dispersed in an 800-cu. ft. room as in a 2-cu. ft. room. Atmospheres containing propylene glycol vapor are invisible, odorless, nonirritating, and apparently nontoxic. The mode of action of propylene glycol vapor has not been fully elucidated, but it is thought that a bactericidal concentration of the glycol rapidly accumulates in the bacterial droplet as a result of contact with and absorption of glycol molecules from the surrounding atmosphere. The bactericidal action of the glycols is thought to be due to their hydroscopic properties.

SOAPS AND SYNTHETIC DETERGENTS

For a long time it has been popularly supposed that some ordinary soaps are mild germicides. However, part of the action which such soaps appear to possess when used on the skin can be accounted for on the basis of mechanical removal of microorganisms by emulsification of the lipoidal secretions of the skin, in which many bacteria become embedded. Although several early workers considered that the germicidal action of soap depended on the alkali produced by hydrolysis, this theory does not explain the specificity of the action of certain soaps on bacteria which has been observed by Eggerth (1931), Bayliss (1936–

1937), Stuart and Pohle (1941), and others. For example, these workers have shown how such factors as the length of the hydrocarbon chain, chemical configuration, *p*H, and serum influence the action of soaps on bacteria. In general, however, when ordinary soaps are tested *in vitro* in dilutions comparable to their concentration in lather, they show little or no killing action for such organisms as *Staphylococcus aureus* [Morton and Klauder (1944)]. Today ordinary soaps are generally employed where detergent, rather than germicidal, action is desired. The so-called surgical or germicidal soaps which are on the market usually contain disinfectants such as mercuric chloride or iodide (0.25 to 2.0 per cent), Metaphen (1 : 500), chloramine-T (7 per cent), diphenolmethane derivatives (for example, G-11), or other germicides. Although certain of these soaps possess a greater bacterial killing power than ordinary soaps, only those containing 1.0 or 2.0 per cent mercuric iodide kill such organisms as *Staphylococcus aureus* in less than 1 minute when diluted 1 : 5; when diluted 1 : 20, about 2 to 4 minutes is required to kill this organism [Morton and Klauder (1944)].

Like other germicides, soaps have certain disadvantages. Ordinary, as well as the so-called germicidal, soaps are often too alkaline for application to sensitive tissues, and they are precipitated by hard water. These are just two examples of their disadvantages.

Because of the deficiencies of ordinary soaps and because of the demands of many industries for new and improved detergents, interface modifiers, wetting and emulsifying agents, and related compounds, at least a thousand individually different compounds with such properties have been synthesized in recent years [Baker, Harrison, and Miller (1941)]. These compounds, in general, are superior to ordinary soaps in wetting and cleansing abilities and have the additional virtue of stability in acid and alkaline solutions. They may be classified into three main groups: (1) *anionic compounds,* such as sodium lauryl sulfate, which ionizes with the hydrophobic group in the anion, thus: $(Na^{+}) + (C_{12}H_{25}OSO_3)^{-}$; (2) *cationic compounds,* such as lauryl pyridinium iodide, which contains the hydrophobic group in the cation, thus: $\left(\langle\bigcirc\rangle N—C_{12}H_{25}\right)^{+} + (I)^{-}$; and (3) *nonionized compounds,* such as the polyglycerol esters. Many of these compounds are now commercially available, and Baker, Harrison, and Miller (1941) and Gershenfeld and associates (1941) have tabulated the names of the more important synthetic detergents, together with their chemical structure and the manufacturers (Table 39). It will be seen that many of the compounds in the table are quaternary ammonium compounds or complex alkyl sulfates.

Although most of the synthetic detergents have been patented, they have not been described to any great extent in the scientific journals. Therefore only a few typical results will be presented here. Dunn

TABLE 39

TRADE NAME AND COMPOSITION OF SEVERAL DETERGENTS

[From Baker, Harrison, and Miller (1941)]

	Trade Name	Chemical Composition
Cationic	Zephiran (Alba Pharmaceutical Co.)	Alkyldimethylbenzyl ammonium chlorides (alkyl = C_8 to C_{18})
	Triton K-12 (Röhm and Haas)	Cetyldimethylbenzyl ammonium chloride
	Triton K-60 (Röhm and Haas)	Lauryldimethylbenzyl ammonium chloride
	Retarder LA (E. I. du Pont)	Stearyltrimethyl ammonium bromide
	Hydrocide (Röhm and Haas)	Alkylhydroxybenzyldimethyl ammonium phosphate
	Damol (Alba Pharmaceutical Co.)	N-N-N′-N′-Tetramethyl-N-N′-didodecyl-β-hydroxypropylene diammonium bromide
	Emulsol-605 (Emulsol Corp.)	$C_{11}H_{23}$—COO—C_2H_4—NH—CO—CH_2—$N(CH_3)_3Cl$
	Cepryn chloride (Wm. S. Merrell Co.)	Cetyl pyridinium chloride
	Emulsol-660B (Emulsol Corp.)	Lauryl pyridinium iodide
	Emulsol-606 (Emulsol Corp.)	Lauryl ester of glycine hydrochloride
Anionic	Cetyl sulfate (Procter and Gamble Co.)	Sodium cetyl sulfate (C_{16})
	Duponol LS (E. I. du Pont)	Sodium oleyl sulfate (C_{18})
	Triton W-30 (Röhm and Haas)	Sodium salt of alkylphenoxy ethyl sulfonate
	Triton 720 (Röhm and Haas)	Sodium salt of alkylphenoxy dialkoxy sulfate
	Igepon T (General Dyestuffs)	R—CO—$N(CH_3)$—$(CH_2)_2$—SO_3Na
	Igepon AP (General Dyestuffs)	R—COO—$(CH_2)_2$—SO_3Na
	Nopcocastor (National Oil Products Co.)	75 per cent sulfonated castor oil
	Tergitol-7 (Carbon and Carbide Corp.)	Sodium alkyl sulfate (alkyl = 3:9-diethyltridecanol-6)(C_{17})
	Drene (Procter and Gamble Co.)	Triethanolamine lauryl sulfate
	Sodium taurcholate (Pfanstiehl Co.)	Sodium taurocholate

(1937, 1938) has published some interesting results on the antiseptic, germicidal, and fungicidal properties of alkyldimethylbenzyl ammonium chloride (Zephiran). For example, when tested by the Food and Drug Administration standard technique, the substance was found to kill organisms when diluted 1 : 2,000 to 1 : 4,000 at 20°C. and 1 : 35,000 to 1 : 95,000 at 37°C. in water; and when diluted 1 : 1,250 to 1 : 5,000 at 20°C. and 1 : 3,250 to 1 : 8,750 at 37°C. in the presence of 20 per cent serum. When the phenol coefficients were calculated for several organisms, the values in Table 40 were obtained.

TABLE 40

GERMICIDAL ACTION OF ALKYLDIMETHYLBENZYL AMMONIUM CHLORIDES IN THE ABSENCE AND PRESENCE OF NORMAL HORSE SERUM

[From Dunn (1937)]

	Average Phenol Coefficients			
	In Water		*In 20 Per Cent Serum*	
Organisms	20°C.	37°C.	20°C.	37°C.
Staphylococcus aureus	279	407	54.2	72
Eberthella typhosa	250	429	23.0	39.8
Escherichia coli	160	358	17.9	31
Streptococcus pyogenes	435	579	63.6	61.5
Cryptococcus hominis	214	395	....	....
Monilia albicans	111	274	....	....
Trichophyton interdigitale	30.8	...	....	....
Microsporon lanosum	400	...	....	....

Baker, Harrison, and Miller (1941) studied the effects of synthetic detergents and wetting agents on the respiration and glycolysis of several Gram-positive and Gram-negative bacteria. They drew the following conclusions: All of the *cationic detergents* in Table 39 are very effective inhibitors of bacterial metabolism at 1 : 3,000 concentration, and several are equally active at 1 : 30,000. Few of the *anionic detergents* inhibit as effectively as the cationic compounds. Gram-positive and Gram-negative bacteria were found to be equally sensitive to the action of the cationic detergents. On the other hand, all the anionic compounds studied selectively inhibit the metabolism of Gram-positive organisms. The inhibitory action of both types of detergents is influenced markedly by hydrogen-ion concentration. Cationic detergents exhibit their maximum activity in the alkaline *p*H range, and the anionic, in the acid range [see also Gershenfeld and Milanick (1941)]. Studies of homologous series of straight-chain alkyl sulfates and sulfoacetates (C_8 to C_{18}) demonstrate that maximum inhibition is exerted by the 12-, 14-, and 16-carbon compounds (lauryl, myristyl, and cetyl). It has been observed that three lauryl esters of amino acids are powerful inhibitors of bacterial metabolism. The effect of such cationic detergents (without the quaternary ammonium structure) has not been studied previously. Certain detergents were found to stimulate bacterial metabolism at concentrations lower than the inhibiting values, this effect being noticed more frequently with the anionic detergents.

Gershenfeld and his associates (1941) have studied the bactericidal effects of many wetting agents, which can be classified as synthetic detergents. They found, for example, that such compounds did not increase the bactericidal or bacteriostatic efficiencies of 16 phenolic, 10 mercurial, and 2 halogen compounds. Some of their results are also discussed on pp. 244 to 245 on the relationship between surface tension and the action of disinfectants.

Further studies of the germicidal action of quaternary ammonium salts and other anionic and cationic synthetic detergents have been made by Cowles (1938), Birkeland and Steinhaus (1939), Rawlins, Sweet, and Joslyn (1943), Joslyn, Yaw, and Rawlins (1943), and Epstein, Harris, and Katzman (1943). These workers have shown that the general configuration of the molecule is as important for the antibacterial effect as the nature of the individual constituents. They postulate that the R groups in the general formula, $R_1R_2R_3R_4NCl$, should consist of 1 long alkyl or similar group, 1 short aryl and 2 low alkyl radicals; the total number of carbon atoms of the long chain should be 12 to 16. The introduction of a halogen into the nucleus of the aryl group does not increase the antibacterial activity but may reduce it.

Rawlins and associates employed some 30 quaternary ammonium salts in their study, and found one to be a much more potent bactericide and fungicide than the others. This compound is *p-tert*-octylphenoxyethoxyethyldimethylbenzyl ammonium chloride:

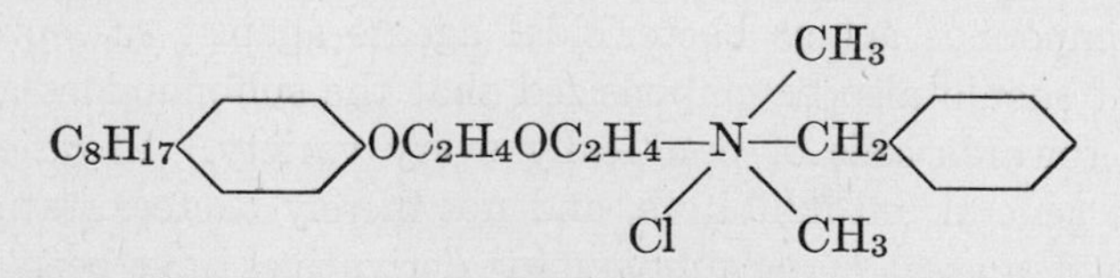

and has been introduced into commerce under the trade name Phemerol. For most bacteria tested *in vitro*, dilutions of 1 : 12,000 or more will kill in 5 minutes at 20°C.; under similar conditions higher fungi are killed by dilutions of 1 : 500 to 1 : 1,000.

In recent years certain other biological effects of some of the synthetic detergents (especially the quaternary bases and the alkyl sulfates) have been studied rather extensively. For example, they have been shown to be relatively nontoxic for rabbits [Gershenfeld and Witlin (1941), to inactivate certain viruses [Stock and Francis (1940), Krueger (1942), Knight and Stanley (1944)], to lyse red blood cells and denature the hemoglobin, to denature egg albumin and serve as useful agents to extract certain photosensitive pigments, such as visual purple and chlorophyll [Anson (1939)], to neutralize tetanus toxin and diphtheria toxin *in vitro*, selectively to lyse Gram-negative bacteria [Bayliss (1937)], to render certain bacteria filterable [Kramer (1939)], to delay the clotting of oxalated human plasma by a staphylococcus culture, to inhibit fibrinolysis by a Group-A strain of hemolytic streptococcus [Neter (1942)], and to affect several other biological systems.

The mode of action of the cationic detergents is apparently similar to the action of the toxic metallic ions and dye cations; that is, they function by the phenomenon of ionic exchange with bacteria and other bodies [see Albert (1942), Valko and DuBois (1944)].

SULFONAMIDE, SULFONE, AND OTHER SULFUR COMPOUNDS

The growing success of the chemotherapeutic treatment of a number of bacterial diseases by means of different sulfonamides has stimulated a great deal of research in this field. Even a fragmentary discussion of the pertinent publications on this subject would far exceed the scope of this book. Therefore, only a few papers will be mentioned briefly; for further details the book by Long and Bliss (1939) and several reviews by Marshall (1939, 1940), Long (1940), Northey (1943), Henry (1943), Fosbinder (1944), and others, where the chemotherapeutic aspects of the problem are discussed in detail, should be consulted. In general, the sulfonamide compounds are bacteriostatic, rather than germicidal, when tested *in vitro*, and for this reason they have no place as general disinfectants; however, under certain conditions these compounds act as bactericidal agents against susceptible bacteria. It should also be emphasized that the sulfonamides act as inhibitors towards cells of practically every variety. In other words, they are general cell inhibitors, and not merely bacteriostatic agents.

Although a great many sulfonamide derivatives have been prepared and tested as chemotherapeutic agents, only a few are used at the present time. The most important of these compounds are listed in Table 41, together with their principal chemotherapeutic uses. Many new sulfonamide compounds are appearing, and as time goes on they will probably replace some of the substances listed in Table 41.

TABLE 41

THE SULFONAMIDE * COMPOUNDS AND THEIR PRINCIPAL USES

Drug and Properties	Formula	Principal Uses
Sulfanilamide (*p*-aminobenzenesulfonamide), white crystals. M.P.: 164.5°–167.0°C. Solubility: 1 g. in 125 ml. H_2O at 20°C.	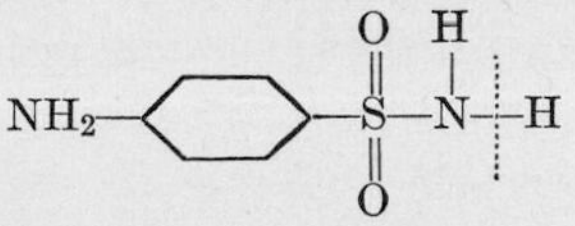 $NH_2-C_6H_4-SO_2-NH-H$	Hemolytic streptococcus. Meningococcus.
Sulfapyridine (2-sulfanilamidopyridine), white crystals. M.P.: 191°–194°C. Solubility: 54 mg. in 100 ml. H_2O at 37.5°C. at *p*H 7.1.	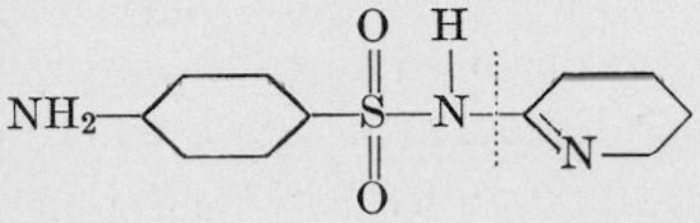 $NH_2-C_6H_4-SO_2-NH-$ Pyridine	Pneumococcus. Gonococcus.
Sulfathiazole (2-sulfanilamidothiazole), white crystalline powder (dimorphic). M.P.: 168°–175°C. (prisms), 200–203.5°C. (rods). Solubility: 96 mg. in 100 ml. H_2O at 37.5°C. at *p*H 7.1.	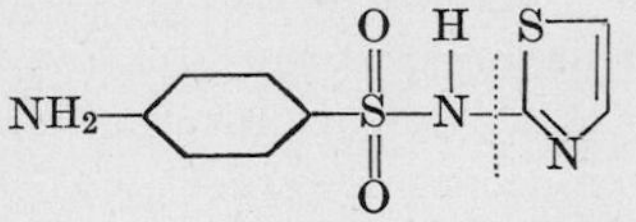 $NH_2-C_6H_4-SO_2-NH-$ Thiazole	Pneumococcus. Gonococcus. Staphylococcus.
Sulfaguanidine (sulfanilylguanidine), white crystalline powder. M.P.: 190°–192.5°C. Solubility: 220 mg. in 100 ml. H_2O at 37.5°C. at *p*H 7.1.	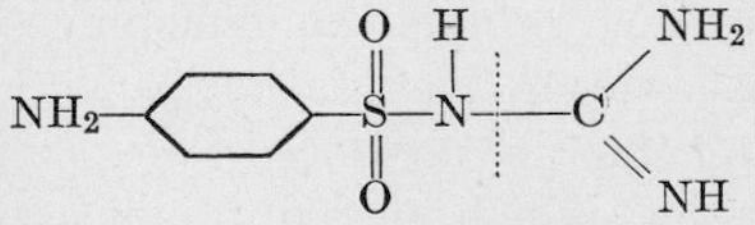 $NH_2-C_6H_4-SO_2-NH-C(NH_2)=NH$ Guanidine	Dysentery.
Sulfadiazine † (2-sulfanilamidopyrimidine), white crystals. M.P.: 253°–256°C. Solubility: 12.3 mg. in 100 ml. H_2O at 37°C.	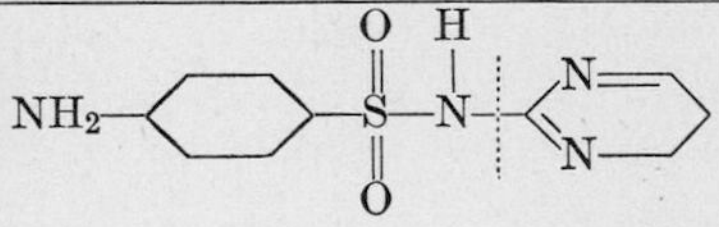 $NH_2-C_6H_4-SO_2-NH-$ Pyrimidine	Pneumococcus. Staphylococcus.
Sulfamyd (*p*-aminosulfonylacetylimide or sulfacetimide), white crystals. M.P.: 181°–182°C. Solubility: 1 : 100 at room temperature.	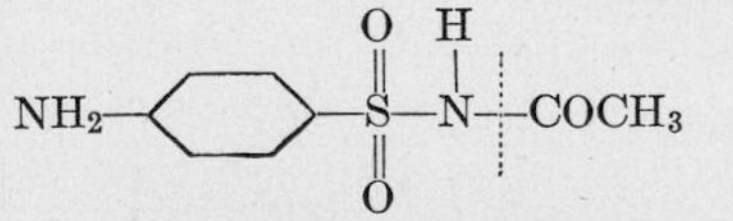 $NH_2-C_6H_4-SO_2-NH-COCH_3$ Acetimide	Urinary tract infections, especially those due to *Escherichia coli*. Gonococcus.

* Sulfonamides may be considered derivatives of sulfanilamide when a hydrogen atom is replaced by a radical or ring structure.

Recently a number of N^4-acyl derivatives of the sulfonamides have been used with considerable success as intestinal antiseptics [see Poth and Ross (1943)]. Of these, sulfasuxidine (succinylsulfathiazole) and sulfathalidine (phthalylsulfathiazole) show a great deal of promise as chemotherapeutic agents for treating dysentery.

† The monomethyl derivative, sulfamerazine (sulfamethyldiazine or 2-sulfamilamido-4-methylpyrimidine), and the dimethyl derivative, sulfamethazine (sulfadimethyldiazine or 2-sulfanilamido-4:6-dimethylpyrimidine), of sulfadiazine have been used with considerable success to treat a number of diseases.

The sulfonamides, like other cell inhibitors, are influenced by environmental conditions. For example, the structure of the drug and its concentration, the size of the inoculum, the age and nature of the culture, the composition of the medium and its *p*H, and the temperature of incubation must be taken into consideration when experimental studies are being made with these compounds. Henry (1943) has discussed these factors in some detail, and his review should be consulted for additional reading on this subject.

Although a number of theories have been suggested to explain the mode of action of sulfanilamide and sulfapyridine, little or nothing is known about the action of some of the newer compounds. It should also be borne in mind that, although the activity *in vivo* of the better-known compounds appears to be directed solely against the invading microorganisms, the recovery of the infected host seems to entail two factors: the drug factor and the host factor. In other words, although the drug can bring the infection under control, it requires the cooperation of the host's defense mechanism to dispose of the infectious agent. Since the host factor is a medical problem and hence does not concern us, no further discussion on this subject will be given here. The drug factor includes the ability of these compounds to inhibit the growth of, or possibly actually kill, susceptible bacteria, as well as their power to neutralize the harmful effects of the toxic products of certain microorganisms. However, whether sulfanilamide or its derivatives have the power of inactivating bacterial toxins is a matter of dispute.

One of the first theories advanced to explain sulfonamide inhibition was based upon data which tended to indicate that oxidative changes, in which molecular oxygen played a role, were responsible for the conversion of *p*-aminobenzenesulfonamide (sulfanilamide) to some truly active compound, such as *p*-hydroxylaminobenzenesulfonamide [see Mayer (1937), Shaffer (1939)]. Probably the greatest single evidence against this theory is that *p*-aminobenzoic acid is unable to antagonize the action of sulfonamide oxidation products and derivatives [Rosenthal (1943), Henry (1943)].

As soon as the hypothesis appeared that the active agent of sulfonamide action was some oxidation product of the parent compound, a second theory was proposed [see Henry (1943)]. This theory was based on the oxidation-reduction potential changes occurring in cultures during sulfonamide action. Preliminary investigations suggested that sulfonamides, in their oxidized form, might poise the E_h of the bacterial cultures at levels too high to permit bacterial multiplication. This theory may be of some importance, but it is considered less likely today, since it has been shown that the sulfonamides will also act at low E_h levels.

The third theory dealing with the mode of action of sulfonamides was the anticatalase theory advanced by Locke, Main, Mellon and their associates (1938, 1939). These investigators noted that oxidized products of sulfanilamide possessed the power of inactivating catalase. It has been known for a long time that, if catalase is inactivated in cultures of pneumococci, peroxide accumulates rapidly and may reach a concentration that is bactericidal for the cells. Thus these workers reasoned that, if oxidized sulfanilamide formed an inactive complex with catalase, peroxide would accumulate and would destroy the bacteria or inhibit their growth. Among the arguments which refute this hypothesis are: (1) some peroxide-resistant organisms are sulfonamide-sensitive; and (2) sulfonamides act in the absence of conditions necessary for the formation of peroxide, that is, under anaerobic conditions.

The fourth theory of importance concerning the mode of action of sulfonamides may be spoken of as the sulfonamide-antagonists theory. One of the most unusual facts about sulfonamide action is that certain substances can counteract it. Several explanations of sulfonamide action have therefore evolved around this point.

Woods (1940), Woods and Fildes (1940), and Fildes (1940) first demonstrated that *p*-aminobenzoic acid counteracts sulfonamide inhibition of bacterial growth, and since that time their observation has been confirmed by many workers, using a variety of experimental conditions [see Henry (1943)]. Woods and Fildes believed that sulfonamides function by interfering with the essential metabolite, *p*-aminobenzoic acid, and thereby inhibit growth. They further proposed that such inhibition requires an inhibitor closely related structurally to the essential metabolite so that it can fit the same enzyme, but sufficiently unrelated to be an inadequate substitute for the essential metabolite. Their theory is thus based on the existence of a competition between sulfanilamide *p*-aminobenzoic acid for an enzyme surface. This theory has been widely accepted by investigators in the field because it correlates very nicely with many experimental observations.

No one disagrees with the fact that *p*-aminobenzoic acid counteracts the inhibitory action of certain sulfonamides, but others are resistant. Also, it should be pointed out that more recent observations on the antagonism of sulfonamides by various substances, other than *p*-aminobenzoic acid, are difficult to explain by this theory. For example, such substances as methionine and some other amino acids, purines, glucose, urethane, and coezymes, have been shown to counteract certain sulfonamides under experimental conditions [see Long (1941), Harris and Kohn (1941), Henry (1943), Rantz and Kirby (1944), Fohlen (1944), and Sevag and Green (1944)]. Whether these substances antagonize by specific interference as does *p*-aminobenzoic acid, form inactive complexes with the sulfonamides or with certain cellular proteins, such as enzymes, or serve merely as growth stimulants has not been fully elucidated. These facts and others, however, cannot be ignored. Thus all that can be said is that, because of additional data brought to light since the initial observations by Woods and Fildes, this theory must be accepted with reservations until more facts are available.

More recently, two other theories have been advanced to explain the mode of action of sulfonamides. Klotz (1944) believes that the inhibition of bacterial growth by sulfonamides may be accounted for quantitatively by assuming that the action is due to a reversible combination between the basic form of the drug and the neutral form of the cellular protein, such as enzymes, and that the law of mass action is applicable. Sevag and Green (1944) and others have formulated a theory based upon experimental data which show that sulfonamides inhibit certain respiratory enzymes. For example, Sevag and Green determined the effect of sulfonamides on the metabolism of tryptophan by *Staphylococcus aureus* and came to the conclusion that sulfonamides inhibit the oxidative-reductive reactions leading to the synthesis of tryptophan but are incapable of inhibiting the utilization of tryptophan when it is added to the medium. Future studies along these two lines will probably elucidate the true mechanism (or mechanisms) of sulfonamide action.

Not all the sulfur compounds which are active antibacterial agents are sulfonamides; a number are sulfones, sulfoxides, and sulfides. Promin (sodium *p,p*′-diaminodiphenyl sulfone-N,N′-didextrose sulfonate), Diasone (disodium formaldehydesulfoxylate diaminodiphenyl sulfone), and other compounds of the sulfone series seem to offer considerable promise at the present time as chemotherapeutic agents for treating experimental tuberculosis in guinea pigs [see Feldman and Hinshaw (1943), Raiziss (1943)]. However, Promin and other sulfones do not exhibit as strong a bacteriostatic action on human tubercle bacilli *in vitro* as do benzophenone and some of its derivatives [Freedlander (1942)].

The bacteriostatic, bactericidal, fungistatic, and fungicidal action of 51 organic sulfur derivatives was studied by Everitt and Sullivan (1940). Of this group of compounds fungistatic activity was manifested by phenylthioarsenite, 4-chloro-2-nitrophenyl sulfur amine, 1:2-naphthoquinone-4-sodium sulfonate, and sulfanilamide. Fungicidal activity was exhibited by mercaptobenzothiazole and phenylbenzothiazole. Bacteriostatic action was very marked with phenothioxine, and bactericidal activity was displayed by mercaptobenzothiazole. Almost all the other compounds tested were ineffective.

THE DYES AND RELATED COMPOUNDS

The natural dyes and the coal-tar dyes and related compounds have played an important role for many years in the study of bacteria and other microorganisms. Since the early days of the science they have been employed to stain bacteria in order to make the cells more readily visible under the microscope, and in more recent years they have also been used extensively in differential culture media as *p*H and oxidation-reduction potential indicators and as antiseptics and disinfectants. The literature on this subject is so voluminous that it is impossible here to give it a just analysis. For details Conn's book, *Biological Stains* (1940), which contains much interesting and valuable information, should be consulted. A brief general discussion on the nature and classification of the compounds will now be given and mention will be made of their use as stains and antiseptics, or for other purposes. Most of the information on the next few pages has been adopted from the book by Conn.

Definition and Classification of the Dyes. In the early days of bacteriology the natural dyes were used extensively, but they have been gradually replaced by synthetic compounds derived from one or more substances found in coal tar, especially derivatives of the cyclic compound benzene (C_6H_6). A dye is usually defined as an organic compound containing both auxochrome and chromophore groups linked to benzene rings. The chromophore group is regarded as being responsible for the colored properties of the compound in which it occurs, whereas the auxochrome radical gives the compound its property of electrolytic dissociation and its affinity for other substances. Many chemical compounds containing a benzene ring are colored because they have a chromophore group in their molecule; they are not dyes, however, because they lack the auxochrome group. These points can be clearly illustrated with the simple nitro compounds. If three hydrogens in a benzene ring are replaced by three nitro groups, trinitrobenzene is formed:

$$C_6H_6 + 3HNO_3 = C_6H_3(NO_2)_3 + 3H_2O$$

(structural diagram: benzene ring + $3HNO_3$ = benzene ring with O_2N, NO_2, NO_2 substituents + $3H_2O$)

Such a nitro derivative of benzene is pale yellow in color because of the chromophore groups (—NO_2), although it is not a dye because it lacks the property of electrolytic dissociation and does not form salts with acids or bases. It is true that such a compound may form a colored coat around cells, but this phenomenon is only mechanical, and the color can be easily removed by mechanical processes. In other words, there is no "take." If, however, an auxochrome group, such as (—OH), is substituted for another hydrogen atom in the trinitrobenzene molecule, the compound 2:4:6-trinitrophenol (known as picric acid) is formed:

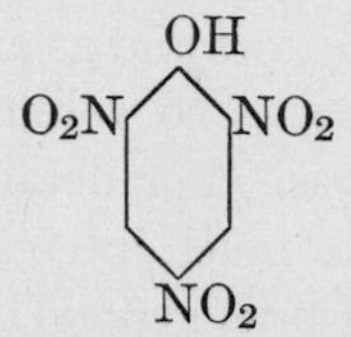

This compound is a typical acid dye and belongs to the group known as the nitro dyes. It is still yellow in color because of the chromophore groups (—NO_2) and is capable of being dissociated electrolytically, forming phenolates with bases. Furthermore, it dyes fibers and tissues by virtue of its auxiliary auxochrome hydroxyl group (—OH).

The dyes may be divided into two large groups: the natural and the synthetic dyes. The natural compounds are of little significance today, since they have been replaced to a large extent by synthetic compounds. Thus we need not concern ourselves here with their taxonomy. Attempts have been made to classify the synthetic dyes on the basis of specific color, but such a method has certain inherent difficulties. The most useful method is one which puts together those compounds having a similar chemical structure. Conn (1940) used this procedure and allocated the important biological dyes into seven groups. These groups, together with certain examples, are listed in Table 42. The solubilities of several of these dyes at 26°C. are shown in Table 43.

AUXOCHROME GROUPS. All true dyes must contain at least one auxochrome radical. The auxochrome groups may be either acidic or basic in character. Specific examples are the acidic hydroxyl group (—OH) and the basic amino group (—NH_2). The hydroxyl group is acidic because of its ability to form hydrogen ions by electrolytic dissociation; the amino group owes its basic character to the property of its nitrogen atom to become pentavalent in aqueous or acid solutions. The greater the number of either one of these two radicals in a compound, the stronger acid or base the compound becomes. If there is one of each, the basic character of the amino group prevails but is considerably weakened by the influence of the acidic hydroxyl group. The strength of both groups is also influenced by other groups or atoms in the compound. For example, the chromophore radical (—NO_2) is not able in itself to give acid properties to a compound, although it helps to make any hydroxyl group in a compound more strongly acidic. The sulfonic group (—SO_2OH) may also be present in certain dyes. The group is strongly acidic in character and possesses salt-forming properties. This radical, however, is so weakly auxochromic that compounds which contain it and a chromophore group are not dyes unless they contain in addition a true auxochrome group.

From the preceding discussion it might be assumed that all dyes are acids or bases. This is not strictly so, because commercially dyes are prepared in the form of salts. Usually the acid dyes are prepared as their sodium, potassium, calcium, barium, or ammonium salts. The basic dyes are prepared as salts of colorless acids, such as acetic, oxalic, hydrochloric, or sulfuric. Both the so-called acid and base dyes are employed in the study of bacteria. The acid dyes seem to have an affinity for cellular cytoplasm and stain such materials intensely, whereas the basic dyes exhibit their greatest affinity for the nuclear material of cells.

Chromophore Groups. According to definition, every dye must contain at least one chromophore group. It is this group or groups which give a compound its color. The chromophores, like the auxochromes, may be either acidic or basic in nature. A few of the groups will be mentioned here for illustrative purposes.

The *acid chromophore* group includes:

1. The nitro group (—NO_2), as found in picric acid.

2. The quinoid ring, $=\langle\quad\rangle=$, as found in the indamines, the xanthenes, and the di- and triphenylmethanes. Included in these groups are such well-known stains as rosolic acid and acid fuchsin.

The *basic chromophore* groups include:

1. The azo linkage (—N=N—), where a benzene ring is attached to each nitrogen atom:

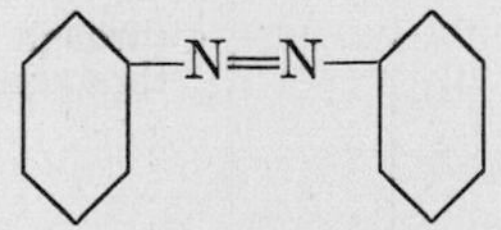

All the dyes of this group may be considered derivatives of azobenzene; the group includes such well-known dyes as Congo red, methyl orange, and Bismarck brown.

TABLE 42

CLASSIFICATION OF THE SYNTHETIC DYES

[Data from Conn's *Biological Stains* and Salle's *Fundamental Principles of Bacteriology*]

Classification	Acid or Base Dye	Chromophore Group Derivation, etc.
I. The nitro dyes Picric acid	 Acid	The chromophore is $—NO_2$, which is strongly acidic. 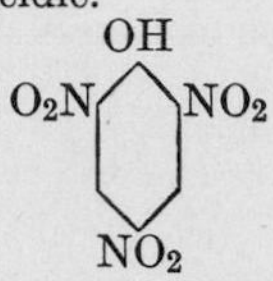 OH O_2N NO_2 NO_2 Picric acid
II. The azo dyes 1. Janus green 2. Bismarck brown 3. Congo red 4. Methyl orange 5. Methyl red 6. Sudan III	 Base Base Acid Weak acid Weak acid Weak acid	The chromophore, —N=N—, joins benzene or naphthalene rings. 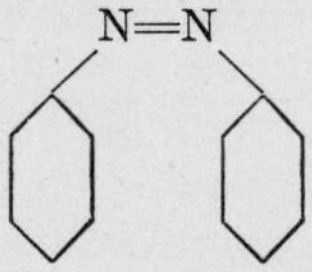 N=N It is possible for the chromophore to occur more than once, forming diazo dyes: 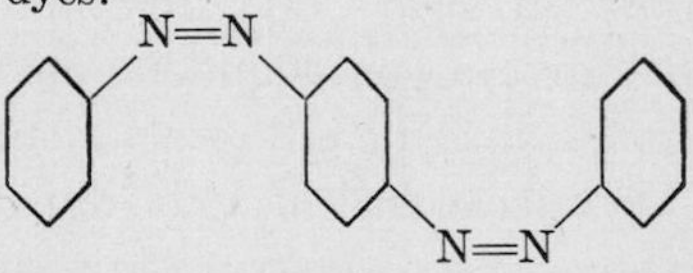 N=N N=N Groups in the benzene ring are usually in the *p*-position to each other. Ordinarily this also holds for auxochrome groups (—OH or $—NH_2$).
III. The anthraquinone dyes Alizarin	 Acid	The oxyquinoid ring is the most important chromophore. The dyes are derivatives of anthracene: 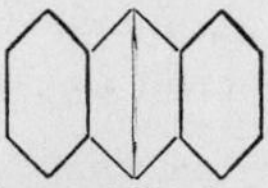 through the oxidized compound anthraquinone: 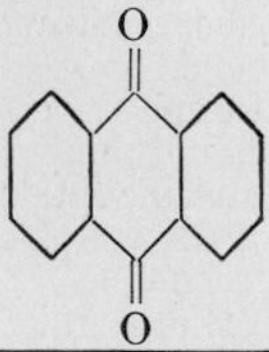 O O

TABLE 42 (*Continued*)

CLASSIFICATION OF THE SYNTHETIC DYES

[Data from Conn's *Biological Stains* and Salle's *Fundamental Principles of Bacteriology*]

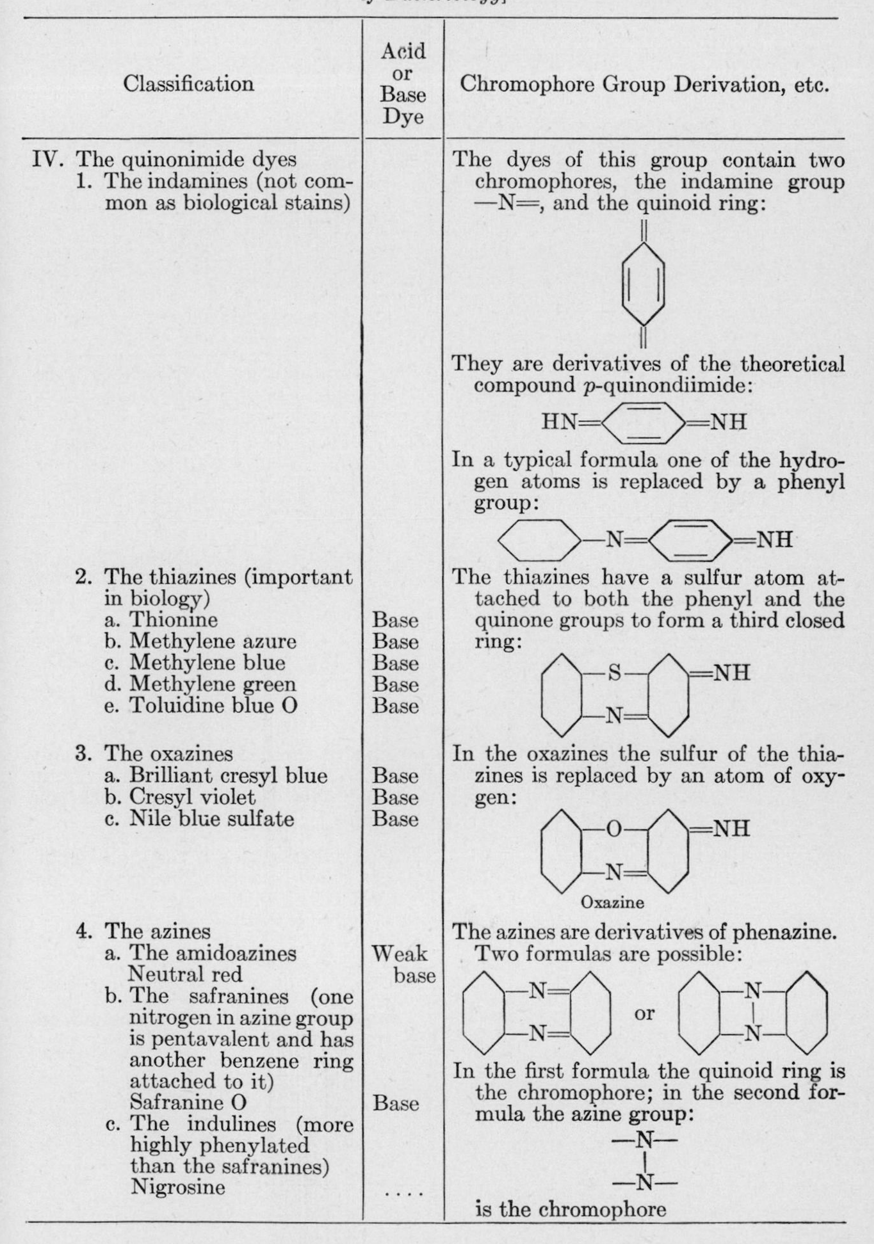

Classification	Acid or Base Dye	Chromophore Group Derivation, etc.
IV. The quinonimide dyes 1. The indamines (not common as biological stains)		The dyes of this group contain two chromophores, the indamine group —N=, and the quinoid ring: They are derivatives of the theoretical compound *p*-quinondiimide: HN= ⬡ =NH In a typical formula one of the hydrogen atoms is replaced by a phenyl group: ⬡ —N= ⬡ =NH
2. The thiazines (important in biology)		The thiazines have a sulfur atom attached to both the phenyl and the quinone groups to form a third closed ring:
a. Thionine	Base	
b. Methylene azure	Base	
c. Methylene blue	Base	
d. Methylene green	Base	
e. Toluidine blue O	Base	
3. The oxazines		In the oxazines the sulfur of the thiazines is replaced by an atom of oxygen: Oxazine
a. Brilliant cresyl blue	Base	
b. Cresyl violet	Base	
c. Nile blue sulfate	Base	
4. The azines		The azines are derivatives of phenazine. Two formulas are possible:
a. The amidoazines Neutral red	Weak base	or
b. The safranines (one nitrogen in azine group is pentavalent and has another benzene ring attached to it) Safranine O	Base	In the first formula the quinoid ring is the chromophore; in the second formula the azine group: —N— | —N—
c. The indulines (more highly phenylated than the safranines) Nigrosine	....	is the chromophore

TABLE 42 (*Continued*)

CLASSIFICATION OF THE SYNTHETIC DYES

[Data from Conn's *Biological Stains* and Salle's *Fundamental Principles of Bacteriology*]

Classification	Acid or Base Dye	Chromophore Group Derivation, etc.
V. The phenylmethane dyes		The phenylmethane dyes include the most important dyes used in bacteriology and industry. The compounds are substituted methanes. One or more hydrogen atoms may be replaced. If 2 hydrogen atoms are replaced by ethyl groups, the compound diethylmethane is formed: 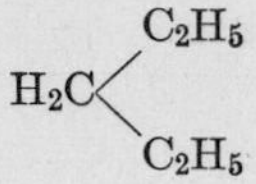
1. The diaminotriphenylmethane dyes		
a. Malachite green	Weak base	
b. Brilliant green	Base	
2. The triaminotriphenylmethane dyes (rosanilines)		C_2H_5 H_2C C_2H_5
a. Basic fuchsin	Base	
b. *para*-Rosaniline	Base	
c. Rosaniline	Base	
d. New fuchsin	Base	
e. Acid fuchsin	Acid	
f. Hofmann's violet	Base	If 2 hydrogens of methane are replaced by phenyl groups, diphenylmethane is formed: 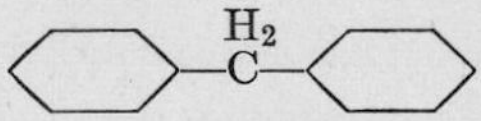
g. Methyl violet	Base	
h. Crystal violet	Base	
i. Methyl green	Base	H_2 —C—
j. Methyl blue (cotton blue)	Base	
		If 3 hydrogens are replaced, triphenylmethane is produced:
		H C
		Such compounds are not dyes, because they lack chromophore and auxochrome groups. However, the introduction of substituted amino and other groups accounts for a large number of dye compounds.
3. Hydroxyphenylmethane dyes Rosolic acid		The hydroxyphenylmethane dyes are triphenylmethane derivatives in which the amino groups of the rosanilines are replaced with hydroxyl groups: 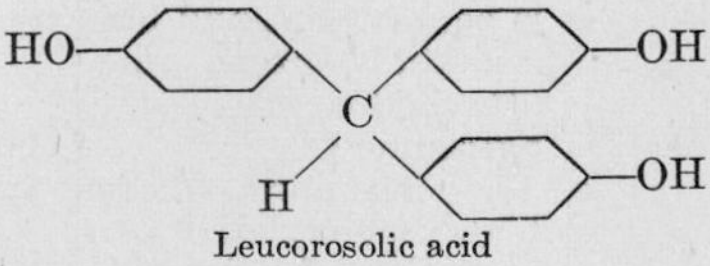
		HO— —OH C H —OH Leucorosolic acid

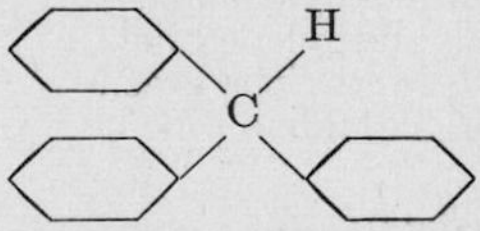

TABLE 42 (*Continued*)

CLASSIFICATION OF THE SYNTHETIC DYES

[Data from Conn's *Biological Stains* and Salle's *Fundamental Principles of Bacteriology*]

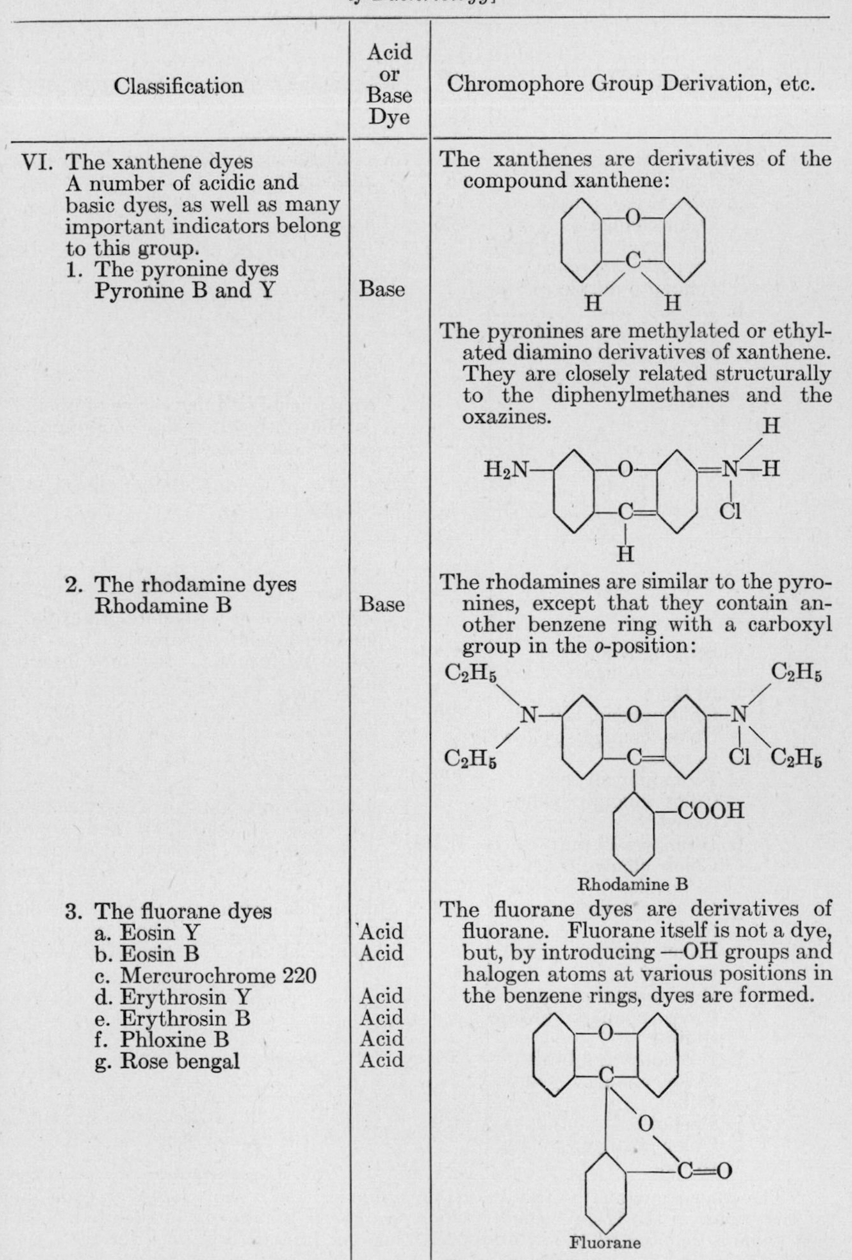

Classification	Acid or Base Dye	Chromophore Group Derivation, etc.
VI. The xanthene dyes A number of acidic and basic dyes, as well as many important indicators belong to this group.		The xanthenes are derivatives of the compound xanthene:
1. The pyronine dyes Pyronine B and Y	Base	The pyronines are methylated or ethylated diamino derivatives of xanthene. They are closely related structurally to the diphenylmethanes and the oxazines.
2. The rhodamine dyes Rhodamine B	Base	The rhodamines are similar to the pyronines, except that they contain another benzene ring with a carboxyl group in the *o*-position: Rhodamine B
3. The fluorane dyes a. Eosin Y b. Eosin B c. Mercurochrome 220 d. Erythrosin Y e. Erythrosin B f. Phloxine B g. Rose bengal	 Acid Acid Acid Acid Acid Acid	The fluorane dyes are derivatives of fluorane. Fluorane itself is not a dye, but, by introducing —OH groups and halogen atoms at various positions in the benzene rings, dyes are formed. Fluorane

TABLE 42 (*Continued*)

CLASSIFICATION OF THE SYNTHETIC DYES

[Data from Conn's *Biological Stains* and Salle's *Fundamental Principles of Bacteriology*]

Classification	Acid or Base Dye	Chromophore Group Derivation, etc.
4. Phenolphthalein and the sulfonephthalein dyes	pK *	A phthalein is a compound of phthalic anhydride: 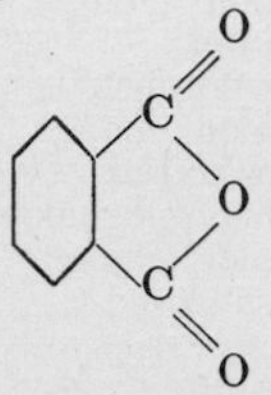 O C O C O with phenol or a derivative of phenol. A sulfonephthalein is a compound of *o*-sulfobenzoic acid, SO_3H COOH with phenol or a phenol derivative.
a. *meta*-Cresol purple. Color change: *acid range*, red to yellow; *alkaline range*, yellow to purple	1.5, 8.3	
b. Thymol blue Color change: *acid range*, red to yellow; *alkaline range*, yellow to blue	1.5, 8.9	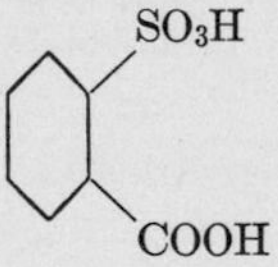
c. Bromophenol blue. Color change: yellow to blue	4.1	Phenolphthalein apparently has the following formula. It is not used as a dye. 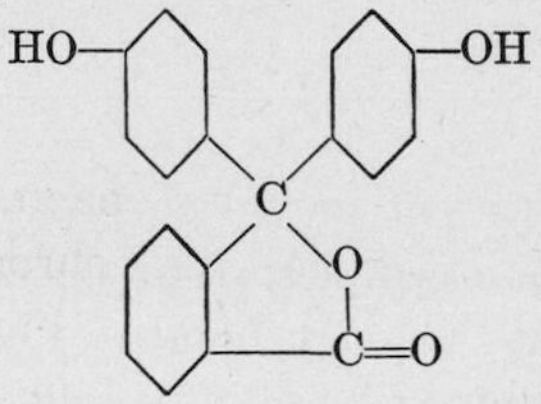 HO— —OH C O C=O
d. Chlorophenol red. Color change: yellow to red	6.0	
e. Bromophenol red. Color change: yellow to red	6.2	
f. Bromocresol purple. Color change: yellow to purple	6.3	
g. Bromochlorophenol blue. Color change: yellow to purple	4.0	Sulfonephthaleins have no practical significance as dyes. Their real use is as indicators. The basic structure is: 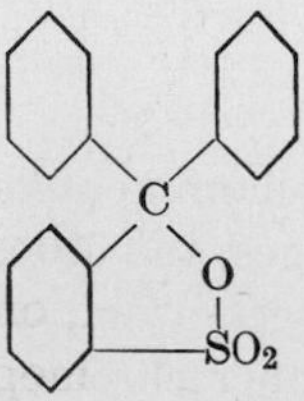 C O SO_2
h. Bromocresol green. Color change: yellow to blue	4.7	
i. Bromothymol blue. Color change: yellow to blue	7.1	
j. Phenol red. Color change: yellow to red	7.9	

* The color change of an indicator takes place within a short range on each side of that point in the H-ion scale at which the dye is 50 per cent dissociated. This pH value is denoted by the symbol pK. (See pp. 75 and 78 of Chapter 1.)

TABLE 42 (*Continued*)

CLASSIFICATION OF THE SYNTHETIC DYES

[Data from Conn's *Biological Stains* and Salle's *Fundamental Principles of Bacteriology*]

Classification	Acid or Base Dye	Chromophore Group Derivation, etc.
k. Cresol red. Color change: yellow to red	8.3	
l. Cresolphthalein. Color change: Colorless to red	9.4	
m. Phenolphthalein Color change: Colorless to red	9.7	
VII. The acridine dyes Small group of dyes closely related to xanthenes. Not of much interest to biologist, although used somewhat as disinfectants.		The acridines are derived from acridine:
Acriflavine	Base	a compound closely related to xanthene.

2. The azine linkage:

—N—
|
—N—

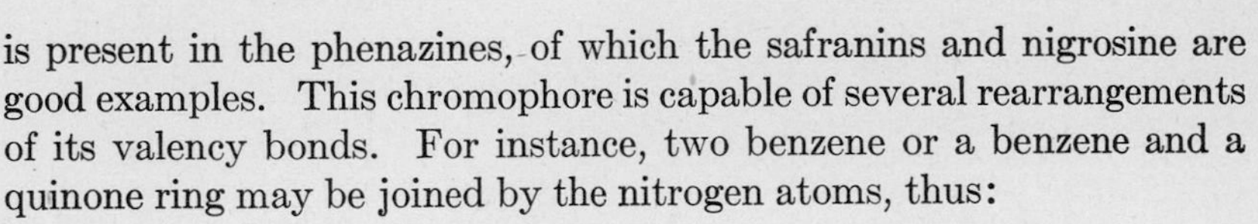

is present in the phenazines, of which the safranins and nigrosine are good examples. This chromophore is capable of several rearrangements of its valency bonds. For instance, two benzene or a benzene and a quinone ring may be joined by the nitrogen atoms, thus:

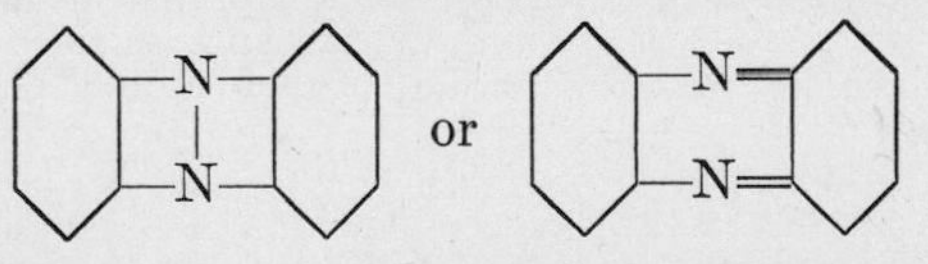

3. The indamine linkage (—N=), is present in the indamines, thiazines, oxazines, and other dyes. Usually two benzene rings are attached to the nitrogen atom, one of them being in the quinoid form and thus adding another chromophore. A typical indamine may have the following basic structure:

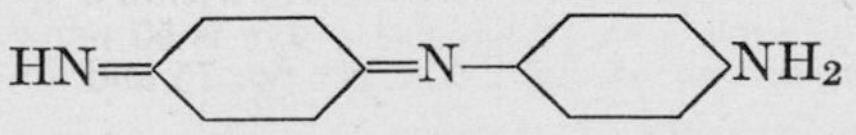

The thiazines have the two rings further joined together by a sulfur atom. Methylene blue, the best example of this class, has the following nucleus:

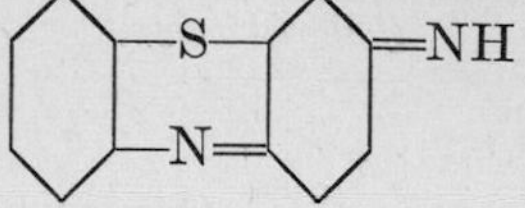

The oxazines have the benzene and quinoid rings joined together by the indamine linkage and by an oxygen atom, thus:

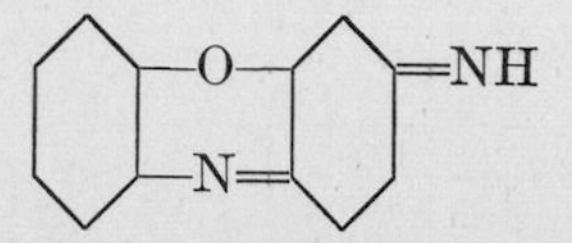

Nile blue sulfate is an example in which this linkage is present.

Further data on these groups will be found in Table 42, based on Conn's (1940) classification of the dyes.

Reduction of Dyes to Leuco Compounds. Although the chromophore groups may differ considerably in structure, they all have one property in common, namely, unsatisfied affinities for hydrogen. Hence they are easily reduced by combining with hydrogen at the double bonds. The nitro group may be reduced to an amino radical; sometimes the double bonds of the quinoid ring may break and allow hydrogen atoms to become attached to the freed valences. In all these cases the reduction destroys the chromophore group, and the compound loses its specific color. It can thus be seen that a dye retains its characteristic color only as long as its affinity for hydrogen is not completely satisfied. Once this affinity has been fulfilled, however, colorless, or leuco, compounds are formed. Dyes may, therefore, be employed as indicators of oxidation and reduction. Two examples, the reduction of fuchsin and the reduction of methylene blue, will illustrate the type of change which takes place:

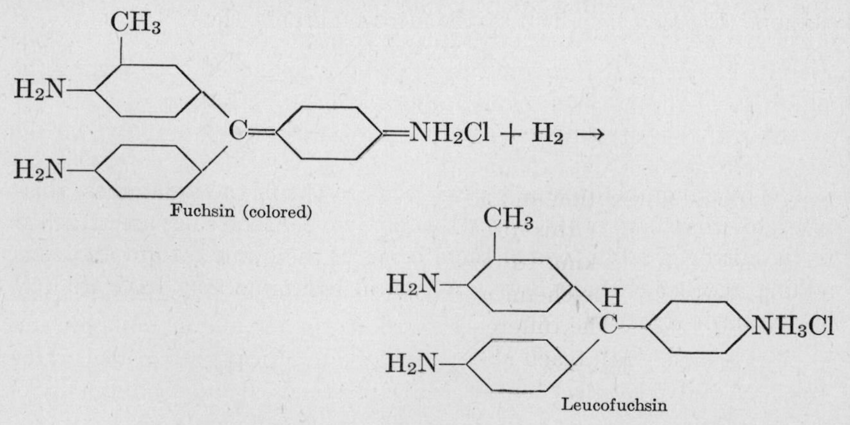

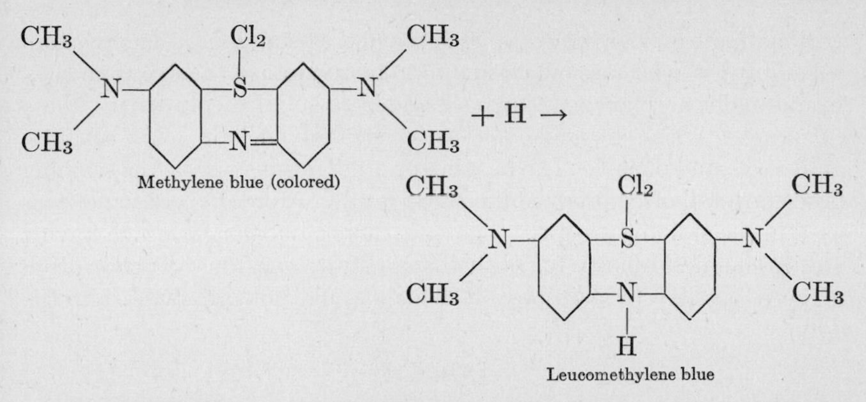

Methylene blue (colored)

Leucomethylene blue

These reactions are reversible under conditions favoring oxidation, that is, in the presence of oxygen or air. Other compounds, known as leuco bases, are often formed in certain dye processes, but they are of little significance to the bacteriologist.

Use of Dyes as Bacterial Stains. Since the true bacteria are colorless and rather difficult to see when viewed with the microscope, they are usually first treated by a special staining procedure. Such a procedure may not only intensify their gross structure but reveal certain bodies embedded in their protoplasm as well. This information is often of great help in classifying certain organisms.

Two main theories have been advanced to explain the phenomenon of staining bacteria and other substances. One theory has a chemical basis; the other is based on physical phenomena. At first thought it would seem that the purely chemical theory is the most logical, because it is believed that some parts of the cell are acid in reaction, whereas others are alkaline. Inasmuch as in certain dyes the color exists in the cation (basic dyes) and in others in the anion (acid dyes), it is natural to expect chemical combinations to take place between the dyes and the bacteria, depending upon the reaction of the bacteria. However, until we know something about the chemical nature of the various cellular elements, it is difficult to draw any conclusions concerning the affinities of the various stains for the cellular components. The exponents of the physical theory have carefully pointed out that all the observed facts can be explained by such physical forces as capillarity and osmosis, absorption and adsorption. (For a discussion of how adsorption enters into this problem see pp. 35 to 41 on adsorption.) Evidence is still lacking to prove or disprove the physical theory, on the one hand, and the chemical theory, on the other; possibly both play important roles. The difference, perhaps, is not one of immense importance, since both teach about the same practical lessons concerning the type of dye to select for any particular purpose and the influence of various factors upon the rate or intensity of staining. Often certain substances which cause organisms to take up more of the dye than they would under normal conditions are added to staining solutions. These substances, which are spoken of as intensifiers, include acids, alkalies, aniline oil, and phenol. The heating of preparations during the staining procedure will often produce the same result. Mordants are sometimes used in the staining process. They are merely substances which have a strong chemical affinity for both the substrate and the dye; they often make it possible to stain objects which would not otherwise take the dye.

TABLE 43

SOLUBILITIES OF SEVERAL COMMON DYES AT 26°C.
[From Conn (1940)]

C.I. * Number	Name of Dye	Per Cent Soluble in *Water*	Per Cent Soluble in 95% *Alcohol*
7	Picric acid	1.18	8.96
133	Janus green	5.18	1.12
142	Methyl orange	0.52	0.08
	Methyl orange (acid)	0.015	0.015
248	Sudan III	Nil	0.15
331	Bismarck brown Y	1.36	1.08
370	Congo red	Nil	0.19
1,027	Alizarin	0.0	0.125
920	Thionine	0.25	0.25
922	Methylene blue ($ZnCl_2$ double salt)	2.75	0.05
	Methylene blue (chloride)	3.55	1.48
924	Methylene green	1.46	0.12
925	Toluidine blue O	3.82	0.57
825	Neutral red (chloride)	5.64	2.45
841	Safranine	5.45	3.41
657	Malachite green (oxalate)	7.60	7.52
676	*para*-Rosaniline (chloride)	0.26	5.93
	para-Rosaniline (acetate)	4.15	13.63
	Rosaniline (chloride)	0.39	8.16
680	Methyl violet	2.93	15.21
678	New fuchsin (chloride)	1.13	3.20
681	Crystal violet (chloride)	1.68	13.87
741	Pyronine B (iodide)	0.07	1.08
749	Rhodamine B	0.78	1.47
768	Eosin Y (Na salt)	44.20	2.18
771	Eosin B (Na salt)	39.11	0.75
773	Erythrosin (Na salt)	11.10	1.87
774	Phloxine (Na salt)	50.90	9.02
779	Rose bengal (Na salt)	36.25	7.53

* C.I. refers to *Colour Index,* edited by F. M. Rowe, published by the Society of Dyers and Colourists, Bradford, Yorkshire, England.

Use of Dyes in Culture Media. Many media are now available in which various dyes have been incorporated to aid in the isolation and recognition of bacteria. Such media find their greatest application in the field of sanitary bacteriology, where such well-known media as eosin-methylene blue agar, Endo's medium, Dominick-Lauter medium, Conradi-Drigalski agar, Salle's crystal violet-lactose broth, brilliant green-bile media, and others have been developed for the detection of *Escherichia coli*. Crystal violet and other dyes are often added to media for the isolation of the tubercle bacillus. The best known of these is probably Petroff's egg medium, to which is added 0.01 per cent crystal violet. It is also possible sometimes to distinguish between *Brucella melitensis*, *Brucella abortus*, and *Brucella suis* on the basis of their ability to grow in the presence of certain aniline dyes. Without entering into the details of the technique, we may say that the general procedure consists of preparing plates of liver agar, *p*H 6.6, containing 1 : 30,000 and 1 : 60,000 thionine, 1 : 25,000 and 1 : 50,000 basic fuchsin, 1 : 50,000 and 1 : 100,000 methyl violet, and 1 : 100,000 and 1 : 200,000 pyronine. (The dyes used must be obtained from the National Aniline Chemical Company of New York.) After inoculation and incubation in 10 per cent CO_2, the following general behavior of the species may be expected. Strains of *B. melitensis* usually grow to some extent in the presence of all four dyes; *B. abortus* strains are inhibited by thionine but grow freely in the presence of the other three; *B. suis* strains grow well in the presence of thionine but are inhibited by basic fuchsin, methyl violet, and pyronine. Though this is the general behavior of the three species, there is considerable variation between different strains of the same species, especially those coming from different parts of the world. For this reason reliance on the method is questioned by many workers. Dyes or indicators are also frequently added to media to detect the lipolytic activity of microorganisms. For further details and references to the literature concerning the use of dyes in culture media the papers by Salle (1927), Petroff and Gump (1935), Chapman and Berens (1935), Chapman (1936), Ritter (1940), and the book by Huddleson (1934) should be consulted.

Use of Dyes as *p*H and Oxidation-Reduction Potential Indicators. Dyes of various types, especially xanthene dyes, are now widely used for the colorimetric determination of *p*H and oxidation-reduction potentials. We have just mentioned how certain dyes can undergo oxidation and reduction with a corresponding change in color; further details on this subject will be found on pp. 52 to 54 of Chapter 1.

Bacteriostatic and Antiseptic Action of Dyes. Churchman (1912) was the first person to investigate thoroughly the harmful action of dyes on bacteria, although several studies had appeared before this date. He found that their action was more inhibitory than germicidal and that varying amounts of dye might produce "cessation of mobility, genesistasis, inhibition of sporulation, and suspension of animation." Working with gentian violet, he observed that, if five drops of a saturated aqueous solution were added to broth cultures of various organisms, the mixtures were allowed to remain for an hour, and transfers were made to fresh agar, the Gram-negative bacteria multiplied satisfactorily, but the Gram-positive forms failed to grow. Churchman next tested a great many different bacteria to determine if there was a perfect correlation between Gram-positiveness and the bacteriostatic action of gentian violet. This was found not to be the case; about 90 per cent of the Gram-positive bacteria was killed by gentian violet or failed to grow in media containing it, but the remaining 10 per cent, comprising principally the acid-fast group, was not affected. Similarly, though approximately 90 per cent of the Gram-negative species was resistant to the dye, the remaining 10 per cent was susceptible.

Since this early work of Churchman, a number of studies have been carried out on the antiseptic or bacteriostatic properties of dyes [see Kligler (1918), Churchman (1926), Gay and Morrison (1921), Browning (1930, 1943), Petroff and Gump (1935), Chapman (1936), Salle, Schechmeister, and McOmie (1940), Smith (1942), Rubbo, Albert, and Maxwell (1942), Panja and Ghosh (1943), Brownlee and Tonkin (1943), Lawrence (1943), Martin (1944), and others]. Several of these studies have been conducted in the hope of using dyes for the therapeutic treatment of wounds and infections. Unfortunately not all the expectations of the advocates have been fulfilled, although the future looks brighter than it did 5 to 10 years ago [see Rubbo, Albert, and Maxwell (1942), Browning (1943), and Martin (1944)]. At the present time the most promising group of antiseptic dyes is the acridines. For example, certain of the mono- and diaminoacridines strongly inhibit various bacteria. Some of the most active of these compounds are (Rubbo, Albert, and Maxwell (1942), Lawrence (1943), Silverman and Evans (1943), and Martin (1944)], 2-aminoacridine, 5-aminoacridine, 2:8-diaminoacridine (proflavine), 2-ethoxy-6:9-diaminoacridine (Rivanol), and 3-chloro-7-methoxy-9-(1-methyl-4-diethylamino) butylaminoacridine·2HCl (Atabrine). Silverman and Evans have also made the interesting observation that the inhibition of Atabrine for *Escherichia coli* can be nullified by the naturally occurring amines, spermidine and spermine, as well as by several synthetic polyamines. The mechanism of this counteraction has not been elucidated.

The dilutions at which several dye compounds are bacteriostatic and lethal for bacteria are given in Tables 44 and 45. More recent data have been published by the workers previously mentioned, but the figures in the tables are sufficient to illustrate the action of dyes on bacteria.

According to Stearn and Stearn (1924), Albert (1942), and others, dyes exhibit their staining and antiseptic powers by the phenomenon of ionic exchange with cells. The cells are rendered partially or completely inactive by this exchange. Thus, the acid dyes, such as acid fuchsin, act through interaction of their acidic ions with the basic groups of bacteria to form feebly ionized compounds:

$$BP—NH_2 + Na^+A^- + H_2O \rightarrow BP—NH_3A + Na^+OH^-$$

where BP refers to the bacterial protein with a free amino group, and A stands for the anion of the dye. In a similar manner the so-called basic dyes, such as the polyphenylmethanes (brilliant green, crystal violet, etc.) and the acridines (proflavine, acriflavine, 5-aminoacridine, etc.), owe their activity to their basic ions, which interact with the acidic groups in bacteria to form slightly ionized complexes:

$$BP—COOH + C^+Cl^- \rightarrow BP—COOC + H^+Cl^-$$

where C stands for the high-molecular-weight cation of the dye.

TABLE 44

HIGHEST DILUTIONS OF VARIOUS DYES WHICH SHOW BACTERIOSTATIC ACTION

[From Petroff and Gump (1935)]

Compound	*Staphylococcus aureus*	*Streptococcus pyogenes*	*Diplococcus pneumoniae*, type I	*Streptococcus fecalis*	*Shigella dysenteriae*	*Vibrio comma*
Gentian violet (methyl violet)	50,000	50,000	50,000	.....	......	......
Ethyl violet	50,000	50,000	50,000	25,000	......	......
Brilliant green	100,000	100,000	200,000	25,000	100,000	100,000
Basic fuchsin	25,000	50,000	50,000	25,000	25,000	10,000
Acridine yellow	25,000	100,000	100,000	.....	25,000	10,000
Proflavine	50,000	100,000	100,000	25,000	10,000	5,000
Neutral acriflavine	100,000	100,000	100,000	25,000	50,000	......
Acriviolet	50,000	100,000	100,000	25,000	50,000	10,000
Cresyl violet	100,000	50,000	150,000	25,000	10,000	......
Methylene blue	100,000	100,000	200,000	50,000	5,000	......
Ethylene blue	100,000	150,000	300,000	25,000	10,000	......
n-Propylene blue	100,000	150,000	300,000	25,000	5,000	5,000

It is of interest to mention here that the anionic and cationic synthetic detergents as well as other substances, such as heavy metal salts, apparently exhibit their activity in a similar manner. In fact, Valko and DuBois (1944) have presented experimental data to show that all these substances act in a similar manner.

Several workers have observed that, in general, the basic dyes, which belong to the group of so-called cationic antiseptics, are much more active than the acid dyes. Two points may be mentioned to explain this difference [Albert (1942)]. In the first place bacteria contain an excess of acidic groups over basic groups, as is indicated by their low isoelectric points. Secondly, quite apart from the —COOH groups, more strongly acid groups (phosphoric) are to be expected in the nuclear apparatus and enzyme systems of the cell. This second point is supported by the work of McIlwain (1941), which shows that acriflavine inhibits the growth of bacteria partly, at least, through interaction with nucleotides.

TABLE 45

Lethal Concentrations of Various Dyes

[From Browning and his associates (1917) and Browning (1930)]

Compound	Lethal Concentration * for *Staphylococcus aureus*: In H_2O + 0.7% Peptone	*Staphylococcus aureus*: In Serum	*Escherichia coli*: In H_2O + 0.7% Peptone	*Escherichia coli*: In Serum
Brilliant green (sulfate)	1 : 10,000,000	1 : 30,000	1 : 130,000	1 : 3,500
Brilliant green (oxalate)	1 : 10,000,000	1 : 100,000	1 : 200,000	1 : 3,500
Malachite green (oxalate and sulfate)	1 : 10,000,000	1 : 40,000	1 : 20,000	1 : 1,000
para-Rosaniline (*para*-Fuchsin)	1 : 100,000	1 : 20,000	(1 : 1,000 fails)	1 : 2,000
Crystal violet (gentian violet)	1 : 4,000,000	1 : 400,000	1 : 8,000	1 : 8,000
Mercurochrome-220 (disodium dibromohydroxymercurifluorescein)	1 : 100,000	1 : 1,000	1 : 100,000	1 : 1,000
Acriflavine	1 : 200,000	1 : 200,000	1 : 20,000	1 : 100,000

* Lowest concentration which killed organisms, as tested by subculture, after incubation at 37°C. for 48 hours.

ESSENTIAL OILS AND SIMILAR COMPOUNDS

The antiseptic and germicidal actions of a large number of essential plant oils have been tested by exposing various microorganisms and their spores to the vapors in closed tubes or by suspending the bacteria in the oils for a given period of time, after which plate counts are made. Oil of celery, Ceylon cinnamon, lavender, geranium, eucalyptus, cloves, thyme, peppermint, dill, rosemary, orange, citronella, fennel, anise, marjoram, juniper, bay, turpentine, and camphor were studied by several early workers [Chamberland (1887), Riedlin (1887), Cadéac and Meunier (1889), and Kobert (1907)]. More recently these and other oils have been studied by Kliewe and Huthmacher (1938) and Blum and Fabian (1943). The vapors of most of these oils have little or no germicidal effect on bacteria and their spores; the oils or vapors from oil of mustard and Ceylon cinnamon appear to be the most active. Direct contact with the oils appears to be more effective than are the vapors. For examples, Cadéac and Meunier (1889) inoculated *Eberthella typhosa* into various pure oils for a given time and then seeded agar plates with the mixture. Ceylon cinnamon oil killed this bacterium after about 12 minutes, clove oil after 25 minutes, thyme oil after 35 minutes, and oil of geranium after 50 minutes. Other essential oils killed the test organism in 24 to 48 hours, some in 4 to 10 days; others were not lethal even in 10 days.

Blum and Fabian (1943) have studied the inhibitory and germicidal action of many spice oils by determining their effect on alcohol production by *Saccharomyces ellipsoideus* and by cultivating acetic acid bacteria in cider containing the oils for 24 hours and then making transfers to fresh cider. The bactericidal power of several essential oils has been evaluated also by Miller (1931) and by Naves (1935) by determining their phenol coefficients; a few values obtained were: thymol 27.6, eugenol 9.7, cinnamic aldehyde 6.1, menthol 5.1, and eucalyptol 1.4.

The preserving action of spices is supposedly due to the essential oils which they contain. This subject has been studied by Hoffmann and Evans (1911) and Bachmann (1918). More recent studies by several investigators indicate that certain natural spices may be highly contaminated with bacteria and should not be added to certain foods unless they are sterilized.

Vapors from crushed garlic and horseradish have been reported to be bactericidal by Walton, Herbold, and Lindegren (1936) and Foter (1940). Vollrath, Walton, and Lindegren (1937) showed that the agent responsible for the bactericidal action of garlic was acrolein, while Foter (1940) found that the active principle in crushed horseradish was allyl thiocyanate. Blum and Fabian (1943) found the deceasing order of germicidal activity of spice components they studied to be: allyl isothiocyanate and carvacrol (equal), cinnamic aldehyde and cinnamyl acetate (equal), eugenol, eugenol methyl ether, and eucalyptol. Vegetable oils which possess bactericidal action themselves seem to deprive other germicides which are dissolved in them of most of their activity. Early workers, for example, found that phenol dissolved in vegetable oils, such as olive or cottonseed oil, was only slightly active. This fact has since been confirmed by McMaster (1919), who also pointed out that mineral oils do not possess this effect on germicides.

The germicidal action of a few of the animal oils has been studied by Harris, Bunker, and Milas (1932), Nélis (1939), Nélis and Thomas (1939), de Potter (1939), and Leusden and Derlich (1940). Harris, Bunker, and Milas found that some of these oils, such as seal oil and tuna oil, give off vapors which are bactericidal, whereas others, such as cod-liver oil and sardine oil, become germicidal only after exposure to sunlight or ultraviolet light. It has been suggested that H_2O_2 is given off by the animal oils, and that its rate of evolution is accelerated by irradiation. Nélis and his associates, on the other hand, report that an aqueous extract of cod-liver oil possesses a marked bactericidal power. Leusden and Derlich found that certain fish-liver oils possess a definite bactericidal and sporicidal action. They used nine different species of bacteria and observed marked differences in resistance. For example, the spores of *Bacillus mycoides* were killed in 5 minutes, whereas pseudoanthrax spores remained alive for at least 24 hours. The bactericidal principle of fish-liver oil is not water soluble, according to these workers.

MISCELLANEOUS COMPOUNDS

The bacteriostatic and germicidal properties of a great many other compounds not mentioned above have been determined by various workers. However, since Klarmann (1939–1944) has reviewed these studies in some detail, only a few examples will be briefly mentioned here.

The action of hydrogen peroxide on the spores of several bacteria was studied by Curran, Evans, and Leviton (1940). They found that the spores died in a logarithmic fashion in the presence of 1 per cent H_2O_2 at 50°C. and *p*H 6.9. According to Mallmann, Botwright, and Churchill (1941), slow oxidizing agents, such as potassium dichromate and sodium azide, exert a strong selective bacteriostatic effect on Gram-negative bacteria. Sodium azide has also been studied in some detail by Lichstein and Soule (1944). They found that 0.1 to 0.3 per cent solutions of sodium azide were bacteriostatic for practically all Gram-negative bacteria, for aerobic spore-forming bacilli, and for a few other Gram-positive bacteria, but streptococci, pneumococci, and anaerobes were resistant. The catalase activity of suspensions of washed bacteria was also found to be markedly inhibited, but, on the other hand, the utilization of glucose and the production of lactic acid by streptococci were not impeded.

The bacteriostatic activity of a series of quinones has been studied by Page and Robinson (1943) and Armstrong, Spink, and Kahnke (1943). Certain of the quinones are quite bacteriostatic, and there seems to be a connection between the oxidation-reduction potentials of these compounds and their antibacterial potencies.

The effect of propamidine (4:4′-diamidinodiphenoxypropane·2HCl) on bacterial activities has been studied by Thrower and Valentine (1943), Bernheim (1943), Kohn (1943), and Snell (1944). The compound is both bacteriostatic and bactericidal for various bacteria, such as streptococci, staphylococci, and lactobacilli, and also affects the activities of certain protozoa. It seems to be of considerable value in treating wound infections, since pus and tissue fluids do not interfere with its action. However, certain polyamines, such as triethylenetetramine and spermidine, counteract its action for some bacteria [see Snell (1944)].

Certain stilbene derivatives also show considerable promise as selective germicides. For example, several workers [see Faulkner (1944)] have shown that *Mycobacterium tuberculosis*, *Corynebacterium diphtheriae*, staphylococci, streptococci, and other Gram-positive organisms are killed when incubated *in vitro* in aqueous media containing 1 : 5,000 to 1 : 500,000 dilutions of diethylstilbesterol (4:4′-dihydroxy-α:β-diethylstilbene, $HO\langle\bigcirc\rangle C(C_2H_5){=}C(C_2H_5)\langle\bigcirc\rangle OH$) and 4-hydroxy-diethylstilbene. Gram-negative bacilli are not affected by such compounds. Furthermore the bactericidal activity of the stilbenes is not related especially to their estrogenic activity.

Numerous other miscellaneous compounds have been tested by various investigators for their inhibitory or germicidal action on bacteria and higher fungi. For example, chlorophyll has some antibacterial properties [Smith (1944)], and diphenyl has a more or less selective fungistatic action for molds. With few exceptions, however, it has no effect on yeasts [Hertz and Levine (1942)].

CHEMICAL NATURE OF ANTAGONISTIC SUBSTANCES (ANTIBIOTICS) PRODUCED BY MICROORGANISMS

For many years it has been known that numerous relations of association and antagonism occur between organisms in nature. Although these relationships have been studied by individuals principally interested in the academic phases of the problem, it has become apparent, particularly in recent years, that certain animal and plant diseases can be controlled by utilizing microorganisms or their products which are antagonistic, lytic, bacteriostatic, or bactericidal for the particular organisms causing the disease. Since this subject has been reviewed in detail by Buchanan and Fulmer (1930), Waksman (1941, 1944), Dubos (1942, 1944), Schmitt (1944), and Hoogerheide (1944) and in bibliographies published by several chemical companies, such as Merck, Squibb, and Winthrop, no attempt will be made here to cover the literature. Only a few pertinent facts dealing with the chemical nature of the antagonistic substances produced by some of the microorganisms will be briefly discussed.

It was once believed that all bacteria produce substances antagonistic for other organisms during certain stages of their development. However, according to Waksman (1941), it is now definitely recognized that only certain species and frequently only specific strains of microorganisms are capable of producing antagonistic substances. These substances vary greatly in their chemical properties, in their toxicity for animals, in their action on various microorganisms, and in the mechanism of their action; however, the differences are often more of degree than of kind.

For classifying the antimicrobial agents of biological origin, Waksman states that the following criteria may be employed: (1) solubility in various reagents; (2) specific chemical nature; (3) specific bacteriolytic, bacteriostatic, and bactericidal properties; (4) toxicity to animals and action *in vivo;* and (5) nature of the organism producing these substances.

Certain of these substances are soluble in water but not in organic solvents; some are soluble in chloroform or in alcohol but not in ether and acetone; others are soluble in these solvents but not in water.

Chemically the antimicrobial agents may be classified as (1) lipids or lipid-like bodies: pyocyanase, clavacin; (2) pigments: actinomycin A, pyocyanine; (3) polypeptides: gramicidin, tyrocidine, lysozyme, actinomycetin; (4) sulfur-bearing compounds: gliotoxin; (5) quinone-like compounds: possibly penicillin; (6) organic bases: streptothricin; (7) other substances: fumigacin, chlorellin, etc.

On the basis of their action, these agents are classified as follows: (1) primarily bacteriostatic: actinomycin, etc.; (2) bacteriostatic and bactericidal: penicillin, gliotoxin, clavacin, etc.; (3) bacteriolytic: gramicidin, actinomycetin, lysozyme. Some are also fungistatic and even fungicidal. In respect to their toxicity for animals they are: (1) practically nontoxic (0.5 g. or more/kg. weight of animal tolerated): penicillin, actinomycetin, streptothricin; (2) fairly toxic (0.05 g. to 0.5 g./kg. lethal): gramicidin, tyrocidine, gliotoxin; (3) highly toxic

(0.15 mg. to 0.1 g./kg. lethal): actinomycin, aspergillic acid. For the most part the antibiotic substances are highly selective in their action upon microorganisms, since two closely related species or even two strains of the same organism can be differentiated.

Few specific facts are available concerning the mode of action of the antibiotic substances, although considerable progress has been made along this line during the past few years [see Dubos, Hotchkiss, and Coburn (1942), Waksman (1943, 1944) Hotchkiss (1943), Schales (1943), Dubos (1944), Welshimer, Krampitz, and Werkman (1944), Geiger and Conn (1945)]. In general, according to Waksman (1943, 1944), the mode of action of these antibiotic substances consists of interfering with cell multiplication by blocking or impeding certain metabolic reactions of microorganisms, for example, (1) by oxidizing a metabolic substance which has to be reduced in the process of microbial nutrition; (2) by combining with the substrate or one of its constituents, rendering it inactive for microbial utilization; (3) by competing with the substrate for an enzyme required by the microorganism for an essential metabolic process; (4) by affecting the surface tension (or interfacial tension) of the microorganism; (5) by influencing the respiratory mechanism of the cell; and (6) by acting as an enzyme system and producing products, such as peroxides, which are injurious to the microbial cell. Penatin (penicillin B, notatin) is known to function as a glucose oxidase and catalyze the following reaction:

$$\text{Glucose} + O_2 \rightarrow \text{Gluconic acid} + H_2O_2$$

It is believed that the bacteriostatic effect of this antibiotic substance can be explained by its ability to produce hydrogen peroxide [see Schales (1943)]. Tyrocidine is a surface-active compound, and it is thought that it exhibits its action by disruption of cell membranes and by denaturation of proteins (enzymes, etc.), thus causing irreversible damage and death [Dubos (1944)]. Gramicidin, like tyrocidine, is a peptide antibiotic, and its activity may be due in part to its content of *d*-amino acids, which may interfere with the utilization of *l*-amino acids by microorganisms [Fox, Fling, and Bollenback (1944)]. Penicillin has been shown to inhibit the activity of urease [Waksman (1944)] and to interfere with the dismutation of pyruvate [Welshimer, Krampitz, and Werkman (1944)]. More recently clavacin (claviformin) has been shown to exhibit its antibiotic activities by combining with the sulfhydryl groups of bacterial enzyme systems or with sulfhydryl-containing metabolites essential to the bacteria [Geiger and Conn (1945)].

Some of the antagonistic substances of microbial origin have been highly purified and crystallized, and their chemical constitution has

TABLE 46

SHOWING CERTAIN SELECTIVE BACTERIOSTATIC AND BACTERICIDAL SUBSTANCES OF MICROBIAL ORIGIN

[From Waksman (1941, 1944), Waksman and Woodruff (1942), and Others]

Substance	Properties	Produced by
Actinomycetin	Water-soluble, protein-like substance. Precipitated by acetone, alcohol, and $(NH_4)_2SO_4$. Thermolabile. Destroyed by strong acids, but not by mild antiseptics. Acts (lysis) primarily against dead bacteria.	*Actinomyces albus*
Actinomycetin (lysozyme)	Water-soluble, but ether-, benzol-, and chloroform-insoluble. Thermostable. Similar to egg-white lysozyme, but not identical.	*Actinomyces violaceus*
Actinomycin A	Orange pigment. Soluble in ether, alcohol, benzol, and chloroform, but not in petrol ether. Thermostable. Highly toxic for animals. Highly bacteriostatic.	*Actinomyces antibioticus*
Actinomycin B	Colorless substance. Soluble in ether, petrol ether, and alcohol, but not in water. Little bacteriostatic action, but bactericidal.	*Actinomyces antibioticus*
Aspergillic acid [1] ($C_{12}H_{20}N_2O_2$)	Crystalline, amphoteric substance. Soluble in sodium bicarbonate solution, alcohol, ether, acetone, benzol, chloroform and pyridine, but insoluble in cold water and petrol ether. Moderately toxic for animals. Bacteriostatic and bactericidal for Gram (+) cocci, but less active against anaerobic bacilli and Gram (−) bacteria.	*Aspergillus flavus*
Chlorellin [2]	Soluble in chloroform, benzol, and 1:2-dichloroethane. Bactericidal for Gram (+) and (−) bacteria.	*Chlorella vulgaris*, etc.
Clavacin [3] (Probably clavatin,[4] claviformin,[5] and patulin [6] are very similar or identical.)	Soluble in ether, chloroform, dilute alkalies, alcohol, and water. Adsorbed on norite. Moderately toxic for animals. Primarily active (bacteriostatic and bactericidal) against Gram (−) bacteria.	*Aspergillus clavatus*, *Penicillium claviforme*
Gliotoxin [7] ($C_{13}H_{14}N_2S_2O_4$) or ($C_{13}H_{16}N_2S_2O_4$)	Soluble in pyridine and dioxane, less so in chloroform and alcohols, and only sparingly so in water. Sensitive to alkalies and light. Highly toxic for animals. Fungicidal, bacteriostatic, and bactericidal.	*Gliocladium fimbriatum*, *Trichoderma*, species, *Aspergillus fumigatus*
Gramicidin [8] ($C_{55}H_{79}N_{11}O_{10}$) or ($C_{74}H_{105}N_{15}O_{13}$)	Soluble in alcohol, ether, and acetone. Crystalline. Moderately toxic for certain cells, but inactive against others. Lytic for Gram (+) bacteria.	*Bacillus brevis*
Gramicidin S [9]	Soluble in alcohol and slightly soluble in acetone. Crystalline polypeptide. Moderately toxic. Prevents growth and kills many Gram (+) and (−) bacteria. See discussion for additional properties.	A thermophilic *Bacillus brevis* type
Helvolic acid [10] ($C_{32}H_{44}O_8$) (Probably fumigacin [11] is very similar or identical.)	Colorless, crystalline, monobasic acid. Soluble in most organic solvents. Thermostable. Bacteriostatic for Gram (+) bacteria; almost inactive against Gram (−) forms.	*Aspergillus fumigatus*

[1] White and Hill (1943), Jones, Rake, and Hamre (1943), Dutcher and Wintersteiner (1944).
[2] Pratt *et al.* (1944).
[3] Waksman, Horning, and Spencer (1942), Conn and Geiger (1944).
[4] Bergel *et al.* (1943).
[5] Chain, Florey, Jennings, and Callow (1942).
[6] Birkinshaw *et al.* (1943).
[7] Johnson, Bruce, and Dutcher (1943), Bruce, Dutcher, Johnson, and Miller (1944), Dutcher Johnson, and Bruce (1944), Menzel, Wintersteiner, and Hoogerheide (1944).
[8] Hotchkiss (1941), Tishler, Stokes, Trenner, and Conn (1941), Gordon, Martin, and Synge (1943).
[9] Gause and Brazhnikova (1944), Belozersky and Passhina (1944).
[10] Chain, Florey, Jennings, and Williams (1943), Menzel, Wintersteiner, and Hoogerheide (1944).
[11] Waksman, Horning, and Spencer (1942).

TABLE 46 (*Continued*)

SHOWING CERTAIN SELECTIVE BACTERIOSTATIC AND BACTERICIDAL SUBSTANCES OF MICROBIAL ORIGIN

[From Waksman (1941, 1944), Waksman and Woodruff (1942), and Others]

Substance	Properties	Produced by
Iodinin[12] ($C_{12}H_8O_4N_2$)	Insoluble in acids, except concentrated H_2SO_4. Soluble in alkalies. Sodium salt transitorily soluble in water. More bacteriostatic for Gram (+) than Gram (−) bacteria.	*Chromobacterium iodinum*
Patulin[13] ($C_7H_6O_4$)	Crystalline substance, soluble in water and most organic solvents. Bacteriostatic for both Gram (+) and (−) bacteria.	*Penicillium patulum*
Penatin[14] (Probably penicillin B[15] and notatin[16] are very similar or identical.)	Yellowish, high-molecular-weight protein; probably a yellow enzyme. Soluble in water, but not in certain organic solvents. Resistant to acids, but destroyed by alkalies. Penatin and notatin nontoxic; penicillin B toxic. Glucose required for antibacterial action. Bacteriostatic and bactericidal; action probably due to liberated H_2O_2.	*Penicillium notatum*
Penicidin[17]	Pale-yellow oil. Soluble in chloroform, benzol, ether, ethyl alcohol, and dilute mineral acids; quickly destroyed by strong alkalies. Diffuses through cellophane and can be adsorbed on charcoal. Bacteriostatic for both Gram (+) and (−) bacteria.	*Penicillium*, species
Penicillin[18] (Probably flavacidin[19] is very similar or identical.)	Soluble in water, alcohol, ether (at *p*H 2.0, but only partly at *p*H 7.2), and acetone. Thermolabile. Low toxicity. Strong bacteriostatic action for most Gram (+) bacteria. See discussion for additional properties.	*Penicillium notatum, etc.*
Pyocyanase	Soluble in several solvents. Lipoidal. Thermostable. Lytic for many bacteria, especially Gram (+) species; activity due largely to unsaturated fatty acids.	*Pseudomonas aeruginosa*
Streptomycin[20]	Very similar to streptothricin, but more active against certain Gram (+) and (−) bacteria.	*Actinomyces griseus*
Streptothricin[21]	Organic base, low in nitrogen. Adsorbed on norite and eluted with dilute mineral acids. Precipitated by ethyl alcohol; insoluble in ether or chloroform. Thermostable. Low in toxicity for animals. Inhibits Gram (−) bacteria; most Gram (+) species more resistant. Bactericidal.	*Actinomyces lavendulae*
Subtilin[22]	Soluble in alcohol and precipitated from it by NaCl. Contains 5.7% N. Inactivated by light, methyl alcohol, and formaldehyde. Active against Gram (+) bacteria.	*Bacillus subtilis*
Tyrocidine[23] ($C_{63}H_{83}N_{13}O_{13} \cdot HCl$)	Crystalline polypeptide. Soluble in absolute alcohol, but insoluble in ether or acetone. Moderately toxic for animals. Lytic for Gram (+) and (−) bacteria.	*Bacillus brevis*

[12] McIlwain (1941, 1943).
[13] Birkinshaw *et al.* (1943).
[14] Kocholaty (1943).
[15] Roberts *et al.* (1943), Van Bruggen *et al.* (1943).
[16] Birkinshaw and Raistrick (1943).
[17] Atkinson (1942, 1943).
[18] See reviews mentioned in discussion.
[19] McKee, Rake, and Houck (1944).
[20] Schatz, Bugie, and Waksman (1944).
[21] Woodruff and Foster (1943), Foster and Woodruff (1943).
[22] Jansen and Hirschmann (1944).
[23] Hotchkiss (1941), Christensen, Edwards, and Piersma (1941), Gordon, Martin, and Synge (1943), Christensen, Uzman, and Hegsted (1945).

been fairly well established, whereas only the proximate chemical composition of others is known, or they have not been characterized. Certain properties of the more important of these substances are given in Table 46, and a few additional remarks about some of them will be made. For more details the literature cited in the discussion should be consulted.

Aspergillic acid has been obtained in a highly purified crystalline form from *Aspergillus flavus* by White and Hill (1943). They reported that the crystals have a pale cream color, a "sweet" odor, a molecular weight of about 224, and an empirical formula of $C_{12}H_{20}N_2O_2$. More recently Dutcher and Wintersteiner (1944) have shown that aspergillic acid is monobasic in character, is optically active, and melts at 93°C. It apparently has the following structural formula:

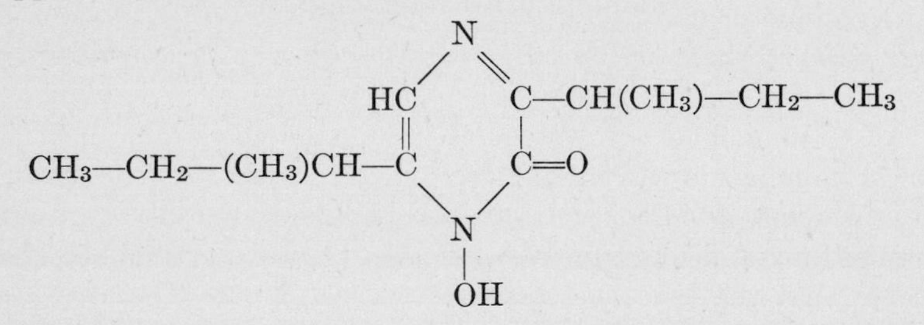

Clavacin, or clavatin, is produced by *Aspergillus clavatus*, has a chemical formula of $C_7H_6O_4$, and melts at about 110°C. [Bergel *et al.* (1943)]. Claviformin, which is very similar in many respects, has been reported to be a compound with an empirical formula of $C_9H_8O_5$ and to melt at 110°C. [Chain, Florey, Jennings, and Callow (1942)]. Patulin also appears to be identical with these substances.

Gliotoxin, the antagonistic substance excreted by *Gliocladium fimbriatum*, has been studied in some detail by Johnson, Bruce, and Dutcher (1943), Bruce, Dutcher, Johnson, and Miller (1944), and Dutcher, Johnson, and Bruce (1944). These workers not only studied the biological properties of gliotoxin, but they also determined its empirical formula, molecular weight (about 326), crystalline form (monoclinic), solubility, ultraviolet absorption curve, optical activity, and degradation products. On the basis of these studies the most logical empirical formula was found to be $C_{13}H_{14}N_2O_4S_2$. When the compound was mixed with selenium and heated to 250°C., the following reaction occurred:

$$C_{13}H_{14}N_2O_4S_2 \xrightarrow[250^\circ C.]{Se} C_{12}H_8N_2O_3 + 2H_2S + [C] + H_2O$$

where [C] might be CO_2, formaldehyde, or methane, and the C_{12} compound is 2-methyl-1:3:4:triketotetrahydropyrazino-[1.2-a]-indole:

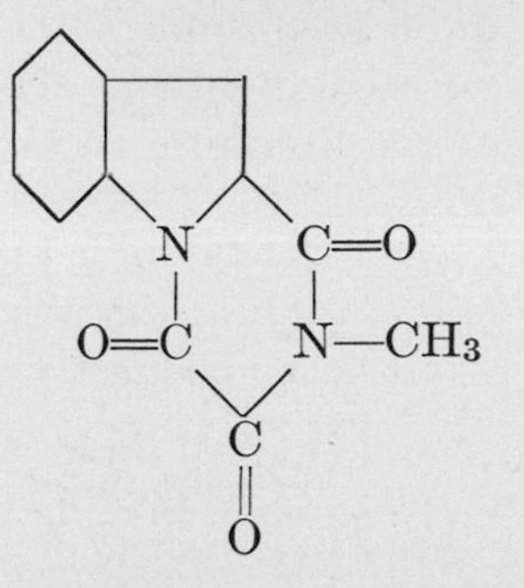

Gramicidin is a polypeptide formed by *Bacillus brevis*, and contains no free amino or carboxyl groups; according to Gordon, Martin, and Synge (1943), there are 24 amino acid residues in the peptide. The total nitrogen and oxygen content is accounted for by α-amino acids and a 1 : 2 aminohydroxy compound which is not an α-amino acid. The known amino acids which have been identified are *l*-tryptophan, glycine, *d*-leucine, *d*-valine, and *l*-alanine. Several alternative empirical formulas for gramicidin have been proposed; however, Hotchkiss (1941) believes that the two most satisfactory ones are $C_{55}H_{79}N_{11}O_{10}$ and $C_{74}H_{105}N_{15}O_{13}$, with molecular weights of 1,054 and 1,413, respectively [see also Tishler, Stokes, Trenner, and Conn (1941)]. Gramicidin crystals are spear-shaped, colorless platelets and melt at 228° to 230°C.

Gramicidin S, or Soviet gramicidin, is similar in many respects to Dubos' gramicidin and tyrocidine, but it appears to be a different type of polypeptide [Belozersky and Passhina (1944)]. Some of its properties are shown in Table 46 and mentioned in the discussion on tyrocidine.

Helvolic acid has been isolated from cultures of *Aspergillus fumigatus* in the crystalline state by Chain, Florey, Jennings, and Williams (1943). It has an elementary composition of $C_{32}H_{44}O_8$, is colorless and nonfluorescent in ultraviolet light, melts at 204.5° to 205.5°C., and titrates as a monobasic acid.

Iodinin, the violet, copper-glinting pigment produced by *Chromobacterium iodinum*, was first studied chemically by Clemo and McIlwain in 1938, but its ability to inhibit bacterial growth remained unknown until McIlwain (1941, 1943) studied this property of the compound. Iodinin melts at 236°C., has a formula of $C_{12}H_8O_4N_2$, and is probably 1:2(?)-dihydroxyphenazine N,N′-dioxide (see pp. 422 to 429 on bacterial pigments in Chapter 5). McIlwain (1943) not only found that iodinin

(2×10^{-6} to 5×10^{-7} *M*) would inhibit bacterial growth, but that its action could be counteracted by certain concentrations (5×10^{-6} to 5×10^{-7} *M*) of pure hydroxyanthraquinones and 2-methyl-1:4-naphthaquinone. This is probably another example of antagonism between structurally related compounds.

Patulin, the bacteriostatic substance formed by *Penicillium patulum*, is very similar to, if not identical with, clavacin, clavatin, and claviformin [Bergel *et al.* (1943)]. Birkinshaw, Michael, Bracken, and Raistrick (1943) have studied the chemistry of crystalline patulin in some detail. It is optically inactive, melts at 111°C., and has an empirical formula of $C_7H_6O_4$. It is believed to be anhydro-3-hydroxymethylenetetrahydro-γ-pyrone-2-carboxylic acid of the following structure:

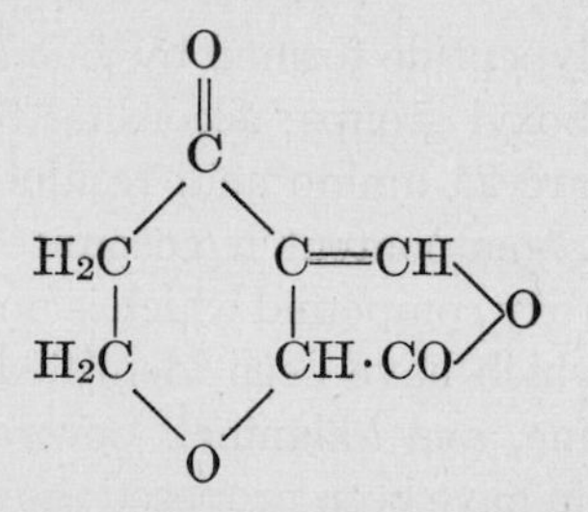

Numerous derivative and decomposition products were prepared and studied to prove this structure.

Penicillin, the antibiotic substance produced by *Penicillium notatum*, was first described by Dr. Alexander Fleming in 1929. Since that time, and especially in the past few years, this substance has been studied very extensively. The impetus for most of the work came after Professor H. W. Florey and his associates (Abraham, Chain, Jennings, and others) demonstrated that penicillin has great value as a chemotherapeutic agent in treating certain diseases and that it can be produced on a commercial scale. At the present time over 20 pharmaceutical plants, built at a cost of about 20 million dollars, are producing penicillin in this country. If these plants have a current production of about 400 billion units [3] (100,000 units = about 130 mg.), per month, daily production would be just about 18 lb. of pure penicillin. However, this amount will treat several hundred thousand serious cases of infection per month.

Penicillin has been obtained as a free acid and in the form of various salts, such as those of barium, calcium, strontium, potassium, and so-

[3] In June, 1943, about 425 million units of penicillin were produced in this country; in February, 1944, this figure rose to 18 billion units; in March, 1944, to 40 billion; in January, 1945, to 394 billion units; and in the early summer of 1945 to about 460 billion units.

dium. In the form of its salts or the acid it is easily oxidized by $KMnO_4$ and H_2O_2 but is less sensitive to reducing agents. The empirical formula [4] of the barium salt has been reported to be $C_{23}H_{30}O_9N_2Ba$ or $C_{24}H_{32}O_{10}N_2Ba$, and that of the strontium salt to be $C_{24}H_{34}O_{11}NSr$. When the molecule is ruptured it supposedly yields: (1) a colorless, water-soluble acid, which on further hydrolysis gives a simple peptide; (2) a yellow, insoluble pigment, $C_{16}H_{20}O_6$ or $C_{16}H_{18}O_5 \cdot H_2O$; (3) acetaldehyde; and (4) carbon dioxide. An interesting point in connection with the growth-inhibiting property of penicillin is that it can be readily overcome by an enzyme called penicillinase [Abraham and Chain (1940), Harper (1943), Woodruff and Foster (1944), Bondi and Dietz (1944), Himes and White (1944), McQuarrie *et al.* (1944)]. This enzyme is formed by several bacteria, such as paracolon bacillus and other coliform bacilli, aerobic spore-forming bacilli, and certain *Shigella*, and cell-free preparations may be employed routinely in culture media for the isolation of penicillin-sensitive bacteria from pathological material containing inhibitory concentrations of the drug. For further reading on penicillin the references cited in the bibliographies published by Merck and Co., Squibb, and Winthrop Chemical Co. and in the review by Schmitt (1944) should be consulted.

Tyrocidine, like gramicidin and gramicidin S, is a polypeptide product of *Bacillus brevis*, but it contains free amino groups. According to Hotchkiss (1941) and Christensen, Edwards, and Piersma (1941), the most probable molecular unit has two amino groups, three amide groups, one weakly acidic or phenolic group, and a molecular weight of

[4] According to the Committee on Medical Research, O.S.R.D., Washington, and the Medical Research Council, London (*Science*, **102**: 627–629), all antibiotics of the penicillin class have the empirical formula $C_9H_{11}O_4SN_2 \cdot R$. In F-penicillin (penicillin I) R is Δ^2-pentenyl,—$CH_2 \cdot CH{=}CH \cdot CH_2 \cdot CH_3$; in dihydro-F-penicillin, R is *n*-amyl; in G-penicillin (penicillin II), R is benzyl; in X-penicillin (penicillin III), R is *p*-hydroxybenzyl; in K-penicillin, R is *n*-heptyl. At present the formulas (as sodium salts) which are receiving the most attention contain a β-lactam structure (I) and an incipient azlactone grouping (II), respectively:

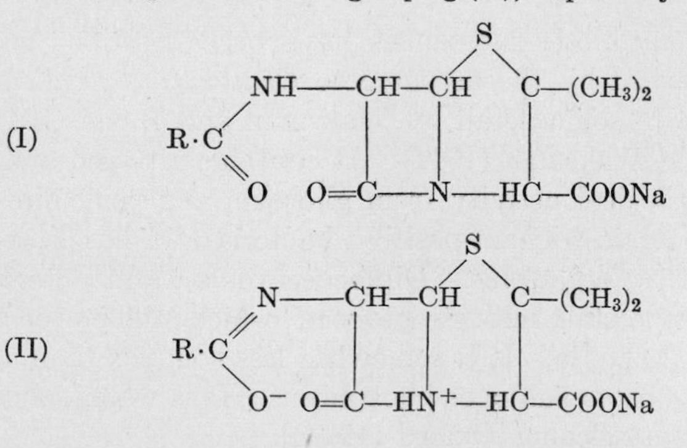

2,534. However, the empirical formula which is most satisfactory for the compound is $C_{63}H_{83}N_{13}O_{13} \cdot HCl$, which corresponds to a molecular weight of 1,267. Tyrocidine has been obtained in the form of crystalline needles which melt at 237° to 240°C. The workers mentioned above detected tryptophan, phenylalanine, tyrosine, alanine, and dicarboxylic amino acids (in part aspartic) in tyrocidine. More recently Gordon, Martin, and Synge (1943) have hydrolyzed (acid) tyrocidine and studied its amino acid composition. Phenylalanine, leucine, proline, valine, tyrosine, ornithine, and glutamic acid were isolated by partition chromatography, and characterized as their acetyl derivatives. Additional evidence was obtained for the occurrence of tryptophan and aspartic acid in this polypeptide. It is of interest that this appears to be the first time ornithine has been isolated by acid hydrolysis from an intact protein or polypeptide. The following data, taken from the papers by Belozersky and Passhina (1944) and Christensen, Uzman, and Hegsted (1945), show some of the relationships between the properties and the composition of tyrocidine, Dubos' gramicidin, and gramicidin S:

	Tyrocidine·HCl	Gramicidin Dubos	Gramicidin S
Melting point, °C.	240	228–230	268–270
Molecular weight	1,260	1,250–1,550	1,060–1,340
Free NH_2 groups	+	−	+
Free COOH groups	+	−	+
Hydrolysis time, hours	2	18	18–20
Total N(Kjeldahl), per cent	14.3	14.8	13.0
Tryptophan	+	+	+
Tyrosine	+	−	−
Dicarboxylic acids	+	±?	−
Phenylalanine	+	−	−
Proline	+	−	+
Ornithine	+	−	+ (18%)
Leucine	+ (8.2%)	+	+
Valine	+ (7.6%)		

Several other antibiotic substances have been described recently. Chaetomin is formed by the ascomycete *Chaetomium cochliodes* and has been studied in some detail by Waksman and Bugie (1944) and Geiger, Conn, and Waksman (1944). It contains nitrogen and sulfur but differs in biological activity from gliotoxin and penicillin. It is primarily active against Gram-positive bacteria and has little effect upon Gram-negative organisms. Diplococcin is an antibacterial protein, elaborated by certain milk streptococci, which inhibits the growth of Gram-positive bacteria. It is somewhat less complex than a metaprotein and contains no sulfur or phosphorus. It is water-soluble but insoluble in absolute alcohol [Oxford (1944)].

REFERENCES

Abraham, E. P., and E. Chain. 1940. *Nature,* **146:**837.

Abraham, E. P., E. Chain, C. M. Fletcher, H. W. Florey, A. D. Gardner, N. G. Heatley, and M. A. Jennings. 1941. *Lancet,* **1941**(2)**:**177–189.

Akatsu, S. 1917. *J. Exptl. Med.,* **25:**363–373.

Albert, A. 1942. *Lancet,* **1942**(2)**:**633–636.

Andrewes, F. W., and K. J. P. Orton. 1903. *Centr. Bakt., I Abt. Orig.,* **35:**645–651, 811–815.

Anderson, J. F., and T. B. McClintic. 1911. *J. Infectious Diseases,* **8:**1–26.

Anson, M. L. 1939. *J. Gen. Physiol.,* **23:**239–246.

Armstrong, W. D., W. W. Spink, and J. Kahnke. 1943. *Proc. Soc. Exptl. Biol. Med.,* **53:**230–234.

Atkinson, N. 1942, 1943. *Australian J. Exptl. Biol. Med. Sci.,* **20:**287–288; **21:**15–16.

Bachmann, F. M. 1918. *Ind. Eng. Chem.,* **10:**121–123.

Baker, A. H., S. R. Finn, and C. C. Twort. 1940. *J. Hyg.,* **40:**560–582.

Baker, A. H. 1941. *Chem. Products,* **4:**25–28.

Baker, Z., R. W. Harrison, and B. F. Miller. 1941. *J. Exptl. Med.,* **73:**249–271; **74:**611–620, 621–637.

Bayliss, M. 1936–1937. *J. Bact.,* **31:**489–504; *J. Lab. Clin. Med.,* **22:**700–704.

Beckwith, T. D., and J. R. Moser. 1933. *J. Am. Water Works Assoc.,* **25:**367–374.

Belozersky, A. N., and T. S. Passhina. 1944. *Lancet,* **1944**(2)**:**716–717; *Am. Rev. Soviet Med.,* **2:**138–140.

Bergel, F., A. L. Morrison, A. R. Moss, R. Klein, H. Rinderknecht, and J. L. Ward. 1943. *Nature,* **152:**750.

Berliner, J. F. T. 1931. *J. Am. Water Works Assoc.,* **23:**1320–1333.

Bernheim, F. 1943. *Science,* **98:**223.

Bidzinski, S. 1926. "Contribution à l'étude de l'action bactéricide des sels de cuivre." Thèse. Nancy, France.

Bigg, E. 1943. *Proc. Soc. Exptl. Biol. Med.,* **53:**120–121.

Bigger, J. W., and J. H. Nelson. 1943. *J. Path. Bact.,* **55:**321–327.

Birkhaug, K. E. 1933. *J. Infectious Diseases,* **53:**250–261.

Birkinshaw, J. H., S. E. Michael, A. Bracken, and H. Raistrick. 1943. *Lancet,* **1943**(2)**:**625–630.

Birkinshaw, J. H., and H. Raistrick. 1943. *J. Biol. Chem.,* **148:**459–460.

Birkeland, J. M., and E. A. Steinhaus. 1939. *Proc. Soc. Exptl. Biol. Med.,* **40:**86–88.

Blum, H. B., and F. W. Fabian. 1943. *Fruit Products J.,* **22:**326–329, 347.

Bondi, A., Jr., and C. C. Dietz. 1944. *J. Bact.,* **47:**426.

Brewer, C. M., and G. L. A. Ruehle. 1934. *Soap,* **10**(10)**:**81–83.

Brewer, C. M. 1943. *Am. J. Pub. Health,* **33:**261–264.

Brewer, J. H. 1939. *J. Am. Med. Assoc.,* **112:**2009–2018.

Brewer, J. H. 1939. *J. Bact.,* **37:**411–413.

Bronfenbrenner, J., A. D. Hershey, and J. Doubly. 1939. *J. Bact.,* **37:**583–597.

Browning, C. H. 1930. Chapter V (pp. 202–207), Vol. I. *A System of Bacteriology in Relation to Medicine.* Medical Research Council, London.

Browning, C. H. 1943. *Brit. Med. J.,* **1943**(1)**:**341–343.

Brownlee, G., and I. M. Tonkin. 1943. *Quart. J. Pharm. Pharmacol.,* **16:**73–78.

Bruce, W. F., J. D. Dutcher, J. R. Johnson, and L. L. Miller. 1944. *J. Am. Chem. Soc.,* **66:**614–616.

Buchanan, R. E., and E. I. Fulmer. 1930. *Physiology and Biochemistry of Bacteria*, Vol. II. Williams and Wilkins Co., Baltimore.
Bucholtz, L. 1875. *Arch. exptl. Path. Pharmakol.*, **4**: 1–81.
Bunyea, H. 1927. *J. Agr. Research*, **34**: 623–630.
Burlingame, E. M., and G. F. Reddish. 1939. *J. Lab. Clin. Med.*, **24**:765–772.
Butterfield, C. T., E. Wattie, S. Megregian, and C. W. Chambers. 1943. *U. S. Pub. Health Service Repts.*, **58**:1837–1866.
Cadéac, and A. Meunier. 1889. *Ann. inst. Pasteur*, **3**:317–326.
Caius, J. F., B. P. B. Naidu, and J. S. Jang. 1927. *Indian J. Med. Res.*, **15**:117–134.
Calloway, N. O., H. Gilman, and C. H. Werkman. 1933. *Proc. Iowa Acad. Sci.*, **40**:81.
Carswell, T. S., and J. A. Doubly. 1936. *Ind. Eng. Chem.*, **28**: 1276–1278.
Castellani, E. 1935. *Boll. sez. ital. Soc. intern. microbiol.*, **7**:396–400.
Chain, E., H. W. Florey, M. A. Jennings, and D. Callow. 1942. *Brit. J. Exptl. Path.*, **23**:202–205.
Chain, E., H. W. Florey, M. A. Jennings, and T. I. Williams. 1943. *Brit. J. Exptl. Path.*, **24**:108–119.
Chamberland, M. 1887. *Ann. inst. Pasteur*, **1**:153–164.
Chang, S. L. 1944. *J. Am. Water Works Assoc.*, **36**:1192–1207.
Chapman, G. H., and C. Berens. 1935. *J. Bact.*, **29**:437–448.
Chapman, G. H. 1936. *J. Bact.*, **32**:199–205.
Charlton, D., and M. Levine. 1937. *Iowa Eng. Exp. Sta. Bull.* 132. 60 pp.
Chick, H., and C. J. Martin. 1908. *J. Hyg.*, **8**:654–697, 698–703.
Chick, H. 1908–1912. *J. Hyg.*, **8**:92–158; **10**:237–286; **12**:414–435.
Chick, H. 1930. Chapter V (pp. 178–207), Vol. I. *A System of Bacteriology in Relation to Medicine.* Medical Research Council, London.
Christensen, H. N., R. R. Edwards, and H. D. Piersma. 1941. *J. Biol. Chem.*, **141**:187–195.
Christensen, H. N., L. Uzman, and D. M. Hegsted. 1945. *J. Biol. Chem.*, **158**:279–281.
Christiansen, J. 1918. *Z. physiol. Chem.*, **102**:275–305.
Churchman, J. W. 1912, 1923, 1926. *J. Exptl. Med.*, **16**:221–247; **37**:543–551; *Proc. Soc. Exptl. Biol. Med.*, **23**:530–534.
Clark, W. C. 1938. *J. Am. Pharm. Assoc.*, **27**:130–132.
Cohen, B. 1922. *J. Bact.*, **7**:183–230.
Conn, H. J. 1940. *Biological Stains*, 4th Ed. Biotech Publications, Geneva, N. Y.
Conn, J. E., and W. B. Geiger. 1944. *J. Bact.*, **47**:422–423.
Costigan, S. M. 1936, 1942. *J. Bact.*, **32**:57–63; *J. Am. Water Works Assoc.*, **34**:353–364.
Cowles, P. B. 1938. *Yale J. Biol. Med.*, **11**:33–38, 127–135.
Cowles, P. B. 1940. *Yale J. Biol. Med.*, **12**:697–704.
Cowles, P. B. 1941. *Yale J. Biol. Med.*, **13**:571–578.
Curran, H. R., F. R. Evans, and A. Leviton. 1940. *J. Bact.*, **40**:423–434.
Dakin, H. D., J. B. Cohen, and J. Kenyon. 1916. *Brit. Med. J.*, **1916**(1):160–162.
Delafield, M. E., E. Straker, and W. W. C. Topley. 1941. *Brit. Med. J.*, **1941**(1):145–150.
de Potter, F. 1939. *Compt. rend. soc. biol.*, **131**:158–160.
Dernby, K. G., and H. Davide. 1923. *Z. Immunitäts.*, **35**:447–449.

De Witt, L. M., and H. Sherman. 1916. *J. Infectious Diseases*, **18**:368–382.
Dodd, M. C., W. B. Stillman, M. Roys, and C. Crosby. 1944. *J. Pharmacol.*, **82**:11–18.
Dorfman, A., L. Rice, S. A. Koser, and F. Saunders. 1940. *Proc. Soc. Exptl. Biol. Med.*, **45**:750–753.
Downie, A. W., L. Stent, and S. M. White. 1931. *Brit. J. Exptl. Path.*, **12**:1–9.
Dubos, R. J. 1941, 1942, 1944. *Bull. N. Y. Acad. Med.*, **17**:405–422; *Ann. Rev. Biochem.*, **11**:659–678; *J. Am. Med. Assoc.*, **124**:633–636.
Dubos, R. J., R. D. Hotchkiss, and A. F. Coburn. 1942. *J. Biol. Chem.*, **146**:421–426.
Dunn, C. G. 1937. *Am. J. Hyg.*, **26**:46–52.
Dunn, C. G. 1938. *Proc. Soc. Exptl. Biol. Med.*, **37**:661–663.
Dutcher, J. D., J. R. Johnson, and W. F. Bruce. 1944. *J. Am. Chem. Soc.*, **66**:617–619, 619–621.
Dutcher, J. D., and O. Wintersteiner. 1944. *J. Biol. Chem.*, **155**:359–360.
Eggerth, A. H. 1931. *J. Exptl. Med.*, **53**:27–36.
Eisenberg, P. 1918. *Centr. Bakt., I Abt. Orig.*, **82**:69–207.
Eisler, M. von. 1909. *Centr. Bakt., I Abt. Orig.*, **51**:546–564.
Ely, J. O. 1939. *J. Bact.*, **38**:391–400.
Epstein, A. K., B. R. Harris, and M. Katzman. 1943. *Proc. Soc. Exptl. Biol. Med.*, **53**:238–241.
Epstein, F. 1897. *Z. Hyg. Infektionskr.*, **24**:1–21.
Erickson, F. J., and F. W. Fabian. 1942. *Food Research*, **7**:68–79.
Everitt, E. L., and M. X. Sullivan. 1940. *J. Wash. Acad. Sci.*, **30**:125–131, 457–463.
Fabian, F. W., and C.-E. A. Winslow. 1929. *J. Bact.*, **18**:265–291.
Falk, I. S. 1923. *Bact. Abstr.*, **7**:33–50, 87–105, 133–147.
Falk, I. S., and C.-E. A. Winslow. 1926. *J. Bact.*, **11**:1–25.
Faulkner, G. H. 1944. *Am. Rev. Tuberc.*, **50**:167–175.
Feasley, C. F., B. H. Gwynn, E. F. Degering, and P. A. Tetrault. 1941. *J. Am. Pharm. Assoc.*, **30**:41–44.
Feldman, W. H., and H. C. Hinshaw. 1943. *Am. Rev. Tuberc.*, **48**:256–260.
Field, J., II, and S. M. Field. 1932. *Proc. Soc. Exptl. Biol. Med.*, **29**:935.
Fildes, P. 1940. *Brit. J. Exptl. Path.*, **21**:67–73.
Flexner, S. 1907. *J. Exptl. Med.*, **9**:105–141.
Fohlen, G. M. 1944. *J. Am. Pharm. Assoc., Sci. Ed.*, **33**:33–41.
Forjaz, A. P., and K. P. Jacobsohn. 1938. *Congr. chim. ind., Compt.-rend. 18me, Congr. Nancy*, **1938**:736–740. (1939. *Chem. Abstr.*, **33**:5977.)
Fosbinder, R. J. 1944. *J. Am. Pharm. Assoc., Sci. Ed.*, **33**:1–10.
Foster, J. W., and H. B. Woodruff. 1943. *J. Bact.*, **45**:408–409; *Arch. Biochem.*, **3**:241–255.
Foster, J. W., and H. B. Woodruff. 1944. *J. Bact.*, **47**:43–58.
Foter, M. J. 1940. *Food Research*, **5**:147–152.
Fox, S. W., M. Fling, and G. N. Bollenback. 1944. *J. Biol. Chem.*, **155**:465–468.
Freedlander, B. L. 1942. *Proc. Soc. Exptl. Biol. Med.*, **51**:153–156.
Friedberger, E., and G. Joachimoglu. 1917. *Biochem. Z.*, **79**:135–151.
Frobisher, M., Jr. 1927. *J. Bact.*, **13**:163–182.
Fuller, A. T. 1942. *Biochem. J.*, **36**:548–558.
Gagna, F. 1939. *Giorn. batteriol. immunol.*, **23**:672–687. (1941. *Chem. Abstr.* **35**:6062.)

Garrod, L. P. 1935. *J. Hyg.*, **35**:219–237.

Gause, G. F., and M. G. Brazhnikova. 1944. *Lancet*, **1944**(2):715–716; *Am. Rev. Soviet Med.*, **2**:134–138.

Gay, F. P., and L. F. Morrison. 1921. *J. Infectious Diseases*, **28**:1–17.

Gegenbauer, V. 1922. *Arch. Hyg.*, **90**:23–81.

Geiger, W. B., J. E. Conn, and S. A. Waksman. 1944. *J. Bact.*, **48**:531–536.

Geiger, W. B., and J. E. Conn. 1945. *J. Am. Chem. Soc.*, **67**:112–116.

Gershenfeld, L., and R. Miller. 1932. *J. Am. Pharm. Assoc.*, **21**:894–903.

Gershenfeld, L., and V. E. Milanick. 1941. *Am. J. Pharm.*, **113**:306–326.

Gershenfeld, L., and D. Perlstein. 1941. *Am. J. Pharm.*, **113**:237–255.

Gershenfeld, L., and B. Witlin. 1941. *Am. J. Pharm.*, **113**:215–236.

Gordon, A. H., A. J. P. Martin, and R. L. M. Synge. 1943. *Biochem. J.*, **37**: 86–92, 313–318.

Gregersen, J. P. 1915. *Centr. Bakt., I Abt. Orig.*, **77**:168–185.

Greig, M. E., and J. C. Hoogerheide. 1941. *J. Bact.*, **41**:557–562.

Guest, H. L., and A. J. Salle. 1942. *Proc. Soc. Exptl. Biol. Med.*, **51**:272–273.

Hager, G. P., and T. C. Grubb. 1942. *J. Infectious Diseases*, **71**:228–231.

Hailer, E., and U. von Bockelberg. 1939. *Arch. Hyg.*, **122**:20–43.

Hansen, K., and E. Blegen. 1935. *Klin. Wochschr.*, **14**:1113.

Harper, G. J. 1943. *Lancet*, **1943**(2):569–571.

Harris, J. S., and H. I. Kohn. 1941. *J. Biol. Chem.*, **141**:989–990.

Harris, R. S., J. W. M. Bunker, and N. A. Milas. 1932. *J. Bact.*, **23**:429–435.

Heinemann, B. 1943. *J. Am. Pharm. Assoc., Sci. Ed.*, **32**:298–301.

Heise, M. D., and W. A. Starin. 1940. *J. Infectious Diseases*, **67**:70–73.

Henry, R. J. 1943. *Bact. Rev.*, **7**:175–262.

Hertz, M. R., and M. Levine. 1942. *Food Research*, **7**:430–441.

Heyman, B., and T. C. Grubb. 1940. *J. Bact.*, **40**:363–371.

Himes, A. T., and H. J. White. 1944. *J. Bact.*, **47**:426–427.

Hirsch, M. M., and M. V. Novak. 1942. *Proc. Soc. Exptl. Biol. Med.*, **50**·376–379.

Hobbs, B. C., and G. S. Wilson. 1942. *J. Hyg.*, **42**:436–450.

Hoffman, C., T. R. Schweitzer, and G. Dalby. 1940–1941. *J. Am. Chem. Soc.*, **62**:988–989; *Ind. Eng. Chem.* (*Ind. Ed.*), **33**:749–751.

Hoffmann, C., and A. C. Evans. 1911. *Ind. Eng. Chem.*, **3**:835–838.

Holwerda, K. 1928–1930. *Mededeel. Dienst Volksgezondheid Nederland. Indië*, **17**:351–398; **19**:290–350.

Hoogerheide, J. C. 1944. *Botan. Rev.*, **10**:599–638.

Hotchkiss, M. 1923. *J. Bact.*, **8**:141–162.

Hotchkiss, R. D. 1941. *J. Biol. Chem.*, **141**:171–185.

Hotchkiss, R. D., and R. J. Dubos. 1941. *J. Biol. Chem.*, **141**:155–162.

Hotchkiss, R. D. 1943. *J. Bact.*, **45**:64–65.

Huddleson, I. F. 1934. *Brucella Infections in Animals and Man.* The Commonwealth Fund, New York.

Jansen, E. F., and D. J. Hirschmann. 1944. *Arch. Biochem.*, **4**:297–309.

Johnson, J. R., W. F. Bruce, and J. D. Dutcher. 1943. *J. Am. Chem. Soc.*, **65**:2005–2009.

Jones, H., G. Rake, and D. M. Hamre. 1943. *J. Bact.*, **45**:461–469.

Joslyn, D. A., K. Yaw, and A. L. Rawlins. 1943. *J. Am. Pharm. Assoc., Sci. Ed.*, **32**:49–51.

Kempf, J. E., and M. H. Soule. 1940. *Proc. Soc. Exptl. Biol. Med.*, **44**:431–434

Kessel, J. F., D. K. Allison, F. J. Moore, and M. Kaime. 1943. *Proc. Soc. Exptl. Biol. Med.*, **53**:71–73.
Klarmann, E., V. A. Shternov, and J. von Wowern. 1929. *J. Bact.*, **17**:423–442.
Klarmann, E., V. A. Shternov, and L. W. Gates. 1934. *J. Lab. Clin. Med.*, **19**:835–851; **20**:40–47.
Klarmann, E. G. 1939–1944. *Soap San. Chemicals*, **15**:111, 113, 115, 117; **16**:109, 111, 113, 115, 117, 119, 121; **18**: 99–101, 101A, 101B, 127; **19**:97, 99, 101, 103–107; **20**:109, 111, 113, 115, 117, 69, 70.
Kliewe, H., and C. K. Huthmacher. 1938. *Deut. Apoth. Ztg.*, **53**:952–955. (1938. *Chem. Abstr.*, **32**:8691.)
Kligler, I. J. 1918. *J. Exptl. Med.*, **27**:463–478.
Klotz, I. M. 1944. *J. Am. Chem. Soc.*, **66**:459–464.
Knaysi, G. 1930. *J. Infectious Diseases*, **47**:293–333.
Knight, C. A., and W. M. Stanley. 1944. *J. Exptl. Med.*, **79**:291–300.
Kobert, K. 1907. *Chem. Centr.*, **1**:419–420.
Kocholaty, W. 1943. *Arch. Biochem.*, **2**:73–86.
Kohn, H. I. 1943. *Science*, **98**:224.
Kokko, U. P. 1939. *Arch. Hyg. Bakt.*, **122**:44–56.
Köser, A. 1926. *Centr. Bakt., I Abt. Orig.*, **99**:164–171.
Kramer, S. P. 1939. *Proc. Soc. Exptl. Biol. Med.*, **42**:448–451.
Krönig, B., and Paul, T. 1897. *Z. Hyg. Infektionskr.*, **25**:1–112.
Krueger, A. P. 1942. *U. S. Naval Med. Bull.*, **40**:622–631.
Kurotchkin, T. J., and H. A. Reimann. 1930. *J. Infectious Diseases*, **46**:36–41.
Lawrence, C. A. 1943. *Proc. Soc. Exptl. Biol. Med.*, **52**:90–91.
Leifson, E. 1935. *J. Path. Bact.*, **40**:581–599.
Leusden, F. P., and R. Derlich. 1940. *Centr. Bakt., I Abt. Orig.*, **146**:284–296.
Levine, A. S., and C. R. Fellers. 1940. *J. Bact.*, **39**:499–515.
Levine, M., and J. H. Buchanan. 1928. *Am. J. Pub. Health*, **18**:1361–1368.
Levine, M., J. H. Buchanan, and J. H. Toulouse. 1927. *Iowa State Coll. J. Sci.*, **2**:19–29.
Levine, M., E. E. Peterson, and J. H. Buchanan. 1927–1928. *Ind. Eng. Chem.*, **19**:1338–1340; **20**:63–65.
Levine, M. 1938. *Food Research*, **3**:141–148.
Lichstein, H. C., and M. H. Soule. 1944. *J. Bact.*, **47**:221–230, 231–238, 239–251, 253–257.
Lipman, C. B. 1909. *Botan. Gazette*, **48**:105–125.
Locke, A., E. R. Main, and R. R. Mellon. 1938. *Science*, **88**:620–621.
Locke, A., and R. R. Mellon. 1939. *Science*, **90**:231–232.
Long, P. H., and E. A. Bliss.1939. *The Clinical and Experimental Use of Sulfanilamide, Sulfapyridine, and Allied Compounds.* The Macmillan Co., New York.
Long, P. H. 1940–1941. *Bull. N. Y. Acad. Med.*, **16**:732–750; *Sigma Xi Quart.*, **29**:149–169.
Lowman, O. E., J. H. Buchanan, and M. Levine. 1931. *Iowa State Coll. J. Sci.*, **5**:251–268.
Madsen, T., and M. Nyman. 1907. *Z. Hyg. Infektionskr.*, **57**:388–404.
Mallmann, W. L., W. E. Botwright, and E. S. Churchill. 1941. *J. Infectious Diseases*, **69**:215–219.
Manninger, W. 1940. *Deut. med. Wochschr.*, **66**:169–170.

Marshall, E. K., Jr. 1939–1940. *Physiol. Rev.*, **19**:240–269; *Bull. N. Y. Acad. Med.*, **16**:723–731.
Marshall, M. S., and A. K. Hrenoff. 1937. *J. Infectious Diseases*, **61**:42–54.
Martin, G. J. 1944. *Medicine*, **23**:79–103.
Martin, J. D., Jr., and C. D. Fowler. 1934. *Ann. Surg.*, **99**:993–996.
Mathews, A. P. 1904. *Am. J. Physiol.*, **10**:290–323; **11**:455–496; **12**:419–443.
Mayer, R.-L. 1937. *Bull. Acad. Méd., Paris, Ser. III*, **117**:727–735.
McCalla, T. M. 1940. *J. Bact.*, **40**:23–32.
McCalla, T. M. 1941. *Proc. Soil Sci. Soc. Am.*, **6**:165–167.
McCulloch, E. C. 1945. *Disinfection and Sterilization*, 2nd Ed. Lea & Febiger, Philadelphia, Penna.
MacDonald, H. 1940. *Illinois Med. J.*, **77**:356–357.
McGuigan, H. 1923. *J. Pharmacol.*, **21**:65–75.
McIlwain, H. 1941. *Biochem. J.*, **35**:1311–1319; *Nature*, **148**:628.
McIlwain, H. 1943. *Biochem. J.*, **37**:265–271; *J. Chem. Soc.*, **1943**:322–325.
McKee, C. M., G. Rake, and C. L. Houck. 1944. *J. Bact.*, **47**:187–197.
McMaster, P. D. 1919. *J. Infectious Diseases*, **24**:378–385.
McQuarrie, E. B., A. J. Liebmann, R. G. Kluener, and A. T. Venosa. 1944. *Arch. Biochem.*, **5**:307–315.
Menzel, A. E. O., O. Wintersteiner, and J. C. Hoogerheide. 1944. *J. Biol. Chem.*, **152**:419–429.
Miller, R. E. 1931. *Am. J. Pharm.*, **103**:324–328.
Minervini, R. 1898. *Z. Hyg. Infektionskr.*, **29**:117–147.
Morton, H. E., and J. V. Klauder. 1944. *J. Am. Med. Assoc.*, **124**:1195–1201.
Nägeli, C. von. 1893. *Denkschr. schweizer. Naturforsch. Ges.*, **33**:1 [cited by Seuderling (1933)].
Naves, Y. R. 1935. *Parfums France*, **13**:273–284.
Nélis, P. 1939. *Compt. rend. soc. biol.*, **130**:329–332.
Nélis, P., and G. Thomas. 1939. *Compt. rend. soc. biol.*, **130**:1074–1076.
Neter, E. 1942. *Proc. Soc. Exptl. Biol. Med.*, **51**:254–256.
Northey, E. H. 1943. *Ind. Eng. Chem.*, **35**:829–836.
Nunheimer, T. D., and F. W. Fabian. 1940. *Am. J. Pub. Health*, **30**:1040–1049.
Oxford, A. E. 1944. *Biochem. J.*, **38**:178–182.
Page, J. E., and F. A. Robinson. 1943. *Brit. J. Exptl. Path.*, **24**:89–95.
Panja, G., and S. K. Ghosh. 1943. *Indian J. Med. Research*, **31**:5–14.
Patterson, A. M. 1932. *Am. J. Pub. Health*, **22**:465–472.
Paul, T. 1909. *Biochem. Z.*, **18**:1–13.
Paul, T., G. Birstein, and A. Reuss. 1910. *Biochem. Z.*, **25**:367–400; **29**:202–278.
Petroff, S. A., and W. S. Gump. 1935. *J. Lab. Clin. Med.*, **20**:689–698.
Phatak, N. M., and C. D. Leake. 1936. *J. Pharmacol.*, **56**:265–268; **58**:155–158.
Phelps, E. B. 1911. *J. Infectious Diseases*, **8**:27–38.
Pilcher, J. D., and T. Sollmann. 1924. *J. Lab. Clin. Med.*, **9**:256–260.
Poth, E. J., and C. A. Ross. 1943. *Texas Repts. Biol. Med.*, **1**:345–370.
Powell, H. M., and W. A. Jamieson. 1931, 1939–1940. *Am. J. Hyg.*, **13**:296–310; *Proc. Indiana Acad. Sci.*, **49**:45–53.
Pratt, R., T. C. Daniels, J. J. Eiler, J. B. Gunnison, W. D. Kumler, J. F. Oneto, L. A. Strait, H. A. Spoehr, G. L. Hardin, H. W. Milner, J. H. C. Smith, and H. H. Strain. 1944. *Science*, **99**:351–352.
Price, P. B. 1939. *Arch. Surg.*, **38**:528–542.

Puck, T. T., O. H. Robertson, and H. M. Lemon. 1943. *J. Exptl. Med.*, **78**:387–406.
Pulvertaft, R. J. V. 1944. *J. Hyg.*, **43**:352–356.
Rahn, O., and J. E. Conn. 1944. *Ind. Eng. Chem.*, **36**:185–187.
Raiziss, G. W., and M. Severac. 1927. *J. Infectious Diseases*, **40**:447–452.
Raiziss, G. W. 1943. *Science*, **98**:350.
Ralston, A. W. 1940. *Oil and Soap*, **17**:89–91.
Ramel, E., and C. Vulliémoz. 1938. *Ann. inst. Pasteur*, **61**:820–822.
Rammelkamp, C. H. 1942. *Proc. Soc. Exptl. Biol. Med.*, **51**:95–97.
Rantz, L. A., and W. M. M. Kirby. 1944. *J. Immunol.*, **48**:29–37.
Rao, I. R. 1933. *Nature*, **132**:480.
Rawlins, A. L., L. A. Sweet, and D. A. Joslyn. 1943. *J. Am. Pharm. Assoc., Sci. Ed.*, **32**:11–16.
Reddish, G. F., and E. M. Burlingame. 1938. *J. Bact.*, **36**:265.
Reichel, H. 1908–1909. *Z. Hyg. Infektionskr.*, **61**:49–67; *Biochem. Z.*, **22**:149–231.
Reid, J. D. 1932. *Am. J. Hyg.*, **16**:540–556.
Rettger, L. F., G. Valley, and W. N. Plastridge. 1929. *Centr. Bakt., I Abt. Orig.*, **110**:80–92.
Rideal, S., and J. T. A. Walker. 1903. *J. Roy. Sanit. Inst.*, **24**:424–441.
Riedlin, G. 1887. *Arch. Hyg.*, **7**:309–339.
Ritter, C. 1940. *Am. J. Pub. Health*, **30**:59–65.
Roberts, E. C., C. K. Cain, R. D. Muir, F. J. Reithel, W. L. Gaby, J. T. Van Bruggen, D. M. Homan, P. A. Katzman, L. R. Jones, and E. A. Doisy. 1943. *J. Biol. Chem.*, **147**:47–58.
Robertson, O. H., E. Bigg, T. T. Puck, and B. F. Miller. 1943. *J. Exptl. Med.*, **75**:593–610.
Rose, S. B., and R. E. Miller. 1940. *Am. J. Med. Sci.*, **199**:338–342.
Rosenthal, S. M., H. Bauer, and E. Elvove. 1939. *U. S. Pub. Health Service Repts.*, **54**:1317–1336.
Rosenthal, S. M. 1943. *U. S. Pub. Health Service Repts.*, **58**:5–9.
Rubbo, S. D., A. Albert, and M. Maxwell. 1942. *Brit. J. Exptl. Path.*, **23**:69–83.
Rudolph, A. S., and M. Levine. 1941. *Iowa State Coll. Eng. Exptl. Sta. Bull.* 150. 48 pp.
Ruehle, G. L. A., and C. M. Brewer. 1931. *U. S. Dept. Agr. Circ.* 198.
Russu, V., and P. Sichet. 1937. *Münch. med. Wochschr.*, **84**:186–188.
Salle, A. J. 1927. *J. Infectious Diseases*, **41**:1–8.
Salle, A. J., and A. S. Lazarus. 1935. *Proc. Soc. Exptl. Biol. Med.*, **32**:665–667, 937–938, 1057–1060.
Salle, A. J., W. A. McOmie, I. L. Shechmeister, and D. C. Foord. 1939. *J. Bact.*, **37**:639–646.
Salle, A. J., I. L. Shechmeister, and W. A. McOmie. 1940. *Proc. Soc. Exptl. Biol. Med.*, **45**:614–617.
Salle, A. J., and M. Korzenovsky, 1942. *Proc. Soc. Exptl. Biol. Med.*, **50**:12–16.
Salle, A. J. 1943. *Fundamental Principles of Bacteriology.* McGraw-Hill Book Co., New York.
Saxl, P. 1924 [cited by Seuderling (1933)].
Saz, A. K., F. R. Johnston, A. Burger, and F. Bernheim. 1943. *Am. Rev. Tuberc.*, **48**:40–50.
Schaffer, J. M., and F. W. Tilley. 1927. *J. Bact.*, **14**:259–273.

Schales, O. 1943. *Arch. Biochem.*, **2**:487–490.

Schatz, A., E. Bugie, and S. A. Waksman. 1944. *Proc. Soc. Exptl. Biol. Med.*, **55**:66–69.

Schmelkes, F. C., and E. S. Horning. 1935. *J. Bact.*, **29**:323–331.

Schmidt, W. H., and A. J. Moyer. 1944. *J. Bact.*, **47**:199–209.

Schmitt, G. F. 1944. *Am. J. Med. Sci.*, **207**:661–678.

Scott, J. P. 1928. *J. Infectious Diseases*, **43**:90–92.

Seuderling, Y. 1933. *Acta Soc. Med. Fenn. Duodecim.*, Ser. A, **16**, Fasc. 2, 1–119.

Sevag, M. G., and M. N. Green. 1944. *Am. J. Med. Sci.*, **207**:686–687.

Shaffer, P. A. 1939. *Science*, **89**:547–550.

Shillinglaw, C. A., and M. Levine. 1943. *Food Research*, **8**:464–476.

Silverman, M., and E. A. Evans, Jr. 1943. *J. Biol. Chem.*, **150**:265–266.

Smith, D. E., E. J. Czarnetzky, and S. Mudd. 1936. *Am. J. Med. Sci.*, **192**:790–808.

Smith, L. W. 1944. *Am. J. Med. Sci.*, **207**:647–654.

Smith, W. W. 1942. *Proc. Soc. Exptl. Biol. Med.*, **51**:324–326.

Snell, E. E. 1944. *J. Biol. Chem.*, **152**:475–476.

Somogyi, R. 1916. *Intern. Z. physik.-chem. Biol.*, **2**:416–429. (1916. *Physiol. Abstr.*, **1**:342.)

Spaulding, E. H. 1939. *Surg. Gynecol. Obstet.*, **69**:738–744.

Sprowls, J. B., and C. F. Poe. 1943. *J. Am. Pharm. Assoc., Sci. Ed.*, **32**:33–40, 41–44.

Starkey, R. L., and S. A. Waksman. 1943. *J. Bact.*, **45**:509–519.

Stearn, A. E., and E. W. Stearn. 1924. *J. Bact.*, **9**:491–510.

Stearn, E. W., and A. E. Stearn. 1926. *J. Bact.*, **11**:345–357.

Stock, C. C., and T. Francis, Jr. 1940. *J. Exptl. Med.*, **71**:661–681.

Stuart, L. S., and W. D. Pohle. 1941. *Soap San. Chemicals*, **17**:34–37, 73–74.

Sturdza, S. A. 1938. *Compt. rend. soc. biol.*, **129**:410–412.

Suter, C. M. 1941. *Chem. Rev.*, **28**:269–299.

Tanner, F. W., and G. Pitner. 1939. *Proc. Soc. Exptl. Biol. Med.*, **40**:143–145.

Tanner, F. W., and F. L. Wilson. 1943. *Proc. Soc. Exptl. Biol. Med.*, **52**:138–140.

Tarr, H. L. A. 1941. *Nature*, **147**:417–418.

Taylor, G. W., and E. N. Harvey. 1934. *Proc. Soc. Exptl. Biol. Med.*, **31**:954–957.

Thrower, W. R., and F. C. O. Valentine. 1943. *Lancet*, **1943**(1):133–136.

Tilley, F. W., and J. M. Schaffer. 1926, 1928, 1931. *J. Bact.*, **12**:303–309; **16**:279–285; *J. Agr. Research*, **42**:93–106.

Tilley, F. W. 1939. *J. Bact.*, **38**:499–510.

Tishler, M., J. L. Stokes, N. R. Trenner, and J. B. Conn. 1941. *J. Biol. Chem.*, **141**:197–206.

Topley, W. W. C. 1915. *Brit. Med. J.*, **1915**(1):237–238.

Traub, E. F., C. A. Newhall, and J. A. Fuller. 1944. *Surg. Gynecol. Obstet.*, **79**:205–216.

Twort, C. C., and A. H. Baker. 1942. *J. Hyg.*, **42**:266–283.

Valko, E. I., and A. S. DuBois. 1944. *J. Bact.*, **47**:15–25.

Van Bruggen, J. T., F. J. Reithel, C. K. Cain, P. A. Katzman, E. A. Doisy, R. D. Muir, E. C. Roberts, W. L. Gaby, D. M. Homan, and L. R. Jones. 1943. *J. Biol. Chem.*, **148**:365–378.

van Niel, C. B. 1943. *Ann. Rev. Biochem.*, **12**:551–586.

Vignati, J., and P. Schnabel. 1928. *Centr. Bakt., I Abt. Orig.*, **109**:464–481.

Vollrath, R. E., L. Walton, and C. C. Lindegren. 1937. *Proc. Soc. Exptl. Biol. Med.*, **36**:55–58.
Waksman, S. A., E. S. Horning, and E. L. Spencer. 1942. *Science*, **96**:202–203.
Waksman, S. A., and H. B. Woodruff. 1942. *Proc. Soc. Exptl. Biol. Med.*, **49**:207–210; *J. Bact.*, **44**:373–384.
Waksman, S. A. 1941, 1943, 1944. *Bact. Rev.*, **5**:231–291; *J. Bact.*, **45**:64; *Am. J. Pub. Health*, **34**:358–364.
Waksman, S. A., and E. Bugie. 1944. *J. Bact.*, **48**:527–530.
Walton, L., M. Herbold, and C. C. Lindegren. 1936. *Food Research*, **1**:163–169.
Watkins, J. H., and C.-E. A. Winslow. 1932. *J. Bact.*, **24**:243–265.
Watson, H. E. 1908. *J. Hyg.*, **8**:536–542.
Weber, G. R. 1942. *Iowa State Coll. J. Sci.*, **17**:155–157.
Weed, L. A., and E. E. Ecker. 1931, 1933. *J. Infectious Diseases*, **49**:440–449; **52**:354–363.
Weiser, H. H. 1937. *Proc. Soc. Exptl. Biol. Med.*, **36**:151–152.
Welch, H., and C. M. Brewer. 1942. *J. Immunol.*, **43**:25–30; *Am. J. Pub. Health*, **32**:261–267.
Welshimer, H. J., L. O. Krampitz, and C. H. Werkman. 1944. *J. Bact.*, **47**:425.
Wheeler, L. M. 1943. *J. Pharmacol.*, **78**:265–275.
White, E. C., and J. H. Hill. 1943. *J. Bact.*, **45**:433–443.
Williams, O. B. 1931. *J. Bact.*, **21**:55–56.
Winslow, C.-E. A., and E. E. Lochridge. 1906. *J. Infectious Diseases*, **3**:547–571.
Winslow, C.-E. A., and M. Hotchkiss. 1922. *Proc. Soc. Exptl. Biol. Med.*, **19**:314–315.
Winslow, C.-E. A., and E. S. Falk. 1923. *J. Bact.*, **8**:215–236, 237–244.
Winslow, C.-E. A., and A. F. Doloff. 1928. *J. Bact.*, **15**:67–92.
Winslow, C.-E. A., and E. T. Haywood. 1931. *J. Bact.*, **22**:49–69.
Withell, E. R. 1942. *J. Hyg.*, **42**:339–353.
Witlin, B. 1942. *Proc. Soc. Exptl. Biol. Med.*, **49**:27–31.
Witz, M. 1940. *Arch. Hyg.*, **124**:243–258.
Woodruff, L. L., and H. H. Bunzel. 1909. *Am. J. Physiol.*, **25**:190–194.
Woodruff, H. B., and J. W. Foster. 1943. *Arch. Biochem.*, **2**:301–315.
Woodruff, H. B., and J. W. Foster. 1944. *J. Bact.*, **44**:425–426.
Woods, D. D. 1940. *Brit. J. Exptl. Path.*, **21**:74–90.
Woods, D. D., and P. Fildes. 1940. *Chem. Ind.*, **59**:133–134.

5

THE CHEMICAL COMPOSITION OF MICROORGANISMS

Since all the functions of bacterial cells are associated with chemical changes, many experiments have been carried out to learn more about the basic chemical composition of the cells themselves. The information obtained from such studies often gives insight into the life processes of the bacterium. Several variable factors, such as the bacterium itself, its age, and the culture medium upon which it is grown, make the determination of the exact chemical composition of any given organism difficult. We can probably assume, however, that bacterial cells are formed from the same general building blocks and cast from the same chemical pattern as other living cells, differing, possibly, only in that they contain certain characteristic groupings. In recent years the chemistry of bacteria has received a great deal of impetus, resulting in the acquisition of much information in several fields of research.

Two techniques have been employed to study the composition of microorganisms: (1) a microscopic method, which yields essentially qualitative results; and (2) a direct chemical analysis of the cells, which may be both qualitative and quantitative. The microscopic method has found its greatest application in studies concerned with the distribution of chemical constituents within the cell. Because of the minute size of many bacteria, however, such a method is of little value in determining the details of their internal structure. On the other hand, when larger forms, such as yeasts, protozoa, and higher fungi are being investigated, much interesting information may be obtained. Several well-known examples involving the use of the microscope and various reagents are: the blue color given by starch granules and the red-brown color by glycogen with dilute iodine solution; the blue color given by cellulose and the violet-like color by chitin in the presence of zinc chloriodide; and the staining of fat and oil globules with osmic acid, Sudan black, Sudan III, or spirit blue. Certain dyes exhibit a selective action and can be used to identify certain cellular constituents. For instance, Sudan III dyes fat globules red but leaves the other components of the cell unstained; and polychrome methylene blue selectively stains metachromatic granules and related bodies which are present in certain bacteria. Even though many data can be obtained by such techniques, they are very crude at their best and possess certain inherent disadvantages. One of the greatest drawbacks is that only groups of substances can be identified, and usually no clue is given concerning the member of the group with which one is dealing. This point can be illustrated by the use of Sudan III, which stains all fats in a similar manner.

The application of direct chemical methods to the analysis of cells is of great value, because they provide a means of actually separating, purifying, and identifying the various cellular components. It can readily be seen that such techniques will require rather large amounts of starting material if appreciable quantities of the components are to be secured. The particular method used to obtain sufficient material to work with will depend somewhat upon the nature of the growth and the food requirements of the organism under investigation. Usually one of the following two methods is used.

1. The Harvesting of Growth from Solid Media. This technique consists briefly of cultivating the test organisms on the surface of a suitable nutrient medium rendered solid by the addition of gelatin or agar. The medium is usually placed in large Kolle flasks, pans, or other suitable containers and sterilized in the autoclave; after which process it is allowed to solidify. The containers are then inoculated and allowed to incubate for a given time at a suitable temperature; finally the growth is washed or scraped from the surface of the medium. This method is extensively used, and under optimum conditions quite large yields are obtained. It does not work well, however, with certain fungi, especially molds, which frequently grow into the substrate and thus resist removal.

2. The Removal of Cells from Liquid Media by Centrifugation or Filtration. The easiest and quickest way to remove bacteria or yeast from liquid media is by centrifugation. One of several types of apparatus may be used. Filtration techniques are not very satisfactory for obtaining large masses of bacterial cells from liquid media, since the cells are too small to be retained by ordinary filter paper; and, if one of the common filter candles is used, the pores soon become clogged. However, the bacterial species and molds which form a firm and compact pellicle on the surface of liquid media can be easily removed by filtration. Whichever procedure is used to obtain a mass of cells, it is necessary to centrifuge and wash the cellular mass a couple of times to be sure that the cells are freed from any adhering media.

Once the cells have been separated from the extraneous substances of the medium, they may be subjected to analysis to determine their water content and the amount and nature of their mineral constituents. In many studies part of the cells are submitted to a special fractionation in order to isolate the various components which may be present. For

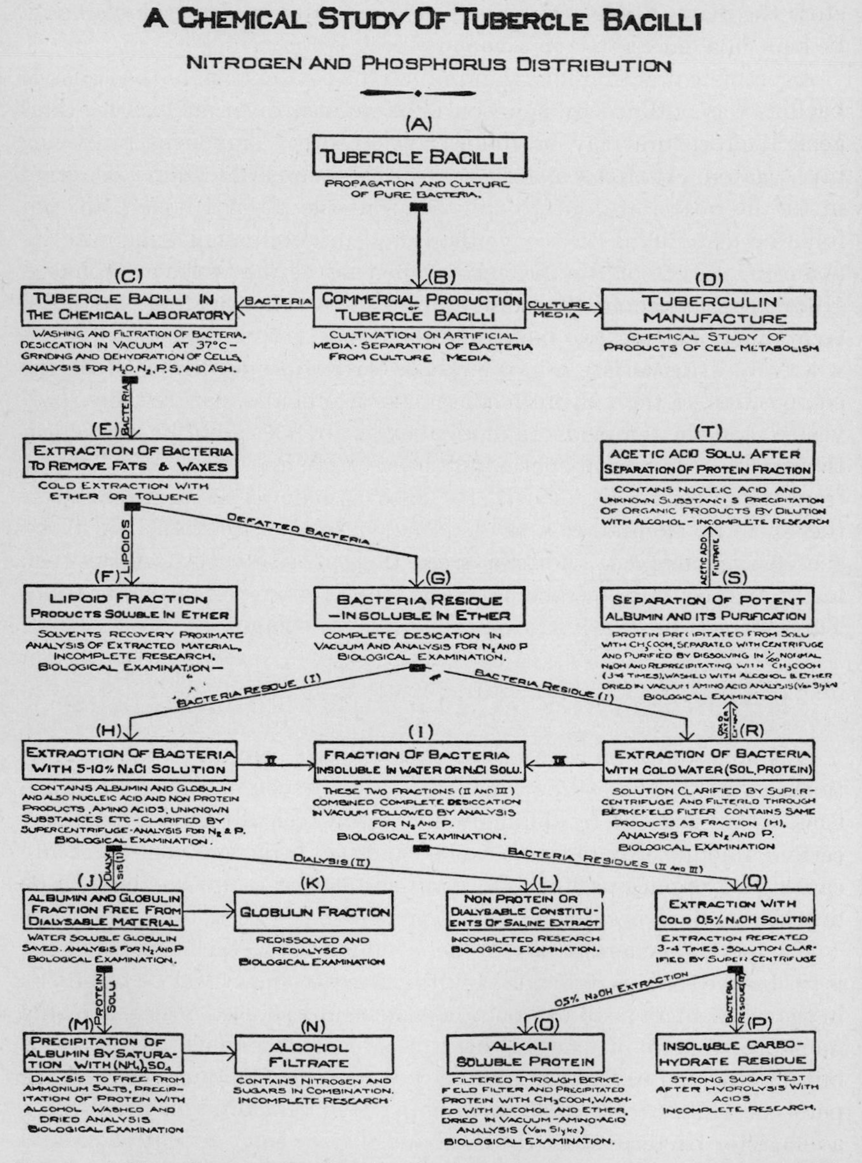

FIG. 1. A Flow Sheet for the Chemical Study of Bacteria. (From Johnson, 1926.)

example, an aqueous extraction will remove some of the bacterial gums; treatment with a weak alkaline buffer solution will eliminate the nucleic acid; an acid buffer solution will dissolve the basic proteins; and solvents such as ether, chloroform, or acetone will educe fats and waxes. Greater yields of these components are often obtained if the cells are disintegrated in a ball mill before they are fractionated. If it is necessary to store the mass of cells until a sufficient quantity is obtained, it should be kept in a dark bottle in a vacuum desiccator.

A complete procedure for the study of the composition of the tubercle bacillus was outlined by Johnson (1926) and is given in Fig. 1. This general procedure may be followed when other organisms are being investigated. Probably many of the discrepancies which have occurred in the literature are due to the fact that the investigators have not followed a standard chemical procedure, such as the one suggested by Johnson. Proof of this fact may be found in the work by Johnson (1926), Anderson (1932), and others who have employed standard techniques. They have been able to repeat their studies many times with very little variation in the results. If certain factors, such as the composition of the culture medium, the age of the culture when harvested, and the temperature of incubation are not carefully controlled, the results obtained in such studies may vary considerably. Table 1 from the paper by Dawson (1919) illustrates how various media alter the chemical composition of *Escherichia coli*. This table needs no special explanation. The differences in chemical composition between individual bacterial species or genera may show even greater variation. This fact will be demonstrated in the next few pages.

THE MOISTURE CONTENT OF MICROORGANISMS

It is now well established that all living cells contain a high proportion of water. The estimation of the moisture content of microorganisms, as carried out by different investigators, has varied widely. A certain amount of variation is to be expected, however, since the truly capsulated organisms undoubtedly retain more moisture than those organisms which are devoid of a large capsule.

The method generally used in determining the water content of cells is to observe the loss in weight resulting from drying at 100°C. to 110°C. in the air or in a vacuum oven at a lower temperature. Results for the moisture content of bacteria have been recorded above 95 per cent, but those given in Tables 1 and 2 will be found to range from 73.35 per cent (*Escherichia coli*) to 87.8 per cent (*Bacillus mycoides*); the average for bacteria seems to be about 80 per cent. Attention should also be called to the work of Friedman and Henry (1938), who have studied the bound water content of vegetative and spore forms of bacteria by the cryoscopic method. This method is based upon the assumption that bound water does not alter the freezing point of a given solution of sucrose. These investigators believe that the heat resistance of bacterial spores is due, in part at least, to the relatively

TABLE 1

VARIATION IN CHEMICAL COMPONENTS OF *Escherichia coli* IN RELATION TO CHEMICAL COMPOSITION OF THE MEDIUM

[From Dawson (1919)]

	Medium *							
	I	II	III	IV	V	VI	VII	VIII
	Per Cent	Per Cent	Per Cent	Per Cent	Per Cent	Per Cent	Per Cent	Per Cent
Water and volatile matter	74.84	7.25	60.25	75.01	74.9	60.69	60.32	79.55
Ash	4.8	2.7	2.5	4.5	4.5	7.83	7.69	2.1
Sulfur (total)	0.06	0.0	0.0	0.1	0.09	0.0	0.0	0.14
Sulfur (loose)	0.0	0.0	0.0	0.02	0.01	0.0	0.0	0.03
Phosphorus, P_2O_5	4.24	3.48	2.38	2.89	3.30	1.69	1.83	0.92
Calcium, CaO	2.66	0.05	1.06	2.62	2.60	2.34	2.34	0.19
Nitrogen, total	2.84	3.02	6.22	2.40	2.11	4.32	5.00	5.02
Nitrogen, amino	0.77	0.89	2.97	0.72	0.69	1.69	1.65	3.01
Protein, coagulation	2.99	0.97	4.66	2.34	2.47	4.05	5.32	5.54
Protein, acid-precipitated	7.42	6.61	9.57	7.32	4.61	6.47	6.93	2.08
Protein, alkaline-precipitated	5.60	7.44	2.80	6.05	5.33	6.63	6.80	4.22
Protein, soluble	0.05	2.25	1.31	0.07	0.10	0.08	1.21	1.10
Protein, insoluble	0.05	0.04	0.09	0.06	0.99	0.07	0.10	0.03
Residue, insoluble	1.00	2.37	2.00	1.40	1.70	0.98	1.49	0.76
Fats	3.99	4.32	4.82	5.77	8.00	†	†	5.07
Carbohydrate	4.00	3.10	2.19	1.38	2.69	3.01	2.88	1.00
Cellulose-like substance	1.00	2.42	2.01	1.41	1.75	1.09	1.52	0.81

* Composition of media: I. Peptone 1.0 per cent, meat extract 1.0 per cent, agar 2.0 per cent. Neutral in reaction. II. Peptone 0.5 per cent, edestin 0.5 per cent, agar 2.0 per cent. Alkaline in reaction. III. Peptone 0.25 per cent, flour proteins 1.0 per cent, agar 2.0 per cent. Alkaline in reaction. IV. Peptone 0.25 per cent, meat extract 1.0 per cent, glucose 1.0 per cent, agar 2.0 per cent. Neutral in reaction. V. Peptone 0.25 per cent, meat extract 1.0 per cent, glucose 1.0 per cent, glycerol 1.0 per cent, agar 2.0 per cent. VI and VII. Peptone 0.25 per cent, butter soap 1.0 per cent, agar 2.0 per cent. VIII. Peptone none; potato juice from whole unskinned potato, freed from starch, 500 g. potato per liter of medium.

† Not determined because of extraneous fat attached to bacterial composition of media.

high percentage of water in the bound state. Their results are included in Table 2. Virtanen and Pulkki (1933), however, have found little difference in the free-moisture content of spores and vegetative cells of bacteria and suggest an enzyme theory for the difference in resistance.

For comparison a few results for yeasts and molds are also included in Table 2. Yeasts average about 75 per cent moisture and molds about 85 per cent.

TABLE 2

WATER (FREE- AND BOUND-) CONTENT OF MICROORGANISMS

Organism	Free Water, per cent	Reference
Mycobacterium tuberculosis	85.9	Cramer (1893)
Corynebacterium diphtheriae	84.5	Nicolle and Alilaire (1909)
Corynebacterium xerosis	84.93	(Kappes) Leach (1906)
Malleomyces mallei	76.49	Nicolle and Alilaire (1909)
Bacillus anthracis	80.0	Dyrmont (1886)
B. anthracis, spores	85.44	Dyrmont (1886)
B. anthracis	8.74	Nicolle and Alilaire (1909)
Bacillus megatherium	79.7	Henry and Friedman (1937)
B. megatherium, spores	58.2	Henry and Friedman (1937)
Bacillus mycoides	87.8	Henry and Friedman (1937)
B. mycoides, spores	70.6	Henry and Friedman (1937)
Pseudomonas aeruginosa	74.99	Nicolle and Alilaire (1909)
Serratia marcescens	78.00	Nicolle and Alilaire (1909)
Escherichia coli	73.35	Nicolle and Alilaire (1909)
Klebsiella pneumoniae	85.55	Nicolle and Alilaire (1909)
K. pneumoniae	84.2	Brieger (1885)
Proteus, species	83.42	Rubner (1904)
Proteus vulgaris	79.99	Nicolle and Alilaire (1909)
Eberthella typhosa	78.93	Nicolle and Alilaire (1909)
Salmonella typhimurium	78.05	Nicolle and Alilaire (1909)
Shigella dysenteriae	78.21	Nicolle and Alilaire (1909)
Vibrio comma	73.38	Nicolle and Alilaire (1909)
V. comma (average for five strains)	88.3	Cramer (1895)
Molds	88.32–85.79	Sieber (1881)
Mold spores	38.87	Cramer (1891)
Yeasts	83.0	von Nägeli (1878)
Yeasts	69.25	Nicolle and Alilaire (1909)
Yeasts	54.0	Beetlestone (1928)
Yeast	70.0	Frey (1930)
	Bound Water, per cent	
Bacillus subtilis	0.0	Friedman and Henry (1938)
B. subtilis, spores	69.0	Friedman and Henry (1938)
Bacillus megatherium	17.7	Friedman and Henry (1938)
B. megatherium, spores	62.6	Friedman and Henry (1938)
Bacillus mycoides	28.2	Friedman and Henry (1938)
B. mycoides, spores	58.7	Friedman and Henry (1938)

THE ELEMENTARY COMPOSITION OF MICROORGANISMS

Very few complete and thorough analyses of the elementary composition of microorganisms have been reported. In most studies only figures for nitrogen and ash are given. The elements will now be discussed under the headings of carbon and phosphorus, nitrogen, and ash content. All figures are listed as percentages of the dry weight.

CARBON AND PHOSPHORUS CONTENT

Bacteria, yeasts, molds, and viruses all possess about the same percentage of carbon. Figures ranging from 22.42 per cent (*Azotobacter chroococcum*) to 64.06 per cent (*Mycobacterium tuberculosis*) have been reported, but most of the values fall within the range of 45 to 55 per cent carbon. Several representative examples are given in Table 3. Northrop (1938) found that purified staphylococcus bacteriophage contain 40.6 to 41.8 per cent carbon, and McFarlane (1939) reported that several purified viruses contain approximately 50 per cent carbon. Determinations on mold tissues give about the same values. The determinations are usually made by converting the dry bacterial mass to

TABLE 3

CARBON CONTENT OF MICROORGANISMS

Organism or Body	Carbon, per cent of dry weight	Reference
Mycobacterium tuberculosis (from broth)	60.12–64.01	De Schweinitz and Dorset (1895)
M. tuberculosis (from protein-free medium)	62.16–63.35	
Malleomyces mallei (from broth)	41.8–44.8	
Azotobacter chroococcum	22.42	Omeliansky and Sieber (1913)
K. pneumoniae	49.44–50.89	Cramer (1893)
Diplococcus pneumoniae	50.55–51.37	
Vibrio, species	50.4–51.76	Linton, Shrivastava, and Mitra (1934)
Staphylococcus bacteriophage protein	40.6–41.8	Northrop (1938)
Influenza A and B virus	53.2, 52.7	Taylor (1944)
Tobacco mosaic virus	50.74–53.25	McFarlane (1939)
Aucuba mosaic virus	49.07–50.46	
Cucumber 3 and 4 virus	50.0–51.0	
Potato "X" virus	47.7–49.5	
Bushy stunt virus	47.0	
Mold (from gelatin medium)	47.01–47.36	Sieber (1881)
Mold (from protein-free medium)	46.03–46.36	
Mold	43.99–56.48	Mazé (1902)

carbon dioxide and water and calculating the carbon as $\frac{3}{11}$ of the CO_2. The percentage of hydrogen can also be calculated as $\frac{1}{9}$ the water.

The phosphorus content of various microorganisms seems to vary from approximately 2.5 to 5.0 per cent. For example, Leach (1906) reported that *Escherichia coli* contains 2.87 per cent phosphorus, Stoklasa (1908) published a figure of 3.94 per cent for *Azotobacter chroococcum*, Stull (1929) found that pneumococcus, Type III, contained 2.92 to 2.94 per cent phosphorus, Northrop (1938) observed that a purified staphylococcus bacteriophage contained 4.6 to 5.0 per cent, and Mesrobeanu (1936) has reported figures of approximately the same magnitude for several different bacteria.

NITROGEN CONTENT

The total nitrogen content of microorganisms is usually calculated by the Kjeldahl method or one of its modifications. The micro-Kjeldahl method is now widely used. There are several inherent drawbacks to such a technique, however, since the Kjeldahl method accounts for only about 85 per cent of the total nitrogen present. The nitrogen of certain compounds (nitro, azo, or azoxy compounds and such ring compounds as pyrimidines and purines) is not detected by this method.

The total nitrogen content of the same bacterial species varies as reported by different investigators, and different bacterial species show an even wider range of total nitrogen (Table 4). Nicolle and Alilaire (1909) reported figures between 8.28 and 10.73 per cent nitrogen for various bacteria, and Linton, Mitra, and Shrivastava (1934) observed that the cholera vibrios vary between 13.75 and 15.57 per cent nitrogen. The usual range for nitrogen seems, therefore, to be from 8 to 15 per cent for bacteria. Fewer data are available on the animal and plant viruses, but they appear to be more uniform in nitrogen content than bacteria, and figures have been reported which vary between 13.0 and 16.5 per cent nitrogen. Northrop (1938) purified a bacteriophage for staphylococcus and found it to contain 14.1 to 14.6 per cent nitrogen. A few comparative figures for yeast and molds are also listed in Table 4. All the values have been calculated on the basis of dry weight.

ASH CONTENT

The ash or mineral content of microorganisms is usually determined after a given weight of cells has been incinerated in a platinum crucible. In several studies both the total ash and the components of the ash have been determined, and in Tables 5 and 6 the results of several such investigations are listed. The figures reported for the ash content of microorganisms vary over a wide range. It will be noted in the accom-

TABLE 4

NITROGEN CONTENT OF MICROORGANISMS

Organism or Body	Nitrogen, per cent of dry weight	Reference
Mycobacterium tuberculosis	8.35–8.8	Kresling (1901)
M. tuberculosis	7.27–9.14	De Schweinitz and Dorset (1895)
M. tuberculosis	10.55	(Agnew) Wheeler (1909)
Corynebacterium diphtheriae	9.75	Tamura (1914)
Corynebacterium xerosis	12.1	(Kappes) Leach (1906)
Malleomyces mallei	14.05–14.8	De Schweinitz and Dorset (1895)
M. mallei	10.47	Nicolle and Alilaire (1909)
Azotobacter chroococcum	8.6–11.3	Stoklasa (1908)
A. chroococcum	1.89–2.18	Omeliansky and Sieber (1913)
Azotobacter agilis	8.15	Greene (1935)
Azotobacter vinelandii	7.55	Greene (1935)
Azotobacter beijerinckii	2.46	Greene (1935)
Azotobacter chroococcum	2.87	Greene (1935)
Acetobacter aceti	4.17–6.51	Kayser (1894)
Acetobacter xylinum	6.9	Alilaire (1906)
Bacillus subtilis	5.964	Wheeler (1909)
Bacillus megatherium	8.349	Wheeler (1909)
Bacillus mycoides	10.3–11.3	Virtanen and Pulkki (1933)
B. mycoides, spores	10.4–11.3	Virtanen and Pulkki (1933)
Bacillus anthracis	6.8	Dyrmont (1886)
B. anthracis, spores	12.44	Dyrmont (1886)
B. anthracis	12.285	Wheeler (1909)
B. anthracis	9.22	Nicolle and Alilaire (1909)
Pseudomonas aeruginosa	10.834	Wheeler (1909)
Ps. aeruginosa	9.79	Nicolle and Alilaire (1909)
Serratia marcescens	10.55	Nicolle and Alilaire (1909)
Escherichia coli	10.65	Leach (1906)
E. coli	10.32	Nicolle and Alilaire (1909)
Klebsiella pneumoniae	9.50	Brieger (1885)
K. pneumoniae	8.33	Nicolle and Alilaire (1909)
Proteus, species	9.81	Rubner (1904)
Proteus vulgaris	6.791	Wheeler (1909)
P. vulgaris	10.73	Nicolle and Alilaire (1909)
Eberthella typhosa	11.55	Wheeler (1909)
E. typhosa	8.28	Nicolle and Alilaire (1909)
Salmonella typhimurium	9.55	Nicolle and Alilaire (1909)
Shigella dysenteriae	8.89	Nicolle and Alilaire (1909)
Vibrio comma	9.79	Nicolle and Alilaire (1909)
V. comma and cholera-like vibrios	13.75–15.57	Linton, Mitra, and Shrivastava (1934)
Brucella melitensis	12.73–13.05	Huston, Huddleson, and Hershey (1934)
Brucella abortus	13.21–13.35	Huston, Huddleson, and Hershey (1934)
Brucella suis	13.66–13.98	Huston, Huddleson, and Hershey (1934)
Sarcina aurantiaca	11.46	Wheeler (1909)

TABLE 4 (*Continued*)

NITROGEN CONTENT OF MICROORGANISMS

Organism or Body	Nitrogen, per cent of dry weight	Reference
Staphylococcus aureus (rough and smooth)	10.82–11.49	Hoffstadt and Clark (1938)
S. aureus (two strains)	12.79, 13.18	Fellowes and Routh (1944)
Diplococcus pneumoniae	10.406	Wheeler (1909)
D. pneumoniae, type III	13.0–13.32	Stull (1929)
D. pneumoniae, type I	9.4	Leineweber, Kautsky, and Famulener (1923)
D. pneumoniae, type II	10.0	
D. pneumoniae, type III	8.0	
D. pneumoniae, type IV	8.8	
Staphylococcus bacteriophage protein	14.1–14.6	Northrop (1938)
Elementary bodies of vaccinia virus	13.3	Hughes, Parker, and Rivers (1935)
Elementary bodies of vaccinia virus	13.0–13.3	MacFarlane and Salaman (1938)
Rabbit papilloma virus	15.0	Beard and Wyckoff (1937)
Influenza A virus	10.0	Taylor (1944)
Influenza B virus	9.7	
Swine influenza virus	9.0	
Rous sarcoma No. 1	15.1–15.5	Pollard (1938)
Tobacco mosaic virus	16.5	Stanley (1937)
Tobacco mosaic virus	14.4–16.6	(Bawden and Pirie) McFarlane (1939)
Cucumber 3 and 4 virus	15.3–15.8	
Potato "X" virus	15.7–17.0	
Bushy stunt virus	16.0	
Yeast	8.38	Frey (1930)
Yeast, top	7.32	Rubner (1904)
Yeast, bottom	9.62	
Yeast	6.32–6.16	Guichard (1894)
Yeast	8.0	von Nägeli (1878)
Molds	5.37–6.88	Sieber (1881)
Molds	2.26–6.63	Mazé (1902)
Aspergillus glaucus	8.26	Marschall (1897)
Penicillium glaucum	7.46	
Mucor stolonifer	8.21	

panying table that results for vegetative bacteria range from 1.34 to 13.86 per cent, for viruses from 0.72 to 5.8 per cent, for yeasts from 6.5 to 10.17 per cent, and for molds from 5.97 to 12.2 per cent total ash; for bacteriophage the figure is 13.0 per cent.

Spores of bacteria and molds seem to have a lower ash content than vegetative cells, but this has not been definitely proved. Partial explanation of these figures may be due to the medium on which the various organisms have been cultivated. Dawson (1919), for example,

TABLE 5

ASH CONTENT OF MICROORGANISMS

Organism or Body	Ash, per cent	Reference
Mycobacterium tuberculosis	2.31–2.72	Kresling (1901)
M. tuberculosis	11.47	(Agnew) Wheeler (1909)
M. tuberculosis	9.56	Tamura (1913)
M. tuberculosis-hominis	2.31–3.94	De Schweinitz and Dorset (1902)
M. tuberculosis-bovis	2.66–2.67	
Mycobacterium avium	3.94–3.96	
M. tuberculosis (Mulford)	5.78	Johnson and Brown (1922)
Mycobacterium lacticola	5.08–8.22	Tamura (1913)
Corynebacterium xerosis	9.52	(Kappes) Leach (1906)
Malleomyces mallei	5.18	De Schweinitz and Dorset (1895)
Azotobacter chroococcum	4.16	Omeliansky and Sieber (1913)
A. chroococcum	4.24	Greene (1935)
Azotobacter agilis	8.23	
Acetobacter xylinum	5.9	Alilaire (1906)
Bacillus subtilis	10.83	Wheeler (1909)
Bacillus anthracis	7.76	
B. anthracis, spores	1.15	Dyrmont (1886)
B. anthracis (rough)	13.57	Damboviceanu and Barber (1931)
B. anthracis (smooth)	12.7	
Bacillus megatherium	10.18	Wheeler (1909)
Bacillus mycoides	5.6	Virtanen and Pulkki (1933)
B. mycoides, spores	5.8	
Pseudomonas aeruginosa	9.04	Wheeler (1909)
Phytomonas tumefaciens	7.03	Damboviceanu and Barber (1931)
Serratia marcescens	8.93–13.86	Cramer (1891)
Escherichia coli	8.61	Leach (1906)
E. coli	8.38	(Agnew) Wheeler (1909)
E. coli	6.43	Damboviceanu and Barber (1931)
Klebsiella pneumoniae	2.97–7.16	Lyons (1897)
Proteus, species	8.06	Rubner (1904)
Proteus vulgaris	10.88	Wheeler (1909)
Eberthella typhosa	5.7	Wheeler (1909)
E. typhosa	6.36	Damboviceanu and Barber (1931)
Salmonella paratyphi	5.46	
Salmonella schottmuelleri	7.15	
Salmonella choleraesuis	6.96	
Shigella dysenteriae (3 strains)	7.19–8.34	
Brucella melitensis	4.54–5.26	Huston, Huddleson and Hershey (1934)
Brucella abortus	4.79–5.14	
Brucella suis	4.29–5.13	
Vibrio comma (average for five strains)	3.6	Cramer (1895)
V. comma	1.34–3.73	
Vibrio strains	2.29–3.04	Linton, Shrivastava, and Mitra (1934)

TABLE 5 (*Continued*)

ASH CONTENT OF MICROORGANISMS

Organism or Body	Ash, per cent	Reference
Staphylococcus aureus (2 strains)	13.60, 13.91	Fellowes and Routh (1944)
Staphylococcus citreus	11.51	Damboviceanu and Barber (1931)
S. aureus	10.99	
Staphylococcus albus	11.20	
Neisseria catarrhalis	6.69	
Sarcina aurantiaca	6.4	Wheeler (1909)
Diplococcus pneumoniae	5.78	
D. pneumoniae, type III	8.48–8.64	Stull (1929)
Staphylococcus bacteriophage protein	13.0	Northrop (1938)
Elementary bodies of vaccinia virus	0.72	Hughes, Parker, and Rivers (1935)
Rous sarcoma No. 1	2.0–5.8	Pollard (1938)
Tobacco mosaic virus	0.53–3.00	McFarlane (1939)
Aucuba mosaic virus	0.11–0.19	
Cucumber 3 and 4 virus	1.0–2.0	
Potato "X" virus	2.0–2.5	
Yeasts	6.5–7.2	Guichard (1894)
Yeast, top	6.54	Rubner (1904)
Yeast, bottom	10.17	
Yeast	8.74	Frey (1930)
Yeast	10.0	Garrod (1935)
Penicillium glaucum, spores	2.94	Cramer (1891)
P. glaucum	6.15	Marschall (1897)
Aspergillus glaucus	5.97	
Mucor stolonifer	6.88	
Rhizopus, species	6.14–12.2	Cramer (1891)

reported ash contents varying from 2.1 to 7.83 per cent for *Escherichia coli* when grown on different media. Similar results have been recorded by Cramer (1897), Tamura (1913), and Damboviceanu and Barber (1931).

More recently Curran, Brunstetter, and Myers (1943) have investigated the elementary inorganic composition of vegetative cells and spores of bacteria by spectrographic analysis. Some of their data are listed in Table 7, where it will be seen that the vegetative cells of several aerobic bacilli are relatively high in potassium and phosphorus, as compared with the spores of the same species. On the other hand, the spores contain more calcium, copper, and manganese than the vegetative cells from which they were derived. Although there is no direct correlation between the inorganic composition of the spores of the various bacteria and their resistance to heat, a high calcium concentration seems somewhat related to enhanced heat tolerance.

TABLE 6

COMPONENTS OF THE ASH OF SEVERAL MICROORGANISMS

Organism	Percentage of Total Ash as									Reference
	P_2O_5	K_2O	Na_2O	MgO	CaO	SiO_2	SO_3	Cl	FeO	
Mycobacterium tuberculosis	55.23	6.35	13.62	11.55	12.64	0.57		–		De Schweinitz and Dorset (1898)
M. tuberculosis	46.97	8.23	11.48	9.81	8.59		10.79	1.25		Tamura (1913)
M. tuberculosis	43.4	7.7	11.6	5.7	9.7		22.8			Goris and Loit (1920)
M. tuberculosis	39.66			8.52	7.16	4.2	10.41			Johnson and Brown (1922)
Mycobacterium lacticola (from broth)	48.29	6.16	9.73	8.73	16.24		15.14	0.99		Tamura (1913)
M. lacticola (from protein-free medium)	67.56	6.05	4.13	20.99	0.061			2.03		Tamura (1913)
Acetobacter xylinum	47.45	+	+	8.0	10.7	0.60	+	+	+	Alilaire (1906)
Azotobacter chroococcum	4.93	2.41								Stoklasa (1908)
Escherichia coli (fixed salts)	33.99	12.95	2.61	5.92	13.77			0.0	3.35	Guillemin and Larson (1922)
E. coli (free salts)	26.84	9.94	19.77	2.04	9.13			7.4	+	Guillemin and Larson (1922)
Yeast	51.09	38.68	1.82	4.16	1.69	1.6	0.57	+	0.06	Belohoubeck, Guichard (1894)
Yeast, top	46.9	36.3	0.2	6.0	1.3	1.8	+	+	4.1	Payen, Guichard (1894)
Yeast, bottom (average)	53.6	30.0	1.3	5.1	2.45		+	+	5.0	Béchamp, Guichard (1894)
Yeast, bottom (average)	46.6	29.8	2.4	4.2	2.2	14.4	+	+	2.1	Liebig, Guichard (1894)
Yeast	54.5	36.5	0.7	5.2	1.4	1.2	0.5	+	+	Frey (1930)
Yeast	42.1	36.2		4.4	1.1	+	+		+	Garrod (1935)

+ = a trace.

TABLE 7

ELEMENTARY INORGANIC COMPOSITION OF VEGETATIVE AND SPORE CELLS AS DETERMINED BY SPECTROGRAPHIC ANALYSIS

[From Curran, Brunstetter, and Myers (1943)]

Organism	Percentage of Dry Weight								Parts per Million of Dry Weight									
	K		Ca		P		Mg		Fe		Al		Cu		Mn		B	
	Veg.*	Sp.*	Veg.	Sp.	Veg.	Sp.	Veg.	Sp.	Veg.	Sp.	Veg.	Sp.	Veg.	Sp.	Veg.	Sp.	Veg.	Sp.
Bacillus coherens	2.0	0.5	0.2	2.7	4.5	1.7	0.9	0.5	560	120	90	300	50	480	40	80	5	10
Bacillus cereus	1.1	0.2	0.2	1.9	1.6	0.9	0.2	0.3	60	170	30	430	20	150	20	30	..	..
Bacillus subtilis	1.3	0.9	0.8	1.6	3.1	1.8	1.1	0.5	100	120	100	90	80	90	20	60	5	10
Bacillus macerans	0.1	0.1	0.1	1.9	6.1	0.6	0.6	0.8	140	220	390	230	50	260	30	40	5	20
1503 †	0.8	0.1	1.0	1.2	1.4	1.1	0.7	0.4	180	80	450	120	40	80	30	60	..	..
1518 †	1.6	0.2	1.0	1.9	2.3	1.3	1.0	0.5	200	130	240	120	40	110	60	70	7	1
Clostridium sporogenes	...	...	0.3	...	1.5	...	0.4	...	470	...	171	...	14	...	8	..	..	..
Medium	1.5		0.1		0.5		0.2		117		15		24		85		148	

* Vegetative cells and spores, respectively.

† 1503 and 1518 are thermophiles (flat-sour types).

There seems to be a general agreement that a high proportion of the total ash of microorganisms consists of phosphorus and potassium. Barber (1932) reported that staphylococci contain ten to twenty times more potassium in their ash than do other bacteria, and *Eberthella typhosa* contains twice as much as *Salmonella paratyphi* and ten times as much as *Salmonella schottmuelleri*. On the other hand, *Salmonella paratyphi* contains twice as much iron as *Salmonella schottmuelleri* and three to four times more than the typhoid organism.

Yeasts show high percentages of phosphorus and potassium. Among the other chief mineral constituents which have been identified are sodium, magnesium, calcium, silicon, and iron. Richards and Troutman (1940) have made a qualitative spectroscopic analysis of the mineral content of yeast (*Saccharomyces cerevisiae*) grown on synthetic and natural media. The elements found were as follows: barium, bismuth, boron, calcium, chromium, copper, gold, iron, lanthanum, lead, magnesium, manganese, phosphorus, platinum, potassium, silver, sodium, thallium, tin, and zinc.

THE PROTEIN AND OTHER NITROGENOUS COMPONENTS OF MICROORGANISMS

The protein content of microorganisms is usually based on their total nitrogen content, as determined by the Kjeldahl method or one of its modifications. The calculation is made by simply multiplying the nitrogen content by the standard factor 6.25. This procedure will lead to some error, since the conversion factor is an average value based on proteins containing 16 per cent nitrogen. Another source of error is the Kjeldahl method itself, which detects only about 85 per cent of the total nitrogen present. The nitrogen present in certain compounds (nitro, nitroso, azo, and azoxy compounds or such ring compounds as purine and pyrimidine bases) is beyond estimation by this method. The values recorded for nitrogen are usually within the range 8 to 15 per cent for bacteria, 13 to 16 per cent for viruses, 5 to 10 per cent for yeasts, and 2.2 to 7.0 per cent for molds, corresponding to protein contents of approximately 50 to 93.7 per cent, 81.2 to 100 per cent, 31.2 to 62.5 per cent, and 13.7 to 43.6 per cent, respectively.

The proteins are essential components of all living cells and are probably the most complex substances synthesized by microorganisms. They can be built up from the very simplest starting materials. Because of their complexity, their lability, their colloidal nature, and the lack of any criterion of purity, they are very difficult substances to study chemically, and we do not know too much about their structure. However, considerable progress has been made in recent years in the determination of their structure [see Bull (1941)]. Since the proteins of bacteria and related bodies are very much like those of higher plants and animals, we assume that they are built up in much the same manner. For instance, amino acids are probably joined together through the carboxyl group of one and the amino group of another to form peptide linkages, thus:

$$R\cdot CHNH_2\cdot COOH + NH_2\underset{\displaystyle COOH}{\underset{|}{CH}}\cdot R = R\cdot CHNH_2\cdot CO\cdot NH\underset{\displaystyle COOH}{\underset{|}{CH}}\cdot R + H_2O$$

If this process is repeated, a tripeptide is formed; and, if it is continued, polypeptides, protamines, and eventually proteins are formed. Other ways of linking amino acids may be present in proteins.

The proteins have very high molecular weights. According to Svedberg (1937), they are multiples of about 35,100, but this value has been questioned by some workers. Several of Svedberg's calculations, obtained with the aid of an ultracentrifuge, are:

Protein	Molecular Weight
Lactalbumin-α	17,600 = ½ × 35,100
Erythrocruorin (*Arca*)	35,100
CO hemoglobin (horse)	70,200 = 2 × 35,100
Serum globulin (horse)	140,400 = 4 × 35,100
Erythrocruorin (*Daphnia*)	421,200 = 12 × 35,100
Hemocyanin (*Nephrops*)	842,000 = 24 × 35,100
Hemocyanin (*Octopus*)	2,950,000 = 84 × 35,100
Hemocyanin (*Helix pomatia*, main compound)	6,740,000 = 192 × 35,100
Hemocyanin (*Busycon*, aggregation compound)	10,100,000 = 288 × 35,100
Tobacco mosaic virus protein	17,000,000 = 470 × 35,100

Complex bacterial proteins can be hydrolyzed into their constituent amino acids, but we know very little about the arrangement of these components in the protein molecule. Little knowledge is available in regard to the nature and amount of coagulable proteins in bacterial cells. Boivin and Mesrobeanu (1934), who observed a total nitrogen figure of 13.7 per cent dry weight for *Escherichia coli*, reported that only 0.65 per cent of this nitrogen was soluble in trichloracetic acid, the remaining 13.05 per cent being precipitated by the acid. They gave figures for other organisms too, but in every case the nitrogen precipitated by trichloracetic acid formed more than 80 per cent of the total nitrogen. It is at present impossible to say whether the coagulable protein is present in the form of globulin or albumin or both. Nicolle and Alilaire (1909), in reviewing the work of other investigators, state that albumins have been isolated from various bacteria, but the presence of globulins is in doubt. However, the work of Linton, Mitra, and Shrivastava (1934) shows that in *Vibrio comma* and cholera-like vibrios the coagulable protein is almost all in the form of globulin, since it is precipitated by half-saturation with ammonium sulfate. Of the noncoagulable nitrogen, Boivin and Mesrobeanu (1934) found that about one-quarter was present as polypeptides or amino acids and about one-quarter as ammonium compounds.

The proteins of the *Mycobacterium tuberculosis* and related acid-fast bacilli have been studied more extensively than those of any other bacteria. By immunological methods it has been possible to show that the protein of the human-type tubercle bacillus is different from that of several other acid-fast bacilli. This entire problem has been reviewed recently by Seibert (1941), and her review should be consulted for many significant data.

A protein with interesting properties has been isolated from the mold *Aspergillus sydowi* by Bohonos, Woolley, and Peterson (1942). It was resistant to hydrolysis by such proteolytic enzymes as pepsin, papain, trypsin, pancreatin, ficin, and a special mold enzyme. It was insoluble in water but soluble in dilute alkali. It contained 11.3 per cent nitrogen, 1.9 per cent ash, 3.5 per cent hexosamine, 9.1 per cent reducing sugar (as glucose), 0.7 per cent phosphorus, 0.5 per cent purine nitrogen, and a trace of sulfur. The amino acids histidine, arginine, lysine, tyrosine, aspartic acid, leucine, proline, and tryptophan were isolated from the protein hydrolysate.

Partially degraded proteins, protamines, peptones, and polypeptides may also be present in microbial cells, as well as such conjugated proteins as glycoproteins, lecithoproteins, phosphoproteins, and nucleoproteins. The nucleoproteins are very important and will now be discussed in more detail.

THE NUCLEOPROTEINS OF BACTERIA

The nucleoproteins, nucleic acids, and similar substances are of great biological significance, since they form the most important constituent of the cell—nuclear material—without which cell life and cell activity would be impossible. In most bacteria the nuclear material seems to be uniformly dispersed throughout the cell, but in others there is some indication that it may be collected in the form of granules. All investigators are agreed that bacteria have a fairly high nucleoprotein content, and figures have been reported ranging from 2.0 per cent to above 5.0 per cent, based on dry weight.

The nucleoproteins are soluble in dilute alkali and can be precipitated from such a solution by weak acids. Their molecules are very complex and upon hydrolysis break down to yield other proteins and nuclein. The nuclein can be further hydrolyzed to nucleic acid and still another protein. It is known that the nucleic acids are composed of phosphoric acid, carbohydrates, and certain purines and pyrimidine bases. The following scheme illustrates one concept of nucleoprotein and its hydrolytic products.

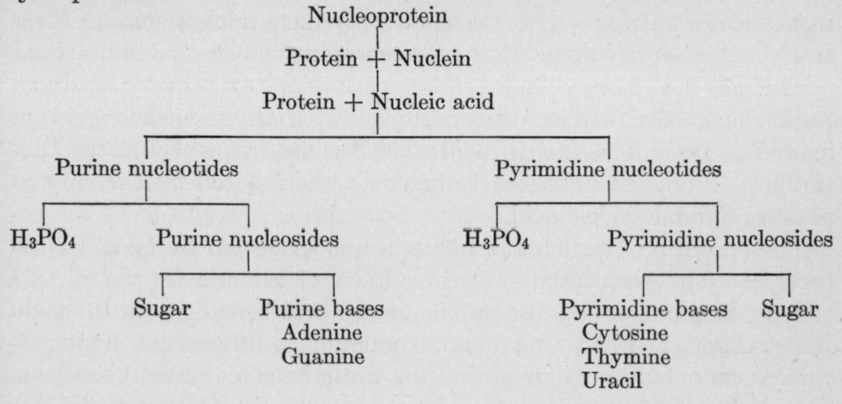

Principally as a result of the work of Kossel, who in 1891 made the first hydrolysis of a protein-free nucleic acid, the nucleic acids became allocated to two groups, that from yeast being representative of one group (ribose nucleic acid) and that from the thymus gland and fish sperm being typical of the other group (desoxyribose nucleic acid). The products of hydrolysis of the two principal nucleic acids may be listed as follows:

Yeast Nucleic Acid

Adenine,
N=C·NH₂ / HC C—NH / N—C—N >CH

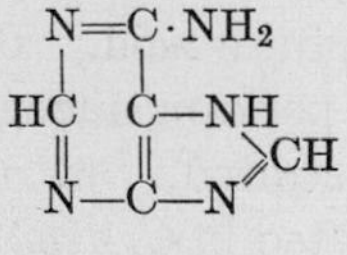

Guanine,
HN—CO / H₂N·C C—NH / N—C—N >CH

Cytosine,
N=C·NH₂ / O=C CH / HN—CH

Uracil,
HN—C=O / O=C CH / HN—CH

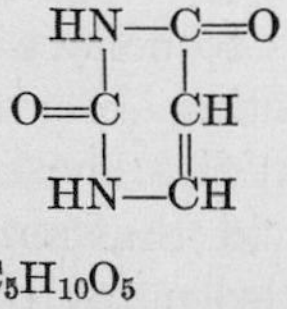

d-Ribose, $C_5H_{10}O_5$

Phosphoric acid, H_3PO_4

Thymonucleic Acid

Adenine

Guanine

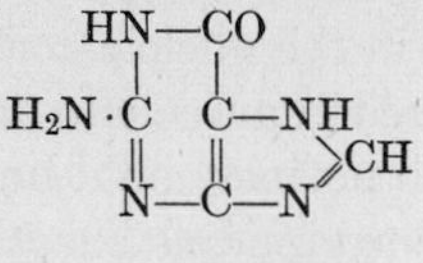

Cytosine

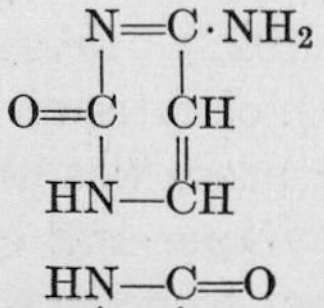

Thymine,
HN—C=O / O=C C·CH_3 / HN—CH

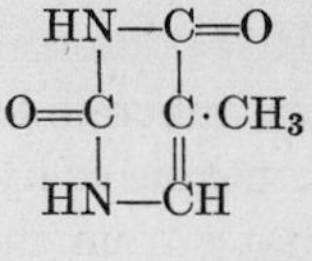

d-2-Desoxyribose, HCOH / CH_2 / HCOH / HCOH / CH_2 (ring closed through O)

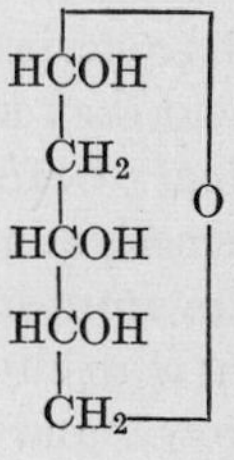

Phosphoric acid

Thus these two nucleic acids differ in composition with regard to the constituent sugar and one pyrimidine base. The striking difference in the physical and chemical properties of these two acids is due to the nature of the sugar component, so that the two classes are now known as the ribose nucleic acids and the desoxyribose nucleic acids, respectively. The earlier distinction between plant nucleic acid and animal nucleic acid has been abandoned upon the definite discovery of ribose nucleic acid derivatives concomitantly with thymonucleic acid in animal tissues. This fact is mentioned because frequently in the bacteriology literature reference is made to the isolated nucleic acid as plant or animal nucleic acid.

The presence of nucleins in bacteria was suspected by many of the early bacteriologists because of the affinity of bacteria for the nuclear stains. Nishimura (1893) was one of the first investigators to study this problem, and he found adenine, guanine, xanthine, and hypoxanthine in an organism which he called a water bacillus. About the same time Aronson (1900) demonstrated nucleoprotein in defatted diphtheria bacilli and determined the presence of xanthine, phosphoric acid, and a pentose sugar. Levene (1904) found the nucleic acid from *Mycobacterium tuberculosis* to contain thymine and uracil. The purines, adenine, guanine, and hypoxanthine, were shown to be present in *Azotobacter chroococcum* by Stoklasa (1908). In 1913–1914 Tamura studied in detail the nucleic acids from *M. tuberculosis* and *Corynebacterium diphtheriae*. From the first of these organisms he isolated a substance which was insoluble in weak acids, salt solution, and water but soluble in dilute alkalies and concentrated sulfuric acid. This material contained 0.7 per cent phosphorus and 9.2 per cent nitrogen. Adenine and probably hypoxanthine were demonstrated, but not guanine and xanthine. Adenine was also demonstrated in *C. diphtheriae*.

Long (1921) determined the purines in the nucleic acid (tuberculinic acid) of the tubercle bacillus and isolated guanine and adenine but did not find xanthine or hypoxanthine. No purines could be demonstrated in the filtrates from the bacteria. The pyrimidine bases of *M. tuberculosis* were studied by Johnson and Brown (1922). From 7 g. of tuberculinic acid they were able to obtain 0.1035 g. of cytosine and 0.0756 g. of thymine. Uracil was not present, and pentose was present in only a very small quantity. Its content of thymine and cytosine and its freedom from uracil led these investigators to believe that they were dealing with thymonucleic acid. An interesting observation was made by Brown and Johnson (1923), who identified levulinic and formic acids after acid hydrolysis of tuberculinic acid, thus indicating that the main sugar present was hexose. It was also noted that the guanine component was more readily split off from the original tuberculinic acid than were the other bases, leaving, apparently, a stable trinucleotide containing adenine, thymine, and cytosine. Analysis for carbon, hydrogen, nitrogen, and phosphorus agreed closely with the theoretical value for an acid to which they gave the following formula:

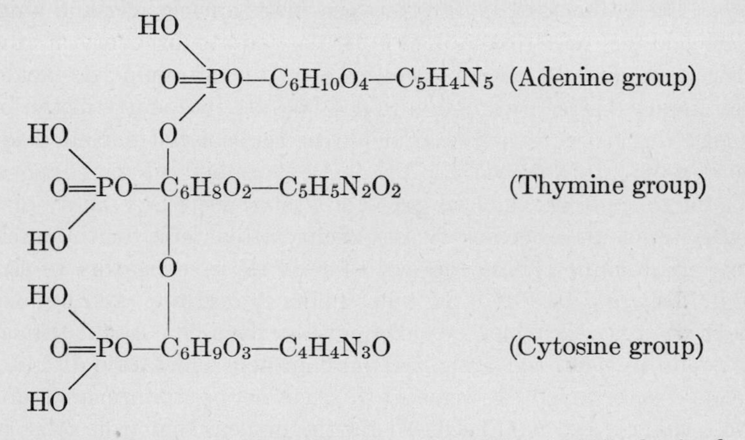

About this same time Johnson and Coghill (1925) obtained as a product of the hydrolysis of tuberculinic acid, 5-methyl cytosine:

```
   N=C·NH₂
   |  |
O=C  C·CH₃
   |  ||
  HN—CH
```

a pyrimidine not previously identified in nature. Its exact relationship to the nucleic acid molecule was not determined. In a closely related organism, *Mycobacterium phlei*, the nucleic acid differs significantly from the tubercle bacillus. Coghill (1931) found that it contained 7.9 per cent phosphorus, 14.9 per cent nitrogen, and 20 per cent pentose; upon hydrolysis it produced adenine, guanine, and the two pyrimidine bases, cytosine and uracil, but not thymine. Thus a composition corresponding very closely to that of yeast nucleic acid was determined. In the following year Coghill and Barnés (1932) published a study of nucleic acid obtained from *Corynebacterium diphtheriae*. In a purified sample they found 8.05 per cent phosphorus, 14.5 per cent nitrogen, 12.4 to 13.8 per cent pentose, and 24 to 29 per cent thymonucleic acid. Three pyrimidine bases, thymine, cytosine, and uracil, were demonstrated, the presence of which indicates that the acid from this organism is a mixture of the two main types or is an entirely different type of nucleic acid.

The presence of nucleic acid in *Escherichia coli* was demonstrated by Schaffer, Folkoff, and Bayne-Jones (1922). Guanine was found, but no pentose, as indicated by a negative orcinol reagent test. Lancefield (1928) and Heidelberger and Kendall (1931) found a nucleoprotein in *Streptococcus pyogenes* and demonstrated that it was the yeast (ribose) type. More recent studies, however, by Sevag, Smolens, and Lackman (1940) and by Sevag and Smolens (1941) have given us further information on the nucleoprotein of *S. pyogenes*. Of the total nucleic acid contained in streptococci it appears that 10 to 30 per cent is desoxyribose (thymus) nucleic acid, the remainder being of the *d*-ribose (yeast) type. Boor and Miller (1931) studied the nucleoprotein substance isolated from the gonococcus and its serological relationship to the meningococcus and pneumococcus. Cross precipitin reactions were obtained, suggesting a common nucleoprotein for all these organisms. Menzel and Heidelberger (1938) have also shown that different fractions of *Mycobacterium phlei* and other acid-fast bacilli contain different amounts of nucleic acid and react differently serologically. More recently Seibert (1941) has reviewed the chemistry of the proteins of the acid-fast bacilli and has discussed the importance of the various components.

Boivin and Mesrobeanu (1934) and Mesrobeanu (1936) have made extensive studies of the purine bases present in *E. coli*, *Proteus vulgaris*, *Salmonella typhimurium*, *Pseudomonas aeruginosa*, and several other organisms. They observed that adenine was the dominant purine base; in *E. coli* it constituted 70 per cent of the purine nucleoside, and in *P. vulgaris*, 63 per cent. Purines were demonstrated in all the bacteria studied. The nucleoproteins of the species of the genus *Brucella* have been studied by Huston, Huddleson, and Hershey (1934), Topping (1934), and Stahl, Pennell, and Huddleson (1939). According to Stahl, Pennell, and Huddleson, the protein-nucleate comprises approximately 14 per cent of the total dry weight of the cells in preparations from smooth strains and about 18 per cent in preparations from intermediate-rough and rough strains. The protein component comprises about 70 to 75 per cent of the protein-nucleate prepared from smooth strains and approximately 60 per cent of the protein-nucleates prepared from rough strains. Guanine, adenine, and cytosine, but not thymine and uracil, were found in the nucleic acids. Both pentose and desoxypentose sugars were present. These data tend to show that there are two nucleic acids present in species of the genus *Brucella;* the other alternative, a nucleic acid composed of both pentose and desoxypentose nucleotides, is possible but improbable. The results of precipitation studies with the protein-nucleates and protein components from smooth-strain preparations show that they are not type specific and that the nucleic acid possesses no precipitating power. Similar preparations from the rough strains reacted only slightly with homologous and heterologous antisera, and here again the nucleic acid possessed no precipitating power.

Mitra (1936) found cytosine and uracil in the nucleic acid from *Vibrio comma*, but thymine was absent. The presence of such components led Mitra to believe that this acid belonged to the ribose (yeast) type of nucleic acid. The yield from the cholera vibrios was only 0.15 per cent. The nucleoprotein from *Bacillus anthracis* yielded adenine and guanine upon hydrolysis, according to Ferramola (1935, 1937).

Thompson and Dubos (1938) and Lavin, Thompson, and Dubos (1938) have reported some very interesting data on the nucleic acid content of a rough culture derived from pneumococcus, type II. They removed the nucleoprotein and nucleic acid from the pneumococcus cells by a carefully controlled process of autolysis which did not completely destroy the cell structure but altered their Gram reaction from positive to negative. A chemical study revealed that the nucleic acid was of the ribose (yeast) type, although it did not give exactly the same N : P ratio as yeast nucleic acid. They believed the protein moiety of the nucleoprotein belonged to the group of protamines or histones. The nucleic acid and nucleoprotein fractions were further studied by determining their ultraviolet absorption spectra. The measurements were made with a Spekker spectrophotometer and a small Hilger quartz spectrograph. Curves were obtained by plotting the absorption coefficient against the wavelengths in angstroms. The absorption coefficient, α, was defined by the expression:

$$\alpha = \frac{1}{cl} \log \frac{I_0}{I}$$

where c = concentration in milligrams per milliliter.
l = cell length in centimeters.
I_0 = intensity of light falling on the cell.
I = intensity of light after passing through the cell thickness of length l (1 cm.).

The curves were further checked by photographs taken with the continuous light from a hydrogen discharge tube. The maximum of the pneumococcus nucleoprotein at 2,600 Å. was not due to tryptophan, which displays a maximum at 2,780 Å; or to tyrosine, which exhibits a maximum at 2,750 Å. It corresponds closely, however, to the maxima observed for pneumococcus (Fig. 2, curve A) and for yeast (curve *B*) nucleic acid. Figure 2, taken from the paper by Lavin, Thompson, and Dubos, shows the relationship of plotted values.

Akasi (1938) made a study of the nucleic acid of the typhoid bacillus of mice (*Salmonella typhimurium*). Starting with 450 g. of fat-freed dried bacilli, he carefully isolated a pure nucleic acid in a yield corresponding to 1.6 per cent. The pure material contained 14.48 per cent nitrogen and 9.03 per cent phosphorus. It gave not only the pentose reaction but also Feulgen's reaction, showing the coexistence of ribose

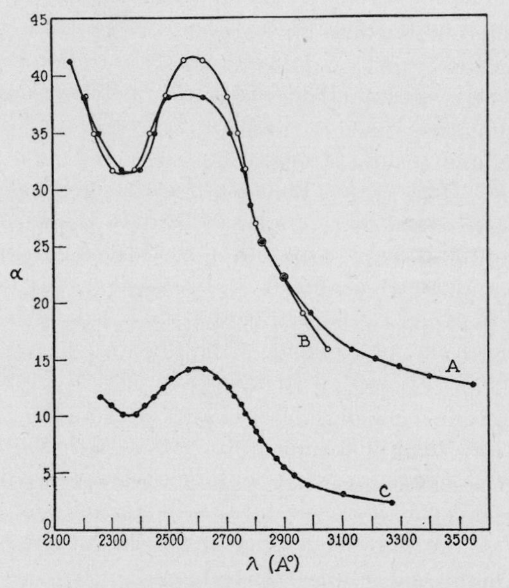

FIG. 2. Absorption Coefficient Curves. Curve *A* = sodium salt of nucleic acid obtained from pneumococcus (0.031 mg./ml.); curve *B* = yeast nucleic acid (0.031 mg./ml.); curve *C* = acetic acid precipitate (nucleoprotein) obtained from supernatant in which pneumococci had become Gram-negative (0.128 mg./ml.). (From Lavin, Thompson, and Dubos, 1938.)

and desoxyribose as a sugar component. The purine bases, guanine and adenine, were isolated in equimolecular proportions, and the pyrimidine bases, thymine, cytosine, and uracil, were identified. The proportion of purine N to total N was 60.2 per cent and that of purine nucleotide P to total P, 53.9 per cent, corresponding to the proportions required for tetranucleotide. The presence of the various components in this acid led Akasi to suggest that possibly a special type of nucleic acid was present in bacteria.

According to LePage and Umbreit (1943), the adenine nucleotide present in the autotrophic bacterium, *Thiobacillus thiooxidans*, is adenosine-3-phosphate rather than adenosine-5-phosphate, which is the usual ester obtained from muscle, yeast, and a number of bacteria (*Escherichia coli*, *Bacillus subtilis*, *Staphylococcus aureus*, and *Pseudomonas fluorescens*). The implication is that either the autotroph has a more primitive metabolism and is unable to convert adenosine-3-phosphate to adenosine-5-phosphate or that it gains some advantage of energy transfer by possession of the different ester. This is the first time this ester has ever been demonstrated in nature.

In summary, we can say that the nucleoproteins which have been isolated from different bacteria by various investigators belong to both the ribose (so-called yeast) and desoxyribose (so-called thymus) groups, and no one type is common to all bacteria. Furthermore, the nucleoprotein of diphtheria bacilli, species of the genus *Brucella*, typhoid bacilli of mice, and certain streptococci is a mixed type, or possibly an unknown type. The autotrophic bacterium *Thiobacillus thiooxidans* contains the purine nucleotide adenosine-3-triphosphate as a component of its nucleoprotein rather than adenosine-5-triphosphate, the type present in most other cells.

Penicillium glaucum consists of 0.9 per cent nucleic acid of the yeast type, according to Akasi (1939). Bacteriophage has the composition of a nucleoprotein, according to Northrop (1938). Likewise some of the viruses contain considerable amounts of nucleoprotein. For example, Hoagland, Lavin, Smadel, and Rivers (1940) studied the properties of nucleic acid obtained from vaccinia virus and found it to be of the thymonucleic acid type; on the other hand, the nucleic acid isolated from proteins of cucumber virus 4 and tobacco mosaic virus is of the yeast type [Knight and Stanley (1941)].

THE AMINO ACIDS OF BACTERIA

When bacterial proteins are hydrolyzed, they yield about the same amino acids as do proteins from other sources. Several examples will serve to illustrate this point. Arginine, histidine, and lysine appear to be almost always present in bacteria and other microorganisms, since they have been isolated many times. Besides these three amino acids, Tamura (1913, 1914) demonstrated *l*-phenylalanine, *l*-proline, valine, tyrosine, and tryptophan in *Mycobacterium tuberculosis* and *Mycobacterium lacticola*, and tyrosine, leucine, isoleucine, *l*-proline, valine, and tryptophan in *Corynebacterium diphtheriae*. Phenylalanine could not be demonstrated in the latter organism. Mitra (1936) in a study on the racemization of the proteins of *Vibrio comma* found the diamino acids, arginine, histidine, and lysine, and the monoamino acids, glycine, alanine, valine, leucine, tyrosine, aspartic acid, glutamic acid, proline, and hydroxyproline. Isoleucine, phenylalanine, serine, and cystine were not identified. Chargaff (1939) has isolated aspartic and glutamic acids from *Phytomonas tumefaciens* and *Corynebacterium diphtheriae* and has demonstrated that they have the normal *l*-(+)-configuration.

Csonka (1935) studied the proteins of *Saccharomyces cerevisiae* and reported the presence of the amino acids, cystine, tryptophan, tyrosine, arginine, histidine, and lysine. Most of the other amino acids have also been demonstrated in yeasts by other investigators [see Meisenheimer (1919, 1921)]. Glycine, alanine, leucine, glutamic acid, and aspartic acid have been found in the protein from *Aspergillus niger* by Abderhalden and Rona (1905), but proline, phenylalanine, and tyrosine were lacking. Woolley and Peterson (1936, 1937) isolated leucine, isoleucine, arginine, histidine, and lysine from the defatted mycelium of *Aspergillus sydowi*.

The amino acids in strains of tobacco mosaic virus and in the related cucumber viruses 3 and 4 have been studied in some detail by Knight and Stanley (1941). Analysis of twelve preparations of tobacco mosaic virus indicated the presence of 3.8, 4.5, and 6.0 per cent of tyrosine, tryptophan, and phenylalanine, respectively. The results obtained for yellow aucuba, green aucuba, Holmes' masked, and other strains of tobacco mosaic virus were the same as those for tobacco mosaic virus within experimental error. On the other hand, pronounced differences were found in Holmes' ribgrass strain of tobacco mosaic virus and cucumber viruses 3 and 4. The tyrosine, tryptophan, and phenylalanine values for the tobacco mosaic viruses were 6.4, 3.5, and 4.3 per cent, respectively, and about 3.8, 1.4, and 10.2 per cent, respectively, for the cucumber viruses. From these results the authors concluded that the mutation of tobacco mosaic virus to form a new strain may be accompanied by changes in the amino acid composition of the virus.

A complete hydrolysis of a protein and the isolation of its various components is a rather long, tedious process and is often not very accurate. Other techniques have, therefore, been sought to determine the nature of a protein without elaborate and detailed amino acid separation. Probably the most successful of these methods is that of Van Slyke, which determines the distribution of nitrogen between the monoamino and diamino groups. The details can be found in the original papers by Van Slyke or in the articles or biochemistry books of several other workers. Only a brief discussion will be given here, so that the accompanying diagram may be better understood.

The nitrogen in protein is generally regarded as being distributed according to the following scheme:

I. *Total Nitrogen*	II. *Amide* N.		
	III. *Humin* N.		
	IV. *Basic* N (precipitated by phosphotungstic acid).	A	Cystine (estimated from sulfur determination). Contains only amino N.
			Lysine.
		B	Arginine. Three-fourths of N is non-amino N.
			Histidine. Two-thirds of N is nonamino N.
	V. *Monoamino* N+. *Nonamino* N (not precipitated by phosphotungstic acid).	A	Glycine, dicarboxylic acids, etc.
			Tryptophan. Half of N is amino N.
		B	Tryptophan. Half of N is nonamino N.
			Proline, Hydroxyproline. Contain only nonamino N.

To determine the distribution of nitrogen in a protein by the Van Slyke method, the protein is first hydrolyzed by strong acid, and the nitrogen in the various groups is estimated as follows:

I. *Total nitrogen* by Kjeldahl technique. A portion of the hydrolysis mixture is oxidized with concentrated H_2SO_4, whereupon the nitrogen is converted into ammonium sulfate. Excess of alkali is added, and the mixture distilled into standard acid.

II. *Amide nitrogen.* A portion of the hydrolyzed solution is evaporated *in vacuo* to remove the excess of acid and is neutralized with magnesium oxide, the *amide nitrogen* distilled off as ammonia *in vacuo* at 40°C. The ammonia is collected in standard acid.

III. *Humin nitrogen.* A black residue remains in the flask used in the previous determination (II) which can be filtered off and the nitrogen estimated by Kjeldahl's method. The *humin nitrogen* is usually attributed to tryptophan.

IV. *Basic nitrogen* and *cystine nitrogen.* The filtrate from III is acidified with H_2SO_4 and phosphotungstic acid is added. This separates the nitrogenous constituents of groups IV and V, those of group IV being precipitated by phosphotungstic acid, those of group V remaining in solution. The precipitate is filtered off and the complex decomposed with barium chloride. A new precipitate, barium phosphotungstate, is formed and can be filtered off. Then:

- *a.* The *total nitrogen* of a portion of fraction IV is determined by the method of Kjeldahl.
- *b.* The *arginine nitrogen* is resolved by boiling a portion of the solution with strong sodium hydroxide. One-half of the arginine nitrogen is converted into ammonia and can be titrated.
- *c.* The *cystine nitrogen* is ascertained from an estimation of the sulfur as sulfate.
- *d.* The *total amino nitrogen* of fraction IV is determined by the

TABLE 8

Distribution of Nitrogen in the Proteins of Microorganisms

	Azotobacter chroococcum		*Azotobacter agilis*, Per Cent [2]	*Corynebacterium diphtheriae*,* Per Cent [3]	*Corynebacterium diphtheriae*	
	Per Cent [1]	Per Cent [2]			Per Cent [4]	Defatted Bacilli, Per Cent [4]
Amide N	9.75 †	17.90 †	13.42 †	.....	12.30 †	11.55
Humin N	3.57	9.62	13.18	24.75	1.29	2.29
Dibasic N	26.47	20.00	26.90	.....	32.86	35.00
Arginine	10.35	16.25	19.19	10.64	15.88	17.16
Histidine	1.63	0.11	0.16	1.03	6.02	7.46
Lysine	14.55	3.14	7.24	4.93	9.69	9.09
Cystine	0.0	0.50	0.31	.....	1.91	1.26
Mono- and nonamino N	60.15	52.50	45.77	.....	53.04	55.39
Amino N	55.33	50.34	44.33	54.62	44.80	47.41
Nonamino N	4.82	2.16	1.44	Unknown N = 3.76 NH_3 = 0.27	8.30	7.97
Total N accounted for	99.95	99.96	99.27	100.00	99.49	104.23

	Mycobacterium lacticola *		*Mycobacterium tuberculosis*,* Per Cent [5]	*Mycobacterium tuberculosis* (Tuberculinic Acid Removed)		
	Broth, Per Cent [5]	Synthetic Medium, Per Cent [5]		Per Cent [6]	Per Cent [7]	Per Cent [7]
Amide N	.....	.....	.....	11.83	13.50	10.23
Humin N	14.52	17.80	15.79	4.11	6.72	6.66
Dibasic N	.....	.....	.....	27.06	26.62	29.71
Arginine	11.69	10.92	7.64	10.63	10.28	12.21
Histidine	1.11	1.11	1.53	11.48	9.13	13.81 ‡
Lysine	1.23	1.18	1.49	3.69	7.21	3.69 ‡
Cystine	0.00	0.00	0.00	1.26	Trace	Trace
Mono- and nonamino N	.....	.....	.....	56.73	55.98	53.40
Amino N	66.74	63.62	66.59	47.39	52.10	50.30
Nonamino N	Unknown N = 3.57 NH_3 = 0.91	Unknown N = 4.86 NH_3 = 0.54	Unknown N = 6.01 NH_3 = 1.15	9.34	3.88	3.10
Total N accounted for	99.77	100.03	100.20	99.73	102.82	100.00

* Not by Van Slyke method.
† Average of different determinations.
‡ Total basic nitrogen determination lost. Calculated by difference.

[1] W. L. Omeliansky and N. D. Sieber. 1913. *Z. physiol. Chem.*, **88**:445.
[2] R. A. Greene. 1935. *Soil Sci.*, **39**:327.
[3] S. Tamura. 1914. *Z. physiol. Chem.*, **89**:289.
[4] J. Hirsch. 1931. *Z. Hyg. Infektionskr.*, **112**:660.
[5] S. Tamura. 1913. *Z. physiol. Chem.*, **87**:84, **88**:190; H. Popper and J. Warkany. 1925. *Z. Tuberk.*, **43**:368.
[6] T. B. Johnson and E. B. Brown. 1922. *J. Biol. Chem.*, **54**:721.
[7] T. B. Johnson and R. D. Coghill. 1925. *J. Biol. Chem.*, **63**:225.

TABLE 8 (*Continued*)

DISTRIBUTION OF NITROGEN IN THE PROTEINS OF MICROORGANISMS

	Escherichia coli		*Vibrio comma* and Cholera-like Vibrios			
	Alanine Glucose Medium, Per Cent [8]	Cystine Glucose Medium, Per Cent [8]	Two Agglutinable Strains Containing Galactose, Per Cent [9]		Two Nonagglutinable Strains Containing Arabinose, Per Cent [9]	
Amide N	11.30	10.80	6.09	7.00	7.22	6.69
Humin N	4.80	5.74	4.06	4.73	4.16	4.40
Dibasic N	38.43	35.61	26.03	25.70	24.80	24.08
Arginine	15.40	16.30	11.22	11.83	12.03	11.35
Histidine	10.61	10.41	5.72	5.26	3.11	3.27
Lysine	12.42	8.90	9.09	8.61	9.66	9.46
Cystine	0.00	0.00	0.00	0.00	0.00	0.00
Mono- and non-amino N	46.10	49.12	64.47	63.45	63.49	64.89
Amino N	42.90	45.71	56.83	55.94	54.84	56.64
Nonamino N	3.20	3.41	7.64	7.52	8.66	8.26
Total N accounted for	100.63	101.27	100.65	100.86	99.66	100.96

	Staphylococcus aureus		*Staphylococcus aureus*		Beer Coccus, Per Cent [12]	*Brucella melitensis* (Smooth), Per Cent [13]	Yeast Protein,§ Per Cent [14]	Casein, Per Cent [15]	Gelatin, Per Cent [15]
	Smooth Strain, Per Cent [10]	Rough Strain, Per Cent [10]	I C Strain, Per Cent [11]	C B Strain, Per Cent [11]					
Amide N	6.79	10.35	13.16	13.98	6.27	10.73	....	10.27	2.25
Humin N	1.22	1.39	4.17	4.90	10.77	3.36	....	1.28	0.07
Dibasic N	28.89	25.32	29.52	29.97	....	19.89	20.0	....	....
Arginine	8.88	5.36	8.55	8.26	4.39	5.39	5.0	7.41	14.7
Histidine	6.35	5.08	9.94	11.25	7.38	6.15	5.0	6.21	4.48
Lysine	13.7	14.88	10.45	9.87	8.55	7.76	10.0	10.03	6.32
Cystine	13.7	14.88	0.58	0.59	0.0	0.0	....	0.2	0.0
Mono- and nonamino N	63.18	62.94	53.61	51.78	.....	.....	....	.....	....
Amino N	59.36	47.04	48.10	45.10	31.09	69.09	58.5	55.81	55.8
Nonamino N	3.83	15.89	.....	.....	31.55	.....	1.6	7.13	14.9
Total N accounted for	100.08	100.00	100.46	100.63	100.00	103.07	99.5‖	98.61	99.02

§ For additional data on yeast protein see R. Block and D. Bolling. 1943. *Arch. Biochem.*, **3**:217.

‖ To make this total, NH_3 = 8.0%, purine and pyrimidine bases = 12%, choline = 0.50%, glycosamine = 0.50%.

[8] H. C. Eckstein and M. H. Soule. 1931. *J. Biol. Chem.*, **91**:395.

[9] R. W. Linton, B. N. Mitra, and D. L. Shrivastava. 1934. *Indian J. Med. Res.*, **21**:635.

[10] R. E. Hoffstadt and W. M. Clark. 1938. *J. Infectious Diseases*, **62**:70.

[11] O. N. Fellowes and J. I. Routh. 1944. *J. Lab. Clin. Med.*, **29**:1054.

[12] C. Enders and K. W. Gergs. 1939. *Biochem. Z.*, **303**:10.

[13] W. H. Stahl, R. B. Pennell, and I. F. Huddleson. 1939. *Mich. State College Tech. Bull.* 168.

[14] J. Meisenheimer. 1919, 1921. *Z. physiol. Chem.*, **104**:229, **114**:205.

[15] B Harrow and C. P. Sherwin. 1937. *A Textbook of Biochemistry.* W. B. Saunders Co., Philadelphia, Pa.

special apparatus devised by Van Slyke. By subtracting the value obtained from the total nitrogen of the fraction, (*a–d*), the *nonamino nitrogen* of the fraction is obtained. This nitrogen comes only from arginine and histidine. From the nonamino value (*a–d*) three-fourths of the value obtained for arginine (*b*) is subtracted. This result is the nonamino nitrogen of the histidine (*e*). When this value (*e*) is multiplied by two-thirds, it gives the *histidine nitrogen* (*f*). The *lysine nitrogen* is equal to a figure obtained by making the following subtractions: Total nitrogen minus arginine nitrogen minus cystine nitrogen minus histidine nitrogen (*a–b–c–f*).

V. *Monoamino nitrogen* and *nonamino nitrogen*. A Kjeldahl determination gives the total nitrogen present in this fraction. Call it *g*.

h. The *amino nitrogen* of fraction V is determined by the Van Slyke apparatus. By subtracting this value from the total nitrogen of the fraction, (*g–h*), the *nonamino nitrogen* of the portion is obtained.

The analyses of proteins made by Van Slyke's method have given much valuable information on the constitution of protein materials. Bacterial proteins have been studied by this technique, and several examples are given in Table 8, which also includes the figures obtained for some different proteins. Several other reports have appeared on the isolation of amino acids from bacteria [Hetler (1927), Burris (1942)], yeasts, and molds, but the figures in the table are typical results. The early work by Vaughan, Vaughan, and Vaughan (1913) and others [Wheeler (1909), Omeliansky and Sieber (1913), and Tamura (1913–1914)] on the amino acid content of bacteria is open to criticism, since the material fractionated by means of the Kossel and Kutscher procedure was an incomplete hydrolysis mixture of bacterial proteins.

PROTEIN SYNTHESIS BY MICROORGANISMS

It is well known that many bacteria can synthesize their cellular proteins from the simplest of starting materials. As we have pointed out, simple amino acids may be combined to form peptides and eventually proteins, but often certain bacteria can carry out all their life processes in a substrate which contains nitrogen in a form simpler than amino acid nitrogen. Just how the various components of a simple medium are linked together to form proteins is not very well understood at this time, although several theories have been advanced. Knoop and Oesterlin (1925, 1927) suggested that the various amino acids might be synthesized from sugars and ammonia in the following steps:

$$\text{I.}\quad \underset{\text{Keto acid}}{R\cdot CO\cdot COOH} + NH_3 = \underset{\text{Hydroxyamino acid}}{R\cdot C(OH)(NH_2)-COOH}$$

The hydroxyamino acid then loses water to form an imino acid, thus:

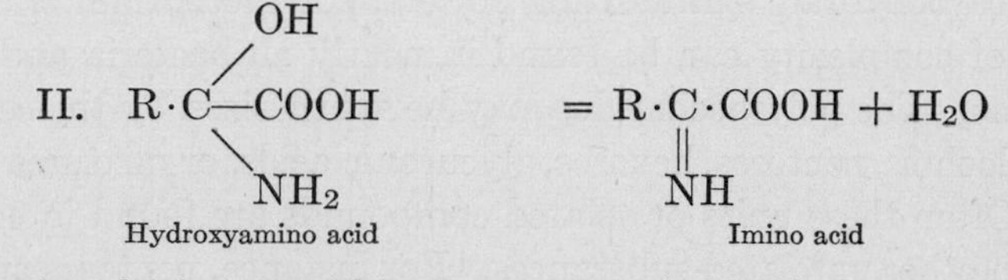

By reduction the imino acid becomes an amino acid, thus:

$$\text{III.}\quad \underset{\text{Imino acid}}{R\cdot C(=NH)\cdot COOH} + 2H = \underset{\text{Amino acid}}{R\cdot CH(NH_2)\cdot COOH}$$

The third (III) step is half of a coupled oxidation-reduction reaction, the other half probably being the dehydrogenation of an intermediate product of sugar breakdown, such as the formation of pyruvic acid from glyceraldehyde phosphate or from methylglyoxal hydrate. If R in the above reactions is a methyl group, then the scheme represents the formation of the amino acid, alanine, from pyruvic acid.

Another example which may be cited is the bacterial synthesis of aspartic acid from fumaric acid and ammonia:

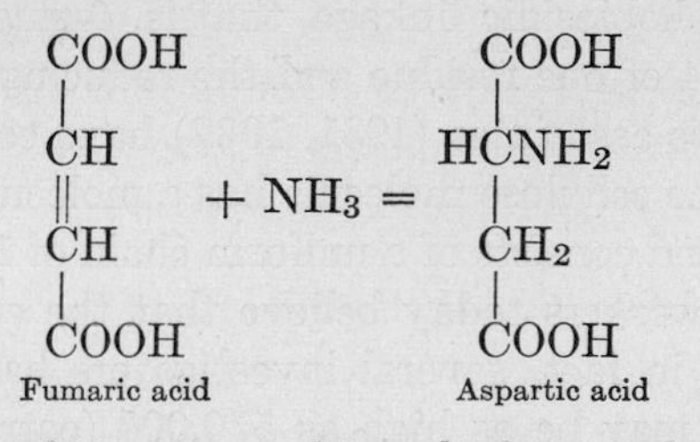

Once the amino acids have been formed, they can be united, probably as peptides, thus:

$$R\cdot CH(NH_2)\cdot COOH + H_2N\cdot CH(R)\cdot COOH = R\cdot CH(NH_2)\cdot CO\cdot NH\cdot CH(R)\cdot COOH + H_2O$$

and the process continued until the various cellular proteins are formed

THE CARBOHYDRATES IN MICROORGANISMS

The carbohydrate content of bacteria and related organisms is subject to considerable variation because of several factors, such as the age of the cells and the amount and the nature of the available nutrient material. Analyses have shown that the carbohydrate content of bacteria varies from 12 to 28 per cent, of yeasts from 25 to 60 per cent, and of molds from 8 to 40 per cent. Even though microorganisms vary in their carbohydrate synthesizing powers, polysaccharides of different degrees of complexity can be found in nearly all bacteria and related organisms. The polysaccharides may be synthesized by the cells from simple alcohols, pentoses, hexoses, glycuronic acids, or mixtures of these units. Often these units or related compounds are found in combination with other unrelated substances. For instance, pentoses and other sugars have been found in the nucleoproteins of many microorganisms. Simpler sugars and hexahydric alcohols also occur in certain organisms.

Let us now briefly discuss several carbohydrates which have been isolated from microorganisms.

CELLULOSE AND PENTOSANS

The cellulose which is synthesized by bacteria is apparently identical with that obtained from other sources, but, since the exact constitution of cellulose is in doubt, this statement lacks proof. By hydrolytic cleavage cellulose yields glucose exclusively, and on acetolysis it gives a yield of 50 per cent of cellobiose octaacetate (4-β-glucosidglucose). This fact has led several workers to believe that cellulose is built up of glucose units in cellobiosidic linkage, that is, β-glucose residues joined between position 4 of one residue and the reducing group of the next.

Haworth and his associates (1931, 1932) have concluded from their early work that the cellulose molecule has a molecular weight of about 20,000 to 40,000 and consists of a uniform chain of 100 to 200 β-glucose residues. Many workers today believe that the cellulose molecule is somewhat larger; in fact, several investigators have figured that its molecular weight may be as high as 570,000 (corresponding to 3,600 glucose units).

Cellulose is insoluble in water, organic solvents, dilute acids, and alkalies but is soluble in ammoniacal copper hydroxide (Schweitzer's reagent), hydrochloric acid-zinc chloride solution (Cross and Bevan's reagent), and several other solvents. On treatment with concentrated sulfuric acid and iodine or with chloriodide of zinc, it gives characteristic blue color on standing, the so-called "cellulose reaction" employed by biologists.

Many workers have claimed that the cell membrane of microorganisms contains cellulose, but there is not too much proof in favor of this belief except for some of the acetic acid bacteria, especially *Acetobacter xylinum.* While studying *Acetobacter aceti,* Brown (1886, 1887) observed a new bacterium to which he assigned the name *Bacterium xylinum* (*Acetobacter xylinum*). When cultured in a suitable nutrient medium containing dextrose, levulose, or mannitol, the new organism produced a very thick membrane on the surface of the medium. This membrane consisted of 35 to 62 per cent cellulose and was readily soluble in ammoniacal copper hydroxide. Upon hydrolysis with strong sulfuric acid the material gave a dextrorotatory sugar in a manner similar to ordinary cellulose. Sucrose, starch, and ethyl alcohol did not support the formation of the cellulose-like substance. A few years later Beijerinck (1898) found that acetic acid bacteria (*Acetobacter pasteurianum* and *Acetobacter rancens*) other than *Acetobacter xylinum* produced slimes capable of giving a positive cellulose reaction. He believed these compounds were closely related structurally to the cell walls of the seeds of most leguminous plants and the ascus-bearing cell of the lichens. Van Wisselingh (1898) employed a special type of cellulose reaction in his study on 100 different fungi including *Bacillus mesentericus, Bacillus megatherium,* yeasts, and molds. He concluded that cellulose was not commonly found in bacteria other than A. *xylinum.* The X-ray diagram of the cellulose membrane formed by *A. xylinum* was found to be similar to β-cellulose by Eggert and Luft (1930), and quite similar results were reported by Sisson (1936).

Tarr and Hibbert (1931) made an extensive study of bacterial cellulose, using *A. xylinum* as their test organism. The optimum nutrient medium necessary for the production of the carbohydrate was determined. Along with other nutrients a small amount of ethyl alcohol was found to be necessary for optimum growth. Hexoses, their anhydrides, or compounds which can be converted into hexoses by bacterial action gave rise to the cellulose-like polysaccharide. No membrane was formed from such carbon sources as arabinose, xylose, or erythritol, but mannitol and glycerol, which can be oxidized to levulose, yield to the production of the complex carbohydrate. When glucose and glycerol were methylated, the polysaccharide formation was inhibited. Levulose served as the best sugar for cellulose synthesis by this bacterium. Hibbert and Barsha (1931) and Barsha and Hibbert (1934) studied the structure of the cellulose synthesized by *A. xylinum* and found it to differ little, if any, from cellulose from other sources.

The presence of pentosans, $(C_5H_8O_4)_x$, in microorganisms has not received a great deal of attention from the bacteriologist in the past. The pentosans are hydrolyzed to pentoses by dilute mineral acids but not by alkali. The pentoses are readily distinguished from other monosaccharides because of their conversion to furfural on boiling with concentrated hydrochloric acid. The amount of furfural formed may be calculated quantitatively by coupling with phloroglucinol and weighing the insoluble product. In this way the amount of pentose may be determined.

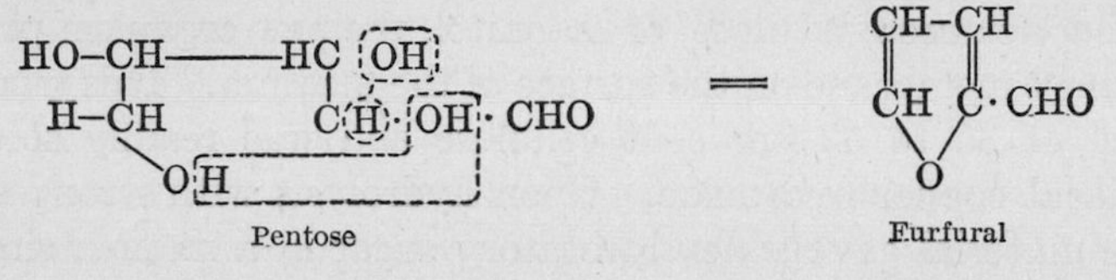

Pentose Furfural

A very useful qualitative test which may be used to test for the presence of pentose in a hydrolyzed bacterial mass is the reagent introduced by Tollens—a solution of orcinol in 18 per cent hydrochloric acid—which gives a deep purple color on boiling with pentoses. In the presence of a small amount of ferric chloride a green color is obtained.

Tamura (1914) was unable to find cellulose in *Corynebacterium diphtheriae*, *Mycobacterium tuberculosis*, and *Mycobacterium lacticola* but isolated a substance possibly of the class of hemicelluloses or pentosans. After separation of the fatty substance from the bacilli and as complete a removal as possible of proteins by alkali, a substance remained which was insoluble in Schweitzer's cellulose reagent and failed to give the iodine reaction of chitin, but was easily hydrolyzed by 3 per cent sulfuric acid. The hydrolysate readily reduced Fehling's solution, and gave the orcinol hydrochloride test for pentoses. An osazone was prepared which gave figures corresponding to the pentose, arabinose. The substance thus appeared to be a pentosan. Laidlaw and Dudley (1925) and Heidelberger and Menzel (1932) demonstrated in the tubercle bacillus polysaccharides which appear to be pentosans, since upon hydrolysis they yield pentose sugars.

Several molds, including *Aspergillus niger* and *Penicillium camembertii*, contain pentosans, according to Dox and Neidig (1911). Hilpert, Becker, and Rossée (1937) believe that most of the cellulose-like material in lichens, molds, and algae is in the form of hemicellulose, since it goes into solution on boiling with alkali or sodium sulfite.

HEXOSANS AND MISCELLANEOUS POLYSACCHARIDES

The synthesis of hexosans and other polysaccharides by bacteria has been established and studied rather extensively. Probably Pasteur (1861) was the first person to show that the slimy fermentation of carbohydrates was bacterial in origin. Since that time extensive studies have been carried out by many investigators, especially of the gummy material produced during sugar processing in the sugar industry, the slime produced in beer, the slime produced in pulp and paper mills, and the ropy fermentation in milk.

Dextran or Glucosan. The mucilaginous fermentation sometimes occurring during the processing of cane and beet sugar is caused by certain microorganisms, especially *Leuconostoc mesenteroides,* acting upon the sucrose. The "gum" produced by this organism was considered to be cellulose by Durin (1876), but Scheibler previously had established its nature as closely related to that of starch and dextrin and had given it the name *dextran.* More recently the structure of dextran synthesized from sucrose by *L. mesenteroides* has been determined by Hassid and Barker (1940), and the antigenic properties of dextran from the same species were studied by Evans, Hawkins, and Hibbert (1941). Stacey and Youd (1938) found that *Leuconostoc dextranicum* produces a pure dextran. After separation and purification the dextran gave a specific rotation of $[\alpha]_D^{20}$ 180° in water, an ash of 0.4 per cent, and a yield of 0.25 per cent nitrogen. Several other organisms produce dextran-like gums, but they are not as important as the organisms just mentioned.

Using a bacterium which had been previously isolated by C. B. Lipman from an old mud brick, Hassid and Chandler (1937) made a study of its polysaccharide-synthesizing property. When cultivated in a medium containing mannitol, the organism produced a nitrogen-free polysaccharide with a specific rotation, $[\alpha]_D$, of +140°, and on hydrolysis it yielded only glucose. The substance was shown to consist of nine or ten anhydroglucose units and to have a molecular weight of 2,765 to 2,980. A few strains of *Streptococcus salivarius* and *Streptococcus bovis* are also able to synthesize from sucrose and raffinose an insoluble carbohydrate which seems to be a dextran [Niven, Smiley, and Sherman (1941)].

Fructosan or Levulan. A great many studies have been made on the synthesis of fructosans by bacteria. Of the early studies the most extensive were by Smith and his associates (1903–1905). They isolated an organism, *Bacillus laviniformans,* which had the power of synthesizing a levulan from sucrose but was unable to produce the substance from glucose, fructose, lactose, or maltose. Upon hydrolysis it yielded only fructose with a specific rotation of $[\alpha]_D$ − 40°. Since the organism showed a marked power to invert sucrose, but other carbohydrates were not attacked, they assumed that levan could be formed only from the so-called nascent fructose and glucose produced by the inversion of sucrose. Owen (1911, 1918, 1923) observed that commercial sugar deterioration is caused by molds, yeast, and bacteria. Such species as *Bacillus vulgatus, Bacillus liodermos, Bacillus megatherium,* and *Bacillus subtilis* possessed the greatest polysaccharide-synthesizing powers, according to Owen. Furthermore, he believed that the levan was formed directly from the sucrose molecule by the extracellular enzyme *levanase*, thus disagreeing with other investigators who believe that the sucrose must first be inverted into nascent fructose and glucose before the polysaccharide can be formed. Kopeloff and Kopeloff (1919, 1920) and Kopeloff, Welcome, and Kopeloff (1920) believed that molds were the most common single group of organisms present in raw sugars. They found that spores of *Aspergillus sydowi* contain an enzyme which is capable of forming levan in sucrose solutions of varying concentrations. The pure gum which was formed melted at 200°C., had a specific rotation of −40°, and upon hydrolysis yielded only levulose. They concluded that the levan was formed from the nascent levulose and dextrose resulting from the inversion of the sucrose, and that the levulose was more important than the dextrose in levan formation.

More recently Harrison, Tarr, and Hibbert (1930) in an excellent study observed that *Bacillus mesentericus*, *Bacillus subtilis*, and an enzyme preparation from *B. mesentericus* were able to synthesize a levan type polysaccharide from simpler carbohydrates. When *B. mesentericus* was cultured in sucrose broth for 10 days at 37.5°C. and the polysaccharide purified by successive precipitations from 95 per cent ethyl alcohol followed by electrodialysis, a quantity of levan sufficient for chemical analysis was obtained. The yield of polysaccharide was about 51 g. per liter of original culture solution. Harrison, Tarr, and Hibbert gave the substance the empirical formula of $(C_6H_{10}O_5)_x$. Hydrolysis gave 97 per cent of the theoretical yield of syrupy fructose, thus proving that levan is made up entirely of fructose units. The anhydrous material could be easily acetylated or methylated. It was insoluble in most organic liquids, but dissolved readily in glycerol or ethylene glycol. Fehling's solution was not reduced. It was a levorotatory polysaccharide with a specific rotation of −43.5°. The chemical investigation of this material showed it to be a polymer of 2:6-anhydrofructofuranose [Hibbert, Tipson, and Brauns (1931)].

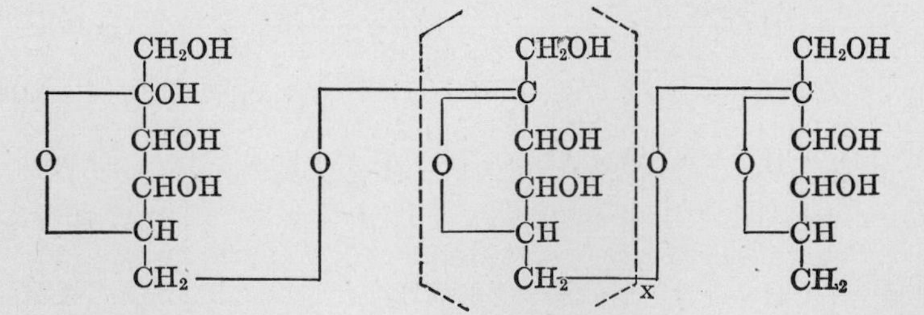

The formation of levan took place in sucrose and raffinose solutions but not in melezitose, lactose, maltose, glucose, fructose, or xylose media. Sucrose, raffinose, and melezitose all contain the fructofuranose residue in their molecule and, since melezitose was not polymerized to levan, these results appeared somewhat puzzling to the investigators. They were explained by the fact that both sucrose and raffinose have a terminal fructofuranose group, whereas in melezitose there is a central anhydrofructose molecule attached at each end to a glucose molecule. The following formulas below will clearly illustrate this point.

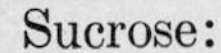

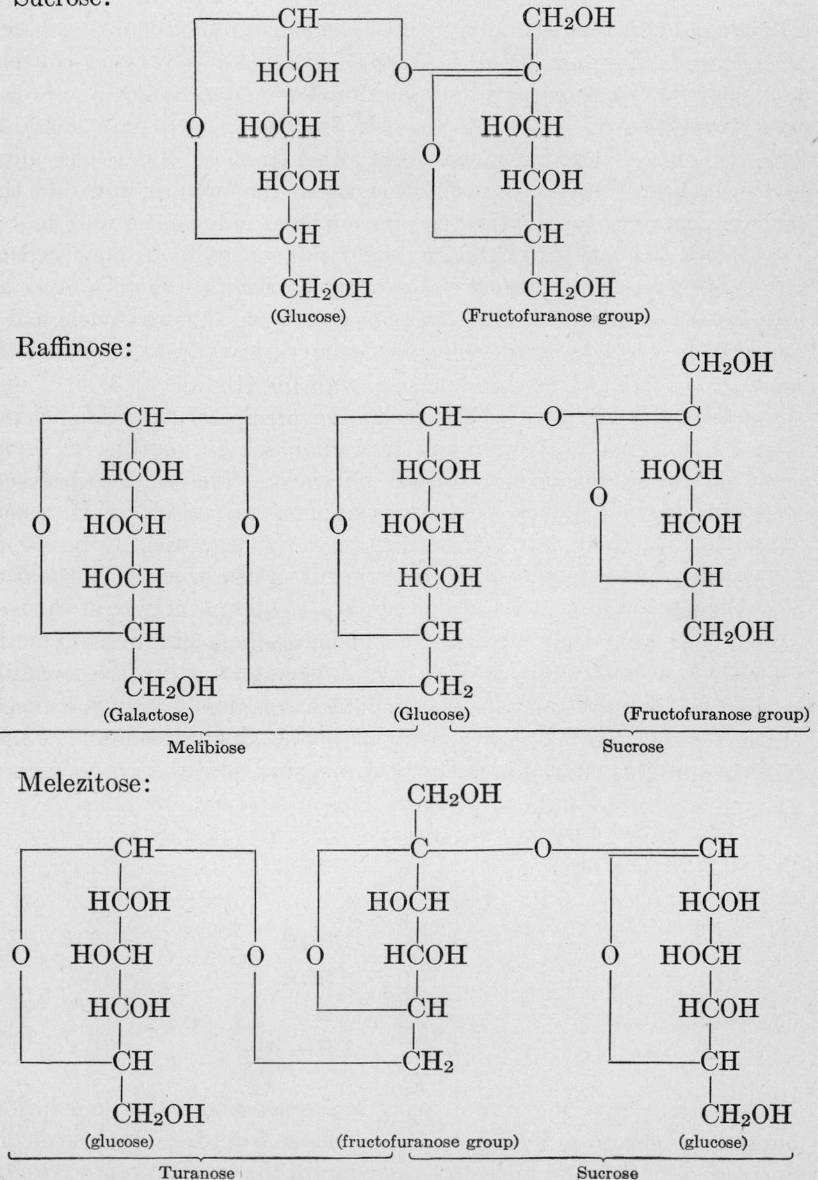

Other sugars containing a terminal fructofuranose residue, such as gentianose, stachyose, and turanose, were not available for this study.

Cooper and Preston (1935), Carruthers and Cooper (1936), and Cooper (1939) have studied organisms representing several genera of bacteria and their ability to produce fructosan polysaccharides from various carbohydrates. Peptone was not essential for polysaccharide synthesis from sucrose, since asparagine, *d*-alanine, and *l*-leucine usually served as a sole source of nitrogen for most of the organisms. Many strains of *Streptococcus salivarius* also synthesize large quantities of a soluble levan from sucrose and raffinose [Niven, Smiley, and Sherman (1941)].

Galactans. There are numerous reports in the literature concerning the production of galactans, arabogalactans, and similar substances by bacteria when they are cultivated in a suitable medium containing carbohydrate. Emmerling (1900) and Schardinger (1902) were among the first to observe that *Aerobacter aerogenes* produced a slime in milk and other carbohydrate-containing media. Schardinger assigned the substance the formula $(C_6H_{10}O_5)_x$ and found that it dissolved in water giving a clear, gelatinous solution. It was optically inactive, nitrogen-free, and did not reduce Fehling's solution. Hydrolysis with dilute acids produced a reducing sugar, and on oxidation with nitric acid both oxalic and mucic acids were formed. Thus the gummy substance was called an arabogalactan. In a series of papers Smith (1903, 1905) described *Bacterium sacchari* and *Bacterium atherstonei* which were galactan-producing organisms. Several other bacteria were also isolated which produced gums of the arabin and parabin groups. Upon hydrolysis these groups yielded both galactose and arabinose, and by oxidation with nitric acid both mucic and oxalic acids were formed. Furfural was demonstrated by distillation with dilute hydrochloric acid, thus proving the presence of a pentose. Kramár (1922) classified the gum or capsular material formed by *Klebsiella pneumoniae* as a galactan.

Miscellaneous Polysaccharides. Buchanan (1909) observed that *Rhizobium leguminosarum* formed a mucilaginous material from fifteen different carbohydrates, as well as from glycerol and from salts of several organic acids. The material in each instance had the same general characteristics, contained no nitrogen, and on hydrolysis yielded reducing sugar. Cooper and Preston (1937) made a similar study of this organism and demonstrated that the gum contained glucuronic acid as one of its components.

Beijerinck and den Dooren de Jong (1923) noted that *Bacillus polymyxa* produces large amounts of slimy material. "This slime," they stated, "is built up of sugars by one or more synthetically acting enzymes that might be named 'cyteses' and should be considered as the genes or factors of the cell-walls." They called this substance a cellulan.

Certain bacteria produce mixed polysaccharides when they are cultivated in suitable media. For example, the pneumococcus synthesizes a substance containing glucose and galactose; tubercle bacilli contain a polysaccharide made up of glucose, arabinose, and mannose; and *Vibrio comma* and cholera-like vibrios synthesize a polymer consisting of glucose, galactose, and arabinose. Beckwith (1931) and Sanborn (1933) have studied the cause of pulp slime in paper and pulp mills and have isolated several organisms thought to be the causative agents. The capsular material of *Bacillus krzemieniewski* is a polymannose of high molecular weight, according to Kleczkowski and Wierzchowski (1940).

The polysaccharides synthesized by several molds have been extensively studied by Haworth, Raistrick, and Stacey (1935), and the subject has been reviewed by Birkinshaw (1937) and Raistrick (1938). Only two examples will be mentioned here. When *Penicillium charlesii* was cultivated in a special medium, it produced two polysaccharides: mannocarolose, $[\alpha]_D + 66°$, consisting only of mannose residues, and mannogalactose, consisting only of galactose residues. The mannocarolose consisted of eight or nine units of *d*-mannose linked together through the 1:6 position. According to the investigators, this is a unique structure for a polymannose. *Penicillium varians* gave rise to a complex polysaccharide called varianose, $[\alpha]_D + 15°$. On acid hydrolysis this substance yielded mixtures of *d*-glucose, *d*-galactose, and a third hexose which was identified as either *l*-altrose or *d*-idose. The three hexoses occurred in the ratio 6 : 1 : 1, respectively. For other interesting information the review by Raistrick (1938) should be consulted.

ANTIGENIC POLYSACCHARIDES

In recent years the literature on antigenic polysaccharides, the so-called soluble specific substances, which are responsible for the serological behavior of many microorganisms, has grown very large. No attempt will be made to cover the literature, since fine reviews are available by Mikulaszek (1935), White (1938), Kimmig (1940), Linton (1940), and others. Also no attention will be given to the interesting studies by Goebel and others [see Goebel (1940)] on the synthesis of antigenic polysaccharides.

In 1917 Dochez and Avery discovered in cell-free filtrates of broth cultures of pneumococcus, types I, II, and III, in human blood serum, in urine during the course of lobar pneumonia and, at times, in the blood of experimentally infected animals, a soluble substance which gave a specific precipitate with antipneumococcic serum of the homologous type. The substance was readily soluble in water, was not destroyed by boiling, was not digested by trypsin or urease, did not dialyze through parchment, and was precipitable by acetone, alcohol, ether, and colloidal iron. The material was, of course, the now well-known soluble-specific substance which has so broadened our conception of pneumococcal immunity and the antigenic structure of bacteria and related bodies. After this report a great many investigations were undertaken, using the pneumococcus as a test organism. As a result no microorganism, except perhaps the tubercle bacillus, has been subjected to such a thorough chemical investigation. The first definite and detailed description of the carbohydrate fraction, or soluble-specific substance of pneumococci, was presented by Heidelberger and Avery (1923). Their material was obtained from an 8-day autolyzed broth culture of pneumococcus, type II, by careful precipitation with alcohol. Because 1.2 per cent of nitrogen was found to be present in this preparation, the authors did not make any claims for its purity.

During the next few years there came from the laboratories of the Rockefeller Institute a series of papers under the authorship of Avery, Heidelberger, and their associates, Goebel, Neill, and Morgan, which contained descriptions of refinements in the methods of preparing these polysaccharides and of their physical, chemical, and immunological properties. The two summarizing articles by Heidelberger (1927), which give a comprehensive discussion of the chemical nature of the antigenic substance of pneumococcus, should be read by all persons interested in this subject. White (1938) has also fully reviewed the subject.

To mention briefly the available data on the pneumococcus, we can say that marked differences have been found between the soluble substances of the various types. Pneumococcus, type I, polysaccharide contains nitrogen, part of which is in the form of amino nitrogen. As it was first isolated, it was not antigenic, but by modified methods, in which treatment with alkali was purposely avoided, the soluble-specific substance was isolated by Avery and Goebel (1933) in the form of an ash-free, acetyl polysaccharide possessing marked acidic properties and the ability to incite antibodies in experimental animals. It was readily soluble in water and gave solutions of high viscosity, which showed a specific optical rotation of about +270°. The naturally acetylated type I polysaccharide was found to contain nitrogen, and it did not reduce Fehling's solution until after hydrolysis with dilute mineral acids. As soon as reducing sugars appeared in the solution, the serological specificity of the acetyl polysaccharide was destroyed. Thus its behavior was identical with that of the deacetylated polysaccharide. The acetylated carbohydrate apparently contained uronic acid in its molecule. It was soluble in water and in 80 per cent acetic acid. Aqueous solutions were precipitated by phosphotungstic acid, silver nitrate, and neutral and basic lead acetate. Unlike the deacetylated preparation, the acetyl polysaccharide was precipitated by tannic acid but not by uranyl nitrate. It gave negative reactions to the biuret, ninhydrin, sulfosalicylic, and picric acid tests. The analyses in Table 9, taken from the paper by Avery and Goebel, show the properties of the polysaccharide of pneumococcus, type I.

The results of the analysis correspond closely with the calculated composition of the acetylated polysaccharide, and this substance is therefore believed by some to approach in its chemical make-up that of the so-called soluble-specific substance as it probably exists in the pneumococcus cell. Avery and Goebel also found that both the acetyl polysaccharide and the deacetylated substance were precipitated by homologous immune serum. On the other hand, when the serum was absorbed with the deacetylated polysaccharide, it still reacted with the acetyl polysaccharide in high dilutions. After absorption with the acetyl polysaccharide the serum was completely exhausted of all precipitins for both forms of the carbohydrate. The deacetylated polysaccharide, therefore, selectively removed from the serum only the precipitins for itself, whereas the acetyl polysaccharide completely removed all the precipitating antibodies for both forms of the specific substance. Further evidence of the specific antigenicity of the acetyl polysaccharide, as compared to the incomplete antigenic action of its deacetylated derivative, was furnished by Avery and Goebel's experiments on the immunizing action of the two carbohydrates on mice. Three injections, each of 0.5 ml. of a 1 : 2,000,000 solution of the acetylated polysaccharide, protected all the mice tested 6 days later against 10^{-5} ml. of a culture of pneumococcus, type I, of which 10^{-8} ml. killed the control mice. A similar series of mice injected with the same amounts of the deacetylated substance, however, was not protected. According to some workers, the experimental evidence presented by Avery and Goebel goes a long way toward reconciling the conflicting differences in some of the various carbohydrate derivatives isolated by other workers from the pneumococcal cell and its products. However, it should be pointed out that Felton and Prescott (1939) have definitely shown that the presence or absence of acetyl groups in pneumococcus, type I, polysaccharide is of no significance for its antigenicity in white mice.

Pneumococcus, type II, polysaccharide is a dextrorotatory carbohydrate, contains little or no nitrogen, and is weakly acidic. As first pre-

TABLE 9

ANALYSES OF THE ACETYL POLYSACCHARIDE OF PNEUMOCOCCUS, TYPE I

[From Avery and Goebel (1933)]

Preparation Number	Source	Acid Equivalent	Specific Rotation	Ash, per cent	Carbon, per cent	Hydrogen, per cent	Total Nitrogen, per cent	Amino Nitrogen, per cent	Acetyl, per cent	Phosphorus, per cent	Reducing Sugars after Hydrolysis, per cent	Highest Dilution of Polysaccharide Reacting with Antipneumococcus Serum
1	Bacterial cells	...	+270	0.0	.....	....	4.89	2.30	5.9	0.0	....	1 : 5,000,000 *
2	Bacterial cells	...	+265	0.0	.....	....	4.86	2.21	6.9	....	....	1 : 5,000,000 *
3	Autolyzed broth cultures	576	+277	0.0	42.55	6.58	4.85	2.22	6.0	0.0	32.0	1 : 5,000,000 *
2A, deacetylated	†	535	+297	0.0	‡	‡	5.05	2.50	0.0	...	27.6	1 : 5,000,000 §

* Type I antipneumococcus serum previously absorbed with Preparation 2A (deacetylated).

† This sample of deacetylated polysaccharide was obtained by alkaline hydrolysis of Preparation 2. This material is identical with the carbohydrate formerly known as the soluble-specific substance of pneumococcus, type I.

‡ An analysis of carbon and hydrogen was made on a sample of deacetylated carbohydrate which had been reprecipitated five times at its isoelectric point. The material contained no ash and had a carbon content of 40.33 per cent and a hydrogen content of 6.23 per cent.

§ Unabsorbed type I antipneumococcus serum.

pared it was nonantigenic; however, work by Schiemann and Casper (1927), Schiemann (1929), and others has demonstrated that it can be isolated in an antigenic form. The chemical and biological analyses of this polysaccharide will be found in Tables 10, 11, and 12. Type III soluble-specific substance is a nitrogen-free polysaccharide but is more strongly acidic than the type II substance and is levorotatory.

Considerable progress in the elucidation of the structure of type III polysaccharide has been made by Goebel and associates [see Reeves and Goebel (1941)] at the Rockefeller Institute. They have shown that the polysaccharide is built up of units of an aldobionic acid, 4-β-glucuronosido-glucose or cellobiuronic acid. In the intact carbohydrate the cellobiuronic acid units are linked through the reducing group of the aldobionic acid to one of the hydroxyl groups of a similar unit.

Heidelberger and Kendall's (1931) study of the type IV specific polysaccharide has brought to light a carbohydrate of a new kind among those with specific properties. The study has also demonstrated the presence in pneumococcus of a serologically inactive polysaccharide closely related to chitin. Brown (1935, 1939) has published results on preparations of the type-specific substances isolated from pneumococci, types I to XXXII. Some of her data are given in Tables 10 and 11. The polysaccharides produced by *Azotobacter chroococcum* and a clover strain of the genus *Rhizobium* are apparently closely related to the specific polysaccharides of pneumococcus, types I and II [Cooper, Daker, and Stacey (1938)].

Similar specific polysaccharides have been isolated from a great many other bacteria. A few representative results are given in Tables 12 and 13. For details the references should be consulted. In passing we should mention the work of Ivánovics and Bruckner (1937) on the capsular substance of *Bacillus anthracis* and *Bacillus mesentericus*, which is apparently identical. This nontoxic polysaccharide contains nitrogen and can be isolated from both capsulated and noncapsulated cells. It seems to be unlike the polysaccharides of the pneumococcus and other cells in that it possesses a peptide linkage, as:

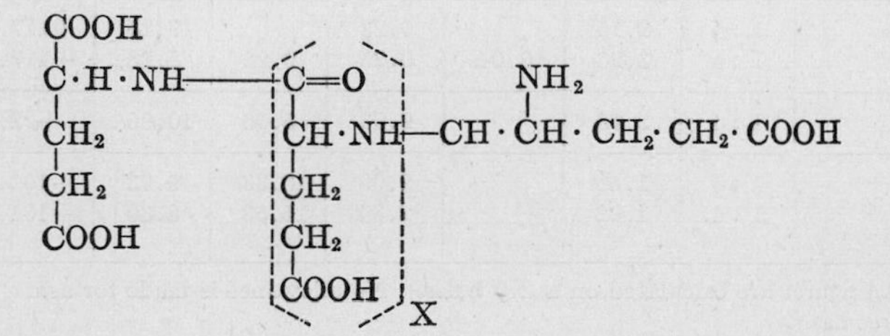

On hydrolysis with acid this material loses its serological activity and yields glutamic acid.

TABLE 10

ANALYTICAL DATA AND SEROLOGIC ACTIVITY OF PREPARATIONS OF THE TYPE-SPECIFIC SUBSTANCES OF THE PNEUMOCOCCUS

[From Rachel Brown (1939)]

Type	Precipitin Titer, millions	Kjeldahl N, per cent	Amino N, per cent	P, per cent	Acetyl, per cent	Ash, per cent	$[\alpha]_D$	Relative Viscosity
I	1 : 4	4.78	1.97	0.32	6.61	9.93	+253.2°	1.69
I	1 : 4	4.84	2.10	0.19	6.83	9.19	+255.6°	1.65
Heidelberger I		4.62± to 5.22	2.0±	0.00± to 0.25	7.1± to 10.0	0.0 * to 3.42	+278° to +294°	1.10 to 1.69
II	1 : 4	0.26		0.06	1.52	5.46	+56.8°	1.76
Heidelberger II		0.14± to 0.73		0.00±	0.4± to 3.8	0.1 * to 3.70	+53° to +58°	1.04 to 1.64
III	1 : 4	0.30		0.00	0.32	14.03	−36.4°	2.34
III	1 : 4	0.11		0.01		13.78	−36.8°	2.40
III	1 : 4	0.09				14.73	−34.8°	2.79
Heidelberger III		0.06± to 0.43		0.00±	0.5± to 0.9	0.2 * to 6.5	−30.7° to −37.3°	1.09 to 3.14
IV	1 : 4	5.24	0.31	0.49	15.51	5.17	+33.2°	1.38
Heidelberger IV		4.7 to 5.9	0.1 to 0.4	<0.1	5.6 to 5.9	0.0 † to 0.3	+17.0° to +37.7°	
V	1 : 4	5.01	0.00	0.25	21.73	3.16	−44.8°	1.06
VIa	1 : 4	0.32		4.24	2.12	14.12	+112.0°	1.12
VIa	1 : 4	0.48		4.03		13.80	+114.4°	1.20
VIb ‡	1 : 4	0.32		3.99	3.75	13.35	+112.8°	1.16
VII	1 : 4	3.19	0.37	1.23	11.06	3.36	+70.8°	1.17
VIII	1 : 4	0.20		0.09	0.41	7.52	+124.4°	2.44
Brown VIII		0.20		0.06		0.73	+126°	
Goebel VIII		0		0		0	+125°	
Heidelberger VIII		0.2±			0.05±	3.1 *	+123°	2.50
IX	1 : 4	3.15		0.23		7.15	+117.2°	1.30
IX	1 : 4	3.26	0.04	0.25	9.22	5.28	+117.2°	1.28
X	1 : 4	2.08		2.93	5.06	10.90	+22.4°	1.12
XI	1 : 4	1.40		2.99	16.33	9.93	+102.0°	1.27
XI	1 : 4	1.62		2.34	15.53	8.30	+101.6°	1.29

NOTE. All figures are calculated on a dry basis. No allowance is made for ash. ± Calculated to the ash-free basis.

* Ash as sodium.

† Ash as calcium.

‡ Originally classified as type XXVI.

TABLE 10 (*Continued*)

ANALYTICAL DATA AND SEROLOGIC ACTIVITY OF PREPARATIONS OF THE TYPE-SPECIFIC SUBSTANCES OF THE PNEUMOCOCCUS

[From Rachel Brown (1939)]

Type	Precipitin Titer, millions	Kjeldahl N, per cent	Amino N, per cent	P, per cent	Acetyl, per cent	Ash, per cent	$[\alpha]_D$	Relative Viscosity
XII	1 : 4	4.69	0.22	0.58	11.07	4.26	+3.6°	1.25
XIII	1 : 4	1.62		3.07	8.80	10.50	−28.8°	1.19
XIII	1 : 4	1.86		3.23	8.23	10.49	−28.4°	1.26
XIV	1 : 4	2.41		0.41	6.99	1.28	+6.8°	1.12
Goebel XIV		1.91 † to 2.08		0	6.6± to 7.7	0.56 to 1.57	+6.5° to +12.6°	
XV	1 : 4	2.46		3.08	9.80	12.24	+32.0°	1.26
XVI	1 : 4	3.16	0.07	2.81	7.51	9.96	+18.4°	1.29
XVII	1 : 8	0.09		2.51	4.28	8.33	+46.2°	1.28
XVIII	1 : 8	0.57		3.07	6.52	9.92	+76.0°	1.71
XIX	1 : 4	3.82	0.16	3.05	7.75	10.69	+32.8°	1.09
XX §	1 : 4	1.56		2.35	10.29	7.97	+7.2°	1.19
XX §	1 : 4	1.50		2.62	12.01	8.76	+4.8°	1.19
XXI	1 : 4	1.20		2.68	7.08	8.82	+66.8°	1.11
XXII	1 : 4	0.69		0.27	5.08	5.92	+95.6°	1.25
XXII	1 : 8	0.42		0.27	4.42	4.75	+94.8°	1.21
XXIII §	1 : 4	0.27		3.77	1.44	12.65	−0.8°	1.30
XXIII §	1 : 4	0.11		3.79	0.87	12.37	−0.4°	1.65
XXIV	1 : 4	1.63		3.03	4.79	10.07	−34.0°	1.56
XXV	1 : 4	4.72	0.15	0.87	14.40	5.52	+128.0°	1.09
XXVII	1 : 8	2.75		3.12	7.02	10.76	+53.2°	1.68
XXVIII §	1 : 4	1.76		6.08	3.87	14.81	+50.0°	1.67
XXVIII §	1 : 4	1.59		5.99	4.21	14.18	+48.8°	1.69
XXIX	1 : 8	1.53		3.22	5.15	10.53	−50.8°	1.22
XXX	1 : 4	1.73		3.06	4.49	10.00	+50.4°	1.25
XXXI	1 : 4	0.90		0.55	7.70	5.80	−20.4°	1.25
XXXII	1 : 4	1.67		6.38	4.60	16.16	+32.0°	1.45

§ Two different strains of the same type used as the source of the soluble-specific substances.

CARBOHYDRATE SYNTHESIS BY MICROORGANISMS

Our knowledge concerning the synthesis of polysaccharides or even simple sugars by bacteria is very incomplete. Kluyver (1931) was of the opinion that the synthesis of carbohydrates involves certain coupled oxidation-reduction processes, as does the synthesis of fats and proteins. He has suggested that the processes may follow the general scheme for the resynthesis of glycogen from lactic acid in the muscle during the recovery period. Since the reactions for the breakdown of glucose to lactic acid and alcohol are discussed in some detail in Chapter 10, pp. 910 to 927 on the mechanism of alcoholic fermentation, they will not be repeated fully here. If the intermediate products and the role played by phosphate are disregarded, the over-all reaction leading from lactic acid to glucose may be written thus:

$$3CH_3CHOH \cdot COOH \rightarrow 3CO_2 + 3H_2O + C_6H_{12}O_6$$

and the over-all reaction from glucose to glycogen may be written:

$$\underset{\text{Glucose}}{C_6H_{12}O_6} \xrightarrow[\text{dextrins, etc.)}]{\text{(Maltose, isomaltose,}} \underset{\text{Glycogen}}{(C_6H_{10}O_5)_x}$$

Until just recently practically nothing has been known about the intermediate steps in this second reaction. Data are now accumulating [see papers by Cori (1940, 1942), Hanes (1940), Cori and Cori (1940, 1943), and Meyerhof (1943)] on this subject, however, which give us further insight into this very interesting phase of the metabolism of carbohydrates in plants and animals. The biochemical setting of the enzymatic processes in their relation to glycogen synthesis by animal and yeast cells may be indicated in the scheme adopted from the paper by Cori (1940). A similar scheme for the plant enzymatic reversible conversion of starch and inorganic phosphate to glucose-1-phosphate will be found in the classical paper by Hanes (1940).

SCHEME FOR GLYCOGEN SYNTHESIS AND BREAKDOWN

[From Cori (1940)]

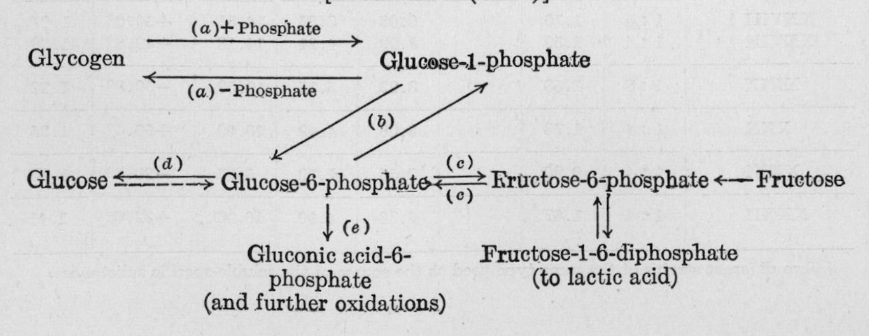

TABLE 11

CHEMICAL PROPERTIES OF PREPARATIONS OF THE TYPE-SPECIFIC SUBSTANCES OF THE PNEUMOCOCCUS

[From Rachel Brown (1939)]

Type of Soluble-Specific Substance (1 Per Cent Solution)	Carbohydrate Tests			Precipitants										
	Reduction by Fehling's Solution before Hydrolysis *	Uronic Acid	Amino Sugar after Hydrolysis	Phosphotungstic Acid	Tannic Acid	Ammonium Sulfate	Barium Chloride	Copper Sulfate	Ferric Sulfate	Lead Acetate	Basic Lead Acetate	Mercuric Nitrate	Silver Nitrate	Uranyl Nitrate
I	−	+	+	+	−	−	+	+	−	+	+	+	+	+
II	−	Weak +	−	−	−	−	−	−	−	−	+	+	−	−
III	−	+	−	+	−	+	+	+	+	+	+	+	+	+
IV	−	−	+	+	−	+	−	−	−	−	+	+	−	+
V	+	−	+	−	−	+	−	−	−	−	+	+	−	−
VIa	−	−	−	−	−	−	−	−	−	−	+	−	−	−
VIb †	−	−	−	−	−	−	−	−	−	−	+	−	−	−
VII	−	−	+	−	−	+	−	−	−	−	−	−	−	−
VIII	−	+	−	−	−	+	+	−	−	+	+	+	+	+
IX	−	+	+	−	−	+	−	−	−	−	−	+	−	−
X	−	−	+	−	−	−	−	−	−	−	−	−	−	−
XI	−	−	−	−	−	+	−	−	−	−	+	−	−	−
XII	−	+	+	−	−	+	−	−	−	+	+	+	−	−
XIII	−	−	+	−	−	+	−	−	−	−	+	−	−	−
XIV	−	−	+	−	+	−	−	−	−	−	+	−	−	−
XV	−	−	+	−	−	+	−	−	−	−	−	−	−	−
XVI	−	−	Weak +	−	−	+	−	−	−	−	+	−	−	+
XVII	−	−	−	−	−	+	−	−	−	−	+	−	−	−
XVIII	−	−	−	−	−	+	−	−	−	−	+	−	−	−
XIX	−	−	+	−	−	+	−	−	−	−	+	−	−	+
XX	−	−	Weak +	−	−	+	−	−	−	−	+	−	−	−
XXI	Weak +	−	Weak +	−	−	−	−	−	−	−	+	−	−	−
XXII	−	+	−	−	−	+	−	−	−	−	+	−	−	−
XXIII	−	−	−	−	−	−	−	−	−	−	+	−	−	−
XXIV	−	−	+	−	−	+	−	−	−	−	+	−	−	−
XXV	−	+	+	−	−	+	−	−	−	−	+	+	−	−
XXVII	−	Weak +	+	−	−	+	−	−	−	−	+	−	−	+
XXVIII	−	−	−	+	−	+	−	−	−	−	+	−	−	−
XXIX	−	−	+	−	−	−	−	−	−	−	+	−	−	−
XXX	−	−	+	−	−	+	−	−	−	−	−	−	−	−
XXXI	−	−	+	−	−	+	−	−	−	−	−	−	−	−
XXXII	Weak +	−	−	−	−	+	−	−	−	−	+	−	−	−

NOTE. + = positive reaction or precipitation; − = no reaction or no precipitation. The biuret, ninhydrin, and iodine tests were negative. Picric and trichloroacetic acids gave no precipitation.

* All tests positive after hydrolysis.

† Originally classified as type XXVI.

TABLE 12

SOME OF THE PHYSICAL, CHEMICAL, AND BIOLOGICAL PROPERTIES OF REPRESENTATIVE BACTERIAL POLYSACCHARIDES

Organism	$[\alpha]_D$	Acid Equivalent	Ash, per cent	Carbon, per cent	Hydrogen, per cent	Nitrogen, per cent	Phosphorus, per cent	Reducing Sugars after Hydrolysis, per cent	Type of		Precipitin Test	Reference
									Antigen	Specificity		
Mycobacterium tuberculosis "H37"	+17.3					0.3			Partial	Species		Enders (1929) Mikulaszek (1935)
M. tuberculosis "H37" (Range of fractions)	+10 to −95	1,000 to 21,800	0.2 to 2.8			0.01 to 1.66	0.1 to 6.46	61.0 to 87.0	Partial		+ −	Heidelberger and Menzel (1932, 1937)
M. tuberculosis-bovis (Two fractions)	+49 +62	15,000 800	1.8 0.7				2.0 3.8				+ −	Menzel and Heidelberger (1939)

Bacillus anthracis	+23.5	160.2				9.24					+	Ivánovics and Bruckner (1937)
Bacillus mesentericus	+19.6 to +22.7	162.8 to 170.5	2.1 to 3.7			9.17 to 10.14 *					+	
Phytomonas tumefaciens			4.8	44.0	7.4	1.7	1.0	40.8	Complete		+	Mesrobeanu (1936)
Escherichia coli			8.30	44.6	7.25	3.09	2.51	38.0	Complete		+	
Aerobacter aerogenes						0.9		66.0	Partial	Type	+	Tomcsik and Kurotchkin (1928)
Klebsiella pneumoniae												
Type A	−103.4	430	0.0	43.9	6.0	0.1		64.0	Partial	Type	+	Heidelberger, Goebel, and Avery (1925)
Type A, purified	−101	430	0.0			0.0		65.0	Partial	Type	+	
Type B	+100	670	0.0	44.6	6.1	0.0		73.0	Partial	Type	+	Avery, Heidelberger, and Goebel (1925)
Type C	+90.0	610	0.0			0.5		75.0	Partial	Type	+	
Type C, purified	+100.0	680	0.0			0.0		73.1	Partial	Type	+	Goebel and Avery (1927)

* Also 0.18 to 0.2% amino nitrogen.

TABLE 12 (*Continued*)

SOME OF THE PHYSICAL, CHEMICAL, AND BIOLOGICAL PROPERTIES OF REPRESENTATIVE BACTERIAL POLYSACCHARIDES

Organism	$[\alpha]_D$	Acid Equivalent	Ash, per cent	Carbon, per cent	Hydrogen, per cent	Nitrogen, per cent	Phosphorus, per cent	Reducing Sugars after Hydrolysis, per cent	Type of Antigen	Type of Specificity	Precipitin Test	Reference
Eberthella typhosa	+103		0.0			4.05	2.06	63.5 to 69.5	Partial		+	Furth and Landsteiner (1928, 1929)
Salmonella schottmuelleri	+94		0.0	43.8	6.5	1.86		3.94 to 67.3	Partial		+	
E. typhosa				45.0		2.47	1.45	45.8	Complete		+	Mesrobeanu (1936)
Salmonella paratyphi				45.5		3.39	1.35	58.8	Complete		+	
S. schottmuelleri				43.8		2.90	1.94	53.6	Complete		+	
Salmonella typhimurium			10.69	46.7	7.4	2.04	2.40	39.8	Complete		+	

S. typhimurium (Range of five fractions)			10.74 to 16.32	38.01 to 43.64	5.84 to 6.46	3.64 to 14.06	1.87 to 3.52	8.90 to 37.80	Complete	Species	+	Raistrick and Topley (1934)
E. typhosa (3 strains)			2.5 to 4.3			4.8 to 5.3			Complete	Species	+	Topley *et al.* (1937)
E. typhosa O "901"			11.7	46.1	7.6	2.6	1.7		Complete		+	Henderson and Morgan (1938)
E. typhosa "Ty 2," Vi strain			11.7	48.7	8.2	2.5	2.1		Complete		+	
E. typhosa "Ty 2," O-specific	+114 to 115					0.2 to 0.4	0.4 to 0.9	83		†		Freeman and Philpot (1942)
Shigella dysenteriae			4.0 to 6.0	45.5	7.6	3.8	1.3		Complete	Species	+	Morgan (1937)
Vibrio comma	+64.0			45.8	7.8				Complete	Species	+	Jermoljewa and Bujanowskaja (1930)
Vibrio luminosus	+36.0					4.2 ‡			Complete	Species	+	Linton and Shrivastava (1933) Mikulaszek (1935)

† Precipitates to a high dilution with *E. typhosa* O-antiserum, but not with Vi-antiserum.
‡ Amino nitrogen.

TABLE 12 (*Continued*)

SOME OF THE PHYSICAL, CHEMICAL, AND BIOLOGICAL PROPERTIES OF REPRESENTATIVE BACTERIAL POLYSACCHARIDES

Organism	$[\alpha]_D$	Acid Equivalent	Ash, per cent	Carbon, per cent	Hydrogen, per cent	Nitrogen, per cent	Phosphorus, per cent	Reducing Sugars after Hydrolysis, per cent	Type of		Precipitin Test	Reference
									Antigen	Specificity		
Brucella abortus	−7.0 to −10.5				1.0 to 4.0						+ −	Hershey, Huddleson, and Pennell (1935)
Staphylococcus aureus												
I C strain	+15.27	463	2.44			8.18	1.06	18.27			+	Fellowes and Routh (1944)
C B strain	+11.70	467	4.63			6.50	1.09	19.20			+	
Streptococcus pyogenes	−33					4.2		28.0	Partial	Species Type	+	Lancefield (1928) Mikulaszek (1935)
Diplococcus pneumoniae												
Type I	+300			43.3 §	5.8	5.0 ‖		28.0	Partial	Type	+	Heidelberger, Goebel, and Avery (1925)
Type II	+74	1,250		45.8	6.4	0.0		70.0	Partial	Type	+	
Type III	−33	340		42.7	5.3	0.0		75.0	Partial	Type	+	

D. pneumoniae												
Type I			0.43			4.37 ¶	0.39		Complete	Type	+	Wadsworth and Brown (1933)
Type II			0.62			2.03	1.72			Type	+	
Type III			1.76			3.41	2.06			Type	+	
Neisseria gonorrhoeae	Inactive					4.2			Partial	Group	+	Miller and Boor (1934)
Neisseria intracellularis						3.7			Partial	Group		
N. intracellularis												
Type I	+56.8		10.2	30.37	6.0	4.9		46.6	Partial	Type	+	Scherp and Rake (1935)
Type II, purified	+56.8		9.59			4.36	8.91	45.2	Partial	Type	+	
Yeast						0.2		83.0	Partial	Species		Tomcsik and Kurotchkin (1928) Mikulaszek (1935)

§ Theory for $(C_6H_{10}O_5)n$: C, 44.4 per cent; H, 6.2 per cent.

‖ Also amino N, 2.5 per cent.

¶ Also amino N, 2.14 per cent.

TABLE 13

TYPICAL REACTIONS EXHIBITED BY BACTERIAL POLYSACCHARIDES WITH DIFFERENT REAGENTS

Organism	Lead Acetate	Aluminum Sulfate or Copper Sulfate	Mercuric Acetate	Phosphotungstic Acid	Uranyl Nitrate	Uranium Acetate	Salicylsulfonic Acid	Trichloroacetic Acid	Picric Acid	Ninhydrin Test	Biuret Test	Molisch Test	Naphthoresorcinol Test for Glucuronic Acid	Orcinol and Phloroglucinol Test for Pentoses	Selivanoff's Test for Ketoses	Iodine Test for Glycogen	Reference
Mycobacterium tuberculosis	−	−	−	−					−			+					Enders (1929)
M. tuberculosis	+	−	−	−	+		−		−	−	−	+	−	−	−	+	Schlossmann (1934)
Aerobacter aerogenes	+?	−		+	−			−			−						Tomcsik (1927)
Klebsiella pneumoniae																	
Type A	+	−		+?	+								+			−	Goebel and Avery (1927)
Type C	+	−		−	+								+			−	
Eberthella typhosa	+	+	+	+		+	−	−	−	+	+	+					Topley *et al.* (1937)
(3 strains)	−	−	−	−		−											
E. typhosa	−	−	−	−	−	−	−	−	−	+	+		−	−	−	−	Henderson and Morgan (1938)
0 "901"																	
E. typhosa	+?	+	+	+		+	−	−	−		+?		−	−	−	−	
"Ty 2," Vi strain				+?			−	−	−	+	+	+					Raistrick and Topley (1934)
Shigella dysenteriae	−	−	−	−		−	−	−	−	−	+		−	−	−	−	Morgan (1937)
Vibrio comma							−				−	+					Jermoljewa and Bujanowskaja (1930), Linton and Shrivastava (1933)
Neisseria gonorrhoeae										−	−	+		−	−		Miller and Boor (1934)
Neisseria intracellularis	+	−	−		+			−			−	+		−		−	Scherp and Rake (1935)

+ = Positive reaction.
+? = Weak or incomplete reaction.
− = Negative reaction.

Enzymes (where no letters are given, enzymes have not been named):

a. Phosphorylase.
b. Phosphoglucomutase.
c. Isomerase.
d. Phosphatase.
e. Glucose-6-phosphate dehydrogenase (Zwischenferment of Warburg).

Adopting this picture, which is known to be incomplete, and anticipating the rigid proof that glycogen formation in animal tissues and starch formation in the plastid of the plant cell is due to the phosphorylase mechanism, we can see that glucose-1-phosphate occupies a position of central metabolic importance. Not only is this ester the direct precursor of starch and glycogen, but it also forms the initial reactant in the sequence of interconversions leading to the formation of fructose diphosphate. According to a view for which evidence is accumulating, these reactions in the formation of fructose diphosphate represent the preliminary steps in the catabolism of hexose in the animal and plant cell. Here the reversible formation of glycogen and starch from glucose-1-phosphate may be regarded as a side reaction, incidental to the essential processes of carbohydrate breakdown associated with cellular respiration.

It must be assumed that there exists in the cell a mechanism by which the primary synthesis of glucose-1-phosphate is effected from hexose (or some simpler compound), together with inorganic phosphate. In this respect the generation of glucose-1-phosphate by the phosphorolysis of starch or glycogen under the action of phosphorylase is to be regarded as a secondary mechanism by which the ester can be reformed readily. Starch and glycogen might be said to constitute an accessible supply of hexose phosphate, a conception which clarifies the traditional statement that both these substances form a reserve of readily available carbohydrate for the plant and the animal.

Although actual proof is lacking that bacterial cells synthesize carbohydrates in a manner analogous to the scheme just discussed, it is quite possible that future studies will reveal a mechanism closely related to that operative in yeast, higher plant, and animal cells. In fact, Stacey (1942) has already isolated an enzyme from *Leuconostoc mesenteroides* growing in association with yeast which is capable of synthesizing a polyglucose having 1 : 6 linkages from sucrose (glucose-1-fructofuranose). Likewise, Kagan, Lyatker, and Tsvasman (1942) have presented evidence for the binding of inorganic phosphate in the presence of sucrose, with the production of glucose-1-phosphate, by cell suspensions of *L. mesenteroides.* More recently Doudoroff, Kaplan, and Hassid (1943) have demonstrated the phosphorolysis and synthesis of sucrose by enzymatic preparations from *Pseudomonas saccharophila.* This process and the competing hydrolytic reaction may be represented by the following scheme:

$$\begin{array}{l} \text{Sucrose} + H_3PO_4 \underset{}{\overset{\text{Phosphorolysis}}{\rightleftarrows}} \text{Glucose-1-phosphate} + \text{Fructose} \\ \quad + \\ \quad H_2O \\ \quad \downarrow \\ \text{Glucose} + \text{Fructose} \end{array}$$

The demonstration of such an enzymatic phosphorolysis in bacteria helps to explain not only the mechanism of sucrose synthesis but also the so-called direct utilization of disaccharides by various microorganisms, which has been claimed by various investigators. Thus it would appear that these findings with bacteria are of significance in comparison with Hanes's and Cori's discovery of the starch-synthesizing and glycogen-synthesizing enzymes which utilize glucose-1-phosphate.

THE LIPIDES OF MICROORGANISMS

The substances to be considered under this heading are usually called *fats, oils, lipoids, lipides,* or *lipins.* Unfortunately there is little uniformity in the definition and usage of these terms. The term lipide will be used here as an inclusive term for the fats and fat-like substances, as well as their breakdown products, such as fatty acids and glycerol. These cellular constituents can usually be extracted by the so-called fat solvents: ether, alcohol, acetone, or chloroform.

The presence of lipides in the cells of microorganisms may be demonstrated by several simple techniques. For example, fat droplets are stained brown or black by osmic acid, deep blue-black by Sudan Black B, red by Sudan III, blue by a slightly alkaline solution of α- or β-naphthol and dimethyl-*p*-phenylenediamine, and yellow by dimethyl amidoazobenzene. When further information is desired, it is usually necessary to employ direct chemical methods, because these tests are very crude at their best and do not differentiate between the various groups of lipides.

The total lipide content of microorganisms is usually determined by extracting a dry, pulverized mass of cells of known weight with ether, or ether plus other fat solvents. The results obtained may be influenced by several factors, such as the composition of the culture medium upon which the organisms are grown, the gaseous environment

TABLE 14

LIPIDE CONTENT OF VARIOUS MICROORGANISMS

Organism or Body	Dry Weight,* per cent	Reference
Mycobacterium tuberculosis—hominis	22.7	Long and Campbell (1922)
M. tuberculosis—bovis	22.3	
Mycobacterium avium	11.0	
Mycobacterium leprae	9.7	
Mycobacterium smegmatis	35.6	
Mycobacterium phlei	20.2	
M. tuberculosis (28 strains)	3.3–14.1	Chargaff and Dieryck (1932)
M. tuberculosis (BCG)	25.4	Chargaff and Levine (1938)
Malleomyces mallei	39.29	De Schweinitz and Dorset (1895)
Corynebacterium diphtheriae	4.9	Chargaff (1933)
Acetobacter aceti	1.56	Alilaire (1906)
Bacillus subtilis	4.4	Long and Campbell (1922)
Bacillus mycoides	0.4	Virtanen and Pulkki (1933)
B. mycoides, spores	0.2	
Phytomonas tumefaciens	7.0–8.1	Chargaff and Levine (1938)
Escherichia coli (alanine medium)	7.8	Eckstein and Soule (1931)
E. coli (cystine medium)	3.6	
E. coli (range of four strains)	4.45–7.91	Williams, Bloor, and Sandholzer (1939)
Escherichia communior (range of three strains)	4.66–6.88	
Shigella paradysenteriae (Flexner)	5.36	
Salmonella typhimurium	4.9	Akasi (1939)
Brucella abortus	5.0–6.0	Stahl (1941)
Staphylococcus albus	2.8	Long and Campbell (1922)
Elementary bodies of vaccinia	8.54	Hughes, Parker, and Rivers (1935)
Rous sarcoma No. 1	35.0–48.0	Pollard (1938)
Blastomyces dermatiditis	8.0–10.0	Peck and Hauser (1938, 1939, 1940)
Monilia albicans	5.3	
Yeast	5.0	von Nägeli (1878)
Yeast	1.72	Frey (1930)
Oöspora lactis	7.5–22.5	Fink, Haehn, and Hoerburger (1937)
Aspergillus glaucus	4.69	Marschall (1897)
Penicillium glaucum	4.13	
Mucor stolonifer	7.03	
Penicillium javanicum	22.2	Ward, Lockwood, May, and Herrick (1935)
Penicillium roquefortii	22.9	
Aspergillus flavus	16.0	
Aspergillus sydowi	5.0–5.2	Pruess, Eichinger, and Peterson (1934)
Aspergillus oryzae	5.0–5.6	
Aspergillus niger	2.6–2.8	
Aspergillus fischeri	6.4–13.4	

* Figures correspond to material extractable by ether, petroleum ether, or alcohol-ether mixtures.

during growth, and the treatment of the cells preparatory to their extraction. For example, Nägeli as early as 1878 showed that the fat content of yeasts and molds could be increased from 5 to 12 per cent when they were grown in well-oxygenated media containing an abundance of carbohydrates but a scarcity of nitrogen. Similarly, Reindel, Niederländer, and Pfundt (1937) have shown that yeast sterols can be increased fivefold, depending upon the medium employed. The figures reported by several investigators are given in Tables 14 and 15, where it will be seen that different bacterial species show a wide variation in their lipide content. The data listed in these two tables are typical, but are in no way complete. They illustrate, however, the high lipide content of the acid-fast bacteria of the genus *Mycobacterium* and the relatively low lipide content of other microorganisms. For more complete information the review by Schwartz (1937) and the references listed in this brief discussion should be consulted.

TABLE 15

ACETONE- AND CHLOROFORM-SOLUBLE MATERIAL IN MICROORGANISMS

[From Nicolle and Alilaire (1909)]

Organism	Acetone Extract, per cent of dry weight	Chloroform Extract, per cent of dry weight
Malleomyces mallei	11.69	8.59
Corynebacterium diphtheriae	7.04	5.23
Bacillus anthracis	6.31	1.48
Pseudomonas aeruginosa	15.77	10.67
Serratia marcescens	9.00	6.60
Escherichia coli	15.25	11.77
Klebsiella pneumoniae	15.45	7.36
Proteus vulgaris	10.87	7.10
Shigella dysenteriae	12.80	10.57
Vibrio comma	8.70	6.77
Yeast	4.22	2.92

NEUTRAL FATS

The neutral, or true, fats are esters formed by a combination of glycerol and fatty acids:

$$\begin{array}{ccccc} H_2COH & & HOCO \cdot R & & H_2C—O—CO \cdot R \\ | & & & & | \\ HCOH & + & HOCO \cdot R & = & HC—O—CO \cdot R + H_2O \\ | & & & & | \\ H_2COH & & HOCO \cdot R & & H_2C—O—CO \cdot R \\ \text{Glycerol} & & \text{Fatty acids} & & \text{Neutral fat} \end{array}$$

In such a neutral fat, if all three of the fatty acid radicals (R) are the same, as in the example shown, the fat is called a *simple triglyceride;* if two or three different fatty acids are present, it is called a *mixed triglyceride.* The simple triglycerides are named according to their fatty acids. For example, the triglyceride of stearic acid is tristearin or stearin; of palmitic acid, tripalmitin or palmitin, etc. The nomenclature of the mixed triglycerides depends upon the position of the fatty acids. For instance:

$$\begin{array}{ll} \alpha & H_2C—O—CO\cdot(CH_2)_{16}CH_3 \\ & \quad | \\ \beta & \;HC—O—CO\cdot(CH_2)_7CH{=}CH(CH_2)_7CH_3 \\ & \quad | \\ \alpha_1 & H_2C—O—CO\cdot(CH_2)_{16}CH_3 \end{array}$$

is called β-oleo-α-α_1-distearin.

As a general rule, the neutral fats and oils are similar in their physical properties to the fatty acids which are present in their molecule. This is particularly true when the fatty acids are of high molecular weight and thus make up a very large part of the fat or oil molecules. Stearic acid, for example, accounts for over 90 per cent of the molecular weight of tristearin and has a melting point of 69.3°C. The melting point of the corresponding neutral fat, tristearin, is 71° to 72°C. The melting points of mixed triglycerides vary to some extent with the position of the fatty radicals. Thus β-palmito-α-α_1-dimyristin melts at 59.8°–60°C., whereas α-palmito-α_1-β-dimyristin melts at 53°C. [Averill, Roche, and King (1929)]. Pure fats are practically never found in bacteria; instead they occur together as complex mixtures which are extremely difficult to separate and purify. Analyses, therefore, are restricted usually to the fatty acids present and the determination of the ratio of saturated to unsaturated fatty acids.

The fats present in microorganisms have been studied by several investigators. The constituent fatty acids, palmitic ($C_{16}H_{12}O_2$), stearic ($C_{18}H_{36}O_2$), and oleic ($C_{18}H_{34}O_2$) have been isolated from most organisms, and such fatty acids as butyric ($C_4H_8O_2$), caproic ($C_6H_{12}O_2$), lauric ($C_{12}H_{24}O_2$), linoleic ($C_{18}H_{32}O_2$), linolenic ($C_{18}H_{30}O_2$), dihydroxystearic ($C_{18}H_{36}O_4$), tuberculostearic ($C_{19}H_{38}O_2$), arachidic ($C_{20}H_{40}O_2$), cerotic ($C_{26}H_{52}O_2$), phthioic ($C_{26}H_{52}O_2$), and myristic ($C_{30}H_{60}O_2$), have been found in the fats of bacteria. Goris and Liot (1920) found the acetone-extractable fraction of *Pseudomonas aeruginosa* to contain the fatty acids, butyric, caproic, oleic, palmitic, stearic, and arachidic. The crude fat, extracted by alcohol and ether, from *Lactobacillus acidophilus* yields lauric, myristic, palmitic, stearic, and oleic acids, as well as an appreciable amount of free dihydroxystearic acid [Crowder and Anderson (1932)]. Dihydroxystearic acid, according to these investigators, is not commonly found free in nature. It is dextrorotatory but is very easily racemized. The highest observed rotation was +7.78, but, after the acid was boiled with dilute alkali, it became optically inactive. The acid was crystallized from ethyl acetate and melted at 106°–107°C. The fat present in *Corynebacterium diphtheriae* consists mainly of free fatty acids, according to Chargaff (1933). The solid-saturated fatty acid was palmitic exclusively and constituted about one-third of the total fatty substance. The main constituent of the liquid-unsaturated fatty acids was a Δ^{9}-hexadecenoic acid, $CH_3(CH_2)_5CH{=}CH(CH_2)_7COOH$, since it could be catalytically hydrogenated to palmitic acid and gave on oxidation with $KMnO_4$ azelaic and *n*-heptoic acids. One per cent of the fatty acids present consisted of an acid having the formula, $C_{14}H_{26}O_2$. The higher unsaturated acids formed a complex mixture, but *diphtheric* acid was isolated from this complex. Chargaff assigned this acid the probable formula of $C_{35}H_{68}O_2$. It melted at 35° to 36°C. and had a specific rotation, $[\alpha]_D^{23}$, of +2.6° in $CHCl_3$. According to Cassagne (1939), the acetone-soluble portion of the diphtheria bacillus increases regularly with the age of the organisms. Dry bacilli from a 4-day culture yielded 4.82 per cent; from an 8-day culture, 6.42 per cent; from a 14-day culture, 7.9 per cent acetone-soluble material.

The lipides of *Malleomyces mallei* have been studied in some detail by Umezu (1940). This investigator found that acetone-soluble fat constitutes 5.1 to 7.6 per cent of the dried bacilli. It consists of soft, golden crystals which melt at 37°–38°C.; it is optically inactive.

Since the acid-fast bacteria of the genus *Mycobacterium* contain so much lipide material, they have been the subject of many chemical studies, the most extensive and complete of which have been carried out by Dr. R. J. Anderson and his associates at Yale University. We cannot even begin to review their investigations at this time, since they have already published over 60 papers pertaining to the chemistry of the lipides of tubercle bacilli and related acid-fast bacteria. Anderson's (1932) review, as well as the papers which have appeared and are appearing in the *Journal of Biological Chemistry*, should be read by all those interested in this subject. The fatty acids which are present in the acetone-soluble fraction of several acid-fast bacteria are listed in Table 16. It will be seen that tuberculostearic acid [Spielman (1934)], probably 10-methylstearic acid, $CH_3 \cdot (CH_2)_7 \cdot \underset{\displaystyle CH_3}{\underset{|}{CH}} \cdot (CH_2)_8 \cdot COOH$, saturated fatty acid, and phthioic acid, also a liquid-saturated fatty acid with a branched chain, are present in large amounts in the acetone-extractable fraction of the three acid-fast bacilli. The phthioic acid has the remarkable biological property of bringing about a proliferation of monocytes, epithelioid cells, and giant cells, with the formation of tubercular tissue, when injected into normal, healthy experimental animals. One of the most interesting points in connection with the neutral fat from the human tubercle bacillus is that it is not in the form of glycerides, but rather as a complex ester of fatty acids with trehalose [Anderson and Newman (1933)].

TABLE 16

FATTY ACIDS PRESENT IN THE ACETONE-SOLUBLE FATS FROM ACID-FAST BACILLI

[From Anderson (1932)]

Fatty Acids	*Mycobacterium tuberculosis*		*Mycobacterium*
	hominis	*bovis*	*phlei*
Butyric, $C_4H_8O_2$	Trace	Trace	Trace
Palmitic, $C_{16}H_{32}O_2$	Large amount	Large amount	Large amount
Stearic, $C_{18}H_{36}O_2$	Small amount	None found	None found
Cerotic, $C_{26}H_{52}O_2$	Trace	Small amount	None found
Linoleic, $C_{18}H_{32}O_2$ / Linolenic, $C_{18}H_{30}O_2$	Small amount	Small amount	Small amount
Tuberculostearic, $C_{19}H_{38}O_2$ / Phthioic, $C_{26}H_{52}O_2$	Large amount	Large amount	Large amount

The fats which have been synthesized and extracted from yeasts usually contain a high proportion of unsaturated fatty acids. Fatty acids, such as butyric, caproic, lauric, palmitic, stearic, oleic, linoleic, linolenic, myristic, arachidic, and isocetinic, have been isolated on various occasions from yeasts [MacLean and Thomas (1920),Täufel, Thaler, and Schreyegg (1936), Fink, Haehn, and Hoerburger (1937)]. An illustration of the amount of fat produced by *Oöspora lactis* when grown in Jena flasks containing a whey-inorganic salt medium may be cited (Table 17). An examination of these data shows that under the conditions of the experiment the maximum yield of crude fat was obtained in 6 days.

The lipide content of different molds varies considerably. The content of mold spores is reported to vary from about 1.0 to 14 per cent, and that of the mycelium ranges from 1.0 to 40 per cent, depending upon the species and upon such other factors as the period of incubation, the type of carbohydrate and nitrogen in the medium, the degree of acidity of the substrate, and the presence in the medium of small amounts of zinc, manganese, or copper. Pruess, Eichinger, and Peterson (1934) cultured 24 molds on two different types of media: (1) a glucose-inorganic salts substrate and (2) a glucose-malt sprouts medium. Results of their analyses of the dried mycelia of the molds are given in Table 18. When the molds were grown on the glucose-inorganic salt (synthetic) medium, the lipide content of the mycelia varied from 1.1 to 19.9 per cent, with an average of 6.0 per cent; on the glucose-malt sprouts substrate a range of 1.5 to 24.4 was obtained, with an average of 8.8 per cent. The average lipide content of all the molds was almost 50 per cent greater when grown on the glucose-malt sprouts

TABLE 17

FAT (DRY SUBSTANCE) PRODUCTION BY *Oöspora lactis* IN A WHEY MEDIUM AT 25°–30°C.

[From Fink, Haehn, and Hoerburger (1937)]

Age, days	Total Yield of Substance, grams	Total Yield of Crude Fat, grams	Total Yield of Crude Fat, per cent	Nitrogen in Substance, per cent
2	1.777	0.133	7.5	5.40
3	3.238	0.349	10.8	3.32
4	3.968	0.531	13.4	3.15
5	4.771	0.796	16.7	2.98
6	5.729	1.290	22.5	2.81
7	6.147	1.352	22.0	2.76
12	5.886	1.152	19.6	2.85
16	5.710	0.948	16.6	3.15

substrate than when cultivated on the synthetic medium. However, some species (*Aspergillus nidulans* and *Paecilomyces variota*) produced more lipide on the chemically defined medium. Ward and his associates (1934, 1935) extracted the crude fat from the dried mycelia of 61 different molds, using ethyl ether as the solvent. Of these molds 10 contained more than 15 per cent crude fat (Table 19). Some of the physical and chemical characteristics of the crude fat extracted from *Penicillium javanicum* are also cited below.

PHYSICAL AND CHEMICAL CHARACTERISTICS OF CRUDE FAT FROM *Penicillium javanicum*

[From Ward and Jamieson (1934)]

Solidification point,	6 to 7°C.	Unsaponifiable matter, per cent	2.0
Melting point,	about 15°C.	Saturated acids (corrected), per cent	30.8
Specific gravity (at 25°)	0.9145	Unsaturated acids (corrected), per cent	60.8
Refractive index (at 25°)	1.4680	Melting point of mixed saturated acids, °C.	52.5
Acid value	10.6	Mean molecular weight of saturated acids	272
Saponification value	191		
Iodine value (Hanus)	84.0		
Reichert-Meissl value	0.3		
Acetyl value	10.7		

TABLE 18

CHEMICAL COMPOSITION OF CERTAIN MOLDS

[From Pruess, Eichinger, and Peterson (1934)]

Organism	Weight of Dry Pad, grams per 100 cu. cm.	Sterol, per cent	Lipide, per cent	Crude Protein (N × 6.25), per cent	Carbohydrate (by Difference), per cent	Free Fatty Acid of Lipide (as Oleic), per cent
	Glucose-Inorganic Salts Medium					
Aspergillus aerea	2.67	0.65	4.7	34.4	60.9 *	....
Aspergillus carbonarius	4.04	0.39	1.1	13.7	85.2	56.3
Aspergillus cinnamomeus	3.63	0.42	3.4	25.0	71.6	....
Aspergillus citrosporus	3.53	0.45	3.9	32.5	63.6	....
Aspergillus clavatus	2.03	0.75	7.6	35.0	57.4	20.0
Aspergillus fischeri	2.62	0.90	6.4	31.2	62.4	15.2
Aspergillus flavipes	2.81	0.75	7.0	36.3	57.7	8.0
Aspergillus fumigatus	3.13	0.82	3.1	31.2	65.7	51.5
Aspergillus fuscus	2.81	0.93	3.0	28.1	68.9	30.2
Aspergillus insuetus	2.52	1.10	13.5	23.7	62.8	13.4
Aspergillus lutea	2.62	0.65	3.8	36.7	59.5	....
Aspergillus melleus	1.98	0.88	3.1	40.6	56.3	44.9
Aspergillus minutus	2.33	0.52	7.4	32.5	60.1	27.4
Aspergillus nidulans	3.45	0.55	19.9	25.6	54.5	9.7
Aspergillus niger	3.14	0.80	2.6	28.1	69.3	....
Aspergillus ochraceous	2.21	0.61	4.5	43.1	52.4	19.7
Aspergillus oryzae	1.17	0.84	5.0	33.7	61.3	19.5
Aspergillus schiemanni	2.39	0.78	4.1	32.5	63.4	34.2
Aspergillus sydowi	2.02	1.09	5.0	26.9	68.1	8.4
Penicillium aurantio-brunneum	1.72	0.87	11.8	23.7	64.5	17.6
Penicillium chrysogenum	1.66	0.91	2.3	43.7	54.0	67.8
Penicillium cyaneum	0.75	0.59	2.4	33.1	64.5	....
Penicillium cyaneo-fulvum	1.06	0.40	3.2	36.3	60.5	39.4
Pecilomyces varioti	1.64	1.25	14.9	30.0	55.1	14.8
Average	2.41	0.75	6.0	31.6	62.5	27.6
	Glucose-Malt Sprouts Medium					
Aspergillus aerea	2.55	0.88	6.1	25.6	68.3 †	....
Aspergillus carbonarius	5.03	0.33	2.1	12.5	85.4	....
Aspergillus cinnamomeus	4.16	0.54	5.0	14.4	80.6	....
Aspergillus citrosporus	2.59	0.57	1.5	25.6	72.9	....
Aspergillus clavatus	2.77	0.86	16.6	22.5	60.9	....
Aspergillus fischeri	2.40	0.84	13.4	28.1	58.5	8.3
Aspergillus flavipes	2.53	0.77	23.0	21.2	55.8	....
Aspergillus fumigatus	2.63	0.26	1.8	24.4	73.8	73.1
Aspergillus fuscus	3.94	0.48	5.7	18.1	76.2	16.9
Aspergillus insuetus	2.32	1.05	24.4	21.9	53.7	15.0
Aspergillus lutea	2.41	0.45	4.8	26.2	69.0	....
Aspergillus melleus	2.55	0.95	3.8	23.7	72.5	36.2
Aspergillus minutus	2.56	1.10	18.3	23.7	58.0	10.6
Aspergillus nidulans	4.16	0.38	16.8	13.1	70.1	7.9
Aspergillus niger	3.87	0.43	2.8	18.1	79.1	....
Aspergillus ochraceous	2.98	0.44	5.2	21.9	72.9	24.3
Aspergillus oryzae	1.45	1.09	5.6	36.3	58.1	19.9
Aspergillus schiemanni	3.47	0.81	5.2	18.1	76.7	38.5
Aspergillus sydowi	2.53	0.86	5.2	20.6	74.2	8.0
Penicillium aurantio-bruneum	2.21	0.77	12.9	20.6	66.5	10.7
Penicillium chrysogenum	1.87	1.16	7.1	15.0	77.9	30.4
Penicillium cyaneum	1.82	0.70	4.4	20.6	75.0	....
Penicillium cyaneo-fulvum	1.71	0.38	8.2	21.9	69.9	41.2
Pecilomyces varioti	1.48	1.70	10.1	26.9	63.0	27.4
Average	2.92	0.78	8.8	22.5	69.6	26.2

* Values in this column include ash; this varies from 2.5 to 8.5 per cent.

† Values in this column include ash; this varies from 1.0 to 4.5 per cent.

For further details on methods and results consult the references just cited and the papers by Strong and Peterson (1934), Lockwood, Ward, May, Herrick, and O'Neill (1934), Prill, Wenck, and Peterson (1935), Kroeker, Strong, and Peterson (1935), Woolley, Strong, Peterson, and Prill (1935), and Bohonos and Peterson (1943).

TABLE 19

CRUDE FAT IN THE DRIED MYCELIA OF CERTAIN MOLDS

[From Ward, Lockwood, May, and Herrick (1935)]

Organism	Crude Fat, per cent
Penicillium bailowiezense	17.0
Penicillium citrinum	18.1
Penicillium hirsutum	18.4
Penicillium soppi	20.2
Penicillium javanicum	22.2
Penicillium roqueforti	22.9
Penicillium oxalicum	24.4
Penicillium piscarum	26–28
Penicillium flavocinerium	28.5
Aspergillus flavus	16.0

WAXES, STEROLS, AND HIGHER ALCOHOLS

The general term wax is applied to many natural products, of which beeswax is the best-known example. Such compounds are usually thought of as fats in which glycerol is replaced by other alcohols. Most of these alcohols have a single hydroxyl group and a relatively high molecular weight. Probably the best known are cetyl alcohol ($C_{16}H_{33}OH$), ceryl alcohol ($C_{26}H_{53}OH$), and myricyl alcohol ($C_{30}H_{61}OH$). Many reports have appeared in the literature in reference to the wax-like substances which bacteria supposedly contain. Of the early work that of Tamura (1913) seems to be the most complete. He isolated an alcohol from the wax fraction of certain acid-fast bacilli and gave it the name *mykol* and the formula $C_{29}H_{56}O$. The compound was particularly interesting because it possessed acid-fast properties.

More recently the chemistry of the wax fraction of several acid-fast bacilli has been studied by Anderson and his associates [see Anderson (1932), Anderson, Crowder, Newman, and Stodola (1936), Cason and Anderson (1937, 1938), Anderson, Creighton, and Peck (1940), and Peck and Anderson (1941)]. These workers have shown that the so-called wax fractions of the acid-fast bacteria are composed mainly of hydroxy acids of very high molecular weight combined with carbohydrates or polysaccharides. In addition to these constituents the waxes yield on saponification small amounts of lower fatty acids and certain characteristic higher alcohols. To distinguish the high-molecular-weight hydroxy acids, which are specific metabolic products of the acid-fast bacteria, Anderson and his associates have designated them as mycolic acids. For example, the acid isolated from the bovine tubercle bacillus was called bovine mycolic acid, the three hydroxy acids from the avian tubercle bacillus were named α-, β-, and γ-mycolic acids; and the principal component of the wax of the timothy bacillus (*Mycobacterium phlei*), a dibasic acid of high molecular weight corresponding approximately to the formula, $C_{70}H_{138}O_6$, was called phleimycolic acid. The mycolic acids either are saturated compounds or have low iodine numbers, and they possess peculiar and interesting properties. They are dextrorotatory and acid-fast. In fact, they are the only substances which Anderson and his coworkers have been able to isolate from acid-fast bacilli which possess the property of acid-fastness.

The waxes from *Mycobacterium phlei* and *Mycobacterium leprae* contain the optically active alcohols, β-octadecanol ($C_{18}H_{35}OH$) and β-eicosanol ($C_{20}H_{39}OH$), and esters of fatty acids with the disaccharide, trehalose. The simpler fatty acids obtained by saponification from the wax (called leprosin) of the leprosy bacillus consist of myristic, palmitic, stearic, tetracosanic, and a new hydroxy acid called leprosinic acid ($C_{44}H_{88}O_3$). The wax of the bovine tubercle bacillus contains several interesting compounds, one of which is a crystalline dihydroxymonomethoxy alcohol ($C_{35}H_{72}O_3$), identical with phthiocerol, which has been found only in the waxes from the human tubercle bacillus. The unsaponifiable matter of the avian tubercle bacillus consists principally of *d*-eicosanol-2, $CH_3(CH_2)_{17}\cdot CHOH\cdot CH_3$, and a specific polysaccharide which on hydrolysis gives principally mannose, *d*-arabinose, galactose, and traces of glucosamine and inositol. According to Chargaff (1933), the chloroform-soluble wax-like substance from the attenuated strain of *Mycobacterium tuberculosis*, BCG, constitutes 11.1 per cent of the total dry weight of the bacteria and is a complex mixture giving on hydrolysis a pentose carbohydrate and palmitic and cerotic acids, as well as an acid-fast wax ($C_{52}H_{104}O_3$). The chloroform-soluble wax in *Malleomyces mallei* has been studied by Umezu (1940). It consists of a white amorphous substance, melting at 169° to 172°C., and constituted but 0.54 per cent of the dried bacilli.

Bacteria which are not acid-fast apparently contain very little, if any, waxy materials, because Chargaff and Levine (1938) reported that *Phytomonas tumefaciens* contained only 0.8 per cent chloroform-soluble wax in the dry material and *Corynebacterium diphtheriae* only 0.3 per cent.

The sterols are monohydroxy alcohols of high molecular weight. A condensed isocyclic system, consisting of three six-membered rings and one five-membered ring, forms the architectural principle common to such compounds. This will be seen in the two following formulas:

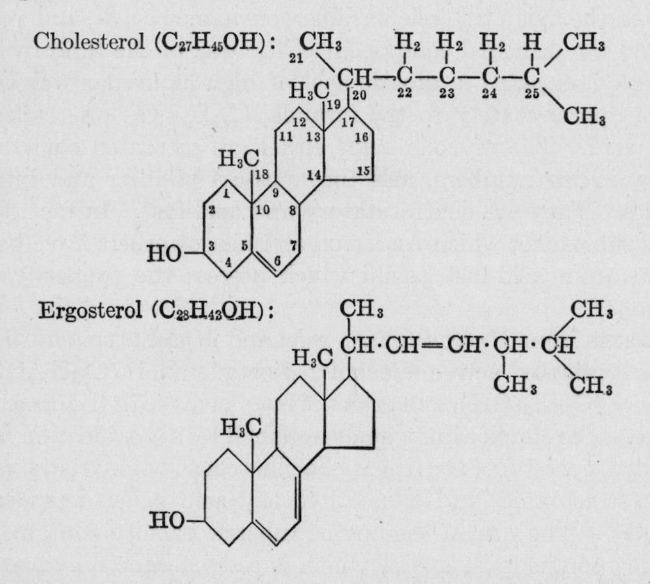

The literature contains many conflicting data concerning the presence of sterols in bacteria and other microorganisms. Several early workers reported their presence in bacteria, but others have doubted this claim. Anderson (1932) did not find any sterols in the lipide fractions of several acid-fast bacilli, Chargaff (1933) did not detect any in the lipides of *Corynebacterium diphtheriae*, and Williams, Bloor, and Sandholzer (1939) found no cholesterol or other sterols in several enteric bacilli studied. Hecht (1935), on the other hand, got a positive test for cholesterol in the petroleum-ether extract of *Escherichia coli*, and Sifferd and Anderson (1936) isolated from *Azotobacter chroococcum* a sterol which had a melting point of 156° to 158° and a $[\alpha]_D$ of $-16°$.

Yeasts are known to contain rather large amounts of sterol. MacLean and Thomas (1920) reported that ergosterol may constitute as much as 20 per cent of yeast fat, and Maguigan and Walker (1940) found that the sterol (ergosterol) content of yeast varied from 0.14

per cent to 1.44 per cent, depending upon the gaseous environment and the medium. The sterols in brewer's yeast were determined by Galimard (1934), who thought they were located in the cell membrane, probably existing as sterol-lecithide-protein complexes. Täufel, Thaler, and Schreyegg (1936) studied the chemistry of the fat from yeasts and found it to contain 19.6 per cent unsaponifiable matter, of which 3.3 per cent consisted of ergosterol and 16.3 per cent squelene. Wieland and his associates (1937) have studied the secondary sterols of yeast. Cryptosterol ($C_{30}H_{49}OH$) and zymosterol ($C_{27}H_{43}OH$) were isolated and studied. Cryptosterol was a secondary alcohol with two double bonds, melting at 138° to 140°C. and having a specific rotation, $[\alpha]_D^{20}$, of 48.7°. Zymosterol was a doubly unsaturated alcohol, and its dihydro derivative melted at 120° to 121°C. and had a specific rotation, $[\alpha]_D^{28}$, of 28.7°. Peck and Hauser (1938, 1939, 1940) found ergosterol in the lipides of certain pathogenic fungi (*Monilia albicans* and *Blastomyces dermatiditis*).

Sterols are also present in the fat-like substance of many molds. For example, Pruess, Gorcica, Greene, and Peterson (1932) made a survey of the sterol content of a great many molds. Some of their data are given in Table 18, where it will be seen that the average sterol content of molds ranges from 0.75 to 0.78 per cent of dry mycelia. Hind (1940) likewise has demonstrated ergosterol in *Penicillium carmino-violaceum*.

PHOSPHATIDES

The terms phosphatide, phospholipide, etc., have been suggested as class names for fat-like substances containing both phosphorus and nitrogen. The most common phosphatide is lecithin, which is probably built up of glycerol esterified with two molecules of fatty acid and one of phosphoric acid to which is attached a choline radical. It may be represented by the following formula:

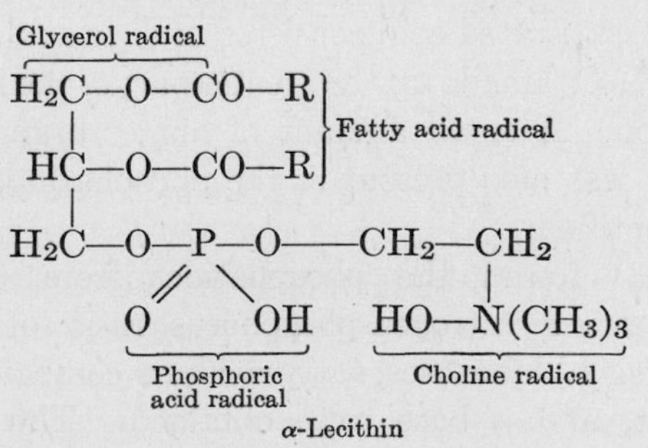

α-Lecithin

A phosphatide is usually classified simply by its ratio of nitrogen to phosphorus, for example, as a monoamino-monophosphatide (N : P = 1 : 1), diamino-monophosphatide (N : P = 2 : 1), or monoamino-diphosphatide (N : P = 1 : 2).

Compounds which can be classified as phosphatides are known to be present in many, if not all, microorganisms, since they have several properties in common with true phosphatides. They form colloidal solutions in water and are soluble in most of the fat solvents, although, when pure, they are insoluble in acetone. They are usually very hygroscopic and are oxidized spontaneously and rapidly when exposed to air and light. Furthermore, they form additional compounds with many inorganic salts, a property which is used extensively in the separation and purification of the phosphatides. Figures for the phosphatide content of non-acid-fast bacteria have been reported as ranging from 0.4 per cent to about 2.0 per cent, whereas figures for the acid-fast bacteria are somewhat higher and vary between 0.6 per cent and 6.5 per cent of total dry bacteria. Nicolle and Alilaire (1909) and other early workers found phosphatides in several bacterial species studied, but few data were given on their composition. For this reason such studies are of only historical interest.

The phosphatide from an attenuated tubercle bacilli, BCG, was studied by Chargaff (1933). It had a nitrogen-phosphorus ratio of about 8 to 1, and the chief constituents were palmitic acid and the carbohydrate, mannose. Anderson, Lothrop, and Creighton (1938) reported that the phosphatide of the human tubercle bacillus contains at least two types of carbohydrates, both of which contain phosphorus in organic combination. One carbohydrate appeared to be a mannose-glycerodiphosphoric acid and the other a glucoside, manninositose phosphoric acid. The fatty acids in the phosphatide prepared from cell residues from tuberculin were determined by Peck and Anderson (1941). The solid-saturated acids consisted mainly of palmitic acid, although traces of stearic and mycolic acids were also found. The principal liquid-unsaturated acid consisted of oleic acid, and tuberculostearic acid ($C_{19}H_{38}O_2$) made up the greater part of the liquid-saturated fatty acid fraction. A small amount of higher branched-chain dextrorotatory acids was also present in the phosphatide, but they were not definitely identified.

Chargaff (1933) found the phosphatides from *Corynebacterium diphtheriae* to have a nitrogen-phosphorus ratio of approximately 1 : 1; on hydrolysis aldohexoses, fatty acids, a compound with a high molecular weight, and a base were obtained. The solid-saturated fatty acid was exclusively palmitic, and the liquid fatty-acid fraction contained a new substance called corynin, $C_{49}H_{97}(OH)_2 \cdot COOH$, which had a melting point of 70° to 71°C. More recently, Chargaff and Levine (1938) purified the phosphatide from *Phytomonas tumefaciens*. According to their analysis, it was a monoamino-monophosphatide (N : P = 2.3 : 3.2). Phospholipides constitute the major portion of the total lipides of enteric bacilli, according to Williams, Bloor, and Sandholzer (1939). With one exception the phospholipides represented about 60 per cent of the total lipide from the various organisms. Similar results have also been obtained by Stahl (1941), using *Brucella abortus* as a test organism.

Yeasts and other fungi are known to contain phosphatides, but less work has been done on their chemical constitution than on that of some of the bacteria, especially the acid-fast bacilli of the genus *Mycobacterium*. However, Peck and Hauser (1938, 1939, 1940) have made a careful study of the phosphatides present in *Blastomyces dermatiditis* and *Monilia albicans*. Of the total lipides (8 to 10 per cent) present in *Blastomyces dermatiditis*, one-third consisted of phosphatide and two-thirds of an acetone-soluble fat, whereas of the total lipides (5.3 per cent) isolated from *M. albicans* 3.0 per cent separated into a phosphatide fraction and 97.0 per cent into an acetone-soluble fraction.

As an example of the isolation of phosphatides from molds the study Woolley, Strong, Peterson, and Prill (1935) may be cited. They found the phospholipides of *Aspergillus sydowi* constituted 0.4 to 0.7 per cent of the dried mycelia and consisted of a mixture of lecithin and cephalin. Glycerophosphoric acid, choline, cholamine, and oleic acid were identified as the chief hydrolysis products. Stearic, palmitic, and a more unsaturated acid were also present in small amounts.

SYNTHESIS OF FATS BY MICROORGANISMS

Although we have little or no information concerning the mechanism of fat synthesis by bacteria, we have fragmentary knowledge concerning the process as brought about by yeast. Haehn and Kinttof in 1925 suggested that the higher fatty acids arise from acetaldehyde, which is formed as an intermediate product in sugar breakdown. They arrived at this conclusion after carrying out extensive studies on the synthesis of fat by the so-called fat yeast, *Endomyces vernalis*. Kluyver (1931) and Fink, Haehn, and Hoerburger (1937) presented the scheme of Haehn and Kinttof in a slightly modified form, and the data presented below are from Kluyver's book. Other possible schemes are also discussed by Fink, Haehn, and Hoerburger (1937) and Reichel (1940) and should be consulted by those interested in this subject.

Glucose is first broken down, probably in the same manner as in alcoholic fermentation, to yield some intermediate product, perhaps methylglyoxal hydrate, which in turn gives pyruvic acid and hydrogen:

$$\text{(I)}\quad \underset{\text{Glucose}}{C_6H_{12}O_6} \rightarrow \underset{\substack{\text{Triose}\\ \text{(Methylglyoxal hydrate?)}}}{2CH_3\cdot CO\cdot C(OH)(OH)H} \rightarrow \underset{\text{Pyruvic acid}}{2CH_3\cdot CO\cdot COOH} + 4H$$

At the same time another intermediate compound, glyceric aldehyde, is reduced to form glycerol:

$$\text{(II)}\quad \underset{\text{Glyceric aldehyde}}{CH_2OH\cdot CHOH\cdot CHO} + 2H \rightarrow \underset{\text{Glycerol}}{CH_2OH\cdot CHOH\cdot CH_2OH}$$

The pyruvic acid formed in equation I is decarboxylated to give acetaldehyde and carbon dioxide:

$$\text{(III)}\quad \underset{\text{Pyruvic acid}}{CH_3\cdot CO\cdot COOH} \rightarrow \underset{\text{Acetaldehyde}}{CH_3\cdot CHO} + CO_2$$

Then two molecules of the acetaldehyde condense to yield aldol:

$$\text{(IV)}\quad \underset{\text{Acetaldehyde}}{CH_3\cdot C(=O)H + H{-}C(H)(H)\cdot CHO} \rightarrow \underset{\text{Aldol}}{CH_3\cdot CHOH\cdot CH_2\cdot CHO}$$

The aldol then loses water with the formation of the unsaturated aldehyde, crotonaldehyde:

$$\text{(V)}\quad \underset{\text{Aldol}}{CH_3\cdot CHOH\cdot CH_2\cdot CHO} \rightarrow \underset{\text{Crotonaldehyde}}{CH_3\cdot CH{=}CH\cdot CHO} + H_2O$$

Crotonaldehyde is reduced by hydrogen to give butyric aldehyde:

$$\text{(VI)}\quad \underset{\text{Crotonaldehyde}}{CH_3\cdot CH{=}CH\cdot CHO} + 2H \rightarrow \underset{\text{Butyric aldehyde}}{CH_3\cdot CH_2\cdot CH_2\cdot CHO} + H_2O$$

The butyric aldehyde condenses with another molecule of acetaldehyde to produce a higher homolog of aldol, namely, β-hydroxycaproic aldehyde:

$$\text{(VII)}\quad \underset{\text{Butyric aldehyde}}{CH_3\cdot CH_2\cdot CH_2\cdot C(=O)H} + \underset{\text{Acetaldehyde}}{H{-}C(H)(H)\cdot CHO} \rightarrow \underset{\beta\text{-Hydroxycaproic aldehyde}}{CH_3\cdot CH_2\cdot CH_2\cdot CHOH\cdot CH_2\cdot CHO}$$

The β-hydroxycaproic aldehyde loses water and yields α-β-hexylene aldehyde:

(VIII) $CH_3 \cdot CH_2 \cdot CH_2 \cdot CHOH \cdot CH_2 \cdot CHO \rightarrow$
β-Hydroxycaproic aldehyde

$CH_3 \cdot CH_2 \cdot CH_2 \cdot CH{=}CH \cdot CHO + H_2O$
α-β-Hexylene aldehyde

In turn this is reduced to caproic aldehyde:

(IX) $CH_3 \cdot CH_2 \cdot CH_2 \cdot CH{=}CH \cdot CHO + 2H \rightarrow$
α-β-Hexylene aldehyde

$CH_3 \cdot CH_2 \cdot CH_2 \cdot CH_2 \cdot CH_2 \cdot CHO$
Caproic aldehyde

This process of condensation with acetaldehyde, dehydration, and reduction continues until an aldehyde compound with a chain of carbon atoms corresponding to one of the higher fatty acids is formed. Oxidation of the aldehyde group (CHO) to a carboxyl group (COOH) then gives the fatty acid. The fatty acids thus produced form esters with glycerol, which arises in the early stages of the process (see equation II). Most of the fats which have been isolated from yeasts are true glycerides and contain fatty acids with an even number of carbon atoms. Therefore this scheme serves to illustrate the mechanism involved. On the other hand, when we try to explain the synthesis of bacterial fats and waxes by such a scheme, we encounter many difficulties. For instance, some of the fats and waxes of the tubercle bacillus are not glycerides or compounds containing well-known alcohols, but rather esters in which glycerol has been replaced by the disaccharide trehalose or even more complex polysaccharides, and instead of all the fatty acids being straight-chain acids, some are known to have branched chains.

THE PIGMENTS OF MICROORGANISMS

A great many microorganisms produce some coloring matter or pigment. Some of the pigments remain confined within the cells, but others are secreted by the cells into the surrounding medium. Often this characteristic is used to classify the pigments as extracellular or intracellular. Further classification can then be made on the basis of solubility in various reagents [see Wolberg (1938)]. Shades of color ranging from red to violet to black are formed by bacteria, especially aerobic species. It has been stated that pigments are never produced by anaerobic bacteria, but this point requires further investigation [see French (1940)]. Higher fungi also produce pigments of many shades.

Pigmentation by microorganisms is governed by a variety of factors. Reid (1936) showed that solid media are usually more favorable than liquid substrates for the detection of color, and that the principal element essential for the production of pigment by bacteria is nitrogen. Certain mineral salts are sometimes necessary, and the reaction(*p*H) of the medium may influence the color of certain pigments. The carbon source, temperature of incubation, oxygen supply, and presence of light are also factors which at times govern pigment production by bacteria and other fungi [Wolberg (1938)].

The literature on this subject is so large that it is impossible to give an extensive review. Only brief mention of some of the more recent studies will be given. For more extensive reading the references at the end of the chapter, particularly the general reviews by Bergmann, (1933, 1934), Godfrin (1934), Reid (1936), Birkinshaw (1937), Wolberg (1938), White (1939), and Heilbron (1942), should be consulted. For references to the older literature volume I by Buchanan and Fulmer (1928) should be consulted. By far the greatest amount of work in this field has been carried out by Raistrick and his associates in England, who have been mainly concerned with mold pigments. Reference to most of their studies will be found in the review by Birkinshaw (1937).

So little is known about the chemical nature and composition of the microbial pigments that a general classification based entirely on such knowledge is impossible at this time. For the most part, however, the pigments isolated to date may be classified as follows [White (1939)]:

Bacterial Pigments	*Fungus Pigments*
Pyrrole derivatives	Benzene derivatives
Phenazines	Diphenyl quinones
Carotenoids	Terphenyl quinones
A naphthoquinone	Anthraquinones
Miscellaneous	Phenanthraquinones
	Oxonium bases
	Hydrocarbons
	Miscellaneous

These two main groups will be discussed separately. A somewhat similar classification was employed by Wolberg (1938). He also tabulated the solubilities of most of the known bacterial pigments.

BACTERIAL PIGMENTS

Because of certain cultural difficulties investigations concerned with bacterial pigments have not produced so many substances as have similar researches on higher fungi. However, two pyrrole derivatives, three phenazines, several carotenoids and the naphthoquinone, phthiocol, have been well characterized (Table 20). As we shall point out shortly, the pigments from higher fungi include many quinones, but none appear to be naphthoquinones, but the only true quinone thus far isolated from bacteria belongs to the naphthoquinone group.

The two *pyrrole* derivatives which have been isolated from bacteria consist of *bacteriochlorophyll* and *prodigiosin.* Bacteriochlorophyll is closely related to, but apparently not identical with, the chlorophyll of green plants. The pigment has been isolated from the photosynthesizing bacteria, *Rhodobacillus palustris, Rhodovibrio,* and *Thiocystis violacea,* which, like higher plants, assimilate carbon dioxide in the light. It is thought to exist in two forms, usually spoken of as bacteriochlorophyll a and b. Bacteriochlorophyll b is the more highly oxidized. These substances are very labile and can be reversibly oxidized and reduced by a number of agents. The empirical formula for bacteriochlorophyll b is $C_{55}H_{72}N_4O_6 \cdot Mg \cdot H_2O$, according to Schneider (1934). Fischer and his associates (1935, 1937, 1938) have shown that the structure for bacteriochlorophyll a is most probably represented by the formula given in Table 20. Van Niel and Arnold (1938) have described a simple and rapid method for the quantitative determination of bacteriochlorophyll. The technique is based on the quantitative extraction of the pigment, its quantitative conversion into bacteriopheophytin, and the spectrophotometric estimation of the bacteriopheophytin in a mixed solvent. The procedure does not have an experimental error of more than 3 per cent. French (1940) has studied the pigment-protein complex in several photosynthetic bacteria including *Spirillum rubrum, Rhodovibrio* species, *Phaeomonas* species, and *Streptocococcus varians.* He found that the absorption curves for the water-soluble cell juice from these organisms all showed approximately the same maxima at 790 and 590 mμ. The second pyrrole derivative which has been fairly well characterized is prodigiosin, the red coloring matter produced by *Serratia marcescens* (*Bacillus prodigiosus*).

The three bacterial pigments which are phenazine derivatives are: *pyocyanin, chlororaphin,* and *1:2-dihydroxyphenazine-di-N-oxide.* Pyocyanin is the dark-blue pigment produced by *Pseudomonas aeruginosa* (*Pseudomonas pyocyanea*), and was the first phenazine derivative to be found in nature. It is decolorized by either oxidation or reduction and, with alkali, is converted into oxidation and reduction products. It has been used in a number of experiments as an accessory respiratory ferment. The most important studies of this pigment are referred to in Table 20. Chlororaphin is a green pigment which has not received a great deal of attention. Likewise, the pigment (1 : 2-dihydroxyphenaz-

TABLE 20

PIGMENTS PRODUCED BY CERTAIN BACTERIA

Pigment	Structural Formula	Bacterium	Reference
Bacteriochlorophyll a ($C_{55}H_{72}N_4O_6Mg$)	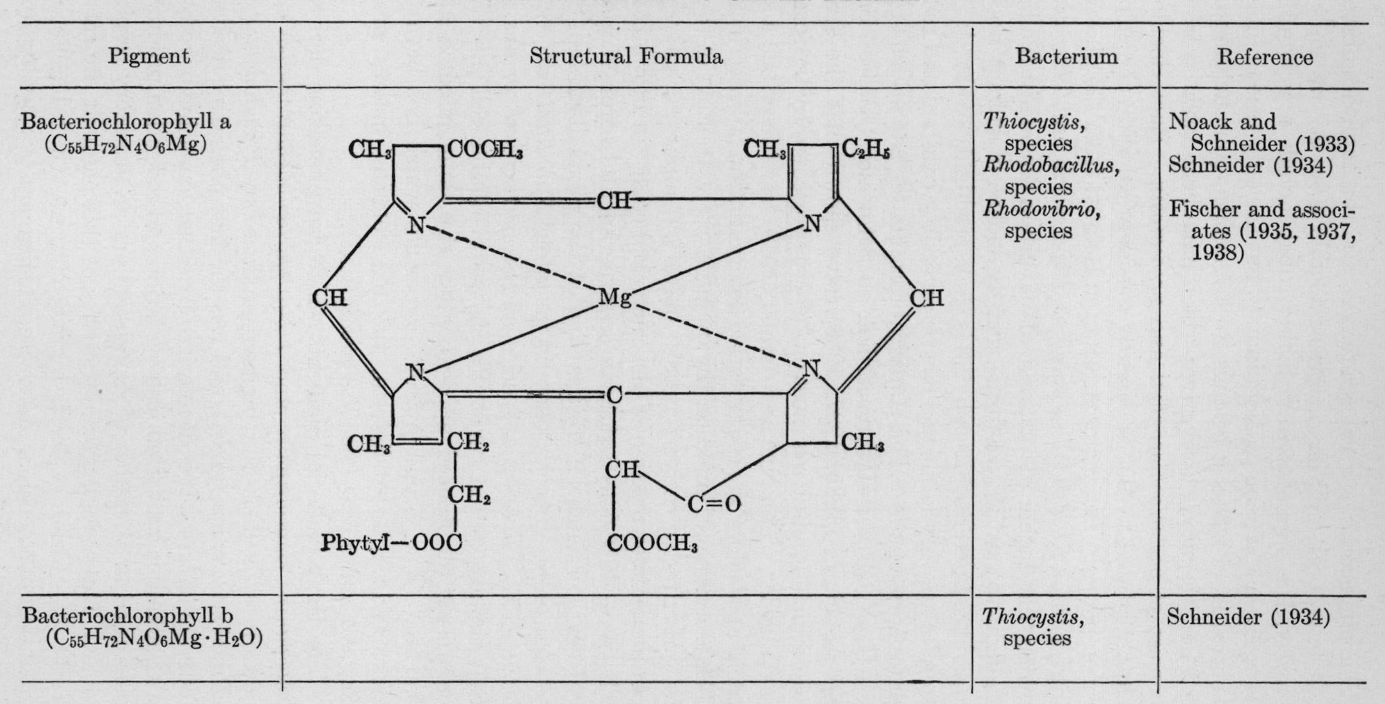	*Thiocystis*, species *Rhodobacillus*, species *Rhodovibrio*, species	Noack and Schneider (1933) Schneider (1934) Fischer and associates (1935, 1937, 1938)
Bacteriochlorophyll b ($C_{55}H_{72}N_4O_6Mg \cdot H_2O$)		*Thiocystis*, species	Schneider (1934)

Chlororaphin (green) ($C_{13}H_8O_2N_2$) M.P. 229°–230°C.	N, N, COOH	*Bacillus chlororaphis*	Kögl and Postowsky (1930) Kögl and Tönnis (1932)
Flavins		Yeasts and bacteria	Warburg (1938) Yamagutchi and Usami (1939)
Iodinin [1:2(?)-dihydroxyphenazine-di-N-oxide] (violet) ($C_{12}H_8O_4N_2$) M.P. 236°C.	O, N, —OH, —OH, N, O	*Chromobacterium iodinum*	Clemo and McIlwain (1938) McIlwain (1943)
Melanin (black)		*Azotobacter chroococcum*	Ungerer (1934)
Phthiocol (2-methyl-3-hydroxy-1:4-naphthoquinone) (yellow) ($C_{11}H_8O_3$) M.P. 173°–174°C.	O, —CH_3, —OH, O	*Mycobacterium tuberculosis*	Anderson and Newman (1933)

TABLE 20 (*Continued*)

PIGMENTS PRODUCED BY CERTAIN BACTERIA

Pigment	Structural Formula	Bacterium	Reference
Prodigiosin (red) ($C_{20}H_{25}N_3O$) M.P. 176°C.	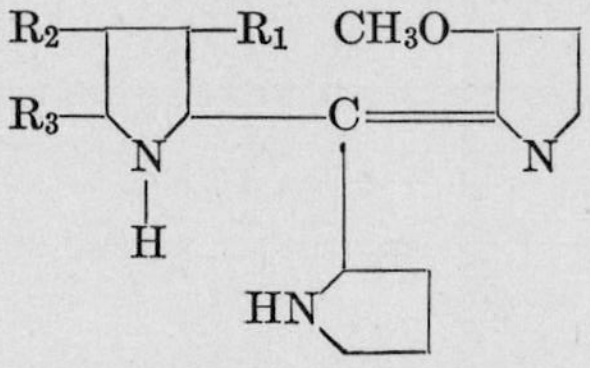 $R_1 + R_2 + R_3 = C_6H_{15}$	*Serratia marcescens*	Wrede and Hettche (1929) Wrede (1932) Wrede and Rothhaas (1933) Ehrismann and Noethling (1936)
Pyocyanin (dark blue) ($C_{26}H_{20}N_4O_2$)	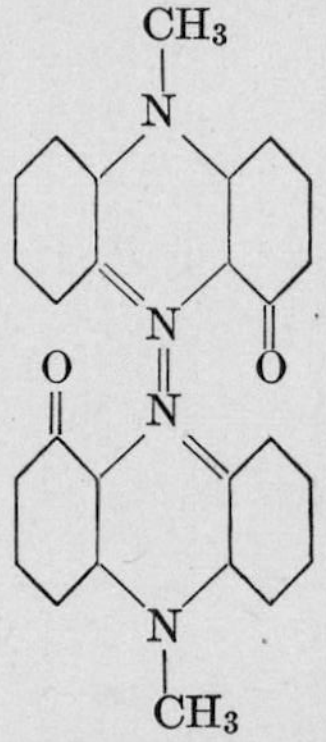	*Pseudomonas aeruginosa*	Wrede and Strack (1929) Friedheim and Michaelis (1931) Friedheim (1931) Kuhn and Schön (1935) Ehrismann and Noethling (1936)

Rhodopin ($C_{40}H_{58}O$) or ($C_{40}H_{56}O$) M.P. 171°C.		*Thiocystis*, species	Karrer, Solmssen, and Koenig (1938)
Rhodoviolascin (blue) ($C_{42}H_{60}O_2$) M.P. 218°C.	$(CH_3)_2\cdot C{=}CH\cdot \overset{OCH_3}{C}{=}CH\cdot \overset{CH_3}{C}{=}[CH\cdot CH{=}CH\cdot \overset{CH_3}{C}]_2{=}CH$ $(CH_3)_2\cdot CH\cdot CH_2\cdot \underset{OCH_3}{CH}\cdot CH_2\cdot \underset{CH_3}{C}{=}CH\cdot CH{=}[CH\cdot \underset{CH_3}{C}{=}CH\cdot CH]_2{=}CH$	*Rhodovibrio*, species *Thiocystis*, species	Karrer and Solmssen (1935, 1936) Karrer and Koenig (1940)
Spirilloxanthin (red) ($C_{48}H_{66}O_3$) M.P. 218–219°C.		*Spirillum rubrum*	van Niel and Smith (1935)
Toxoflavin (yellow) ($C_6H_6N_4O_2$)	Isomer of l-methyl xanthine	*Bacterium cocovenenans*	van Veen and Baars (1937, 1938)
Violacein ($C_{10}H_{12}O_3N$)		*Chromobacterium violaceum*	Tobie (1935, 1936)

ine-di-N-oxide) of *Chromobacterium iodinum* has only recently been investigated from a chemical standpoint.

A large number of *carotenoid* pigments have been isolated from bacteria by various workers. The carotenoids are red, orange, or yellow pigments which are soluble in the solvents: ether, chloroform, benzol, and carbon disulfide. They derive their name from carotene, $C_{40}H_{56}$, the unsaturated hydrocarbon present in carrots, egg yolk, and butter. The xanthophylls, $C_{40}H_{56}O_2$, also belong to this general group. Such compounds are usually distinguished by chromatographic analysis. Most of the carotenoids give the lipocyan test, a deep-blue color with concentrated sulfuric acid. Those bacteria which produce bacteriochlorophyll also contain carotenoids, and it has been shown that the two types of pigment are present in the same ratio as in the higher plants. Several of the carotenoids isolated have been found to be identical with those already known, for example, β- and γ-carotene, lycopene, and xanthophylls, but many are new. For example, Karrer and his associates (1935, 1936, 1938, 1940) have studied the carotenoids of the purple bacteria and described the following new pigments: *rhodoviolascin, rhodopin, rhodopurpurin, flavorhodin. Lycopene* and β-carotene were also present. *Spirillum rubrum* forms the purple pigment, *spirilloxanthin,* which contains one hydroxyl group and fifteen double bonds, as well as other carotenoid pigments [van Niel and Smith (1935)]. French (1940) has also reviewed the work on carotenoids in certain photosynthetic bacteria.

The carotenoids, however, are by no means restricted to occurrence with bacteriochlorophyll, since a number of bacteria which are not photosynthetic also produce such pigments. For instance, Reader (1925) isolated a new carotenoid, coralin, from *Streptothrix corallinus.* Chargaff (1933, 1934) and Chargaff and Lederer (1935) isolated two carotenoids from *Sarcina lutea,* zeaxanthin and β-carotene from *Sarcina aurantiaca,* and zeaxanthine from *Staphylococcus aureus* and studied the carotenoids in two acid-fast bacilli. Ingraham and Steenbock (1935) demonstrated kryptoxanthin, α- and β-carotene, lutein, zeaxanthin, and azafrin in a study of the production of carotenoids by *Mycobacterium phlei;* and leprotin, a carotenoid hydrocarbon similar to β-carotene, was found by Grundmann and Takeda (1937) in an acid-fast bacteria isolated from a leprous lesion. Nakamura (1936) was of the opinion that the yellow pigment produced by *S. lutea* was very closely related to kryptoxanthin, but Lederer (1938) called this carotenoid sarcinene. Lederer also isolated a similar compound from *Bacterium halobium,* to which he assigned the name bacterioruberin. More recently Takeda and Ohta (1941) have studied the carotenoid pigments of *S. lutea* and report the isolation of a new xanthophyll, which they call sarcinaxanthin. The pigment melts at 149° to 150°C. and has absorption maxima at 480, 451, and 423 mμ in chloroform and benzene. The pigments from variants of *Micrococcus tetragenus* have been studied spectrometrically by Reimann and Eckler (1941). The following pigments were recognized in the respective type strains: yellow strain—xanthophyll; white strain—no pigment; pink strain—rhodoxanthin; mucoid-pink strain—lycopene; pink-yellow strain—α-carotin or rubixanthin and other unidentified pigments; brown strain—γ-carotin or rubixanthin and other unidentified pigments. Stahly, Sesler, and Brode (1942) have also developed an accurate and simple method for measuring bacterial pigments by the use of the spectrophotometer and the photoelectric colorimeter. The spectrometer is employed first to determine the absorption spectra data for each specific pigment. These data are then applied in the use of the photoelectric colorimeter for the measurement of the pigment in a bacterial suspension. For example, one filter is chosen to transmit the light waves which are unabsorbed by the bacterial pigment; a second filter transmits the light which is affected most by the pigment. The colorimeter reading with the first filter represents turbidity; that with the second filter, turbidity plus pigment. Calculations can then be made to obtain the photometric density due to pigment for a standard turbidity. Using this technique, Sobin and Stahly (1942) studied twelve carotenoid pigments isolated from fourteen different bacteria, including five species of the genus *Flavobacterium*, three of *Sarcina*, two of *Micrococcus*, two of *Erwinia*, and one each of *Bacterium* and *Cellulomonas*. Some bacteria produced only one pigment, whereas others produced several. Pigments whose absorption maxima were identical with those of Δ-carotenoid and rubixanthin were found in all strains of *S. aureus* studied.

The only naphthoquinone which has been isolated from bacteria is the yellow pigment, *phthiocol*, which Anderson and Newman (1933) demonstrated in human tubercle bacilli.

A great many other pigments are produced by bacteria, but their constitutions are not yet clear. They include *caryocyanine* from *Bacterium caryocyaneus* [Godfrin (1934)]; a lyochrome from *Pseudomonas fluorescens* [Giral (1936)]; the blue pigment, *indigoidine*, from *Pseudomonas indigofera* [Elazari-Volcani (1939)]; *melanin* from *Azotobacter chroococcum* [Ungerer (1934)], *Bacillus niger*, and related species; *toxoflavin* from *Bacterium cocovenenans* [van Veen and Baars (1937, 1938)] and other *flavins* from many bacteria [Yamagutchi and Usami (1939)]; *violacein* ($C_{10}H_{12}O_3N$), a quinone imine, from *Chromobacterium violaceum; cytochromes;* and other pigments concerning whose chemistry even less is known.

TABLE 21

PIGMENTS PRODUCED BY CERTAIN HIGHER FUNGI

Pigment	Structural Formula	Fungus	Reference
Aspergillin (brown)	Similar to humic acids from peats	*Aspergillus niger*, spores	Quilico (1933)
Atromentin (brown) ($C_{18}H_{12}O_6$)	HO—C₆H₄—(ring: =O, —OH, HO—, =O)—C₆H₄—OH	*Paxillus atromentosus*	Kögl and Becker (1928)
Aurantin (yellow) ($C_{16}H_{22}O_3$)		*Oöspora aurantia*	Birkinshaw (1937)
Aurofusarin (orange-yellow) ($C_{30}H_{20}O_{12}$) M.P. above 360°C.		*Fusarium culmorum*	Ashley, Hobbs, and Raistrick (1937)
Auroglaucin (golden-orange) ($C_{19}H_{22}O_3$) M.P. 146°–152°C.	OH, OH, C_5H_9 on ring —CO—(CH=CH)$_3$—CH_3	*Aspergillus glaucus*, species	Gould and Raistrick (1934) Cruickshank, Raistrick, and Robinson (1938)

Boletol (blue) ($C_{15}H_8O_7$) M.P. 253°C.	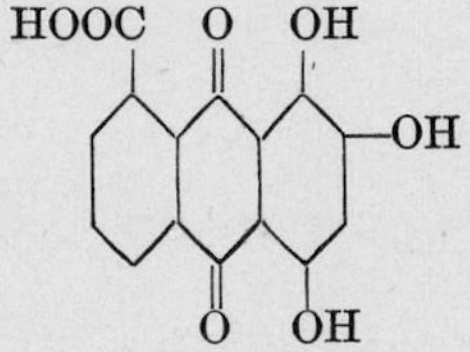	*Boletus luridus* *Boletus satanas*	Kögl and Deijs (1934)
β-Carotene (yellow)		*Mucor hiemalis* *Phycomyces blakesleeanus*	Birkinshaw (1937)
Carviolacin (red to orange) ($C_{20}H_{16}O_7$) Carviolin (red to orange) ($C_{16}H_{12}O_6$)	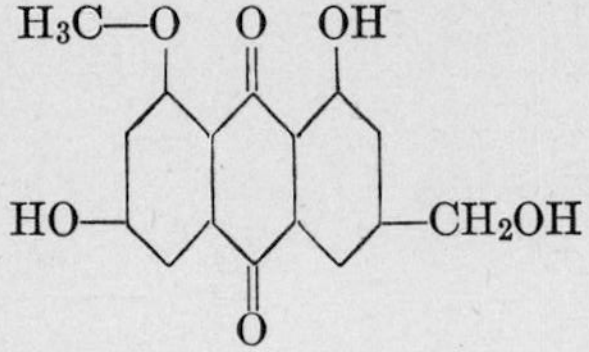	*Penicillium carmin-oviolaceum*	Hind (1940)
Catenarin [β-(hydroxymethyl)-1:5:8-trihydroxyanthraquinone] (red) ($C_{15}H_{10}O_6$) M.P. 246°C.	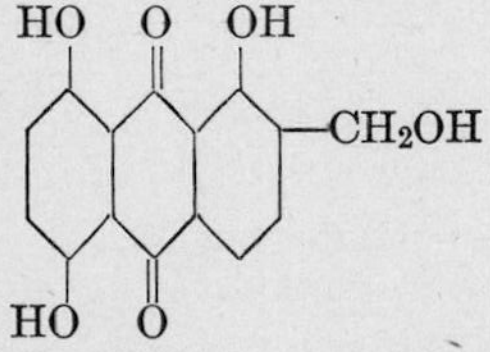	*Helminthosporium catenarium* *Helminthosporium gramineum* *Helminthosporium tritici-vulgaris* *Helminthosporium velutinum*	Raistrick, Robinson, and Todd (1934)

TABLE 21 (*Continued*)

PIGMENTS PRODUCED BY CERTAIN HIGHER FUNGI

Pigment	Structural Formula	Fungus	Reference
Chrysogenin (yellow) ($C_{18}H_{22}O_6$)		*Penicillium chrysogenum* *Penicillium notatum*	Clutterbuck, Lovell, and Raistrick (1932)
Citrinin (yellow) ($C_{13}H_{14}O_5$) M.P. 166°–170°C.	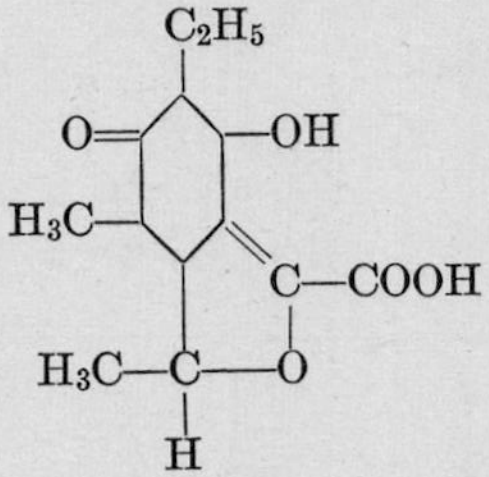 C_2H_5; O=; —OH; H_3C—; C—COOH; H_3C—C—O; H	*Penicillium citrinum*	Hetherington and Raistrick (1931)
Citromycetin (lemon-yellow) ($C_{14}H_{10}O_7 \cdot 2H_2O$) M.P. 283°–285°C.	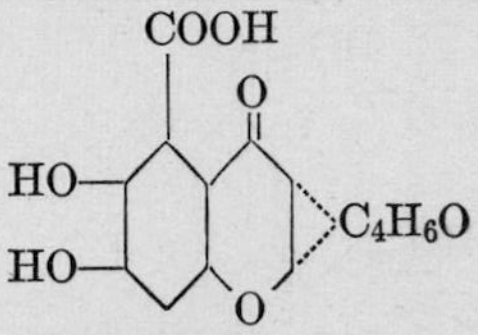 COOH; O; HO—; HO—; C_4H_6O; O	*Citromyces glaber* *Citromyces pfefferianus*	Hetherington and Raistrick (1931)

Cynodontin (probably 1:4:5:8-tetrahydroxy-2-methylanthraquinone) (bronze-like) ($C_{15}H_{10}O_6$) M.P. 260°C.	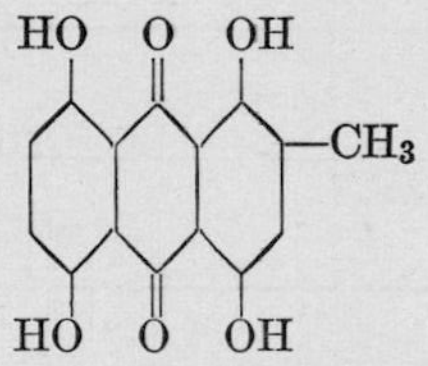 HO O OH —CH_3 HO O OH	*Helminthosporium cynodontis* *Helminthosporium euchlenae*	Raistrick, Robinson, and Todd (1933)
Emodic acid (4:5:7-trihydroxyanthraquinone-2-carboxylic acid) (orange) ($C_{15}H_8O_7$) M.P. 363°–365°C.	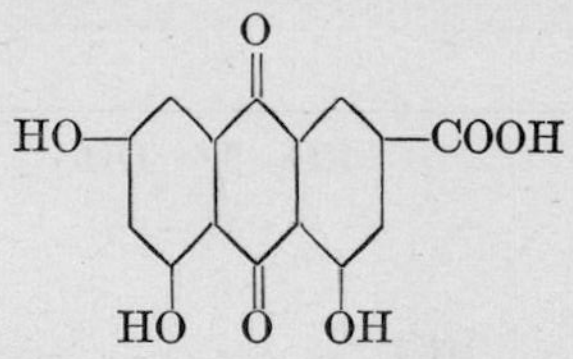 O HO— —COOH HO O OH	*Penicillium cyclopium*	Anslow, Breen, and Raistrick (1940)
Ergochrysin (yellow) ($C_{28}H_{28}O_{12}$) M.P. 266°C.		Ergot	Bergmann (1932)
Erythroglaucin (ruby-red) ($C_{16}H_{12}O_6$) M.P. 205°–206°C.		*Aspergillus ruber* *Aspergillus glaucus*, species	Ashley, Raistrick, and Richards (1939) Gould and Raistrick (1934)
Flavoglaucin (lemon-yellow) ($C_{19}H_{28}O_3$) M.P. 97°–105°C.		*Aspergillus glaucus*, species	Gould and Raistrick (1934)
Fulvic acid (yellow) ($C_{14}H_{12}O_8$) M.P. 246°C.		*Penicillium Brefeldianum* *Penicillium flexuosum* *Penicillium griseofulvum*	Oxford, Raistrick, and Simonart (1935)

TABLE 21 (*Continued*)

PIGMENTS PRODUCED BY CERTAIN HIGHER FUNGI

Pigment	Structural Formula	Fungus	Reference
Fumigatin (3-hydroxy-4-methoxy-2:5-toluquinone) (maroon) ($C_8H_8O_4$) M.P. 116°C.	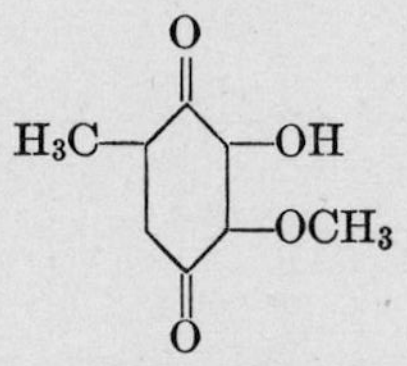 O, H_3C, OH, OCH_3, O	*Aspergillus fumigatus*	Anslow and Raistrick (1938)
Helminthosporin (2-methyl-4:5:8-trihydroxyanthraquinone) (dark-maroon crystals) ($C_{15}H_{10}O_5$) M.P. 226°–227°C.	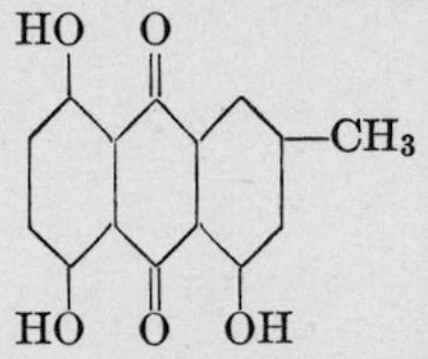 HO, O, CH_3, HO, O, OH	*Helminthosporium gramineum*	Charles, Raistrick, Robinson, and Todd (1933)
Lactarazulene (blue) ($C_{15}H_{18}$) Lactaroviolin (red-violet) ($C_{15}H_{14}O$)		*Lactarius deliciosus*	Willstaedt (1935, 1936, 1939)
Monascoflavin (yellow) ($C_{17}H_{22}O_4$)		*Monascus purpureus*	Birkinshaw (1937)
Monascorubrin (red) ($C_{22}H_{24}O_5$)		*Monascus purpureus*	Birkinshaw (1937)

Muscarufin (orange-red) ($C_{25}H_{16}O_9$) M.P. 275.5°C.	COOH, O, —(CH=CH)$_2$—COOH, HO—, O, COOH	*Amanita muscaria*	Kögl and Erxleben (1930)
Oösporin (purple-brown with $FeCl_3$) ($C_{10}H_{14}O_2$)		*Oöspora aurantia*	Birkinshaw (1937)
Penicilliopsin (orange) ($C_{30}H_{24}O_8$) M.P. 330°C.		*Penicilliopsis clavariae-formis*	Oxford and Raistrick (1940)
Phenicin (yellow, red, or violet, depending on *p*H) ($C_{14}H_{10}O_6$) M.P. 230°–231°C.	O, O, H_3C—, —OH, HO—, —CH_3, O, O	*Penicillium pheiceum*	Posternak (1938)
Physcion (red-orange) ($C_{16}H_{12}O_5$) M.P. 203°–204°C.	O, H_3CO—, —CH_3, HO, O, OH	*Aspergillus glaucus*, species	Ashley, Raistrick, and Richards (1939)

TABLE 21 (*Continued*)

PIGMENTS PRODUCED BY CERTAIN HIGHER FUNGI

Pigment	Structural Formula	Fungus	Reference
Polyporic acid (2:5-diphenyl-3:6-dihydroxybenzoquinone) (yellow) ($C_{18}H_{12}O_4$) M.P.206°–207°C.		*Polyporus ridulans*	Kögl (1925)
Ravenelin (3-methyl-1:4:8-trihydroxyxanthone) ($C_{14}H_{10}O_5$) M.P. 267°–268°C.		*Helminthosporium ravenelii* *Helminthosporium turcicum*	Raistrick, Robinson, and White (1936)
Rubrofusarin (red) ($C_{15}H_{12}O_5$) M.P. 210°–211°C.		*Fusarium culmorum*	Ashley, Hobbs, and Raistrick (1937)
Sclerotiorine (yellow-brown in alkali) ($C_{20}H_{20}O_5Cl$) M.P. 206°–207°C.		*Penicillium sclerotiorum*	Curtin and Reilly (1940)

Spinulosin (6-hydroxyfumigatin (blue-purple) ($C_8H_8O_5$) M.P. 200°C.	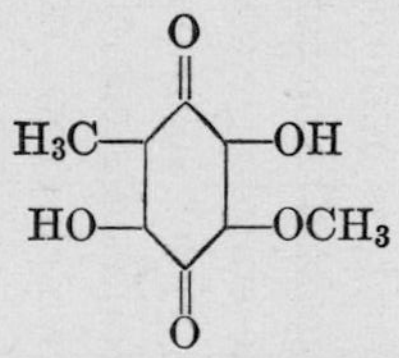 O; H_3C—; —OH; HO—; —OCH_3; O	*Penicillium spinulosum*	Anslow and Raistrick (1938)
Telephoric acid (indigo-blue) ($C_{20}H_{12}O_9$)	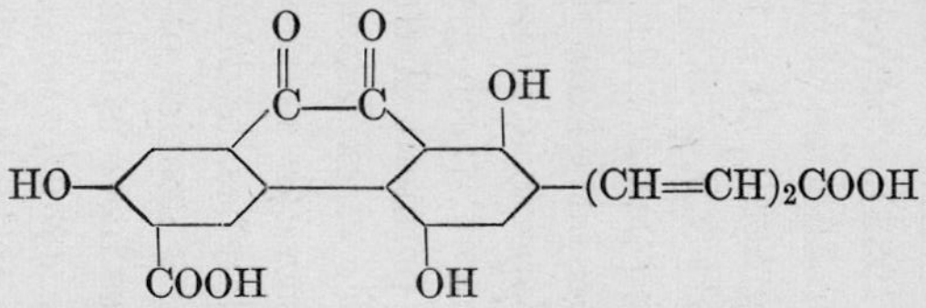 O O; C—C; OH; HO—; —$(CH{=}CH)_2COOH$; COOH; OH	*Telephora*, species	Kögl, Erxleben, and Jänecke (1930)
Tritisporin [1:3:5:8-tetrahydroxy-6-(or 7)-(hydroxymethyl) anthraquinone] (red-brown) ($C_{15}H_{10}O_7$) M.P. 260°–262°C.	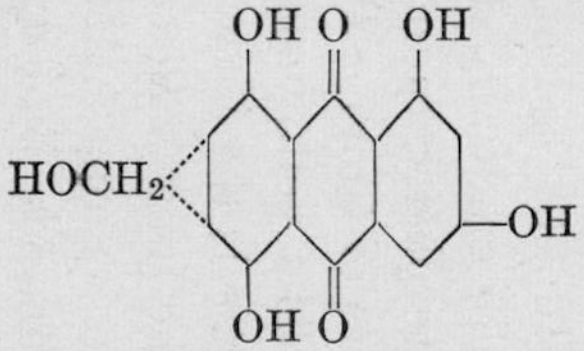 OH O OH; $HOCH_2$; —OH; OH O	*Helminthosporium tritici-vulgaris*	Raistrick, Robinson, and Todd (1934)
Verdazulene (green) ($C_{15}H_{16}$)		*Lactarius deliciosus*	Willstaedt (1939)
Xylindein (malachite-green) ($C_{34}H_{26}O_{11}$)		*Peziza aeruginosa* (wood-rotting fungus)	Rommier (1868) White (1939)

FUNGUS PIGMENTS

The pigments produced by certain higher fungi have been more completely investigated than those from bacteria. One of the most important reasons for this difference is the ease of cultivating certain molds on simple subtrates. Of the pigments isolated from molds and related fungi the anthraquinone group has the most representatives. Several pigments are listed in Table 21, together with references to their investigators. Unfortunately space does not permit a discussion of the chemistry of these compounds. For details the references should be consulted.

Of the benzene derivatives isolated from higher fungi three are derivatives of toluquinone, and two are quinol products. The toluquinones are represented by *fumigatin*, *apinulosin*, and *citrinin*. The two quinols, hydroquinones, are *auroglaucin* and *flavoglaucin*. The only diphenyl quinone which has been obtained from fungi is called *phenicin;* it was first isolated by Friedheim from *Penicillium pheiceum* and has been synthesized by Posternak (1938). Several intermediate semiquinones may be formed by partial reduction of phenicin; for this reason it is believed to be a respiratory pigment. It is yellow in strongly acid solutions (*p*H 1.0 to 3.0), red at *p*H 4.9 to 6.0, and violet in alkaline solutions. The color gradually disappears when the *p*H is maintained above 8.5. Three terphenyl quinones have been recognized as metabolic pigmented products of fungi. *Polyporic* acid is the simplest example of this group. It is a yellow pigment which gives violet solutions in alkalies. *Atromentin* is the brown pigment of the top and stem of the fruiting body of the fungus *Paxillus atromentosus*, which grows in the spring on old tree stumps. *Muscarufin* is thought to occur in the organism as a glucoside but undergoes hydrolysis during isolation. In an examination of a great many species of the genus *Helminthosporium* Raistrick and his associates have isolated several different anthraquinones, such as *catenarin*, *cynodontin*, *emodic acid*, *helminthosporin*, and *tritisporin*. *Boletol* and other pigments also belong to this group. Two representatives of the phenanthraquinone group may be mentioned which occur in higher fungi. They are *telephoric acid* and *xylindein*.

Four oxonium bases have been isolated from fungi. These are *ravenelin* from *Helminthosporium ravenelii*, *rubrofusarin* from *Fusarium culmorum*, *lactaroviolin* from *Lacterium deliciosus*, and *citromycetin*, the yellow coloring matter from *Citromyces glaber*.

Among the hydrocarbon pigments of the higher fungi, α-, β-, and γ-carotene, lycopene, and several other carotenoid hydrocarbons have been isolated from yeasts. Tischer (1937, 1938, 1939) studied the carotenoids of the fresh-water alga, *Hematococcus pluvialis* and *Aphani-*

zomenon flos-aquae, and demonstrated the presence of β-carotene, lutein, and zeaxanthin, as well as a new carotenoid, *hematoxanthin*, with an absorption maximum at 478 mμ. Besides these carotenoids, Tischer isolated and described the following new polyene pigments from *A. flos-aquae: aphanin*, $C_{40}H_{54}O$, with absorption maxima at 505 and 474 mμ; *aphanicin*, $C_{80}H_{106}O_3$, which contains twelve double bonds; and *aphanizophyll* and *flavacin*, which were not fully characterized. A new carotenoid, *torulene*, has recently been isolated by Fromageot and Tchang (1938) from *Rhodotorula sanniei*. Other hydrocarbons of interest, belonging to the azulene group, are *lactarazulene* and *verdazulene*, which have been isolated from *Lactarius deliciosus* by Willstaedt (1935, 1936, 1939).

Other miscellaneous fungus pigments have been described, but their composition has not been completely solved. Examples include *aspergillin*, the complex brown pigment of the spores of *Aspergillus niger*, *aurantin* from *Oöspora aurantia*, *fulvic* acid from certain *Penicillium* species, and *monascoflavin* and *monascorubrin* from *Monascus purpureus*. Certain of their properties will be found in Table 21. For other details the references should be consulted.

BACTERIA AND OTHER FUNGI AS A SOURCE OF VITAMINS FOR HIGHER ANIMALS

Probably the members of the vitamin B-complex are the principal vitamins which are synthesized by microorganisms, although it is known that bacteria synthesize compounds which exhibit vitamin K activity, as well as compounds which resemble other well-known vitamins. The earlier work on this subject, however, is difficult to classify with our present knowledge of the various fractions of the vitamin B-complex.

Wollman (1921), Wollman and Vagliano (1922), Slanetz (1923), and Cunningham (1924) were unable to demonstrate vitamin A or vitamin B in *Lactobacillus bulgaricus*(?), *Azotobacter chroococcum*, *Bacterium lactis-acidi*, *Serratia marcescens*, *Bacillus mycoides*, *Bacillus subtilis*, *Rhizobium leguminosarum*, *Micrococcus agilis*, and the tubercle bacillus. Cooper (1914) and Weill, Arloing, and Dufourt (1922) could not demonstrate vitamin B activity in *Escherichia coli* when the organisms were fed to pigeons that were on a diet of polished rice. Damon (1923, 1924) reviewed some of the early work on this subject and in his own investigations showed that the timothy bacillus, *Mycobacterium smegmatis*, and *Mycobacterium moelleri*, when fed to rats in the dry form (7.5 per cent of the diet), served as a source of vitamin B. *Klebsiella pneumoniae* and *Bacillus adherens* were both negative.

Sunderlin and Werkman (1928) demonstrated vitamin B synthesis by *B. subtilis*, *B. adherens*, *B. mycoides*, *E. coli*, *A. chroococcum*, and *R. leguminosarum*. Schieblich (1929, 1930, 1931, and 1933) obtained positive results for vitamin B synthesis with *Bacillus vulgatus*, *Bacillus mesentericus*, *B. mycoides*, *B. mycoides-ruber*, *Bacillus ellenbachensis*, *S. marcescens*, *Bacterium lactis-aerogenes*, and *Vibrio alcaligenes*. He used the pigeon as a test organism in many of his experiments. Peskett (1933) makes reference to several other important articles dealing with the synthesis of vitamins by microorganisms.

Along this line is the interesting work by Bechdel, Honeywell, Dutcher, and Knutsen (1928), and Guerrant and Dutcher (1935), dealing with the synthesis of vitamin B by the bacterial flora present in the intestine of animals. Bechdel, Honeywell, Dutcher, and Knutsen isolated from the rumen of the cow a new bacterium, *Flavobacterium vitarumen*, which was found to be a potent synthesizer of vitamin B. This subject was also studied by Kon, Kon, and Mattick (1938) in an investigation of factors governing potato-starch refection in rats and by Abdel-Salaam and Leong (1938), who studied the synthesis of vitamin B_1 by the intestinal bacteria of the rat. Guha (1932) found that *Bacillus vulgatus* was not able to synthesize sufficient B_1 in a simple synthetic medium to make the process convenient for the concentration of the vitamin. According to Guha, the organism is able to synthesize "bios" in quite large quantities. More recently, Wegner, Booth, Elvehjem, and Hart (1940) have studied the synthesis of six members of the vitamin B-complex in the rumen of the cow. Significant amounts of these vitamins were formed in the rumen when the animals were fed a ration very low in these compounds, and the investigators concluded that the synthesis was very likely due to bacterial action. Similar results have been observed since 1940 by other workers using different animals.

Early work by Nelson, Fulmer, and Cessna (1921), Harden and Zilva (1921), and MacDonald (1922) showed that various higher fungi, especially yeasts, were able to synthesize vitamin B. *Monilia candida* was found to effect a vitamin B synthesis by Hoet, Leclef, and Delrue (1924), and Sunderlin and Werkman observed similar results with *Torula rosea* and *Oidium lactis*. Copping and Roscoe (1937) found yeasts to vary in vitamin B_1 (thiamin) from 20 to 140 μg. per gram. Williams and Spies (1938) state that there is evidence of vitamin B_1 synthesis in some of the higher fungi such as *Mucor*, *Rhizopus nigricans*, *Aspergillus niger*, and other species.

The medium on which the various microorganisms are cultivated seems to be an important factor in the synthesis of vitamin B, since Pavcek, Peterson, and Elvehjem (1937) observed the thiamin content of yeast to vary from 12 to 40 μg. per gram, depending upon the substrate.

Passing mention should be made of vitamin A synthesis by marine diatoms and other organisms, as reported by Jameson, Drummond, and Coward (1922) and Hjort (1922). Also, Norris, Simeon, and Williams (1937) observed that certain of the marine algae were a good source of vitamin B and vitamin C. The vitamin B was determined by feeding rats, and the vitamin C content was titrated with 2,6-dichlorophenolindophenol.

Further data on the synthesis of vitamins by various bacteria will be discussed in Chapter 7, Bacterial Nutrition.

THE PYROGENS OF MICROORGANISMS

The administration of transfusion fluids, such as plasma, and of vaccines, antisera, or other bacterial preparations is frequently accompanied by reactions which produce high temperatures and chills in man and animals. These reactions are due to substances called pyrogens, which are thought to be of microbial origin.

Most of the studies on this subject have been concerned with methods of testing for the presence of pyrogens in solutions or ways to eliminate them from solutions. Robinson and Flusser (1944), however, have isolated the pyrogens from different bacteria and have studied them chemically. The elementary analyses of these substances are given in Table 22. The pyrogen isolated from the typhoid preparation had a molecular weight of about 62,000, and was homogeneous in nature. When between 25 and 50 μg. of this substance was given per kilo of rabbit, a rise in temperature of about 2.5°C. was observed. Tests indicated that the pyrogens from all the organisms were carbohydrate in character, and similar results have been reported by others [Tui, Hope, Schrift, Powers, Wallen, and Schmidt (1944)].

TABLE 22

THE CHEMICAL COMPOSITION OF BACTERIAL PYROGENS

[From Robinson and Flusser (1944)]

	Eberthella typhosa + para A and B, per cent	*Pseudomonas aeruginosa*, per cent	*Proteus vulgaris*, per cent
Carbon	39.28	38.75	35.83
Hydrogen	6.95	6.53	6.06
Nitrogen	0	0	0
Phosphorus	0.38	2.38	0.29
Ash	4.43	12.18	8.33

REFERENCES

Abdel-Salaam, A., and P. C. Leong. 1938. *Biochem. J.*, **32**:958–963.
Abderhalden, E., and P. Rona. 1905. *Z. physiol. Chem.*, **46**:179–186.
Akasi, S. 1938–1939. *J. Biochem. Japan*, **28**:355–370; **29**:13–20, 21–29.
Alilaire, E. 1906. *Compt. rend.*, **143**:176–178.
Anderson, R. J. 1932. *Physiol. Rev.*, **12**:166–189.
Anderson, R. J., and M. S. Newman. 1933. *J. Biol. Chem.*, **101**:499–504; **103**:197–201.
Anderson, R. J., J. A. Crowder, M. S. Newman, and F. H. Stodola. 1936. *J. Biol. Chem.*, **113**:637–647.
Anderson, R. J., W. C. Lothrop, and M. M. Creighton. 1938. *J. Biol. Chem.*, **125**:299–308.
Anderson, R. J., M. M. Creighton, and R. L. Peck. 1940. *J. Biol. Chem.*, **133**:675–693.
Anslow, W. K., and H. Raistrick. 1938. *Biochem. J.*, **32**:687–696, 803–806.
Anslow, W. K., J. Breen, and H. Raistrick. 1940. *Biochem. J.*, **34**:159–168.
Aronson, H. 1900. *Arch. Kinderheilk.*, **30**:23–30.
Ashley, J. N., B. C. Hobbs, and H. Raistrick. 1937. *Biochem. J.*, **31**:385–397.
Ashley, J. N., H. Raistrick, and T. Richards. 1939. *Biochem. J.*, **33**:1291–1303.
Averill, H. P., J. N. Roche, and C. G. King. 1929. *J. Am. Chem. Soc.*, **51**:866–872.
Avery, O. T., M. Heidelberger, and W. F. Goebel. 1925. *J. Exptl. Med.*, **42**:709–725.
Avery, O. T., and W. F. Goebel. 1933. *J. Exptl. Med.*, **58**:731–755.
Barber, C. 1932. *Bull. Assoc. Inst. sup. fermentations Gand.*, **32**:20 (*Chem. Abstr.*, **26**:2762).
Barsha, J., and H. Hibbert. 1934. *Can. J. Research*, **10**:170–179.
Beard, J. W., and R. W. G. Wyckoff. 1937. *Science*, **85**:201–202.
Bechdel, S. I., H. E. Honeywell, R. A. Dutcher, and M. H. Knutsen. 1928. *J. Biol. Chem.*, **80**:231–238.
Beckwith, T. D. 1931. *J. Bact.*, **22**:15–22.
Beetlestone, N. C. 1928. *J. Inst. Brewing*, **34**:22–38.
Beijerinck, M. W. 1898. *Centr. Bakt., II Abt.*, **4**:209–216.
Beijerinck, M. W., and L. E. den Dooren de Jong. 1923. *Proc. Konink. Akad. Wetenschappen Amsterdam*, **25**:279–287.
Bergmann, E. 1933–1934. *Ergeb. Physiol.*, **35**:158–300; **36**:347–414.
Bergmann, W. 1932. *Ber. deut. chem. Ges.*, **65**:1489–1494.
Birkinshaw, J. H. 1937. *Biol. Rev. Cambridge Phil. Soc.*, **12**:357–392.
Block, R. J., and D. Bolling. 1943. *Arch. Biochem.*, **3**:217–226.
Bohonos, N., D. W. Woolley, and W. H. Peterson. 1942. *Arch. Biochem.*, **1**:319–324.
Bohonos, N., and W. H. Peterson. 1943. *J. Biol. Chem.*, **149**:295–300.
Boivin, A., and L. Mesrobeanu. 1934. *Arch. roumaines path. exptl. microbiol.*, **7**:95–133.
Boor, A. K., and C. P. Miller, Jr. 1931. *Proc. Soc. Exptl. Biol. Med.*, **28**:1046–1048.
Bourne, G., and R. Allen. 1935. *Australian J. Exptl. Biol. Med. Sci.*, **13**:165–174.
Brieger, L. 1885. *Z. physiol. Chem.*, **9**:1–7.
Brown, A. J. 1886, 1887. *J. Chem. Soc. London*, **49**:172–187, 432–439; **51**:643.
Brown, E. E., and T. B. Johnson. 1923. *J. Biol. Chem.*, **57**:199–208.

Brown, R. 1935. *Proc. Soc. Exptl. Biol. Med.*, **32**:859–860.
Brown, R. 1939. *J. Immunol.*, **37**:445–455.
Buchanan, R. E. 1909. *Centr. Bakt., II Abt.*, **22**:371–396.
Buchanan, R. E., and E. I. Fulmer. 1928. *Physiology and Biochemistry of Bacteria*, Vol. I. Williams and Wilkins Co., Baltimore.
Bull, H. B. 1941. *Advances Enzymology*, **1**:1–42.
Burris, R. H. 1942. *J. Biol. Chem.*, **143**:509–517.
Carruthers, A., and E. A. Cooper. 1936. *Biochem. J.*, **30**:1001–1009.
Cason, J., and R. J. Anderson. 1937, 1938. *J. Biol. Chem.*, **119**:549–551; **126**:527–541.
Cassagne, H. 1939. *Compt. rend. soc. biol.*, **131**:693–695.
Chargaff, E., and J. Dieryck. 1932. *Biochem. Z.*, **255**:319–329.
Chargaff, E. 1933. *Z. physiol. Chem.*, **217**:115–137; **218**:223–240.
Chargaff, E. 1933. *Compt. rend.*, **197**:946–948.
Chargaff, E. 1934. *Ann. inst. Pasteur*, **52**:415–423.
Chargaff, E., and E. Lederer. 1935. *Ann. inst. Pasteur*, **54**:383–388.
Chargaff, E., and M. Levine. 1938. *J. Biol. Chem.*, **124**:195–205.
Chargaff, E. 1939. *J. Biol. Chem.*, **130**:29–33.
Charles, J. H. V., H. Raistrick, R. Robinson, and A. R. Todd. 1933. *Biochem. J.*, **27**:499–511.
Clemo, G. R., and H. McIlwain. 1938. *J. Chem. Soc. London*, **1938**:479–483.
Clutterbuck, P. W., R. Lovell, and H. Raistrick. 1932. *Biochem. J.*, **26**:1907–1918.
Coghill, R. D., and O. D. Bird. 1929. *J. Biol. Chem.*, **81**:115–122.
Coghill, R. D. 1931. *J. Biol. Chem.*, **90**:57–63.
Coghill, R. D., and D. Barnés. 1932. *Anales soc. españ. fís. quím.*, **30**:208–221.
Cooper, E. A. 1912, 1914. *J. Hyg.*, **12**:436–462; **14**:12–22.
Cooper, E. A., and J. F. Preston. 1935. *Biochem. J.*, **29**:2267–2277.
Cooper, E. A., and J. F. Preston. 1937. *J. Soc. Chem. Ind.*, **56**:1T–5T.
Cooper, E. A., W. D. Daker, and M. Stacey. 1938. *Biochem. J.*, **32**:1752–1758.
Cooper, E. A. 1939. *J. Soc. Chem. Ind.*, **58**:229–231.
Copping, A. M., and M. H. Roscoe. 1937. *Biochem. J.*, **31**:1879–1902.
Cori, C. F. 1940. *Endocrinology*, **26**:285–296.
Cori, C. F. 1942. *Proc. Am. Soc. Brewing Chemists*, 5th Annual Meeting, May 25–27. 9 pp.
Cori, G. T., and C. F. Cori. 1940. *J. Biol. Chem.*, **135**:733–756.
Cori, G. T., and C. F. Cori. 1943. *J. Biol. Chem.*, **151**:57–63.
Cramer, E. 1891, 1893, 1895, 1897. *Arch. Hyg.*, **13**:71–112; **16**:151–195; **22**:167–190; **28**:1–15.
Crowder, J. A., and R. J. Anderson. 1932. *J. Biol. Chem.*, **97**:393–401.
Cruickshank, J. H., H. Raistrick, and R. Robinson. 1938. *J. Chem. Soc. London*, **1938**:2056–2064.
Csonka, F. A. 1935. *J. Biol. Chem.*, **109**:703–715.
Cunningham, R. L. 1924. *Am. Rev. Tuberc.*, **9**:487–490.
Curran, H. R., B. C. Brunstetter, and A. T. Myers. 1943. *J. Bact.*, **45**:485–494.
Curtin, T. P., and J. Reilly. 1940. *Biochem. J.*, **34**:1419–1421.
Damboviceanu, A., and C. Barber. 1931. *Arch. roumaines path. exptl. microbiol.*, **4**:5–40.
Damon, S. R. 1923, 1924. *J. Biol. Chem.*, **56**:895–902; *J. Path. Bact.*, **27**:163–169.
Dawson, A. I. 1919. *J. Bact.*, **4**:133–148.

De Schweinitz, E. A., and M. Dorset. 1895, 1898. *J. Am. Chem. Soc.*, **17**:605–611; **20**:618–620.
De Schweinitz, E. A., and M. Dorset. 1902. *Centr. Bakt., I Abt. Orig.*, **32**:186–192.
Doudoroff, M., N. Kaplan, and W. Z. Hassid. 1943. *J. Biol. Chem.*, **148**:67–75.
Dox, A. W., and R. E. Neidig. 1911. *J. Biol. Chem.*, **9**:267–269.
Durin, E. 1876. *Compt. rend.*, **83**:128–131.
Dyrmont, A. 1886. *Arch. Exptl. Path. Pharmakol.*, **21**:309–317.
Eckstein, H. C., and M. H. Soule. 1931. *J. Biol. Chem.*, **91**:395–404.
Eggert, J., and F. Luft. 1930. *Z. physik. Chem., B*, **7**:468–470.
Ehrismann, O., and W. Noethling. 1936. *Biochem. Z.*, **284**:376–382.
Elazari-Volcani, B. 1939. *Arch. Mikrobiol.*, **10**:343–358.
Emmerling, O. 1900. *Ber. deut. chem. Ges.*, **33**:2477–2479.
Enders, C., and K. W. Gergs. 1939. *Biochem. Z.*, **303**:10–12.
Enders, C., and K. Röed. 1939. *Biochem. Z.*, **301**:1–8.
Enders, J. F. 1929. *J. Exptl. Med.*, **50**:777–786.
Evans, T. H., W. L. Hawkins, and H. Hibbert. 1941. *J. Exptl. Med.*, **74**:511–518.
Fellowes, O. N., and J. I. Routh. 1944. *J. Lab. Clin. Med.*, **29**:1054–1061.
Felton, L. D., and B. Prescott. 1939. *J. Bact.*, **38**:579–593.
Ferramola, R. 1935. *Rev. inst. bacteriol. dept. nacl. hig.*, **7**:32–41.
Ferramola, R. 1935, 1937. *Ann. assoc. quím. Argentina*, **23**:93–105; **25**:1813.
Fink, H., H. Haehn, and W. Hoerburger. 1937. *Chem. Ztg.*, **61**:689–693, 723–726, 744–747.
Fischer, H., and J. Hasenkamp. 1935. *Liebig's Ann.*, **515**:148–164.
Fischer, H., and R. Lambrecht. 1937. *Z. physiol. Chem.*, **249**:I–III.
Fischer, H., W. Lautsch, and K. Lin. 1938. *Liebig's Ann.*, **534**:1–22.
Freeman, G. G., and J. St. L. Philpot. 1942. *Biochem. J.*, **36**:340–356.
French, C. S. 1940. *J. Gen. Physiol.*, **23**:469–481, 483–494.
Frey, C. N. 1930. *Ind. Eng. Chem.*, **22**:1154–1162.
Friedheim, E. A. H. 1931. *J. Exptl. Med.*, **54**:207–221.
Friedheim, E., and L. Michaelis. 1931. *J. Biol. Chem.*, **91**:355–368.
Friedman, C. A., and B. S. Henry. 1938. *J. Bact.*, **36**:99–105.
Fromageot, C., and J. L. Tchang. 1938. *Arch. Mikrobiol.*, **9**:424–433.
Fukumoto, J., and H. Shimomura. 1937. *J. Agr. Chem. Soc. Japan*, **13**:613–620.
Furth, J., and K. Landsteiner. 1928, 1929. *J. Exptl. Med.*, **47**:171–184; **49**:727–743.
Galimard, J. 1934. Thesis in Pharmacology, Paris (1937. *Chem. Abstr.*, **31**:4445).
Garrod, L. P. 1935. *J. Hyg.*, **35**:219–237.
Giral, F. 1936. *Anales soc. españ. fís. quím.*, **34**:667–693 (1937. *Chem. Abstr.*, **31**:6280).
Godfrin, P. 1934. "Contribution à l'étude des bactéries bleues et violettes." These, Nancy, France.
Goebel, W. F., and O. T. Avery. 1927. *J. Exptl. Med.*, **46**:601–607.
Goebel, W. F. 1940. *J. Exptl. Med.*, **72**:33–48.
Goris, A., and A. Liot. 1920. *Ann. inst. Pasteur*, **34**:497–546.
Gould, B. S., and H. Raistrick. 1934. *Biochem. J.*, **28**:1640–1656.
Greene, R. A. 1935. *Soil Sci.*, **39**:327–336.
Grundmann, C., and Y. Takeda. 1937. *Naturwissenschaften*, **25**:27.
Guerrant, N. B., and R. A. Dutcher. 1935. *J. Biol. Chem.*, **110**:233–243.

Guerrant, N. B., R. A. Dutcher, and R. A. Brown. 1937. *J. Nutrition*, **13**:305–315.
Guha, B. C. 1932. *Indian J. Med. Research*, **19**:977–983.
Guichard, P. 1894. *Bull. soc. chim. Paris*, Ser. 3, **11**:230–239.
Guillemin, M., and W. P. Larson. 1922. *J. Infectious Diseases*, **31**:349–355.
Hanes, C. S. 1940. *Proc. Roy. Soc. London, B*, **129**:174–208.
Harden, A., and S. Zilva. 1921. *Biochem. J.*, **15**:438–439.
Harrison, F. C., H. L. A. Tarr, and H. Hibbert. 1930. *Can. J. Research*, **3**:449–463.
Hassid, W. Z., and W. L. Chandler. 1937. *J. Biol. Chem.*, **117**:203–207.
Hassid, W. Z., and H. A. Barker. 1940. *J. Biol. Chem.*, **134**:163–170.
Haworth, W. N., E. L. Hirst, and H. A. Thomas. 1931. *J. Chem. Soc. London*, **1931**:824–829.
Haworth, W. N., and H. Machemer. 1932. *J. Chem. Soc. London*, **1932**:2270–2277.
Haworth, W. N., H. Raistrick, and M. Stacey. 1935. *Biochem. J.*, **29**:612–621, 2668–2678.
Hecht, E. 1935. *Z. physiol. Chem.*, **231**:279–280.
Heidelberger, M., and O. T. Avery. 1923. *J. Exptl. Med.*, **38**:73–79.
Heidelberger, M., W. F. Goebel, and O. T. Avery. 1925. *J. Exptl. Med.*, **42**:701–707, 727–745.
Heidelberger, M. 1927. *Physiol. Rev.*, **7**:107–128; *Chem. Rev.*, **3**:403–423.
Heidelberger, M., and F. E. Kendall. 1931. *J. Exptl. Med.*, **53**:625–639; **54**:515–531.
Heidelberger, M., and A. E. O. Menzel. 1932. *Proc. Soc. Exptl. Biol. Med.*, **29**:631–633.
Heidelberger, M., and A. E. O. Menzel. 1937. *J. Biol. Chem.*, **118**:79–100.
Heilbron, I. N. 1942. *J. Chem. Soc. London*, **1942**:79–89.
Henderson, D. W., and W. T. J. Morgan. 1938. *Brit. J. Exptl. Path.*, **19**:82–94.
Henry, B. S., and C. A. Friedman. 1937. *J. Bact.*, **33**:323–329.
Hershey, A. D., I. F. Huddleson, and R. B. Pennell. 1935. *J. Infectious Diseases*, **57**:183–185.
Hetherington, A. C., and H. Raistrick. 1931. *Phil. Trans. Roy. Soc. London, B*, **220**:209–244, 269–295.
Hetler, D. M. 1927. *J. Biol. Chem.*, **72**:573–585.
Hibbert, H. and J. Barsha. 1931. *Can. J. Research*, **5**:580–591.
Hibbert, H., and F. Brauns. 1931. *Can. J. Research*, **4**:596–604.
Hibbert, H., R. S. Tipson, and F. Brauns. 1931. *Can. J. Research*, **4**:221–239.
Hilpert, R. S., D. Becker, and W. Rossée. 1937. *Biochem. Z.*, **289**:179–192.
Hind, H. G. 1940. *Biochem. J.*, **34**:67–72, 577–579.
Hirsch, J. 1931. *Z. Hyg. Infektionskr.*, **112**:660–667.
Hjort, J. 1922. *Proc. Roy. Soc. London, B*, **93**:440–449.
Hoagland, C. L., G. I. Lavin, J. E. Smadel, and T. M. Rivers. 1940. *J. Exptl. Med.*, **72**:139–147.
Hoet, J., G. Leclef, and G. Delrue. 1924. *Arch. intern. physiol.*, **23**:284–298.
Hoffstadt, R. E., and W. M. Clark. 1938. *J. Infectious Diseases*, **62**:70–82.
Hughes, T. P., R. F. Parker, and T. M. Rivers. 1935. *J. Exptl. Med.*, **62**:349–352.
Huston, R. C., I. F. Huddleson, and A. D. Hershey. 1934. *Mich. Agr. Exp. Sta. Tech. Bull.* 137.

Ingraham, M. A., and H. Steenbock. 1935. *Biochem. J.*, **29**:2553–2562.
Ivánovics, G., and V. Bruckner. 1937. *Z. Immunitäts.*, **90**:304–318; **91**:175–176.
Jameson, H. L., J. C. Drummond, and K. H. Coward. 1922. *Biochem. J.*, **16**:482–485.
Jermoljewa, Z. W., and I. S. Bujanowskaja. 1930. *Z. Immunitäts.*, **68**:346–350.
Johnson, T. B., and E. B. Brown. 1922. *J. Biol. Chem.*, **54**:721–730.
Johnson, T. B., and R. D. Coghill. 1925. *J. Biol. Chem.*, **63**:225–231.
Johnson, T. B. 1926. *Am. Rev. Tuberc.*, **14**:164–171.
Kagan, B. O., S. N. Lyatker, and E. M. Tsvasman. 1942. *Biokhimiya*, **7**:93–108 (1943. *Chem. Abstr.*, **37**:4760).
Karrer, P., and U. Solmssen. 1935, 1936. *Helv. Chim. Acta*, **18**:1306–1315; **19**:3–5, 1019–1024.
Karrer, P., U. Solmssen, and H. Koenig. 1938. *Helv. Chim. Acta*, **21**:454–455.
Karrer, P., and H. Koenig. 1940. *Helv. Chim. Acta*, **23**:460–463.
Kayser, E. 1894. *Ann. inst. Pasteur*, **8**:737–784.
Kimmig, J. 1940. *Klin. Wochschr.*, **19**:858–862.
Kleczkowski, A., and P. Wierzchowski. 1940. *Soil Sci.*, **49**:193–195.
Kluyver, A. J. 1931. *The Chemical Activities of Micro-organisms.* University of London Press, London.
Knight, C. A., and W. M. Stanley. 1941. *J. Biol. Chem.*, **141**:29–38, 39–49.
Knoop, F., and H. Oesterlin. 1925, 1927. *Z. physiol. Chem.*, **148**:294–315; **170**:186–211.
Kögl, F. 1925. *Liebig's Ann.*, **447**:78–85.
Kögl, F., and H. Becker. 1928. *Liebig's Ann.*, **465**:211–242.
Kögl, F., and H. Erxleben. 1930. *Liebig's Ann.*, **479**:11–26.
Kögl, F., H. Erxleben, and L. Jänecke. 1930. *Liebig's Ann.*, **482**:105–119.
Kögl, F., and J. J. Postowsky. 1930. *Liebig's Ann.*, **480**:280–297.
Kögl, F., and B. Tönnis. 1932. *Liebig's Ann.*, **497**:265–289.
Kögl, F., and W. B. Deijs. 1934. *Liebig's Ann.*, **515**:10–33.
Kon, P. M., S. K. Kon, and A. T. R. Mattick. 1938. *J. Hyg.*, **38**:1–24.
Kopeloff, N., and L. Kopeloff. 1919, 1920. *La. State Agr. Exp. Sta. Bulls.* 166 and 170.
Kopeloff, N., C. J. Welcome, and L. Kopeloff. 1920. *La. State Agr. Exp. Sta. Bull.* 175.
Kramár, E. 1922. *Centr. Bakt., I Abt. Orig.*, **87**:401–406.
Kresling, K. 1901. *Centr. Bakt., I Abt. Orig.*, **30**:897–909.
Kroeker, E. H., F. M. Strong, and W. H. Peterson. 1935. *J. Am. Chem. Soc.*, **57**:354–356.
Kuhn, R., and K. Schön, 1935. *Ber. deut. chem. Ges.*, **68**:1537–1539.
Laidlaw, P. P., and H. W. Dudley. 1925. *Brit. J. Exptl. Path.*, **6**:197–201.
Lancefield, R. C. 1928. *J. Exptl. Med.*, **47**:469–480, 481–491.
Lavin, G. I., R. H. S., Thompson, and R. J. Dubos. 1938. *J. Biol. Chem.*, **125**:75–78.
Leach, M. F. 1906. *J. Biol. Chem.*, **1**:463–502.
Lederer, E. 1938. *Bull. soc. chim. biol.*, **20**:611–634.
Leineweber, F., R. Kautsky, and L. W. Famulener. 1923. *Proc. Soc. Exptl. Biol. Med.*, **20**:543–545.
LePage, G. A., and W. W. Umbreit. 1943. *J. Biol. Chem.*, **148**:255–260.
Levene, P. A. 1904. *J. Med. Research*, **12**:251–258.
Linton, R. W., and D. L. Shrivastava. 1933. *Indian J. Med. Research*, **21**:91–100

Linton, R. W., B. N. Mitra, and D. L. Shrivastava. 1934. *Indian J. Med. Research,* **21**:635–638.

Linton, R. W., D. L. Shrivastava, and B. N. Mitra. 1934. *Indian J. Med. Research,* **22**:309–312.

Linton, R. W. 1940. *Bact. Rev.,* **4**:261–319.

Lockwood, L. B., G. E. Ward, O. E. May, H. T. Herrick, and H. T. O'Neill. 1934. *Centr. Bakt., II Abt.,* **90**:411–425.

Long, E. R. 1921. *Am. Rev. Tuberc.,* **4**:842–846.

Long, E. R., and L. K. Campbell. 1922. *Am. Rev. Tuberc.,* **6**:636–641.

Lyons, R. E. 1897. *Arch. Hyg.,* **28**:30–42.

MacDonald, M. B. 1922. *J. Biol. Chem.,* **54**:243–248.

MacFarlane, M. G., and M. H. Salaman. 1938. *Brit. J. Exptl. Path.,* **19**:184–191.

MacLean, I. S., and E. M. Thomas. 1920. *Biochem. J.,* **14**:483–493.

Maguigan, W. H., and E. Walker. 1940. *Biochem. J.,* **34**:804–813.

Marschall. 1897. *Arch. Hyg.,* **28**:16–29.

Mazé, P. 1902. *Ann. inst. Pasteur,* **16**:346–378.

McFarlane, A. S. 1939. *Biol. Rev. Cambridge Phil. Soc.,* **14**:223–242.

McIlwain, H. 1943. *J. Chem. Soc.,* **1943**:322–325; *Biochem. J.,* **37**:265–271.

Meisenheimer, J. 1919, 1921. *Z. physiol. Chem.,* **104**:229–283; **114**:205–249.

Menzel, A. E. O., and M. Heidelberger. 1938, 1939. *J. Biol. Chem.,* **124**:89–101, 301–307; **127**:221–236.

Mesrobeanu, L. 1936. I. "Les antigènes glucido-lipidiques des bactéries (Étude chimique et biologique). II. Contribution à l'étude des corps puriques de la cellule bactérienne." Thèses, University of Strasbourg. 192 pp. Masson et Cie, Paris.

Meyerhof, O. 1943. *Am. Brewer,* **76**:26–29, 74, 76.

Mikulaszek, E. 1935. *Ergeb. Hyg.,* **17**:415–496.

Miller, C. P., and A. K. Boor. 1934. *J. Exptl. Med.,* **59**:75–82.

Mitra, B. N. 1936. *Indian J. Med. Research,* **23**:573–578, 579–588; **24**:1–4.

Morgan, W. T. J. 1937. *Biochem. J.,* **31**:2003–2021.

Nägeli, von. 1878. *J. prakt. Chem.,* N.F., **17**:403–428.

Nakamura, T. 1936. *Bull. Chem. Soc. Japan,* **11**:176–179.

Nelson, V. E., E. I. Fulmer, and R. Cessna. 1921. *J. Biol. Chem.,* **46**:77–81.

Nicolle, M., and E. Alilaire. 1909. *Ann. inst. Pasteur,* **23**:547–557.

Nishimura, T. 1893. *Arch. Hyg.,* **18**:318–333.

Niven, C. F., Jr., K. L. Smiley, and J. M. Sherman. 1941. *J. Biol. Chem.,* **140**:105–109.

Noack, K., and E. Schneider. 1933. *Naturwissenschaften,* **21**:835.

Norris, E. R., M. K. Simeon, and H. B. Williams. 1937. *J. Nutrition,* **13**:425–433.

Northrop, J. H. 1938. *J. Gen. Physiol.,* **21**:335–366.

Omeliansky, W. L., and N. O. Sieber. 1913. *Z. physiol. Chem.,* **88**:445–459.

Owen, W. L. 1911, 1918, 1923. *La. State Agr. Exp. Sta. Bulls.* 125, 162; *J. Bact.,* **8**:420–445.

Oxford, A. E., H. Raistrick, and P. Simonart. 1935. *Biochem. J.,* **29**:1102–1115.

Oxford, A. E., and H. Raistrick. 1940. *Biochem. J.,* **34**:790–803.

Pasteur, L. 1861. *Bull. soc. chim.,* **2**:30–31.

Pavcek, P. L., W. H. Peterson, and C. A. Elvehjem. 1937. *Ind. Eng. Chem.,* **29**:536–541.

Peck, R. L., and C. R. Hauser. 1938–1940. *J. Am. Chem. Soc.,* **60**:2599–2603; **61**:281–284; *J. Biol. Chem.,* **134**:403–412.

Peck, R. L., and R. J. Anderson. 1941. *J. Biol. Chem.*, **138**:135–140; **140**:89–96.
Peskett, G. L. 1933. *Biol. Rev.*, **8**:1–45.
Pollard, A. 1938. *Brit. J. Exptl. Path.*, **19**:124–129.
Popper, H., and J. Warkany. 1925. *Z. Tuberk.*, **43**:368–371.
Posternak, T. 1938. *Helv. Chim. Acta*, **21**:1326–1337.
Prill, E. A., P. R. Wenck, and W. H. Peterson. 1935. *Biochem. J.*, **29**:21–33.
Pruess, L. M., H. J. Gorcica, H. C. Greene, and W. H. Peterson. 1932. *Biochem. Z.*, **246**:401–413.
Pruess, L. M., E. C. Eichinger, and W. H. Peterson. 1934. *Centr. Bakt., II Abt.*, **89**:370–377.
Quilico, A. 1933. *Gazz. chim. ital.*, **63**:400–410.
Raistrick, H., R. Robinson, and A. R. Todd. 1933, 1934. *Biochem. J.*, **27**:1170–1175; **28**:559–572.
Raistrick, H., and W. W. C. Topley. 1934. *Brit. J. Exptl. Path.*, **15**:113–130.
Raistrick, H., R. Robinson, and D. E. White. 1936. *Biochem. J.*, **30**:1303–1314.
Raistrick, H. 1938. *Ergeb. Enzymforsch.*, **7**:316–349.
Reader, V. 1925. *Biochem. J.*, **19**:1039–1046.
Reeves, R. E., and W. F. Goebel. 1941. *J. Biol. Chem.*, **139**:511–519.
Reichel, L. 1940. *Angew. Chem.*, **53**:577–579.
Reid, R. D. 1936. *Centr. Bakt., II Abt.*, **95**:379–389.
Reimann, H. A., and C. Eckler. 1941. *J. Bact.*, **42**:435.
Reindel, F., K. Niederländer, and R. Pfundt. 1937. *Biochem. Z.*, **291**:1–6.
Richards, O. W., and M. C. Troutman. 1940. *J. Bact.*, **39**:739–746.
Robinson, E. S., and B. A. Flusser. 1944. *J. Biol. Chem.*, **153**:529–534.
Rommier, M. A. 1868. *Compt. rend.*, **66**:108–110.
Rubner, M. 1904. *Arch. Hyg.*, **48**:260–311.
Sanborn, J. R. 1933. *J. Bact.*, **26**:373–378.
Schaffer, A. J., C. Folkoff, and S. Bayne-Jones. 1922. *Bull. Johns Hopkins Hosp.*, **33**:151.
Schardinger, F. 1902. *Centr. Bakt., II Abt.*, **8**:144–147.
Scherp, H. W., and G. Rake. 1935. *J. Exptl. Med.*, **61**:753–769.
Schieblich, M. 1929–1931, 1933. *Biochem. Z.*, **207**:458–461; **220**:394–398; **225**:212–215; **233**:371–374; **259**:19–26.
Schiemann, O., and W. Casper. 1927. *Z. Hyg. Infektionskr.*, **108**:220–257.
Schiemann, O. 1929. *Z. Hyg. Infektionskr.*, **110**:567–580.
Schlossmann, K. 1934. *Acta Commentations Univ. Tartu*, A27, No. 7. 47 pp.
Schneider, E. 1934. *Z. physiol. Chem.*, **226**:221–254.
Schwartz, W. 1937. *Angew. Chem.*, **50**:294–296.
Seibert, F. B. 1941. *Bact. Rev.*, **5**:69–95.
Sevag, M. G., J. Smolens, and D. B. Lackman. 1940. *J. Biol. Chem.*, **134**:523–529.
Sevag, M. G., and J. Smolens. 1941. *J. Biol. Chem.*, **140**:833–845.
Sieber, N. 1881. *J. prakt. Chem., N.F.*, **23**:412–421.
Sifferd, R. H., and R. J. Anderson. 1936. *Z. physiol. Chem.*, **239**:270–272.
Sisson, W. A. 1936. *J. Phys. Chem.*, **40**:343–359.
Slanetz, E. J. 1923. *Abstracts Bact.*, **7**:352.
Smith, R. G. 1903, 1905. *Centr. Bakt., II Abt.*, **10**:61–63; **11**:698–703; **15**:380–384.
Sobin, B., and G. L. Stahly. 1942. *J. Bact.*, **44**:265–276.
Spielman, M. A. 1934. *J. Biol. Chem.*, **106**:87–96.

Stacey, M., and F. R. Youd. 1938. *Biochem. J.*, **32**:1943–1945.
Stacey, M. 1942. *Nature*, **149**:639.
Stahl, W. H., R. B. Pennell, and I. F. Huddleson. 1939. *Mich. Agr. Exp. Sta. Tech. Bull.* 168.
Stahl, W. H. 1941. *Mich. Agr. Exp. Sta. Tech. Bull.* 177:29–34.
Stahly, G. L., C. L. Sesler, and W. R. Brode. 1942. *J. Bact.*, **43**:149–154.
Stanley, W. M. 1937. *Am. J. Bot.*, **24**:59–68.
Stoklasa, J. 1908. *Centr. Bakt., II Abt.*, **21**:620–632.
Strong, F. M., and W. H. Peterson. 1934. *J. Am. Chem. Soc.*, **56**:952–955.
Stull, A. 1929. *J. Biol. Chem.*, **82**:641–650.
Sunderlin, G., and C. H. Werkman. 1928. *J. Bact.*, **16**:17–33.
Svedberg, T. 1937. *Chem. Rev.*, **20**:81–98.
Takeda, Y., and T. Ohta. 1941. *Z. physiol. Chem.*, **268**:I–II.
Tamura, S. 1913, 1914. *Z. physiol. Chem.*, **87**:85–114; **88**:190–198; **89**:289–303, 304–311.
Tarr, H. L. A., and H. Hibbert. 1931. *Can. J. Research*, **4**:372–388.
Täufel, K., H. Thaler, and H. Schreyegg. 1936. *Z. Untersuch. Lebensm.*, **72**:394–404.
Taylor, A. R. 1944. *J. Biol. Chem.*, **153**:675–686.
Thompson, R. H. S., and R. J. Dubos. 1938. *J. Biol. Chem.*, **125**:65–74.
Tischer, J. 1937, 1938, 1939. *Z. physiol. Chem.*, **250**:147–154; **251**:109–128; **260**:257–261.
Tobie, W. C. 1935, 1936. *J. Bact.*, **29**:223–227; *Proc. Soc. Exptl. Biol. Med.*, **34**:620–622.
Tomcsik, J. 1927. *Proc. Soc. Exptl. Biol. Med.*, **24**:810–812.
Tomcsik, J., and T. J. Kurotchkin. 1928. *J. Exptl. Med.*, **47**:379–388.
Topley, W. W. C., H. Raistrick, J. Wilson, M. Stacey, S. W. Challinor, and R. O. J. Clark. 1937. *Lancet*, **1937**(1):252–256.
Topping, L. E. 1934. *J. Path. Bact.*, **39**:665–668.
Tui, F. W. C., D. Hope, M. H. Schrift, J. Powers, A. Wallen, and L. Schmidt. 1944. *J. Lab. Clin. Med.*, **29**:58–62.
Umezu, M. 1940. *Rept. Inst. Sci. Research Manchoukuo*, **4**:273–285 (1941. *Chem. Abstr.*, **35**:1825).
Ungerer, E. 1934. *Z. Pflanzenernähr. Düngung Bodenk., Abt. A.*, **36**:287–290.
van Niel, C. B., and J. H. C. Smith. 1935. *Arch. Mikrobiol.*, **6**:219–229.
van Neil, C. B., and W. Arnold. 1938. *Enzymologia*, **5**:244–250.
van Veen, A. G., and J. K. Baars. 1937, 1938. *Proc. Konink. Akad. Wetenschappen Amsterdam*, **40**:498–505; *Rec. trav. chim.*, **57**:248–264.
Van Wisselingh, W. 1898. *Jahrb. wiss. Botan.*, **31**:619–687.
Vaughan, V. C., V. C. Vaughan, Jr., and J. W. Vaughan. 1913. *Protein-Split Products in Relation to Immunity.* Lea and Febiger, Philadelphia.
Virtanen, A. I., and L. Pulkki. 1933. *Arch. Mikrobiol.*, **4**:99–122.
Wadsworth, A., and R. Brown. 1933. *J. Immunol.*, **24**:349–368.
Warburg, O. 1938. *Ergeb. Enzymforsch.*, **7**:210–245.
Ward, G. E., and G. S. Jamieson. 1934. *J. Am. Chem. Soc.*, **56**:973–975.
Ward, G. E., L. B. Lockwood, O. E. May, and H. T. Herrick. 1935. *Ind. Eng. Chem.*, **27**:318–322.
Wegner, M. I., A. N. Booth, C. A. Elvehjem, and E. B. Hart. 1940. *Proc. Soc. Exptl. Biol. Med.*, **45**:769–771.
Weill, E., F. Arloing, and A. Dufourt. 1922. *Compt. rend. soc. biol.*, **87**:50–52.

Wheeler, S. M. 1909. *J. Biol. Chem.*, **6**:509–552.

White, B. 1938. *The Biology of Pneumococcus.* The Commonwealth Fund, New York.

White, D. E. 1939. *Australian Chem. Inst. J. Proc.*, **6**:313–330.

Wieland, H., and Y. Kanaoka. 1937. *Liebig's Ann.*, **530**:146–151.

Wieland, H., H. Pasedach, and A. Ballauf. 1937. *Liebig's Ann.*, **529**:68–83.

Williams, C. H., W. R. Bloor, and L. A. Sandholzer. 1939. *J. Bact.*, **37**:301–313.

Williams, R. R., and T. D. Spies. 1938. *Vitamin B_1 (Thiamin) and Its Use in Medicine.* The Macmillan Co., New York.

Willstaedt, H. 1935, 1936, 1939. *Ber. deut. chem. Ges.*, **68**:333–340; **69**:997–1001; *Atti X cong. intern. chim.*, **3**:390–397 (1940. *Chem. Abstr.*, **34**:3753).

Wolberg, A. 1938. *Med. Doświadczalna Spoleczna*, **23**:372–396.

Wollman, E. 1921. *Compt. rend. soc. biol.*, **85**:801–803.

Wollman, E., and M. Vagliano. 1922. *Compt. rend. soc. biol.*, **86**:832–833.

Woolley, D. W., F. M. Strong, W. H. Peterson, and E. A. Prill. 1935. *J. Am. Chem. Soc.*, **57**:2589–2591.

Woolley, D. W., and W. H. Peterson. 1936, 1937. *J. Biol. Chem.*, **114**:84–90; **118**:363–370.

Wrede, F. 1932. *Z. physiol. Chem.*, **210**:125–128.

Wrede, F., and A. Rothhaas. 1933. *Z. physiol. Chem.*, **215**:67–78; **219**:267–274.

Wrede, F., and O. Hettche. 1929. *Ber. deut. chem. Ges.*, **62**:2678–2685.

Wrede, F., and E. Strack. 1929. *Ber. deut. chem. Ges.*, **62**:2051–2057.

Yamagutchi, S., and S. Usami. 1939. *Cytologia*, **9**:419–429.

6

BACTERIAL ENZYMES AND BACTERIAL RESPIRATION

For many years chemists have known that the velocity of certain reactions can be accelerated by adding small amounts of certain inorganic or organic substances to reacting mixtures. For example, hydrogen and oxygen gases do not combine very rapidly at ordinary temperatures. However, if a mixture of the two gases is passed over a small amount of colloidal platinum, the union takes place instantly. Water also plays a very important role in certain chemical reactions. Sometimes it accelerates a reaction, whereas in other instances, especially when it is a product of the reaction, it may inhibit or retard a reaction. Hydrogen and chlorine gases, when dry and pure, do not unite to any extent to form hydrogen chloride, but, if a trace of water is present, the rate of the reaction is greatly increased. As we shall point out later, water also enters into all biological systems.

Substances which possess the remarkable power of affecting the speed of chemical reactions are called *catalysts* or *catalytic agents*, and their activity is known as *catalysis*. The word catalysis is derived from Greek and means literally "down-loosening." Catalysts may be either inorganic or organic in nature. Although the inorganic catalysts are extremely important in many chemical and biological reactions, we shall give little attention to them here. Catalysts are often termed positive or negative; that is, they may increase or decrease the rate of a reaction. The positive catalysts are probably more important. In older conceptions catalysts were looked upon as mysterious chemical compounds which in some way accelerated chemical reactions. Furthermore, it was agreed that all catalysts had two properties in common: (1) a catalyst never initiated a new reaction but merely changed the rate of a reaction already in progress, and (2) the catalyst neither was used up in the process nor appeared in the principal end products of the reaction. As our information has increased on this subject, it has been necessary to make certain revisions in the older viewpoints. The newer conception is that a catalyst may actually initiate certain chemical reactions; and, although it does not appear, as a rule, in the end products of the reaction, the catalytic surface itself undoubtedly enters into the reaction at some stage and forms labile compounds with the reactive molecules of the substrate. These labile compounds are then rearranged or altered while associated with the catalyst and break down with the formation of new products and the regeneration of the catalyst.

Enzymes may be defined as organic catalytic agents which are elaborated by living cells and which may act independently of the life processes of the cells. According to Waksman and Davison (1926), the word enzyme was first suggested and employed by Kühne in 1867 to replace the term unorganized ferment since a great deal of confusion existed in the older literature as a result of the indiscriminate use of the word ferment. The word enzyme is derived from the Greek and means literally "in yeast" or "in leaven." Enzymes are also frequently called biochemical catalysts and biocatalysts, but, since there are many biochemical catalysts, Tauber (1937) proposed the following classification to assure a distinct differentiation between true enzymic and nonenzymic catalysts:

1. *Specific cell-independent, biochemical catalysts or enzymes:* catalysts which are produced by the living cell, but whose action is independent of the living cell, and which are destroyed if their solutions are heated long enough. *Examples:* pepsin, trypsin, maltase, lipase.

2. *Specific, cell-dependent, biochemical catalysts:* catalysts produced by living cells, active *in vitro* as well as *in vivo*, their activity, however, depending on the unimpaired cell. They are destroyed on heating, and their activity ceases on mechanical destruction of the cell. *Examples:* the catalyst affecting synthesis of urea in the liver, and the dehydrogenetic function of certain bacteria which is inactivated on cell destruction (toluol).

3. *Nonspecific biochemical catalysts:* catalysts elaborated by the living cell, their action being independent of the life process of the cell. They are not destroyed to any extent when their solutions are heated. *Examples:* glutathione, ascorbic acid, cytochrome, adenylic acid.

It is now generally recognized that enzymes play a dominant part in all the physiological processes of living cells. In fact, Willstätter, a leader in enzyme investigation, says, "We may regard life as a system of cooperating enzymatic reactions." The hydrolytic processes in digestion, the oxidizing and reducing reactions in respiration, the disintegrations in cell metabolism, and undoubtedly the synthetic processes as well—all depend upon catalysts for their activation and acceleration. In performing such duties in the mildest of reagents, the enzymes of the living cell affect a vast number of complicated reactions which so far are beyond the powers of the organic chemist to understand. Enzymes are present in bacteria, yeasts, molds, and other microorganisms in great variety. Some of the harmful effects of pathogenic organisms are caused by enzymes or products of enzyme activity, for example, the true bacterial toxins, which are substances synthesized by the organisms. Yeasts and other organisms cause fermentation by virtue of enzymes, and the proteolytic action of cheese bacteria and molds is well known. Since most life processes involve enzyme activity of one sort or another, the healthy functioning of an organism depends largely upon the proper equilibrium between the various factors involved.

ENZYME NOMENCLATURE AND TERMINOLOGY

A great many enzymes have been described in the literature [see Oppenheimer (1925–1937)], although the existence of some of them has not been definitely established. Since our knowledge of the true nature of many enzymes is very vague, we are forced to classify and study them by their activities and by the effects of various factors on these activities.

In the early days of bacteriology, as we have mentioned, enzymes were called ferments, and two types were recognized. *Organized* or *formed ferments* were thought to be directly connected with the life of the microorganism, or were possibly considered the living cell itself, whereas *unorganized* or *unformed ferments* were believed to be agents which operated outside the cell and, once formed, were independent of the vital processes of the cell. This distinction was of course arbitrary, and, as our knowledge increased, it became less and less tenable. Therefore, in order to avoid the use of these confusing terms, Kühne proposed the term enzyme for these bodies.

At least four systems of nomenclature for enzymes have been proposed. They are:

1. Substituting the ending *-ase* for the last part of the substance or substrate decomposed, for example:

Substrate	*Enzyme*
Lactose	Lactase
Maltose	Maltase
Urea	Urease
Protein	Protease

2. Combining the ending *-ase* with the name of one of the end products formed in the reaction, as *alcoholase.*

3. Combining the ending *-ase* with the name of the reaction taking place, such as *hydrolase, oxidase,* and *reductase.*

4. Employing classical names which have no relation to the process involved, such as rennin, tryspin, pepsin, emulsin, and zymase. Such names often designate specific preparations which may contain a number of enzymes.

The first system of terminology, as proposed by Duclaux, 1898–1899, is now generally employed in enzymology; this system, in combination with the third, is frequently used for classification purposes. It has also been suggested that synthesizing enzymes should be named by the addition of the ending *-ese* to the substance formed, but this terminology has not been accepted.

Many times it is convenient to classify enzymes in respect to their relationship to the cell; that is, extracellular enzymes, which are formed by the cell and then secreted outside, where they exhibit their activity, and intracellular enzymes, which are formed by the cell and retained inside it throughout their life. However, there is no absolute distinction between these two types of enzymes.

Often a cell secretes not the complete enzyme but rather a mother substance called a *proenzyme* or *zymogen*, which is transformed into an active enzyme outside the cell by means of chemicals, as in the action of HCl on pepsinogen, or by special substances known as *kinases*. Other terms which are used in enzymology are: *antienzyme*, which is an immune body that inhibits or interferes with enzyme activity; *activator* and *inhibitor*, which are chemicals of relatively low molecular weight, usually inorganic in nature, that accelerate or inhibit enzyme activity, respectively; and *coenzyme*, which refers to an organic compound of relatively low molecular weight which is necessary for the action of certain enzymes. Compounds which can be allocated to the coenzyme group are discussed in more detail on pp. 464 to 487.

THE ISOLATION OR PREPARATION OF ENZYMES

The modern methods of obtaining concentrated enzyme preparations may be placed in two general categories. The first is the *adsorption method*, which was introduced by early workers and was further improved by Willstätter and his associates. It is based on the separation of the enzyme from extraneous matter by adsorption on a suitable colloid, such as kaolin, certain aluminum hydroxides, or other specially prepared gels, and the subsequent freeing or elution of the enzyme from the adsorbent. This method of purification is based on the greater affinities of the adsorbent for the enzyme than for the impurities; by repeating the procedure several times a concentration of the enzyme is obtained. However, the adsorption procedure is often the cause of enormous loss in active enzyme material. The second method, or group of methods, is that used chiefly by various American workers. The enzymes in these procedures are dissolved in suitable solvents and concentrated by "salting out," by precipitation with various reagents, or by electrophoretic methods. Changes in hydrogen-ion concentration and temperature, dialysis, and other measures are also often employed either to rid the medium of impurities or to concentrate or crystallize the enzyme. Frequently a combination of several of these techniques is employed.

When an enzyme is present in a secretion, such as milk or saliva, it is often possible to collect the secretion and use it directly in enzyme studies. However, if the enzyme to be isolated is present within the animal or plant tissues or inside bacterial cells, it must first be liberated. This procedure may be accomplished by one or more of the following means: (1) physical methods, such as chopping, grinding with sand or broken glass, alternate freezing or thawing, crushing in a press, or wet-crushing in a specially designed mill for microorganisms [Booth and Green (1938)]; (2) preliminary weakening of the cell wall by extraction of lipides or other components; (3) simple extraction of the enzyme with a suitable solvent; (4) autolysis; and (5) the action of enzymes (other than autolytic) upon the cell wall. Once the enzyme has been liberated, the processes of isolation and purification may be started immediately, or the material may first be dried and stored. Drying and storing are often used with microorganisms because of the necessity to collect considerable cellular material, and in the drying process a portion of the protein present is denatured and can be discarded. On the other hand, the drying may have a deleterious effect upon the enzyme, especially if it is carried out in the air.

GENERAL PROPERTIES OF ENZYMES

Enzymes either are colloids or are so closely associated with colloids that they have not been isolated in a noncolloidal state. Therefore their physical and chemical properties are those of colloids. In general, enzyme solutions exhibit the Tyndall effect; they may be precipitated by various colloidal reagents; they are changed, injured, or denatured by heat; they may act as protective colloids; and they dialyze very slowly or not at all. This property of not dialyzing readily is employed in the purification of certain enzymes, since it permits the removal of inorganic salts and organic compounds of low molecular weight. Sometimes, however, this procedure inactivates the enzyme by removing an essential activator (inorganic) fraction or a coenzyme; in other cases dialysis must be employed sparingly because certain enzymes are comparatively small and pass through a parchment membrane.

An interesting (and physiologically important) property of enzymes is the reversibility of their reactions. This property has long been known for certain esterases and has been assumed to be applicable, theoretically at least, to all enzymatic reactions. However, it often cannot be demonstrated, as, for example, in those reactions in which intramolecular rearrangements take place together with the primary reaction. Some 20 years ago Falk (1924) listed the following enzymes as having been found definitely to accelerate synthetic changes: lipase, emulsin, trypsin, pepsin, kephirlactase, maltase, and oxynitrilase. Since that time considerable progress has been made in this field [see Sumner and Somers (1943)].

Although little or nothing is known about the chemical constitution of the microbial enzymes, several enzymes from other sources have been concentrated by various methods and obtained in crystalline form, and their composition has been analyzed by definite chemical methods. Some of the physical and chemical properties of several crystalline enzymes are given in Table 1. Thus far all these enzymes have been demonstrated to be proteins.

TABLE 1

CERTAIN PROPERTIES OF A FEW CRYSTALLINE ENZYMES *

[From Sumner (1935), Northrop (1939), Kunitz (1940), and others]

		Pepsin	Trypsin	Carboxy-peptidase	Yellow Oxidation Enzyme	Ribo-nuclease
Form of Crystals		Hexahedral	Short prisms	Long prisms	Short cubical prisms	Long plates or fine needles
Elementary composition	Carbon	51.61	50.0	52.6	51.5	48.2
	Hydrogen	6.86	7.1	7.2	7.37	6.2
	Nitrogen	14.63	15.0	14.4	15.9	16.1
	Chlorine	0.0	2.85	....	....	....
	Sulfur	0.42	1.1	0.47	....	3.6
	Phosphorus	0.09	0.0	0.0	0.043	....
	Ash	1.78	1.0	0.68	....	0.1
Amino N as per cent of total N		5.26	9.3	....	....	6.95
Diffusion coefficient, cm.^{2}/day		0.047	0.023	....	....	0.092
Approximate particle weight		37,000	36,500	....	70–75,000	15,000±
Isoelectric point (pH)		2.75	7–8	....	5.2	8.0
Optimum activity (pH), experimental		2.75–3.0	8–9	....	5–6	....

* Analytical data are also available for trypsinogen, chymotrypsin, chymotrypsinogen, urease, pepsinogen, papain, and lipase.

Two separate schools of thought exist concerning the chemical nature of enzymes. Both are probably correct if certain minor modifications are accepted. The carrier or "Träger" theory of the Willstätter group may be expressed as follows:

> Enzymes contain a special reactive group which either combines with, or possesses some particular affinity for, definite groupings in the substrate, thus accounting for the specificity of enzyme behavior. This special reactive group is attached to a colloidal carrier, and enzyme action is determined in part by the affinity of the active groups for the substrate and in part by the colloidality of the entire aggregate. When the colloidal properties of the aggregate are destroyed, then the activity of the enzyme disappears.

The opposing viewpoint or theory has been advanced principally by American workers, who believe that enzymes are specific and definite chemical compounds, probably all proteins, and that the arrangement of the groupings in the protein molecule not only is responsible for the enzyme activity but likewise determines enzyme specificity. The Träger theory was adopted by Willstätter in 1922 before there was any definite evidence as to the type of compound which might constitute the prosthetic group. More recently it has been shown by several workers that the prosthetic group in cytochrome c, catalase, and peroxidase is an iron-porphyrin residue, but in each instance the porphyrin residue is associated with a specific protein. Therefore the characteristics of the enzyme and its specificity are determined not by the prosthetic group alone but likewise by the specific protein with which it is associated. For example, in catalase the iron-porphyrin residue (hematin) will feebly decompose H_2O_2 by itself, but, when associated with the specific protein which accompanies it in the enzyme catalase, the combination is approximately ten million times more active in decomposing H_2O_2 than is the porphyrin residue alone. Another interesting example is the yellow oxidation enzyme of Warburg and Christian. In this enzyme the prosthetic group is a riboflavin-phosphoric acid ester which is associated with a specific protein. Neither the prosthetic groups nor the specific protein possesses enzymatic activity alone. However, when the two components are combined in the proper proportions, they exhibit such activity.

Sumner (1933) has raised the question of whether enzymatic behavior should be attributed to a part of the enzyme or whether the whole complex should be taken into consideration, and furthermore whether one part of an enzyme can be considered more important than another. If the catalase activity of hematin increases ten million times by association with its colloidal carrier (protein), then it must be assumed that the colloidal carrier is almost as important as the prosthetic group. In certain enzymes, such as pepsin, trypsin, and urease, no specific prosthetic group has yet been discovered. However, Northrop and others are of the opinion that the enzymatic activity in such cases is due to a particular arrangement of the amino acids in the molecule. If this theory is correct, it will probably be difficult to determine the exact nature of the specific groupings responsible for their activity, although a true prosthetic group is not yet entirely ruled out. Therefore, at present sufficient evidence is available to demonstrate that the Träger theory of Willstätter, with minor modifications, accounts for the enzymatic behavior of certain enzymes. Those enzymes which do not now fit into this group may actually belong here, or they may be specific proteins. In catalase, peroxidase, the yellow oxidation enzyme, and others the prosthetic group-protein linkages are of the nature of either salts or adsorption affinities. Such linkages can be broken by relatively simple physical techniques. On the other hand, in certain other enzymes such linkages may exist as carbon-to-carbon or carbon-to-nitrogen bonds, and the breaking of such bonds would require such drastic treatment that the protein would be destroyed.

ENZYME SPECIFICITY, MECHANISM, AND KINETICS

As a general rule, enzymes are specific to a high degree; that is, a given enzyme will attack only certain compounds or groups of compounds. Since this attack is apparently always directed to a definite type of linkage in the substrate molecule, there are several exceptions to the general rule of specificity. However, it may be stated definitely that certain broad boundaries are never crossed. For example, lipases do not split proteins or carbohydrates, carbohydrases are unable to saponify fats or attack proteins, and proteases exhibit no activity in the presence of true carbohydrates or lipides. There are also many examples of very specific activity. Urease apparently acts only on urea, dipeptidases attack dipeptides but not tripeptides or polypeptides, and polypeptidases will split tripeptides and polypeptides but are unable to hydrolyze dipeptides. In this respect some of the oxidizing enzymes are very interesting. Tyrosinase acts on tyrosine, $HO-C_6H_4-CH_2 \cdot CHNH_2 \cdot COOH$, on *p*-cresol, $HO-C_6H_4-CH_3$, and on catechol, $C_6H_4(OH)-OH$, but not on guaiacol, $CH_3O-C_6H_4-OH$. Laccase, on the other hand, attacks catechol and guaiacol, but not tyrosine or *p*-cresol.

Several theories have been proposed to explain the mechanism of enzyme action. Most of these theories have postulated a union of the enzyme and the substrate to form an intermediate product which then breaks down, producing the decomposition products and the regenerated enzyme:

(a) Substrate + Enzyme ⇄ Substrate-enzyme intermediate compound.

(b) Substrate-enzyme intermediate compound → Decomposition products + Enzyme.

Definite proof of the existence of an intermediate compound is available for certain enzyme reactions, such as those between catalase and monoethyl hydrogen peroxide [Stern (1936)] and cytochrome c peroxidase and hydrogen peroxide [Abrams, Altschul, and Hogness (1942)]. It seems probable that similar enzyme-substrate combinations exist in other enzyme reactions, but definite proof is lacking, because methods for identifying intermediates are not available and sometimes the intermediate exists for only a short period of time.

A great deal has been written about the kinetics of enzyme reactions. Often it has been observed that enzymatic reactions partly or wholly obey the law of mass action and the other physicochemical laws of true solutions. However, our knowledge of the stability, rates of diffusion, and energies of colloidal systems is in most instances too inadequate to draw final conclusions and to fit colloidal behavior completely into the scheme of the classical physicochemical systems. Therefore it is not surprising that many workers have found that enzymatic reactions deviate somewhat from the theoretical values as calculated by the monomolecular reaction equation. Since several books [Waldschmidt-Leitz and Walton (1929), Tauber (1937), Elvehjem, Wilson, *et al.* (1939), and Sumner and Somers (1943)] are available in which this subject is treated in some detail, no further discussion will be given here.

ACTION OF PHYSICAL AND CHEMICAL AGENTS ON ENZYMES AND ENZYME ACTIVITY

Since enzymes either are colloids or are closely associated with them, it can be assumed that their activities are influenced by many of the physical and chemical agents which alter colloids. The action of certain of these agents on enzymes has already been discussed in Chapters 3 and 4 on the effects of physical and chemical agents on bacteria, and more complete details will be found in books dealing specifically with enzymes. Therefore only a brief discussion will be given here.

Effect of Radiations. It is generally agreed that visible light rays have little effect on most enzymes. On the other hand, ultraviolet light, X-rays, and other electromagnetic radiations may show an inhibitory action or sometimes may even denature the protein component of enzymes.

Effect of Desiccation, Pressure, and Agitation. Certain enzymes lose their activity while being dried, but most enzymes are fairly stable if they are desiccated by special techniques. Mechanical pressures ranging between 5,000 and 6,000 kg. per sq. cm. will inactivate enzymes such as pepsin and rennin (see Chapter 3). Little research has been done on the effect of agitation on enzymes, but it has been reported that rennin is very sensitive to shaking and that violent agitation may destroy the activity of other enzymes.

Effect of Temperature. The minimum, optimum, and maximum temperatures for activity have been determined for many enzymes. Most animal enzymes have an optimum around 40°C., but the optimum for plant enzymes is usually somewhat higher, and one extreme has been reported of a plant rennin exhibiting optimum activity at a temperature of 80° to 85°C. The enzymes elaborated by psychrophilic, mesophilic, and thermophilic bacteria must have an optimum somewhere near the optimum growth temperature for these groups of bacteria. It should be emphasized in all these cases, however, that there can be no optimum temperature for enzyme activity which does not take time into consideration.

In general, most enzyme solutions are quickly inactivated by heating above 50° to 80°C., although there are several exceptions such as trypsin preparations, which may be heated to boiling for a short time without much loss of activity, providing the solution has an acid reaction. Further exception to the general rule must exist in the case of thermophilic microorganisms that have an optimum growth temperature at or above 70°C. Many dry enzyme preparations can stand temperatures of 100° to 120°C. before their activity is destroyed.

The velocity of enzymatic reactions is accelerated as the temperature is increased to the optimum, above which there is a decrease in velocity until the temperature destroys all enzyme activity. Many experiments have been carried out on the effect of temperature on enzyme activity. Usually the effect has been analyzed on the assumption that enzymatic reactions follow simple physicochemical laws; that is, monomolecular chemical reactions. When such data are analyzed and the temperature coefficients calculated (see Chapter 4 for equations), it is usually found that the values (Q_{10}) are not 2 to 3, as they generally are when reactions are catalyzed by inorganic catalysts, but are somewhat lower. This fact is shown in Table 2, where coefficients $\left(\frac{k_{t+10}}{k_t}, \text{ or } Q_{10}\right)$ of several enzyme reactions are tabulated.

TABLE 2

Temperature Coefficients (Q_{10}) for Several Enzyme Reactions

Enzyme	Substrate	Temperature, Range, °C.	Q_{10}	Reference
Liver lipase	Ethyl butyrate	0–10	1.72	Kastle and Loevenhart (1900)
		10–20	1.36	
		20–30	1.10	
Pancreatic lipase	Ethyl butyrate	0–10	1.50	
		10–20	1.34	
		20–30	1.26	
Malt amylase	Starch	20–30	1.96	Lüers and Wasmund (1922)
		30–40	1.65	
Clostridium acetobutylicum amylase	0.1% starch	10–20	1.42	Johnston and Wynne (1935)
		20–30	1.45	
		30–40	1.44	
		35–45	1.46	
	1.0% starch	10–20	2.14	
		20–30	1.74	
		30–40	1.35	
		35–45	1.25	
Clostridium perfringens mucinase	Mucin	0–10	1.70	Robertson, Ropes, and Bauer (1940)
		10–20	1.80	
		20–30	1.70	
		30–40	1.80	
		40–50	1.8	
Yeast sucrase	Sucrose	25–35	1.61	Nelson and Bloomfield (1924)
Yeast maltase	Maltose	10–20	1.90	Lintner and Kröber (1895)
		20–30	1.44	
		30–40	1.28	
Bacterial succinic oxidase	Succinate	30–40	2.0	Quastel and Whetham (1924)
		40–50	2.1	
		50–60	2.1	
Lactic dehydrogenase (from gonococci)	Lactate	25–35	2.23	Barron and Hastings (1933)

Effect of Reaction (*p*H). Since enzymes appear to have the properties of lyophilic colloids, it might be expected that their activity would be influenced by the *p*H of the dispersion medium. In general this assumption is true. All enzyme preparations have an optimum *p*H, at which they exhibit their greatest activity. This optimum, however, may vary considerably for different enzymes and is influenced by such factors as the type of substrate, the source of the enzyme material, the time, the temperature, and the buffer substances present. A few optimum values for several different enzymes are given in

Table 3. Since there can be no such thing as optimum hydrogen-ion concentration independent of time, *p*H-activity curves are frequently plotted for enzymes. Two examples are given in Figs. 1 and 2 to illustrate this point.

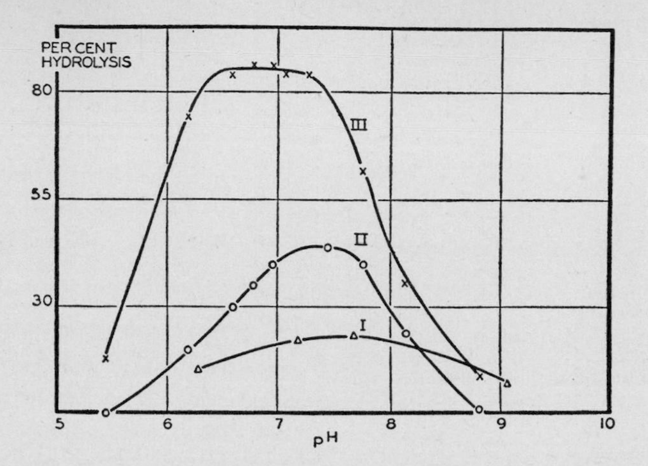

Fig. 1. *p*H Optima for Hydrolysis of Leucyldiglycine by *Bacillus subtilis* (I, Acetone-Precipitated Enzyme Solution, after 1-hr. incubation) and by *Clostridium sporogenes* (II, after 1-hr. incubation; III, after 4-hr. incubation, at 40° C.). (From Berger, Johnson, and Peterson, 1938.)

Effect of Miscellaneous Chemical Compounds. Since enzymes are protein in nature, they are affected by many of the so-called protein reagents, such as heavy metals (copper, silver, mercury, lead) and

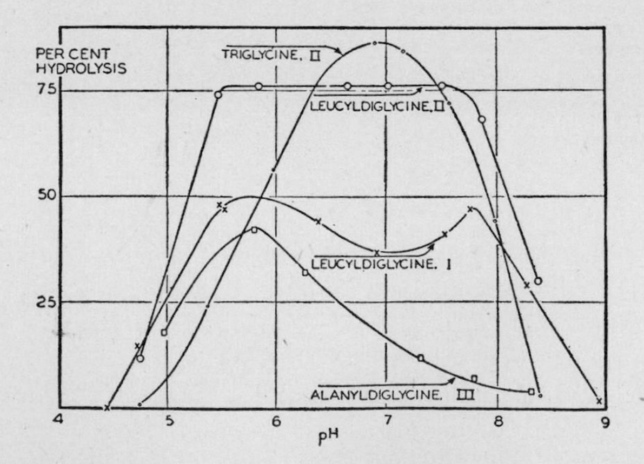

Fig. 2. *p*H Optima for *Leuconostoc mesenteroides* against Three Tripeptides. (Incubation for 1 hr. at 40° C. Roman numerals refer to different enzyme preparations.) (From Berger, Johnson, and Peterson, 1938.)

TABLE 3

VARIATION OF THE OPTIMUM *p*H FOR ENZYME ACTIVITY WITH THE SOURCE OF THE ENZYME MATERIAL, THE TYPE OF SUBSTRATE, AND THE BUFFER

Enzyme	Source	Optimum *p*H	Reference
Amylase (diastase)	*Aspergillus oryzae*	5.3–5.5	Caldwell and Tyler (1931)
	Pancreas	6.8	(Sherman *et al.*) Tauber (1937)
	Malt	4.4–5.2	
Dextrinase	*A. oryzae*	4.0	Maslow and Davison (1926)
Lactase	Almond	4.2	(Willstätter *et al.*) Tauber (1937)
	Yeast	7.0	
	Escherichia coli	7.0–7.5	Knopfmacher and Salle (1941)
	E. coli-mutabile	7.0–7.5	Deere, Dulaney, and Michelson (1939)
Maltase	Yeast	6.7–7.2	(Willstätter *et al.*) Tauber (1937)
	A. oryzae	4.0	(von Euler) Waksman and Davison (1926)
Sucrase (invertase)	Yeast, fresh	4.4–5.2	(von Euler *et al.*) Waksman and Davison (1926)
	Aspergillus niger	2.5–3.5	(Kanitz) Waksman and Davison (1926)
Carboxylase	Yeast and *Fusaria*	6.2–6.4	Tytell and Gould (1941)
l-Lysine decarboxylase	*Bacterium cadaveris*	6.0	Gale and Epps (1943)
Aspartase	*E. coli*	7.1	Virtanen and Tarnanen (1932)
Aspartase II	*E. coli*	7.0–8.0	Gale (1938)
l-Amino acid oxidase	*Proteus vulgaris*, etc.	6.8	Stumpf and Green (1944)
Urease	Urobacteria	7.9–8.0	Mischoustin (1932)
Urease, crystalline	Jack bean		
Acetate buffer		6.4	Howell and Sumner (1934)
Citrate buffer		6.5	
Phosphate buffer		6.9	
Peptidases *			
Substrate			
Leucylglycine	*Pseudomonas aeruginosa* (filtrate)	8.4	Gorbach (1930)
Leucyldiglycine	*Ps. aeruginosa* (filtrate)	8.4	
Diglycine	*Pseudomonas fluorescens*	8.4	Gorbach and Pirch (1936)
Leucylglycine	*Ps. fluorescens*	8.4	
Leucyldiglycine	*Ps. fluorescens*	8.4	
Leucylglycine	*Caseicoccus*, Gorini	4.8, 7.0	Gorbach (1937)
Leucyldiglycine	*Gastrococcus*, Gorini	4.8	
Benzoyldiglycine	*Staphylococcus aureus*	8.0	Imaizumi (1938)
Leucyldiglycine	*Staphylococcus aureus*	8.0	
	Eberthella typhosa	8.0	
Chloroacetyl-phenylalanine	*S. aureus*	7.0	
	E. typhosa	7.0	
	Bacillus subtilis	7.0	
Phosphatases	*Aerobacter aerogenes*	5.6, 5.6, 6.2 †	Pett and Wynne (1938)
	B. subtilis (Marburg)	10.7, 6.6, 6.6	
	B. subtilis (Michigan)	6.5, 6.0, 6.2	
	Alcaligenes fecalis	8.7, 8.5, 7.6	
	Clostridium acetobutylicum	5.1, 6.0, 7.0	
	Propionibacterium jensenii	7.0, 6.0, 7.0	
	Saccharomyces cerevisiae	4.0, 6.5, ..	
	Mammalian tissues	8.9, 8.9, ..	
	Erythrocytes	6.0, 6.6, ..	
	Soya bean	5.3, ...	

* For other values see papers I and II by Berger, Johnson, and Peterson (1938).
† Glycerophosphate, hexose phosphate, and pyrophosphate, respectively.

alkaloid reagents. The effect of such compounds is usually considered to be *nonspecific,* since almost all enzyme reactions under the influence of these reagents are inhibited. Furthermore, the inhibition produced by these substances is usually irreversible. In addition to the protein reagents there are a large number of chemicals which appear to exhibit a selective inhibition for certain enzyme reactions. Such inhibition is more or less *specific* and is often reversible. Compounds such as the fluorides and cyanides, iodoacetate, carbon monoxide, *p*-aminophenol, and urethane are only a few of the chemicals which belong to the group of specific or selective inhibitors. For complete details on this subject Chapter VII by Cohen (1939) in *Respiratory Enzymes* by Elvehjem, Wilson, *et al.* should be consulted.

Some common solvents, as water, dilute alcohol, glycerol, and dilute acids and alkalies, are employed in the preparation of certain enzyme solutions. However, many enzymes can be precipitated from such solutions by strong alcohol or acetone and by various concentrations of ammonium sulfate and other salts. In general, strong oxidizing agents are very injurious to enzymes.

In many enzyme systems the presence or absence of neutral electrolytes has a profound effect on the reaction. For example, certain enzymes are practically inactive in the absence of neutral electrolytes, and others require the presence of specific ions before they attack their substrate.

ACTIVATORS AND COENZYMES

For many years the terms activator and coenzyme were used very loosely to describe any substance which accelerated enzyme processes. No sharp distinction was made between the two terms. However, as now generally used, *activator* is reserved for those nonspecific substances which merely accelerate enzymic processes, whereas *coenzyme* refers to those organic substances which are absolutely essential in order for the enzyme to manifest itself at all. The new coenzyme concept visualizes the coenzyme as the prosthetic group of the enzyme; what was formerly considered to be the enzyme proper is now generally recognized as a part of the enzyme, namely, as the bearer protein.

However, the terminology employed by various investigators to designate the complete enzyme, the protein portion, and the coenzyme has not been standardized, and the following synonymous terms will be found in the literature:

Enzyme	*Protein Fraction*	*Coenzyme*
Holoenzyme	Apoenzyme	Coenzyme
Symplex	Träger	Active group
Ferment protein	Protein	Prosthetic group
	Pheron	Agon
		Cozymase

Activators are heat-stable dialyzable substances of relatively low molecular weight. Usually only trace amounts are necessary to activate a system. Often they may be replaced by other substances and, therefore, are relatively nonspecific. A few examples may be cited to make this point clear: (1) Hydrochloric acid, the activator which converts pepsinogen into active pepsin, may be replaced by other inorganic and organic acids, for the hydrogen-ion concentration is the activating factor; (2) sodium chloride, the activator of pancreatic amylase, may be replaced by any of a large number of salts; the chlorides, however, activate best; sulfates are inert; (3) certain cations, such as calcium, magnesium, and manganese, accelerate the activity of other enzymes; and (4) hydrocyanic acid or hydrogen sulfide must activate the proteolytic enzyme, papain, before it can attack peptones, although more complex proteins are supposedly hydrolyzed by papain when these activators are absent.

Coenzymes may be defined as fairly thermostable, dialyzable organic compounds which are relatively specific in nature and are indispensable components of one or more enzymes. In a number of cases the coenzymes can be separated from their "carrier" proteins by simple physical means. When this is possible, the union between the two components

TABLE 4

THE RELATIONSHIP BETWEEN CERTAIN COENZYMES, THEIR PROTEIN BEARERS, AND THE ENTIRE ENZYME

[From Oppenheimer and Stern (1939), Sumner and Somers (1943)]

Coenzyme (Agon or Prosthetic or Active Group)	Protein Bearer (Apoenzyme, Träger, or Pheron)	Enzyme (Holoenzyme or Symplex)	Action
1. Diphosphopyridine nucleotide (cozymase, coenzyme I, codehydrogenase I, etc.)	+ Protein A =	Alcohol dehydrogenase	Oxidation of their respective substrates
	+ Protein B =	Lactic acid dehydrogenase	
	+ Protein C =	Malic acid dehydrogenase	
	+ Protein D =	Triosephosphate dehydrogenase	
2. Triphosphopyridine nucleotide (codehydrogenase II, etc.)	+ Protein E =	Hexose phosphate dehydrogenase	Oxidation of their respective substrates
	+ Protein F =	Glucose dehydrogenase	
	+ Protein G =	Glutamic acid dehydrogenase	
3. Cocarboxylase	+ Protein H =	Carboxylase	Decarboxylation of pyruvic acid
4. Isoalloxazine-adenine nucleotides	+ Protein I =	*d*-Amino acid oxidase	Oxidation of *d*-alanine, etc.
	+ Protein J =	Xanthine oxidase	Oxidation of xanthine, etc.
5. Adenylic acid	+ Protein K =	Phosphorylase	Formation of glycogen or starch from Cori ester; involved in sucrose synthesis.
6. Glutathione	+ Protein L =	Glyoxalase	Conversion of methylglyoxal to lactic acid

must not be very firm. On the other hand, certain enzymes either contain no prosthetic group in the form of a coenzyme or else the bond between the protein carrier and the coenzyme is so strong that it cannot be broken except by such drastic treatment that the protein component is also destroyed.

In the last few years remarkable progress has been made in the study of the coenzymes [see extensive reviews by Baumann and Stare (1939), Oppenheimer and Stern (1939), Green (1940), and Parnas (1943)]. The best-known coenzymes of these will now be briefly mentioned. They include the pyridine nucleotides, cocarboxylase, the alloxazine systems (the adenine-flavin-dinucleotides and flavin nucleotides), the adenosine triphosphate-adenosine monophosphate (adenylic acid) system, and miscellaneous coenzymes. Table 4 from Oppenheimer and Stern (1939) and Sumner and Somers (1943) shows certain interesting facts about some of the coenzymes, their protein carriers, and the complete enzymes. The data are self-explanatory.

THE PYRIDINE COENZYMES

As shown in Table 4, two known coenzymes belong to the pyridine group. Many names have been assigned to these two coenzymes, but, since their chemical composition is known, Baumann and Stare (1939) have suggested that they be called by their proper chemical names, that is, diphosphopyridine nucleotide (abbreviation DPN) and triphosphopyridine nucleotide (TPN).

Diphosphopyridine nucleotide was first isolated from yeast by Harden and Young in 1904–1906, and later the name cozymase was assigned to this crystalloidal, thermostable substance whose presence is essential to the process of fermentation. According to Myrbäck (1933), yeast is still one of the best natural sources for the coenzyme, although fairly high concentrations have also been demonstrated in other microorganisms, such as *Lactobacillus helveticus* [von Euler and Nilsson (1926)] and *Streptococcus lactis* [Myrbäck and von Euler (1924)]. On the other hand, such organisms as *Penicillium glaucum* [Myrbäck and von Euler (1924)] and *Aerobacter aerogenes* [von Euler and Myrbäck (1929)] yield little DPN. Diphosphopyridine nucleotide has likewise been demonstrated in a great many animal and plant tissues. Baumann and Stare (1939) and Oppenheimer and Stern (1939) mention that it is present in large amounts in muscle, liver, red blood cells, and retina; less has been found in blood serum, bone marrow, connective tissue, mushrooms, and seeds and root tips of certain higher plants.

Triphosphopyridine nucleotide was first isolated from red blood cells by Warburg and Christian (1931) and has since been isolated by them

(1935, 1936) from other cells, including yeast. As a matter of fact, they claim or believe that TPN is a "ubiquitous cell constituent."

The pyridine nucleotides (DPN and TPN) have a molecular weight of about 700, dissolve in water, pass readily through membranes, and remain fairly stable up to 80°C. They are insoluble in fat solvents and can be precipitated by them, as well as by phosphotungstic acid and tannic acid. Both coenzymes form salts with barium, lead, mercury, silver, and zinc, many of these salts being insoluble in water or dilute alcohol. The two nucleotides can be separated by virtue of the unequal solubility of their barium salts in dilute alcohol and by differential adsorption in an Al_2O_3 column, where DPN is less strongly adsorbed than is TPN. The chemical structure for each of these nucleotides, as suggested by von Euler and Schlenk (1937), may be written as follows:

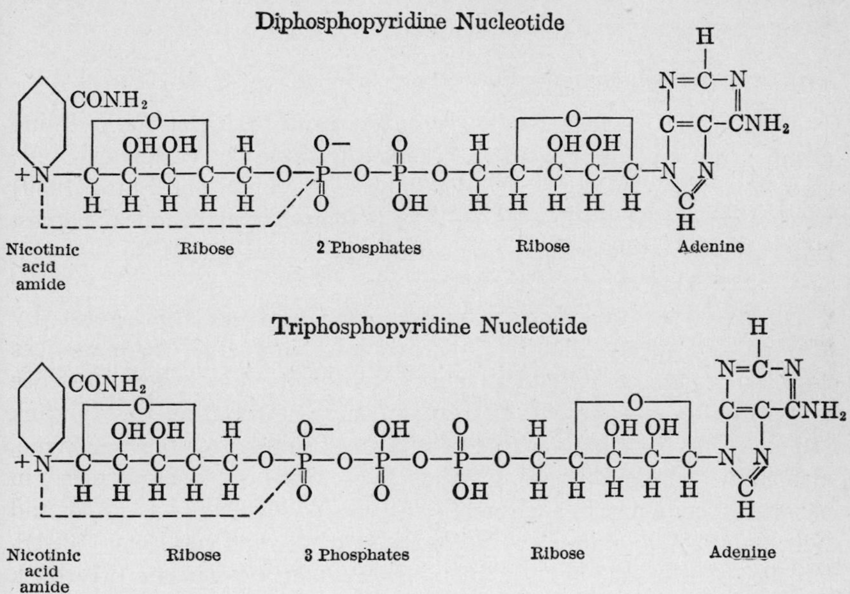

On reduction the nicotinic acid amide residue supposedly undergoes the following change:

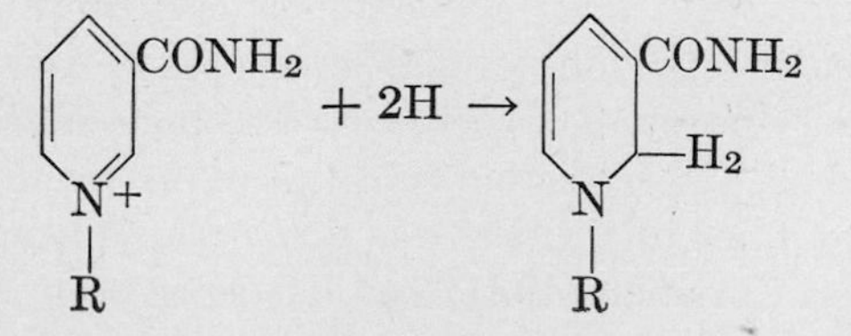

The chemical structure and hydrolytic products of the pyridine nucleotides have been studied in some detail by Warburg and Christian (1936), von Euler and Schlenk (1937), Schlenk (1942), and others. On hydrolysis DPN yields the following products, as might be assumed from the preceding formula:

1 mol. nicotinic acid amide + 1 mol. adenine + 2 mols. pentose + 2 mols. phosphoric acid;

and triphosphopyridine nucleotide (TPN):

1 mol. nicotinic acid amide + 1 mol. adenine + 2 mols. pentose + 3 mols. phosphoric acid.

In 1942 Schlenk proved that the pentose in DPN was *d*-ribose. Also he believes that one of the phosphoric acid groups in TPN may be attached to the adenylic portion of the molecule, thus:

$$\text{Nicotinic}^{+}\text{ acid amide–Pentose—}\underset{\underset{\text{O}}{\|}}{\overset{\overset{\text{O}^-}{|}}{\text{P}}}\text{—O—}\underset{\underset{\text{O}}{\|}}{\overset{\overset{\text{OH}}{|}}{\text{P}}}\text{—}\underset{\underset{\text{H}_2\text{PO}_3}{|}}{\text{Pentose}}\text{–Adenine,}$$

rather than as indicated in the older formula.

DPN has been converted into TPN by chemicals ($POCl_3$), enzymes, and microorganisms [Lwoff and Lwoff (1937)], but, because of the apparent specificity of each nucleotide, this conversion is thought to be uncommon. The reactive part of both molecules (DPN, TPN) is the nicotinic acid amide residue, which readily and reversibly takes on hydrogen. The nucleotides are easily reduced to the dihydrides by sodium hydrosulfite but are readily reoxidized by shaking with methylene blue or with the yellow enzyme in the presence of air.

A great deal of work has been done by many investigators on the mode of action or the function of the pyridine coenzymes in cellular respiration. Briefly, we can say that, when they are combined with a specific protein to form a coenzyme–dehydrogenating enzyme system, their function is to aid in the transportation of hydrogen (or electrons) from a specific substrate, activated by the dehydrogenase, to some other hydrogen acceptor and eventually to oxygen. The following scheme has been postulated as one example of the general phenomenon of hydrogen transport:

$$\text{Substrate} + \underset{\text{Dehydrogenase}}{\underset{\uparrow\ \text{(TPN)}}{\text{Coenzyme}}} + H_2O \rightarrow \text{Oxidized substrate} + \text{Reduced coenzyme}$$

$$\text{Reduced coenzyme} + \underset{\text{(Yellow enzyme)}}{\text{Flavoprotein}} \rightarrow \text{Coenzyme} + \text{Reduced flavoprotein}$$

$$\text{Reduced flavoprotein} + O_2 \rightarrow \text{Flavoprotein} + H_2O_2$$

The over-all reaction being:

$$\text{Substrate} + O_2 + H_2O \rightarrow \text{Oxidized substrate} + H_2O_2$$

The first reaction takes place when the substrate and specific dehydrogenase come in contact. The substrate loses two atoms of hydrogen and becomes oxidized, whereas the coenzyme portion of the dehydrogenase gains two hydrogens and becomes reduced. Specifically, the hydrogen is accepted by the pyridine ring (nicotinic acid amide) residue of the coenzyme molecule. In the second reaction the hydrogen, originally coming from the substrate but in combination with the coenzyme portion of the specific enzyme system, is transferred to the yellow enzyme or some other related flavoprotein. In this case the hydrogen apparently unites with the alloxazine ring, or the flavin portion, of the yellow enzyme. The pyridinoprotein enzyme then returns to its original state and becomes available to react with more substrate. The third reaction consists of a similar hydrogen transfer, the H_2 uniting with molecular O_2 to form H_2O_2 and thus freeing the flavoprotein. Both the pyridinoprotein and flavoprotein may be reduced and regenerated many times without being used up.

Although the foregoing scheme gives us some idea of the role played by the coenzyme in enzymatic processes, the reactions which take place within the living cell are undoubtedly more complex than this simple analysis indicates. Many substrates are broken down in the living bacterial cell, each probably requiring a specific dehydrogenase. Also many other enzymes and compounds other than flavoprotein may function in transporting hydrogen from reduced DPN to molecular oxygen; this is especially true of the cytochromes. Most enzyme systems are quite specific in their requirements for pyridine nucleotides (coenzymes); thus they may require either DPN or TPN, but one coenzyme usually cannot replace the other in such enzyme systems. However, there are exceptions to this general rule. Both pyridine coenzymes undergo the same general type of reduction and oxidation, and each is capable of reacting with several substrates, since they are a common component of several specific dehydrogenases.

In addition to its ability to serve as a hydrogen carrier, the diphosphopyridine nucleotide residue of an enzyme may also function in the transfer of phosphate. In this respect it resembles adenylic acid, which will be discussed shortly. This property is not surprising, because one-half of the DPN molecule is adenylic acid. It is interesting to note that the transfer of phosphate by means of such coenzymes is remarkably sensitive to inorganic ions. Sodium ions inhibit the transfer of phosphate by either DPN or adenylic acid, but particularly by DPN. [Ohlmeyer and Ochoa (1938)]. This inhibition by sodium ions can be counteracted by the addition of manganese, and, if the reaction is carried out in solutions of potassium or ammonium salts rather than sodium salts, the transfer of phosphate will take place even in the absence of manganese. The exact role played by these various ions is still vague, and the mechanism by which DPN transports phosphate is not well understood.

The diphosphopyridinoprotein and triphosphopyridinoprotein enzymes play very important roles in many biological oxidation processes. Since this subject is clearly discussed by Green (1940) and Sumner and Somers (1943), only a few examples will be briefly mentioned here.

The *diphosphopyridine nucleotide* is essential for certain specific enzymes to catalyze the oxidation of:

1. Ethyl alcohol to aldehyde.
2. β-Hydroxybutyrate to acetoacetate.
3. $l(+)$-Lactate to pyruvate or $l(-)$-malate to oxaloacetate.

$$\text{Lactate} + \text{DPN} \rightleftarrows \text{Pyruvate} + \text{Reduced DPN}$$

$$\text{Malate} + \text{DPN} \rightleftarrows \text{Oxaloacetate} + \text{Reduced DPN}$$

4. Glucose to gluconic acid.
5. $l(+)$-Glutamic acid to α-ketoglutaric acid and NH_3. Apparently the first oxidation product in this case is the imino acid, which then spontaneously hydrolyzes into α-ketoglutaric acid and NH_3:

$$COOHCH_2 \cdot CH_2 \cdot CHNH_2 \cdot COOH + DPN \xrightleftharpoons{\text{Enzyme}} COOHCH_2 \cdot CH_2 \cdot C{:}NHCOOH + \text{Reduced DPN}$$

$$COOHCH_2 \cdot CH_2 \cdot C{:}NHCOOH + H_2O \rightleftarrows COOHCH_2 \cdot CH_2 \cdot COCOOH + NH_3$$

This reaction is reversible. This fact means that ketoglutaric acid can be reductively aminated to form glutamic acid and suggests that the following equilibrium exists:

$$COOHCH_2 \cdot CH_2 \cdot C{:}NHCOOH \rightleftarrows COOHCH_2 \cdot CH_2 \cdot COCOOH + NH_3$$

It is possible that this type of reaction accounts for the synthesis of some of the amino acids in the cell.

6. Hexose to lactic acid in animal tissues and to alcohol and CO_2 in yeast; as well as some of the intermediate products in the glycolysis and fermentation of hexose by various organisms. For example, the oxidation of 3-phosphoglyceraldehyde to 3-phosphoglyceric acid by the tri-

osephosphoric enzyme requires DPN. The formic enzyme which catalyzes the oxidation of formate to CO_2 and H_2O also requires this coenzyme.

7. The diphosphopyridine nucleotide also catalyzes certain *dismutations*, *mutases*, and *isomerases*. For example, a mutase is defined as "an enzyme or enzyme system which catalyzes the oxidation of one molecule of its substrate at the expense of the reduction of another molecule." Thus the enzyme discovered by Parnas in mammalian liver produces the following dismutation of aldehyde:

$$\text{Aldehyde} + \text{DPN} \rightarrow \text{Acetate} + \text{Reduced DPN}$$

$$\text{Reduced DPN} + \text{Aldehyde} \rightarrow \text{Alcohol} + \text{DPN}$$

One molecule of aldehyde is oxidized to acetate, and simultaneously another is reduced to ethyl alcohol.

A number of isomerases from muscle tissue, yeast, and bacteria have been studied by Meyerhof, Lohmann, and their associates and by Utter and Werkman (1941). All these enzymes apparently require DPN before they can catalyze the reaction. For example, Meyerhof has presented evidence for the existence of two isomerases which catalyze the following successive rearrangements of 3-phosphoglycerate:

$$\begin{array}{ccccc} \text{COOH} & & \text{COOH} & & \text{COOH} \\ | & & | & & | \\ \text{HCOH} & \rightleftarrows & \text{HCOPO}_3\text{H}_2 & \rightleftarrows & \text{COPO}_3\text{H}_2 \\ | & & | & & \| \\ \text{H}_2\text{COPO}_3\text{H}_2 & & \text{H}_2\text{COH} & & \text{H}_2\text{C} \\ \text{3-Phosphoglyceric acid} & & \text{2-Phosphoglyceric acid} & & \text{Phosphopyruvic acid} \end{array}$$

Other interesting data on yeast isomerase are mentioned in the discussion of alcoholic fermentation, pp. 915 to 919, and the paper by Utter and Werkman (1941) should be consulted for information on isomerase in bacteria.

Triphosphopyridine nucleotide is essential for certain enzyme systems, but less is known about the role of TPN systems in cellular respiration than about the DPN systems. Three important examples may be cited, but with the probable exception of (2), they have not been reversed experimentally; that is, reduced TPN does not react with the oxidized substrate.

1. *Hexosemonophosphoric enzyme.* In 1931–1932 Warburg and Christian reported that they had isolated an enzyme from yeast and red blood corpuscles which catalyzed the oxidation of glucose-6-phosphate to 6-phosphogluconate:

$$\underset{\text{Glucose-6-phosphate}}{H_2O_3PO \cdot CH_2 \cdot (CHOH)_4 \cdot CHO} \rightarrow \underset{\text{6-Phosphogluconate}}{H_2O_3PO \cdot CH_2 \cdot (CHOH)_4 \cdot COOH}$$

2. *Glutamic enzyme.* An enzyme has been isolated from bottom yeast by von Euler, Adler, and Eriksen (1937) which catalyzes the oxidation of $l(+)$-glutamic acid, $COOH(CH_2)CHNH_2COOH$, to NH_3 and α-ketoglutaric acid, $COOH(CH_2)_2COCOOH$. The coenzyme TPN is needed as the specific oxidizing agent for the substrate and cannot be replaced by DPN.

3. *Isocitrate enzyme.* Adler, von Euler, Günther, and Plass (1939) isolated an enzyme from acetone-dried heart muscle which catalyzed the oxidation of isocitrate (but not citrate) to α-ketoglutarate. One possible way in which this reaction could take place is:

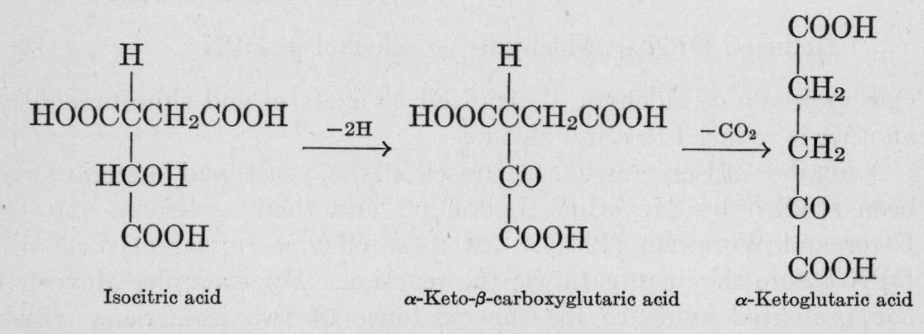

Triphosphopyridine nucleotide is apparently necessary for this reaction to take place. The end product of the reaction may be a potential source of glutamic acid if NH_3 is present, according to Adler and associates. This fact can be demonstrated by the following equations:

$$\text{Isocitrate} + \text{TPN} \rightarrow \alpha\text{-Ketoglutarate} + CO_2 + \text{Reduced TPN}$$

$$\alpha\text{-Ketoglutarate} + NH_3 \rightarrow \alpha\text{-Iminoglutarate}$$

$$\alpha\text{-Iminoglutarate} + \text{Reduced TPN} \rightarrow \text{Glutamate} + \text{TPN}$$

The pyridinoprotein enzymes are probably essential for the growth of all microorganisms. Certain organisms, however, can apparently synthesize the prosthetic group (DPN or TPN) of the enzyme, as well as the protein carrier, from simple ammonium salts. Other organisms which require DPN or TPN are unable to synthesize the coenzymes from simple ammonium salts but can effect such a synthesis if supplied with the proper units, that is, nicotinamide, pentose, and adenylic acid. Still other organisms apparently require partially synthesized coenzymes or the intact pyridine nucleotide molecules to carry out their activities, since they are unable to synthesize the compounds when they are supplied with the separate component parts. *Escheri-*

chia coli is a good example of an organism which can synthesize the nucleotides in a medium where the only source of nitrogen is an ammonium salt. *Staphylococcus aureus, Shigella dysenteriae, Corynebacterium diphtheriae*, some of the species of the genus *Proteus*, and probably many other organisms can synthesize one of the pyridine nucleotides if supplied with nicotinic acid amide, which is one of the essential components of both DPN and TPN. To the third category belongs *Hemophilus parainfluenzae*, which must be supplied with the nicotinamide riboside (nicotinamide + pentose) or the intact nucleotide molecule for growth, since it can neither synthesize the coenzyme from simple materials nor hook the individual organic components together. The work on *H. parainfluenzae* has been carried out principally by Lwoff and Lwoff (1937), who have shown that "growth factor V" may be replaced by pure DPN or TPN. Nicotinic acid or its amide and adenylic acid are unable to serve as factor V; but Schlenk and Gingrich (1942) and Gingrich and Schlenk (1944) have shown that *H. parainfluenzae* can proceed with the synthesis of DPN or TPN if the first step, the linkage between nicotinamide and pentose, is accomplished.

It is also of interest that the Lwoffs have devised an extremely sensitive microbiological test for the pyridine nucleotides in which they can detect as little as 0.004 μg. of the coenzymes in biological fluids. The Lwoff test for DPN or TPN has been applied to the estimation of these substances in the blood of normal persons and pellagrins by Kohn (1938), Kohn and Klein (1940), and others. Such studies have shown that both groups of individuals possess greater amounts of the coenzymes in their blood after nicotinic acid has been administered. When cultures of *H. parainfluenzae* are grown under conditions in which factor V is the only limiting factor, glucose, hexosemonophosphate, pyruvate, fumerate, malate, ethyl alcohol, asparagine, and valine are all oxidized very slowly. On the other hand, when either of the pyridine coenzymes is added, the organism rapidly oxidizes all the substrates.

COCARBOXYLASE (DIPHOSPHOTHIAMIN)

As early as 1911 Neuberg demonstrated that yeast and plants contain an enzyme (carboxylase) which decarboxylates α-keto acids, converting them into the corresponding lower aldehydes. For example, the decarboxylation of pyruvic acid by yeast follows the equation:

$$\underset{\text{Pyruvic acid}}{CH_3 \cdot CO \cdot COOH} \rightarrow \underset{\text{Acetaldehyde}}{CH_3 \cdot CHO} + CO_2$$

We now know that mammals and certain bacteria act differently on pyruvic acid; these reactions will be discussed in the next few pages.

Before 1932 it was not known that carboxylase required a coenzyme. However, in that year Auhagen demonstrated that, when dried yeast was washed with alkaline phosphate, it lost its power to decarboxylate pyruvic acid because a coenzyme was washed out. The coenzyme has since been isolated from liver, kidney, heart, blood, and a large number of vegetables [Auhagen (1932), Tauber (1937)].

It is now known that cocarboxylase is a distinct chemical entity. Preparation of pure crystalline cocarboxylase was first accomplished by Lohmann and Schuster (1937), who obtained only about 700 to 800 mg. from 100 kg. of brewer's yeast. After careful chemical analysis they found that the coenzyme was the pyrophosphoric acid ester of thiamin (vitamin B_1):

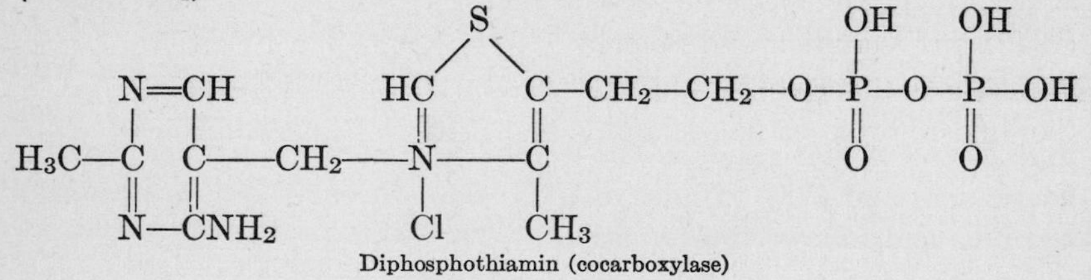

Diphosphothiamin (cocarboxylase)

Cocarboxylase has now been synthesized from thiamin by enzymatic and chemical methods. Stern and Hofer (1937) converted thiamin into its pyrophosphoric acid ester by treatment with phosphorus oxychloride, and Weijlard and Tauber (1938) obtained good yields of crystalline cocarboxylase by a similar method, except that the ester was obtained by treating thiamin with a mixture of ortho- and pyrophosphoric acid. Silverman and Werkman (1938, 1939) have shown that propionic acid bacteria can synthesize thiamin in vitamin B_1-deficient medium. Undoubtedly the thiamin serves as a precursor to cocarboxylase.

Diphosphothiamin is a rather stable compound with a melting point of about 242°C. It is readily soluble in water. Hydrolysis with 1.0 *N* HCl for 15 minutes liberates one of the two phosphoric acid residues, and the coenzyme becomes inactive. The second phosphoric group, however, is removed only after several hours' boiling with 1.0 *N* HCl [Tauber (1939)]. Very little is known about the function and mode of action of cocarboxylase, although considerable interesting data will be found on this subject in the paper by Stern and Melnick (1940). Recent studies by Green, Herbert, and Subrahmanyan (1940) indicate that the enzyme carboxylase is a diphosphothiamin-magnesium protein. It can be resolved into its component parts (protein, magnesium, cocarboxylase) by a variety of procedures, and there is good reason to believe that the metal plays the role of a "cement" substance which binds the specific protein to the prosthetic group (cocarboxylase).

Cocarboxylase definitely functions in the decarboxylation of pyruvic acid in yeast and *Fusaria* [Tytell and Gould (1941)], and the hypothesis has been advanced that in other microorganisms and tissues vitamin B_1 serves as a precursor for the coenzyme. It has been shown by Krebs and Johnson (1937), Lipmann (1937), Barron and Lyman (1939), Still (1941), Green and his associates (1941), Stotz, Westerfeld, and Berg (1944), and others, however, that animal tissues and certain bacteria (*Lactobacillus delbrückii*, staphylococci, gonococci, and *Escherichia coli*) do not decarboxylate pyruvic acid to form acetaldehyde in the direct manner that yeast does, but instead help catalyze it to other compounds. For example, Barron and his associates and Still have obtained enzyme preparations from gonococci, staphylococci, and *E. coli* which catalyze the aerobic oxidation of pyruvic acid to acetic acid and CO_2. Under anaerobic conditions the dismutation of pyruvic acid follows this equation:

$$2CH_3 \cdot CO \cdot COOH \xrightarrow{+H_2O} CH_3 \cdot COOH + CO_2 + CH_3 \cdot CHOH \cdot COOH$$

where one molecule of pyruvic acid is oxidized to acetic acid and CO_2, and another is reduced to lactic acid.

The oxidation of pyruvic acid requires cocarboxylase, adenine-flavin-dinucleotide or a similar carrier, inorganic phosphate, and other inorganic ions, such as magnesium or manganese. Some explanation of this process has been given in the interesting studies by Lipmann [See Lipmann and Tuttle (1944)] and Utter, Krampitz, and Werkman (1944). Using *L. delbrückii*, *Micrococcus lysodeikticus*, and other cells, these workers have presented evidence which indicates that acetyl phosphate is an intermediate in the oxidation of pyruvate to acetate and CO_2, and that the reaction is coupled with the phosphorylation of adenylic acid to form adenosine triphosphate. According to Lipmann, the following reactions explain the process:

$$\underset{\text{Pyruvic acid}}{CH_3 \cdot CO \cdot COOH} + H_3PO_4 \xrightarrow{-2H} \underset{\text{Acetyl phosphate}}{CH_3 \cdot COOPO_3H_2} + CO_2$$

$$2CH_3 \cdot COOPO_3H_2 + \text{Adenylic acid} \longrightarrow 2CH_3 \cdot COOH + \text{Adenosine triphosphate}$$

The two hydrogens liberated in the oxidation of pyruvic acid to acetylphosphate are accepted by an adenine-flavin-dinucleotide system. The resulting reduced dinucleotide is in turn reoxidized by oxygen under aerobic conditions or by pyruvate plus riboflavin in an anaerobic environment.

It has also been pretty well established by Green and his associates and by others [see Stotz, Westerfeld, and Berg (1944)] that a diphosphothiamin enzyme system from animal tissues is involved in a reaction where acetaldehyde and pyruvic acid undergo condensation to form acetoin (acetylmethylcarbinol). It is believed that pyruvic acid is first decarboxylated to acetaldehyde, which then undergoes condensation with a second molecule of pyruvic acid to yield acetoin as in the reactions:

$$\underset{\text{Pyruvic acid}}{CH_3 \cdot CO \cdot COOH} \rightarrow CH_3 \cdot CHO + CO_2$$

$$CH_3 \cdot CHO + CH_3 \cdot CO \cdot COOH \rightarrow CH_3 \cdot CHOH \cdot CO \cdot CH_3 + CO_2$$

It is quite possible that certain bacteria also produce acetoin by this mechanism.

Still other carboxylase enzymes have been described recently, but it is still too early to say whether they contain diphosphothiamin as a prosthetic group. These enzymes are discussed later in the chapter on pp. 586 to 589 on carboxylase and other decarboxylases.

THE ALLOXAZINE (FLAVIN) SYSTEMS

The chemical nature of the water-soluble, yellow-green, fluorescent pigment now referred to as *riboflavin* (synonymous with cytoflav, lactoflavin, vitamin G, and vitamin B_2, as used by many English and German investigators) commanded the attention of chemists as early as 1879. It was not until about 1932, however, that scientists gave proper attention to this pigment.

In 1932 Warburg and Christian announced the isolation of a "yellow ferment" from bottom yeast (Lebedew juice). They were also able to resolve the enzyme into a colorless protein and a yellow prosthetic group by treatment with methyl alcohol. The yellow color of this new oxidation enzyme disappeared when aqueous solutions were treated with reducing agents but reappeared when they were shaken with oxygen. Together with a second enzyme obtained from yeast and a coenzyme from red blood cells, this yellow enzyme constituted a system capable of oxidizing Robison's hexose monophosphoric acid ester. The yellow ferment was reversibly reduced to its leuco form during the process but could be regenerated by shaking the solution with molecular oxygen. In this system the yellow enzyme, by virtue of its easily reversible oxidation-reduction reactions, acted as a hydrogen-transporting substance between the substrate and molecular oxygen. Further research showed that this pigmented enzyme was present in all types of living cells, including yeast and bacteria.

As we have already mentioned, Warburg and Christian (1933) separated the yellow enzyme into two components: a protein fraction and a colored fraction (riboflavin). In this connection it should be mentioned that neither of these components was catalytically active when tested alone. However, if they were added together in a certain concentration, the enzymatic activity was regenerated. These brilliant researches constitute the first separation and identification of the prosthetic or chemically active grouping of an enzyme.

The actual synthesis of riboflavin was reported almost simultaneously from three different laboratories [see review by Theorell (1935)]. The compound was found to have the following formula:

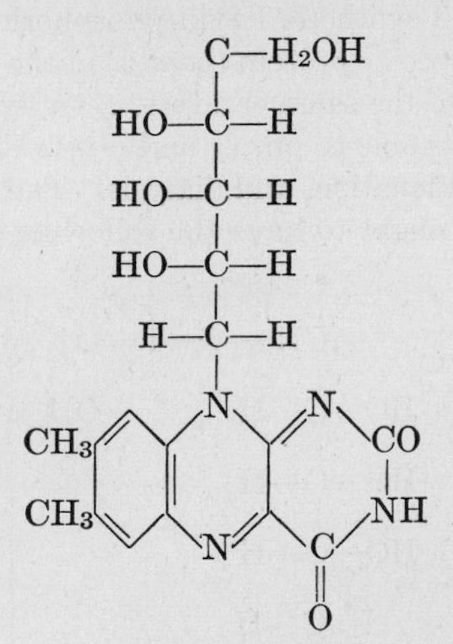

Riboflavin [vitamin B_2 or G, 6,7-dimethyl-9-(1'-*d*-ribityl)isoalloxazine]

Riboflavin is slightly soluble in water (11 mg. in 100 ml. at 25°C.), less soluble in alcohol, and insoluble in the ordinary fat solvents. It is stable in strong mineral acids but is sensitive to alkali. It is irreversibly decomposed by light.

The unique, as well as complicated, oxidation-reduction system of the flavins has attracted unusual attention and also has stimulated a considerable volume of literature. The normal potential of riboflavin referred to the normal hydrogen electrode is approximately −0.21 volts (*p*H 7.0). For details on this subject the paper by Stern (1934) should be consulted.

When riboflavin is combined with phosphoric acid, the prosthetic group of the yellow enzyme of Warburg and Christian is formed. As synthesized by Kuhn and Rudy (1936), it has the following formula:

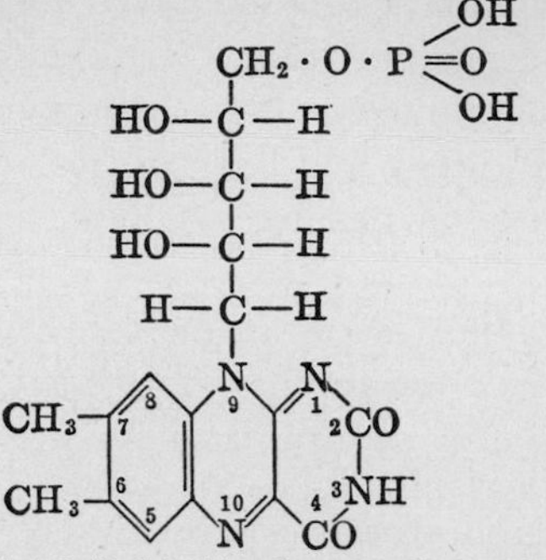

6,7-Dimethyl-9-(*d*-ribityl)isoalloxazine-5′-phosphoric acid

Both the natural and synthetic flavin phosphoric acids are capable of combining with the specific protein (bearer) of the yellow enzyme, forming chromoproteins of the same catalytic activity.

Theorell (1934) was able to purify and crystallize the yellow enzyme by cataphoresis, fractionation, and dialysis. The prosthetic group and protein bearer are thought to have the following mode of attachment:

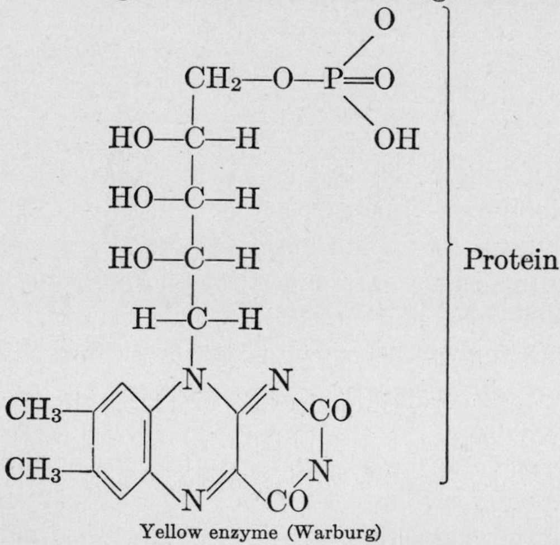

Yellow enzyme (Warburg)

The coenzyme or prosthetic group of the *d*-amino acid oxidase also belongs to this group of interesting compounds. Krebs (1932, 1933) described an enzyme capable of oxidizing many amino acids by the following reaction:

$$\underset{\displaystyle NH_2}{R\cdot \underset{|}{CH}\cdot COOH} + \tfrac{1}{2}O_2 \rightarrow R\cdot CO\cdot COOH + NH_3$$

In 1936 Das demonstrated that Krebs's *d*-amino acid oxidase required a thermostable factor for its activity, and later Warburg and Christian (1938) showed that the coenzyme was adenine-alloxazine-dinucleotide. Warburg and Christian gave a detailed procedure for the isolation of the pure coenzyme from liver, kidney, and yeast; although the highest yield was obtained from yeast, they secured approximately 65 mg. from 50 kg. of kidney and liver tissues. It is believed that this coenzyme is widespread in nature, and it is undoubtedly formed by bacteria.

Warburg and Christian made an elementary analysis of the pure barium salt of this coenzyme and found it to have an empirical formula of $BaC_{27}H_{31}N_9P_2O_{15}$ and an approximate molecular weight of 920. The structure of the adenine-flavin-dinucleotide may be represented schematically as follows:

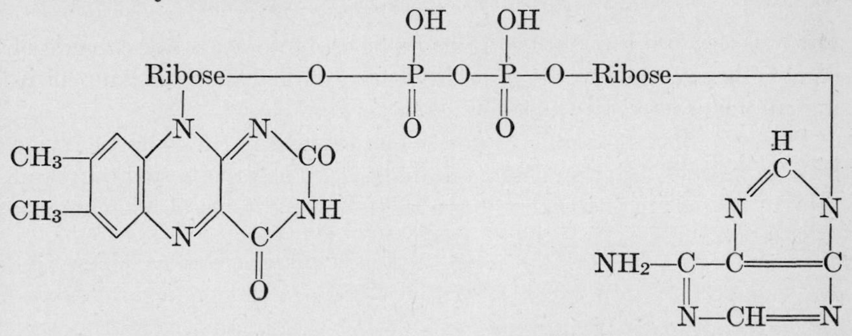

The absorption spectrum and chemical properties are very similar to those of riboflavin. Neutral aqueous solutions of this coenzyme retain their activity for some time if kept cold, but normal NaOH or HCl destroys its activity in a short time. Reversible reduction with loss of the yellow color may be accomplished with $Na_2S_2O_4$ at *p*H 7.5.

The mode of action of the coenzyme (adenine-alloxazine-dinucleotide) of the *d*-amino acid oxidase is very similar to that of the old yellow enzyme of Warburg. The alloxazine ring of the coenzyme molecule accepts hydrogen from the *d*-amino acid, forming a reduced compound and the corresponding imino acid. The reduced coenzyme then may be regenerated to the pigmented form by shaking with molecular oxygen [Baumann and Stare (1939)]. The role played by this adenine-alloxazine-dinucleotide in bacterial metabolism has not been definitely established, although it undoubtedly exists in certain organisms and probably functions in a manner similar to that just described.

That the original yellow enzyme and *d*-amino acid oxidase are not the only enzymes which have a flavin prosthetic group is borne out by reports by Ball (1938, 1939), stating that xanthine oxidase also belongs to this group. Publications from Warburg's laboratory [see review by Warburg (1938)] and by Haas and his associates (1940) and others also make it clear that there exists in nature a whole class of yellow enzymes, or alloxazine proteids, which differ in the constitution of their prosthetic group as well as that of the bearer protein and which show a well-defined specificity. Some ten of these flavoproteins have been described up to now; the more important ones which have been demonstrated in microorganisms are listed in Table 5. For more details the papers cited below this table, books on enzyme chemistry, and the articles in the *Annual Review of Biochemistry* should be consulted.

Several workers have calculated the amount of flavin present in various microorganisms. For example, Yamagutchi and Usami (1939) determined the flavin content of two yeasts and fifteen bacterial species. Per gram of dry weight, *Micrococcus citreus, Pseudomonas aeruginosa*, and *Escherichia coli* contained more than 10 to 15 μg. of flavin, whereas all the other bacteria and yeasts studied contained less than 10 μg., and *Serratia marcescens* contained less than 1.5 μg.

ADENOSINE TRIPHOSPHATE–ADENOSINE MONOPHOSPHATE (ADENYLIC ACID) SYSTEM

The function of the adenine-nucleotide coenzymes [1] in muscle and yeast metabolism has been studied extensively by several workers, who have demonstrated their role to be that of transferring energy-rich phosphate bonds to carbohydrates and other substances [see Green and

[1] To conserve space the following abbreviations will be used for these coenzymes: AMP for adenosine monophosphate (adenylic acid), ADP for adenosine diphosphate, and ATP for adenosine triphosphate. The formulas for these compounds are:

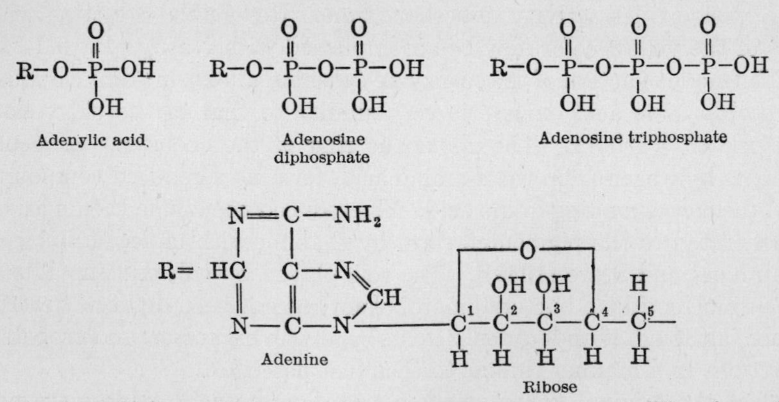

Adenylic acid from *Thiobacillus thiooxidans* and certain yeast differs from the above form in that the phosphate group is linked to position 3 of the ribose residue.

TABLE 5

SOME OF THE YELLOW ENZYMES, THE NATURE OF THEIR COENZYMES (PROSTHETIC GROUPS), THEIR SOURCES, AND THEIR ACTION

Coenzyme	Protein	Enzyme	Source	Action
Mononucleotide isoalloxazine-*d*-ribose-phosphate	+ Protein A =	Old yellow enzyme [1]	Yeast	Transfer of hydrogen from TPN to O_2 in the oxidation of hexose monophosphate
	+ Protein B =	Cytochrome c reductase [2]	Yeast	Reduction of cytochrome c by reduced TPN
Dinucleotide isoalloxazine-*d*-ribose-$(H_2PO_3)_2$-*d*-ribose-adenine	+ Protein C =	The Haas enzyme [3]	Yeast	Similar to old yellow enzyme
	+ Protein D =	Xanthine oxidase (Schardinger enzyme) [4]	Milk, liver, microorganisms (?)	Oxidation of xanthine to uric acid, etc.
	+ Protein E =	*d*-amino oxidase [5]	Animal organs, bacteria, yeast, etc.	Oxidation of *d*-amino acids to imino acids
	+ Protein F =	Diaphorase I [6]	Animal and plant tissues, bacteria, yeast, etc.	Oxidation of the reduced forms of DPN and TPN, respectively, in the presence of methylene blue
	+ Protein G =	Diaphorase II [6]		
Probably a flavin, but not fully characterized	+ Protein H =	Glucose oxidase (penatin, notatin, penicillin B, etc.) [7]	Molds, bacteria, etc.	Oxidation of glucose to gluconic acid
	+ Protein I =	*l*-Lysine decarboxylase [8]	*Bacterium cadaveris*	Decarboxylation of *l*-lysine to cadaverine
	+ Protein J =	Acetoacetic acid decarboxylase [9]	*Clostridium acetobutylicum*	Decarboxylation of acetoacetic acid to acetone

[1] Review by Warburg (1938).
[2] Haas, Horecker, and Hogness (1940).
[3] Haas (1938).
[4] Ball (1938, 1939).
[5] Krebs (1932, 1933).
[6] Dewan and Green (1938), Adler *et al.* (1939).
[7] Coulthard *et al.* (1942), Schales (1943).
[8] Gale and Epps (1943).
[9] Davies (1943).

Colowick (1944), Kalckar (1944)]. The transfer of phosphate from one linkage to another can occur either intramolecularly (for example, glucose-1-phosphate ⇄ glucose-6-phosphate) or intermolecularly. Intramolecular exchange of phosphate can apparently take place in the absence of the adenine nucleotides, but intermolecular transfer reactions require the presence of these coenzymes. The better known intermolecular phosphate transfer reactions, in which ATP, ADP, and AMP take part, have been discussed in some detail by Green and Colowick (1944); they classify the reactions as follows:

ATP formation	ADP + Acetyl phosphate ⇄ ATP + Acetate ADP + Phosphopyruvate ⇄ ATP + Pyruvate ADP + 1:3-Diphosphoglycerate ⇄ ATP + 3-Phosphoglycerate
Internucleotide phosphate transfer	ADP + ADP ⇄ ATP + AMP
ATP utilization	ATP + Glucose ⇄ ADP + Glucose-6-phosphate ATP + Fructose-6-phosphate → ADP + Fructose-1:6-diphosphate
Storage of energy-rich phosphate bonds	ATP + Creatine ⇄ ADP + Phosphocreatine ATP + Arginine ⇄ ADP + Phosphoarginine

It can be seen from this outline that the adenine nucleotides can take part in a wide variety of enzymatic reactions in which ADP or AMP accepts phosphate from other phosphate compounds formed at the expense of metabolism. The energy-rich phosphate bond of the ATP so formed can then be utilized: (1) by a hydrolytic enzyme known as adenosine triphosphatase (myosin), or (2) for the phosphorylation of other compounds which either undergo further metabolism or serve as a storage for energy-rich phosphate bonds.

Adenosine Triphosphate Formation. A number of phosphate compounds probably arise during normal metabolism which are capable of phosphorylating ADP or AMP to form ATP. At present, however, only acetyl phosphate, phosphopyruvate, and diphosphoglycerate are well known. One of these reactions may be cited here to illustrate ATP formation. According to Lipmann [see Lipmann and Tuttle (1944)], the oxidation of pyruvate by pyruvic dehydrogenase from bacteria and other cells is coupled with the phosphorylation of adenylic acid in the following way:

$$\underset{\text{Pyruvic acid}}{CH_3 \cdot CO \cdot COOH} + H_3PO_4 \xrightarrow{-2H} \underset{\text{Acetyl phosphate}}{CH_3 \cdot COOPO_3H_2} + CO_2$$

$$2\ CH_3 \cdot COOPO_3H_2 + AMP \longrightarrow 2\ \underset{\text{Acetic acid}}{CH_3 \cdot COOH} + ATP$$

It is well known that inorganic phosphate is taken up by plant and animal tissues and by microorganisms [see Macfarlane (1936, 1939),

Wiggert and Werkman (1938), O'Kane and Umbreit (1942), and pp. 916 to 926 on the mechanism of alcoholic fermentation in Chapter 10]. Probably the cells use a mechanism such as the one just described to form a complex between inorganic phosphate and organic compounds.

Internucleotide Phosphate Transfer. ATP may be formed in a somewhat different manner than the one just described. In muscle metabolism a water-soluble heat-stable enzyme, myokinase, catalyzes the reversible reaction:

$$2\ \text{ADP} \rightleftarrows \text{ATP} + \text{AMP}$$

where a labile phosphate is transferred from one molecule of ADP to another (phosphate dismutation), yielding ATP and AMP. Myokinase appears to be specific for adenine nucleotides, since it has no effect on inosine triphosphate [see Kalckar (1944)]. To what extent this enzyme occurs in bacteria and other cells is not known.

Adenosine Triphosphate Utilization. Several examples can be cited to illustrate the utilization of ATP in biological systems; these include the enzymatic phosphorylation of adenosine, thiamin, riboflavin, free hexoses, and other compounds containing alcoholic hydroxyl groups. In yeast metabolism the enzyme hexokinase catalyzes the one-step transfer of phosphate from ATP to hexoses:

$$\text{ATP} + \underset{\text{(Glucose)}}{\text{Hexose}} \rightarrow \text{ADP} + \underset{\text{(Glucose-6-phosphate)}}{\text{Hexose monophosphate}}$$

This enzyme is probably present in all cells that ferment glucose. Yeasts and other cells also contain an enzyme which can catalyze the reaction of ATP with fructose-6-phosphate:

$$\text{ATP} + \text{Fructose-6-phosphate} \rightarrow \text{ADP} + \text{Fructose-1:6-diphosphate}$$

It is also of interest that Colowick and Kalckar (1943) have shown that a combination of yeast hexokinase and animal myokinase can catalyze the two-step reaction:

$$\text{ATP} + 2\ \text{Hexose} \rightarrow \text{AMP} + 2\ \text{Hexose monophosphate}$$

Storage of Energy-Rich Phosphate Bonds. In the classification shown on p. 482, the storage of energy-rich phosphate bonds is illustrated by two reactions. Probably other similar reactions occur in nature. It is generally believed that in vertebrates the reaction, ATP (ADP) + Creatine $\rightleftarrows$ ADP (AMP) + Phosphocreatine, goes from left to right during "resting" muscle metabolism; when ATP is needed for other purposes, the reaction can proceed in the opposite direction and furnish a supply of this substance.

Studies of the various enzymatic reactions by which phosphate is transferred to and removed from the adenine nucleotides have revealed two facts about these coenzymes. They are: (1) The terminal phosphate of ATP is much more easily removed than is that of ADP; for example, only the terminal phosphate of ATP can be split off by the hydrolytic enzyme adenosinetriphosphatase (myosin) or transferred to glucose by hexokinase. (2) The terminal phosphate of ADP is much more readily phosphorylated by phosphopyruvate or 1:3-diphosphoglycerate than is AMP.

MISCELLANEOUS COENZYMES

Several other substances have been studied by various investigators which answer to the description of coenzymes; that is, they are fairly heat-stable, dialyzable organic compounds of relatively low molecular weight. Knowledge of their exact function in the respiration of bacteria and other cells, however, is very incomplete. For this reason they will be only briefly mentioned here. Other so-called coferments and other similar substances not cited here have been described in the biochemical literature, but at the present time they are outside the scope of bacteriology. Future studies, however, will undoubtedly show their importance in the metabolism of the bacterial cell.

Diaphorase (Coenzyme Factor, Coenzyme Dehydrogenase). Until recently it was quite generally believed that the reoxidation of the reduced pyridine nucleotides was accomplished by the yellow enzyme, which was in turn reduced to the leuco flavoprotein. This substance then reacted with molecular oxygen or with hemin systems in the ferric form to regenerate the oxidized form of the yellow enzyme. However, the recent researches by Adler and his associates (1937, 1939), Dewan and Green (1938), and others indicate that, at least in certain animal tissues, not the yellow enzyme but a different enzyme (called *diaphorase* by Adler and *coenzyme factor* by Dewan and Green) is responsible for the specific dehydrogenation of the reduced pyridine nucleotide-protein enzyme systems. In turn, then, the diaphorase forms the coupling link between the pyridine enzymes and the hemin systems of the cell (cytochrome-cytochrome oxidase). Abraham and Adler (1940) have shown that two different diaphorases occur in animal tissues. Diaphorase I reacts specifically with coenzyme I (diphosphopyridine nucleotide) and diaphorase II with coenzyme II (triphosphopyridine nucleotide). Diaphorase II was shown to be less specific than diaphorase I. Diaphorases have been demonstrated in bacteria (*Escherichia coli, Proteus vulgaris,* and *Bacillus subtilis*) and yeast, as well as in animal tissues [Green and Dewan (1938)]. Several workers have shown that the colored group in the diaphorases (I and II) is an adenine-flavin-dinucleotide. For this reason these coenzymes should probably be discussed with the other flavin coenzymes. However, until a little more is known about the diaphorases, we prefer to list them here [see paper by Haas, Horecker, and Hogness (1940)].

Coenzyme R. Allison, Hoover, and Burk (1933) and Hoover and Allison (1935) extracted a substance from commercial cane sugar and other plant and animal tissues which they called *coenzyme R,* because it played an important role in the nutrition and respiration of the root nodule bacteria (*Rhizobia*). Since coenzyme R is now known to be closely related to, if not identical with, the growth factor biotin, it is of only historical interest. A discussion of biotin will not be given here, since it seems better to consider it in Chapter 7 on bacterial nutrition.

Glyoxalase Coenzyme. Coenzyme activity has been attributed to glutathione (GSH) by Lohmann (1932) and others, who believe that it reacts with methylglyoxal to form a complex which in turn serves as a substrate for the enzyme glyoxalase (present in yeast and bacteria). The end products of this enzyme reaction would be lactic acid, and regenerated glutathione.

$$CH_3\cdot CO\cdot CHO + GSH \rightleftarrows CH_3\cdot CO\cdot CHO\text{—}HSG \xrightarrow[\text{Glyoxalase}]{H_2O} CH_3\cdot CHOH\cdot COOH + GSH$$

Although there are considerable data to support this reaction, recent studies have cast some doubt on the nature of the intermediate product [see Behrens (1941)], which is apparently only very slowly acted upon by glyoxalase. Many workers have been of the opinion that the sulfhydryl group of glutathione plays a necessary role in the coenzyme action. However, this in itself is not the only requirement for coenzyme action, since cysteine, cysteinylglycine, thioglycolic acid, hydrogen sulfide, and thioneine are inactive. Behrens (1941) has tested several compounds closely related in structure to glutathione to see whether they are capable of acting as coenzymes. Isoglutathione (α-glutamylcysteinylglycine), differing from glutathione only in that the glutamic acid residue is attached through the α-carboxyl instead of the γ-carboxyl group, and asparthione (β-aspartylcysteinylglycine), the aspartic acid analog of glutathione, were both found to be capable of acting as coenzymes for glyoxalase.

Glutathione and related compounds may also function in other important respiratory systems. For example, Bigwood and Thomas (1935) observed that purified cytochrome c is readily reduced by glutathione, and it may be that hydrogen is transferred to the hemin systems in this manner.

Lysine Decarboxylase Coenzyme. The decarboxylation of *l*-lysine to cadaverine by the paracolon organism, *Bacterium cadaveris*, requires a flavin coenzyme [Gale and Epps (1943)]. The coenzyme has not been fully characterized. The known flavin coenzymes will not replace it in the reaction.

THE ROLE OF COENZYMES

A question which might be raised is how enzymes function in the various enzymatic processes. In the older literature coenzymes were thought to be accessory substances which merely assisted or accelerated enzyme reactions by activating the hydrogen of the substrate in such a manner that it was more easily removed by the various specific dehydrogenases. As more data have accumulated on cellular or biological processes, this view has been somewhat altered. It is now quite generally believed that biological oxidation is accomplished by means of a chain of complex reactions in which hydrogen or electrons from the substrate are transported by one substance, or probably by a series of compounds, until eventually they combine with oxygen. The role played by the various coenzymes in this chain of reactions is therefore probably that of actually uniting with hydrogen and then passing it on to some other compound in the chain which has a greater affinity for the hydrogen than the compound to which it is attached. Compounds which make up the links in the chain through which hydrogen passes are the specific dehydrogenases and their coenzymes, the cytochromes, and cytochrome oxidase. Many other naturally occurring substances, such as glutathione, pigments, and dicarboxylic acids, often insert themselves in the dehydrogenation chain and may supply alternate routes for the transfer of hydrogen from the substrate to oxygen. Irrespective of the route traveled by hydrogen, various more or less specific dehydrogenases are essential as master escorts.

There is still some question concerning the union of the enzyme and coenzyme in the dehydrogenation chain. One school [see review by Theorell (1935)] believes that the substrate and specific dehydrogenase unite to form a substrate-dehydrogenase complex which contains activated hydrogen. This complex then gives up hydrogen to a coenzyme. On the other hand, Warburg (1938) and Warburg and Christian (1939) emphasize the combination of protein and coenzyme, which then becomes the active hydrogen-transporting enzyme system. The protein component gives the hydrogen-transporting enzyme specificity and determines whether the coenzyme will accept hydrogen from the substrate. Baumann and Stare (1939) have made the following interesting and conservative statement concerning the enzyme-coenzyme relationship:

The enzyme-coenzyme relationship might be pictured as follows: reaction between coenzyme and substrate takes place when the proper dehydrogenase, a large molecule, seizes the coenzyme with one hand, the substrate with the other, and bumps the two together. The coenzyme takes hydrogen from the substrate, and the reduced coenzyme breaks away. It can then pass its hydrogen on to a suitable acceptor, either as free reduced coenzyme or in the presence of some other specific protein.

CLASSIFICATION OF ENZYMES

Enzymes may be classified in several different ways; the system employed must depend chiefly upon the particular interest of the individual. The ideal classification would be based on the chemical composition of the enzymes, but as yet this is not possible. Quite generally, enzymes are grouped according to the type of chemical reaction which they catalyze. For example, the enzymes which hydrolyze compounds are called hydrolytic enzymes or *hydrolases,* and those which oxidize and reduce the substrate are spoken of as *oxidases* and *reductases* or simply as *oxidoreductases.*

As we have previously mentioned, enzymes are named according to the substrate acted upon, rather than on the basis of their chemical make-up. Thus they are frequently classified on the same basis. For instance, those enzymes which hydrolyze esters are called *esterases;* those which hydrolyze carbohydrates, *carbohydrases;* and those which hydrolyze proteins, *proteinases.* This system is excellent as a secondary classification but has certain inherent disadvantages if used alone. Another method of organization which is frequently used for bacterial enzymes is based on the location of the enzyme in respect to the cell. Many enzymes, or their precursors, are excreted from the bacterial cell and are referred to as *extracellular enzymes* or *exoenzymes,* whereas others reside within the cell during its life and are termed *intracellular enzymes* or *endoenzymes.* Usually the extracellular enzymes are hydrolytic in nature and the intracellular enzymes are oxidoreductive. The classification used in Table 6 was proposed in part by Waksman and Davison (1926), and, as will be seen, it includes two of the systems just mentioned.

Now let us turn to a closer examination of the enzymes listed in Table 6, and briefly discuss their occurrence in various bacteria and related microorganisms. Many bacteria have not been examined for the presence or absence of specific enzymes, and actual proof that all the enzymes listed in this table are present in microorganisms is also lacking at this time. Furthermore, it is probable that several of the enzymes listed are really enzyme mixtures. Future studies will undoubtedly break down many of these mixtures. To make a complete list of the various enzymes which occur in bacteria and other microorganisms is, therefore, impossible. Only a few representatives will be cited here to give the student some idea of the widespread nature of enzymes in microbes. For more complete data on this subject the books by Waksman and Davison (1926), Buchanan and Fulmer (1930), and Oppenheimer (1925–1937) or the reviews by Waksman (1922) and Dubos (1940) should be consulted.

A. Hydrolytic Enzymes (Hydrolases)

I. ESTERASES

The hydrolysis or synthesis of esters by the so-called esterases of microorganisms follows the general equation:

$$R \cdot COOR' + H_2O \rightleftarrows R \cdot COOH + R'OH$$

When R·COOH is a higher fatty acid and R′OH is glycerol, the enzyme responsible for the reaction is called a glyceridase or, usually, a lipase. If, however, R·COOH is any other organic acid or if the acid is inorganic and R′OH is a simple alcohol (aliphatic or aromatic) or a carbohydrate, then the reaction is said to be catalyzed by some other esterase, such as butyrase or phosphatase. Some workers believe that the lipases and other esterases are not absolutely specific.

1. Lipases (Glyceridases). The true lipases hydrolyze neutral fats into glycerol and higher fatty acids but do not readily attack lower esters. The most favorable temperature for lipase activity is about 40°C., although many lipolytic bacteria grow and produce lipase at much lower temperatures. The optimum reaction (*p*H) may vary some with the source of the enzyme, the substrate, and the buffer employed, but a neutral to a weakly acid or alkaline reaction has been used many times by various workers with reproducible results. Several methods have been proposed for the study of lipase activity by microorganisms. Since the enzymatic hydrolysis yields fatty acids, a crude qualitative test can be made by adding an indicator, such as litmus, to the test solution. More reliable tests are those perfected by Berry (1933), Collins and Hammer (1934), and Jensen and Grettie (1937). Berry worked with the test originated by Carnot and Mauban. It consists of growing organisms on a solid medium having fat dispersed throughout. When good growth occurs, the plates are flooded with saturated copper sulfate solution. If hydrolysis has taken place, the freed fatty acids react with the copper sulfate to give an insoluble blue soap. In the method perfected by Collins and Hammer and by

Jensen and Grettie the organisms are cultivated on beef infusion or nutrient agar containing emulsified fat and Nile-blue sulfate as an indicator. This indicator has the property of staining triglycerides and neutral fats red, whereas the various fatty acids show a distinct blue color. Thus when it is employed in a medium containing fat droplets, the color will be red, and any lipase activity on the part of the organisms will change the color to blue. For the proper use of Nile-blue sulfate and other basic dyes to demonstrate lipolysis by microorganisms the paper by Knaysi (1941) should be consulted. Quantitative methods of estimating the action of lipase usually involve the titration, with a standard solution of alkali, of the fatty acids liberated from fats [Trussell and Weed (1937)].

Enzymes capable of hydrolyzing neutral fats are quite widespread in nature, and both intracellular and extracellular lipases have been described from a considerable number of bacteria, yeasts, and molds. The early studies on microbial lipases have been reviewed recently by Jensen and Grettie (1937) and by Horowitz-Wlassowa and Livschitz (1935). Thus only a few representative studies will be mentioned here. Of the early investigations on lipolytic enzymes the most extensive study is that of Söhngen (1910–1911), who demonstrated that such enzymes show a variable resistance to heat. For example, the lipases of such organisms as *Achromobacter punctatum* and *Pseudomonas aeruginosa* were found to be considerably more resistant to heat than those of *Achromobacter lipolyticum*, *Bacillus stutzeri*, *Pseudomonas fluorescens*, *Oidium lactis*, *Aspergillus niger*, *Penicillium glaucum*, and *Clostridium butyri*. According to Lowenstein, Fleming, and Neill (1929), the lipase of *Escherichia coli* is an endocellular heat-labile substance. In this respect it agrees with the lipase of pneumococci [Avery and Cullen (1920)], *Clostridium perfingens* [Fleming and Neill (1927)], and *Bacillus anthracis* but differs from the lipase of *Clostridium botulinum*, which is an extracellular enzyme [Neill and Fleming (1927)]. Collins and Hammer (1934) included 159 cultures in their study, including such species as *Achromobacter connii*, *Pseudomonas fragi*, *Pseudomonas mucidolens*, *Pseudomonas myxogenes*, and others of the genera *Serratia*, *Pseudomonas*, *Bacterium*, and *Micrococcus*. Their data show that hydrolysis of the simple triglycerides of the saturated fatty acids becomes more difficult as the molecular weight increases, and there is little variation in the percentage of bacteria which hydrolyze the different natural and hydrogenated fats. Horowitz-Wlassowa and Livschitz (1935) studied the decomposition of fats and oils by several bacteria and molds. Their study indicated that the greater number of bacterial species bring about an initial hydrolysis of fats, although a few species like *Aerobacter aerogenes* may oxidize the fats directly. Vercellana (1936) could not demonstrate lipase activity in *Brucella melitensis*, *Brucella abortus*, *Vibrio comma*, *Staphylococcus aureus*, *Streptococcus pyogenes*, or *Pseudomonas aeruginosa*. Jensen and Grettie (1937) observed that certain strains of bacteria elaborate lipases and oxidases which act on fats and produce both free fatty acids and oxidation products. Some of these enzymes were active at −17°C.(1.4°F.) and caused rancidity in bacon fat after a period of 4 months to a year. Moisture-free fats did not support growth of the microorganisms tested, but as little as 0.3 per cent water allowed some organisms to initiate growth and produce lipolysis.

2. Butyrases and Other Simple Esterases. Bacterial enzymes which act on the esters of some of the lower fatty acids have not been studied very extensively in bacteria. The decomposition of ethyl butyrate by butyrase is cited in Table 6 as one example of the activity of this group of enzymes. Another example is the hydrolysis of acetyl choline by choline esterase:

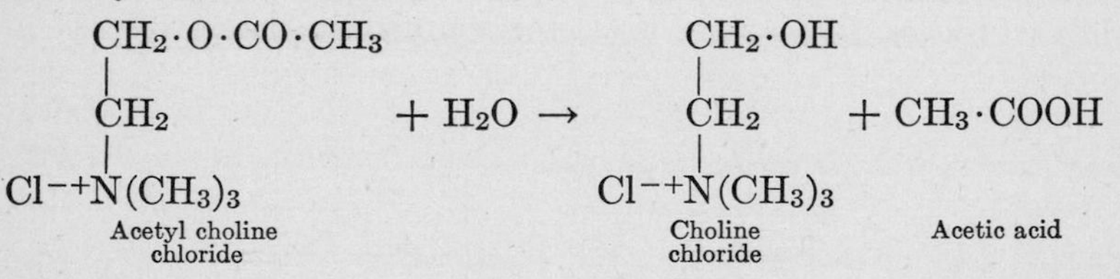

This enzyme has been studied mostly in animal tissues and fluids but has been demonstrated also in type I pneumococcus by Schaller (1942).

3. Phosphatases. In nature numerous enzymes (phosphatases) occur which are concerned with the hydrolytic cleavage of phosphate bonds. For classification purposes it is convenient to allocate these enzymes to the three following classes [Green and Colowick (1944)]:

Class of Enzymes and Examples	*Substrate*	*Products*
1. Phosphomonoesterases: Glycerophosphatase, Phytase	R–C–O–P(OH)(OH)=O	R–C–OH + HO–P(OH)(OH)=O
2. Phosphodiesterases: Glycerophosphate-lecithinase	R–C–O–P(=O)(OH)–O–C–R′	R–C–OH + HO–P(=O)(OH)–O–C–R′
3. Pyrophosphatases: Adenosinetriphosphatase, Carboxylasephosphatase	R–O–P(=O)(OH)–O–P(=O)(OH)–OH	R–O–P(=O)(OH)–OH + HO–P(=O)(OH)–OH

Many of the reactions catalyzed by the phosphatases are irreversible under physiological conditions. According to Lipmann's terminology, the pyrophosphate bonds are energy-rich, but the phosphoric ester bonds are energy-poor; thus the pyrophosphatases liberate a great deal more free energy for cellular activities than do the phosphoesterases.

The phosphatases have been demonstrated in many bacteria, yeasts [Rae and Eastcott (1940)], and molds, as well as in highly purified vaccinia elementary bodies [Macfarlane and Salaman (1938)]. A few specific examples will now be given.

Lecithinase, the enzyme which hydrolyzes lecithin, has been regarded by many workers in the past as a mixture of two or more enzymes, one being a lipase which splits off the fatty acid residues and the other hydrolyzing the remaining product to choline and glycerophosphoric acid. We now know that lecithin may be attacked at more than one place in the molecule by different enzymes, but true lipases do not hydrolyze lecithins. The places where lecithin can be hydrolyzed are indicated by the four dotted lines in the following formula:

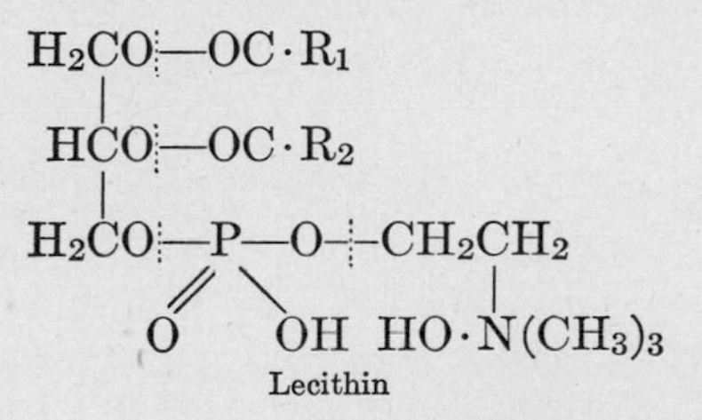

Lecithin

The animal and plant lecithinases A and B are more or less specific in that they remove only one or both of the fatty acids (R_1 and R_2) from lecithin. The phosphodiesterase, glycerophosphate-lecithinase, can act upon lecithin to produce the corresponding diglyceride and phosphoryl choline. This enzyme is thought to occur in several cells, and it has been demonstrated in type A *Clostridium perfringens* (*Clostridium welchii*) toxin by Macfarlane and Knight (1941). It is probably identical with the specific α-toxin, which is the lethal, hemolytic, and necrotic substance predominant in type A culture filtrates. The fourth cleavage of lecithin is brought about by choline-phosphate-lecithinase, a phosphomonoesterase, which acts upon lecithin or phosphoryl choline to form choline and phosphoric acid. Several other investigators have reported that bacteria and other microorganisms can hydrolyze lecithin, but intact organisms, rather than enzyme preparations, have usually been employed. For example, Stoklasa (1911) demonstrated that *Bacillus subtilis, Bacillus mycoides,* and *Proteus vulgaris* hydrolyzed lecithin, and Scales (1914) recorded similar results with the mold *Aspergillus terricola.* Toda (1930) and Toda and Urabe (1935) also reported that many bacteria produce an active lecithinase. *Serratia marcescens, Pseudomonas aeruginosa, Eberthella typhosa,* several acid-fast bacilli, and certain other organisms were included in their studies. The enzyme formed by *S. marcescens* worked best at 40°C., and its action was not destroyed when the cells were killed by heat. In regard to their lecithinase activity the acid-fast bacilli may be ranked in the following diminishing order: *Mycobacterium leprae,* avian, frog, bovine, and human strains of *Mycobacterium tuberculosis.*

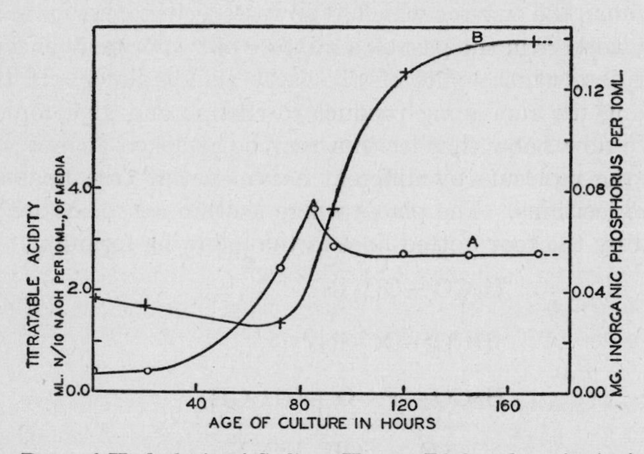

FIG. 3. Rate of Hydrolysis of Sodium Hexose Diphosphate in Active Culture of *Clostridium acetobutylicum.* *A* = titratable acidity; *B* = liberation of inorganic phosphorus. (From Heard and Wynne, 1933.)

Glycerophosphatase, which hydrolyzes the phosphoric acid ester of glycerol, is apparently quite widespread among microorganisms. In 1911 Neuberg and Karczag first demonstrated this enzyme in yeast, and it has since been found in several bacterial species (*Aerobacter aerogenes, Bacillus subtilis, Alcaligenes fecalis, Clostridium acetobutylicum,* and *Propionibacterium jensenii*) by Wynne and his associates [Heard and Wynne (1933), Pett and Wynne (1933, 1938)], who have made extensive studies in this field. Glycerophosphatase has also been demonstrated in bovine and human tubercle bacilli [Kawabata (1934)] and in several molds, including *Aspergillus oryzae* [Proskuryakov (1936)] and *Rhizopus japonicus* [Miyagawa (1936)].

Hexosephosphatase has been found in yeasts and bacteria by several workers. For example, Heard, Pett, and Wynne studied the rate of hydrolysis of the ester by several organisms, as well as the effect of various factors, such as *p*H and salts, on the rate of the reaction

Attempts to demonstrate the synthetic activity of the phosphatase failed. Some of their data on the rate of hydrolysis of 0.04 per cent sodium hexose diphosphate in a glucose-peptone medium by *Clostridium acetobutylicum* are shown in Fig. 3. From this figure it will be seen that the enzyme responsible for the hydrolysis of the ester did not come into effective action until the second phase of the fermentation. In this phase there was little or no increase in cells; in fact, there was frequently a decrease. Also during this period part of the accumulated acetic and butyric acids was converted into acetone and butyl alcohol, which accounts for the decrease in the titratable-acidity curve (*A*). The marked increase in the rate of ester hydrolysis in the second period suggests either that some of the cells had become more permeable to the enzyme or that the enzyme might have been liberated from cells which had actually undergone autolysis. It is not unlikely that a small part of the liberated inorganic phosphate had its origin in the complex esters of the cell. The slight decrease in free phosphate in the early stage of the fermentation suggests the formation of such esters during the active growth of the bacteria.

Phytase is an enzyme which has the ability to hydrolyze the inositol-phosphoric acid ester, phytin. The reaction proceeds according to the equation given in Table 6. The enzyme has been demonstrated in the molds, *Aspergillus niger*, *Aspergillus fumigatus*, and *Aspergillus clavatus* by Dox and Golden (1911) and in twelve species of the genus *Aspergillus* by Kawahara (1929). It is also quite possible that certain other microorganisms contain this particular enzyme, although a systematic study has not been made.

Nucleotidase has been little studied in microorganisms but is undoubtedly present in *Bacillus subtilis* and other bacteria. For example, MacFadyen (1934) stated that the breakdown of nucleotides can occur in the following three ways (P = phosphate, R = ribose, N = base):

$$1.\ \mathrm{PRN} \rightarrow \mathrm{P} + \mathrm{RN}$$

$$2.\ \mathrm{PRN} \rightarrow \mathrm{P} + \mathrm{R} + \mathrm{N}$$

$$3.\ \mathrm{PRN} \rightarrow \mathrm{PR} + \mathrm{N}$$

From the data which were obtained with *Bacillus subtilis* he was able to show that the four nucleotides of yeast nucleic acid were disintegrated mainly into the phosphoric acid ester of ribose and nitrogenous bases, in accordance with the third of the foregoing reactions.

Leahy, Sandholzer, and Woodside (1939) and Leahy, Stokinger, and Carpenter (1940) have demonstrated a phosphatase in twenty-three different Gram-negative bacilli and species of the genus *Neisseria*

TABLE 6

Classification of Certain Enzymes Which Have Been Demonstrated in Microorganisms

(Data from Waksman and Davison's *Enzymes*, Salle's *Fundamental Principles of Bacteriology*, and Others)

Name of Enzyme	Substrate	Reaction and End Products Formed
A. HYDROLYTIC ENZYMES (HYDROLASES)		
I. *Esterases*	Esters	Acids + Alcohols
1. Lipases	Fats (glycerides)	Higher fatty acids + Glycerol $H_2C{-}O{-}CO{-}(CH_2)_{16}CH_3$ / $HC{-}O{-}CO{-}(CH_2)_{16}CH_3$ / $H_2C{-}O{-}CO{-}(CH_2)_{16}CH_3$ (Tristearin) $+ 3H_2O \rightarrow$ H_2COH / $HCOH$ / H_2COH (Glycerol) $+ 3CH_3(CH_2)_{16}COOH$ (Stearic acid)
2. Butyrase and other simple esterases	Lower esters (esters of alcohols other than glycerol)	Lower fatty acids + Alcohols $C_3H_7COOC_2H_5 + H_2O \rightarrow C_3H_7COOH + C_2H_5OH$ Ethyl butyrate, Butyric acid, Ethyl alcohol
3. Phosphatases (see discussion)		
Lecithinase	Lecithin	Choline + Glycerophosphoric acid + Fatty acids $H_2C{-}O{-}CO{-}R$ / $HC{-}O{-}CO{-}R_1$ } Fatty acid radicals / $H_2C{-}O{-}P(=O)(OH){-}O{-}CH_2{-}CH_2{-}N(CH_3)_3{-}OH$ (Lecithin) $+ H_2O \rightarrow HOCH_2CH_2N(CH_3)_3OH$ (Choline) $+$ H_2COH / $HCOH$ / $H_2C{-}O{-}P(=O)(OH){-}OH$ (Glycerophosphoric acid) $+ RCOOH + R_1COOH$ (Fatty acids)
Hexosephosphatases	Hexose phosphates	Hexose + Phosphoric acid

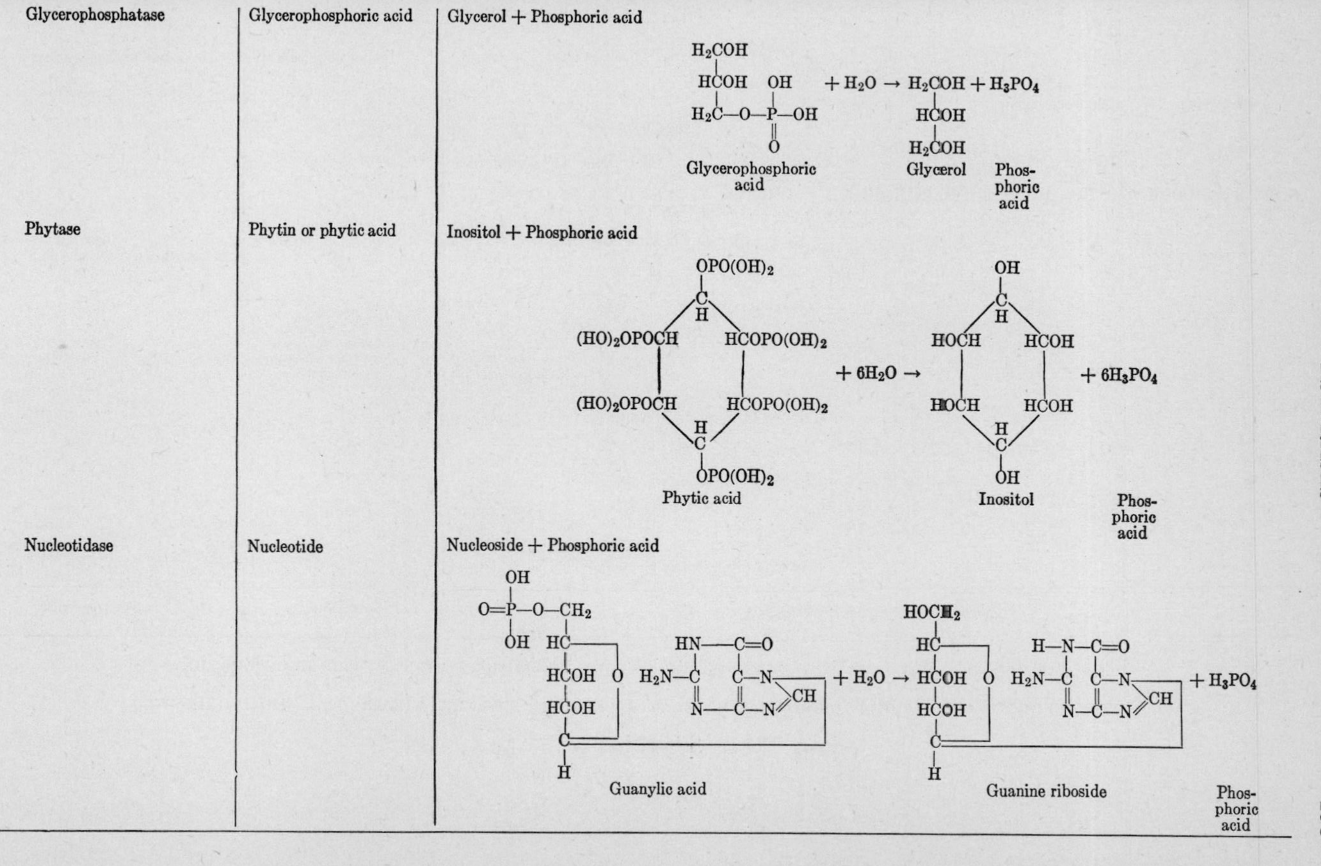

Glycerophosphatase	Glycerophosphoric acid	Glycerol + Phosphoric acid	Glycerophosphoric acid $+ H_2O \rightarrow$ Glycerol $+ H_3PO_4$ (Phosphoric acid)
Phytase	Phytin or phytic acid	Inositol + Phosphoric acid	Phytic acid $+ 6H_2O \rightarrow$ Inositol $+ 6H_3PO_4$ (Phosphoric acid)
Nucleotidase	Nucleotide	Nucleoside + Phosphoric acid	Guanylic acid $+ H_2O \rightarrow$ Guanine riboside $+ H_3PO_4$ (Phosphoric acid)

TABLE 6 (*Continued*)

CLASSIFICATION OF CERTAIN ENZYMES WHICH HAVE BEEN DEMONSTRATED IN MICROORGANISMS

(Data from Waksman and Davison's *Enzymes*, Salle's *Fundamental Principles of Bacteriology*, and Others)

Name of Enzyme	Substrate	Reaction and End Products Formed
4. Sulfatase	Ethereal sulfates	Phenol (or its homologs) + Salts of sulfuric acid $C_6H_5O{\cdot}SO_3K + H_2O \rightarrow C_6H_5OH + KHSO_4$ Phenyl sulfate → Phenol
II. *Carbohydrases* 1. Polysaccharidases Cellulase	Polysaccharides Celluloses	Lower saccharides Cellobiose $(C_6H_{10}O_5)n + nH_2O \rightarrow$ Cellobiose (Glucose-4-β-glucoside) Cellulose
Cytases or hemicellulases	Hemicelluloses	Dextrins + Monosaccharides $(C_6H_{10}O_5)n + nH_2O \rightarrow (C_6H_{10}O_5)n + C_6H_{12}O_6$ Hemicellulose → Dextrin + Glucose

Diastase or amylases	Starch and dextrins	Dextrins + Maltose $(C_6H_{10}O_5)n + nH_2O \rightarrow (C_6H_{10}O_5)n +$ [Maltose structure] Starch Dextrin Maltose (Glucose-4-α-glucoside)
Pectinase Inulase or inulinase	Pectic substances Inulin	Reducing sugars, etc. Fructose $(C_6H_{10}O_5)n + nH_2O \rightarrow C_6H_{12}O_6$ Inulin Fructose
2. Trisaccharidases Raffinase	Trisaccharides Raffinose	Disaccharides + Monosaccharides Melibiose + Fructose [Raffinose structure] $+ H_2O \rightarrow$ [Melibiose structure] + [Fructose structure] Raffinose Melibiose (Glucose-6-α-galactoside) Fructose

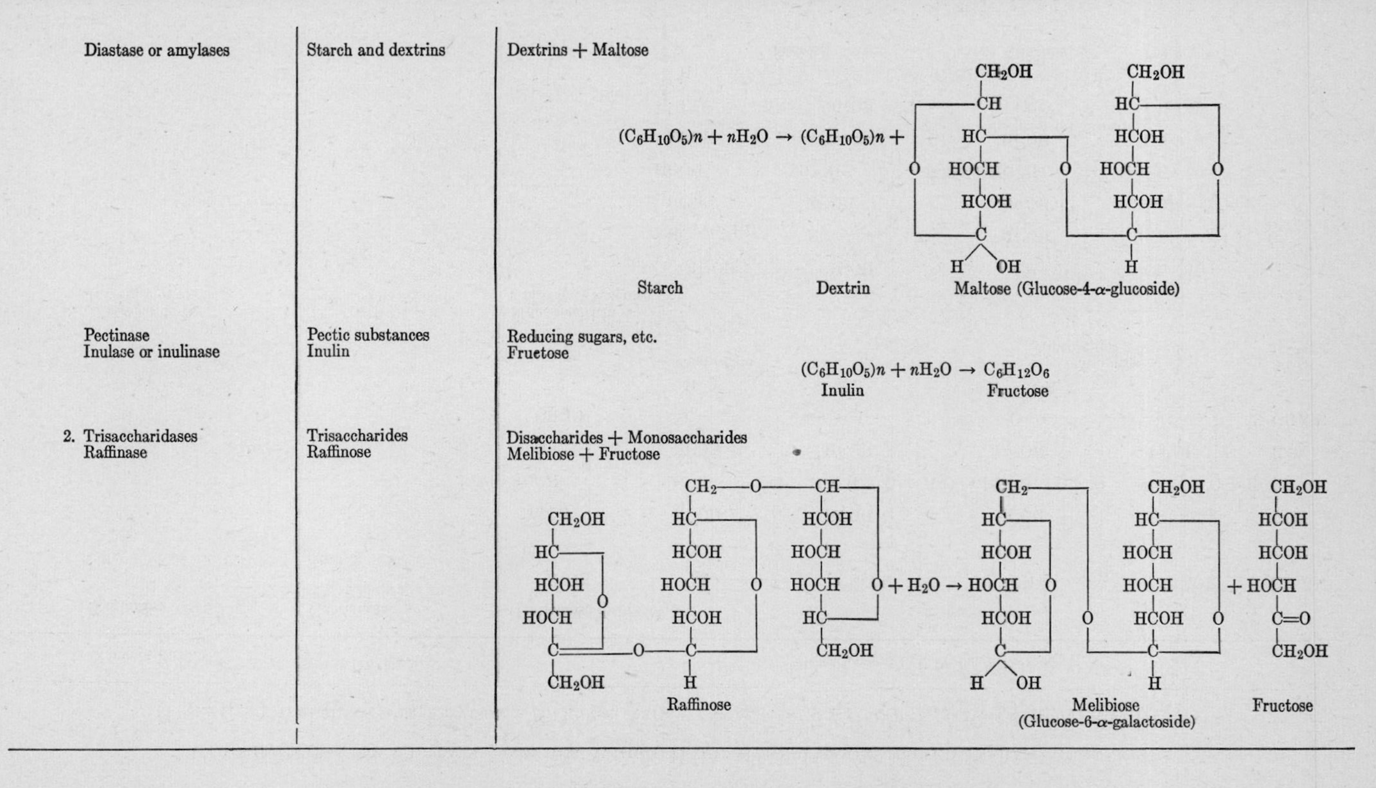

TABLE 6 (*Continued*)

CLASSIFICATION OF CERTAIN ENZYMES WHICH HAVE BEEN DEMONSTRATED IN MICROORGANISMS

(Data from Waksman and Davison's *Enzymes*, Salle's *Fundamental Principles of Bacteriology*, and Others)

Name of Enzyme	Substrate	Reaction and End Products Formed
Gentianase	Gentianose	Gentiobiose + Fructose 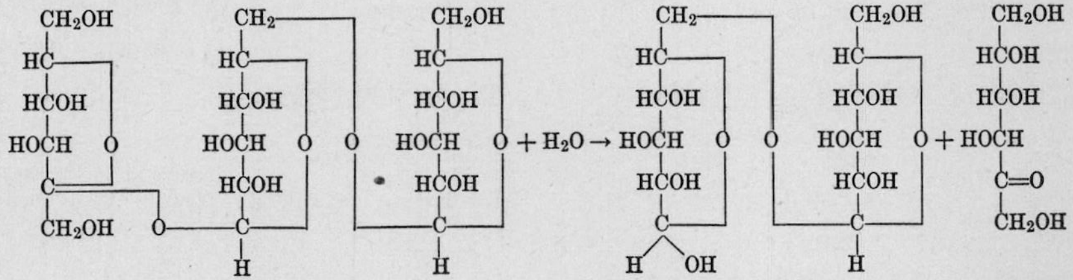 Gentianose $+ H_2O \rightarrow$ Gentiobiose (Glucose-6-β-glucoside) + Fructose
3. Disaccharidases Invertase or Sucrase	Disaccharides Sucrose (cane sugar)	Monosaccharides Glucose + Fructose 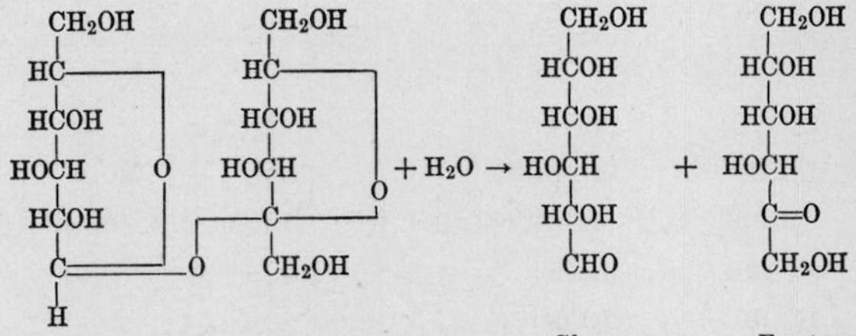 Sucrose $+ H_2O \rightarrow$ Glucose + Fructose

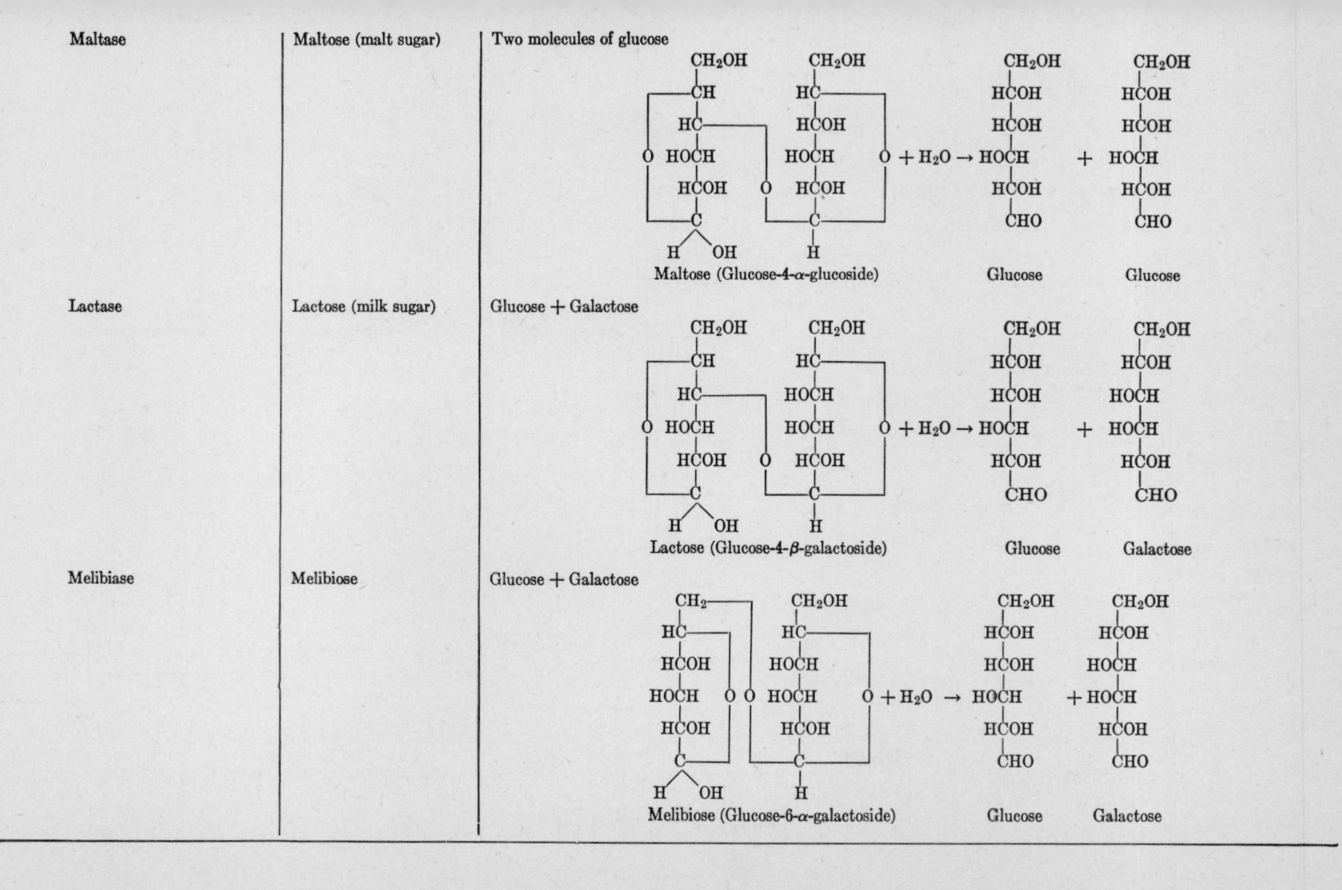

Maltase	Maltose (malt sugar)	Two molecules of glucose	Maltose (Glucose-4-α-glucoside) + H_2O → Glucose + Glucose
Lactase	Lactose (milk sugar)	Glucose + Galactose	Lactose (Glucose-4-β-galactoside) + H_2O → Glucose + Galactose
Melibiase	Melibiose	Glucose + Galactose	Melibiose (Glucose-6-α-galactoside) + H_2O → Glucose + Galactose

TABLE 6 (*Continued*)

CLASSIFICATION OF CERTAIN ENZYMES WHICH HAVE BEEN DEMONSTRATED IN MICROORGANISMS

(Data from Waksman and Davison's *Enzymes*, Salle's *Fundamental Principles of Bacteriology*, and Others)

Name of Enzyme	Substrate	Reaction and End Products Formed
Cellobiase	Cellobiose	Glucose

```
CH2OH           CH2OH                          CH2OH        CH2OH
 |               |                              |            |
HC-------+      HC-------+                     HCOH         HCOH
 |       |       |       |                      |            |
HCOH     |   +---CH      |                     HCOH         HCOH
 |       |   |   |       |                      |            |
HOCH     O   |  HOCH     O + H2O  ->           HOCH    +    HOCH
 |       |   |   |       |                      |            |
HCOH     |   O  HCOH     |                     HCOH         HCOH
 |       |   |   |       |                      |            |
 C=======+===+   C-------+                     CHO          CHO
 |              / \
 H            HO   H
Cellobiose (Glucose-4-β-glucoside)             Glucose      Glucose
```

Name of Enzyme	Substrate	Reaction and End Products Formed
4. Glucosidases α-Glucosidase	Glucosides α-Glucosides	Glucose + Other products Glucose + Alcohol or phenol residue

```
   CH2OH                      CH2OH
    |                          |
   HC-------+                 HCOH
    |       |                  |
   HCOH     |                 HCOH
    |       |                  |
   HOCH     O + H2O  ->       HOCH      + CH3OH
    |       |                  |
   HCOH     |                 HCOH
    |       |                  |
    C-------+                 CHO
   / \
  H   O—CH3
 α-Methyl                     Glucose     Methyl
 glucoside                                alcohol
```

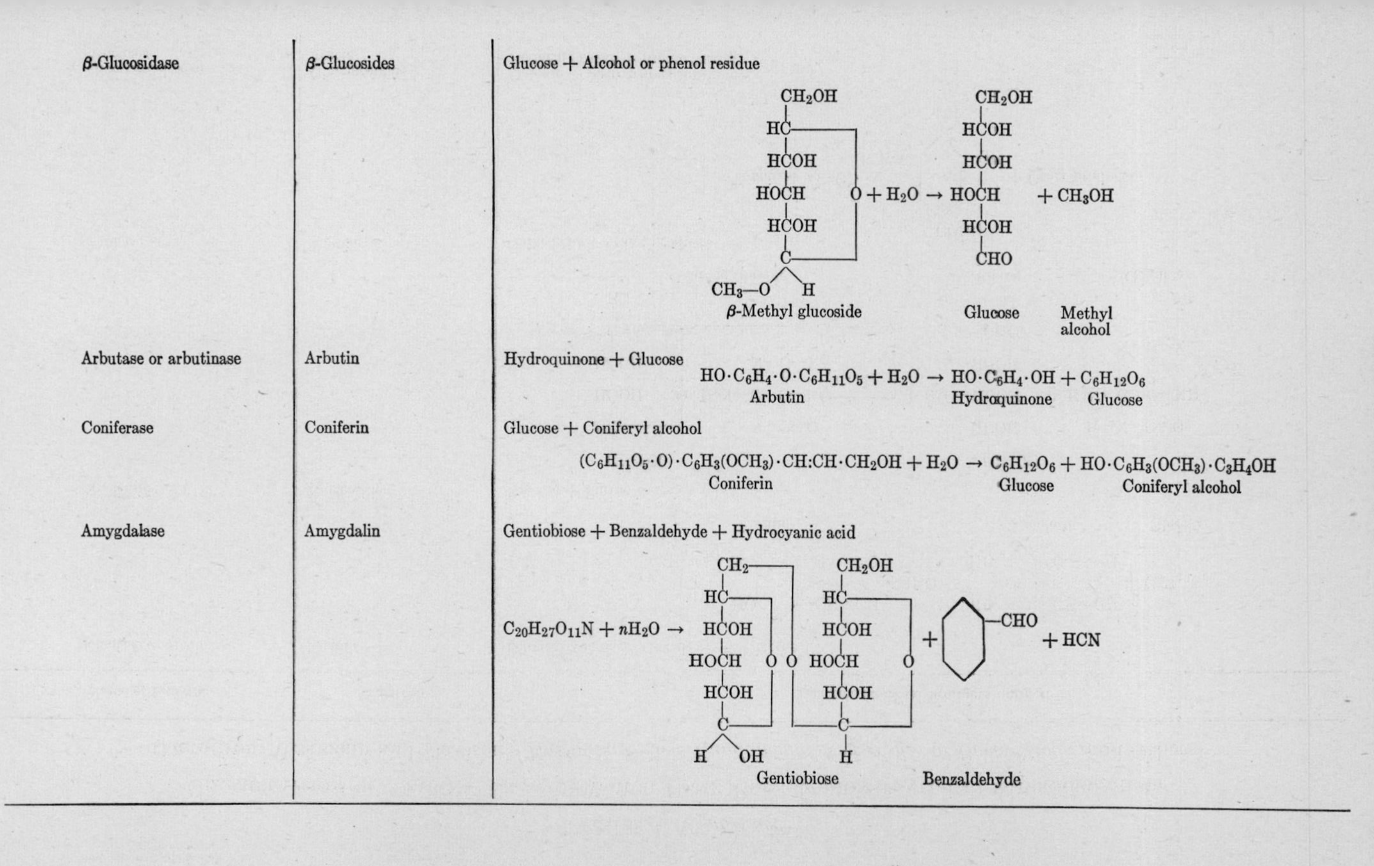

β-Glucosidase	β-Glucosides	Glucose + Alcohol or phenol residue β-Methyl glucoside + H_2O → Glucose + CH_3OH (Methyl alcohol)
Arbutase or arbutinase	Arbutin	Hydroquinone + Glucose $HO\cdot C_6H_4\cdot O\cdot C_6H_{11}O_5 + H_2O \rightarrow HO\cdot C_6H_4\cdot OH + C_6H_{12}O_6$ Arbutin → Hydroquinone + Glucose
Coniferase	Coniferin	Glucose + Coniferyl alcohol $(C_6H_{11}O_5\cdot O)\cdot C_6H_3(OCH_3)\cdot CH{:}CH\cdot CH_2OH + H_2O \rightarrow C_6H_{12}O_6 + HO\cdot C_6H_3(OCH_3)\cdot C_3H_4OH$ Coniferin → Glucose + Coniferyl alcohol
Amygdalase	Amygdalin	Gentiobiose + Benzaldehyde + Hydrocyanic acid $C_{20}H_{27}O_{11}N + nH_2O \rightarrow$ Gentiobiose + Benzaldehyde + HCN

TABLE 6 (*Continued*)

CLASSIFICATION OF CERTAIN ENZYMES WHICH HAVE BEEN DEMONSTRATED IN MICROORGANISMS

(Data from Waksman and Davison's *Enzymes*, Salle's *Fundamental Principles of Bacteriology*, and Others)

Name of Enzyme	Substrate	Reaction and End Products Formed
Esculase or esculinase	Esculin	Dihydroxycumarin (Esculetin) + Glucose $C_6H_{11}O_5$—O—(ring; HO; —CH=CH—; —O—CO) $+ H_2O \rightarrow$ HO, HO—(ring; —CH=CH—; —O—CO) $+ C_6H_{12}O_6$ Esculin → Esculetin + Glucose
Nucleosidase	Nucleoside	Pentose + Purine bases Guanine riboside $+ H_2O \rightarrow$ Ribose (CH_2OH—HCOH—HCOH—HCOH—CHO) $+$ Guanine (H_2N—C; H—N—C=O; C—NH; N—C—N; C—H)
Tannase	Tannin	Gallic acid + Other products Tannin $+ nH_2O \rightarrow$ (ring: COOH, HO, OH, OH) + Other products
5. Glucoproteinases Mucinase	Glucoproteins Mucin	Glucose + Nitrogenous substances Reducing sugar + Amino sugars

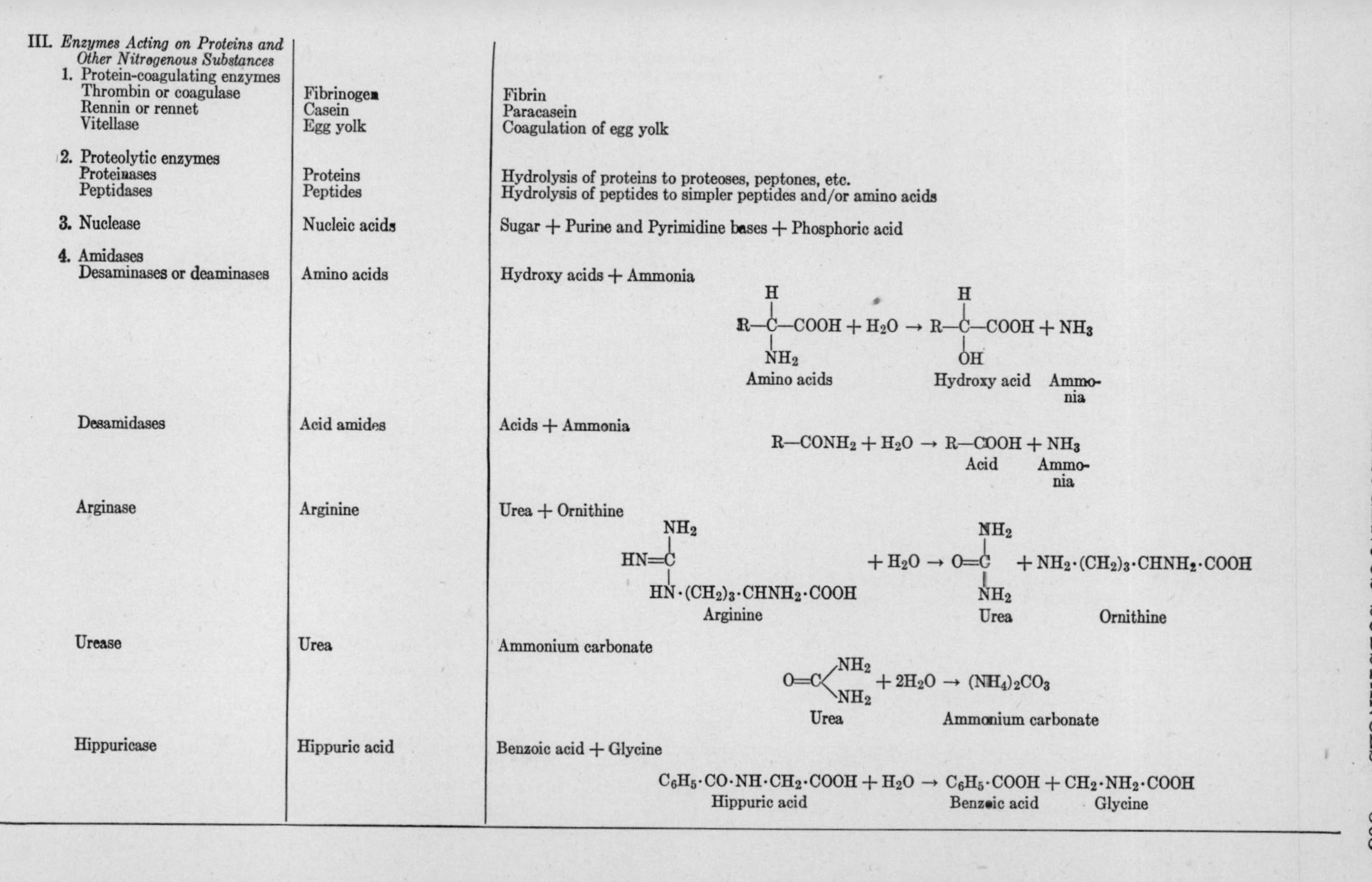

III. *Enzymes Acting on Proteins and Other Nitrogenous Substances*		
1. Protein-coagulating enzymes		
Thrombin or coagulase	Fibrinogen	Fibrin
Rennin or rennet	Casein	Paracasein
Vitellase	Egg yolk	Coagulation of egg yolk
2. Proteolytic enzymes		
Proteinases	Proteins	Hydrolysis of proteins to proteoses, peptones, etc.
Peptidases	Peptides	Hydrolysis of peptides to simpler peptides and/or amino acids
3. Nuclease	Nucleic acids	Sugar + Purine and Pyrimidine bases + Phosphoric acid
4. Amidases		
Desaminases or deaminases	Amino acids	Hydroxy acids + Ammonia $R{-}CH(NH_2){-}COOH + H_2O \rightarrow R{-}CH(OH){-}COOH + NH_3$ Amino acids → Hydroxy acid + Ammonia
Desamidases	Acid amides	Acids + Ammonia $R{-}CONH_2 + H_2O \rightarrow R{-}COOH + NH_3$ Acid + Ammonia
Arginase	Arginine	Urea + Ornithine $HN{=}C(NH_2){-}HN{\cdot}(CH_2)_3{\cdot}CHNH_2{\cdot}COOH + H_2O \rightarrow O{=}C(NH_2)_2 + NH_2{\cdot}(CH_2)_3{\cdot}CHNH_2{\cdot}COOH$ Arginine → Urea + Ornithine
Urease	Urea	Ammonium carbonate $O{=}C(NH_2)_2 + 2H_2O \rightarrow (NH_4)_2CO_3$ Urea → Ammonium carbonate
Hippuricase	Hippuric acid	Benzoic acid + Glycine $C_6H_5{\cdot}CO{\cdot}NH{\cdot}CH_2{\cdot}COOH + H_2O \rightarrow C_6H_5{\cdot}COOH + CH_2{\cdot}NH_2{\cdot}COOH$ Hippuric acid → Benzoic acid + Glycine

TABLE 6 (*Continued*)

CLASSIFICATION OF CERTAIN ENZYMES WHICH HAVE BEEN DEMONSTRATED IN MICROORGANISMS]

(Data from Waksman and Davison's *Enzymes*, Salle's *Fundamental Principles of Bacteriology*, and Others)

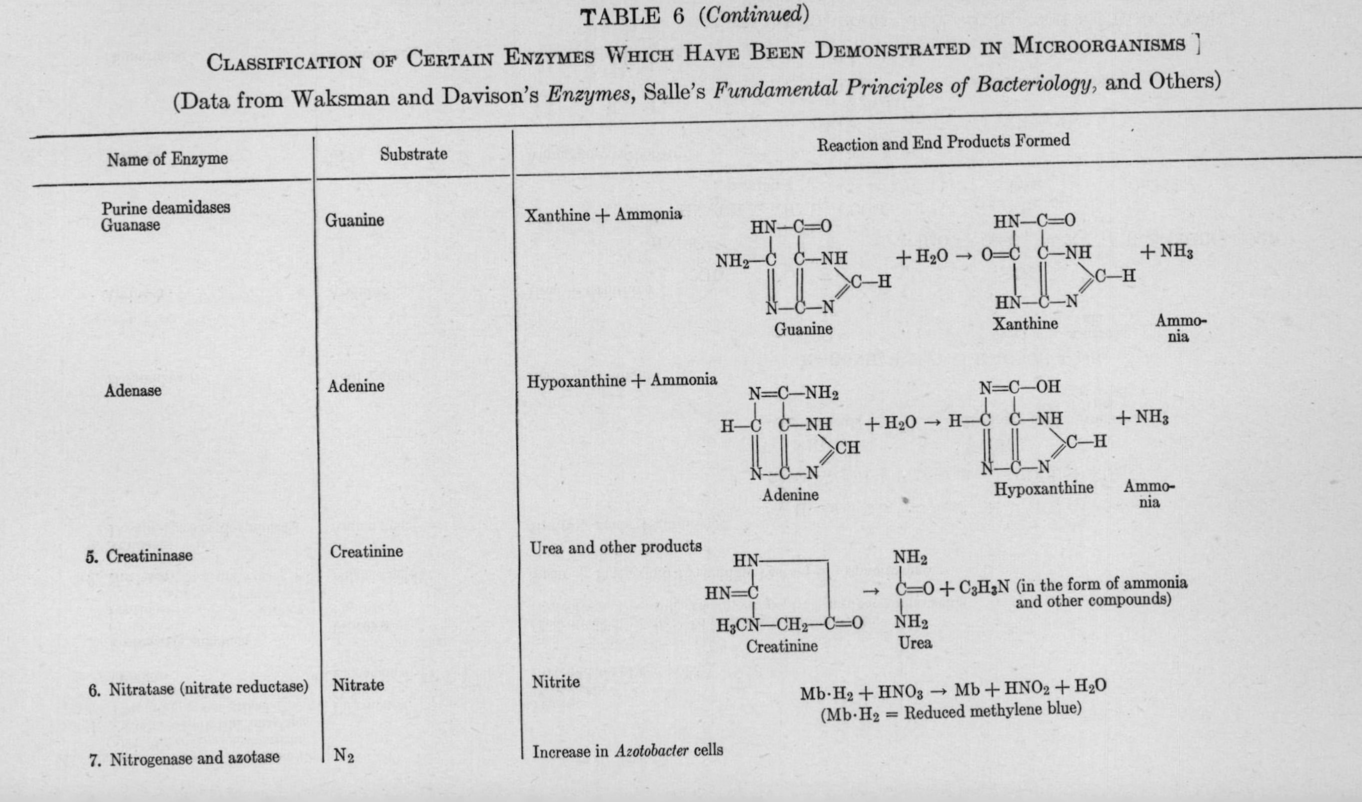

Name of Enzyme	Substrate	Reaction and End Products Formed
Purine deamidases Guanase	Guanine	Xanthine + Ammonia Guanine $+ H_2O \rightarrow$ Xanthine $+ NH_3$ (Ammonia)
Adenase	Adenine	Hypoxanthine + Ammonia Adenine $+ H_2O \rightarrow$ Hypoxanthine $+ NH_3$ (Ammonia)
5. Creatininase	Creatinine	Urea and other products Creatinine $\rightarrow$ Urea $+ C_3H_3N$ (in the form of ammonia and other compounds)
6. Nitratase (nitrate reductase)	Nitrate	Nitrite $Mb \cdot H_2 + HNO_3 \rightarrow Mb + HNO_2 + H_2O$ ($Mb \cdot H_2$ = Reduced methylene blue)
7. Nitrogenase and azotase	N_2	Increase in *Azotobacter* cells

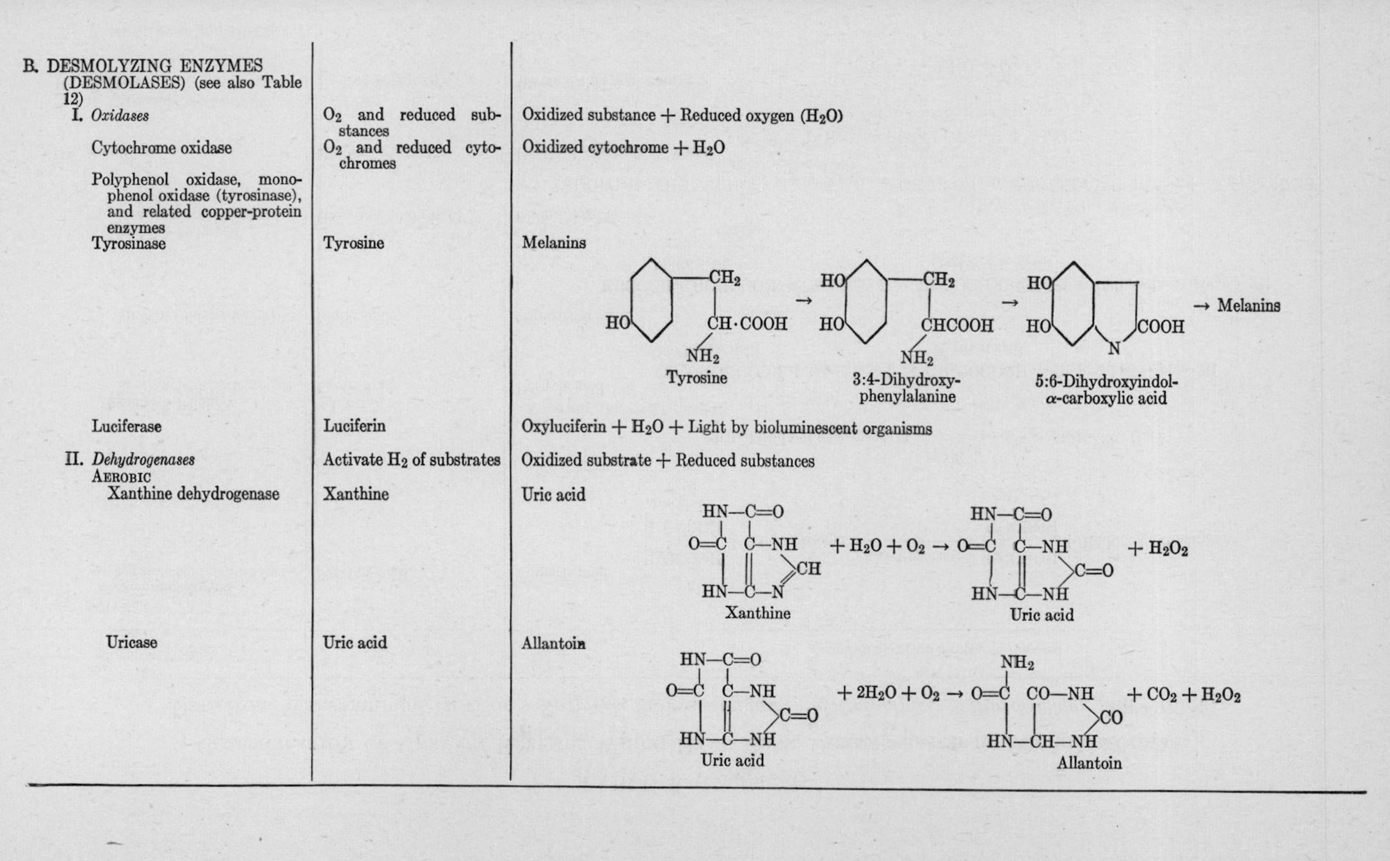

B. DESMOLYZING ENZYMES (DESMOLASES) (see also Table 12)		
I. *Oxidases*	O_2 and reduced substances	Oxidized substance + Reduced oxygen (H_2O)
Cytochrome oxidase	O_2 and reduced cytochromes	Oxidized cytochrome + H_2O
Polyphenol oxidase, monophenol oxidase (tyrosinase), and related copper-protein enzymes		
Tyrosinase	Tyrosine	Melanins Tyrosine → 3:4-Dihydroxyphenylalanine → 5:6-Dihydroxyindol-α-carboxylic acid → Melanins
Luciferase	Luciferin	Oxyluciferin + H_2O + Light by bioluminescent organisms
II. *Dehydrogenases*	Activate H_2 of substrates	Oxidized substrate + Reduced substances
AEROBIC		
Xanthine dehydrogenase	Xanthine	Uric acid Xanthine + H_2O + O_2 → Uric acid + H_2O_2
Uricase	Uric acid	Allantoin Uric acid + $2H_2O$ + O_2 → Allantoin + CO_2 + H_2O_2

TABLE 6 (*Continued*)

Classification of Certain Enzymes Which Have Been Demonstrated in Microorganisms

(Data from Waksman and Davison's *Enzymes*, Salle's *Fundamental Principles of Bacteriology*, and Others)

Name of Enzyme	Substrate	Reaction and End Products Formed
ANAEROBIC Cytochrome-linked Succinic acid dehydrogenase	Succinic acid	Fumaric acid $H_2CCOOH{-}H_2CCOOH$ (Succinic acid) + 2 Cytochrome $\xrightarrow{\text{Dehydrogenase}}$ $HCCOOH{=}HCCOOH$ + Reduced cytochrome 2 Reduced cytochrome + O $\xrightarrow{\text{Oxidase}}$ 2 Cytochrome + H_2O
Coenzyme I-linked Lactic acid dehydrogenase	Lactic acid	Pyruvic acid $CH_3CHOHCOOH$ (Lactic acid) + Coenzyme I ⇄ $CH_3COCOOH$ (Pyruvic acid) + Reduced coenzyme·2H
Malic acid dehydrogenase	Malic acid	Oxaloacetic acid $HOOCCH_2CHOHCOOH$ (Malic acid) + Coenzyme I ⇄ $HOOCCH_2COCOOH$ (Oxaloacetic acid) + Reduced coenzyme I·2H
Coenzyme II-linked Hexose monophosphate dehydrogenase	Glucose-6-phosphate	6-Phosphogluconate $CH_2OPO_3H_2(CHOH)_4CHO$ + Coenzyme II → $CH_2OPO_3H_2(CHOH)_4COOH$ + Reduced coenzyme II·2H
III. *Peroxidase*	Various substrates	Oxidized substrate + Water $P{\cdot}H_2O_2 + S{\cdot}H_2 \rightarrow P + S + 2H_2O$ (P = Peroxidase; S = Substrate)
IV. *Catalase*	Hydrogen peroxide	Water + Molecular oxygen $2H_2O_2 \rightarrow 2H_2O + O_2$

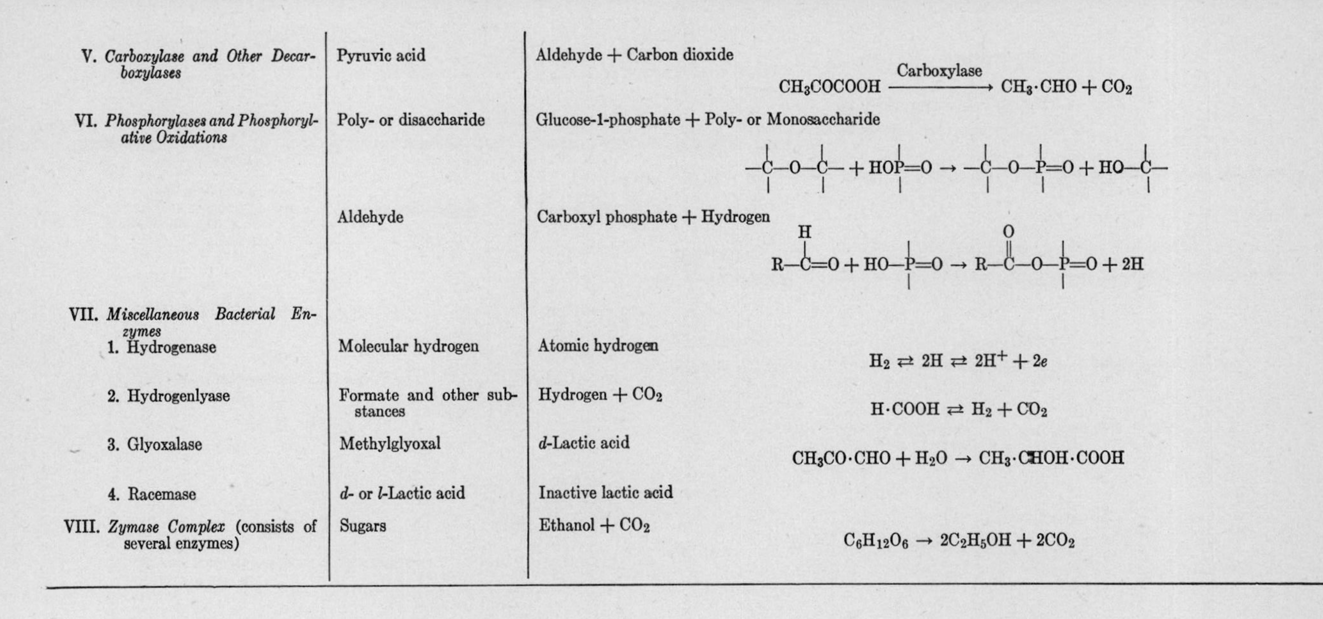

V. *Carboxylase and Other Decarboxylases*	Pyruvic acid	Aldehyde + Carbon dioxide	$CH_3COCOOH \xrightarrow{\text{Carboxylase}} CH_3 \cdot CHO + CO_2$
VI. *Phosphorylases and Phosphorylative Oxidations*	Poly- or disaccharide	Glucose-1-phosphate + Poly- or Monosaccharide	$-\overset{\vert}{\underset{\vert}{C}}-O-\overset{\vert}{\underset{\vert}{C}}- + HO\overset{\vert}{\underset{\vert}{P}}{=}O \rightarrow -\overset{\vert}{\underset{\vert}{C}}-O-\overset{\vert}{\underset{\vert}{P}}{=}O + HO-\overset{\vert}{\underset{\vert}{C}}-$
	Aldehyde	Carboxyl phosphate + Hydrogen	$R-\overset{H}{\overset{\vert}{C}}{=}O + HO-\overset{\vert}{\underset{\vert}{P}}{=}O \rightarrow R-\overset{O}{\overset{\Vert}{C}}-O-\overset{\vert}{\underset{\vert}{P}}{=}O + 2H$
VII. *Miscellaneous Bacterial Enzymes*			
1. Hydrogenase	Molecular hydrogen	Atomic hydrogen	$H_2 \rightleftarrows 2H \rightleftarrows 2H^+ + 2e$
2. Hydrogenlyase	Formate and other substances	Hydrogen + CO_2	$H \cdot COOH \rightleftarrows H_2 + CO_2$
3. Glyoxalase	Methylglyoxal	*d*-Lactic acid	$CH_3CO \cdot CHO + H_2O \rightarrow CH_3 \cdot CHOH \cdot COOH$
4. Racemase	*d*- or *l*-Lactic acid	Inactive lactic acid	
VIII. *Zymase Complex* (consists of several enzymes)	Sugars	Ethanol + CO_2	$C_6H_{12}O_6 \rightarrow 2C_2H_5OH + 2CO_2$

which hydrolyzes disodium phenyl phosphate. The optimal activity occurred at *p*H values of 4.7 to 7.2; each strain possessed an individual optimum.

4. **Sulfatase,** the enzyme or enzymes which hydrolyze various esters of sulfuric acid, has been demonstrated in several microorganisms. For example, Tankó (1932) studied the sulfatases from bacteria of the *Pseudomonas nonliquefaciens* group and observed that the sulfatase which hydrolyzed chondroitinsulfuric acid was also active against the simpler sulfate esters of glucose and sucrose. On the other hand, the chondrosulfatase differed from phenolsulfatase, which attacks only aromatic compounds. Neuberg and Cahill (1936) also isolated a bacterial enzyme capable of liberating sulfuric acid and reducing sugars from chondroitin. Phenolsulfatase has also been demonstrated in certain molds, such as *Aspergillus oryzae.*

II. CARBOHYDRASES

The enzymes which belong to the carbohydrase group are very widespread among the microorganisms. In fact, a microbial enzyme which will attack every naturally occurring carbohydrate can probably be found. Enzymes which hydrolyze sugars are usually classified on the basis of the complexity of the carbohydrate which they attack, for example, polysaccharidases, trisaccharidases, disaccharidases, and glucosidases.

1. **Polysaccharidases.** CELLULASE AND HEMICELLULASES. The decomposition of cellulose and hemicellulose in nature is probably the result of associated microbial action, although several pure cultures of bacteria, molds, and actinomyces which will hydrolyze cellulose have been isolated and studied. Such hydrolytic enzymes are generally regarded to be extracellular, but statements occur in the literature to the effect that they may also be intracellular. Of the early studies of cellulose-dissolving bacteria the one by Kellerman, McBeth, Scales, and Smith (1913) is very complete and has an extensive bibliography. Bradley and Rettger (1927) and Cowles and Rettger (1931) have also made extensive studies on the aerobic and anaerobic bacteria which decompose cellulose. Since Thaysen and Bunker (1927) have reviewed the early literature on this subject in great detail in their book *Microbiology of Cellulose, Hemicellulose, Pectin, and Gums,* this work should be consulted for further details on the decomposition of these substances. More recently, however, cellulase activity has been demonstrated in several bacteria by Simola (1931). He prepared cell-free enzyme solutions which hydrolyzed cellulose to

cellobiose and glucose. Optimum enzyme activity occurred at 37°C. between *p*H 6.0 and 7.0. Grassmann and his associates (1931, 1933) have shown that an extract from *Aspergillus oryzae* contained a cellulase and a hemicellulase. The cellulase had exceptional power to act on polysaccharides of high molecular weight (cellulose, cellodextrin, and somewhat on cellohexose). Its action on tri- and tetrasaccharides was slight; in fact, it had no action on polysaccharides with a molecular weight below 1,000. Cellobiase acted on compounds of lower molecular weight.

Closely related to this group of enzymes are those which attack selectively the gums and polysaccharides produced by bacteria. It has been found by Dubos, Hirst, and others that certain enzymes can attack the cellular structures of pneumococci and of group C streptococci and, indeed, can protect experimental animals against infection with these pathogenic agents. As far as is known, the capsular polysaccharides of these organisms are not decomposed by enzymes of plant or animal origin, nor are they attacked by common species of microorganisms. It is possible, however, to isolate enzymes from certain microorganisms (soil-sporulating bacilli and leeches) which hydrolyze the specific microbial polysaccharides. These polysaccharidases are directed against single specific substances, namely, the capsular polysaccharides, and are neither bacteriolytic nor bactericidal in character.

Diastase or Amylase. Enzymes of this group hydrolyze starch. Under favorable conditions the end product of the reaction is maltose, as is shown in Table 6. The reaction, however, is more complex than this simple equation indicates, since several intermediate compounds are produced. Also, ordinary amylase preparations contain several enzymes, such as α-amylase, β-amylase, and amylophosphatase. The so-called α-amylase produces maltose (usually α-maltose) very slowly from starch but destroys quite rapidly the ability of starch to give a blue color with iodine. This enzyme is sometimes spoken of as the dextrinizing enzyme; it is fairly heat-stable but is sensitive to weak acid. β-Amylase, on the other hand, produces maltose (usually β-maltose) rapidly from starch but does not destroy its power to give a blue color with iodine for a long time. This enzyme is frequently called the saccharifying enzyme; it is heat-labile but resistant to weak acid. Amylophosphatase liquefies starch jelly without producing sugar. The so-called liver amylase is now believed to be nothing more than the enzyme phosphorylase, which catalyzes the breakdown of glycogen in the presence of inorganic phosphate to glucose-1-phosphate (Cori ester).

The amylase activity of an organism may be measured in several ways. For example, if a small amount of an amylase-producing culture is added to starch paste containing phenol to prevent growth, a decrease in viscosity, a disappearance of the characteristic blue color with iodine, and the formation of reducing sugar (maltose) take place. These changes, however, do not always follow the same order or occur at the same rates. Sometimes there is a rapid liquefaction paralleled by a slow maltose formation, whereas at other times there is a very rapid formation of maltose but a slow disappearance of products which give a blue color with iodine. Because of these inherent irregularities it has been quite generally assumed that there are several amylases, or that most amylase preparations contain several different enzymes.

A great many reports have appeared on the amylase activity of microorganisms; in fact, the enzyme has been found in bacteria, yeasts, molds, and actinomyces [Waksman (1922)]. More work, however, has been done on the diastase activity of fungi, particularly *Aspergillus oryzae* than on any other group of organisms. The important factors, such as temperature, *p*H, buffer, and substrate, governing the activity of mold amylase have been studied by Luippold (1929), Leopold and Starbanow (1943), Hao, Fulmer, and Underkofler (1943), and others. Practical use is now being made of fungal amylases as saccharifying agents in the alcoholic fermentation of corn (see pp. 903 to 904 on alcoholic fermentation in Chapter 10). Amylase activity by yeasts has been reported by Fermi (1892), Ono (1935), and several other workers, in spite of the fact that it has been stated in the literature that few, if any, of the true yeasts produce the enzyme. Ono (1935) found that yeast amylase exhibits optimum activity at *p*H 6.0 to 6.6 between 22.5° and 30°C.

A great many bacteria show diastase activity, but only a few examples will be cited here. Fermi (1892) found that diastase was elaborated by *Bacillus anthracis*, *Bacillus subtilis*, *Bacillus megatherium*, *Vibrio comma*, *Gaffkya tetragena*, and most actinomyces tested. The enzyme was formed to a very small extent by *Escherichia coli*, *Klebsiella pneumoniae*, several staphylococci, and red and white yeasts; *Pseudomonas aeruginosa*, *Staphylococcus citreus*, *Vibrio metchnikovi*, rose-colored yeasts, and *Oidium lactis* produced none at all. The significance of the conversion of starch and some of its fractions to crystalline Schardinger dextrins by an amylase preparation from *Bacillus macerans* has been discussed by Kerr (1943) and Wilson, Schoch, and Hudson (1943). Wilson, Schoch, and Hudson believe that macerans amylase

> . . . attacks the nonaldehydic terminus of the starch molecule, progressively producing crystalline Schardinger dextrins from some basic configuration in the starch, and stopping this action only when some irregularity is encountered in the molecular structure. In this connection, it is suggested that the limit dextrin from this enzymolysis may afford a suitable starting material for isolation of new starch fractions and the identification of "irregularities" in configuration.

Diastase activity by several anaerobic bacilli has been reported on several occasions. For example, Johnston and Wynne (1935) found that the diastase of *Clostridium acetobutylicum* has an optimum *p*H of 4.8 to 5.0, with a range of approximately *p*H 2.0 to 7.5. The enzyme activity was retarded by sodium acetate, phosphate, and chloride, a reaction which is in contrast to the results recorded for the activity of diastase from other sources. Fleming and Neill (1927) have also reported amylase activity by *Clostridium perfringens.* Besides the studies just mentioned on extracellular diastase activity by aerobic and anaerobic bacteria, many other examples could be given, including the report on the intracellular diastase activity of the pneumococcus [Avery and Cullen (1920)].

PECTINASE. Many bacteria and molds have been studied which are able to catalyze the hydrolysis of various pectins [Thaysen and Bunker (1927)]. Upon hydrolysis, pectins yield pectic acids, which in turn break down to sugars and acids, such as galacturonic acids. It is thought that pectinase and protopectinase, in combination with other enzymes, are responsible for the retting of flax and the autolysis of fruits and other vegetable products. An early study was made by Jones (1905) on the pectinase activity of several bacteria, and more recently Makrinov (1932), Werch, Jung, Day, Friedemann, and Ivy (1942), and others have investigated the fermentation of pectin by aerobic and anaerobic bacteria. According to Werch and associates, the most active pectin-decomposing bacteria isolated from the intestinal tract of dogs belong to the following groups: *Aerobacillus, Lactobacillus, Micrococcus,* and *Enterococcus.* Harter and Weimer (1921) studied the production of pectinase by various molds of the genus *Rhizopus,* and Menon (1934) made a comparison of the enzyme activity in extracts from six different species of parasitic fungi. Much interesting information on pectic enzymes will be found in the review by Kertesz (1936).

INULASE (INULINASE). The enzyme inulase hydrolyzes the polysaccharide inulin to fructose in a manner similar to that shown in the equation in Table 6. Several workers have studied and described microorganisms which are capable of fermenting inulin. However, the presence of true inulase in these organisms, as demonstrated by the formation of fructose, has rarely been demonstrated. Many molds apparently produce this enzyme, although *Aspergillus niger* and *Aspergillus oryzae* are the most active. Pringsheim and his associates (1931, 1932) and Asai (1937) have made extensive studies of the inulase activity of certain molds. Asai reported that *Aspergillus, Penicillium,* and *Citromyces* species were active enzyme producers, whereas *Rhizopus oryzae* and *Mucor alternans* were negative. The most active enzyme preparations hydrolyzed 80 per cent of inulin in 14 to 24 hours at a temperature of 50 to 55°C. and a *p*H of 4.1. The presence of inulinase in yeasts has been questioned by many workers, although Sacchetti (1934) reported the enzyme in three different species. For example, *Saccharomyces fragilis* produced more fructose from inulin in 17 hours than *Aspergillus niger* did in 14 days. Several bacteria ferment inulin, but the enzyme system has not been systematically studied. In pneumococci the enzyme is located intracellularly [Avery and Cullen (1920)].

2. Trisaccharidases. RAFFINASE. The trisaccharide raffinose is made up of *d*-fructose, *d*-glucose, and *d*-galactose. When hydrolyzed by the enzyme raffinase, this trisaccharide breaks up into fructose and the disaccharide melibiose, which consists of *d*-glucose and *d*-galactose. The melibiose fraction many then be further hydrolyzed by another enzyme, *melibiase,* which splits the molecule into dextrose and galactose. The presence and activity of raffinase in microorganisms have not been studied to any extent, although this carbohydrate is fermented by several molds, yeasts, and bacteria. Only a few studies will be cited here. Bourquelot (1896) and Dox (1910) demonstrated raffinase activity in the molds *Aspergillus niger* and *Pencillium camembertii,* and Kalanthar (1898) reported similar activity in yeast. Many bacteria which ferment sucrose also attack raffinose and presumably contain raffinase. The enzyme was found to be intracellular in the pneumococcus and *Clostridium perfringens* by Neill and Avery (1924) and Fleming and Neill (1927).

GENTIANASE AND OTHER TRISACCHARIDASES. The enzyme gentianase catalyzes the hydrolysis of the trisaccharide gentianose and yields fructose and the disaccharide gentiobiose. Gentiobiose may then be further hydrolyzed to glucose by the enzyme *gentiobiase.*

Other trisaccharides, such as *melezitose,* are fermented by certain bacteria and must therefore contain enzymes which are capable of attacking these compounds. However, specific enzyme studies have not been reported.

3. Disaccharidases. INVERTASE (SUCRASE). This enzyme has been known since about 1860, when Berthelot discovered that under its influence dextrorotatory cane sugar was transformed into levorotatory invert sugar. Berthelot described the enzyme as a "ferment inversio" and first isolated it from yeast. Since that time many microorganisms have been studied which exhibit invertase activity. The enzyme is produced by a majority of yeasts and molds and to a lesser extent by actinomyces and bacteria [Waksman (1922)]. Bottom yeasts contain less invertase than top yeasts, and some species of *Torula* and many wild sugar yeasts are unable to produce the enzyme. Adams, Richtmyer, and Hudson (1943) have recently studied the activity of five highly purified invertase preparations obtained from both brewers' and bakers' yeast. The enzyme was not specific for sucrose alone because the fructofuranoside linkages in raffinose, stachyose, and other sugars were also hydrolyzed. Isosucrose, α- and β-dextrins, and melezitose were not attacked. Invertase activity in the molds *Aspergillus niger*, *Aspergillus oryzae*, *Penicillium glaucum*, and *Penicillium camembertii* has been extensively studied by many workers [see also Kertesz (1931), Kirsanova (1936)]. Few of the bacteria produce invertase. Positive results have been obtained with *Bacillus megatherium*, *Bacillus mesentericus*, *Proteus vulgaris*, *Pseudomonas fluorescens*, *Clostridium perfringens*, and to some extent with *Vibrio comma* and *Vibrio metchnikovi*. Many other species, like the acetic acid bacteria and *Eberthella typhosa*, however, are unable to produce invertase. Hotchkiss (1935) showed that *Escherichia coli-communior* exhibited sucrase activity, but the enzyme was absent in *E. coli*.

MALTASE. The enzyme maltase catalyzes the hydrolysis of maltose to two molecules of glucose, according to the equation given in Table 6. Maltase is apparently elaborated by a great many bacteria, yeasts, and molds. In Waksman's (1922) review maltase activity is credited to many yeasts, including the beer and wine yeasts and *Monilia candida*, and to many molds of the genus *Aspergillus* and the *Mucors*, as well as to many bacteria. More recently, intracellular maltase activity has been demonstrated in *Corynebacterium diphtheriae* [Sugg, Fleming, and Neill (1927)], meningococci [Neill and Gaspari (1927)], *Diplococcus pneumoniae* [Fleming and Neill (1927)], *Clostridium botulinum* [Neill and Fleming (1927)], and both *Escherichia coli* and *E. coli-communior* (Hotchkiss (1935)]. Hofmann (1934) and Leibowitz and Hestrin (1942) have also demonstrated maltase activity in certain yeasts, and

Hestrin (1940) has extensively studied the specificity of mold maltase. Hestrin's mold-enzyme preparation hydrolyzed maltose, maltosazone, and maltobionic acid, as well as several other sugars.

LACTASE. Lactase converts lactose to glucose and galactose. It is generally postulated that organisms which ferment lactose contain the enzyme lactase, but actual proof of this is lacking, since the products of hydrolysis are not always recovered. Waksman (1922) listed a great many microorganisms which exhibit lactase activity, including *Escherichia coli*, *Lactobacillus bulgaricus*, *Streptococcus lactis*, *Oidium lactis*, and other yeasts and molds. Fleming and Neill (1927) demonstrated an intracellular lactase in *Clostridium perfringens*, and Lowenstein, Fleming, and Neill (1929) observed a similar endoenzyme in *E. coli*. The lactase activity of *E. coli-mutabile* was studied by Deere, Dulaney, and Michelson (1939) and Deere (1939), who classified the enzyme as constitutive but state, "The cultural behavior of the organism would lead one to class its lactase as an adaptive enzyme." More recently, Knopfmacher and Salle (1941) have studied extensively the lactase activity of *E. coli*. Their original paper should be consulted for many interesting data. Myrbäck and Vasseur (1943) have shown that *Saccharomyces fragilis* and *Torula cremoris* ferment lactose more rapidly than they do its hydrolytic products (glucose plus galactose). Thus they believe that these organisms ferment lactose directly by an enzyme system other than lactase.

MELIBIASE. The enzyme melibiase, which hydrolyzes the disaccharide melibiose to glucose and galactose, has been demonstrated in bacteria, yeasts, and molds, although proof of its occurrence as shown by the isolation of end products is lacking. No recent studies have appeared on this enzyme.

CELLOBIASE. Cellobiase catalyzes the hydrolysis of the disaccharide cellobiose (or cellose) into two molecules of glucose. The enzyme is rather widely distributed among the microorganisms, but quantitative data concerning its activity are not available.

4. Glucosidases. The glucosidases are enzymes which catalyze the hydrolysis of glucosides. A glucoside is usually defined as a compound which, upon hydrolysis, yields sugars (glucose) or sugars and other products. Therefore, sucrose may be regarded as a fructose glucoside, maltose as a glucose glucoside, and lactose as a galactose glucoside. Other compounds which do not yield sugars only, however, also belong to this group of compounds and may be attacked by enzymes. A few typical glucosidases are given in Table 6 and will be discussed briefly for illustrative purposes. It should be kept in mind that enzymes which act on other glucosides, fructosides, pentosides sorbosides, and similar compounds also exist in microorganisms, but they are not well understood.

α- AND β-GLUCOSIDASES. Several enzymes are known which are capable of rupturing α- and β-glucosidic linkages. Often, however, their specificity has not been studied very extensively. In fact, it is believed by many that, since α-glucosidase is identical with maltase and β-glucosidase is the same as amygdalase of emulsin, too many distinctions or groups should be avoided. In Table 6 we have listed examples of enzymes which attack α- and β-methyl glucosides merely to illustrate how such enzymes act. Much information on the glucosidases will be found in the books by Waldschmidt-Leitz and Walton (1929), and Buchanan and Fulmer (1930) and in the papers by Neuberg and Hofmann (1932) and Hofmann (1934, 1936).

PHENOL, ALCOHOL, AND RELATED GLUCOSIDASES. Several enzymes are known which hydrolyze certain glucosides consisting of glucose and some other compounds, such as a phenol, alcohol, aldehyde, or base. A few examples may be given.

Arbutinase (*arbutase*) catalyzes the hydrolysis of the glucoside arbutin into glucose and hydroquinone, according to the equation given in Table 6. Several reports have appeared in the literature dealing with the presence of this enzyme in microorganisms. For example, Brunstein (1901) demonstrated arbutinase in the molds *Aspergillus niger*, *Aspergillus oryzae*, and *Penicillium glaucum*, and Neuberg and Hofmann (1932) observed the enzyme in a special enzyme preparation from yeast. Its presence has also been demonstrated in bacteria, including *Escherichia coli* and other intestinal organisms [Twort (1907)], *Bacillus mycoides* [Glinka-Tschernorutzky (1930)], and several other bacteria [Verona and Lucchetti (1931)]. Glinka-Tschernorutzky reported the enzyme to be a firmly bound endoenzyme, but this finding has not been confirmed. Two other phenol glucosides may be mentioned. *Iridinase*, an enzyme which hydrolyzes iridin to glucose and irigenin, is present in *E. coli* and other related species; and *phloridzinase*, which catalyzes the hydrolysis of phloridzin to glucose and phloretin, has been demonstrated in several intestinal bacteria [Twort (1907)], as well as in other bacteria [Verona and Lucchetti (1931)].

Two alcohol glucosidases are *coniferase* and *salicinase*. Coniferase hydrolyzes coniferin to glucose and coniferyl alcohol. Its presence in microorganisms has not been extensively studied, although Twort (1907) found that *E. coli*, *Aerobacter aerogenes*, *Aerobacter cloacae*, and *Klebsiella pneumoniae* were able to ferment coniferin. *Salicinase* splits salicin into glucose and saligenin (salicyl alcohol) ($HO \cdot C_6H_4 \cdot CH_2OH$). Its presence in intestinal bacteria is assumed, since Twort (1907) found that six intestinal bacteria, including *E. coli*, ferment salicin. Although salicin is commonly used in the bacteriological laboratory today, quantitative data on microbial salicinase activity are not available.

Amygdalase is an example of an enzyme which hydrolyzes aldehyde glucosides, since benzaldehyde, hydrogen cyanide, and gentiobiose are the end products of the hydrolysis of amygdalin. The enzyme has been demonstrated in the molds, *Aspergillus niger*, *Aspergillus glaucus*, *Penicillium glaucum*, by Brunstein (1901) and others. Yeast also contains the enzyme [Neuberg and Hofmann (1932)], and Twort (1907) has found it in several intestinal bacteria, its presence having since been demonstrated on several occasions by other workers.

According to the equation given in Table 6, *esculase* (*aesculinase*, *esculinase*) hydrolyzes the oxycumarin glucoside esculin to glucose and dioxycumarin (esculetin). Several bacteria and molds are known to ferment this compound, and apparently they produce the specific enzyme. Orla-Jensen (1934) found that esculin was split by lactic acid bacteria, many coli-aerogenes bacteria, *Leuconostoc mesenteroides*, and most streptococci, with the exception of *Streptococcus agalactiae* and *Streptococcus thermophilus*. Jame, Crosnier, and Morel (1935) studied the action of several intestinal bacteria on esculins, using ferric citrate as an indicator. No action was shown by *Salmonella paratyphi*, *Shigella dysenteriae*, *Vibrio comma*, *Pseudomonas aeruginosa*, and *Proteus vulgaris*, but *Escherichia coli*, pneumobacillus, and *Salmonella schottmuelleri* hydrolyzed esculin. Irregular effects were produced by *Salmonella hirschfeldii*, *Eberthella typhosa*, and *Proteus morganii*.

The enzyme of the *nucleosidase* group split the nucleosides to sugar (pentose) and purine and pyrimidine bases. One example is listed in Table 6. Little work has been done on enzymes of this class, but there is every reason to suppose that they are present in various microorganisms, including bacteria.

TANNASE. The enzyme tannase is placed at this point in the classification since it has been studied rather extensively in reference to the hydrolysis of the glucose-gallic acid combination. Its proper location, however, may be with the esterases. Tannins vary considerably in composition, some being glucosides consisting of gallic acid and glucose, whereas others apparently contain phloroglucinol in place of glucose and protocatechuric acid instead of gallic acid. The enzyme tannase has been demonstrated in several molds by a number of workers. For example, Nicholson, Nierenstein, Pool, and Price (1931) observed that, in addition to tannase, *Aspergillus niger* produces an enzyme, *pyrogallase*, which acts on gallic acid. Tannase has also been isolated from the mycelium of *A. niger* by Dyckerhoff and Armbruster (1933), who found that their enzyme preparation hydrolyzed several related compounds besides tannin. This enzyme has not been studied recently in bacteria or other microorganisms.

5. Glucoproteinases. The glucoproteinases catalyze the hydrolysis of glucoproteins, such as the mucins, which yield albuminous substances and carbohydrates on hydrolysis. Enzymes of this group are not true carbohydrases; neither are they true proteinases. Therefore they are placed here provisionally until they are better characterized. Only one example will be cited.

MUCINASE. This enzyme or group of enzymes was first isolated from broth cultures of *Clostridium perfringens* by Robertson, Ropes, and Bauer (1940). It degrades mucin in two distinct steps: the first results in a loss of viscosity and change in precipitability with acetic acid; the second liberates free amino sugars and reducing substances and is probably a hydrolytic reaction. The enzyme has been purified and concentrated 900 times by adsorption on calcium phosphate from a 50 per cent acetone solution, but very little is known about its general properties. Mucinase activity is not peculiar to *Clostridium perfringens*, being present in varying concentrations in the broth cultures of several other microorganisms (*Streptococcus bovis*, *Streptococcus hemolyticus*, *Streptococcus viridans*), but is entirely absent in others (*Escherichia coli*, *Bacillus subtilis*, *Proteus vulgaris*, *Clostridium tetani*, *Staphylococcus aureus*).

III. ENZYMES ACTING ON PROTEINS AND OTHER NITROGENOUS COMPOUNDS

Many very extensive studies have been published on the activities of the proteolytic and related enzymes of microorganisms. Only some of the more recent or representative reports will be mentioned here, however, because many of the early studies have been reviewed by Waksman (1922) and Buchanan and Fulmer (1930).

1. Protein-Coagulating Enzymes. Several microbial enzymes have been described in the literature which are capable of coagulating native protein solutions. They will now be briefly discussed.

THROMBIN. Reports in the early literature stated that certain bacteria are capable of producing thrombin or some similar substance which increases the rate of blood coagulation. Much (1908) regarded the enzyme as a thrombokinase. More recently it has been established that certain pyogenic staphylococci produce a *coagulase* which clots human plasma [Gross (1931), Chapman *et al.* (1934)]. The nature of these enzymes has not been determined, but, in view of the recent study by Almquist *et al.* (1938) on vitamin K production by bacteria, it would seem that some correlation between these studies might be established.

RENNIN (RENNET). A number of studies have been published on the chemical action of the enzyme rennin, but we shall not attempt to review the results. For much interesting information on this point the student is referred to the books on enzyme chemistry by Tauber (1937) and Sumner and Somers (1943). A rennin-like enzyme is apparently produced by a great many bacteria, yeasts, molds, and actinomyces. As brought out by Buchanan and Fulmer (1930), however, identification of the enzyme purely on the basis of milk coagulation is not sufficient, because many organisms produce enough acid in milk to change the reaction (*p*H) to such a degree that the casein is precipitated. It is quite generally assumed that most proteolytic bacteria produce a rennet-like enzyme, although few quantitative data are available. Wahlin (1928) and Gorini (1930, 1933) have studied the elaboration of rennin by bacteria, especially by *Serratia marcescens.* They found that the enzyme was more heat-stable, less susceptible to oxalates, and apparently less susceptible to the casein concentration than was calf rennin. Also, the bacterial rennin coagulated heated milk more readily than did calf rennin.

VITELLASE. The enzyme vitellase was first described by Lagrange (1926), who demonstrated its ability to coagulate egg yolk. He found that *Bacillus sinicus, Bacillus anthracoides,* and several molds produced the enzyme. The reaction occurred in an acid medium in the absence of calcium and was complete in a few hours at 37°C. Apparently this work has not been confirmed.

2. Proteolytic Enzymes. For many years a proteolytic enzyme was merely classified as a pepsin, trypsin, or erypsin. Such a simple division became inadequate as our knowledge increased on this subject. In a more useful classification these enzymes, whether of animal, plant, or microbial origin, are divided into two primary classes: *proteinases* and *peptidases.* The proteinases hydrolyze natural proteins, including some conjugated proteins, and certain simpler synthetic substrates which contain a peptide linkage (—CO—NH—), whereas the peptidases split only simple peptides. The *proteinases* are also sometimes classified as *endopeptidases,* because their point of attack against natural proteins is the middle of a long peptide chain; the *peptidases* are called *exopeptidases* since their point of attack is the end of a peptide chain. This differentiation into endo- and exopeptidases may be misleading when applied to the proteolytic enzymes of bacteria, because quite frequently the same prefixes (endo- and exo-) are used to designate the relationship of the enzyme to the cell. Also recent studies by Bergmann, Fruton, and their associates [see Fruton (1941)] refute the old claim that the action of proteolytic enzymes, such as pepsin, is confined only to proteins of high molecular weight and that simpler substrates are never attacked.

The following general classification of these enzymes, based on the nature of the group attacked and other properties, is now widely quoted in the literature:

A. *Proteinases (proteases)*
   1. Pepsins (gastric pepsins)
   2. Trypsins (plant and animal trypsins, etc.)
   3. Chymotrypsin (animal pancreas)
   4. Papains (plant papains)
   5. Other proteolytic enzymes (cathepsin, ficin, bromelin, etc.)
   6. Protaminases (hydrolysis of protamines, peptone-like substances)

B. *Peptidases*
   1. Hydrolysis of —CO—NH—, but not —CO—N<
      a. Carboxypeptidase
      b. Aminopolypeptidase
      c. Prolinase
      d. Dipeptidase
   2. Hydrolysis of —CO—N<, but not —CO—NH—
      a. Prolidase

Following this classification, we will now briefly discuss the proteolytic enzymes produced by bacteria. For more details on the reactions catalyzed by the proteolytic enzymes a book on enzyme chemistry and the numerous papers by Bergmann and his associates [1932, to date; also the review by Fruton (1941)] should be consulted.

a. Bacterial Proteinases. The proteinases catalyze the hydrolysis of natural proteins and certain simpler substrates but are inactive against the lower degradation products of proteins (certain peptides and amino acids). Bergmann and his associates believe that one essential difference between the animal proteinases and the peptidases is that the animal proteinases do not require a free α-amino or α-carboxyl group near the peptide linkage which is to be split; in fact, their activity may be inhibited by the proximity of such groups. Although additional information is available [see Bergmann and Fruton (1941)] on the specificity and other properties of certain animal proteases, little or nothing is known about the properties of cell-free bacterial proteases. As a matter of fact, in most of the studies using microorganisms intact cells, rather than cell-free enzyme preparations, have been employed.

The proteolytic powers of bacteria vary enormously from one species to another, and even two strains of the same species may behave differently at times. The literature on this subject is very large and contains many contradictory statements concerning the nature and type of substrate attacked, the optimum time, temperature, and *p*H for activity, the effect of activators, inhibitors, nutrition, and other factors. Much of the early work on bacterial proteinases will be found in the review by Waksman (1922) and in the books by Buchanan and Fulmer (1930) and Stephenson (1939). Only a few representative studies will be mentioned in the next few pages because it is difficult to evaluate some of the early work on this subject in the light of our present knowledge of proteolytic enzymes.

From a historical standpoint it is interesting to note that Bitter in 1886 was the first person to demonstrate that the liquefaction of gelatin and coagulation of egg white was accomplished by proteolytic enzymes elaborated by microorganisms. This observation was soon confirmed and extended by many other early workers. It was not until 1915–1918, however, that Sperry, Berman, and Rettger and others showed that few, if any, highly purified native proteins are attacked by aerobic or anaerobic bacteria, unless some other simpler nitrogenous substance is present which the bacteria can readily utilize for protoplasmic synthesis.

The true bacterial proteinases usually diffuse into the culture medium and can be separated from the cells by filtration techniques. The type of medium upon which the proteolytic bacteria are cultivated often greatly influences the activity of the enzymes which they elaborate. Many of the earlier investigators noted the absence of filterable enzymes when organisms were grown on chemically defined media, but since then it has been reported that such enzymes are formed if the media are nutritionally balanced. The optimum reaction for the proteinase activity of bacteria varies from approximately *p*H 7.0 to 8.0, with maximum activity occurring at about 7.2 [Imaizumi (1938), Maschmann (1937–1939), Weil and his associates (1937, 1939), Elberg and Meyer (1939)]. In this respect the proteinases of bacteria may differ somewhat from those of plant and animal origin, since the optimum *p*H for pepsin is about 2.0 to 4.0; for trypsin, 8.0 to 9.0; and for papain and other plant proteinases acting on gelatin, about 5.0. The optimum temperature for the action of the proteinases, regardless of their source, is between 35° and 40°C. Their activity rapidly diminishes above 50°C. Certain bacterial proteinases are quite thermostable. For example, Virtanen and Tarnanen (1932) showed that the filterable proteinases elaborated by a strain of *Pseudomonas fluorescens* retained about 72 per cent of their activity when heated for 10 minutes at 90°C. and 48 per cent at 110°C. but were inactivated in the same time at 115°C.

Elberg and Meyer (1939) studied the extracellular proteolytic system of *Clostridium parabotulinum* and found that the proteinases which catalyze the hydrolysis of gelatin and casein could be inactivated by sodium cyanide, hydrogen peroxide, and copper salts. The proteinases elaborated by several aerobic and anaerobic bacteria have also been studied extensively by Maschmann (1937–1939), Imaizumi (1938), Console and Rahn (1938), and Weil, Kocholaty, and Smith (1939). In general these workers have shown that the extracellular proteinases of such anaerobic bacilli as *Clostridium histolyticum*, *Clostridium sporogenes*, *Clostridium perfringens*, *Clostridium putrificum*, and *Clostridium botulinum* catalyze the hydrolysis of gelatin, casein, Witte peptone, and clupein. In certain species the hydrolysis of gelatin required no activation. In other substrates, however, activation by cysteine or some other —SH compound and inorganic ions such as Fe^{++} was necessary before the enzymes exhibited their maximum activity. The proteinase systems of facultative anaerobes, such as *Proteus vulgaris*, resembled the proteinases of the *Clostridia* in activation behavior, whereas the proteinases of certain aerobic organisms, such as *Bacillus mycoides*, were partially inhibited by cysteine but were activated by a combination of cysteine and ferrous iron.

The proteinases of yeasts and molds have been studied quite extensively. The early literature on this subject has been reviewed by Waksman (1922) and Buchanan and Fulmer (1930). More recently, however, Hecht and Civin (1936) isolated a proteolytic enzyme from yeast which exhibited its greatest activity at *p*H 1.8 and resembled pepsin. An enzyme resembling trypsin was also found, but in a concentration considerably less than that of the pepsin-like enzyme. Berger, Johnson, and Peterson (1937) noted that *Aspergillus parasiticus* secretes proteinases which hydrolyze gelatin, lactalbumin, casein, egg albumin, and edestin to the extent of 82 to 100 per cent. Many other interesting data will be found in these studies by Hecht and Civin and by Berger, Johnson, and Peterson.

Other systems which are sometimes classified as proteinases include pyocyanase, the bacteriolytic enzyme elaborated by *Pseudomonas aeruginosa* and first described by Emmerich and Löw in 1898, bacterial hemolysins, and bacteriophage.

b. Bacterial Peptidases. The peptidases split the intermediate degradation products of proteins and certain synthetic peptides but are without action on proteins and single amino acids. Most peptidases require peptide hydrogen for their action and differ from the proteinases in that they attack only terminal linkages; for this reason the peptidases are usually divided into several classes. These classes will be discussed in the next few pages.

Many early workers reported that bacteria, yeasts, and molds possess peptidases. More recently, extensive studies have been carried out by Gorbach (1930), Imaizumi (1938), Berger, Johnson, and Peterson (1938), Elberg and Meyer (1939), Maschmann (1939), Berger, Johnson, and Baumann (1941), and Johnson (1941).

Carboxypeptidase. The enzyme carboxypeptidase requires a carboxyl group for its action and attacks the end of the peptide chain which bears this particular group. The necessary groups for carboxypeptidase are seen in the following peptide structure:

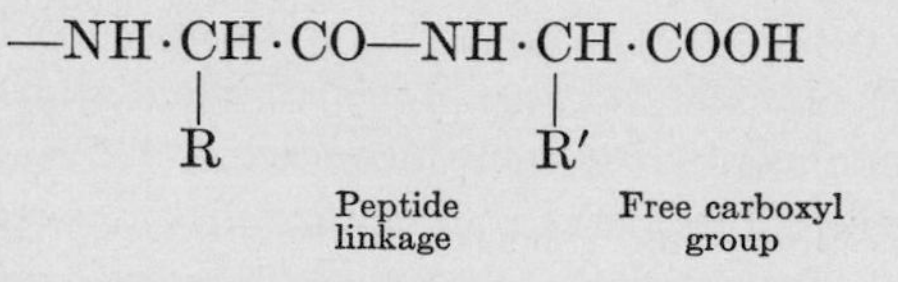

In 1934 Bergmann and his associates pointed out that the carboxypeptidase isolated from the pancreas differs from most of the other enzymes of this class, since its activity is not limited to the hydrolysis of true polypeptides. For example, it hydrolyzes chloracetyl-*l*-tyrosine (I) easily, as well as pyruvoylphenylalanine (II), *d*-tyrosyl-*l*-arginine (III), and *d*-tyrosyl-*l*-tyrosine.

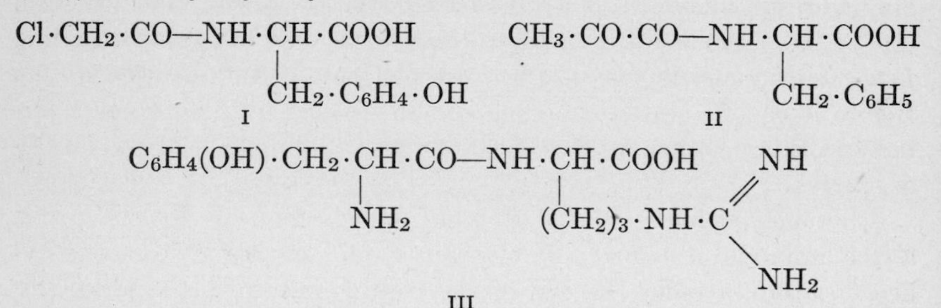

It will be seen that all these peptides contain a free carboxyl group attached to the carbon atom adjacent to the peptide linkage. The presence of the carboxyl group in this position is essential if the compound is to be split by a carboxypeptidase. In pyruvoylphenylalanine (II) the carbon atom linked to the carboxyl group of the peptide linkage does not bear a hydrogen atom. The fact that such a compound is split by carboxypeptidase distinguishes the enzyme from the dipeptidases. Although these three or four dipeptides are attacked by carboxypeptidase, most dipeptides are resistant to the enzyme, because the free amino group adjacent to the peptide linkage exerts an inhibitory effect on its action. However, in tyrosylarginine (III) and tyrosyltyrosine the inhibitory effect is not strong enough to prevent the action of carboxypeptidase.

Bergmann, Zervas, and Schleich (1934) have shown also that, even though chloracetyl-*l*-tyrosine (I) is attacked by carboxypeptidase, the corresponding N-methyl derivative (IV) is not split. This fact led them to conclude that the peptide hydrogen is indispensable for the

$$\begin{array}{l} Cl\cdot CH_2\cdot CO\text{—}N(CH_3)\cdot \underset{|}{C}H\cdot COOH \\ \qquad\qquad\qquad\qquad\quad CH_2\cdot C_6H_4\cdot OH \end{array}$$

IV

action of this enzyme. The configuration of the amino acid carrying the free carboxyl group is often of considerable importance in determining the catalytic activity of carboxypeptidase. For example, the pancreatic enzyme will split carbobenzoxyglycyl-*l*-alanine, but not the corresponding *d*-alanine compound [Bergmann and Fruton (1937)]. On the other hand, extracts from certain bacteria have the ability to split the *d* form of certain peptides almost as rapidly as the *l* form.

Only a few bacteria have been tested for their ability to form carboxypeptidase. Since the extracellular proteolytic system of *Clostridium parabotulinum* does not decompose chloracetyl-*l*-tyrosine, it indicates that the enzyme is absent in this organism [Elberg and Meyer (1939)]. Similar results have been reported by Berger, Johnson, and Peterson (1938), who studied the endoenzymes of several bacteria, including *Leuconostoc mesenteroides*, *Escherichia coli*, and *Bacillus megatherium*. Before it can be stated that bacteria in general do not produce carboxypeptidase, other studies must be carried out on a great variety of species.

Aminopolypeptidase. This enzyme, which requires for its action a free amino group or a basic nitrogen atom carrying at least one hydrogen atom, attacks the end of the peptide chain which carries this group. For example, Grassmann and Dyckerhoff (1928), working with yeast and animal peptidases, have shown that *dl*-leucylglycylglycine (V) is hydrolyzed to *dl*-leucine and glycylglycine, and glycylglycine-*l*-leucine (VI) gives glycine and glycyl-*l*-leucine.

$$\begin{array}{l} C_4H_9\underset{|}{C}H\cdot CO\underset{\uparrow}{\text{—}}NH\cdot CH_2\cdot CO\text{—}NH\cdot CH_2\cdot COOH \\ \quad NH_2 \end{array}$$

V

$$\begin{array}{l} \underset{|}{C}H_2\cdot CO\underset{\uparrow}{\text{—}}NH\cdot CH_2\cdot CO\text{—}NH\cdot \underset{|}{C}H\cdot COOH \\ NH_2 \qquad\qquad\qquad\qquad\qquad\quad C_4H_9 \end{array}$$

VI

Bergmann and Fruton (1937) have shown that pure aminopolypeptidase is incapable of splitting *l*-alanylsarcosylglycine (VII), a compound which does not carry a hydrogen atom on the peptide linkage adjacent to the free amino group, that is, on the peptide linkage which is normally split by aminopeptidase.

$$\underset{\displaystyle NH_2}{CH_3 \cdot \underset{|}{CH}} \cdot CO\text{—}N(CH_3) \cdot CH_2 \cdot CO\text{—}NH \cdot CH_2 \cdot COOH$$

VII

They conclude, therefore, that this enzyme requires a peptide hydrogen for its action and thus in this respect resembles carboxypeptidase, dipeptidase, and prolinase. For additional reading on this subject the review by Johnson and Berger (1941) should be consulted.

Most of the bacteria so far studied are able to hydrolyze *dl*-leucylglycylglycine and thus possess aminopolypeptidase. Gorbach (1930) observed that the culture filtrate of *Pseudomonas aeruginosa* contained aminopolypeptidase which had an optimum *p*H of 8.4. Weil and Kocholaty (1937) determined the activity of the same enzyme from *Clostridium histolyticum* filtrates, and Elberg and Meyer (1939) observed the enzyme in the cell-free filtrates of *Clostridium parabotulinum* cultures, using a medium buffered at *p*H 7.8. Maschmann (1937–1939) found aminopolypeptidase in the supernatant fluids of several bacterial cultures, including *Clostridium botulinum*, *Clostridium sporogenes*, *Clostridium perfringens*, *Serratia marcescens*, *Ps. aeruginosa*, and other anaerobic and aerobic bacteria. Intracellular aminopolypeptidase has been demonstrated in several common bacteria, such as *Staphylococcus aureus* and *Eberthella typhosa* [Imaizumi (1938)], *Leuconostoc mesenteroides*, *Phytomonas tumefaciens*, *Proteus vulgaris*, *Pseudomonas fluorescens*, *Bacillus subtilis*, *Bacillus megatherium*, *Clostridium butylicum*, and *Escherichia coli* [Berger, Johnson, and Peterson (1938), Berger, Johnson, and Baumann (1941)]. The *p*H-activity curves for several of these enzymes were carefully determined. Tissue extracts from animal sources hydrolyze *d*-leucyl peptides much more slowly than the *l*-leucyl forms, but, as pointed out by Berger and his associates, extracts from some bacteria have the ability to split the *d* form almost as rapidly as the *l* form. For example, peptidases from *L. mesenteroides* and *Cl. butylicum* are able to hydrolyze *d*-leucyldiglycine at least one-fifth to one-half as rapidly as *dl*-leucyldiglycine, but extracts from *B. megatherium* and *Ps. fluorescens* exhibit more optical specificity and split the *d* form much more slowly than the *l* form.

Johnson (1941) has highly purified an aminopolypeptidase from brewers' yeast. It behaves as a homogeneous protein on electrophoresis and ultracentrifugal sedimentation and has a molecular weight of about 700,000. The enzyme hydrolyzes the peptide linkage adjacent to the free amino group of the peptide chain. It splits tripeptides much more rapidly than dipeptides. A carboxyl group is not needed for its activity. Zinc ions and halide ions appear to be essential activators.

Prolinase and Prolidase. Prolinase has been shown by Grassmann, Dyckerhoff, and Schoenebeck (1929) to be capable of splitting peptides in which the carboxyl group of proline participates in the peptide linkage, for example, prolylglycine (VIII). Such peptides are apparently resistant to the action of all other enzymes, although they contain the linkage —CO—NH—.

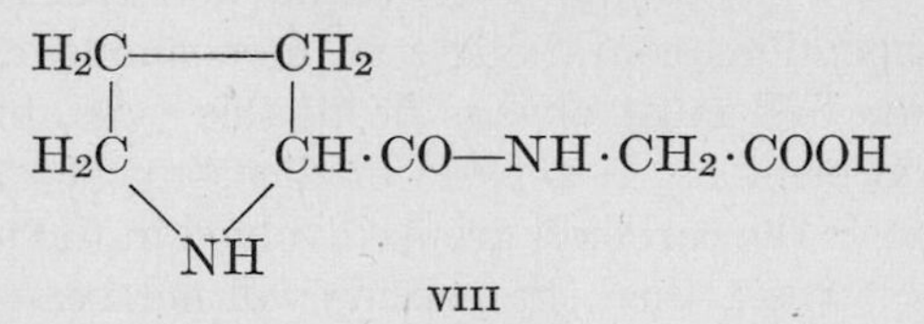

VIII

Berger, Johnson, and Peterson (1938) used *dl*-prolylglycine and *dl*-prolyldiglycine in their study on the intracellular peptidases of *Leuconostoc mesenteroides*, but the compounds were attacked very slowly, if at all. Additional studies are needed on this subject before it can be stated definitely whether this enzyme is produced by bacteria.

Bergmann and Fruton (1937) have shown that ordinary preparations of aminopeptidase contain a second enzyme, *prolidase*, capable of splitting peptides in which the imino group of proline is bound in the peptide linkage; that is, it splits the linkage —CO—N<. Examples of such a linkage are found in glycylproline and *l*-alanyl-*l*-proline (IX).

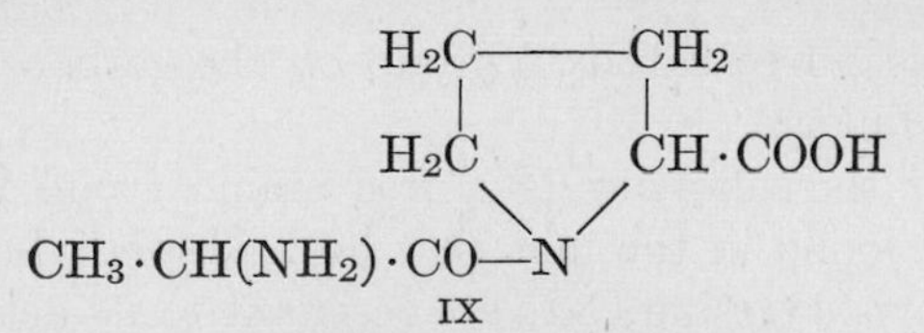

IX

The action of this enzyme seems to be limited to the splitting of peptide linkages containing proline nitrogen. The presence of prolidase in bacteria has apparently not been studied.

Dipeptidase. The activity of dipeptidases is limited to the hydrolysis of dipeptides and requires the presence of free amino and carboxyl groups, peptide hydrogen, and hydrogen in the position α and α', as indicated in the following formula [Bergmann and Zervas (1934), Grassmann and Schneider (1934), Bergmann *et al.* (1935)]:

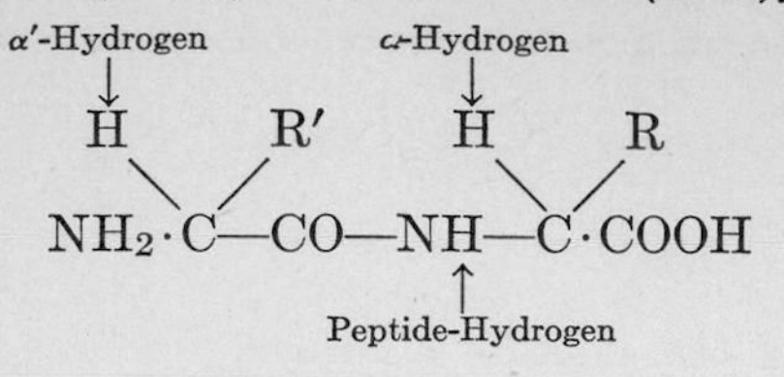

In such peptides one carbon atom adjacent to the peptide linkage carries a free amino group, and the other carries a free carboxyl group. All peptides containing naturally occurring amino acids, but not those with imino acids linked through a normal peptide bond, contain such groups, and all are split by dipeptidases. A normal peptide bond is one between the α-NH_2 group of one amino acid and the α-COOH of another. In dipeptides containing two monoamino monocarboxylic acids the peptide link must always be of this type, but it need not when one of the members is a basic or dicarboxylic amino acid. If either the amino or the carboxyl group involved in the peptide linkage is not in the α-position, then the peptide will not be split by dipeptidase; this enzyme will not split β-*l*-aspartylglycine [Grassmann and Schneider (1934)] nor β-*l*-aspartyl-*l*-tyrosine:

$$\begin{array}{l}COOH\cdot \underset{\displaystyle NH_2}{\underset{|}{CH}}\cdot CH_2CO\text{—}NH\cdot \underset{\displaystyle COOH}{\underset{|}{CH}}\cdot CH_2\cdot C_6H_4\cdot OH\end{array}$$

because in both the free amino group is further removed from the peptide linkage than it is in normal dipeptides (α-peptides). Nor will it split glycyl-*p*-aminobenzoic acid [Bergmann *et al.* (1935)]:

$$\underset{\displaystyle NH_2}{\underset{|}{CH_2}}\cdot CO\text{—}NH\cdot C_6H_4\cdot COOH$$

because it lacks a free carboxyl group on the carbon atom adjacent to the peptide linkage.

Evidence for the necessity of a free amino group for dipeptidase action is to be found in the fact that both N-methyl-*dl*-leucylglycine (X) and sarcosyl-*l*-tyrosine (XI) are resistant to its action [Bergmann *et al.* (1935)].

$$(CH_3)_2\cdot CH\cdot CH_2\cdot \underset{\displaystyle NH\cdot CH_3}{\underset{|}{CH}}\cdot CO\text{—}NH\cdot \underset{\displaystyle COOH}{\underset{|}{CH_2}}$$

X

$$\underset{\displaystyle NH\cdot CH_3}{\underset{|}{CH_2}}\cdot CO\text{—}NH\cdot \underset{\displaystyle COOH}{\underset{|}{CH}}\cdot CH_2\cdot C_6H_4\cdot OH$$

XI

It is also known that a free carboxyl group is necessary for the activity of dipeptidase. This is shown by the fact that, according to Bergmann and his associates, dipeptidase is unable to hydrolyze glycyl-*p*-nitraniline.

$$\begin{array}{l} CH_2\cdot CO\text{—}NH\text{—}C_6H_4\cdot NO_2 \\ | \\ NH_2 \end{array}$$

The necessity of the peptide hydrogen for dipeptidase activity is shown by the fact that this enzyme will not hydrolyze glycylsarcosine (XII), glycyl-*l*-proline, or *l*-alanyl-*l*-proline.

$$\begin{array}{lcr} CH_2CO\text{—}N(CH_3)\cdot & & CH_2 \\ | & & | \\ NH_2 & & COOH \\ & \text{XII} & \end{array}$$

Considerable evidence has accumulated which points to the fact that the α- and α'-hydrogen atoms are essential for dipeptidase activity. Bergmann and Zervas (1934), for example, found that a purified dipeptidase could not split *l*-alanylaminoisobutyric acid, aminoisobutyrylglycine (XIII), or glycyldehydrophenylalanine (XIV).

$$\begin{array}{lcr} (CH_3)_2C\cdot CO\text{—}NH\cdot & & CH_2 \\ | & & | \\ NH_2 & & COOH \\ & \text{XIII} & \end{array} \qquad \begin{array}{lcr} CH_2\cdot CO\text{—}NH\cdot C:CH\cdot C_6H_5 & & \\ | & & | \\ NH_2 & & COOH \\ & \text{XIV} & \end{array}$$

For more information on the absolute specificity of the dipeptidases, concerning which there is some controversy, Tauber (1937) and Johnson and Berger (1941) should be consulted.

Very few studies are available on the hydrolysis of dipeptides by bacteria and other microorganisms. Berger, Johnson, and Peterson (1938) reviewed the early literature on this subject and presented some interesting experimental data of their own. Some of their results will be found in Table 7. The interesting observations by Gauze (1942) on the peptidase activities of sinistral (normal) and dextral (abnormal) strains of *Bacillus mycoides* may also be mentioned. Autolysates from sinistral strains of this organism are unable to attack *d*-leucylglycine, but the dextral strains easily split the unnatural isomer of the dipeptide. Thus it is believed that the inversion of the colony form on the part of the organism is associated with the optical inversion of its proteolytic enzymes. Other studies in which the dipeptidase activity of bacteria has been given attention are those by Gorbach (1937), Imaizumi (1938), Maschmann (1937–1939), Berger, Johnson, and Baumann (1941), and Johnson and Berger (1941).

3. Nucleases. The designation nuclease should probably be confined to enzymes which hydrolyze the various plant and animal nucleic

TABLE 7

HYDROLYSIS * OF SYNTHETIC PEPTIDES BY *Escherichia coli* AND *Bacillus megatherium* PEPTIDASES

[From Berger, Johnson, and Peterson (1938)]

Substrate	*Escherichia coli* Peptidase † (Aerobic Preparation)			*Bacillus megatherium* Peptidase †		
	Per Cent Hydrolysis of One Linkage					
	1 Hour	*6 Hours*	*24 Hours*	*1 Hour*	*6 Hours*	*24 Hours*
dl-Alanylglycine	94	100	107	41	88	94
dl-Leucylglycine	41	100	101	13	47	83
dl-Leucylmethylamine	4	9	12	1	5	5
Diglycine	50	84	90	9	31	49
Glycylmethylamine	2	4	12	0	0	0
Sarcosylglycine	0	5	23	0	0	3
Sarcosyl-*l*-tyrosine	0	2	4	0	1	10
dl-Alanyldiglycine	67	184	201	11	47	138
dl-N-Methylalanyldiglycine	4	20	58	4	5	65
dl-Leucyldiglycine	34	162	202	36	102	136
dl-N-Methylleucyldiglycine	5	13	83	1	1	7
Triglycine	40	140	183	0	1	18
Sarcosyldiglycine	6	29	169	1	3	35
Benzoyldiglycine	0	1	1	0	0	0
Tetraglycine	33	164	272	2	4	16
Chloroacetyl-*l*-tyrosine	0	0	1	1	1	6

* Data are expressed as per cent hydrolysis of one optical component of racemic peptides. Thus 200 per cent splitting of alanyldiglycine means that two linkages (presumably of the natural form of the peptide) have been completely hydrolyzed with the formation of three amino acid molecules.

† In all determinations 0.40 ml. crude *E. coli* enzyme solution (corresponding to 36.9 mg. wet cells), and 0.30 ml. crude *B. megatherium* enzyme solution (corresponding to 50 mg. wet cells), respectively, were used per 3 ml. of reaction mixture.

acids with the formation of nucleotides. Often included in this group, however, are enzymes which split nucleic acids into all their simpler constituents.

The most complete study on bacterial nuclease is that by MacFadyen (1934), who studied the activity of *Bacillus subtilis*, *Bacillus vulgatus*, and *Bacillus megatherium.* He showed that a 3.2 per cent solution of yeast nucleic acid was 80 to 85 per cent decomposed by

B. subtilis nuclease in 48 hours at *p*H 6.6. The decomposed solution was fractionated into undecomposed nucleic acid by the use of uranyl chloride (1.25 per cent) in trichloracetic acid (10 per cent); at *p*H 6.8 the nucleic acid was precipitated, but the nucleotides and smaller units remained in solution. The supernatant solution was then treated with lead acetate at *p*H 6.8 to remove the nucleotides. From this procedure four fractions were obtained: (1) the sodium carbonate solution of the uranyl trichloracetic precipitate; (2) the filtrate from the uranyl chloride precipitation; (3) the supernatant after treatment with neutral lead acetate and removal of lead; (4) the unfractionated culture mixture. Each fraction was then analyzed for total nitrogen and inorganic and total phosphorus. Some of the typical results on fractions 1 and 2 are summarized in Table 8, which also shows the most favorable *p*H for the nuclease activity of *B. subtilis.*

TABLE 8

OPTIMUM HYDROGEN-ION CONCENTRATION FOR DISINTEGRATION OF YEAST NUCLEIC ACID (3.2 PER CENT) BY CULTURES OF *Bacillus subtilis* AT 37.5° C. FOR 48 HOURS

[From MacFadyen (1934)]

*p*H	Total Nitrogen (N)		Nuclease Activity (*c*) †	Total Phosphorus (P)		Nuclease Activity (*f*) ‡	P : N Ratio	
	Fraction 1 * (*a*)	Fraction 2 (*b*)		Fraction 1 (*d*)	Fraction 2 (*e*)		Fraction 1 $\frac{d}{a}$	Fraction 2 $\frac{e}{b}$
	mg.	mg.	per cent	mg.	mg.	per cent		
6.0	12.9	14.9	53.6	7.18	8.72	54.9	0.56	0.59
6.6	5.8	22.9	80.0	2.48	13.52	84.5	0.43	0.59
7.2	7.1	20.8	71.0	3.54	12.46	78.0	0.50	0.60
7.8	12.7	14.7	53.6	7.42	8.51	53.4	0.58	0.58
8.2	17.9	9.4	34.4	10.51	5.43	34.1	0.59	0.58

* Fraction 1, carbonate solution of the uranyl chloride precipitate; Fraction 2 the uranyl chloride supernatant fluid.

† $c = \frac{b}{b + a} \times 100.$

‡ $f = \frac{e}{d + e} \times 100.$

4. Amidases. The enzymes of this general group open carbon-nitrogen linkages in amino acids and acid amides. Usually two subgroups are recognized on the basis of the substrate which they attack: (1) the *desaminases* (*aminoacidases*), which liberate ammonia from amino acids; and (2) the *desamidases* (*amidases*), which split acid amides and related compounds to ammonia and/or other products. Only a few examples will be mentioned here, because some of the enzymes of the two subgroups have not been studied very extensively in bacteria, and the available data on the enzymatic production of ammonia from various amino acids can better be allocated to Chapter 9 on nitrogen metabolism.

ARGINASE. The enzyme arginase hydrolyzes arginine to urea and ornithine, according to the equation given in Table 6. Its activity may be recognized by the increase in formol titration after hydrolysis, since arginine has only one NH_2 group which reacts with formalin, urea has none, and ornithine has two.

Arginase activity has been demonstrated in bacteria, yeasts, and molds. For example, Hino (1924) found the enzyme in young killed cultures of *Pseudomonas aeruginosa* and *Pseudomonas fluorescens*, but it was absent in several other species examined. More recently, Tomota (1940, 1941) has reported that acetone-ether dried powders from *Staphylococcus aureus*, *Staphylococcus albus*, *Staphylococcus citreus*, and *Bacillus subtilis* possess strong arginase activity. Powder obtained from *Sarcina* was fairly active, but powders from streptococci, *Mycobacterium phlei*, *Proteus*, *Pseudomonas aeruginosa*, and *Serratia marcescens* showed weak and variable arginase activity. Some of the properties of the preparations obtained from staphylococci may be cited as rather typical data. The enzyme has an optimum activity at pH 9.0 and is strongly activated by 0.002 to 0.0005 M $MnSO_4$ or 0.001 to 0.0005 M $CdSO_4$. Neither Ni, Co, nor Fe ions exert any effect, but the earth alkalies (Ca, Ba ions) are inhibitory. The enzyme will withstand 50°C. for 30 minutes but is inactivated between 65° and 80°C.; it is inactivated by chloro- or iodoacetic acids but is resistant to the action of animal proteases.

Ackermann (1931) has obtained citrulline, $NH_2 \cdot CO \cdot HN \cdot CH_2 \cdot CH_2 \cdot CH_2 \cdot CHNH_2 \cdot COOH$, from arginine, and Horn (1933) reported similar results with *Pseudomonas aeruginosa*. The reaction probably takes place by a hydrolytic deamination of arginine:

$$\begin{matrix} NH \\ NH_2 \end{matrix} \!\!> C \cdot NH \cdot (CH_2)_3 \cdot CHNH_2 \cdot COOH$$

UREASE. Urease hydrolyzes urea to ammonium carbonate and/or to CO_2 and NH_3, according to the general equation given in Table 6.

There is some question as to whether the reaction proceeds directly to the carbonate, or whether ammonium carbamate is an intermediate product.

$$H_2N \cdot CO \cdot NH_2 + H_2O \rightarrow H_2N \cdot CO_2 \cdot NH_4$$

$$H_2N \cdot CO_2 \cdot NH_4 + H_2O \rightarrow (NH_4)_2CO_3$$

Even though most workers are of the opinion that carbamate is an intermediate product, they are not all in agreement as to whether it is the only one.

Detailed descriptions of the urea-fermenting bacteria were published by several early workers, especially by Viehoever (1913), whose publication covers some 50 pages. More recently, Gibson (1935) has published a description and classification of the bacteria which actively decompose urea. In addition to the well-known species, such as *Bacillus pasteurii* and *Sarcina ureae*, he recognized several new bacilli which were quite active in decomposing urea. Wohlfeil and Weiland (1937) reported that *Proteus* strains, *Corynebacterium pseudodiphtheriae*, and *Mycobacterium pseudotuberculosis* produce urease, but *Escherichia coli* and several other species never produce the enzyme. Utzino, Imaizumi, and Nakayama (1938) also found that urea was easily hydrolyzed by *Proteus vulgaris* or *Staphylococcus aureus*, moderately attacked by *Bacillus subtilis* and *Pseudomonas aeruginosa*, but only slightly decomposed by intestinal bacteria, such as *Eberthella typhosa.*

The yeasts, *Torula rubescens*, *Torula rubra*, and *Schizosaccharomyces santawensis*, produce urease, according to Sakaguchi and Shizume (1937), and a similar activity is exhibited by the molds, *Aspergillus niger* and *Penicillium glaucum* [Miwa and Yoshii (1934)].

HIPPURICASE (HISTOZYME). This desamidase hydrolyzes hippuric acid to benzoic acid and glycine (Table 6). It also attacks certain homologs of hippuric acid, such as *d*-α-benzoylaminobutyric acid, *l*-benzoyl leucine and benzoyl-α-alanine, but exhibits no action on benzoyl-β-alanine and other similar compounds [Waksman and Davison (1926)]. The enzyme has been demonstrated in several plant and animal tissues, as well as in several fungi, such as *Aspergillus oryzae* [Neuberg and Rosenthal (1924)]. The occurrence of the enzyme in bacteria has not been studied very extensively. Seo (1908) reported that several bacteria, including *Staphylococcus aureus*, were able to catalyze the hydrolysis of hippuric acid, and he demonstrated benzoic acid and glycine as the end products. More recently, Tomota and Saito (1940) observed that dried (acetone-ether extracts) preparations of *Bacillus subtilis*, staphylococci, sarcinae, and the timothy bacillus attacked hippuric acid, but those from *Escherichia coli*, *Proteus vulgaris*, and *Serratia marcescens* were unable to alter the compound.

Purine Desamidases. There are a great number of known substances of the so-called purine group. Guanine and adenine, however, are the only naturally occurring purine bases in the nucleic acids. The oxypurines, xanthine and hypoxanthine, are derived from these by the action of acids or enzymes. Purine, the mother substance of the purine bases, does not occur in nature but has been synthesized and has the following structure, the ring being numbered according to the diagram:

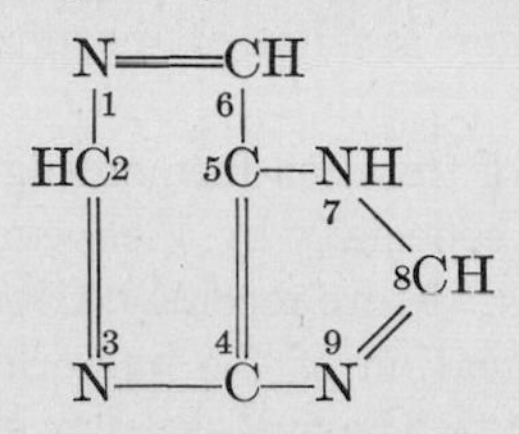

The microbial enzymes which attack the various purine derivatives have not been studied very extensively. Therefore, only one or two examples will be cited here.

Guanase is an enzyme which deaminates guanine to produce xanthine and ammonia, according to the equation given in Table 6. Under aerobic conditions xanthine may be further broken down to uric acid by the enzyme, xanthine oxidase. Guanase has been demonstrated in yeast by Straughn and Jones (1909), but has not been studied very extensively in other microorganisms. Barker and Beck (1941) included guanine in their study of the anaerobic decomposition of purines by the enzymes of *Clostridium acidi-urici* and *Clostridium cylindrosporum*. Their data show that the enzyme systems and intermediate compounds known to be involved in the breakdown of purines by animal and plant tissues and by aerobic microorganisms are not involved in the dissimilation processes of these anaerobic bacteria. For example, the products formed by the anaerobic decomposition of guanine are ammonia, carbon dioxide, and acetic acid. Although the detailed mechanism of the anaerobic processes is obscure, Barker and Beck believe that the processes represent oxidations in which carbon dioxide acts as the ultimate hydrogen acceptor and is reduced to acetic acid.

Adenase deaminates adenine to produce hypoxanthine and ammonia. The hypoxanthine (6-oxypurine) may then be oxidized to xanthine (2:6-dioxypurine) by the enzyme, hypoxanthine oxidase. The presence of adenase in microorganisms has received little attention in the past from the bacteriologist. More recently, however, Lutwak-Mann (1936) has studied the decomposition of adenine compounds by several bacteria. The following compounds were decomposed aerobically and anaerobically: adenosinetriphosphoric acid, muscle adenylic acid, yeast adenylic acid, adenosine, and adenine. The first three were both deaminated and dephosphorylated, but adenosine and adenine were only deaminated. The end product of decomposition was hypoxanthine.

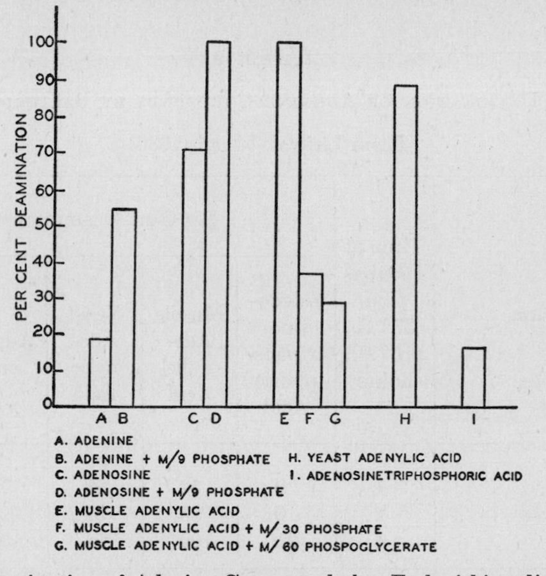

Fig. 4. Deamination of Adenine Compounds by *Escherichia coli* after 1 hr. of Incubation. (From Lutwak-Mann, 1936.)

Some of the interesting data in Lutwak-Mann's article are shown in Table 9 and Figs. 4 and 5. In Fig. 4 it will be seen that the presence of phosphate increases the deamination of adenine and adenosine but

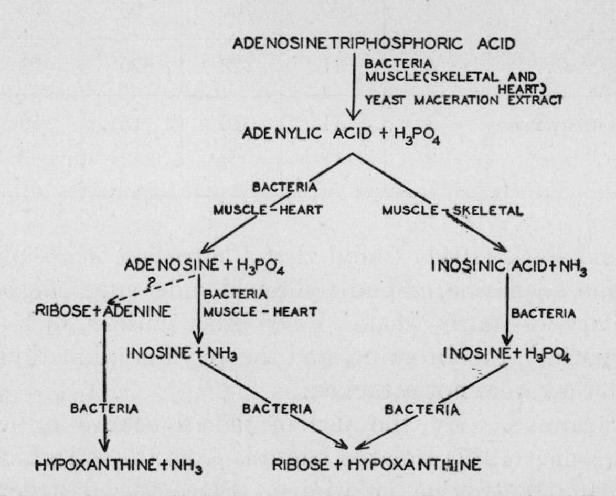

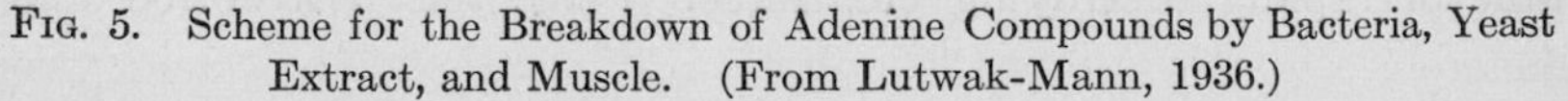

Fig. 5. Scheme for the Breakdown of Adenine Compounds by Bacteria, Yeast Extract, and Muscle. (From Lutwak-Mann, 1936.)

decreases the percentage of muscle adenylic acid decomposed by *Escherichia coli.* Figure 5 shows a comparison between Lutwak-Mann's results with bacteria and those already known for frog, skeletal, and heart muscles and also for yeast maceration extract.

TABLE 9

DEAMINATION OF ADENINE COMPOUNDS BY BACTERIA

[From Lutwak-Mann (1936)]

Organism	Time of Incubation (37° C., *p*H 7.0), hours	Per Cent Deamination of				
		Adenosine-triphosphoric Acid	Muscle Adenylic Acid	Yeast Adenylic Acid	Adenosine	Adenine
Shigella dispar	1	0	52	28	76	8
	2	0	83	57	93	25
	4	21	100	94	100	51
Aerobacter cloacae	1	14	82	38	86	34
	2	29	93	67	93	54
	4	58	100	88	100	79
Aerobacter aerogenes	1	94	94	83	87	50
	2	98	94	86	92	66
	4	100	100	95	100	83
Streptococcus fecalis	4	11	20	20	18	18
Pseudomonas aeruginosa	1	11	10	15	50	47
	2	18	20	15	96	82

Barker and Beck (1941) found that *Clostridium acidi-urici* deaminated adenine, adenosine, and adenylic acid under anaerobic conditions, but its activity was fairly weak. When other purines, such as caffeine (trimethyl purine), theobromine, and theophylline (dimethyl purines), were tested, they were not attacked.

5. Creatininase. By the use of media containing creatinine, Dubos and Miller (1937) isolated bacteria from the soil which are capable of rapidly destroying creatinine. Since this destruction takes place only in the presence of air, it is evident that an oxidative enzyme system of some type is involved. However, little is known about the mechanism other than the fact that a molecule of urea and one of ammonia are formed from each molecule of creatinine. Therefore the enzyme may be tentatively placed in the group which acts on nitrogenous substances rather than with the true oxidases.

Since most other compounds which give a positive Jaffe test for creatinine are not attacked (Table 10), use of the bacterial enzyme

TABLE 10

Enzymatic (Bacterial) Decomposition of Jaffe-Reactive Substances Related to or Associated with Creatinine (Incubated 1 Hour at 37° C., *p*H 7.0)

[From Dubos and Miller (1937)]

Compound	Percentage Decomposition Measured by Change in Jaffe Reaction * Enzyme Preparation NC	HR
Creatinine	100	100
5-Methylcreatinine	0	0
Dimethylcreatinine	0	0
Acetylcreatinine	10 †	..
4- (or 5-) Benzoylcreatinine	0	0
5-Benzylcreatinine	0	0
2-Benzylcreatinine	0	0
Glycocyamidine	10 †	5
5-Methylglycocyamidine	10 †	0

* This reaction is based upon the characteristic property possessed by creatinine of yielding a definite color reaction (red creatinine picrate) in the presence of picric acid in alkaline solution.

† Acetylcreatinine does not undergo further destruction when the incubation period is prolonged, whereas glycocyamidine and 5-methylglycocyamidine are completely decomposed if the incubation is continued for some hours.

preparations is considered a valuable tool in creatinine determination. Because one molecule of urea is always formed from creatinine by the enzyme, Dubos and Miller believe that a quantitative urea determination is more reliable for the estimation of creatinine than is the Jaffe test.

6. Nitratase (Nitrate Reductase). The enzyme nitratase was first observed in *Escherichia coli*, by Green, Stickland, and Tarr (1934). Although it is probably a true desmolase, it will be discussed here as an enzyme which acts upon nitrogenous substances. When nitrate is added to a mixture of the enzyme preparation (crushed cells of *E. coli*) and reduced methylene blue ($Mb \cdot H_2$), it is rapidly reduced to nitrite, and simultaneously the indicator is oxidized to its colored form:

$$Mb \cdot H_2 + HNO_3 \rightarrow Mb + HNO_2 + H_2O$$

This reaction has not yet been demonstrated to be reversible.

7. Nitrogenase and Azotase. Burk (1934) and others have given the name *azotase* to the total system responsible for the nitrogen-fixation reaction in *Azotobacter*. The system includes the specific enzyme, *nitrogenase*, and the activators and other components necessary for the fixation. Azotase differs markedly from the majority of enzyme systems in one respect. Its activity is normally limited to the extent of growth; that is, the amount of nitrogen fixed is directly proportional to the amount of cell synthesis. The elaborated nitrogen compounds occur in the cell bodies chiefly as protein and are not ordinarily liberated into the culture medium by young active cultures. The following enzyme mechanism has been postulated by Burk for nitrogen fixation by *Azotobacter:*

$$N_2 + E \rightleftarrows N_2E \text{ (Rapid reaction)}$$
$$N_2E \rightarrow E + P \text{ (Slow reaction)}$$

where N_2 is atmospheric nitrogen, and the symbol E refers to the specific enzyme, nitrogenase, which combines reversibly with the nitrogen molecule to form the substrate-enzyme complex, N_2E. This complex then splits irreversibly into E and nitrogenous products, P, which are actually in the form of *Azotobacter* cells.

From this brief discussion it should not be assumed that azotase is the only enzyme complex in *Azotobacter* cells, because, besides nitrogenase, they contain numerous dehydrogenases, cytochrome, catalase, malonate carboxylase, and numerous other systems not directly involved in the nitrogen-fixation process.

B. Desmolyzing Enzymes (Desmolases)

Another large group of enzymes is that involved in the processes of respiration and metabolism within the cell. They are often referred to as desmolyzing enzymes or, simply, as desmolases. Such enzymes are principally, though not exclusively, concerned with oxidation, reduction, and decarboxylation changes in organic compounds. The enzymes of this group can be sharply differentiated from the hydrolases which have just been discussed. Hydrolases are usually extracellular and catalyze the severing of the secondary bonds of carbon with oxygen or nitrogen; that is, they activate reactions which do not lead to any marked change in free energy. Desmolases, on the other hand, are intracellular and catalyze the severing of bonds in compounds which lead to the release of considerable energy. This point can be better illustrated by presenting a few figures showing the approximate energy liberated from 1 g. of substrate by the action of different extracellular and intracellular enzymes:

Extracellular Enzymes	kg. cal.	*Intracellular Enzymes*	kg. cal.
Lipase	4.1–4.3	Lactic acid dehydrogenase	82.0
Amylase	7.3–7.8	Alcohol dehydrogenase	149.5
Sucrase (invertase)	8.8–9.3	Urease	239.0
Maltase	5.1–5.6	Vinegar oxidase	2,530.0

The utility of a compound as a food or energy source for an organism depends also upon the degree of oxidation which takes place in the cell; the more complete the oxidation, the greater the available energy. The energy (calories) liberated with varying degrees of oxidation of glucose under aerobic and anaerobic conditions may be cited as an example:

Complete aerobic oxidation

$$C_6H_{12}O_6 + 6O_2 \rightarrow 6CO_2 + 6H_2O + 674 \text{ kg. cal.}$$

Partial aerobic oxidation

$$C_6H_{12}O_6 + 9O_2 \rightarrow \underset{\text{Oxalic acid}}{6C_2H_2O_4} + 6H_2O + 493 \text{ kg. cal.}$$

Anaerobic oxidation

$$C_6H_{12}O_6 \rightarrow \underset{\text{Lactic acid}}{2CH_3CHOHCOOH} + 22.5 \text{ kg. cal.}$$

$$C_6H_{12}O_6 \rightarrow \underset{\text{Ethyl alcohol}}{2C_2H_5OH} + 2CO_2 + 22 \text{ kg. cal.}$$

$$C_6H_{12}O_6 \rightarrow \underset{\text{Acetic acid}}{3CH_3COOH} + 15 \text{ kg. cal.}$$

From this brief consideration it can be seen that with incomplete oxidation more of a given substrate must be broken down to supply the energy needs of an organism.

The desmolases have been characterized by several workers as the enzymes *par excellence* of metabolism, by which the cell obtains the energy necessary for growth, movement, and other activities. Since the activities of the desmolases are bound so intimately to the life processes of the cell, they are now generally called respiratory enzymes. The term respiration has undergone a continual expansion in meaning since it was first introduced into biology. Originally respiration was coined to denote the process of inhaling air into and expelling it from the lungs of animals, that is, breathing. It was then expanded to cover the transfer of oxygen to and the removal of carbon dioxide and water from tissues. Later the term was extended beyond the phenomenon of gaseous exchange and used to denote the general oxidation processes of cells. Now that it is finally recognized that these processes are almost always concerned with the energy requirements of cells, the term respiration has come to mean any energy-producing (exothermic) biological reaction occurring under either aerobic or anaerobic conditions. Hence it follows that respiratory enzymes are enzymes which catalyze the chemical reactions taking place in respiration.

As we have just stated, respiration in its widest sense must include all those processes in the cell whereby the potential energy stored in the chemical compounds of varying degrees of complexity is set free to furnish the energy required by an organism for its vital activities. The goal is effected by processes of oxidation; the result is the production of energy and the formation of simpler chemical substances, such as CO_2 and H_2O. Since it may be stated that all living cells consume free or combined oxygen and eliminate CO_2, then it follows that the amount of oxygen utilized in respiration must be related to the energy liberated during oxidation. The ratio of the CO_2 produced to the O_2 consumed in aerobic respiration, that is, the respiratory quotient (r.q.), yields additional information about the nature of the foodstuffs oxidized. The ratio of this exchange is the same whether the volumes are expressed in cubic centimeters, in percentages, or as millimeters of pressure. Thus in the complete combustion of carbohydrate (glucose), $C_6H_{12}O_6 + 6O_2 \rightarrow 6CO_2 + 6H_2O$, the theoretical respiratory quotient is 1.0 $\left(\text{r.q.} = \frac{6CO_2}{6O_2} = \frac{6}{6} = 1.0\right)$, and in fat and protein the ratio is approximately 0.7 and 0.8, respectively.

The respiratory quotients of microorganisms, as a rule, have been computed from the analysis of the gases over the cultures, but the values thus obtained can be considered at best only approximate. The direct use of analytical data, uncorrected for the changes in pressure, is wrong, since it gives an apparent r.q. which is usually higher than the real quotient. A more common error is the failure to determine the amount of CO_2 dissolved free or chemically combined in the medium. Another point which must be considered is the period of incubation, which, with some organisms, may be without appreciable effect; with others, on account of secondary changes in the medium, such as decarboxylation, a longer period may result in an increased CO_2 production and hence in a higher final value.

The respiratory quotients for several bacteria and protozoa are presented in Table 11. These values were taken from the report by Soule (1928) and are comparable, since all the experiments were carried out under the same conditions. Similar data will be found in the extensive studies of microbic respiration by Novy, Soule, Roehm, and Novy (1925). A comparison of the experimental quotients with the theoretical values given in the last line of the table is of special interest. In every case, except with *Corynebacterium diphtheriae*, the addition of glucose to the medium increased the quotient, a result which shows that, when glucose is present, it is utilized more or less completely by these organisms as a source of energy. If only glucose were oxidized in the glucose-agar media, the quotient would be theoretically 1.0. As is evident in the table, this value is closely approximated by several organisms. On the other hand, it is also clear that some combustion of the proteins or amino acids (for example, glycine and asparagine each have a quotient as high as 1.33) in the media is taking place at the same time that glucose is being oxidized. As a result, the observed r.q. represents a sum of all the oxidations.

TABLE 11

AVERAGE OF CORRECTED REAL RESPIRATORY QUOTIENTS OBTAINED IN JAR EXPERIMENTS

[From Soule (1928)]

Organism	Plain Agar	Glycerol Agar	Glucose Agar	Blood Agar	Glucose-Blood Agar
Mycobacterium tuberculosis-hominis	.....	0.856	0.992	.....	.....
M. tuberculosis-bovis	0.888	0.903	1.036	.....	.....
Malleomyces mallei	0.841	0.859	0.972	0.848	.....
Corynebacterium diphtheriae	0.921	0.802	0.906	0.942	
Bacillus subtilis	0.912	0.843	1.278	.....	
Trypanosoma lewisi	.....	.....	.....	0.822	0.938
Leishmania tropica	.....	.....	.....	0.875	0.951
Leishmania donovani	.....	.....	.....	0.862	0.968
Theoretical value	0.81	0.857	1.00	0.81	1.00

Another factor which tends to raise the respiratory quotient above the theoretical value is the decarboxylation of amino acids and other organic acids, because CO_2 is liberated without a corresponding O_2 intake.

THEORIES ON BIOLOGICAL OXIDATION-REDUCTION

Several theories have been advanced to explain how the energy-liberating oxidation-reduction processes function or take place in biological systems. Only the two most important theories will be mentioned here; the others are principally of historical importance and are discussed in some detail in certain books on enzyme chemistry and by Buchanan and Fulmer (1930).

Wieland's Theory for the Explanation of Biological Oxidation. According to Wieland (1922), biological oxidation processes are based on an "activation" or "mobilization" of hydrogen in the substrate by specific enzymes, followed by a catalytic transfer of the hydrogen from the oxidizable material to some other substance. Thus the oxidation of alcohol to aldehyde, which takes place in the cell, is ascribed to the removal of two atoms of hydrogen from the alcohol molecule according to the following equation:

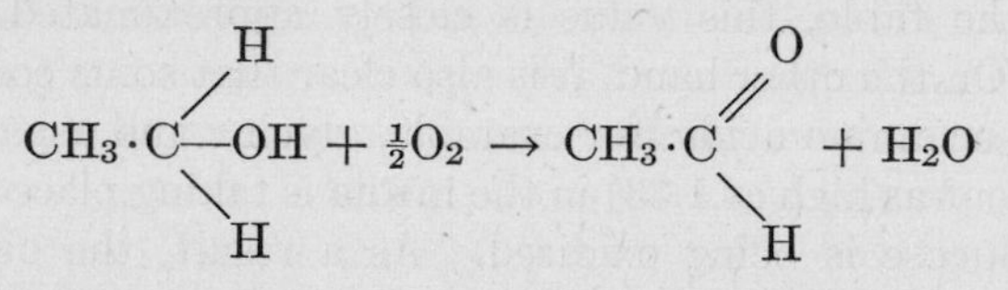

Another cellular process, the formation of acids from aldehydes, proceeds by dehydrogenation by way of the aldehyde hydrate:

$$CH_3 \cdot CHO + H_2O \rightarrow CH_3 \cdot C(OH)(OH)H$$

after which the dehydrogenation takes place as:

$$CH_3 \cdot C(OH)(OH)H + \text{Acceptor} \rightarrow CH_3 \cdot C(OH){=}O + H_2 \cdot \text{Acceptor},$$

which may then be followed by the reaction:

$$H_2 \cdot \text{Acceptor} + \tfrac{1}{2}O_2 \rightarrow \text{Acceptor} + H_2O$$

This concept of the activation of hydrogen has received additional support through the finding that it is possible, even in biological systems, to replace oxygen in the various reactions by other hydrogen acceptors. This point has already been illustrated by the foregoing reaction. Therefore, according to Wieland's viewpoint, oxygen takes part in the dehydrogenation reaction only in the role of a hydrogen acceptor and can be replaced by other acceptor substances, such as methylene blue, or other easily reducible compounds. For example, from some lactic-acid-forming bacteria a heat-labile enzyme may be extracted which can oxidize lactic acid to pyruvic acid in the absence of oxygen. This fact can be ascertained by the addition of methylene blue, which combines with the hydrogen mobilized by the enzyme and is therefore converted to its leuco form. On the addition of molecular oxygen the leuco form is reconverted to oxidized methylene blue and, at the same time, yields two atoms of hydrogen for the formation of water. In other living cells there are similarly acting, heat-labile enzymes, *dehydrogenases*, which are capable of mobilizing the hydrogen of specific substrates and liberating it in atomic form.

Warburg's Theory for the Explanation of Biological Oxidation. It has been known for some time that the presence of a heavy metal, probably iron, is necessary for cellular oxidations to take place. Since iron occurs only in small amounts in cells, it cannot react stoichiometrically, but rather must do so in a catalytic manner. No free iron is present in tissues. On the contrary, it is bound in the form of *heme* (or hematin), which is a constituent of many substances that are now known to be involved in the transportation of oxygen in biological systems.

With these facts in mind Warburg (1925) advanced his theory to explain the mechanism of the oxidations which are required to produce the flow of energy necessary for the maintenance of life. Although his theory is supported by good experiments, it is basically contrary to Wieland's contention. Thus, according to Warburg, respiring cells contain "respiratory ferments" (X·Fe), organic bivalent-iron compounds (hemins), which are able to react with oxygen in some way to produce more highly oxidized iron compounds:

$$X\cdot Fe + O_2 \rightarrow X\cdot FeO_2$$

This process is often referred to as molecular oxygen activation, but in reality it can be nothing more than iron catalysis. Once the oxidized-iron complex is formed, it is then able to react or oxidize other organic substances (A) and is again reduced to bivalent iron, according to the equation:

$$X\cdot FeO_2 + 2A \rightarrow X\cdot Fe + 2AO$$

An examination of these equations will show that the iron moves in a cycle; hence the theory is sometimes spoken of as Warburg's iron cycle. Warburg has also demonstrated that substances like HCN, H_2S, and CO, which are able to form noncatalytic compounds with iron, inhibit biological oxidations.

It is quite generally believed that a large part of the respiration of animal tissues and other cells is due to a catalyst which behaves like an iron compound and is poisoned by HCN, H_2S, CO, and similar substances. As several workers have brought out, however, other types of systems may play an important part in aerobic biological respiration. Two statements may be given to support this claim: (1) According to Dixon, most tissues and cells are inhibited only to an extent of 40 to 60 per cent by H_2S, CO, and HCN, and for this reason Warburg's respiratory ferment can account for only 60 per cent of the respiration at the most. Furthermore it must be remembered that cyanide poisons many systems, such as peroxidases, several oxidases, and catalase, besides the respiratory ferment. (2) Since xanthine oxidase is an aerobic dehydrogenase and is not inhibited by H_2S, NaN_3, or CO, the oxidation brought about by this enzyme apparently cannot be due to an iron catalysis.

If the primary reaction of respiration takes place between molecular oxygen and iron, and molecular oxygen can react in the cell only by this method and not with other organic molecules, then this fact would seem definitely to exclude the possibility of molecular oxygen serving as a direct acceptor for hydrogen, in accordance with the views of Wieland. Therefore, on the surface the theories of Warburg and Wieland are contradictory in respect to the manner in which oxygen acts. As we shall point out on the next few pages, however, the theories are not necessarily contradictory; on the contrary, they may be complementary when the entire biological system is considered.

In 1925 Kluyver and Donker developed a theory of microbiological respiration which combines the Wieland hypothesis explaining biochemical oxidations by means of the catalytic transfer of hydrogen atoms with Warburg's theory of the activation of oxygen. Kluyver and Donker develop their ideas as follows:

Respiration, the process by which cells derive the energy necessary for growth from their substrates, can take place aerobically and anaerobically. *Aerobic respiration,* which they term *oxidative dissimilation,* consists of the transformation of the substrates in the presence of oxygen into compounds which are eventually excreted, these changes necessitating the taking up of free oxygen. The energy released goes into the formation of cell constituents (assimilation). In *anaerobic respiration* the energy is obtained from chemical reactions in which free oxygen takes no part; this process Kluyver and Donker term *fermentative dissimilation.* They regard the mechanism of the transfer catalysis as being due to the affinity of the protoplasm of the cell for certain atoms of the substrate, leading first to the formation of a loose compound between the protoplasm and the substrate. This reaction results in a loosening of the bonds binding the affected atoms to the rest of the molecule; in the presence of a suitable acceptor these so-called activated atoms are removed. The relative affinities of the protoplasm for oxygen and hydrogen are not independent, but reciprocal. Thus a high affinity for hydrogen implies a low affinity for oxygen, and vice versa. The action of the acetic acid bacteria in transforming ethyl alcohol into acetic acid led Wieland to extend his theory of catalytic dehydrogenation to biochemical oxidations (aerobic respiration, oxidative dissimilation). Kluyver and Donker made a close examination of fermentative sugar-dissimilation processes (anaerobic respiration) and concluded that all the diverse reactions which take place can be wholly explained by a similar mechanism.

According to these authors, then, all respiration processes are fundamentally the same, and the observed diversities are only "a consequence of the gradual variation in affinity of the different kinds of protoplasm for hydrogen." Furthermore, a logical consequence of their theory is that it is no longer necessary to assume the existence of a separate enzyme for every single reaction brought about by microorganisms. They admit that different hydrolytic enzymes are required for complex carbohydrates, fats, and proteins; but, when dealing with oxidative dissimilation, such as the transformation of ethyl alcohol to acetic acid by *Acetobacter* species, they postulate only a single oxido-reduction promoting agent as the catalyst. The differences which are ascribed to enzymes such as catalase, carboxylase, and alcoholoxidase, are, according to Kluyver and Donker, due to differences in the affinity of the protoplasm for hydrogen.

On the basis of the foregoing theories, Kluyver and Donker present a scheme for bringing together into groups those species of bacteria which agree in general in their morphological and respiratory activities. The respiratory activities are based on those dissimilation processes in which glucose acts as substrate. The groups are arranged in the order of the affinity for hydrogen possessed by the protoplasm of the microorganisms included in them. For example, Group I contains those bacteria whose affinity for hydrogen is high, but whose corresponding oxygen affinity is low. On the other hand, Group VII contains those organisms whose affinity for hydrogen is so low that it has no significance for hydrogen activation, but whose affinity for oxygen is considerable.

GROUP I. Aerobic organisms with strong oxidative (dehydrogenating) powers. Characterized by their very great affinity for hydrogen. When oxygen (or methylene blue) is present as a hydrogen acceptor, glucose undergoes a direct dehydrogenation, and gluconic acid is formed. Under optimum conditions gluconic acid, as a rule, is not found as a metabolism product, but after this first change a whole series of further dehydrogenations takes place until finally some CO_2 and H_2O are produced. *Examples:* several kinds of molds and acetic acid bacteria.

Group II. Aerobic organisms with weaker oxidative (dehydrogenating) powers. Glucose is not dehydrogenated to gluconic acid but is first converted into compounds of the three-carbon type, such as methyl glyoxal ($CH_3 \cdot CO \cdot CHO$). *Examples:* higher plants, muscular tissues of higher animals, and many aerobic spore-forming bacteria.

Group III. Organisms which cause alcoholic fermentation. The affinity of these microorganisms for hydrogen is again weaker. The preliminary conversion of glucose to methylglyoxal is followed by a dehydrogenation to pyruvic acid. The pyruvic acid produced is then converted by an intramolecular change into CO_2 and acetaldehyde. The acetaldehyde then acts as a hydrogen acceptor in the dehydrogenation of methylglyoxal. Kluyver's views on the degradation of glucose, especially the formation of methylglyoxal, may have to be modified in the light of more recent researches. *Examples:* alcohol yeasts, molds such as *Mucor racemosus.*

Group IV. The bacteria of the colon group. The hydrogen affinity is smaller than that of Group III bacteria and decreases in the order of the three subgroups listed.

a. *Eberthella typhosa* subgroup.
b. *Escherichia coli* subgroup.
c. *Aerobacter aerogenes* subgroup.

Group V. The true lactic acid bacteria. The protoplasm of these organisms is characterized by its sensitivity toward oxygen. The affinity for hydrogen is again smaller than that of the organisms of the foregoing groups and decreases in the order of the two following subgroups.

a. Heterofermentative lactic acid bacteria, which produce lactic acid and other metabolic products. *Examples: Lactobacillus brevis, Lactobacillus buchneri.*
b. Homofermentative lactic acid bacteria, whose dehydrogenation powers are so small that practically nothing but lactic acid is formed. *Examples: Lactobacillus caucasicus, Lactobacillus helveticus, Lactobacillus acidophilus, Lactobacillus delbrueckii.*

Group VI. The propionic acid bacteria. The hydrogen affinity is again smaller than that of the previous group, and consequently the oxygen affinity becomes more pronounced, that is, the organisms are sensitive to oxygen. Lactic acid functions as an acceptor and is converted into propionic acid.

Group VII. The butyl alcohol, butyric acid, and related anaerobic bacteria. The protoplasm of the organisms of this group is characterized by its low affinity for hydrogen. The organisms are very sensitive to oxygen.

More recently, Keilin (1929, 1933) has formulated a theory of cellular respiration which, like that of Kluyver and Donker, combines the Wieland and Warburg points of view but gives a more concrete picture of the actual mechanism of respiration. He believes that the dehydrogenases act as hydrogen activators and permit the reduction of oxygen which has been catalyzed or transported by hemes (respiratory pigments, such as the cytochromes). Such a reduction would result in the formation of water. The functional relationship between the intracellular hematin compounds (cytochromes) and the respiratory enzymes such as dehydrogenases and oxidases is schematically represented as follows:[2]

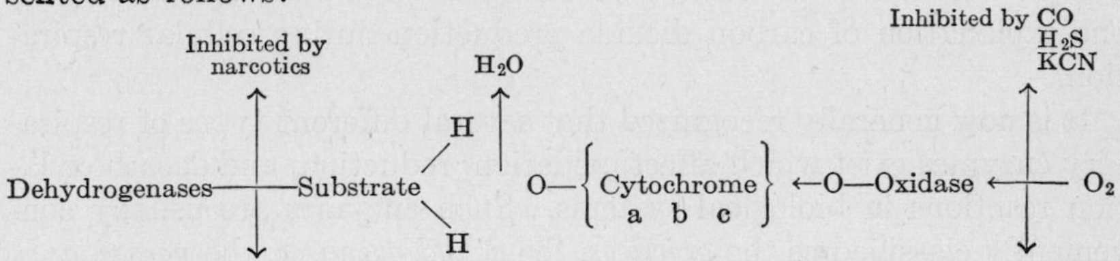

In the form in which Keilin has unified the points of view of Warburg and Wieland it can be seen that they are not necessarily contradictory, but, on the contrary, they are complementary when the entire respiratory system is considered. Oxidation and reduction are fundamentally transfers of electrons (Fe^{++}-e → Fe^{+++}); therefore, whether oxygen is added or hydrogen is removed, there is a loss of an electron. On the other hand, the process of reduction consists of the gain of an electron. Just as it has been found that CO and KCN prevent the oxidation of cytochrome, so its reduction is prevented by narcotics (urethane or alcohol). By reason of this fact each system can be examined independently of the other. In the presence of a suitable dehydrogenase the cytochrome-oxidase-oxygen system may be replaced by an appropriate hydrogen acceptor, such as methylene blue. Narcotics apparently interfere with the action of the dehydrogenases in such a way that they can no longer mobilize the hydrogen of the substrate. In the absence of active or atomic hydrogen the reduction of cytochrome ceases.

The scheme presented on this page for cellular respiration can account for the water formed during respiration. It should be kept in mind, however, that there are enzymes and carriers other than those

[2] This type of respiratory process does not exclude other possibilities, such as (1) the existence of other nonhematin carriers, (2) the direct interreaction between an oxidase and hydrogen donators, and (3) the interaction between hydrogen donators and molecular oxygen. As presented here, it merely shows the relationship between Wieland's and Warburg's theories.

described on these pages. They may function in coordination with those listed or provide for alternate paths of transportation for hydrogen and oxygen. For example, *catalase* and *peroxidase* cause the liberation of oxygen from peroxides. Glutathione, which is a tripeptide of cystine, glycine, and glutamic acid, may act as a hydrogen acceptor. It does so by virtue of the sulfur group (—S—S—) of the cystine constituent of two molecules of glutathione, which may be reduced to H—S—S—H. Certain four-carbon acids may also function as hydrogen acceptors and donators. Finally, mention may be made of *carboxylase*, which acts directly on the carboxyl group of certain compounds and causes the release of carbon dioxide. Its action may be one explanation of carbon dioxide production during cellular respiration.

It is now generally recognized that several different types of respiratory enzymes exist which affect oxidation, reduction, and decarboxylation reactions in biological systems. Such enzymes are usually conveniently classified as the *oxidases*, the *dehydrogenases*, the *peroxidases*, *catalase*, and *carboxylase*. The data listed in Table 12 have been derived largely from the work of Potter (1939). Since catalase and peroxidase exhibit the same general structure as most of the oxidases and since they differ from them only in that they activate peroxides rather than molecular oxygen, they are included in this classification. A somewhat similar classification has been employed by Franke (1940) in his excellent review on the desmolases.

The next few pages will be devoted to a brief discussion of some of the more important desmolases and their application to bacteria. The general facts concerning the enzymes will be presented in an introductory manner, and the enzymes will be discussed in the same order as they are listed in Table 12. For complete details on this phase of the subject the monographs by Elvehjem and associates (1939), Oppenheimer and Stern (1939), Green (1940), and Sumner and Somers (1943), and the reviews by Franke (1940, 1943) should be consulted.

I. OXIDASES

The oxidases elaborated by various cells have been studied by many workers; the literature is too extensive to be reviewed here. Also, in the past the oxidases have not always been clearly differentiated from the dehydrogenases. As a result there is considerable confusion in the literature with respect to proper nomenclature. In view of these facts only a few general remarks will be presented here to acquaint the student with the subject.

Oxidases have been defined by Meldrum (1934) as "oxidative catalysts which reduce only molecular oxygen and whose action is independ-

TABLE 12

PROPERTIES AND CLASSIFICATION OF OXIDASES, DEHYDROGENASES, PEROXIDASES, AND CATALASE

[From Potter (1939) and Others]

I. OXIDASES

General properties: (1) presumably activate oxygen and are inactive in the absence of oxygen; (2) do not reduce dyes; (3) catalyze direct reaction of metabolites and oxygen; (4) produce H_2O; (5) are inhibited by cyanide and other poisons; (6) require neither coenzymes nor cytochrome systems.

Examples

1. Cytochrome oxidase (indophenol oxidase?).
2. Ascorbic acid oxidase.
3. Polyphenol oxidase, monophenol oxidase (tyrosinase), and related copper-protein enzymes.
4. Luciferase.

II. DEHYDROGENASES

AEROBIC

General properties: (1) activate hydrogen of metabolites; (2) reduce dyes; (3) act in absence of oxygen when suitable dyes are present; (4) catalyze direct reaction between metabolites and oxygen; (5) produce peroxide in the presence of oxygen; (6) may or may not be inhibited by cyanide, H_2S, or NaN_3; (7) require neither coenzyme nor cytochrome systems.

Examples

1. Xanthine oxidase or Schardinger enzyme.
2. *d*-Amino acid dehydrogenase.
3. Amine oxidases.
4. Uricase.

ANAEROBIC (DIFFERENTIATED ACCORDING TO THE FIRST CARRIER)

General properties: (1) activate hydrogen of the metabolites; (2) catalyze reaction between metabolites and carriers; (3) may or may not be inhibited by various concentrations of urethane, iodoacetate, etc.

Examples

Class A. Cytochrome-linked

1. Succinic dehydrogenase.
2. α-glycerophosphate dehydrogenase.
3. Lactic dehydrogenase (yeast and gonococcus).
4. Formic dehydrogenase (*Escherichia coli*).

Class B. Coenzyme I-linked (DPN, diphosphopyridine nucleotide, cozymase).

1. Lactic dehydrogenase.
2. Malic dehydrogenase.
3. β-Hydroxybutyric dehydrogenase.
4. Glucose dehydrogenase.
5. Alcohol dehydrogenase.
6. Aldehyde mutase.
7. Triose phosphate dehydrogenase.
8. Dihydroxyacetone dehydrogenase.
9. l-(+)-Glutamic acid dehydrogenase.

Class C. Coenzyme II-linked (TPN, triphosphopyridine nucleotide).

1. Hexose monophosphate dehydrogenase.
2. Isocitric acid dehydrogenase.

III. PEROXIDASES

General properties: (1) oxidize substrates with H_2O_2. The H_2O_2 cannot be replaced by O_2 or by oxidation-reduction dyes; (2) are reversibly inhibited by NaF, KCN, and H_2S; (3) are iron-porphyrin protein enzymes.

IV. CATALASE

General properties: (1) breaks down H_2O_2 to O_2 and H_2O; (2) is an iron-porphyrin protein enzyme; (3) inhibitors like KCN and H_2S prevent the reduction of ferric catalase by H_2O_2, but NaN_3 and NH_2OH stabilize ferro catalase and prevent its reoxidation by molecular oxygen.

ent of hydrogen peroxide." Although this definition is quite satisfactory, it is not too descriptive. With the information which is now available the oxidases may be differentiated from the dehydrogenases in the following manner: oxidases appear to be metallo (iron or copper) proteins, and are therefore inhibited by substances which stabilize the metallic groups. Although, in general, cyanide, H_2S, CO, and NaN_3 poison or stabilize the oxidases, there are a number of individual exceptions. Oxidases fail to work under anaerobic conditions and do not form hydrogen peroxide as a result of their reduction of oxygen.

Lipton, Arnold, and Berger (1939) list six enzymes which, they consider, satisfactorily meet the criteria of true oxidases. They are: (1) cytochrome oxidase (indophenol oxidase?); (2) ascorbic acid oxidase; (3) polyphenol oxidases; (4) laccase; (5) tyrosinase (tyrosine oxidase); and (6) dopa oxidase. The presence of some of these enzymes in bacteria has been studied very little, if at all. For this reason we shall only briefly discuss the subject here. In addition, we shall present a few remarks about *luciferase*.

1. Cytochrome Oxidase (Indophenol Oxidase?). Cytochrome oxidase is one of the most widely distributed oxidizing enzyme systems found in the cells of aerobic organisms, and its presence has been demonstrated in bacteria, yeasts, fungi, algae, higher plants, and animals. The enzyme specifically catalyzes the oxidation of the ferro cytochromes (cellular respiratory pigments) by molecular oxygen; reduced cytochromes a and c are not auto-oxidizable in air at physiological hydrogen-ion concentrations.

The cytochromes are iron-porphyrin proteins similar to hemoglobin and are usually referred to as respiratory pigments. Three or four well-characterized components make up the cytochrome system; the three best-known are referred to as cytochromes a, b, and c and give characteristic absorption bands when the reduced forms are examined with a spectroscope. Sometimes a fourth and a fifth unit are also recognized in the cytochrome complex of certain cells. In such cases component d is the fused β bands of the three more important bands, and a_3 is a new member discovered in 1939 by Keilin and Hartree. Each of the components exists in an oxidized and reduced form. The reduced compounds exhibit well-marked absorption spectra, with intense bands occupying (in bacteria) the following approximate positions [Frei, Riedmüller, and Almasy (1934)]:

Cytochrome a, 5,900–6,000 Å. (Avg. for 18 bacterial species, 5,950 Å.)
Cytochrome b, 5,550–5,653 Å. (Avg. for 19 bacterial species, 5,615 Å.)
Cytochrome c, 5,472–5,550 Å. (Avg. for 10 bacterial species, 5,505 Å.)
Cytochrome d, 5,200–5,313 Å. (Avg. for 19 bacterial species, 5,254 Å.)

In a similar study Fujita and Kodama (1934) examined forty-five bacterial species and classified them into six groups based on the appearance of intense absorption bands in the following positions:

$$a = 600\text{–}605\ m\mu, \quad a' = 587\text{–}595\ m\mu,$$
$$b = 558\text{–}567\ m\mu, \quad a'' = 625\text{–}635\ m\mu,$$
$$c = 547\text{–}555\ m\mu, \quad b' = 552\text{–}563\ m\mu,$$
$$d_1 = 528\text{–}532\ m\mu, \quad d' = 527\text{–}532\ m\mu.$$
$$d_2 = 518\text{–}522\ m\mu,$$

Some bacteria contain several components, whereas others have only one or none at all. The typical yeast cytochrome spectrum consists of four bands with their respective maxima at 604 (a), 565 (b), 550 (c), and 520–530 (d) mμ. Many yeasts, however, show considerable variation, and usually there is general loss of distinction of the cytochrome spectrum when the cells are dried at temperatures above 60°C. [Fink and Lechner (1940)].

Cytochrome c is the most stable component of the cytochrome complex and is the only one which has been extracted and studied *in vitro*. In fact, Theorell and Åkesson (1939) have highly purified the pigment by electrophoresis and have found that it contains approximately 0.43 per cent iron, 3.3 per cent histidine, and 4.7 per cent lysine and has a molecular weight of about 13,000. Theorell has also proposed the following structure for one form of cytochrome c:

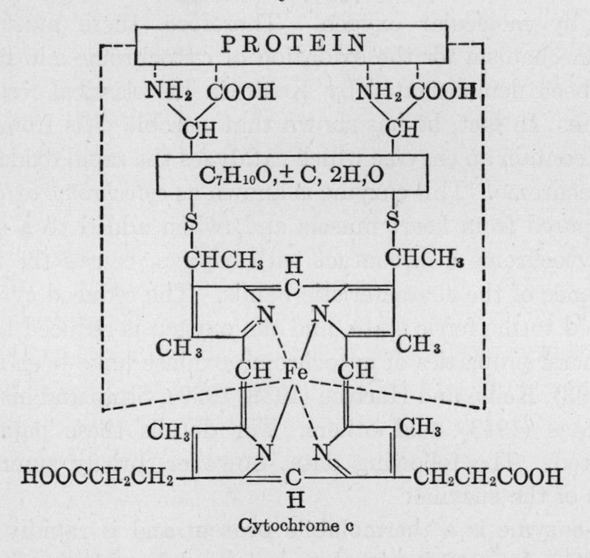

Cytochrome c

Outstanding features of the iron-porphyrin protein structure are the thio- linkages and the peptide linkages between the protein and one or both of the amino and carboxy groups. Although the formula conveys some idea of the graphic structure of cytochrome c, the mode of linkage of the iron and porphyrin to the protein is so obscure at present that no more attention will be given to these subjects. When cytochrome c is reduced by chemical means, such as by hyposulfite or cysteine, the sole chemical change is the reduction of the trivalent iron in the porphyrin to the divalent state. Since there is but one Fe-porphyrin for each molecule of cytochrome c, only one equivalent of hydrogen or one electronic equivalent is involved in the reduction of each molecule. The oxidation of reduced cytochrome by chemical means, such as by H_2O_2 or ferricyanide, converts iron from the ferrous to the ferric state. The protein which is attached to the prosthetic group (Fe-porphyrin) plays no role in the process of oxidation-reduction. However, the peculiarities which distinguish cytochrome c from a large number of closely related pigments are due to the specific protein. Comparatively little is known about the other components of the cytochrome complex, except that they are iron-porphyrin proteins and are very unstable. Most of our information on their properties has been derived from the spectroscopic study of crude preparations [see Sumner and Somers (1943)].

The spectrum bands of reduced cytochrome c persist even when a vigorous stream of oxygen is passed through physiologically neutral solutions. In other words, cytochrome c does not undergo direct oxidation by molecular oxygen. Therefore, there must be some catalytic mechanism for the oxidation of cytochrome c in living cells. This has been demonstrated by Keilin in his classical researches on cytochrome. In fact, he has shown that aerobic cells from a variety of sources contain an enzyme which catalyzes the rapid oxidation of reduced cytochrome. This enzyme is known as *cytochrome oxidase*. It is easily prepared from heart muscle and, when added to a solution of reduced cytochrome c in contact with oxygen, causes the immediate disappearance of the characteristic bands. The reduced cytochrome c is converted to the ferric state, and the oxygen is reduced to water.

The general properties of cytochrome oxidase have been studied by Keilin (1933), Keilin and Hartree (1938, 1939), Stotz and his associates (1938), Haas (1943), and others. For details these papers should be consulted. The following data, however, briefly summarize the properties of the enzyme:

1. The enzyme is a thermolabile protein and is rapidly destroyed above 60°C. Its activity is also destroyed by drying, freezing and thawing, and by treatment with strong alcohol or acetone. Some

progress has been made in highly purifying the enzyme [Haas (1943)].

2. The enzyme specifically catalyzes the oxidation of the ferro cytochrome by molecular oxygen. Hemoglobin and other ferrous porphyrin compounds are not oxidized in the presence of the enzyme. For a long time cytochrome oxidase was attributed the property of catalyzing the oxidation of *p*-phenylenediamine. This error arose from the fact that older preparations of the enzyme contained small amounts of the cytochromes, which can directly oxidize *p*-phenylenediamine by themselves. Preparations of cytochrome oxidase which contain no cytochrome have no influence on the aerobic oxidation of *p*-phenylenediamine. In this respect it should be mentioned that the cytochrome oxidase-cytochrome c system can also catalyze the oxidation of cysteine, catechol, adrenaline, and ascorbic acid.

3. There is a rough parallelism between the respiratory activity of all aerobic cells and the concentration of both cytochrome and cytochrome oxidase. The higher is the concentration of cytochrome and oxidase, the greater is the respiratory activity. This interesting correlation led Keilin to the view that the respiratory process proceeds mainly through the cytochromes and that cytochrome oxidase is an essential catalyst in aerobic events. There are many kinds of evidence which strongly support this view.

4. One of the most striking characteristics of cytochrome oxidase activity is its extraordinary sensitivity to 0.001 *M* concentrations of KCN, H_2S, or NaN_3. The enzymatic activity is also inhibited by CO in the dark; this inhibition is diminished by the action of light. Carbon monoxide inhibition is determined by the ratio of the partial pressure of CO to O_2 in the gas space. The larger the ratio, the greater is the inhibition. The affinity of the enzyme for oxygen is five to nine times as great as that for carbon monoxide, so that it is necessary to have a large excess of CO to obtain effective inhibition.

Apparently very few substances are capable of direct oxidation through the cytochromes, although preliminary processes of oxido-reduction may bring other substances into the system. In other words, reduced cytochrome c does not react directly with oxygen, but, as we have already mentioned, it is oxidized through the enzyme, cytochrome oxidase, with which it seems to be closely associated in the cell. It is a well-known fact that cytochrome and its specific oxidase play a very important role in biological oxidations. In fact, several workers have estimated that about two-thirds of the normal respiration of animal tissue goes through cytochrome. This cytochrome system is often represented schematically by the following series of reactions:

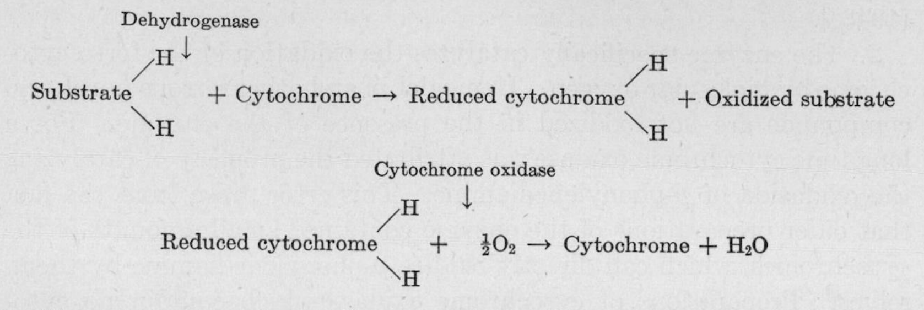

Here the oxygen has to be activated or catalyzed by oxidases (cytochrome oxidase); therefore the over-all process may be represented by the following equation:

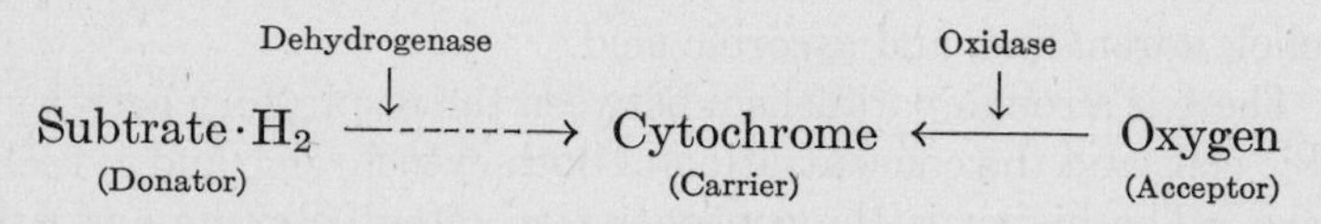

We can see in this simple example that five substances take part in the oxidation: a hydrogen donator (substrate), oxygen (hydrogen acceptor), a specific dehydrogenase to mobilize the hydrogen in the substrate, cytochrome oxidase to activate the oxygen, and cytochrome (carrier). The end product of this reaction is water. Although this example represents a system by which simple oxidation-reduction reactions may take place in the cell, it is by no means complete. Many other *intermediary substances*, which are ephemeral hydrogen acceptors and donators, may come into play as a result of cellular metabolism and complicate the system. Especially is this true in the portion of the above reaction where hydrogen is transported from the substrate to cytochrome.

It has already been mentioned that most, if not all, aerobic bacteria contain the cytochrome components, and it is generally assumed that they are also endowed with cytochrome oxidase, since cytochromes a and c are unable to react directly with oxygen at physiological hydrogen-ion concentrations. Facultative anaerobes possess one or two of the cytochrome pigments and must contain a specific oxidase. The strict anaerobes contain no cytochrome at all and seem to be devoid of cytochrome oxidases also. These points are illustrated with specific examples in Table 13. For further information on this subject the papers by Frei (1935), Farrell (1935), and Edwards and Rettger (1937) and the references listed by these workers should be consulted.

2. Ascorbic Acid (Vitamin C) Oxidase. This enzyme has been studied rather extensively in certain plant and animal tissues but has

TABLE 13

Distribution of Absorption Bands of Reduced Cytochrome, Cytochrome Oxidase, Peroxidase, and Catalase in Bacteria

[Data from Keilin (1933) and Frei, Riedmüller, and Almasy (1934)]

Organism	Cytochrome a	b	c	d	Cytochrome Oxidase	Peroxidase	Catalase
Mycobacterium tuberculosis	+	+	+	+	+	+	+?
Bacillus subtilis	+	+	+	+	+	+	+
Bacillus anthracis	+	+	+	+	+	+	+
Bacillus mesentericus	+	+	+	+	+	+	+
Bacillus mycoides	−	+	−	+			
Azotobacter chroococcum	−	+	+	+			
Azotobacter vinelandii	−	+	+	+			
Acetobacter xylinum	−	−	+	+			
Acetobacter pasteurianum	−	−	+	+			
Sarcina aurantiaca	+	+	−	+			
Sarcina lutea	+	+	+	+	*	*	*
Staphylococcus aureus	+	+	−	+			
Staphylococcus albus	+	+	−	+			
Staphylococcus citreus	+	+	−	+			
Vibrio comma	+	+	+	+			
Pneumococcus, type I	+	+	−	+			
Meningococcus	−	−	+	+			
Gonococcus	−	−	+	+			
Pseudomonas aeruginosa	+	+	+	+	+	+	+
Serratia marcescens	+	+	−	+	−	+	+
Escherichia coli	−	+	−	+	−	+	+
Salmonella paratyphi	+	+	−	+	−	+	+
Salmonella pullorum	+	+	−	+	−	+	+
Proteus vulgaris	+	+	−	+	−	+	+
Shigella dysenteriae	+	+	−	+	−	+	+
Streptococcus lactis	−	−	−	−	−	+	+
Streptococcus pyogenes	−	−	−	−	−	+, −	−
Streptococcus agalactiae	−	−	−	−	−	−	−
Lactobacillus acidophilus	−	−	−	−	*	*	*
Lactobacillus delbrückii	−	−	−	−			
Clostridium perfringens	−	−	−	−	−	−	−
Clostridium tetani	−	−	−	−	−	−	−
Clostridium sporogenes	−	−	−	−	*	*	*
Clostridium putrificum	−	−	−	−			
Clostridium botulinum	−	−	−	−	−	−	−
Clostridium histolyticum	−	−	−	−	−	−	−

* Not tested.

been given little attention by the bacteriologist. Kendall and Chinn (1938), Young and Rettger (1943), and others have reported that certain strains of intestinal bacteria are capable of fermenting ascorbic acid, but nothing is known about the mechanism of the reaction, other than that the decomposition is carried beyond the reversible dehydro stage. Facts are also unavailable to explain why certain bacteria retard the oxidation of ascorbic acid when grown in a medium containing a readily fermentable carbohydrate [Esselen (1939)].

Ascorbic acid oxidase from such plants as squash catalyzes the oxidation of ascorbic acid to dehydroascorbic acid by molecular oxygen, thus:

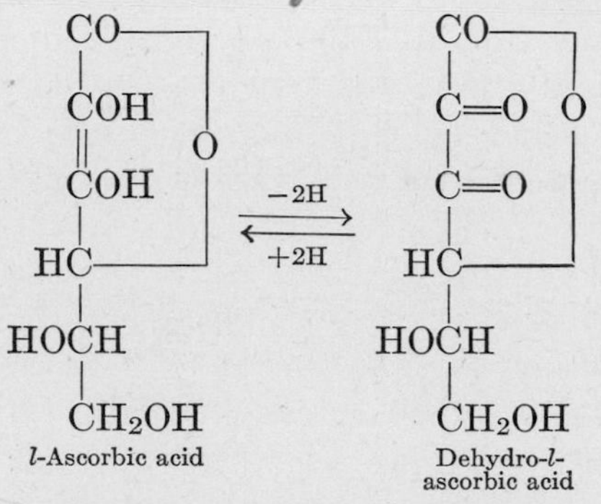

l-Ascorbic acid   Dehydro-*l*-ascorbic acid

The best source of ascorbic acid oxidase is certain varieties of squash. The enzyme exhibits its optimum activity at *p*H 6.0; it is completely inhibited by .001 *M* cyanide but not by H_2S or by CO. Oxygen cannot be replaced by methylene blue or other acceptors. The dehydroascorbic acid can be reduced to ascorbic acid by treatment with H_2S. Several workers [see Powers, Lewis, and Dawson (1944)] have highly purified ascorbic acid oxidase. It is metallo protein, containing about 0.24 per cent copper.

In animal tissues it is thought that ascorbic acid is linked in a coordinated chain of reactions, where it is alternately oxidized to dehydroascorbic acid and reduced to its original form. *In vitro* and *in vivo* experiments by Penney and Zilva (1943) have shown also that dehydroascorbic acid can be converted to 2:3-diketogulonic acid ($HOOC \cdot CO \cdot CO \cdot CHOH \cdot CHOH \cdot CH_2OH$) with comparative ease in both the presence and the absence of oxygen. Thus they have proposed the following scheme of reactions:

$$\text{Ascorbic acid} \rightleftarrows \text{Dehydroascorbic acid} \rightarrow \text{Diketogulonic acid}$$

The significance of this change in metabolism has not been elucidated.

Several mechanisms are known for the oxidation of ascorbic acid in plants, but little is known of the systems which reduce dehydroascorbic acid. Szent-Györgyi has postulated that ascorbic acid plays the same role in plants as does cytochrome in animal tissues, but it seems premature to arrive at any conclusions concerning the role of the vitamin in plants, animals, or bacteria.

3. Polyphenol Oxidase, Monophenol Oxidase (Tyrosinase), and Related Copper-Protein Enzymes. The respiratory pigment of certain arthropods and molluscs is a specific copper-protein compound called hemocyanin. Strictly speaking, there is not one hemocyanin but a group of chemically distinct hemocyanins, which are widely distributed in nature. They are differentiated by their percentage of copper, which varies from 0.17 to 0.38 per cent, depending upon the source, their solubility, their sensitivity to acid, and their crystallizability. Since the hemocyanins (Cu-protein enzymes) have not been studied very extensively in bacteria, they will be only briefly mentioned here.

Copper is found in living organisms as the prosthetic group of *hemocyanin, polyphenol oxidase, laccase, monophenol oxidase* (*tyrosinase*), *hemocuprein, hepatocuprein,* and *ascorbic acid oxidase.* Ascorbic acid oxidase has already been discussed, and the other Cu proteins will now be mentioned briefly.

Hemocyanin may be considered the prototype of the family of Cu proteins in the same sense that hemoglobin is the model of the Fe-porphyrin proteins. The metal is present in hemocyanin in the cuprous form; the function of the respiratory pigment is oxygen transportation. The formation of a compound with molecular oxygen, however, does not involve oxidation of the cuprous hemocyanin to the cupric form. Instead, oxyhemocyanin is a compound that contains loosely bound oxygen, which dissociates at low oxygen tensions, and is not an oxidation product of hemocyanin.

Polyphenol oxidase, laccase, and monophenol oxidase (tyrosinase) are enzymes which catalyze the oxidation of certain benzenoid compounds (see Table 6 for reactions). Polyphenol oxidase and laccase are believed by some workers to undergo a cyclic transformation from the cupric to the cuprous form, and vice versa, in the course of their catalytic activity, but little is known about the changes in monophenol oxidase (tyrosinase). Hemocuprein and hepatocuprein are the only other Cu proteins which have been isolated from vertebrate tissues, and their catalytic function, if any, is still unknown.

Although polyphenol oxidase and laccase are principally plant enzymes, they have been described in the tissues of arthropods and certain molluscs, as well as in various bacteria [Happold (1930)]. There is no evidence of the enzymes in vertebrate tissues. Monophenol oxidase (tyrosinase) has been found to be widely distributed in nature, it has been highly purified by Jensen and Tenenbaum (1943), who found it contains about 0.2 per cent copper. Tyrosinase occurs in some cells and tissues in the form of protyrosinase, which, according to Bodine and his associates, can be converted to tyrosinase by certain synthetic detergents and other agents. A tyrosinase-like enzyme is produced by a few bacteria and higher fungi. Stapp (1923) was unable to demonstrate tyrosinase in a number of bacterial species, but one, *Vibrio tyrosinatica*, was very active against tyrosine. According to Almon and Fred (1933), some of the *Rhizobia* of the bean, alfalfa, and soyabean groups exhibit tyrosinase activity. Skinner (1938) studied the tyrosinase reaction of the actinomyces and came to the conclusion that it was due to tyrosine metabolism.

4. Luciferase. The enzyme luciferase is concerned with bioluminescence, which is actually a chemiluminescence in which some of the energy from the catalytic oxidation of a definite organic compound (luciferin) is emitted as light. In Chapter 3 we discussed the production of light by bacteria; therefore we will only mention here a few properties of the enzyme system believed to be responsible for this phenomenon.

The isolation and purification of the oxidizable compound, luciferin, and the oxidizing enzyme, luciferase, have been successful only in certain animals, such as the ostracod crustacean. The technical details of such procedures have been fully reviewed by Harvey (1941). The exact chemical nature of luciferin is as yet unknown, but it is probably not a proteose or a phospholipide, as has been previously supposed. Several workers believe that it may be one of the polyhydroxybenzenes, many of which are oxidized in two steps and have oxidation-reduction potentials in the same region as that of the luciferin system. Chakravorty and Ballentine (1941), working with highly purified extracts of luciferin, found that it contains a $—COCH_2OH$ side chain, which is oxidatively degraded to $—COOH$ in the luminescent reaction. The luciferin molecule is quite small, since its molecular weight appears to be less than 1,000.

Apparently five reactions in series are involved in luminescence. The steps may be represented as follows [Harvey (1941) and Johnson, van Schouwenburg, and van der Burg (1939)]:

(1) L (Reversibly oxidized luciferin) + $X \cdot H_2$ (Substrate) $\rightleftarrows$ LH_2 (Luciferin) + X

(2) LH_2 + A (Luciferase) $\rightarrow$ $A \cdot LH_2$ (Luciferase-luciferin complex)

(3) $A \cdot LH_2 + \frac{1}{2}O_2 \rightarrow A \cdot LH_2O$

(4) $A \cdot LH_2O \rightarrow$ A′ (Excited luciferase) + L (Oxidized luciferin) + H_2O

(5) $A' \rightarrow A + h\nu$ (A quantum of light)

A logical question is: What is the origin of the oxidized luciferin of equation 1? Although nothing is known of the precursor of the luciferin-oxidized luciferin system, it appears certain that luciferin contains neither sulfur nor halogen, but only carbon, hydrogen, oxygen, and possibly nitrogen.

Luminous bacteria are very convenient material for luminescence studies. However, one disadvantage in using them is that a cell-free luciferin-luciferase reaction cannot be demonstrated, despite many attempts. All procedures which have been used so far to extract the luminous substances from bacteria have failed, and destruction of the cell also destroys its ability to luminesce. Most authorities assume, however, that luciferin and luciferase are present.

Most of the research on luminous bacteria has been centered around the relationship between certain respiratory processes and luminescence and the effect of various physical and chemical agents on the production of light by the organisms. Since the organisms grow well on ordinary bacteriological media, no difficulties are encountered in obtaining starting material. The optimum temperature for light production is 27°C., luminescence decreasing at higher and lower temperatures. The organisms respire and luminesce well between *p*H values of 5.9 and 8.3. Johnson and Harvey (1938) have observed the general respiration of well-washed suspensions of *Achromobacter fischeri* to be practically the same in isotonic sodium phosphate, sea water, and pure 0.5 *M* sodium chloride but diminished in isotonic potassium or magnesium chloride and sucrose and practically abolished in calcium chloride. Luminescence was found to be more sensitive than respiration, since it was almost quenched in calcium or magnesium chloride, greatly affected in potassium chloride, and somewhat affected in sucrose. The oxygen consumption of luminous bacteria is greatly reduced in the presence of cyanide, and the light intensity is also affected, but to a far less degree. Carbon monoxide inhibits respiration but may actually increase the luminescence of *Photobacterium phosphoreum* [van Schouwenburg and van der Burg (1940)]. Azide has been found to have an equally inhibiting effect on both respiration and luminescence of bacteria in a glucose medium, but only in a relatively high concentration (0.01 *M*). Both arsenite and iodoacetate reduce the general respiration and luminescence in small concentrations, but fluoride and pyrophosphate do not inhibit either process, even in high concentrations. Urethane and other similar narcotics possess the ability of greatly affecting the luminescence of bacteria without lowering the oxygen consumption to any great extent. This evidence, as well as other facts, indicates that the oxygen consumed for luminescence is a small percentage of the total respiration.

II. DEHYDROGENASES

A dehydrogenase may be defined as an enzyme which activates or mobilizes the hydrogen of a substrate so that it can pass on to some spontaneously reducible substance. With a few exceptions, such as uricase, the dehydrogenases act in either the presence or the absence of molecular oxygen; this fact aids in distinguishing them from the true oxidases, which have not yet been found to act in the absence of molecular oxygen. It is also quite generally realized that the mobilized hydrogen from a given substrate may be transported over a number of ephemeral intermediate substances before it ultimately combines with a final hydrogen acceptor, such as oxygen.

Like other enzymes, the individual dehydrogenases are named according to the substrate which they attack. However, from a classification standpoint, it is often desirable to group the various dehydrogenases on the basis of the *first carrier* which accepts the hydrogen from the substrate-dehydrogenase complex. This method has been employed by Potter (1939) and others, and we shall use it here (see Table 12). For example, the *aerobic dehydrogenases*, such as xanthine oxidase, *d*-amino acid dehydrogenase, and uricase, transfer the activated hydrogen from the substrate-enzyme complex directly to oxygen and thus reduce oxygen to H_2O_2. Although it is difficult to distinguish the aerobic dehydrogenases from the oxidases, they may be differentiated on the basis that oxidases reduce only molecular oxygen, whereas aerobic dehydrogenases can reduce other substances besides oxygen. It should be kept in mind, however, that this may be only a quantitative difference and that actually there is no sharp line of demarcation between these two groups of enzymes. The so-called *anaerobic dehydrogenases* also activate the hydrogen of the substrate, but instead of molecular oxygen being the first carrier, other substances serve instead, for example, cytochrome, coenzyme I (diphosphopyridine nucleotide, DPN), or coenzyme II (TPN).

Two methods have been extensively used for the study of dehydrogenation respiration. They are: (1) the *Thunberg* dye-reduction technique, in which a nontoxic dye, such as methylene blue, of the proper potential serves as the hydrogen acceptor, and (2) the *Warburg* apparatus, by which the amount of oxygen consumed by a certain volume of bacterial suspension is measured. The reactions, written in a simple manner, are:

$$\text{(1)}\quad \text{Donator-H}_2 + \text{Methylene blue} = \underset{\text{(Oxidized)}}{\text{Donator}} + \underset{\text{(Reduced, colorless)}}{\text{Methylene blue-H}_2}$$

$$\text{(2)}\quad \text{Donator-H}_2 + \text{Oxygen} = \text{Donator} + H_2O$$

The Thunberg technique was first extensively used in bacteriology by Quastel and Whetham (1924, 1925) who employed nonproliferating bacteria ("resting bacteria") as a source of enzymatic material. In the past few years, however, the Warburg apparatus has been used more frequently for respiration studies than has the Thunberg technique.

The number of individual substances which can serve as hydrogen donators for bacteria is very numerous, and even single species, such as *Escherichia coli*, can dehydrogenate a great many substances. Such compounds as the lower members of the fatty acid series, dicarboxylic, hydroxy, and amino acids, polyhydric alcohols, and various sugars have been studied as hydrogen donators for bacteria. This point may be illustrated further by citing the study by Steinbach (1940). Using the Warburg apparatus, he found that the following substances served as hydrogen donators for:

Pseudomonas aeruginosa: glucose, lactate, fumarate.

Pasteurella avicida: glucose, lactate, pyruvate, succinate, fumarate, citrate, alanine, leucine, and asparaginate, but not malonate or glutaminate.

Mycobacterium tuberculosis: lactate, pyruvate, succinate, and glycerophosphate did not serve as donators.

Brucella abortus: glucose, lactate, pyruvate, succinate, fumarate, maleinate, malate, oxaloacetate, citrate, glycerophosphate, acetaldehyde, formaldehyde, and the amino acids alanine, leucine, glutaminate, and asparaginate, but not malonate.

Escherichia coli: lactate, pyruvate, succinate, fumarate, oxaloacetate, citrate, and alanine, but not malonate or leucine.

Salmonella choleraesuis: glucose, succinate, glutaminate, and asparaginate, but not fumarate.

Clostridium septicum: lactate and glutaminate.

Clostridium novyi: lactate and leucine.

Clostridium chauvoei: glucose.

The oxygen uptake by the various species was different and varied also with the nature of the donator. For example, with *Pseudomonas aeruginosa* the oxygen uptake varied from 194 cu. mm. O_2 per hour per milligram dry weight (bacteria alone) to 467 cu. mm. O_2 per hour per milligram dry weight with 3 donators; with *Pasteurella avicida*, from 5 cu. mm. (bacteria alone) to 195 cu. mm. with 9 donators; with *Brucella abortus*, from 3 cu. mm. to 58 cu. mm. with 17 donators; with *Escherichia coli*, from 5 cu. mm. to 147 cu. mm. with 7 donators; with *Salmonella choleraesuis*, from 4 cu. mm. to 100 cu. mm. with 4 donators; with *Clostridium septicum*, from 0.05 cu. mm. to 1.98 cu. mm. with 2 donators; with *Clostridium chauvoei* the uptake was 0.06 cu. mm. with 1 donator; and with *Clostridium novyi*, from 0.38 cu. mm. to 2.8 cu. mm per hour with 2 donators. Although this list of donators is incomplete for some of the organisms, we may draw the conclusions that certain of the aerobic bacteria (*Ps. aeruginosa, P. avicida*) consume more oxygen than others (*E. coli, S. choleraesuis*), and that the anaerobes utilize very little oxygen, as is to be expected, but they consume some. Steinbach also found that the nature of the donator influenced the respiration of the cells. For instance, with *P. avicida, B. abortus,* and *E. coli,* lactate and succinate were the best and second-best donators, respectively, followed by fumarate and then oxaloacetate and citrate.

Many of the substrates which undergo dehydrogenation in the presence of bacteria are likewise acted upon by animal tissues. Probably the best examples are lactate and succinate. On the other hand, such substances as formic acid and hydrogen are apparently attacked only by certain bacteria. The formic dehydrogenase catalyzes the reactions $HCOOH + A \rightarrow AH_2 + CO_2$, where A represents the oxidized form of a suitable hydrogen acceptor [Quastel and Whetham (1925), Stickland (1929), Gale (1939)]; the hydrogenase catalyzes the reaction $H_2 + A \rightarrow AH_2$ and thus effects reductions by converting molecular hydrogen to an active form [Stephenson and Stickland (1931–1933)].

The desmolases of bacteria seem to be more difficult to separate from the cells than the corresponding enzymes of animal and plant tissues. For this reason cell-free extracts have not been extensively studied, except in certain dehydrogenases from *E. coli* and a few other bacteria. Some separation can be accomplished, however, by exposing bacterial cell suspensions to special treatment [Quastel and Wooldridge (1927, 1928), Booth and Green (1938), Wiggert, Silverman, Utter, and Werkman (1940)]. Briefly, the techniques consist of exposing a bacterial suspension or mass to abnormal conditions, such as high-frequency sound waves, alternate freezing and thawing, unfavorable hydrogen-ion concentrations, high concentrations of salt and other chemicals, grinding by special methods, and other techniques which crush or destroy the cells. After such treatments the cellular debris is removed by centrifugation and filtration, and the cell-free extracts are ready for investigation. In this connection the study by Wooldridge and Glass (1937) is very important and interesting. They reported that, although the formic, lactic, and succinic dehydrogenases of *E. coli* are still active in cells no longer viable, the activity of glucose dehydrogenase and amino acid dehydrogenases is greatly reduced in dead cells, and that the amount of dehydrogenase activity per cell is greatest during the phase of logarithmic growth.

Most workers in the past have not used cell-free extracts in their studies of the dehydrogenase activities of bacteria; rather they have subjected the bacteria to different chemicals, such as toluene, benzene, phenol, chloroacetic acid, and permanganate for various intervals of time to determine the effect of these compounds on the dehydrogenases of nonproliferating bacteria [see Bach and Lambert (1937)]. After such treatment the suspension of cells is usually centrifuged and washed, and then a comparison is made of the enzymatic activity of the treated cells and an untreated preparation. Instead of a general destruction of the whole dehydrogenase system taking place under such conditions, what usually happens as the treatment becomes more drastic is that only certain systems drop out or are destroyed, others being left practically unaltered. Also a variation in the type of treatment may result in different sets of mechanisms being lost or retained. These points are well illustrated in Tables 14, 15, and 16, where it will be seen

TABLE 14

REDUCTION TIMES (DEHYDROGENASE ACTIVITY) AFTER EXPOSURE OF *Escherichia coli* TO VARIOUS CHEMICALS

[From Quastel and Wooldridge (1927)]

Substrate (Donator), Concentrations 0.007 *M*	Control, Normal Organisms	Treatment of Cellular Suspension *						
		(a)	(b)	(c)	(d)	(e)	(f)	(g)
	Reduction Time, minutes							
Succinic acid	14.2	34	∞	21.5	∞	69	∞	∞
Lactic acid	7.7	17	54	8.7	25	10	∞	∞
Formic acid	4.0	7.2	14.2	4.7	25.7	9.2	49	∞
Glucose	5.2	9.0	55	∞	∞	∞	∞	∞
Fructose	5.5	10.5	....	∞	∞	∞	∞	∞

* Each vacuum tube contained 2.0 ml. phosphate buffer *p*H 7.4, 1.0 ml. 1/5,000 methylene blue, 1.0 ml. donator, 1.0 ml. bacterial suspension, and 2.0 ml. saline.

(a) 1.0% NaCl, 17 huors, *p*H 7.0.
(b) 1.0% NaCl + 1.0% $NaNO_2$, 17 hours, *p*H 7.0.
(c) Toluene, 5 minutes.
(d) Propyl alcohol, 30 minutes.
(e) Chloroform, 4 hours.
(f) Cyclohexanol, 5 minutes.
(g) Cyclohexanol, not removed

that the exposure of cells of *E. coli* to various chemical agents does not affect the dehydrogenation of all donators to an equal extent when the Thunberg-methylene blue-reduction method is employed. The data in Table 14 show in general that the mechanism causing the activation of hydrogen of the sugars is the most sensitive to chemical treatment and is the first to disappear, followed by the succinic, lactic, and formic acid systems in that order. When other "poisons" are selected, however, they may alter this order of elimination. For example, it will be seen in Table 15 that formic dehydrogenase was the first to disappear (having the longest reduction time) when the cells are treated with $KMnO_4$, KCN, or H_2O_2, whereas the same enzyme was the most resistant to the reagents, such as toluene and propyl alcohol,

TABLE 15

REDUCTION TIMES (DEHYDROGENASE ACTIVITY) AFTER EXPOSURE OF *Escherichia coli* TO VARIOUS CHEMICALS

[From Quastel and Wooldridge (1927)]

Substrate (Donator), Concentrations 0.007 *M*	Control, Normal Organisms	Treatment of Cellular Suspension		
		$KMnO_4$ 0.001%, 1 hour, *p*H 7.4, 37°C.	KCN 0.01%, 1 hour, *p*H 7.4, 37°C.	H_2O_2 5% of 20 vol., 30 minutes, *p*H 7.4, 37°C.
	Reduction Time, minutes			
Succinic acid	13.5	92	49	203
Lactic acid	8	29	28	50
Formic acid	5.5	180	∞	∞
Glucose	8	27.5	15	∞

employed in the preceding experiment (Table 14). The data in Table 16 also show that a concentration of 10^{-4} *N* of silver sulfate has no effect on formic dehydrogenase, but several other enzymes are inhibited. Bach and Lambert (1937) have also studied the effect of a large number of inhibitors on the dehydrogenases of *Staphylococcus aureus*.

The effects of several salts on the dehydrogenase activity of yeast and macerated yeast extract were determined by Hock (1939). He used the methylene blue-reduction technique of Thunberg and found that the cations inhibited the reduction time according to the following order: mercury, copper, gold, thorium, lanthanum, barium, manganese, potassium.

Whether each specific bacterium contains enough separate enzymes to dehydrogenate every substance oxidized by it is a debatable question which will not be discussed here. Some workers [see Kluyver and Donker (1925)] are of the opinion that a general mechanism (affinity for hydrogen) accounts for most dehydrogenation activity, and that it is not necessary to postulate a separate enzyme for the great variety of compounds which a bacterium may be able to decompose. On the

TABLE 16

EFFECT OF SILVER IONS ON SOME ENZYMES OF *Escherichia coli*

[From Yudkin (1937)]

Enzyme	Methylene Blue Reduction Time in the Presence of the Following Concentrations of Ag_2SO_4, minutes			
	0	$N \times 10^{-6}$	$N \times 10^{-5}$	$N \times 10^{-4}$
Glucose dehydrogenase	7.5	7.5	13.5	>120 *
Succinic dehydrogenase	36.0	41.0	75.0	>120 *
Lactic dehydrogenase	10.5	10.0	27.0	>120 *
Formic dehydrogenase	6.5	6.75	6.5	7.0
Hydrogenase	28.0	28.0	37.0	>120 *
	H_2 Evolved per Hour, microliters			
Formic hydrogenlyase	112	105	73	0

* Not reduced in 2 hours. Intervals above this length not used.

other hand, the fact remains that enzymes are fairly specific, and, although several enzymes may contain the same prosthetic group, their activity is governed also by the protein carrier, which is usually different for each enzyme.

A few typical dehydrogenases will now be briefly discussed. Some of the other ones which are listed in Table 12 have not been studied very extensively, if at all, in bacteria and will not be mentioned. For reviews on the subject of the dehydrogenases Chapter 2 by Potter (1939) in the treatise, *Respiratory Enzymes*, the books by Green (1940) and Sumner and Somers (1943), and the reviews by Franke (1940, 1943) should be consulted. All these works contain a great deal of interesting and valuable information from which the author has drawn freely in the preparation of the data in this chapter.

Aerobic Dehydrogenases. 1. XANTHINE OXIDASE (SCHARDINGER'S ALDEHYDE OXIDASE). This enzyme was apparently first studied by Schardinger in 1902, who observed that aldehydes will reduce methylene blue in the presence of milk. In 1922 Hopkins and his associates discovered an enzyme in many animal tissues which oxidized xanthine to uric acid. They called the enzyme xanthine oxidase. For a long time it was assumed that this enzyme was distinct from the Schardinger enzyme. However, the extensive studies by Dixon and his coworkers in Cambridge, England, have shown that xanthine oxidase catalyzes both oxidations [see Booth (1938) and Dixon (1938)]. In fact, it has been found that the enzyme oxidizes some thirty-five nontoxic aromatic and aliphatic aldehydes and nine purines related to xanthine and hypoxanthine. A satisfactory explanation of how one enzyme can catalyze the oxidation of two classes of substances as widely different as aldehydes and purines is not yet available. There is one interesting difference, however, between purine and aldehyde activation. Whereas the maximum rate of oxidation of purines occurs at low concentrations (0.00015 M), the maximum rate with aldehydes takes place at relatively high concentrations (0.06 M). This fact apparently means that the affinity of the enzyme for purines is approximately 400 times greater than for aldehydes.

Xanthine and hypoxanthine are oxidized to uric acid by xanthine oxidase, and oxygen is simultaneously reduced to H_2O_2 (see Table 6):

$$\text{Xanthine} + O_2 \xrightarrow[\text{Oxidase}]{\text{Xanthine}} \text{Uric acid} + H_2O_2$$

The pH optimum for this reaction covers a wide range of from 5.5 to 9.0. The enzyme is irreversibly inactivated by cyanide in the absence of substrate, but uric acid will protect it against this inhibitor. It is not affected by carbon monoxide or toluene. Hydrogen peroxide destroys the enzyme, providing catalase is not present.

Xanthine oxidase (or dehydrogenase) is a flavoprotein enzyme which is quite widely distributed in nature, especially in milk and the livers of certain animals. The purest preparations have been obtained from milk by Ball (1939) and others. It has been reported to be absent in yeasts and apparently has not been studied a great deal in bacteria and other fungi. Barker and Beck (1941) studied the anaerobic decomposition of xanthine, hypoxanthine, and several related purines by *Clostridium acidi-urici*, but the end products were ammonia, carbon dioxide, and acetic acid, rather than uric acid. Therefore, the enzyme systems and intermediate compounds known to be involved in purine breakdown by animal tissues, plants, and probably aerobic microorganisms are evidently not concerned in the dissimilation processes by this anaerobic bacterium. Although the mechanism is obscure, Barker and Beck believe that these dissimilations represent oxidations in which CO_2 acts as the ultimate hydrogen acceptor and is reduced to acetic acid. However, the Schardinger aldehyde enzyme has been observed in several microorganisms, and possibly the failure to demonstrate xanthine oxidase activity can be explained on the grounds that xanthine was not tried as a substrate.

2. *d*-Amino Dehydrogenase (*d*-Amino Oxidase). An enzyme which catalyzes the oxidation of *d*- or unnatural α-amino acids has been isolated from liver and kidney by Krebs. One of the main differences between this enzyme and the *l*-amino acid oxidases is the ease with which it can be extracted from ground tissues; the *l*-amino acid oxidases seem to be more firmly bound to the insoluble particles of the cell. Warburg and his associates, Negelein and Brömel (1939), and others have highly purified the specific protein of *d*-amino acid oxidase. It is a flavoprotein with a molecular weight of approximately 65,000, and, although it appears to be on the borderline between the oxidases and aerobic dehydrogenases, it functions as a true dehydrogenase. The amino acids are thought to be oxidized first to the corresponding unsaturated imino acids, thus:

$$\underset{\displaystyle NH_2}{\underset{|}{R\cdot CH\cdot COOH}} + \text{Acceptor} \rightarrow \underset{\displaystyle NH}{\underset{\|}{R\cdot C\cdot COOH}} + \text{Acceptor}\cdot 2H$$

The amino acid oxidase apparently functions in this reaction, since the hydrolysis of the imino acid to the keto acid and ammonia is thought to be an uncatalyzed reaction:

$$\underset{\displaystyle NH}{\underset{\|}{R\cdot C\cdot COOH}} + H_2O \rightarrow \underset{\displaystyle O}{\underset{\|}{R\cdot C\cdot COOH}} + NH_3$$

Certain bacteria presumably oxidize the unnatural amino acids, although their enzyme has not been studied in cell-free extracts. Bernheim, Bernheim, and Webster (1935), and Webster and Bernheim

(1936) studied the oxidation of thirteen amino acids by "resting" *Proteus vulgaris* and *Pseudomonas aeruginosa*. In *P. vulgaris* only the natural optical isomers were oxidized, except in alanine and serine, where both isomers were attacked. *Ps. aeruginosa* also oxidized the *d*-forms of alanine, serine, tyrosine, and proline.

The amino acids present in cells are usually all of the levo configuration. Thus, it is not known why certain cells are endowed with a specific enzyme of this type, unless its role is to destroy dextro amino acids which may be formed as a result of the racemization of the natural amino acids [Sumner and Somers (1943)]. It is also of interest to note that several workers believe that certain tumors are rich in *d*-amino acids and low in *d*-amino acid oxidase.

3. Amine Dehydrogenase (Tyramine Oxidase, Histaminase, etc.). The monoamine oxidases, such as tyramine oxidase, specifically catalyze the oxidation of primary (tyramine), secondary (adrenaline), and tertiary (hordenine) amines, according to the general equation:

$$RCH_2NH_2 + H_2O + O_2 \rightarrow RCHO + NH_3 + H_2O_2$$

Since amino acids are not attacked, these enzymes can be differentiated from the amino acid dehydrogenases. Certain diamine oxidases, such as histaminase, are also known. To be attacked by a diamine oxidase a substrate must contain two amine groups.

Certain bacteria can utilize amines as a source of nitrogen and apparently contain enzymes which catalyze their oxidation. However, specific enzyme studies are not available on the oxidation of amines by bacteria.

4. Uricase. In the presence of oxygen, uricase converts uric acid to allantoin, as is shown in Table 6. The enzyme has been obtained from animal tissues in a highly purified state; it is a metalloprotein containing 0.09 per cent zinc, 0.2 per cent iron, and 14.4 per cent nitrogen [Davidson (1942)].

Several bacteria and molds are known which are capable of oxidizing uric acid [see Morris and Ecker (1924), Barker and Beck (1941, 1942)], and the utilization of uric acid as a source of nitrogen by *Aerobacter aerogenes* helps to differentiate it from *Escherichia coli* and other closely related species [see Koser (1918), Mitchell and Levine (1938)]. Specific enzyme preparations from microorganisms, however, have not been studied.

Anaerobic Dehydrogenases. Class A. Cytochrome-Linked Dehydrogenases. *1. Succinic Dehydrogenase.* The succinic enzyme is very widespread in nature. It has been demonstrated in almost every tissue in the animal body and has also been found in many microorganisms and higher plants. The enzyme converts succinic acid into fumaric acid according to the equation given in Table 6. Molecular oxygen, methylene blue, or similar hydrogen acceptors are required for its action. In the presence of oxygen the enzyme functions by way of the cytochrome-cytochrome oxidase system, thus:

$$\underset{\uparrow \atop \boxed{\text{Dehydrogenase}}}{\text{Succinate}} + 2\ \text{Cytochrome} \rightarrow \text{Fumarate} + 2\ \text{Reduced cytochrome}$$

$$2\ \text{Reduced cytochrome} + \tfrac{1}{2}O_2 \xrightarrow{\text{Oxidase}} 2\ \text{Cytochrome} + H_2O$$

or in the presence of methylene blue and no cytochrome, as:

$$\underset{\uparrow \atop \boxed{\text{Dehydrogenase}}}{\text{Succinate}} + \text{Methylene blue} \rightarrow \text{Fumarate} + \underset{\text{(Methylene white)}}{\text{Leuco methylene blue}}$$

$$\text{Leuco methylene blue} + O_2 \rightarrow \text{Methylene blue} + H_2O_2$$

Although it has been generally accepted that succinodehydrogenase reacts directly with the cytochrome system, experiments by Hopkins, Lutwak-Mann, and Morgan (1939), Straub (1942), and others indicate that there may be some intermediate substance or enzyme system which functions between them. This unknown intermediate is destroyed by exposure to acid, alcohol, or pancreatin and cannot be replaced by any known coenzyme. Straub calls this unknown intermediate carrier the SC-factor.

Succinodehydrogenase is slightly inhibited by certain concentrations of fumaric, malic, and other acids which have a similar structure. Malonic acid causes strong inhibition, but the inhibition is neutralized by the presence of fumarate. Malonate inhibits succinic oxidation because, although it itself is not oxidized, it is more readily adsorbed on the dehydrogenase than is succinate [Elliott (1941)]. Selenite and arsenite produce almost complete inhibition, and fluoride is partially toxic at very high concentrations, but cyanide and pyrophosphate have little or no toxic action.

It has been postulated by several workers that the energy liberated by succinodehydrogenase is utilized by various cells to synthesize cellular components or is used for the synthesis of energy-rich phosphate bonds.

Succinic acid and other C_4-dicarboxylic acids seem to play a very important role in the respiration of animal tissues and may function in a similar manner in bacteria [see review by Krebs (1941)]. Szent-Györgyi and associates [see Laki, Straub, and Szent-Györgyi (1937)] have postulated an interesting theory to explain the role of such acids in respiratory processes. They observed that the oxygen uptake during glycolysis of minced breast muscle of pigeon gradually decreased with time under ordinary conditions. However, when a few micrograms of succinate, fumarate, malate, or oxaloacetate were added to the system,

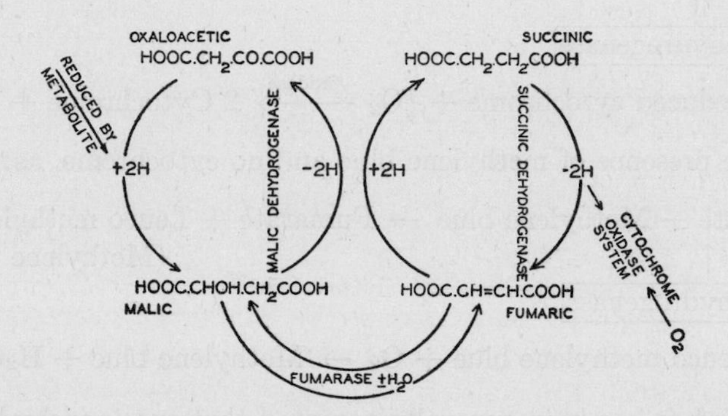

FIG. 6. The Szent-Györgyi Scheme for the Catalytic Activity of the C_4-Dicarboxylic Acids.

the rate of decline in respiration was stabilized. From this observation they concluded that the dicarboxylic acids acted as respiratory catalysts rather than as metabolites. To explain this catalytic activity of the C_4-dicarboxylic acids they constructed the scheme (C_4-dicarboxylic acid cycle) shown in Fig. 6, which needs but little explanation. Oxaloacetate, which may arise from the carboxylation of pyruvic acid ($CH_3 \cdot CO \cdot COOH + CO_2 \rightarrow HOOC \cdot CH_2 \cdot CO \cdot COOH$) or by other mechanisms, is reduced to malate in cooperation with the oxidation of some other intermediate cellular metabolite, such as triosephosphate. Part of the malate is then converted to fumarate by the enzyme fumarase until an equilibrium is established. In the presence of appropriate enzymes, fumarate oxidizes some of the malate to oxaloacetate and in so doing is reduced to succinate. Coenzyme I presumably mediates these hydrogen transfers. Succinodehydrogenase then cooperates with the cytochrome oxidase-oxygen system to reoxidize the succinate to fumarate. The cycle may then be repeated again and again. According to this scheme, the C_4-dicarboxylic acids act in a catalytic capacity as intermediators between metabolites, on the one hand, and the cytochrome-oxygen system, on the other. Also with such a cycle it is possible for certain metabolites to be indirectly oxidized by the cytochrome system, although they themselves are unable to react directly with the cytochromes. For more details of the mechanism of the Szent-Györgyi–C_4-dicarboxylic acid cycle Green (1940) and Elliott (1941) should be consulted.

It has already been stated that succinic acid dehydrogenase has been demonstrated in many bacteria. So, too, have the dehydrogenases of the other C_4-dicarboxylic acids [see review by Krebs (1941)]. The most complete studies of this subject are those by Quastel and Whetham (1924), Quastel, Stephenson, and Whetham (1925), Quastel and Wooldridge (1927, 1928), and Krebs (1937); their papers should be consulted for many interesting details. For example, they have shown that resting cells of *Escherichia coli* convert succinic acid to fumaric acid in the presence of methylene blue; by starting with leuco methylene blue and fumaric acid, the reaction is reversed. When the organism is grown anaerobically with glycerol or lactate plus fumarate in the medium, the fumarate serves as a hydrogen acceptor for the oxidation of the substrates. Krebs also presented evidence to show that in *E. coli* fumarate catalyzes the aerobic oxidation of glucose, malate, lactate, acetate, glycerol, glyceraldehyde, butyrate, pyruvate, acetoacetate, *l*-(+)-glutamate, and molecular hydrogen. The oxidation of lactate, malate, and formate can take place independently of fumarate, but most of the aerobic oxidation of the other substances seems to be mediated by fumarate-succinate. Oxaloacetate also appears to be a hydrogen carrier in *E. coli* and other bacteria.

Sykes (1939) has studied the influence of certain germicides on the succinodehydrogenase of *E. coli.* His results show that the concentrations of certain phenolic compounds required to inhibit completely the succinodehydrogenase are only slightly higher than the concentrations which are lethal for the organism.

2. α-Glycerophosphate Dehydrogenase. This enzyme was first observed by Meyerhof in 1919, but it was not until 1936 that Green made a systematic study of its properties [see Green (1940)]. Although the enzyme has been demonstrated in yeast, most of the studies have been concerned with preparations from animal tissues, skeletal muscle being one of the best sources of the enzyme. Animal tissues apparently contain two separate enzymes which are capable of catalyzing the oxidation of α-glycerophosphate; one is a typical pyridinoprotein which will be described later with triosephosphoric acid dehydrogenase; the other is independent of the pyridine nucleotides and functions through the cytochromes. This second enzyme catalyzes the oxidation of *l*-(+)-α-glycerophosphate ($CH_2OH \cdot CHOH \cdot CH_2OPO_3H_2$) to glyceraldehyde phosphate ($OHC \cdot CHOH \cdot CH_2OPO_3H_2$) by way of cytochrome, thus:

α-Glycerophosphate + 2 Cytochrome →
↑
Dehydrogenase

Glyceraldehyde phosphate + 2 Reduced cytochrome

4 Reduced cytochrome + O_2 → 4 Cytochrome + $2H_2O$
↑

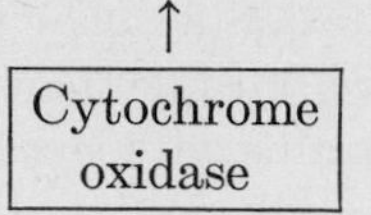

The product (glyceraldehyde phosphate) of this reaction is very unstable and usually breaks down to phosphoric acid and other compounds, such as methylglyoxal. Other closely related compounds, such as *d*-(+)-glycerophosphate, glycerol, and β-glycerophosphate, are not attacked. Besides cytochrome, other hydrogen acceptors, such as methylene blue and pyocyanin (from *Pseudomonas aeruginosa*), can cooperate with the enzyme to produce the reaction. Flavin, flavoproteins, ascorbic acid, and glutathione cannot function in this capacity.

3. Lactic Dehydrogenase (*Yeast and Bacteria*). An enzyme has been demonstrated in yeast [see Green (1940)] and in several bacteria, including the gonococcus [Barron and Hastings (1933)], which catalyzes the oxidation of lactic acid and α-hydroxybutyric acids to the corresponding keto acids. The enzymes apparently function in cooperation with the cytochromes, but the pyridine coenzymes may also be involved. Although Barron and Hastings did not definitely identify their oxygen-activation system with the cytochrome-cytochrome oxidase system, they spoke of it as a hemin compound and described the oxidation of the active substrate (lactate) in terms of electronic exchange. In other words, the reducing system (lactate) becomes oxidized while the oxidizing system (hemin compound) is being reduced. Molecular oxygen then reoxidizes the ferrous hemin to ferric hemin, and the hemin is again ready to act as an oxidizing agent. The chain of reactions may be expressed as follows:

(1) $2CH_3 \cdot CHOH \cdot COO^- + 4Fe^{+++} \rightleftarrows$
Lactate
$2CH_3 \cdot CO \cdot COO^- + 4Fe^{++} + 4H^+$
Pyruvate

(2) $4Fe^{++} + 2O_2 \rightleftarrows 4Fe^{+++} + 4O^-$

(3) $4H^+ + 4O^- \rightarrow 2H_2O_2$

(4) $2H_2O_2 + \text{Catalase} \rightarrow 2H_2O + O_2$

The iron in the above equations may be in the form of the hemin cytochrome.

Lactic acid dehydrogenase is one of the few bacterial enzymes which has been separated from the cell. It is prepared by allowing washed suspensions of *E. coli* to autolyze in the presence of 1 per cent fluoride for several days. The cellular debris is then removed by filtering through kieselguhr, and the enzyme is precipitated by saturation with ammonium sulfate and redissolved with considerable loss of activity [Stephenson (1928)].

It is impossible at this time to state whether the lactic dehydrogenase of microorganisms is the same as that of muscle, which is known to be linked through coenzyme I. Little is known concerning this detail in microbial enzymes.

4. Formic Dehydrogenase (*E. coli*). Most of our information concerning formic dehydrogenase is due to Gale (1939), who has prepared and studied cell-free extracts from *E. coli*. The enzyme catalyzes the oxidation of formate to carbon dioxide:

$$HCOOH + \text{Acceptor} \rightarrow CO_2 + \text{Reduced acceptor}$$

Purified preparations of the enzyme do not catalyze the oxidation of formate by molecular oxygen, except when an added carrier, such as methylene blue, is present. However, crude preparations catalyze the oxidation of formate by molecular oxygen in the absence of an added carrier. Since the crude preparations contain both cytochrome b and cytochrome oxidase, it is believed that they account for the reaction with oxygen in the absence of an added carrier. During the process of purification the oxidase-cytochrome b system is destroyed, and this fact accounts for the need of an added carrier when purified preparations of the enzyme are employed.

A formic dehydrogenase has also been isolated from dried peas, but it differs from the enzyme just described in that it requires coenzyme I rather than cytochrome.

Class B. Coenzyme I-Linked Dehydrogenases. *1 and 2. Lactic and Malic Dehydrogenases.* The lactic enzyme is very widely distributed in animal tissues, and it is not definitely known whether this enzyme is identical with the one discussed under cytochrome-linked dehydrogenases. Both catalyze the same general reaction, but they differ in that this enzyme functions by way of coenzyme I:

$$\text{Lactate} + \text{Coenzyme I} \rightleftarrows \text{Pyruvate} + \text{Reduced coenzyme I}$$

The enzyme catalyzes the oxidation of *l*-(+)-lactate to pyruvate. α-Hydroxybutyrate is also attacked, but much more slowly than is lactate. Lactamide, *d*-(−)-lactate, tartronate, serine, malonate, glycerate, and citrate will not serve as substrates.

The malic dehydrogenase, which catalyzes the oxidation of malic acid ($HOOC \cdot CHOH \cdot CH_2 \cdot COOH$) to oxaloacetic acid ($HOOC \cdot CO \cdot CH_2 \cdot COOH$), is very similar in its properties to the lactic dehydrogenase. It too requires coenzyme I for its activity:

$$\text{Malate} + \text{Coenzyme I} \rightleftarrows \text{Oxaloacetate} + \text{Reduced coenzyme I}$$

The malic enzyme has been demonstrated in muscle extracts and yeasts. It is undoubtedly present in many bacteria, such as *E. coli* [Gale and Stephenson (1939)] and *Aerobacter aerogenes* [Barker (1936)]. The fermentation of malic acid by *A. aerogenes* gives rise to essentially the same products as are formed by this organism from glucose, that is, formic, acetic, and succinic acids and carbon dioxide. In all probability the course of the reaction is by way of oxaloacetic acid, which is then decarboxylated to yield pyruvic acid ($CH_3COCOOH$).

3. β-Hydroxybutyric Dehydrogenase. This enzyme, like the lactic and malic dehydrogenases, functions by way of coenzyme I. The enzyme has been studied quite extensively by Green and his associates and others [see Green (1940)], who have isolated it principally from heart muscle. It is probably present in microorganisms, although no systematic studies have appeared in the literature. The enzyme catalyzes the oxidation of β-hydroxybutyric acid ($CH_3 \cdot CHOH \cdot CH_2 \cdot COOH$) or its salts to acetoacetic acid ($CH_3 \cdot CO \cdot CH_2 \cdot COOH$) by way of the prosthetic group, coenzyme I, thus:

$$\beta\text{-Hydroxybutyrate} + \text{Coenzyme I} \rightleftarrows \text{Acetoacetate} + \text{Reduced coenzyme I}$$

In nature this oxidation reaction may cooperate through coenzyme I with a simultaneous reduction, such as the reduction of aldehyde to alcohol:

$$\beta\text{-Hydroxybutyrate} + \text{Coenzyme I} \xrightarrow{\text{Enzyme}} \text{Acetoacetate} + \text{Reduced coenzyme I}$$

$$\text{Reduced coenzyme I} + \text{Aldehyde} \xrightarrow{\text{Enzyme}} \text{Alcohol} + \text{Coenzyme I}$$

or the reduction of other substances (oxaloacetate or pyruvate):

$$\beta\text{-Hydroxybutyrate} + \left\{\begin{array}{c}\text{Oxaloacetate}\\ \text{or}\\ \text{Pyruvate}\end{array}\right. \xrightarrow[\text{Enzymes}]{\text{Coenzyme}} \text{Acetoacetate} + \left\{\begin{array}{c}\text{Malate}\\ \text{or}\\ \text{Lactate}\end{array}\right.$$

Such reactions are known as coenzyme I-linked, and the butyrate is spoken of as the reducing half and the other systems as the oxidizing half. Since the acetoacetic acid formed in the above reactions is relatively unstable, it may decompose spontaneously, yielding acetone and carbon dioxide:

$$CH_3 \cdot CO \cdot CH_2 \cdot COOH \rightarrow CH_3 \cdot CO \cdot CH_3 + CO_2$$

However, Davies (1943) has shown in *Clostridium acetobutylicum* that this reaction is catalyzed by a specific decarboxylase.

4. Glucose Dehydrogenase. Glucose dehydrogenase from animal tissues catalyzes the oxidation of *d*-glucose, $CH_2OH(CHOH)_4CHO$, to gluconic acid, $CH_2OH(CHOH)_4COOH$, with the cooperation of coenzyme I (DPN) or coenzyme II (TPN). It seems to be one of the few enzymes which can function in the presence of either coenzyme I or coenzyme II. Gluconic acid is the only breakdown product which has been observed, and *d*-glucose is the only sugar that will serve as a substrate. This enzyme was first isolated and studied by Harrison in 1931, who used acetone-dried liver as a source for the enzyme. The literature on this subject is fully reviewed by Potter (1939) and Green (1940).

A few bacteria are known which can produce gluconic acid from glucose, but cell-free extracts have not been employed. For example, Lockwood, Tabenkin, and Ward (1941) studied the production of gluconic acid and 2-ketogluconic acid from glucose by species of the genera *Pseudomonas* and *Phytomonas*. *Pseudomonas ovalis* produced only gluconic acid from glucose, converting approximately 92 per cent of the fermented sugar to gluconic acid. Four species of the genus *Phytomonas* also produced 40 to 80 per cent gluconic acid from glucose. Several molds also ferment glucose to gluconic acid, but the specific enzyme responsible has not been isolated [see Porges, Clark, and Aronovsky (1941)].

5. Alcohol Dehydrogenase. This enzyme has been isolated from liver and yeast, although it is doubtful if the enzymes are identical, since preparations from liver are not inhibited by .01 *M* iodoacetic acid, whereas those from yeast are inhibited by .001 *M* iodoacetic acid.

Certain bacteria undoubtedly possess an enzyme with similar properties, but little or no information is available on this point.

Liver and yeast alcohol dehydrogenases catalyze the oxidation of simple primary or secondary aliphatic alcohols to their corresponding aldehydes or ketones:

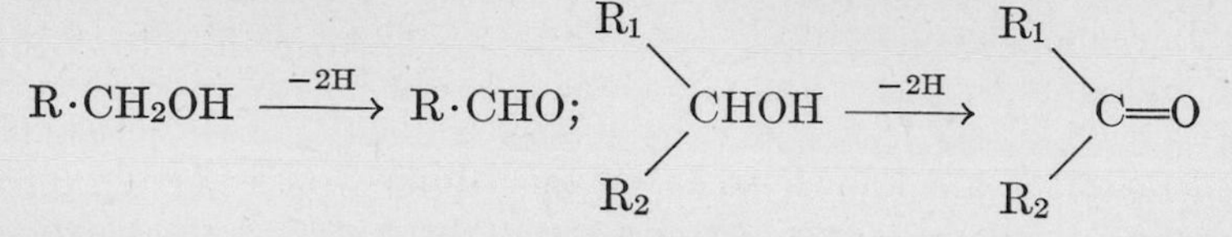

Coenzyme I presumably mediates the hydrogen transfers, although other components may also function in the complete system. If ethyl alcohol and isopropyl alcohol were substituted in the foregoing examples, acetaldehyde and acetone, respectively, would be the end products. Physiologically the enzyme catalyzes both the aerobic oxidation of alcohol and the anaerobic reduction of acetaldehyde. Apparently sugars, hydroxy acids, and polyhydroxy alcohols will not serve as substrates.

6. Aldehyde Mutase. For a long time it has been recognized that an alcohol dehydrogenase and an aldehyde dehydrogenase (Schardinger enzyme, xanthine oxidase) exist which will oxidize alcohols to aldehydes, and aldehydes to acids respectively. Now to complicate the picture further another enzyme, aldehyde mutase, has been found in animal tissues which dismutes aldehydes to acids and alcohols, providing coenzyme I is present. It will be recalled that a mutase catalyzes the dismutation of a substance, that is, an oxidation-reduction between two molecules of the substrate, whereby one is oxidized and the other reduced, thus:

$$2CH_3CHO + H_2O \rightarrow CH_3CH_2OH + CH_3COOH$$

The dismutation of aldehyde by its mutase takes place in two steps by cooperation with coenzyme I:

$$\text{Aldehyde} + \text{Coenzyme I} \rightarrow \text{Acetate} + \text{Reduced coenzyme I}$$

$$\text{Reduced coenzyme I} + \text{Aldehyde} \rightarrow \text{Alcohol} + \text{Coenzyme I}$$

The evidence indicates that aldehyde mutase is distinct from alcohol dehydrogenase and aldehyde dehydrogenase [Dixon (1938)]. Actually, however, the enzyme is equivalent to an alcohol and aldehyde enzyme combined. Acetaldehyde, propionaldehyde, and butyraldehyde are most rapidly attacked by the aldehyde mutase; the higher members of the series and aromatic aldehydes (benzaldehyde) are dismuted very slowly, if at all.

The aldehyde mutase probably exists in bacteria and other microorganisms, but it has not been studied systematically in cell-free extracts from organisms other than yeast [von Euler and Brunius (1928)].

7 and 8. Triose phosphate and Dihydroxyacetone Phosphate Dehydrogenases. These enzymes have been studied principally in connection with muscle glycolysis and yeast fermentation. However, they are also undoubtedly present in certain bacteria, such as *E. coli* [Still (1940, 1941)]. The triose phosphate enzyme catalyzes the oxidation of 3-phosphoglyceraldehyde ($OHC \cdot CHOH \cdot CH_2OPO_3H_2$) to 1:3-diphosphoglycerate ($H_2O_3POCO \cdot CHOH \cdot CH_2OPO_3H_2$):

$$\text{3-Phosphoglyceraldehyde} + H_3PO_4 + \text{Coenzyme I} \rightleftarrows \text{1:3-diphosphoglycerate} + \text{Reduced coenzyme I}$$

The enzyme probably functions in certain coupled oxidation-reduction reactions in intermediate cellular metabolism.

Dihydroxyacetone phosphate dehydrogenase may function in several reactions of importance in intermediary metabolism. For instance, it may act as an isomerase and catalyze the conversion:

$$\underset{\text{Dihydroxyacetone phosphate}}{HOCH_2 \cdot CO \cdot CH_2OPO_3H_2} \rightleftarrows \underset{\text{3-Phosphoglyceraldehyde}}{OHC \cdot CHOH \cdot CH_2OPO_3H_2}$$

For further details about these enzymes Green (1940) and Sumner and Somers (1943) should be consulted.

9. l-(+)-Glutamic Dehydrogenase. The oxidation of natural glutamic acid by animal tissue extracts in cooperation with coenzyme I or II has been known for several years. It is also known that certain bacteria can reductively deaminate and oxidize glutamic acid, but in most cases the end products have not been determined (see pp. 863 to 864 on the decomposition of amino acids by bacteria). Furthermore, in bacteria, cell-free extracts have not been employed, and it has not been shown that a coenzyme functions in the process. The glutamic enzyme of yeast is specific for coenzyme II, and that from higher plants is specific for coenzyme I [Green (1940)].

The glutamic acid dehydrogenase from animal sources oxidizes glutamic acid to α-ketoglutaric acid and ammonia. Apparently the imino acid is an intermediate, and it spontaneously hydrolyzes into the end products:

$$\underset{\text{Glutamic acid}}{HOOC \cdot (CH_2)_2 \cdot CHNH_2 \cdot COOH} + \text{Coenzyme I} \rightarrow HOOC.(CH_2)_2 \cdot C{:}NH \cdot COOH + \text{Reduced coenzyme I}$$

$$\underset{\alpha\text{-Iminoglutaric acid}}{HOOC \cdot (CH_2)_2 \cdot C{:}NH \cdot COOH} + H_2O \rightarrow \underset{\alpha\text{-Ketoglutaric acid}}{HOOC \cdot (CH_2)_2 \cdot CO \cdot COOH} + NH_3$$

The above reactions are also known to be reversible; that is, by starting with a mixture of α-ketoglutaric acid, NH_3, and reduced coenzyme I, a synthesis of glutamic acid is effected. Since in biological systems α-ketoglutaric acid may arise by other mechanisms (see isocitric acid dehydrogenase), it seems probable that the reductive amination of α-ketoglutaric acid to form glutamic acid may account for the synthesis of some of the amino acids in the cell.

Class C. Coenzyme II-Linked Dehydrogenases. At least four enzymes are known which catalyze the oxidation of their substrates in cooperation with coenzyme II (TPN). The better known are the hexose monophosphate, phosphogluconate, isocitrate, and glutamic acid enzymes. The glutamic acid enzyme functions with either coenzyme I or coenzyme II. It has already been discussed. According to Green (1940), very little is known concerning the role of coenzyme II systems in cellular respiration. With the exception of the oxidation of glutamic acid the coenzyme II systems have not been reversed; that is, the reduced coenzyme does not react with the oxidized substrate.

1. Hexose Monophosphate Dehydrogenase. This enzyme was first demonstrated in red blood cells and yeast by Warburg and Christian in 1931–1932. Since that time it has been studied by several other workers, especially by Negelein and Gerischer (1936), who highly purified the yeast enzyme by precipitation with 70 per cent saturation of $(NH_4)_2SO_4$, followed by dialysis and precipitation with 10 per cent alcohol at *p*H 4.8 and 0°C. The distribution of the hexose monophosphate enzyme in bacteria is not known, although it undoubtedly exists in many organisms. The enzyme from both red blood cells and yeast catalyzes the oxidation of glucose-6-phosphate, $H_2O_3POCH_2$-$(CHOH)_4CHO$, to 6-phosphogluconate, $H_2O_3POCH_2(CHOH)_4COOH$. In crude enzyme preparations the phosphogluconate may be further oxidized. In highly purified preparations, however, only the hexose monophosphate is oxidized, indicating that another enzyme is responsible for the activation of the phosphogluconate.

2. Isocitric Acid Dehydrogenase. Citric acid is widely distributed in common foods and is consistently present in small amounts in animal tissues and excreta. Various workers have shown that, when citrate is administered orally in large amounts, only a small amount is recovered in the excreta (urine). Therefore it is clear that citrate can be metabolized. It is interesting to note, however, that, when the C_4-dicarboxylic acids, pyruvate, and a few other compounds are fed to experimental animals and human beings, a large amount of citrate and α-ketoglutarate occurs in the urine.

Even though it has been known for some time that mammalian and other tissues can oxidize citrate rapidly, it has only been comparatively recently that the main course of the oxidation has been studied. In fact, it was not until 1937–1938, when Martius and Knoop published their studies, that the problem assumed real importance. They postulated that the oxidation of citric acid or its salts occurs as follows:

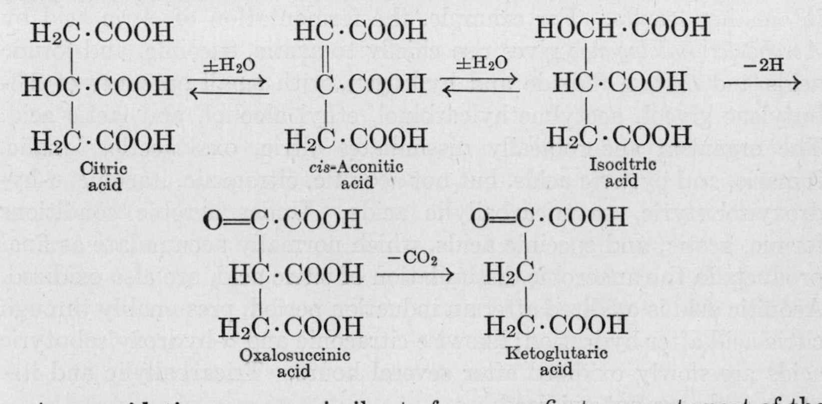

A nonoxidative enzyme similar to fumarase first converts part of the citrate to *cis*-aconitate and isocitrate until an equilibrium is established, the equilibrium values of the concentrations of the three reactants being 80, 4, and 16 per cent, respectively, at *p*H 7.0. The isocitrate is then irreversibly dehydrogenated by an enzyme which is now known as isocitric acid dehydrogenase. This dehydrogenation is mediated principally by coenzyme II (TPN), although coenzyme I also seems to function in a very much weaker capacity. The first oxidation product is thought to be oxalosuccinate, which breaks down spontaneously with the liberation of CO_2 to give α-ketoglutarate. In the presence of other enzymes the α-ketoglutarate can be oxidized and decarboxylated to give succinate ($HOOC \cdot CH_2 \cdot CH_2 \cdot COOH$). Another interesting point in connection with the oxidation of isocitrate has been observed by Adler, von Euler, Günther, and Plass (1939). They have shown that the end product of the citrate oxidation may be synthesized to glutamic acid by the appropriate enzyme and NH_3 in cooperation with coenzyme II and certain salts (Mg^{++}, Mn^{++}):

$$\text{Isocitrate} + \text{Coenzyme II} \rightarrow \alpha\text{-Ketoglutarate} + \text{Reduced coenzyme II} + CO_2$$

$$\alpha\text{-Ketoglutarate} + NH_3 \rightarrow \alpha\text{-Iminoglutarate}$$

$$\alpha\text{-Iminoglutarate} + \text{Reduced coenzyme II} \rightarrow \text{Glutamate} + \text{Coenzyme II}$$

This type of reaction may account for the synthesis of some of the amino acids in the cell.

It is not known definitely whether the oxidation of citrate by bacterial enzymes follows the general scheme just discussed. Brewer and Werkman (1939, 1940) have studied the aerobic and anaerobic dissimilation of citric acid by coliform bacteria and have reported some interesting results. For example, the fermentation of citric acid by *Aerobacter indologenes* gives rise chiefly to acetic, succinic, and formic acids and carbon dioxide and hydrogen, with small amounts of 2,3-butylene glycol, acetylmethylcarbinol, ethyl alcohol, and lactic acid. The organism anaerobically dissimilates citric, oxaloacetic, *l*-malic, fumaric, and pyruvic acids, but not aconitic, citraconic, itaconic, α-hydroxyisobutyric, or tricarballylic acids. Under aerobic conditions formic, acetic, and succinic acids, which normally accumulate as final products in the anaerobic dissimilation of citric acid, are also oxidized. Aconitic acid is oxidized after an induction period, presumably through citric acid after hydration; likewise citraconic and α-hydroxyisobutyric acids are slowly oxidized after several hours. Tricarballylic and itaconic acids are not oxidized.

Passing mention should be made of the *Krebs citric acid cycle*, since several workers believe that this scheme outlines the principal mechanism of the oxidative breakdown of carbohydrate in muscle and related tissues. The cycle was first proposed in 1937 by Krebs and his associates [see the paper by Krebs and Eggleston (1940) for references to most of their work], who found that added citrate (or isocitrate) behaved similarly to the C_4-dicarboxylic acids in that it catalytically promoted the respiration of pigeon muscle suspension, especially if glycogen, hexose diphosphate, or α-glycerophosphate were also present. Since citrate promoted respiration catalytically, that is, caused a greater O_2 uptake than its own oxidation could account for, Krebs and his associates believed that citrate was oxidized and regenerated. When arsenite or malonate was added, they found that citrate disappeared. Arsenite inhibits the oxidation of α-keto acids, and in its presence α-ketoglutarate accumulated in the expected amount. With malonate to inhibit succinate oxidation the expected amount of succinate was found. Finally, on incubating oxaloacetate with minced muscle anaerobically, Krebs and his associates found a synthesis of citrate. The two additional C atoms were presumed to have come from carbohydrate derivatives. Though the synthesis involved oxidation, anaerobic conditions were necessary to prevent further oxidation of the citrate; the oxidation was believed to take place at the expense of the reduction of other molecules of oxaloacetate to malate. Krebs and his colleagues believed, therefore, that a cycle of reactions takes place according to the diagram shown in Fig. 7, in which the arrows indicate conversion of one substance to the next.

In this scheme pyruvic acid in the presence of oxygen can condense with oxaloacetic acid or its salts to form citric acid and CO_2. In turn, citrate is broken down through the compounds illustrated in Fig. 7 to oxaloacetic acid. The net effect of the citric acid cycle is the complete oxidation of the carbohydrate derivative, or "triose." Also, according to this scheme, succinate can arise from added oxaloacetate both by oxidation by way of citrate and by reduction through malate and

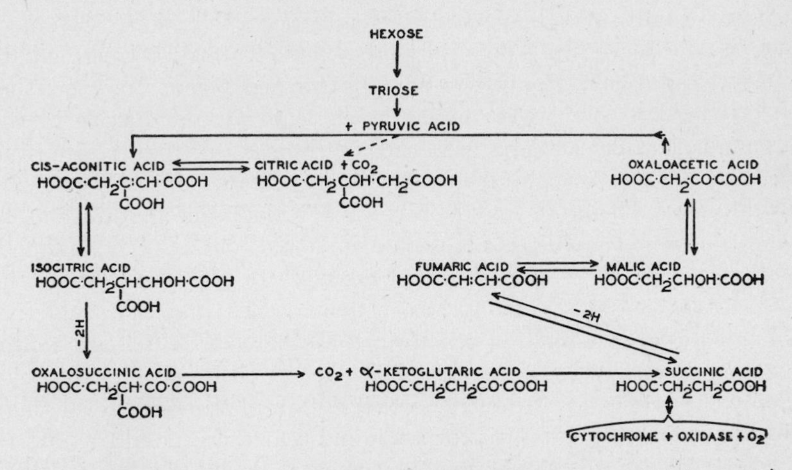

FIG. 7. Krebs's Citric Acid Cycle. (From Franke, 1940, and Krebs, 1942.)

fumarate. The succinate formed by either process may then react with the cytochrome-cytochrome oxidase system to form water and in turn become reduced to fumarate. Krebs has furthermore presented evidence which harmonizes his theory with the C_4-dicarboxylic scheme of Szent-Györgyi. Both embody the conception of a metabolic cycle playing a catalytic role, where the main compounds are broken down and regenerated and energy is released by transferring hydrogen from a "triose" to oxygen through the cooperation of this cycle and the cytochrome-cytochrome oxidase system.

Many of Krebs' experimental results have been confirmed by other workers who also believe that the citric acid cycle is the main pathway for carbohydrate metabolism in certain animal tissues. His results and conclusions have also been subjected to considerable criticism, however, and some investigators even question the existence and importance of a cycle containing citric acid [see review by Elliott (1941)]. For example, Stare, Lipton, and Goldinger (1941) have shown that the conditions required for the existence of the citric acid cycle are not completely fulfilled in chopped avian muscle. In fact, their experimental observations appear to favor a cycle involving a conversion of pyruvic acid to α-ketoglutarate, without citrate as an intermediary, followed by the Szent-Györgyi series of conversions of the dicarboxylic acids to oxaloacetate. Furthermore, they believe that the occasional catalysis of respiration observed when citrate is added to muscle is due not to the citrate itself, but rather to the C_4 acids and α-ketoglutarate which may be formed from it. Citrate may serve as a "stock-room" for the essential catalysts and exert an effect on respiration only when they are low.

More recently, Wood, Werkman, Hemingway, and Nier (1942) have presented evidence which definitely precludes citrate as an intermediate in the dissimilation of pyruvic acid by minced pigeon liver. Using labelled carbon (C^{13}), they have shown that carbon dioxide in the medium is fixed or participates in the synthesis of α-ketoglutarate from pyruvate. The α-ketoglutarate contains fixed carbon in only one carboxyl group. Therefore they believe that, if the α-ketoglutarate arose from the symmetrical citrate molecule, it should contain equal amounts of fixed carbon in its two carboxyl groups. It is proposed that the C_4-dicarboxylic acids are formed by two mechanisms, one reductive through the carbon-fixation reaction, the other oxidative by a tentative and modified Krebs cycle which does not involve citric acid. Finally they believe, "Although certain details of the Krebs cycle may be wrong, there is good basis for assuming that the general framework is correct." For additional reading on the citric acid cycle Krebs (1942) and Green and Stumpf (1944) should be consulted.

Certain bacteria have played a very important part in helping to solve some of the reactions in the citric acid cycle. For details of these studies the references just mentioned, especially the recent paper by Wood, Werkman, and their associates, should be consulted.

III. PEROXIDASES

The enzyme peroxidase, or possibly a group of similar enzymes, is widely distributed in plant tissues, certain animal tissues, and microorganisms. The best natural source is horseradish roots. The enzyme catalyses the oxidation of a variety of compounds by means of H_2O_2, which cannot be replaced by other oxidants, such as molecular oxygen or oxidation-reduction dyes. In the presence of oxidizable substances ($S \cdot H_2$) the decomposition of H_2O_2 by peroxidase (P) is very rapid and is accompanied by the oxidation of the substance. The reaction may be represented as follows:

$$P + H_2O_2 \rightarrow P \cdot H_2O_2$$

$$P \cdot H_2O_2 + S \cdot H_2 \rightarrow P + S + 2H_2O$$

Examples of oxidations affected by peroxidase derived from horseradish are *o*-diphenols to quinones, nitrite to nitrate, adrenaline, tryptophan, and tyrosine to colored products, reduced glutathione and ascorbic acid to their respective oxidized forms, and indicators and dyes, such as leucomalachite green, to their colored state. Cytochrome c peroxidase from yeast is unique in that it only catalyzes the oxidation by hydrogen peroxide of reduced (ferro) cytochrome c [Abrams *et al.* (1942)].

A great many papers have been published on peroxidase activity since the term was first coined by Linossier in 1898. Although Willstätter and his colleagues were mainly responsible for the first isolation and purification of peroxidase, the most complete works on the chemistry of this enzyme are by Keilin and his associates, Theorell, and Gjessing and Sumner [see Sumner and Somers (1943)], who have obtained it in a highly purified and active form. By means of adsorption, precipitation, and electrophoresis techniques Theorell in 1940 was able to obtain a horseradish-peroxidase preparation in a high degree of purity. Furthermore, he separated this preparation into two fractions, which he called peroxidase 1 and peroxidase 2. Highly purified peroxidase 1 formed a precipitate with picric acid, whereas peroxidase 2 did not; and in the electrophoresis apparatus at *p*H 7.5, peroxidase 1 migrated to the cathode, whereas peroxidase 2 went to the anode. The absorption spectrum of peroxidase conforms to that of iron-porphyrin compounds in the ferric state, such as methemoglobin, and consists of four bands at 645 (or 640), 583, 548, and 498 mμ. Upon the addition of $Na_2S_2O_4$, peroxidase undergoes reduction, turning distinctly red, and the four-banded spectrum is replaced by two bands at 594.5 and 558 mμ. This reduced divalent enzyme forms a reversible compound with CO. Oxidized peroxidase combines reversibly with NaF, H_2S, and KCN, and these reagents are known to inhibit peroxidase activity. Until the work of Keilin and his associates the valence of the iron in the enzyme-substrate complex remained unknown. They showed that, unlike catalase, peroxidase remains in the ferric form during the whole cycle of the catalysis and, furthermore, that there is no evidence to support the view that the substances oxidized are activated by the enzyme.

As a result of their spectroscopic studies under varying conditions Keilin and Mann (1937) concluded that, because of its resemblance to methemoglobin, peroxidase may be considered a compound of protohematin with a native globin. If this is true, it would appear that the same hematin compound in combination with different native proteins forms the following three distinct compounds: methemoglobin, peroxidase, and catalase. Each of these substances has many properties in common, but the three show striking differences in the nature and magnitude of their catalytic activities.

In spite of all the work which has been done on the peroxidase activity of animal, plant, and microbial tissues, it has not been shown definitely that the enzyme serves any real physiological function in the cell. In animal tissues there is no real evidence even for the existence of any peroxide upon which the enzyme might act, since H_2O_2 has never been definitely demonstrated in animal tissues. This difficulty may be accounted for, however, on the basis that peroxidase acts at extremely low concentrations of H_2O_2, and, if reducing substances are present, the peroxide can be removed by this mechanism as quickly as it is formed. Or, since reduced cytochrome and reduced glutathione are readily oxidized by peroxide, they may keep the concentration of H_2O_2 in tissues at a low level. Finally, catalase, which appears to be present to some extent in all aerobic cells, would destroy any great accumulation of peroxide in tissues. In bacteria, on the other hand, the production of hydrogen peroxide has been definitely demonstrated on several occasions [Main and Shinn (1939) and Hadley, Hadley, and Eathen (1941)]. Furthermore, evidence for the formation of peroxide in biological systems is to be found in the fact that H_2O_2 is capable of performing various oxidations which are typical of intermediary metabolism, and it should be mentioned again that the original Wieland hypothesis calls for the formation of H_2O_2 as a result of biological dehydrogenation.

Peroxidase activity in bacteria has been observed by Callow (1926), Anderson (1930), Farrell (1935), Frei, Riedmüller, and Almasy (1934), Edwards and Rettger (1937), and others. In general, these studies have shown that most aerobic bacteria exhibit peroxidase activity, whereas the anaerobes are inactive. A few data are cited in Table 13 to illustrate this point.

IV. CATALASE

Like peroxidase, catalase is an enzyme concerned with the removal or utilization of H_2O_2 formed by the primary enzyme systems of the cell. It catalyzes the decomposition of hydrogen peroxide into water and molecular oxygen, thus:

$$2H_2O_2 \xrightarrow{\text{Catalase}} 2H_2O + O_2$$

Catalase was discovered in 1901 by Loew and is now thought to be an indispensable constituent of almost all aerobic cells. Although the enzyme can be demonstrated in practically all aerobic cells, the best yields for large-scale studies are obtained when horse or ox liver is used as a starting material. In fact, the enzyme has been obtained in crystalline form from these two substances. Catalase activity is not exhibited by anaerobic bacteria but has been demonstrated in many aerobic and facultative anaerobic bacteria (Table 13) by McLeod and Gordon (1922–1925), Callow (1923), Virtanen and Karström (1925), Frei, Riedmüller, and Almasy (1934), Farrell (1935), Edwards and Rettger (1937), van Schouwenburg (1940), and many others [see Swenson and Humfeld (1942)]. Ruehle (1923) has also observed that certain bacterial spores exhibit catalase activity. On the basis of the presence of catalase in bacteria McLeod and Gordon (1923) have devised the following scheme for classification:

Class	*Catalase Production*	*Sensitiveness to H_2O_2*	*Examples of Bacteria in Each Class*
I. Potential peroxide producers	Nil	Very great	Strict anaerobes: *Clostridium perfringens* (0.00032–0.0004% *), *Clostridium tetani* (0.00027–0.00033%), *Clostridium septicum, Clostridium chauvoei, Clostridium sporogenes*
II. Peroxide producers			
a.	Nil	Moderate	Microaerophilic bacteria: Many streptococci, certain sarcinae, and lactic acid bacilli: *Streptococcus pyogenes* (0.0085%), *Lactobacillus acidophilus* (0.0027–0.005%)
b.	Nil	Slight	Pneumococci (±0.02%)
III. Nonproducers of catalase or peroxide	Nil	Moderate	Dysentery (Shiga) (0.0037–0.006%) and certain streptococci (0.0085%)
IV. Catalase producers			
a.	Very slight	Marked	*Vibrio comma* (0.00069%)
b.	Slight	Moderate	Typhoid-paratyphoid (0.0033%), *Hemophilus influenzae* (0.005–0.0033%)
c.	Strong	Variable	*Corynebacterium diphtheriae* (0.0017–0.003%), *Bacillus anthracis* (0.0031%), *Escherichia coli* (0.0032–0.0042%), *Staphylococcus aureus* (0.0044–0.0037%), *Bacillus subtilis* (0.015%), *Proteus*, yeast, various soil and tubercle bacilli, meningococcus
d.	Very strong	Slight or moderate	*Corynebacterium hoffmannii* (>0.006%), *Pseudomonas aeruginosa*, *Serratia marcescens* (0.0085%), *Gonococcus*

* Average inhibitory concentration of peroxide.

Chemical analyses of highly purified preparations of catalase by various investigators have shown that it is an iron-porphyrin protein containing about 0.1 per cent iron and 15.5 per cent nitrogen, with a molecular weight between 225,000 and 300,000. When examined spectroscopically, catalase shows three bands: I, 629.5 mμ; II, 544 mμ; III, 506.5 mμ. These bands can be modified in either position or intensity by means of reagents which are known to poison catalase activity [Keilin and Hartree (1936)]. The iron-porphyrin component of catalase is unique among the iron-porphyrins in three respects: (1) its ferro form is not oxidized by ferricyanide; (2) its ferric form is not reduced by hyposulfite; and (3) it can be reduced only by H_2O_2. Otherwise the iron-porphyrin of catalase behaves as if it were combined with globin, since the ferro form reacts with CO and the ferric form with NaF, NaN_3, KCN, and H_2S.

The mode of action of catalase has been studied by Keilin and Hartree (1938), Stern (1939), and by others. The results of various experiments have shown that the enzyme is reduced by peroxide and reoxidized by molecular oxygen. What apparently happens is that H_2O_2 combines and reacts with the enzyme, and the decomposition of H_2O_2 complex is brought about by a sequence of events in which the ferric form of catalase is reduced to the ferro form and the enzyme is then reoxidized by the liberated oxygen. The intermediary, catalase —H_2O_2, has not yet been definitely demonstrated, but there is some evidence that it exists. Keilin and Hartree suggest that the sequence of events for the decomposition of hydrogen peroxide by catalase may be represented by the following two equations:

$$(1)\quad \underset{\text{(Catalase)}}{4Fe^{+++}} + 2H_2O_2 \rightarrow \underset{\text{(Catalase)}}{4Fe^{++}} + 4H^+ + 2O_2$$

$$(2)\quad \underset{\text{(Catalase)}}{4Fe^{++}} + 4H^+ + O_2 \rightarrow \underset{\text{(Catalase)}}{4Fe^{+++}} + 2H_2O$$

$$2H_2O_2 = 2H_2O + O_2$$

In reaction 1 the H_2O_2 supposedly reduces the iron in catalase to the ferrous (Fe^{++}) state, liberating gaseous oxygen; in reaction 2 the reduced catalase is assumed to be oxidized to its original form by one molecule of oxygen. The sum of these two reactions is the catalytic decomposition of hydrogen peroxide into water and molecular oxygen. Evidence is now accumulating which tends to disprove Keilin and Hartree's theory of catalase action [see Sumner and Somers (1943), Green and Stumpf (1944)]. However, until more specific data are available, the above theory can be used tentatively as an example to explain the mode of action of catalase.

The catalytic decomposition of H_2O_2 by catalase follows very closely a monomolecular chemical reaction. For this reason von Euler and Josephson in 1926 expressed the activity of the enzyme in terms of Kataläse fähigkeit (catalase capability) units; that is, Kat. f. = k/g, where g is the dry weight of the enzyme preparation expressed as grams per milliliter, and k is the velocity constant of a monomolecular reaction or a measure of the relative concentration of the enzyme in the digestion mixture. The velocity constant is usually determined as follows: A known amount (usually 35 ml.) of H_2O_2(0.005 to 0.0015 M) is titrated with 0.04 N potassium permanganate to give x ml. To the same amount of peroxide plus phosphate buffer (0.006 M) at pH 6.8

and 0°C. is added a known amount of a catalase solution. After 5 minutes the reaction is stopped by adding 5 ml. of 6 *N* sulfuric acid, and the residual peroxide is again titrated with permanganate to give *y* ml. The velocity constant is then calculated from the expression, $k = 1/5 \ln x/y$. Several workers, for example, have used horse-liver catalase preparations which have *k* values as high as 50,000 to 63,000. The amount of the enzyme in a solution can also be accurately estimated spectrophotometrically. From such measurements it has been calculated that one molecule of catalase can decompose 4.4×10^4 molecules of H_2O_2 per second at 0°C., and that one milligram of catalase iron can produce 2,740 liters of oxygen from H_2O_2 per hour at 0°C.

Virtanen and Karström (1925) and van Schouwenburg (1940) have calculated the catalase content per cell of several bacteria by substituting the value of the number of cells for grams of enzyme in the catalase capability equation. Some of their data are cited in Table 17. Virtanen and Karström employed both sugar-free and glucose broths in their study and found that there was some variation in the results. The values in Table 17 are for the sugar-free broth. The organisms used by van Schouwenburg were all luminous bacteria grown on nutrient agar containing 3 per cent NaCl. More recently, Huddleson and Stahl

TABLE 17

THE CATALASE ACTIVITY OF SINGLE CELLS OF VARIOUS BACTERIA

[From Virtanen and Karström (1925) and van Schouwenburg (1940)]

Organism	Catalase Activity, $\left(\frac{k \times 10^{-9}}{\text{no. of cells}}\right)$
Micrococcus flavus	0.63
Kurthia zopfii	0.62
Micrococcus freudenreichii	0.49–0.50
Micrococcus aurantiacus	0.49
Pseudomonas aeruginosa	0.41
Micrococcus sulfureus	0.33
Alcaligenes viscosus	0.19
Serratia marcescens	0.13
Bacillus asterosporus	0.11
Corynebacterium cremoides	0.09
Escherichia coli	0.04–0.004
Aerobacter aerogenes	0.04–0.008
Photobacterium fischeri	1.08
Bacillus pierantonii	0.53
Photobacterium harveyii	0.18
Photobacterium phosphoreum	0.18
Micrococcus splendidus	0.15
Bacillus sulla-sepius	0.12

(1943) have studied the catalase activity of the species of the genus *Brucella* as a criterion of virulence. In general, catalase activity follows this decreasing order: *Brucella suis, Brucella melitensis, Brucella abortus.* Species must be identified, however, before attempting to correlate virulence with enzymatic activity. Swenson and Humfeld (1943) have reviewed the early literature on the catalase activity by bacteria and have studied its production by *Proteus vulgaris.* They observed that *P. vulgaris* produces two forms of catalase during all its culture cycle, except in the early lag phase. They called one of these forms active catalase and the other activable catalase. Activable catalase could be converted to the active form by an activator, such as Kolmer's cholesterinized antigen, but only in the presence of viable cells. Since activable catalase could not be extracted by acetone, it was regarded as an integral part of the living cell.

V. CARBOXYLASE AND OTHER DECARBOXYLASES

The yeast enzyme which catalyzes the decarboxylation of pyruvic acid is a diphosphothiamin metalloprotein called *carboxylase.* Diphosphothiamin, however, is also known to be the prosthetic group of a series of enzymes, all of which are concerned in the breakdown of pyruvic acid. The best-known examples are the carboxylase of yeast [Green, Herbert, and Subrahmanyan (1940)] and the pyruvic oxidases of *Lactobacillus delbrückii* [Lipmann (1939)], *Neisseria gonorrheae, Staphylococcus aureus, Streptococcus pyogenes, Streptococcus fecalis* [Barron and Lyman (1939), Krebs (1937)], and *Escherichia coli* [Still (1941), Kalnitsky and Werkman (1943)]. Animal tissues also contain an enzyme which oxidizes pyruvic and other α-ketomonocarboxylic acids. The reactions which the yeast and bacterial enzymes are known to catalyze may be represented as follows:

Yeast carboxylase:

$$CH_3 \cdot CO \cdot COOH \rightarrow CH_3 \cdot CHO + CO_2$$

Bacteria (aerobically):

$$CH_3 \cdot CO \cdot COOH + \tfrac{1}{2}O_2 \rightarrow CH_3 \cdot COOH + CO_2$$

Bacteria (anaerobically):

$$2CH_3 \cdot CO \cdot COOH + H_2O \rightarrow CH_3 \cdot COOH + CO_2 + CH_3 \cdot CHOH \cdot COOH$$

The second reaction is probably not a one-step reaction, but instead passes through acetylphosphate, which is coupled with the phosphorylation of adenylic acid (see pp. 473 to 476 on cocarboxylase). In the third reaction a dismutation occurs, whereby one molecule of pyruvic acid is oxidized to acetic acid and CO_2, and another is reduced to lactic acid. Besides these three reactions it is of interest that Quastel and Webley (1939) have noted that thiamin accelerates the oxidation of acetate by propionic acid bacteria which have been grown in a thiamin-deficient medium. This is one of the first suggestions that thiamin may be concerned in oxidations other than α-keto acids. It is also probable that carboxylase is involved in acetylmethylcarbinol (acetoin) production by bacteria (see p. 476 on cocarboxylase for reactions).

No one has succeeded in isolating the pure protein portion of the thiaminoprotein enzymes, although Green and his associates (1940) have prepared carboxylase from top yeast in a highly purified form and have been able to resolve the enzyme into its component parts (protein, magnesium, diphosphothiamin) by a variety of procedures. There is little information concerning the role of the prosthetic group in the decarboxylation or oxidation of pyruvic acid. The sensitivity of the gonococcus pyruvic enzyme to various reagents is unlike that of yeast carboxylase. Low concentrations of NaF (0.001 *M*), HCN, and α-naphthol inhibit almost completely the bacterial enzyme, but have little or no effect on the yeast enzyme.

Certain ions, especially Mg^{++}, Mn^{++}, and phosphate, accelerate the activity of the thiaminoprotein enzymes, although their exact role is not known. To illustrate this point a few results from the classical study by Lohmann and Schuster (1937) may be cited. They added various amounts of Mg^{++}, and Mn^{++}, together with a constant amount of diphosphothiamin, to washed yeast suspensions and then measured their effect by recording the amount of CO_2 evolved from pyruvic acid.

Diphosphothiamin Added, μg.	+	Mg^{++}, μg.	+	Mn^{++} μg.	Amount of CO_2, μl., Evolved in 30 minutes	60 minutes
3		0		0	34	50
3		10		0	38	70
3		30		0	116	210
3		100		0	175	302
3		0		1	50	93
3		0		10	165	289

Lipmann (1939) has shown that adenine-flavin-dinucleotide is also an important catalyst in pyruvic oxidases from bacteria. Using aqueous suspensions of acetone-dried *Lactobacillus delbrückii*, he found that little, if any, oxygen was utilized in the presence of pyruvic acid. When a few micrograms of diphosphothiamin (cocarboxylase) or adenine-flavin-dinucleotide was added to the system, some oxygen was utilized in 60 minutes; when both substances were added together, a large increase in the rate of oxygen uptake was noted. The diphosphothiamin could not be replaced by thiamin (vitamin B_1); and riboflavin, riboflavin phosphate, and the Warburg-Christian flavoprotein were unable to serve in place of the adenine-flavin-dinucleotide.

Diphosphothiamin Added, μg.	Adenine-flavin-dinucleotide Added, μg.	Oxygen Uptake, μl.
15	0	5
0	20	15
15	20	248

Several other decarboxylase enzymes, which are not so well characterized as the ones just mentioned, have also been isolated from bacteria. They will now be discussed briefly.

An enzyme known as oxaloacetic decarboxylase has been demonstrated in *Micrococcus lysodeikticus* by Krampitz and Werkman (1941) and Krampitz, Wood, and Werkman (1943). The enzyme catalyzes the decarboxylation of oxaloacetic acid to pyruvic acid and also the reverse reaction:

$$\underset{\text{Oxaloacetic acid}}{HOOC \cdot CH_2 \cdot CO \cdot COOH} \rightleftarrows \underset{\text{Pyruvic acid}}{CH_3 \cdot CO \cdot COOH} + CO_2$$

It is believed that the carboxylation reaction is involved in the CO_2-utilization axiom of Wood and Werkman. The enzyme is heat-labile and apparently requires Mg^{++} and Mn^{++} for its activity, whereas diphosphothiamin and thiamin have no effect:

Substrate *	Microliters of CO_2 Evolved in Presence of					
	No Addition	Mg^{++}	Mn^{++}	Diphosphothiamin (Cocarboxylase)	Mg and Diphosphothiamin	Mg and Thiamin
Oxaloacetate (anaerobic)	52	928	927	48	934	922
Oxaloacetate (aerobic)	54	925	922	49	916	918

* Total volume of reactants, 2.0 ml.: 0.025 *M* oxaloacetate, 0.006 *M* $MgCl_2$ or $MnSO_4$ and 25 μg. diphosphothiamin (cocarboxylase) or thiamin, respectively; 20-mg. cell (dry weight) per Warburg cup; 0.124 *M* PO_4 buffer at *p*H 6.8. Aerobic experiments contained air in gas space; anaerobic contained N_2. Temperature: 30°C. Time: 1 hour.

Davies (1943) has isolated an enzyme from *Clostridium acetobutylicum* which catalyzes the decarboxylation of acetoacetic acid to acetone:

$$CH_3 \cdot CO \cdot CH_2 \cdot COOH \rightarrow CH_3 \cdot CO \cdot CH_3 + CO_2$$

The enzyme is quite stable, has a *p*H optimum of 5.0, and is specific. The enzyme has been highly purified, and it is tentatively suggested that riboflavin phosphate may be the prosthetic group.

The paracolon organism, *Bacterium cadaveris*, produces an enzyme which specifically decarboxylates *l*-lysine to form cadaverine:

$$\underset{NH_2}{\underset{|}{CH_2}} \cdot (CH_2)_3 \cdot \underset{NH_2}{\underset{|}{CH}} \cdot COOH \rightarrow \underset{NH_2}{\underset{|}{CH_2}} \cdot (CH_2)_3 \cdot \underset{NH_2}{\underset{|}{CH_2}} + CO_2$$

Some fifteen other amino acids, including *d*-lysine, are not attacked [Gale and Epps (1943)]. The enzyme can be inactivated by dialysis and thus requires a coenzyme. The coenzyme is widely distributed in nature but is not identical with any of the known ones; however, it appears to be a flavin-like compound.

VI. PHOSPHORYLASES AND PHOSPHORYLATIVE OXIDATIONS

The occurrence of phosphate in metabolic processes has already been indicated in the discussions of the adenosine triphosphate-adenosine monophosphate coenzyme system and other enzymatic reactions, such as the hydrolytic cleavage of phosphate esters by the *phosphatases*. However, many of the reactions catalyzed by the phosphatases are irreversible under physiological conditions; and, although the hydrolysis of the terminal pyrophosphate bond of a compound such as adenosine triphosphate $\left(R{-}O{-}\overset{O}{\overset{\|}{\underset{OH}{\underset{|}{P}}}}{-}O{-}\overset{O}{\overset{\|}{\underset{OH}{\underset{|}{P}}}}{-}O{-}\overset{O}{\overset{\|}{\underset{OH}{\underset{|}{P}}}}{-}OH\right)$ yields considerable free energy, the hydrolysis of simple phosphoric esters $\left(R{-}\overset{H}{\overset{|}{\underset{H}{\underset{|}{C}}}}{-}O{-}\overset{O}{\overset{\|}{\underset{OH}{\underset{|}{P}}}}{-}OH\right)$ liberates a relatively small amount of free energy [Lipmann (1941)].

For some time it has been known that inorganic phosphate is essential for certain biological reactions. However, it has been only within the past several years that Warburg, Meyerhof, Cori, Lipmann, and their associates have shown us how inorganic phosphate is taken up by organic compounds and utilized in biological reactions. Two main types of reactions are now known which can accomplish the addition of phosphate to organic compounds [Green and Colowick (1944)]. One is catalyzed by phosphorylase enzymes and is therefore called phosphorolysis:

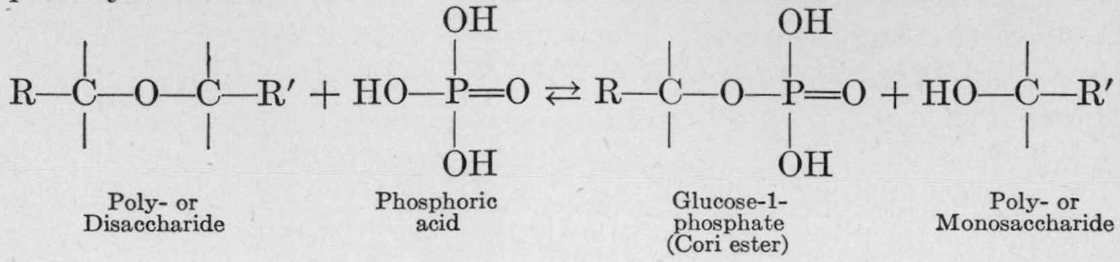

The other involves the addition of inorganic orthophosphate to compounds containing a double bond and is accompanied by a dehydration. Reactions of this type are usually spoken of as phosphorylative oxidations. The phosphorylative oxidation of an aldehyde to a carboxyl phosphate may be cited as one example of this type of reaction:

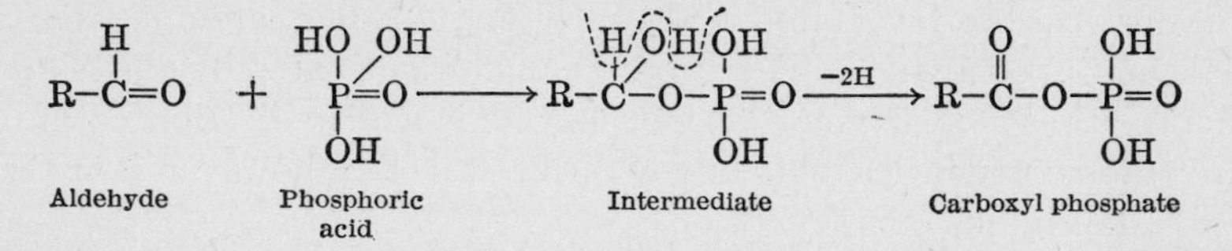

Phosphorylase enzymes have been shown to catalyze: (1) the first step in the degradation of polysaccharides (starch or glycogen) or, since the reaction is reversible, the last step in their synthesis from simpler units; and (2) the conversion of sucrose into glucose-1-phosphate and fructose. Since the substrates are different in these two reactions, the enzymes which catalyze the degradation or synthesis of polysaccharides are usually spoken of as *polysaccharide phosphorylases*, whereas the others are called *disaccharide phosphorylases*.

The polysaccharide phosphorylases are widely distributed in animals, plants, and microorganisms, and they all have many properties in common. However, muscle phosphorylase requires adenylic acid as a coenzyme, but plant phosphorylase either does not or else contains adenylic acid in such a firm union that it is impossible to separate it by dialysis. It is also of interest that a trace of glycogen is necessary for the synthesis of glycogen by animal phosphorylase, whereas a trace of soluble starch or maltose is required by the corresponding plant enzyme. Hehre (1943) has observed an interesting analogy between starch synthesis from glucose-1-phosphate by potato phosphorylase and dextran synthesis from sucrose by an enzyme preparation from *Leuconostoc mesenteroides*. In each reaction the substrate contains the basic unit of the final polymer product, but fructose instead of phosphate is liberated by the bacterial enzyme. Since inorganic phosphate was unnecessary in the bacterial system, it is believed that the synthesis of the dextran from sucrose does not require the mediation of a phosphorylated sugar substrate but instead occurs by direct condensation of the sucrose units. The synthesis of a levan polysaccharide consisting of fructose (levulose) units from sucrose by *Bacillus subtilis*, *Bacillus polymyxa*, and *Aerobacter levanicum* is another similar example [Hestrin, Avineri-Shapiro, and Aschner (1943)].

Disaccharide phosphorylase is very similar to the polysaccharide phosphorylases, except that it is involved in the phosphorolysis of sucrose to glucose-1-phosphate and fructose:

$$\text{Sucrose} + H_3PO_4 \rightleftarrows \underset{\text{(Cori ester)}}{\text{Glucose-1-phosphate}} + \text{Fructose}$$

This reaction is reversible, and only the Cori ester and fructose can be utilized for sucrose synthesis; however, when either *l*-sorbose or *d*-ketoxylose is substituted for fructose in the foregoing reaction two new sugars are formed which appear to be analogs of sucrose [Doudoroff, Hassid, and Barker (1944)]. The disaccharide phosphorylase system has been demonstrated in bacteria (*Leuconostoc mesenteroides*, *Pseudomonas saccharophila*), and it is quite probable that it is involved in the synthesis of sucrose by sugar cane and other plants [see Green and Colowick (1944)]. Doudoroff (1943) has extracted sucrose phosphorylase from dried bacteria and has obtained it relatively free from invertase and phosphatase by ammonium sulfate precipitation. As in plant polysaccharide phosphorylase, a coenzyme is not needed by the sucrose phosphorylase, and glucose inhibits the phosphorylytic process.

As we have mentioned, phosphorylative oxidation is another way by which inorganic phosphate can be taken up by biological systems and bound to organic compounds. The skeleton equation given may be used to illustrate the oxidation of 3-phosphoglyceraldehyde to 1:3-diphosphoglyceric acid, which is one of the intermediate reactions in alcoholic fermentation (see Chapter 10). Another example has already been mentioned in this chapter in the discussion on the role of acetyl phosphate in the oxidation of pyruvic acid (see pp. 475 and 482 on the coenzymes cocarboxylase and the adenosine triphosphate-adenosine monophosphate system). Several other examples of phosphorylative oxidation will be found in the excellent review by Green and Colowick (1944).

VII. MISCELLANEOUS BACTERIAL ENZYMES

Some of the bacterial enzymes, which have not been as well characterized as the ones mentioned, will be discussed under this heading. They include: (1) *hydrogenase*, (2) *hydrogenlyase*, (3) *glyoxalase*, and (4) *racemase*, and (5) *penicillinase*.

1. Hydrogenase. Stephenson and Stickland (1931–1932) described an enzyme in several bacteria which catalyzes the reduction of various substances by molecular hydrogen. The enzyme is comparable to the dehydrogenases, its substrate being molecular hydrogen. To this enzyme Stephenson and Stickland assigned the name hydrogenase. It must be assumed that the enzyme activates molecular hydrogen in some way, and this activation can be conveniently expressed as $H_2 \rightleftarrows 2H^+ + 2e$ without implying anything about the nature of the reaction.

By means of this enzyme hydrogen reduces oxygen, methylene blue, nitrate, and fumarate; sulfate, sulfite, and thiosulfate are reduced to sulfide. Hydrogenase likewise reduces a number of one-carbon compounds (CO_2, CO, formaldehyde, and methyl alcohol) to methane or other substances. For example, the following reaction has been postulated for the reduction of carbon dioxide to methane:

$$4H_2 + CO_2 \rightarrow CH_4 + 2H_2O$$

This reaction takes place if an additional mechanism is present to activate the CO_2 as a hydrogen acceptor.

The methylene blue-reduction technique has been widely employed to study the distribution of hydrogenase in various bacteria, and the data given in Table 18 show that those organisms which exhibit strong hydrogenase activity are able to reduce methylene blue in a relatively short time, providing molecular hydrogen is present. It is now believed that the enzyme hydrogenase is present in a great many microbial cells. The reason certain organisms, such as *Aerobacter aerogenes*, do not readily display their hydrogenase has been explained by Ordal and Halvorson (1939) and Ordal and Tsuchiya (1939). These workers have shown that it is very important to have the cell suspensions sufficiently diluted when studying the hydrogenase activity of bacteria; otherwise reducing matter associated with the cells masks the activity of this enzyme.

In the true methane-producing bacteria (*Hydrogenomonas*) and certain other organisms hydrogenase holds a vital position, since the oxidation of hydrogen is the main reaction by which these bacteria obtain energy. Lee and Umbreit (1940), for example, have studied pure cultures of hydrogen-oxidizing bacteria. One culture was allocated to the genus *Hydrogenomonas*, and another was a heterotrophic rod resembling members of the genus *Flavobacterium*. Carbon dioxide was essential for the hydrogen-oxidizing process.

According to Nakamura (1940), hydrogenase participates in the formation of luciferin by light-producing bacteria (*Micrococcus phosphoreus*). The enzyme has also been demonstrated in *Proteus vulgaris*

[Hoberman and Rittenberg (1943)], *Azotobacter* species, certain freshly isolated *Rhizobia* [Phelps and Wilson (1941), Lee and Wilson (1943)], and green algae [Gaffron (1942)]. It is assumed that hydrogenase plays a role in nitrogen fixation and photosynthesis, and the demonstration of this enzyme in strictly aerobic organisms seems to indicate a generalized importance of hydrogenase catalysis in many types of cells.

TABLE 18

DISTRIBUTION OF HYDROGENASE IN BACTERIA AS DETERMINED BY THE METHYLENE BLUE-REACTION TECHNIQUE

[From Stephenson and Stickland (1931–1932)]

Organism	Methylene Blue Reduction Time, minutes: With H_2	Without H_2	Hydrogenase
Escherichia coli (4 strains)	8–11$\frac{1}{4}$	75–120	+
E. coli-acidilactici	9$\frac{1}{4}$	>150	+
Aerobacter aerogenes	9$\frac{1}{2}$	15$\frac{1}{2}$	?
Alcaligenes fecalis	27$\frac{1}{2}$	28	–
Pseudomonas aeruginosa	65	63	–
Serratia marcescens	>60	>60	–
Bacillus megatherium	>120	>120	–
Bacillus subtilis	>120	>120	–
Clostridium sporogenes	>150	>150	–
Vibrio rubentschickii	17	>150	+
Vibrio? #182	4	>180	+
Yeast	......	......	–
Heart muscle	......	......	–

The preparation of purified dry powders of cell-free hydrogenase from cultures of *Escherichia coli-communior* has been reported by Bovarnick (1941). Results of inhibitor studies by Hoberman and Rittenberg (1943), Wilson and Wilson (1943), and others indicate that hydrogenase is probably an iron-containing compound.

2. Hydrogenlyase. Another bacterial enzyme which may be mentioned here is hydrogenlyase, supposedly produced by the coliform organisms and other bacteria. Hydrogenlyase is regarded as an adaptive enzyme; that is, it is formed only when the organisms are grown in the presence of a specific substrate, such as formate. It is also supposedly produced by *E. coli* and other bacteria in the presence of glucose or glycerol, which yields formic acid as a result of its fermentation. However, some specific factor in the medium appears to be necessary, since in general the enzyme is manufactured only when the organisms are grown on a tryptic digest of casein. When the bacteria are cultivated on synthetic media containing formate, good growth results, but no hydrogenlyase is produced. With *E. coli* maximum production of the enzyme occurs in 2 hours and before the organisms have doubled in number. The enzyme is labile to poisons of all kinds and exhibits optimum activity when the reaction is *p*H 7.0.

The apparent relationship of bacterial formic hydrogenlyase to formic dehydrogenase and hydrogenase may be shown as follows:

(1) Hydrogenase activates molecular hydrogen;

$$H_2 + X \rightleftarrows XH_2$$

(2) Formic dehydrogenase catalyzes the reaction;

$$H \cdot COOH + X \rightleftarrows XH_2 + CO_2$$

(3) Formic hydrogenlyase catalyzes the reaction;

$$H \cdot COOH \rightleftarrows H_2 + CO_2$$

X represents an intracellular hydrogen carrier or, experimentally, a dye such as methylene blue.

According to the foregoing equations, a combination of formic dehydrogenase and hydrogenase should perform the same function as hydrogenlyase; that is, it should liberate H_2 and CO_2 from formate. Stephenson and her associates [see Stephenson (1937)] have expressed the opinion, however, that formic hydrogenlyase cannot be regarded as a combination of these two enzymes. They arrived at this opinion after studying *Shigella dispar*, which they found possessed hydrogenase and formic dehydrogenase but was unable to liberate gas from formate. As a result of more recent research the conclusions of Stephenson and her associates seem to lack sufficient experimental proof. Ordal and Halvorson (1939), Ordal and Tsuchiya (1939), and Waring and Werkman (1944), for example, have obtained results which show that the production of CO_2 and H_2 from formate by certain bacteria is due to the combined action of (1) formic dehydrogenase, (2) an intermediate electron carrier containing iron, and (3) hydrogenase. It is believed that the reason the organism (*S. dispar*) studied by Stephenson and her associates displayed hydrogenase and formic dehydrogenase activity but lacked hydrogenlyase is that the organism lacked the intermediate electron carrier (2). Thus it seems unnecessary at present to postulate that formic hydrogenlyase is a separate and distinct enzyme.

Additional data on hydrogenlyase will be found in the papers by Stephenson and Stickland (1932–1933), Yudkin (1932), Farkas, Farkas, and Yudkin (1934), Woods (1936), Stephenson (1937), Yudkin (1938), Hoberman and Rittenberg (1943), and Waring and Werkman (1944).

3. Glyoxalase. Glyoxalase is an enzyme which is widely distributed in animal tissues and microorganisms such as yeast and bacteria [Lohmann (1932), Still (1941)]. Its exact physiological function is not yet fully understood, although it is known to catalyze the conversion of methyl glyoxal to *d*-lactic acid:

$$CH_3 \cdot CO \cdot CHO + H_2O \rightarrow CH_3 \cdot CHOH \cdot COOH$$

This reaction involves an internal Cannizzaro or intramolecular oxido-reduction, with the keto group of methyl glyoxal being reduced to the alcohol and the aldehyde group simultaneously oxidized to the acid. In 1932 Lohmann discovered that purified preparations of glyoxalase were unable to catalyze the conversion of methyl glyoxal except in the presence of the tripeptide, glutathione:

$$\underbrace{HOOC \cdot CHNH_2 \cdot (CH_2)_2 \cdot CO}_{\text{Glutamic acid}}–\underbrace{NHCH \cdot (CH_2SH) \cdot CO}_{\text{Cysteine}}–\underbrace{NHCH_2 \cdot COOH}_{\text{Glycine}}$$

The —SH group of glutathione can be oxidized by oxygen to the disulfide form in the presence of certain catalysts, such as metals, thus:

$$2GSH + O_2 \rightarrow GSSG + H_2O_2$$

where G represents the tripeptide residue. Glutathione is almost universally distributed in animal tissues, as well as in plants and bacteria. This fact has led biochemists to an intensive search for its physiological function. So far, however, the only significant positive finding in enzymology is Lohmann's discovery of its role as a coenzyme for glyoxalase.

The mechanism of the action of glutathione as a coenzyme for glyoxalase has been studied by several workers [see Behrens (1941)]. It has been suggested that glutathione (abbreviated GSH) forms an addition compound with methyl glyoxal, which then serves as the substrate for glyoxalase according to the following equation:

$$CH_3 \cdot CO \cdot CHO + GSH \rightleftarrows$$
$$CH_3 \cdot CO \cdot CHOH–SG \xrightarrow[H_2O]{\text{Glyoxalase}} CH_3 \cdot CHOH \cdot COOH + GSH$$

The glutathione is then regenerated to its original form, and lactic acid is produced. The only difficulty in accepting this scheme is that, when the addition compound of methyl glyoxal and glutathione is prepared in the laboratory and used as the substrate, it is only very slowly acted upon by the enzyme. Thus it must be questioned as an intermediate. The mechanism whereby the internal oxidation takes place is therefore not clear.

The glyoxalase activity of yeast and bacteria has been studied by Lohmann (1932) and Still (1941). Still found that under suitable conditions a cell-free enzyme preparation from *Escherichia coli* almost completely converted methyl glyoxal to lactic acid. In fact, in one experiment lactic acid was present to the extent of 2.08 mg. when 2.17 mg. was the theoretical amount expected.

4. Racemase. Certain bacteria, such as *Staphylococcus ureae*, *Clostridium butylicum*, and *Lactobacillus plantarum*, contain an enzyme called racemase, which is capable of converting either *d*- or *l*-lactic acid into the racemic mixture [see Katagiri and Kitahara (1937), Christensen, Peterson, and Johnson (1938), and Katagiri and Murakami (1939)]. The same, or a similar, enzyme in *L. plantarum* also racemizes *l*-2-phosphoglyceric acid. In young cultures racemase is confined to the cells, but in old cultures it appears in the medium too. It is most active at *p*H 5.0, is inhibited by cyanide (0.05 *M*), and is destroyed by heat. Racemase appears to be a dehydrogenase, but it is not the same as lactic acid dehydrogenase.

5. Penicillinase. An interesting point in connection with the growth-inhibiting property of penicillin is that it can be destroyed by an enzyme known as penicillinase. This enzyme was first discovered by Abraham and Chain in 1940 and has since been studied by several workers [see Chapter 4 and McQuarrie, Liebmann, Kluener, and Venosa (1944)]. The enzyme is formed by several bacteria, such as paracolon bacillus and other coliform bacilli, aerobic spore-forming rods, and certain *Shigella* species. According to McQuarrie *et al.* (1944), penicillinase is precipitated from the medium in which the organisms have been cultivated by acetone, alcohol, dioxane, Na-tungstate, and saturated $(NH_4)_2 SO_4$, It does not dialyze through a cellophane membrane. Highly purified solutions of the enzyme are extremely labile, being 66 per cent destroyed in 20 minutes and over 95 per cent in 1 hour at 45°C. The most active *p*H at 37°C. is 7.1. The enzyme is inhibited by iodoacetic acid and amyl acetate and partially inhibited by indole-3-acetic acid. It is activated by *dl*-phenylalanine.

VIII. ZYMASE COMPLEX

The term zymase, as now generally used, is restricted to the enzyme systems which function in the alcoholic fermentation, that is, produce alcohol and carbon dioxide from sugar. In the past the term was often used in a much broader sense to incorporate all intracellular enzymes, regardless of whether they attacked carbohydrates or proteins.

Only a brief outline of the zymase complex will be given here to complete the discussion of enzymes. Further details will be found in the reference books dealing with enzyme chemistry. The literature on this subject has grown very large since Buchner's classical experiments in 1897 with fermentation of cell-free yeast juice.

The exact number of specific enzymes, coenzymes, and activators of the zymase complex is not known. The term zymase merely represents the effect of a number of enzyme systems which together bring about alcoholic fermentation. Tauber (1937) states that the action of the following enzymes is known to be specific:

1. *Hexokinase* converts hexose into a more reactive form (enol ?).

2. *Phosphatase* hydrolyzes and synthesizes enol-sugar-phosphoric acid esters. Magnesium is an essential activator.

3. *Oxydoreductase* (*mutase, dehydrase*) rearranges aldehydes (Cannizzaro reaction) and requires cozymase (DPN) as a coenzyme.

4. *Carboxylase* acts on pyruvic acid. It requires the coenzyme cocarboxylase. Of these four enzyme systems carboxylase has probably been obtained in the highest state of purity. According to Green, Herbert, and Subrahmanyan (1940), carboxylase is a diphosphothiamin-magnesium protein. They have been able to resolve the enzyme into its component parts (protein, magnesium, cocarboxylase) by a variety of procedures and believe that the metal plays the role of a cement substance which binds the specific protein to the prosthetic group (cocarboxylase or phosphorylated thiamin).

Since the discovery that magnesium and other salts, as well as coenzymes, are necessary in yeast fermentation the following terminology of the various systems has also been used:

Zymase for the enzyme complex free from all activators and coenzymes.

Holozymase for the fermentation complex plus all activators and coenzymes.

Apozymase for diphosphopyridine nucleotide (cozymase)-free holozymase.

Atiozymase for Mg^{++}-free and cocarboxylase-free apozymase.

Although the term zymase complex is usually used in connection with yeasts which are responsible for alcoholic fermentation, certain bacteria, such as *Pseudomonas lindneri* (*Termobacterium mobile*), also produce essentially the same products and therefore must have a zymase complex similar to that of yeast [Schreder, Brunner, and Hampe (1933)].

ENZYME VARIATION AND ADAPTATION IN MICRO-ORGANISMS

In the study of biology it must always be kept in mind that one is dealing not with static material, but rather with systems which are constantly undergoing change or variation. With higher organisms variation is usually considered as differences among individuals. However, with microorganisms, where observations are almost always recorded from large populations, such individual variations cannot be appreciated, and the term variation must here mean a general change in the average characteristics of the cells under investigation. Biological variation in all types of organisms may be conditioned by alterations in the environment. In most instances the change is in the nature of an adaptation to the altered conditions, the variants being physiologically more suited to the changed environment than were the original organisms. Adaptation of this nature is a fundamental property of living matter.

It is also of interest and importance in studies of microbial variation to observe the effect of environmental changes on the enzymatic make-up of the organism. Many persons have been interested in this subject, and the reviews by Karström (1938), Yudkin (1938), Rahn (1938), Dubos (1940), Rhoades (1941), and Lindegren (1944) should be consulted for the details of many interesting experiments. After studying the enzymatic make-up of certain bacteria which had been grown on a variety of media, Karström (1930) concluded that bacterial enzymes could be divided into two general groups:

1. Constitutive enzymes, which are always formed by a given organism and are independent of the composition of the medium on which it grows. They may be produced in varied amounts in the presence of the specific substrates, but they are always present in the cells. Such enzymes may be considered essential enzymes.

2. Adaptive enzymes, which are produced by a given organism only as the result of chemical stimulation when the cells are grown in the presence of the specific substrate. Such enzymes may be of value to the cell, but they must be considered nonessential enzymes. The terms mutation, modification, acclimatization, training, and adaption have all been used to describe examples of this type.

Most of the constitutive enzymes bring about the respiratory and synthetic processes in bacteria, whereas the majority of the adaptive enzymes may be classified as hydrolases, since they break down the more complex nutrient materials to a stage where they can be attacked by the constitutive enzymes.

Since the mechanism of the production of enzymes in the presence of the substrate may be of more than one type, and since enzyme formation may be conditioned by substances unrelated to the substrate, it may be of interest to consider some of the possible ways whereby enzymes arise in cultures previously not possessing them. In those instances where enzyme formation is associated with the presence of its substrate, there are theoretically two possible ways in which this production may be brought about. They are: (1) adaptation by natural selection, and (2) adaptation due to chemical environment. Mention should be made also of the instances recorded in the literature where substances unrelated to the substrate stimulate enzyme formation [Yudkin (1938)].

ADAPTATION BY NATURAL SELECTION

In adaptations of this type it must be supposed that there exists in all cultures a small but definite number of cells possessing the particular enzyme. Since the organisms used have usually been picked or cultivated from a single-cell colony, a biochemical variation or mutation of definite, though low, frequency must be imagined in order to account for the existence of cells containing the enzyme. Enzymes arising by some such mutation become, according to the hypothesis of natural selection, of physiological value to the organism. The cells possessing them are therefore at an advantage and tend to multiply at the expense of others. A bacterial strain is thus formed in which the majority of the members possesses the enzyme in question.

Many examples of adaptations of this sort are recorded. For example, as early as 1907 Massini observed that, when certain strains of *Escherichia coli* were plated on Endo's medium, the first colonies to develop were white, an indication that the lactose was not fermented, probably because of the absence of sufficient lactase. However, after several days red lactose-fermenting secondary colonies developed as papillae on the tops of the white colonies. When the white colonies were subcultured on fresh Endo's medium, the phenomenon was repeated; but, if the red papillae were carefully removed and subcultured on the same medium, only red colonies developed after incubation. Massini considered the appearance of the lactose-fermenting secondary colonies as a mutation and, in accordance with Neisser's terminology, called his strain *Bacterium coli-mutabile.* Lewis (1934) showed that the mode of origin of such strains was natural selection working on a spontaneous variation in the culture and that, although the sugar acted as a selective agent, it did not exert a specific exciting stimulus to variation. Similar results have been reported with other bacteria and yeasts.

The training of an organism to enhance reactions normally but slowly performed is often possible by serial subculture into media containing the new substrate. Bacteria may also be trained to grow in media previously insufficient to support growth and, as Fildes, Knight, and their associates [see Knight (1936)] have pointed out, this fact may be regarded as due to the development in the organisms of the requisite synthetic enzymes. In many instances, it appears that the mode of enzyme production is selection, since it has often been recorded that attempts to train any given strain of organism succeed in only a few of several simultaneous experiments, and that the attempts are more likely to be successful if large inocula are employed. When large inocula are used, then, training consists of selecting one type of cell from what might almost be considered a mixed culture. Each subculture into the appropriate medium increases the proportion of the mutant cells, since these are at a physiological advantage in that they have at their disposal an additional source of energy or of material which they can use for building protoplasm.

Organisms possessing enzymes which arise as mutations are likely to retain these enzymes in the absence of the substrate, since mutations are generally permanent. The same statement holds true for trained organisms, providing the period of training is sufficiently long.

ADAPTATION DUE TO CHEMICAL ENVIRONMENT

Another way in which microbial enzymes may be produced is that in which an adaptive enzyme arises in response to its chemical environment. Such enzymes can probably be compared to acquired characters in higher organisms. Adaptive enzymes appear and reach their maximum development during the growth of the first culture in the medium containing their specific substrate. They fail to appear as soon as the culture is transferred to a medium not containing this specific substrate. Usually, however, such cultures still retain their power to develop the character if they are subjected to conditions similar to those in which the parent culture developed it.

Although the production of adaptive enzymes of this type need not be associated with cellular multiplication, all the evidence available indicates that it involves the synthesis of new protoplasm. In fact, the phase of physiological youth appears to be the most optimum time in the culture cycle for the formation of such enzymes (see Chapter 2). It has been suggested by Dubos (1940) that ". . . the synthetic process is, so to speak, oriented or guided by the chemical structure of the substrate, which thus determines the specificity of the enzyme." Adaptive enzymes exhibit great specificity toward the substrates which have stimulated their production. Karström has shown, for example, that the adaptive enzymes of *Leuconostoc mesenteroides* (*Betacoccus arabinosaceus*) can differentiate between different monosaccharides and different polysaccharides, and Dubos has demonstrated that the enzymes which hydrolyze the capsular polysaccharides of pneumococci distinguish between polysaccharides which give rise to cross reactions in specific antisera.

Adaptation of this type can be illustrated by many experiments, but only two, one with bacteria and the other with yeast, will be mentioned here to acquaint the student with the kind of results which have been obtained by various workers. Karström cultivated the lactic acid organism, *L. mesenteroides*, on media containing only one of a series of sugars. After incubation the cells were separated from the media and carefully washed. They were then tested for their ability to ferment different carbohydrates (Table 19). From the data in the table it will be seen that the enzymes which catalyze the fermentation of glucose, fructose, mannose, and sucrose are constitutive, since they are produced when the organism is grown on sugar-free or any sugar-containing medium. The enzymes which attacked galactose, arabinose, maltose, and lactose are adaptive, because they are formed only in the presence of their specific substrate (an exception is maltase, which was formed also in the carbohydrate-free medium). That the galactose-fermenting enzyme appeared when *L. mesenteroides* was grown in the presence of lactose is not surprising, since lactose is made up of galactose and glucose residues. Other examples of adaptive enzymes produced by bacteria will be found on pp. 603 to 605 on the use of enzymes and pp. 593 to 594 on hydrogenlyase.

TABLE 19

THE CONSTITUTIVE AND ADAPTIVE ENZYMES PRODUCED BY
Leuconostoc mesenteroides

[From Karström (1930)]

Organisms Grown in a Medium Containing	Sugars Subsequently Fermented					
	Glucose, Fructose, Mannose	Galactose	Arabinose	Sucrose	Maltose	Lactose
Glucose (2%)	+	−	−	−	−	−
Sucrose (2%)	+	−	−	+	−	−
Galactose (0.8%)	+	+	−	+	−	−
Arabinose (0.8%)	+	−	+	+	−	−
Maltose (2%)	+	−	−	+	+	−
Lactose (1%)	+	+	−	+	−	+
No sugar	+	−	−	+	+	−

+ = fermented; − = not fermented.

The second example which will be mentioned of adaptation due to chemical environment is the work by Rhoades (1941). He studied nine strains of yeast of the species *Saccharomyces cerevisiae*, *Saccharomyces ellipsoideus*, *Saccharomyces carlsbergensis*, and *Schizosaccharomyces pombe* with regard to the constitutive or adaptive nature of their enzymes toward the fermentation of glucose, mannose, sucrose, raffinose, galactose, maltose, alpha-methylglucoside, and trehalose. All strains of yeast readily fermented the first four sugars, regardless of the carbon source in which the cells had been grown; that is, these sugars were attacked by constitutive enzymes. In contrast, the other carbohydrates employed were fermented by adaptive enzymes as a result of a specific chemical stimulation of the yeast cells by growth in the presence of the specific substrate. The interesting paper by Lindegren (1944) on the selection and hybridization of industrial yeasts should be consulted for information on this subject.

STIMULATION OF ENZYMES BY UNRELATED SUBSTANCES

So far we have considered the effect of the specific substrate on enzyme production. It is also known that the production of certain enzymes is conditioned by the presence in the culture medium of substances entirely unrelated to the homologous substrate. In a series of papers from 1916–1918, Jacoby studied the production of urease by bacteria and claimed that the formation of an enzyme may be limited by substances in the medium which are needed by the cell as "bricks" ("Bausteine") for the building up of the enzyme molecule. The carbohydrates, for instance, can be classified into four groups according to their efficacy in stimulating urease production in *Proteus vulgaris*, and from this fact Jacoby concluded that the chemical group,

$$\begin{array}{cccc} & H & OH & \\ & | & | & \\ — & C \cdot & C \cdot & CHO \\ & | & | & \\ & HO & H & \end{array}$$

is necessary for the formation of the enzyme. Haines (1932–1933) has studied the effect of the medium on the production of bacterial gelatinase and observed that certain inorganic ions greatly stimulate the formation of the enzyme. Finally, Quastel (1937) showed that, although the production of catalase, urease, and fumarase by *Micrococcus lysodeikticus* varies greatly according to the medium in which the organism is grown, the presence of urea does not stimulate urease, nor does that of succinate or fumarate excite fumarase production. On the other hand, the presence of glucose in the nutritional medium stimulates the formation of urease and suppresses that of catalase in the organism. According to Quastel, the classification into adaptive and constitutive enzymes is inadequate to explain such results. Rather, he suggests that all these results are best interpreted by assuming that the enzymes are themselves metabolites, whose rate of formation and destruction varies with the conditions of growth.

The effect of the substrate could then be due either to contributing the necessary organic molecule for the synthesis of the enzyme or to affecting its stability (for instance, by combining with it). The adaptive stimulation caused by the homologous substrate would be only one particular application of these principles.

USE OF MICROBIAL ENZYMES

It is well known that several large industries have been built up on the function of microorganisms. For example, the brewing industry, the production of wines and distilled spirits, and the manufacture of industrial alcohol all depend on alcohol fermentation by the complex system of enzymes elaborated by yeast cells. The activity of bacterial enzymes is illustrated in the use of acetic acid organisms in connection with vinegar and acetic acid manufacture, of certain *Clostridia* in the production of acetone and other solvents, and of *Lactobacillus delbrückii* for the formation of lactic acid. Gluconic acid and some of its derivatives are produced on a commercial scale by utilizing certain bacteria, such as *Acetobacter* or *Pseudomonas,* as well as by *Aspergillus niger* acting on glucose. The manufacture of citric acid from sugar by *A. niger* has grown to such an extent that over 26,000,000 lb. is produced in the United States per year. Mention may also be made of the use in the Orient of certain fungi for the production of various condiments, such as soya sauce, from soya beans and for the manufacture of the Japanese national beverage, *sake,* from a mixture of soya beans and wheat. Further examples to which such processes apply are the retting of flax, the curing and fermentation of coffee and cacao beans and tea leaves, the production of pickles, sauerkraut, and silage, the making of leaven bread and pastries, and the preparation and ripening of many cheeses. In most of these processes more than one enzyme is involved.

It is possible in certain instances, where the reaction desired is of limited scope and can be attributed to a particular enzyme or mixture of enzymes, to afford a marked improvement in the degree of control of the process by using purified enzyme preparations from suitable microorganisms or other cells. Such enzymes can often be utilized under standardized and controlled conditions, even aseptic, if necessary, to produce a larger yield and a better product. According to Wallerstein (1939), the history of the use of enzyme preparations in a number of industrial processes where they are employed today has often followed this sequence of events. First, conditions involving the presence of mixtures of many microorganisms were used. For instance, in the tanning industry the steeping or sweating of hides was accomplished by "puering" with dog or bird excreta, and in the textile industry desizing was accomplished by soaking fabrics in stagnant water ("rotten steep"). Such practices were then followed by controlling conditions to make them more favorable for the development of the particular microorganisms involved in the processes. Later, with the realization that the reactions were due to specific enzymes, it became possible to take advantage of the elimination of viable organisms and the employment of standard preparations of the enzymes themselves. In such industrial uses enzymes like malt diastase, pancreatic extracts, and papain, from sources other than microorganisms, have long been used for a variety of purposes. Among the enzyme preparations from microorganisms which have been employed industrially are amylase from *Aspergillus oryzae*, invertase from yeast, and amylase and proteases from *Bacillus subtilis*. Conditions governing the commercial production of these enzyme preparations have been discussed in some detail by Wallerstein (1939).

Commercially prepared enzymes are now widely employed in many industries. For example, in the food industry standardized invertase preparations are used in the manufacture of certain noncrystallizable chocolates with soft-cream centers and the preparation of stable and noncrystallizable sirups. Bacterial amylases are being employed to dissolve the cocoa starch in so-called chocolate sirups so as to prevent their subsequent thickening; they are also being applied in the brewing industry for the liquefaction of unmalted cereals, such as wheat, corn, and rice. Proteolytic enzymes from bacteria are useful in the clarification and maturing of malt beverages and the correction of protein haze. Enzyme preparations are also used in the textile industry. Prior to weaving, warp threads require strengthening or "sizing." In cotton and rayon weaving, sizing is usually accomplished by impregnating or coating the threads or the fibers with gelatin or casein or solutions of raw starch which have been modified by liquefaction with amylase to make them more penetrating. After weaving, such fabrics must be freed of the adhering sizing material before they can be dyed and bleached. Amylases and proteases, depending on the nature of the fabric and the size, find wide application in this field. Similarly, bacterial proteases may be employed for the degumming of silk.

Bacterial amylases are used in the paper industry for preparing sizing pastes; proteolytic enzyme preparations may be applied in the stripping of the gelatin coating from photographic plates and motion picture films for the recovery of silver salts; and similarly bacterial enzyme preparations are used in the so-called "bating" procedure in the leather industry and may be employed in the manufacture of deproteinized rubber.

Enzymes are also used as laboratory reagents. Examples of this use are the procedures in which urease is employed to determine the urea content of blood and urine, and the methods for the analysis of starch in plant materials by amylase preparations (Taka-diastase) from *Aspergillus oryzae*. More recently, Dubos and Miller [see Dubos (1940–1941)] have developed a highly specific bacterial enzyme technique for the determination of creatinine in biological fluids, and Dubos and others have used bacterial enzymes for the decomposition of the capsular polysaccharides of pneumococci.

Other interesting uses of various enzyme preparations will be found in the books by Waksman and Davison (1926) and Tauber (1943) and the papers by Wallerstein (1939) and Dubos (1940–1941).

REFERENCES

Abraham, E. P., and E. Adler. 1940. *Biochem. J.*, **34**:119–127.

Abrams, R., A. M. Altschul, and T. R. Hogness. 1942. *J. Biol. Chem.*, **142**:303–316.

Ackermann, D. 1931. *Z. physiol. Chem.*, **203**:66–69.

Adams, M., N. K. Richtmyer, and C. S. Hudson. 1943. *J. Am. Chem. Soc.*, **65**:1369–1380.

Adler, E., H. von Euler, and H. Hellström. 1937. *Arkiv Kemi Mineral. Geol.*, 12 B, No. 38.

Adler, E., H. von Euler, and G. Günther. 1939. *Nature*, **143**:641–642.

Adler, E., H. von Euler, G. Günther, and M. Plass. 1939. *Biochem. J.*, **33**:1028–1045.

Allison, F. E., S. R. Hoover, and D. Burk. 1933. *Science*, **78**:217–218.

Almon, L., and E. B. Fred. 1933. *Centr. Bakt., II Abt.*, **88**:302–304.

Almquist, H. J., C. F. Pentler, and E. Mecchi. 1938. *Proc. Soc. Exptl. Biol. Med.*, **38**:336–338.

Altschul, A. M., H. Persky, and T. R. Hogness. 1941. *Science*, **94**:349–350.

Anderson, L. R. 1930. *J. Bact.*, **20**:371–379.

Asai, T. 1937. *J. Agr. Chem. Soc. Japan*, **13**:1165–1176.

Auhagen, E. 1932. *Z. physiol. Chem.*, **204**:149–167.

Avery, O. T., and G. E. Cullen. 1920. *J. Exptl. Med.*, **32**:547–569, 571–582.

Bach, D., and J. Lambert. 1937. *Compt. rend. soc. biol.*, **126**:298–300, 300–302.

Ball, E. G. 1938. *Science*, **88**:131.

Ball, E. G. 1939. *J. Biol. Chem.*, **128**:51–67; *Cold Spring Harbor Symposia Quant. Biol.*, **7**:100–110.

Barker, H. A. 1936. *Proc. Konink. Akad. Wetenschappen Amsterdam*, **39**:674–683.

Barker, H. A., and J. V. Beck. 1941. *J. Biol. Chem.*, **141**:3–27.

Barker, H. A., and J. V. Beck. 1942. *J. Bact.*, **43**:291–304.

Barron, E. S. G., and A. B. Hastings. 1933. *J. Biol. Chem.*, **100**:155–182.

Barron, E. S. G., and C. M. Lyman. 1939. *J. Biol. Chem.*, **127**:143–161.

Baumann, C. A., and F. J. Stare. 1939. *Physiol. Rev.*, **19**:353–388.

Behrens, O. K. 1941. *J. Biol. Chem.*, **141**:503–508.

Berger, J., M. J. Johnson, and W. H. Peterson. 1937–1938. *Enzymologia*, **4**:31–35; *J. Biol. Chem.*, **124**:395–408; *J. Bact.*, **36**:521–545.

Berger, J., and M. J. Johnson. 1940. *J. Biol. Chem.*, **133**:157–172.

Berger, J., M. J. Johnson, and C. A. Baumann. 1941. *J. Biol. Chem.*, **137**:389–395.

Bergmann, M., L. Zervas, H. Schleich, and F. Leinert. 1932. *Z. physiol. Chem.*, **212**:72–84.

Bergmann, M., and L. Zervas. 1934. *Z. physiol. Chem.*, **224**:11–17.

Bergmann, M., L. Zervas, and H. Schleich. 1934. *Z. physiol. Chem.*, **224**:45–51.

Bergmann, M., L. Zervas, and J. S. Fruton. 1935. *J. Biol. Chem.*, **111**:225–244.

Bergmann, M., and J. S. Fruton. 1937. *J. Biol. Chem.*, **117**:189–202.

Bergmann, M., and J. S. Fruton. 1941. *Advances in Enzymol.*, **1**:63–98.

Berman, N., and L. F. Rettger. 1918. *J. Bact.*, **3**:367–388.

Bernheim, F., M. L. C. Bernheim, and M. D. Webster. 1935. *J. Biol. Chem.*, **110**:165–172.

Berry, J. A. 1933. *J. Bact.*, **25**:433–434.

Bigwood, E.-J., and J. Thomas. 1935. *Compt. rend. soc. biol.*, **120**:69–72.

Booth, V. H. 1938. *Biochem. J.*, **32**: 494–502, 503–507.

Booth, V. H., and D. E. Green. 1938. *Biochem. J.*, **32**:855–861.

Bourquelot, E. 1896. *Compt. rend. soc. biol.*, **48**:205–207.

Bovarnick, M. 1941. *Proc. Soc. Exptl. Biol. Med.*, **47**:191–193.

Bradley, L. A., and L. F. Rettger. 1927. *J. Bact.*, **13**:321–345.

Brewer, C. R., and C. H. Werkman. 1939–1940. *Enzymologia*, **6**:273–281; **8**:318–326.

Brunstein, A. 1901. *Botan. Centr. Beihefte*, **10**:1–50.

Buchanan, R. E., and E. I. Fulmer. 1930. *Physiology and Biochemistry of Bacteria*, Vol. III. Williams & Wilkins Co., Baltimore.

Burk, D., C. K. Horner, and H. Lineweaver. 1932. *J. Cellular Comp. Physiol.*, **1**:435–449.

Burk, D. 1934. *Ergeb. Enzymforsch.*, **3**:23–56.

Caldwell, M. L., and M. G. Tyler. 1931. *J. Am. Chem. Soc.*, **53**:2316–2320.

Callow, A. B. 1923. *J. Path. Bact.*, **26**:320–325.

Callow, A. B. 1926. *Biochem. J.*, **20**:247–252.

Chakravorty, P. N., and R. Ballentine. 1941. *J. Am. Chem. Soc.*, **63**:2030–2031.

Chapman, G. H., C. Berens, A. Peters, and L. Curcio. 1934. *J. Bact.*, **28**:343–363.

Christensen, W. B., W. H. Peterson, and M. J. Johnson. 1938. *J. Biol. Chem.*, **123**:XXI–XXII.

Cohen, P. P. 1939. "Inhibition of Dehydrogenases and Related Systems," Chapter VII of *Respiratory Enzymes* by Elvehjem and Associates. Burgess Publishing Co., Minneapolis, Minn.

Collins, M. A., and B. W. Hammer. 1934. *J. Bact.*, **27**:473–485, 487–496.

Colowick, S. P., and H. M. Kalckar. 1943. *J. Biol. Chem.*, **148**:117–126.

Console, A. D., and O. Rahn. 1938. *J. Bact.*, **36**:47–52.

Coulthard, C. E., R. Michaelis, W. F. Short, G. Sykes, G. E. H. Skrimshire, A. F. B. Standfast, J. H. Birkinshaw, and H. Raistrick. 1942. *Nature*, **150**:634–635

Cowles, P. B., and L. F. Rettger. 1931. *J. Bact.*, **21**:167–182.

Das, N. B. 1936. *Biochem. J.*, **30**:1080–1087, 1617–1621.

Davidson, J. N. 1942. *Biochem. J.*, **36**:252–258.

Davies, R. 1943. *Biochem. J.*, **37**:230–238.

Deere, C. J. 1939. *J. Bact.*, **37**:473–483.

Deere, C. J., A. D. Dulaney, and I. D. Michelson. 1939. *J. Bact.*, **37**:355-363.
Dewan, J. G., and D. E. Green. 1938. *Biochem. J.*, **32**:626–639.
Dixon, M. 1938. *Enzymologia*, **5**:198–225.
Doudoroff, M. 1943. *J. Biol. Chem.*, **151**:351–361.
Doudoroff, M., W. Z. Hassid, and H. A. Barker. 1944. *Science*, **100**:315–316.
Dox, A. W. 1910. *U. S. Dept. Agr., Bur. Animal Industry Bull.* 120.
Dox, A. W., and R. Golden. 1911. *J. Biol. Chem.*, **10**:183–186.
Dubos, R. J., and B. F. Miller. 1937. *J. Biol. Chem.*, **121**:429–445.
Dubos, R. J. 1940–1941. *Bact. Rev.*, **4**:1–16; *Bull. N. Y. Acad. Med.*, **17**:405–422.
Dyckerhoff, H., and R. Armbruster. 1933. *Z. physiol. Chem.*, **219**:38–56.
Edwards, O. F., and L. F. Rettger. 1937. *J. Bact.*, **34**:489–515.
Elberg, S. S., and K. F. Meyer. 1939. *J. Bact.*, **37**:541-565.
Elliott, K. A. C. 1941. *Physiol. Rev.*, **21**:267–306.
Elvehjem, C. A., and Associates, 1939. *Respiratory Enzymes.* Burgess Publishing Co., Minneapolis, Minn.
Esselen, W. B. 1939. *Food Research*, **4**:329–334.
Euler, H. von, and R. Nilsson. 1926. *Z. physiol. Chem.*, **155**:186–194.
Euler, H. von, and E. Brunius. 1928. *Z. physiol. Chem.*, **175**:52–67.
Euler, H. von, and K. Myrbäck. 1929. *Z. physiol. Chem.*, **181**:1–14.
Euler, H. von, and F. Schlenk. 1937. *Z. physiol. Chem.*, **246**:64–82.
Euler, H. von, E. Adler, and T. S. Eriksen. 1937. *Z. physiol. Chem.*, **248**:227–241.
Evans, W. C., W. R. C. Handley, and F. C. Happold. 1941. *Biochem. J.*, **35**:207–212.
Falk, K. G. 1924. *The Chemistry of Enzyme Action.* Chemical Catalog Co., New York.
Farkas, A., L. Farkas, and J. Yudkin. 1934. *Proc. Roy. Soc. London, B*, **115**:373–379.
Farrell, M. A. 1934–1935. *J. Bact.*, **27**:24–25; **29**:411–435.
Fermi, C. 1892. *Centr. Bakt.*, **12**:713–715.
Fink, H., and R. Lechner. 1940. *Biochem. Z.*, **304**:425–435.
Fleming, W. L., and J. M. Neill. 1927. *J. Exptl. Med.*, **45**:169–174, 947–959.
Frei, W., L. Riedmüller, and F. Almasy. 1934. *Biochem. Z.*, **274**:253–267.
Frei, W. 1935. *Centr. Bakt., I Abt. Orig.*, **134**:26–35.
Franke, W. 1940. *Angew. Chem.*, **53**:580–593.
Franke, W. 1943. *Angew. Chem.*, **56**: 55–60, 71–75.
Fruton, J. S. 1941. *Wallerstein Labs. Commun.*, **4**:121–130.
Fujita, A., and T. Kodama. 1934. *Biochem. Z.*, **273**:186–197.
Gaffron, H. 1942. *J. Gen. Physiol.*, **26**:195–217.
Gale, E. F. 1938–1939. *Biochem. J.*, **32**:1583–1599; **33**:1012–1027.
Gale, E. F., and M. Stephenson. 1939. *Biochem. J.*, **33**:1245–1256.
Gale, E. F., and H. M. R. Epps. 1943. *Nature*, **152**:327–328.
Gauze, G. F. 1942. *Biokhimiya*, **7**:25–31 (1943. *Chem. Abstr.*, **37**:4760).
Gibson, T. 1935. *J. Bact.*, **28**:295–311, 313–322; **29**:491–502.
Gingrich, W., and F. Schlenk. 1944. *J. Bact.*, **47**:535–550.
Glinka-Tschernorutzky, H. 1930. *Biochem. Z.*, **226**:62–66.
Gorini, C. 1930, 1933. *J. Bact.*, **20**:297–298; *Arch. Mikrobiol.*, **4**:123–130.
Gorbach, G. 1930, 1937. *Arch. Mikrobiol.*, **1**:537–576; *Enzymologia*, **3**:65–74.
Gorbach, G., and E. Pirch. 1936. *Enzymologia*, **1**:191–198.
Grassmann, W., and H. Dyckerhoff. 1928. *Ber. deut. chem. Ges.*, **61**:656–670.

Grassmann, W., H. Dyckerhoff, and O. von Schoenebeck. 1929. *Ber. deut. chem. Ges.*, **62**:1307–1310.

Grassmann, W., and H. Rubenbauer. 1931. *Münch. med. Wochschr.*, **78**:1817–1819.

Grassmann, W., L. Zechmeister, G. Tóth, and R. Stadler. 1933. *Liebig's Ann.*, **503**:167–179.

Grassmann, W., and F. Schneider. 1934. *Biochem. Z.*, **273**:452–462.

Green, A. A., and S. P. Colowick. 1944. *Ann. Rev. Biochem.*, **13**:155–186.

Green, D. E., L. H. Stickland, and H. L. A. Tarr. 1934. *Biochem. J.*, **28**:1812–1824.

Green, D. E., and J. G. Dewan. 1938. *Biochem. J.*, **32**:1200–1203.

Green, D. E. 1940. *Mechanisms of Biological Oxidations.* Cambridge University Press, Cambridge.

Green, D. E., D. Herbert, and V. Subrahmanyan. 1940. *J. Biol. Chem.*, **135**:795–796.

Green, D. E., W. W. Westerfeld, B. Vennesland., and W. E. Knox. 1941. *J. Biol. Chem.*, **140**:683–684.

Green, D. E., and P. K. Stumpf. 1944. *Ann. Rev. Biochem.*, **13**:1–24.

Gross, H. 1931. *Centr. Bakt., I Abt. Orig.*, **122**:354–361; **123**:212–218.

Haas, E., B. L. Horecker, and T. R. Hogness. 1940. *J. Biol. Chem.*, **136**:747–774.

Haas, E. 1938, 1943. *Biochem. Z.*, **298**:378–390; *J. Biol. Chem.*, **148**:481–493.

Hadley, F. P., P. Hadley, and W. W. Eathen. 1941. *J. Infectious Diseases*, **68**:264–277.

Haines, R. B. 1932–1933. *Biochem. J.*, **26**:323–336; **27**:466–474.

Hao, L. C., E. I. Fulmer, and L. A. Underkofler. 1943. *Ind. Eng. Chem.*, **35**:814–818.

Happold, F. C. 1930. *Biochem. J.*, **24**:1737–1743.

Harter, L. L., and J. L. Weimer. 1921. *J. Agr. Research*, **22**:371–377.

Harvey, E. N. 1941. *Ann. Rev. Biochem.*, **10**:531–552.

Heard, R. D. H., and A. M. Wynne. 1933. *Biochem. J.*, **27**:1655–1659.

Hecht, M., and H. Civin. 1936. *J. Biol. Chem.*, **116**:477–488.

Hehre, E. J. 1943. *Proc. Soc. Exptl. Biol. Med.*, **54**:240–241.

Hestrin, S. 1940. *Enzymologia*, **8**:193–203.

Hestrin, S., S. Avineri-Shapiro, and M. Aschner. 1943. *Biochem. J.*, **37**:450–456.

Hino, S. 1924. *Z. physiol. Chem.*, **133**:100–115.

Hoberman, H. D., and D. Rittenberg. 1943. *J. Biol. Chem.*, **147**:211–227.

Hock, C. W. 1939. *Plant Physiol.*, **14**:797–807.

Hofmann, E. 1934, 1936. *Biochem. Z.*, **272**:133–143, 417–425; **287**:271–275.

Hoover, S. R., and F. E. Allison. 1935. *Trans. 3rd Intern. Congr. Soil Sci.* (Oxford, Eng.), **1**:158–160.

Hopkins, F. G., C. Lutwak-Mann, and E. J. Morgan. 1939. *Nature*, **143**:556–557.

Horn, F. 1933. *Z. physiol. Chem.*, **216**:244–247.

Horowitz-Wlassowa, L. M., and M. J. Livschitz. 1935. *Centr. Bakt., II Abt.*, **92**:424–435.

Hotchkiss, M. 1935. *J. Bact.*, **29**:391–398.

Howell, S. F., and J. B. Sumner. 1934. *J. Biol. Chem.*, **104**:619–626.

Huddleson, I. F., and W. H. Stahl. 1943. *Mich. State Coll. Agr. Exp. Sta. Tech. Bull.* 182, 57–63.

Imaizumi, M. 1938. *J. Biochem. Japan*, **27**:45–64, 65–79, 199–211, 213–225, 227–230.

Jame, L., R. Crosnier, and F. Morel. 1935. *Compt. rend. soc. biol.*, **119**:849–850.

Jensen, L. B., and D. P. Grettie. 1937. *Food Research*, **2**:97–120.
Jensen, H., and L. E. Tenenbaum. 1943. *J. Biol. Chem.*, **147**:737–738.
Johnson, F. H., and E. N. Harvey. 1938. *J. Cellular Comp. Physiol.*, **11**:213–232.
Johnson, F. H., K. L. van Schouwenburg, and A. van der Burg. 1939. *Enzymologia*, **7**:195–224.
Johnson, M. J. 1941. *J. Biol. Chem.*, **137**:575–586.
Johnson, M. J., and J. Berger. 1941. *Advances Enzymology*, **2**:69–92.
Johnston, W. W., and A. M. Wynne. 1935. *J. Bact.*, **30**:491–501.
Jones, L. R. 1905. *N. Y. Agr. Exp. Sta. Tech. Bull.* 11, 291–368. Geneva, N. Y.
Kalanthar, A. 1898. *Z. physiol. Chem.*, **26**:88–101.
Kalckar, H. M. 1944. *J. Biol. Chem.*, **153**:355–367.
Kalnitsky, G., and C. H. Werkman. 1943. *Arch. Biochem.*, **2**:113–124.
Karström, H. 1930. "Über die Enzymbildung in Bakterien und über einigie physiologische Eigenschaften der untersuchten Bakterienarten." Thesis, Helsingfors University, Helsinki, Finland.
Karström, H. 1938. *Ergeb. Enzymforsch.*, **7**:350–376.
Kastle, J. H., and A. S. Loevenhart. 1900. *Am. Chem. J.*, **24**:491–525.
Katagiri, H., and K. Kitahara. 1937. *Biochem. J.*, **31**:909–914.
Katagiri, H., and S. Murakami. 1939. *J. Agr. Chem. Soc. Japan*, **15**:1141–1142.
Kawabata, S. 1934. *Japan. Lit. Tuberk.-Forsch.*, **3**:49–51 (1936. *Chem. Abstr.*, **30**:8284).
Kawahara, T. 1929. *Bull. Agr. Chem. Soc. Japan*, **5**:7–8.
Keilin, D. 1929, 1933. *Proc. Roy. Soc. London, B*, **104**:206–252; *Ergeb. Enzymforsch.*, **2**:239–271.
Keilin, D., and E. F. Hartree. 1936, 1938, 1939. *Proc. Roy. Soc. London, B*, **121**:173–191; **124**:397–405; **125**:171–186; **127**:167–191.
Keilin, D., and T. Mann. 1937. *Proc. Roy. Soc. London, B*, **122**:119–133.
Kellerman, K. F., L. G. McBeth, F. M. Scales, and N. R. Smith. 1913. *Centr. Bakt., II Abt.*, **39**:502–522.
Kendall, A. I., and H. Chinn. 1938. *J. Infectious Diseases*, **62**:330–336.
Kerr, R. W. 1943. *J. Am. Chem. Soc.*, **65**:188–193.
Kertesz, Z. I. 1931, 1936. *Plant Physiol.*, **6**:249–264; *Ergeb. Enzymforsch.*, **5**:233–258.
Kirsanova, V. A. 1936. *Biokhimiya*, **1**:386–389.
Kluyver, A. J., and H. J. L. Donker. 1925. *Proc. Konink. Akad. Wetenschappen Amsterdam*, **28**:297–313.
Knaysi, G. 1941. *J. Bact.*, **42**:587–589.
Knight, B. C. J. G. 1936. "Bacterial Nutrition." *Med. Res. Council (London) Special Rept. Ser.* 210.
Knopfmacher, H. P., and A. J. Salle. 1941. *J. Gen. Physiol.*, **24**:377–397.
Kohn, H. I. 1938. *Biochem. J.*, **32**:2075–2083.
Kohn, H. I., and J. R. Klein. 1940. *J. Biol. Chem.*, **135**:685–689.
Koser, S. A. 1918. *J. Infectious Diseases*, **23**:377–379.
Krampitz, L. O., and C. H. Werkman. 1941. *Biochem. J.*, **35**:595–602.
Krampitz, L. O., H. G. Wood, and C. H. Werkman. 1943. *J. Biol. Chem.*, **147**:243–253.
Krebs, H. A. 1932, 1933, 1937, 1941, 1942. *Klin. Wochschr.*, **11**:1744–1748; *Z. physiol. Chem.*, **217**:191–227; *Biochem. J.*, **31**:661–671, 2095–2124; *Nature*, **147**:560–570; *Biochem. J.*, **36**:IX.

Krebs, H. A., and W. A. Johnson. 1937. *Biochem. J.*, **31**:645–660.
Krebs, H. A., and L. V. Eggleston. 1940. *Biochem. J.*, **34**:1383–1395.
Kuhn, R., and H. Rudy. 1936. *Ber. deut. chem. Ges.*, **69**:1974–1977.
Kunitz, M. 1940. *J. Gen. Physiol.*, **24**:15–32.
Lagrange, E. 1926. *Ann. inst. Pasteur*, **40**:242–251.
Laki, K., F. B. Straub, and A. Szent-Györgyi. 1937. *Z. physiol. Chem.*, **247**:I–II.
Leahy, H. W., L. A. Sandholzer, and M. R. Woodside. 1939. *J. Bact.*, **38**:117.
Leahy, H. W., H. E. Stokinger, and C. M. Carpenter. 1940. *J. Bact.*, **40**:435–440.
Lee, S. B., and W. W. Umbreit. 1940. *Centr. Bakt., II Abt.*, **101**:354–363.
Lee, S. B., and P. W. Wilson. 1943. *J. Biol. Chem.*, **151**:377–385.
Leibowitz, J., and S. Hestrin. 1942. *Biochem. J.*, **36**:772–785.
Leopold, H., and M. P. Starbanow. 1943. *Biochem. Z.*, **314**:232–249.
Lewis, I. M. 1934. *J. Bact.*, **28**:619–639.
Lindegren, C. C. 1944. *Wallerstein Labs. Commun.*, **7**:153–168.
Lintner, C. J., and E. Kröber. 1895. *Ber. deut. chem. Ges.*, **28**:1050–1056.
Lipmann, F. 1937, 1939. *Enzymologia*, **4**:65–72; *Nature*, **143**:436; **144**:381–382.
Lipmann, F. 1941. *Advances Enzymology*, **1**:99–162.
Lipmann, F., and L. C. Tuttle. 1944. *J. Biol. Chem.*, **153**:571–582.
Lipton, M. A., A. Arnold, and J. Berger. 1939. "The Oxidases, Catalase, and Peroxidase," Chapter III in *Respiratory Enzymes* by Elvehjem and Associates. Burgess Publishing Co., Minneapolis, Minn.
Lockwood, L. B., B. Tabenkin, and G. E. Ward. 1941. *J. Bact.*, **42**:51–61.
Lohmann, K. 1932. *Biochem. Z.*, **254**:332–354.
Lohmann, K., and P. Schuster. 1937. *Biochem. Z.*, **294**:188–214.
Lowenstein, L., W. L. Fleming, and J. M. Neill. 1929. *J. Exptl. Med.*, **49**:475–479.
Lüers, H., and W. Wasmund. 1922. *Fermentforsch.*, **5**:169–235.
Luippold, E. 1929. *Jahrb. wiss. Botan.*, **70**:26–56.
Lutwak-Mann, C. 1936, 1938. *Biochem. J.*, **30**:1405–1412; **32**:1364–1374.
Lwoff, A., and M. Lwoff. 1937. *Proc. Roy. Soc. London, B*, **122**:352–359, 360–373.
MacFadyen, D. A. 1934. *J. Biol. Chem.*, **107**:297–308.
Macfarlane, M. G. 1936, 1939. *Biochem. J.*, **30**:1369–1379; **33**:565–578.
Macfarlane, M. G., and M. H. Salaman. 1938. *Brit. J. Exptl. Path.*, **19**:184–191.
Macfarlane, M. G., and B. C. J. G. Knight. 1941. *Biochem. J.*, **35**:884–902.
Main, E. R., and L. E. Shinn. 1939. *J. Biol. Chem.*, **128**:417–423.
Makrinov, I. A. 1932. *Centr. Bakt., II Abt.*, **85**:339–348.
Martius, C. 1938. *Z. physiol. Chem.*, **257**:29–42.
Martius, C., and F. Knoop. 1937. *Z. physiol. Chem.*, **246**:I–II.
Maschmann, E. 1937, 1938, 1939. *Biochem. Z.*, **294**:1–33; **295**:1–10, 351–368, 391–399, 400–401, 402–404; **297**:284–296; **300**:89–112; **302**:332–368.
Maslow, H., and W. C. Davison. 1926. *J. Biol. Chem.*, **68**:95–99.
McLeod, J. W., and J. Gordon. 1922, 1923, 1925. *Biochem. J.*, **16**:499–506; *J. Path. Bact.*, **26**:326–331, 332–343; **28**:147–153.
McQuarrie, E. B., A. J. Liebmann, R. G. Kluener, and A. T. Venosa. 1944. *Arch. Biochem.*, **5**:307–315.
Meldrum, N. U. 1934. *Cellular Respiration.* Methuen and Co., London.
Menon, K. P. V. 1934. *Ann. Botany*, **48**:187–210.
Meyer, K., E. Chaffee, G. L. Hobby, and M. H. Dawson. 1941. *J. Exptl. Med.* **73**:309–326.
Meyerhof, O. 1939. *New Engl. J. Med.*, **220**:49–56.
Mischoustin, E. N. 1932. *Centr. Bakt., II Abt.*, **87**:150–166.

Mitchell, N. B., and M. Levine. 1938. *J. Bact.*, **36**:587–598.
Miwa, T., and S. Yoshii. 1934. *Science Repts. Tokyo Bunrika Daigaku*, **1**:243–270 (1934. *Chem. Abstr.*, **28**:5854).
Miyagawa, K. 1936. *J. Agr. Chem. Soc. Japan*, **12**:74–81.
Morris, J. L., and E. E. Ecker. 1924. *J. Infectious Diseases*, **34**:592–598.
Much, H. 1908. *Biochem. Z.*, **14**:143–155.
Myrbäck, K., and H. von Euler. 1924. *Ber. deut. chem. Ges.*, **57**:1073–1076.
Myrbäck, K. 1933. *Ergeb. Enzymforsch.*, **2**:139–168.
Myrbäck, K., and E. Vasseur. 1943. *Z. physiol. Chem.*, **277**:171–180.
Nakamura, H. 1940. *Acta Phytochim (Japan)*, **11**:239–247.
Needham, D. M. 1937. *Ann. Rev. Biochem.*, **6**:395–418.
Negelein, E., and W. Gerischer. 1936. *Biochem. Z.*, **284**:289–296.
Negelein, E., and H. Brömel. 1939. *Biochem. Z.*, **300**:225–239.
Neill, J. M., and O. T. Avery. 1924. *J. Exptl. Med.*, **40**:405–422.
Neill, J. M., and W. L. Fleming. 1927. *J. Exptl. Med.*, **45**:937–946.
Neill, J. M., and E. L. Gaspari. 1927. *J. Exptl. Med.*, **45**:151–162.
Nelson, J. M., and G. Bloomfield. 1924. *J. Am. Chem. Soc.*, **46**:1025–1043.
Neuberg, C., and W. M. Cahill. 1936. *Enzymologia*, **1**:22–38.
Neuberg, C., and E. Hofmann. 1932. *Biochem. Z.*, **256**:450–461.
Neuberg, C., and O. Rosenthal. 1924. *Biochem. Z.*, **145**:186–188.
Nicholson, W. N., M. Nierenstein, J. C. Pool, and N. V. Price. 1931. *Biochem. J.*, **25**:752–755.
Northrop, J. H. 1939. *Crystalline Enzymes*, Columbia University Press, New York.
Novy, F. G., M. H. Soule, H. R. Roehm, and F. G. Novy, Jr. 1925. "Microbic Respiration," reprinted from *J. Infectious Diseases*, **36**:109–167, 168–232, 245–308, 343–382.
Ohlmeyer, P., and S. Ochoa. 1938. *Biochem. Z.*, **293**:338–350.
O'Kane, D. J., and W. W. Umbreit. 1942. *J. Biol. Chem.*, **142**:25–30.
Ono, K. 1935. *J. Agr. Chem. Soc. Japan*, **11**:803–807.
Oppenheimer, C. 1925–1937. *Die Fermente und ihre Wirkung*, 5th Ed., 4 Vols. Georg Thieme, Leipzig (1925–1929); suppl. W. Junk, The Hague (1936–1937).
Oppenheimer, C., and K. Stern. 1939. *Biological Oxidation.* W. Junk, The Hague.
Ordal, E. J., and H. O. Halvorson. 1939. *J. Bact.*, **38**:199–220.
Ordal, E. J., and H. M. Tsuchiya. 1939. *Rept. Proc. 3rd Intern. Congr. Microbiol.*, **1939**:217–219.
Orla-Jensen, A. D. 1934. *Acta Path. Microbiol. Scand.*, **11**:312–322.
Parnas, J. K. 1943. *Nature*, **151**:577–580.
Penney, J. R., and S. S. Zilva. 1943. *Biochem. J.*, **37**:403–417.
Pett, L. B., and A. M. Wynne. 1933, 1934, 1938. *Biochem. J.*, **27**:1660–1671; **28**:365–371; **32**:563–566.
Phelps, A. S., and P. W. Wilson. 1941. *Proc. Soc. Exptl. Biol. Med.*, **47**:473–476.
Porges, N., T. F. Clark, and S. I. Aronovsky. 1941. *Ind. Eng. Chem.*, **33**:1065–1067.
Potter, V. R. 1939. "Dehydrogenases," Chapter II in *Respiratory Enzymes* by C. A. Elvehjem and Associates. Burgess Publishing Co., Minneapolis, Minn.
Powers, W. H., S. Lewis, and C. R. Dawson. 1944. *J. Gen. Physiol.*, **27**:167–180.
Pringsheim, H., and W. G. Hensel. 1931. *Ber. deut. chem. Ges.*, **64**:1431–1434.
Pringsheim, H., and P. Ohlmeyer. 1932. *Ber. deut. chem. Ges.*, **65**:1242–1248.

Proskuryakov, N. 1936. *Microbiology (USSR)*, **5**:32–39.
Quastel, J. H. 1924, 1937. *Biochem. J.*, **18**:365–380; *Enzymologia*, **2**:37–42.
Quastel, J. H., and M. D. Whetham. 1924, 1925. *Biochem. J.*, **18**:519–534; **19**: 520–531, 645–651.
Quastel, J. H., M. Stephenson, and M. D. Whetham. 1925. *Biochem. J.*, **19**:304–317.
Quastel, J. H., and W. R. Wooldridge. 1927, 1928, 1929. *Biochem. J.*, **21**:148–168, 1224–1251; **22**:689–702; **23**:115–137.
Quastel, J. H., and D. M. Webley. 1939. *Nature*, **144**:633–634.
Rae, J. J., and E. V. Eastcott. 1940. *J. Biol. Chem.*, **136**:443–447.
Rahn, O. 1938. *Growth*, **2**:363–367.
Rhoades, H. E. 1941. *J. Bact.*, **42**:99–115.
Robertson, W. van B., M. W. Ropes, and W. Bauer. 1940. *J. Biol. Chem.*, **133**:261–276.
Ruehle, G. L. A. 1923. *J. Bact.*, **8**:487–491.
Sacchetti, M. 1934. *Ind. saccar. ital.*, **27**:49–54 (1934. *Chem. Abstr.*, **28**:3517).
Sakaguchi, K., and Y. Shizume. 1937. *J. Agr. Chem. Soc. Japan*, **13**:309–312.
Salle, A. J. 1943. *Fundamental Principles of Bacteriology.* McGraw-Hill Book Co., New York.
Scales, F. M. 1914. *J. Biol. Chem.*, **19**:459–472.
Schales, O. 1943. *Arch. Biochem.*, **2**:487–490.
Schaller, K. 1942. *Z. physiol. Chem.*, **276**:271–274.
Schlenk, F. 1942. *Symposium on Respiratory Enzymes*, pp. 104–133. University of Wisconsin Press, Madison.
Schlenk, F. 1942. *J. Biol. Chem.*, **146**:619–625.
Schlenk, F., and W. Gingrich. 1942. *J. Biol. Chem.*, **143**:295–296.
Schreder, K., R. Brunner, and R. Hampe. 1933. *Wochschr. Brau.*, **50**:233, 237, 243–245.
Seo, Y. 1908. *Arch. Exptl. Path. Pharmakol.*, **58**:440–449.
Silverman, M., and C. H. Werkman. 1938, 1939. *Proc. Soc. Exptl. Biol. Med.*, **38**:823–827; *J. Bact.*, **38**:25–32; *Enzymologia*, **5**:385–387.
Simola, P. E. 1931. *Ann. Acad. Sci. Fennicae*, Ser. A., **34**:1–115.
Skinner, C. E. 1938. *J. Bact.*, **35**:415–424.
Söhngen, N. L. 1910, 1911. *Proc. Konink. Akad. Wetenschappen Amsterdam*, **19**:689–703; **20**:126–130.
Soule, M. H. 1928. "Gas Metabolism of Bacteria," Chapter 18, pp. 250–267 in *The Newer Knowledge of Bacteriology and Immunology*, ed. by E. O. Jordan and I. S. Falk. University of Chicago Press, Chicago.
Sperry, J. A., and L. F. Rettger. 1915. *J. Biol. Chem.*, **20**:445–459.
Stapp, C. 1923. *Biochem. Z.*, **141**:42–69.
Stare, F. J., M. A. Lipton, and J. M. Goldinger. 1941. *J. Biol. Chem.*, **141**:981–987.
Steinbach, K. F. 1940. "Investigations into Bacterial Respiration with Special Reference to Hydrogen Donators." Thesis, University of Zuerich. Printed by J. Hagmann, Zuerich.
Stephenson, M. 1928. *Biochem. J.*, **22**:605–614.
Stephenson, M., and L. H. Stickland. 1931, 1932, 1933. *Biochem. J.*, **25**:205–214, 215–220; **26**:712–724; **27**:1517–1527, 1528–1532.
Stephenson, M. 1937. *Ergeb. Enzymforsch.*, **6**:139–156.
Stephenson, M. 1939. *Bacterial Metabolism*, Longmans, Green and Co., New York

Stern, K. G. 1934, 1936, 1938, 1940. *Biochem. J.*, **28**:949–964; *J. Biol. Chem.*, **114**:473–494; *Enzymologia*, **5**:190–197; *Ann. Rev. Biochem.*, **9**:1–42.
Stern, K. G., and J. W. Hofer. 1937. *Enzymologia*, **3**:82–95.
Stern, K. G., and J. L. Melnick. 1940. *J. Biol. Chem.*, **135**:365–369.
Stickland, L. H. 1929. *Biochem. J.*, **23**:1187–1198.
Still, J. L. 1940, 1941. *Biochem. J.*, **34**:1177–1182, 1374–1382; **35**:380–389, 390–391.
Stoklasa, J. 1911. *Centr. Bakt., II Abt.*, **29**:385–519.
Stotz, E., A. M. Altschul, and T. R. Hogness. 1938. *J. Biol. Chem.*, **124**:745–754.
Stotz, E., A. E. Sidwell, and T. R. Hogness. 1938. *J. Biol. Chem.*, **124**:733–744.
Stotz, E., W. W. Westerfeld, and R. L. Berg. 1944. *J. Biol. Chem.*, **152**:41–50.
Straub, F. B. 1942. *Z. physiol. Chem.*, **272**:219–226.
Straughn, M. N., and W. Jones. 1909. *J. Biol. Chem.*, **6**:245–255.
Stumpf, P. K., and D. E. Green. 1944. *J. Biol. Chem.*, **153**:387–399.
Sugg, J. Y., W. L. Fleming, and J. M. Neill. 1927. *J. Exptl. Med.*, **46**:909–916.
Sumner, J. B. 1933, 1935. *Science*, **78**:335; *Ann. Rev. Biochem.*, **4**:37–58.
Sumner, J. B., and G. F. Somers. 1943. *Chemistry and Methods of Enzymes.* Academic Press, Inc., New York.
Swenson, T. L., and H. Humfeld. 1942. *J. Agr. Research*, **65**:391–403.
Sykes, G. 1939. *J. Hyg.*, **39**: 463–469.
Tankó, B. 1932. *Biochem. Z.*, **247**:486–490.
Tauber, H. 1937. *Enzyme Chemistry.* John Wiley & Sons, New York.
Tauber, H. 1939. *J. Chem. Education*, **16**:10–15.
Tauber, H. 1943. *Enzyme Technology.* John Wiley & Sons, New York.
Thaysen, A. C., and H. J. Bunker. 1927. *The Microbiology of Cellulose, Hemicellulose, Pectin, and Gums.* Oxford University Press, Oxford.
Theorell, H. 1934, 1935. *Biochem. Z.*, **272**:155–156; **275**:30–36; **278**:263–290.
Theorell, H., and Å. Åkesson. 1939. *Science*, **90**:67.
Toda, T. 1930. *Centr. Bakt., I Abt. Orig.*, **117**:489–494.
Toda, T., and K. Urabe. 1935. *Japan. Lit. Tuberk.-Forsch.*, **4**:44 (1936. *Chem. Abstr.*, **30**:8286).
Tomota, S. 1940, 1941. *J. Biochem. Japan*, **32**:307–315, 401–403, 405–417; **33**:205–214.
Tomota, S., and H. Saito. 1940. *Tohoku J. Exptl. Med.*, **39**:211–214.
Trussell, R. E., and L. A. Weed. 1937. *J. Bact.*, **33**:381–388.
Truszkowski, R. 1930. *Acta Biol. Expt. (Warsaw)*, **5**:257–315 (1930. *Chem. Abstr.*, **26**:5590).
Twort, F. W. 1907. *Proc. Roy. Soc. London, B*, **79**:329–336.
Tytell, A. A., and B. S. Gould. 1941. *J. Bact.*, **42**:513–526.
Utter, M. F., and C. H. Werkman. 1941. *J. Bact.*, **42**:665–676.
Utter, M. F., L. O. Krampitz, and C. H. Werkman. 1944. *J. Bact.*, **47**:412.
Utzino, S., M. Imaizumi, and M. Nakayama. 1938. *J. Biochem. Japan*, **27**:257–264.
van Heyningen, W. E. 1940. *Biochem. J.*, **34**:1540–1545.
van Schouwenburg, K. L. 1940. *Enzymologia*, **8**:344–352.
van Schouwenburg, K. L., and A. van der Burg. 1940. *Enzymologia*, **9**:34–42.
Vercellana, G. 1936. *Centr. Bakt., I Abt. Orig.*, **136**:225–230.
Verona, O., and G. Lucchetti. 1931. *Boll. soc. intern. Microbiol. Sez. Ital.*, **3**:477–482.
Viehoever, A. 1913. *Centr. Bakt., II Abt.*, **39**:209–359.

Virtanen, A. I., and H. Karström. 1925, 1931. *Biochem. Z.*, **161**:9–46; *Acta Chem. Fennica, B*, **7**:17.
Virtanen, A. I., and J. Tarnanen. 1932. *Biochem. Z.*, **250**:193–211; *Z. physiol. Chem.*, **204**:247–258.
Wahlin, J. G. 1928. *J. Bact.*, **16**:355–373, 375–386.
Waksman, S. A. 1922. *Abstracts Bact.*, **6**:265–299, 331–360.
Waksman, S. A., and W. C. Davison. 1926. *Enzymes.* Williams & Wilkins Co., Baltimore.
Waldschmidt-Leitz, E., and R. P. Walton. 1929. *Enzyme Actions and Properties.* John Wiley & Sons, New York.
Wallerstein, L. 1939. *Ind. Eng. Chem.*, **31**:1218–1224.
Warburg, O. 1925, 1938. *Science*, **61**:575–582; *Ber. deut. chem. Ges.*, **58**:1001–1011; *Ergeb. Enzymforsch.*, **7**:210–245.
Warburg, O., and W. Christian. 1931, 1932, 1933, 1935, 1936, 1938, 1939. *Biochem. Z.*, **242**:206–227; **254**:438–458; **266**:377–411; **282**:157–205, 221–223; **287**:291–328; *Ber. deut. chem. Ges.*, **69**:228; *Biochem. Z.*, **298**:150–168, 368–377; **303**:40–68.
Waring, W. S., and C. H. Werkman. 1944. *Arch. Biochem.*, **4**:75–87.
Webster, M. D., and F. Bernheim. 1936. *J. Biol. Chem.*, **114**:265–271.
Weijlard, J., and H. Tauber. 1938. *J. Am. Chem. Soc.*, **60**:2263–2264.
Weil, L., and W. Kocholaty. 1937. *Biochem. J.*, **31**:1255–1267.
Weil, L., W. Kocholaty, and L. deS. Smith. 1939. *Biochem. J.*, **33**:893–897.
Werch, S. C., R. W. Jung, A. A. Day, T. E. Friedemann, and A. C. Ivy. 1942. *J. Infectious Diseases*, **70**:231–242.
Wieland, H. 1922. *Ergeb. Physiol.*, **20**:477–518.
Wiggert, W. P., and C. H. Werkman. 1938. *Biochem. J.*, **32**:101–107.
Wiggert, W. P., M. Silverman, M. F. Utter, and C. H. Werkman. 1940. *Iowa State Coll. J. Sci.*, **14**:179–186.
Wilson, E. J., Jr., T. J. Schoch, and C. S. Hudson. 1943. *J. Am. Chem. Soc.*, **65**:1380–1383.
Wilson, J. B., and P. W. Wilson. 1943. *J. Gen. Physiol.*, **26**:277–286.
Wilson, P. W. 1939. "Physical-Chemical Theory of Enzyme Reactions," Chapter X in *Respiratory Enzymes* by C. A. Elvehjem and Associates. Burgess Publishing Co., Minneapolis, Minn.
Wohlfeil, T., and P. Weiland. 1937. *Centr. Bakt., I Abt. Orig.*, **138**:388–400.
Wood, H. G., C. H. Werkman, A. Hemingway, and A. O. Nier. 1942. *J. Biol. Chem.*, **142**:31–45.
Woods, D. D. 1936. *Biochem. J.*, **30**:515–527.
Wooldridge, W. R., and V. Glass. 1937. *Biochem. J.*, **31**:526–531.
Yamagutchi, S., and S. Usami. 1939. *Cytologia*, **9**:419–429.
Young, R. M., and L. F. Rettger. 1943. *J. Bact.*, **46**:351–363.
Yudkin, J. 1932, 1937, 1938. *Biochem. J.*, **26**:1859–1871; *Enzymologia*, **2**:161–170; *Biol. Rev.*, **13**: 93–106.

7

BACTERIAL NUTRITION

A great many studies on the nutritional requirements of bacteria have appeared in the literature during the past few years. Although there have been several stimuli for these studies, two seem to be the most important. First, we have had very little knowledge of the basal or essential nutritional requirements of bacteria, especially of pathogenic bacteria. In the past many microorganisms have had to be cultivated on media containing complex mixtures of organic substances of unknown chemical composition, because their basal nutritional needs were unknown. Thus some knowledge of the requirements of these organisms would permit the use of much simpler culture media and would greatly simplify their cultivation for all types of morphological, biochemical, and immunological studies. Undoubtedly many of the discrepancies in the literature, as well as failures to isolate bacteria from various materials, have been due to lack of this information. Many times such difficulties have been unavoidable because, for example, it is almost an impossibility to make two different preparations of media containing complex organic substances of unknown chemical composition and have them the same.

In the second place, a great deal of interesting research has been reported since the discovery that certain microorganisms, like higher forms of life, require various accessory growth factors, or vitamins, for development in media free from proteins or their higher cleavage products. Four or five of the vitamins of the B-complex were shown to be of importance in the nutrition of microorganisms before they were demonstrated to be essential for higher forms of life. Thus many of the facts which have been observed in microbial nutrition have been directly applicable to other phases of nutrition.

No attempt will be made to cover the literature on the subject of microbial nutrition because the general reviews by Knorr (1925), Sergent (1928), Peskett (1933), Knight (1936), Burrows (1936), Lwoff (1938), Koser and Saunders (1938), Janke (1939), Trager (1941), Williams (1941), Schopfer (1943), and Peterson and Peterson (1945) have very adequately summarized the early work. Only a few typical studies of bacterial nutrition will be discussed with brief mention from time to time of similar studies of other cells.

GENERAL REQUIREMENTS FOR GROWTH

In general, bacteria have very diversified growth requirements. For example, certain organisms can synthesize new protoplasm and carry out all their life activities in simple aqueous media containing only ammonia, carbonate, and traces of inorganic salts; other bacteria are more deficient in synthetic powers and therefore must find in their environment more complex organic substances, such as amino acids and sugar, if they are to live. Some organisms can activate (use) atmospheric oxygen in their oxidative processes; some must obtain their oxygen from substances within the medium and are sensitive to atmospheric oxygen; others can exist under either aerobic or anaerobic conditions. Certain bacteria show optimum growth at *p*H 1.0 to 3.0, others at *p*H 10 or above. Some organisms exhibit their normal activities at temperatures below 0°C. and others at those above 65°C., whereas certain species are peculiar and will die rapidly if the temperature varies but a few degrees from 37.5°C.

For an organism to carry on its life processes, it must be supplied with material which can be transformed into new protoplasm, as well as substances which can serve as a source of energy for this transformation and for other cellular activities, such as motility. As Knight (1936) has pointed out, studies of the nutrition of bacteria involve a determination of not only the essential components necessary for growth, but also the optimum concentration and combination of chemical substances which will support life on continued subculture. Thus the term nutritional requirements means not only the natural food of the organism, but also the fundamental substances which the organism must get from its environment in order to live, grow, and reproduce. For example, garbage may serve as a suitable food for rats, but it is not one of their nutritional requirements, in the sense in which thiamin or riboflavin and certain amino acids are necessary for optimum development. One needs only to refer to *A Compilation of Culture Media for the Cultivation of Microorganisms* by Levine and Schoenlein (1930) to see at once that a great deal more is known about the food of bacteria than about their fundamental nutritional requirements.

The fundamental problem in the nutrition of any organism (animal, plant, or microbe) is the construction of a medium, or diet, of known composition which will permit optimum growth and reproduction. With bacteria this problem has led to the development of chemically defined or synthetic media, that is, media composed of known purified chemicals. In the past it has not been difficult to find carbon, nitrogen, and mineral compounds which could be utilized by bacteria. For certain species, however, various extracts of plant and animal tissues of unknown and often variable composition also had to be present in media before growth would occur. Because of this fact it has been difficult to define completely the requirements of many bacteria. The isolation, purification, and, finally, the identification of some of the active or essential components in the various extracts constitute important achievements in bacterial chemistry during the past decade.

Before the nutritional requirements of several individual bacterial species are discussed, a few brief remarks should be made concerning the general conditions necessary for the growth of bacteria. These requirements will be discussed under the following headings: the role of water, the inorganic requirements, the organic requirements, and the gaseous requirements. Although these four points are of fundamental importance in studies of the nutrition of bacteria, they are not the only general points which must be considered. For example, the age and condition of the inoculum may also be very important in certain cases, and an effort should always be made to keep the inoculum constant. Also, the reaction (*p*H) of the substrate has a marked effect on the growth of bacteria.

THE ROLE OF WATER

It is well known that water plays an extremely important role in all living processes. One needs only to read the review by Barnes and Jahn (1934), however, to realize ". . . the importance of water as a neglected component in chemical and biological systems." Water has many peculiar physical properties, such as maximum density at 4°C., high surface tension, and minimum compressibility at 50°C., but its great power as a solvent makes it an indispensable component of all biological systems.

Water is the vehicle by means of which all needed substances are brought to the cell and waste products are carried away. Cellular absorption, secretion, diffusion, and excretion could not take place without water. Since it serves as a solvent or dispersion medium for all other constituents of protoplasm, it is one of the most important and abundant substances in the living cell. Water exists not only as a pure solvent but also as water of hydration, combined with carbohydrates, proteins, and other substances. Furthermore, it is formed by the polymerization or synthesis of compounds and by the oxidation (dehydrogenation) of hydrogen-containing substances. Such water is called metabolic water; from 10 to 14 g. of metabolic water are formed per 100 cal. in the ordinary diet.

Although considerable information is available [see the reviews by Adolph (1933), Gortner (1932, 1934), and Barnes and Jahn (1934)] concerning the role of water in higher plants and animals, practically nothing is known about water metabolism in bacteria and other microorganisms. Little thought is usually given to this problem in studies of the nutrition of bacteria, merely because all bacteriological media contain a high percentage of water and it is assumed that they satisfy the water requirements of bacteria. The bacterial cell must be endowed with exceptional powers, however, to maintain precisely the balance between water and other cellular constituents in such an environment. We ordinarily think of water as passing freely into and out of the cell, because we are in the habit of regarding the plasma membrane as permeable to water, but this conception is not valid. The water supply of the cell must be very accurately controlled by the regulatory power of the membrane or by the protoplasm itself.

The importance of bound water, heavy water, and the various polymers of water [H_2O, $(H_2O)_2$, $(H_2O)_3$, etc.] in the metabolism of bacteria is unknown, but under certain conditions such waters must markedly influence bacterial activities. For example, in Chapter 3 we mentioned that bound water may account for the resistance of the bacterial spores to adverse conditions. It is also known that high concentrations of heavy water may be toxic to bacteria. Very little attention has been given to the effect of the various polymers of water on the growth of bacteria. Hegarty and Rahn (1934), however, observed that the growth rate of *Escherichia coli* was slower in media prepared from freshly distilled water (predominantly mono- and dihydrol) than from freshly melted ice water (predominantly trihydrol). They attributed the retardation of growth in the freshly distilled water to a lack of higher water polymers, which seem to be favorable, or necessary, for growth. Barnes and Jahn (1934) have also observed that the growth of certain protozoa is increased in water rich in trihydrol, $(H_2O)_3$. For example, when *Euglena gracilis* was cultivated in water high in monohydrol, the cell count increased 32 per cent in 10 to 16 days, whereas in water rich in trihydrol the count increased 105 per cent in the same time interval. Barnes is of the opinion that the higher-polymerized water molecules are of primary importance in many physiological processes and that they may account for the unexpected richness of the microflora of the arctic oceans.

THE INORGANIC REQUIREMENTS [1]

The continued life of bacteria, like that of other organisms, is dependent upon the presence of inorganic salts in their protoplasm and

[1] The literature on the inorganic requirements of plants, animals, and microorganisms has been reviewed in a comprehensive bibliography published (1939–1944) by the Chilean Nitrate Educational Bureau, Inc., New York.

in their surrounding medium. Salts serve bacteria in their metabolic activities both as constituents of substances formed, such as protoplasm, and as part of catalysts (enzymes) or activators of reactions. They function also as physical agents in establishing and maintaining osmotic pressure, concentration equilibria, and electric balance between the cell and its substrate.

Very little is known about the salt requirements of various bacteria or their exact function in such cells. Part of our ignorance of this subject is due to the fact that certain elements are effective in great dilution and may be present as a "trace" in the organic ingredients and other salts which are commonly used in preparing bacteriological media. Table 1, for instance, shows the extent to which certain organic substances commonly employed in preparing culture media are contaminated with inorganic materials.

TABLE 1

PRESENCE OF SEVERAL TRACE ELEMENTS † IN ORGANIC COMPOUNDS USED TO CULTURE MICROORGANISMS

[From Steinberg (1938)]

Substance	Group in Periodic Table																			
	I					II					III		IV				V		VII	VIII
	Li	Na	K	Cu	Ag	Mg	Ca	Zn	Sr	Ba	B	Al	Si	Ti	Sn	Pb	P	V	Mn	Fe
Bactopeptone, Difco	+	+	+	+	−	+	+	−	+	+?	−	+	+	−	−	+	+	−	+	+
Peptone, Witte	−	+*	+	+	−	+*	+*	−	+*	+	+	+	+*	−	+	+	−	+?	+	+*
Malt extract, Difco	−	+	+	+	−	+*	+*	−	+	+	−	+	+	+?	+	+	+	+?	+	+
Yeast extract, Difco	−	+*	+*	+	−	+*	+*	−	+*	+	−	+	+	−	−	+	−	+?	+	+*
i-Inositol, Pfanstiehl	−	−	−	+	−	+*	+*	−	−	−	−	+	+	−	−	+	−	+?	+	+*
Casein, Pfanstiehl	−	+	−	+	+	+	−	+?	−	−	−	−	−	−	−	+	+	−	−	−

+* = strong trace; +? = doubtful; − = negative or data not recorded.
† Demonstrated with a Bausch & Lomb large-sized quartz spectrograph and carbon arc.

Only very rigorous and specially designed experiments can determine the exact inorganic salt requirements of an organism. Usually such experiments are carried out either by determining the elements in the ash of a given organism or by cultivating it on synthetic substrates to which salts of known purity can be added. An elementary analysis of bacterial ash is of limited value because the organisms may contain nonessential elements, especially if they have been cultivated on media containing nonessential substances. Such analyses are, however, useful in determining the gross inorganic salts necessary for a medium. The second procedure for determining the salt requirements of an organism may also lead to erroneous results unless the ingredients of the synthetic media employed have been subjected to spectroscopic analysis. Although such experiments have been carried out with plants, animals, and higher fungi [Foster (1939), Steinberg (1935–1941)], only a few attempts have been made with bacteria [see Steinberg (1938), Waring and Werkman (1943, 1944), Young, Begg, and Pentz (1944), and the references in the following discussion].

The "trace"-element requirements of plants, animals, and higher fungi are now receiving considerable attention; similar studies of bacteria are needed before we can draw any general conclusions concerning their salt requirements. Until a few years ago it was thought that only ten elements (carbon, hydrogen, oxygen, nitrogen, sulfur, phosphorus, potassium, calcium, magnesium, and iron) were necessary for plant life, but we now know that this number is wholly inadequate. Although sodium was not listed in the first ten elements necessary for plant life, it was known that common salt was essential for animals, especially herbivorous ones. In recent years the list of elements occurring in plants and animals, and therefore possibly necessary for life, has lengthened considerably. The following list includes those elements so far reported as occurring in plants and animals:

Carbon	Sodium [2]	Manganese [2]	Arsenic	Beryllium
Hydrogen	Chlorine	Copper [2]	Selenium	Cadmium
Oxygen	Iodine	Zinc [2]	Thallium [2]	Chromium [2]
Nitrogen	Bromine	Tin [2]	Titanium	Cesium
Potassium [2]	Fluorine	Aluminum	Silver [2]	Cerium
Calcium [2]	Silicon	Rubidium	Molybdenum	Gold [2]
Phosphorus [2]	Boron [2]	Cobalt	Vanadium	Lanthanum [2]
Magnesium [2]	Lithium	Lead [2]	Radium	Thorium
Sulfur	Barium [2]	Nickel	Germanium	Zirconium
Iron [2]	Strontium	Mercury	Gallium	

At present it is impossible to say whether every one of the fifty elements found in plants and animals is essential, but certainly more than ten or twelve are needed for some forms of life. In this connection it is of interest to mention the work of Calvery (1942). He re-

[2] These elements have also been demonstrated in yeast by qualitative spectroscopic analysis [Richards and Troutman (1940)].

viewed the literature on the occurrence, nutritional value, and toxicity of a number of elements which are present in small quantities (20 p.p.m. per gram or less) in foods. With this information he was able to classify the trace elements into the following four classes:

1. *Nutritive trace elements,* or those which have been shown to play a definite role in normal biological processes: cobalt, copper, iron, iodine, manganese, and zinc. Physiological significance has also been ascribed to arsenic, aluminum, barium, bromine, fluorine, nickel, rubidium, and silicon, but, as Calvery has pointed out, their essential nature in higher animals has not been fully established except, possibly, that of fluorine.

2. *Nonnutritive and nontoxic trace elements,* or those which have not been demonstrated to be required by higher forms of life but which cause no deleterious effects when given to animals in quantities up to 100 p.p.m. of diet: aluminum, beryllium, boron, chromium, silicon, strontium, tin, titanium, and nickel.

3. *Nonnutritive and toxic trace elements,* or those which cause harmful effects in animals when administered in amounts of 100 p.p.m. or less in the diet: silver, bismuth, cadmium, fluorine, mercury, lead, arsenic, antimony, barium, bromine, selenium, thallium, molybdenum, vanadium, and thorium.

4. *Miscellaneous trace elements,* or those which have been reported to be present in foods but whose significance in nutrition is unestablished and whose toxicology has not been thoroughly investigated: cesium, germanium, gold, lanthanum, lithium, rubidium, thorium, zirconium.

We have mentioned that there is very little definite information concerning the general salt requirements of bacteria. However, since a few facts are available concerning the metabolic function of the elements in microorganisms, and since several studies with bacteria have produced some interesting information, these elements should be discussed here. The first four elements in the preceding list need not be mentioned, since they, together with phosphorus and sulfur, are essential components of all living cells.

Potassium. The function of potassium in organisms appears to be primarily catalytic. This is true of numerous other elements which do not enter into the composition of tissue or serve directly as food for producing energy. Actually, however, the exact role of potassium in the living cell is still unknown.

In spite of the fact that textbooks on plant and animal physiology and biochemistry state that potassium is necessary for all organisms, there is some evidence available to question such statements where bacteria are concerned. After reviewing the literature on this subject and carrying out personal researches as well, Rahn (1936) concluded that certain bacteria require no potassium for growth. Some of his results are summarized in Table 2, which needs no special explanation other than to call attention to the fact that rubidium and cesium can partially replace potassium in the nutrition of certain organisms. Braun and Mündel (1929) and Mueller (1935) have also demonstrated that potassium either is essential for or stimulates the growth of the diphtheria bacillus, and Davies (1942) has shown that this element is an essential factor in the fermentation of maize meal by *Clostridium acetobutylicum.*

Potassium is known to be necessary for the optimum growth of many other microorganisms, for example, the *Chlorella* species. It is also an activator for certain enzyme systems [see Quastel and Webley (1942)].

TABLE 2

POTASSIUM REQUIREMENTS OF VARIOUS ORGANISMS

[From Rahn (1936) and others]

Organism	K Necessary	K Can Be Replaced by					
		Na	Li	Rb	Cs	U	Ra
Aspergillus niger	+	−	−	+*	+*		
Yeast	+	−	−	+	−	−	(Thorium, −)
Chlorella species	+	−	−	+*	±		
Mycobacterium tuberculosis	+	−	−	+*	−	−	−
Bacillus subtilis	+	−		+		−	−
Azotobacter species	+	−					
Rhizobium species	+	−					
Colon-typhoid group	−						
Pseudomonas aeruginosa	−						
Pseudomonas fluorescens	−						
Serratia marcescens	−						
Staphylococcus aureus	+?						

+* Formation of spores poor or absent, crop reduced, or variable results.

Calcium. Calcium is important in the nutrition of plants and animals, though its complete function is unknown. It apparently plays a catalytic role, but it is also known to be bound to proteins, lipides, and cell-wall constituents. Little is known about the calcium requirements of bacteria, although some bacterial processes may demand calcium. For example, several investigators [see Burk (1934)] have claimed that calcium is specifically required for nitrogen fixation by *Azotobacter* and *Rhizobium* species, but more recent studies [see Wilson (1940)] question whether calcium is specific for this reaction. Boltjes (1935) found that calcium played a very important part in the nitrification process with *Nitrosomonas* species, although the reaction took place slowly without its addition. Another example of a bacterial process which appears to require calcium ions is gelatinase formation by various bacteria [Merrill and Clark (1928), Haines (1932, 1933)].

Calcium is not essential for growth of the nitrogen-fixing alga, *Nostoc muscorum*, in the presence of combined nitrogen, but in a nitrogen-free medium nitrogen fixation is retarded in its absence. Growth of some other algae, such as *Chlorella vulgaris*, is not influenced by calcium. This element is apparently essential, however, for normal growth and spore formation of certain molds in the genera *Aspergillus* and *Penicillium*.

Phosphorus. Phosphorus plays a very important role in the living world and has been recognized as an essential element for plants and animals for many years. Although bacteria have not been studied systematically in so far as their phosphorus requirements are concerned, phosphates have been reported to be essential for the diphtheria bacillus [Braun and Mündel (1929)], for certain strains of dysentery bacilli [Horster (1930)], and for *Pseudomonas aeruginosa* [Robinson (1932)], and we can probably assume that all bacteria require this element. Phosphorus is also required for yeasts and molds [Mann (1943)]. The importance of phosphate in the utilization of carbohydrates by plants, animals, and microorganisms is well known, even though its exact function has not been fully elucidated.

Magnesium. Magnesium has been known to be important in metabolic processes for many years. It is a component of bacteriochlorophyll and is apparently essential for nitrogen fixation by *Azotobacter* species, for the normal growth of *Escherichia coli* [Young, Begg, and Pentz (1944)], for gelatinase activity by bacteria [Merrill and Clark (1928), Haines (1932, 1933)], and for other enzymatic processes, especially those involving phosphorylation [Utter and Werkman (1942)]. This element also has been shown to be essential for certain higher fungi and algae; sometimes it can be replaced by manganese.

Sulfur. Sulfur is a constituent of protein and therefore necessary to its synthesis by living cells. Such sulfur-containing substances as cystine, methionine, glutathione, insulin, thiamin, and biotin play important roles in cellular metabolism. The sulfur bacteria are an outstanding instance in which nature has raised this element to a high position in the physiology of the cell. These bacteria use sulfur as a source of energy in the synthesis of protoplasm and more complex foods.

Animals and certain microorganisms require organic sulfur compounds for growth, but plants and some microorganisms can utilize inorganic forms of sulfur. In microorganisms sulfur (sulfate, sulfide, etc.) improves pigment formation (*Pseudomonas aeruginosa*), is required for yeast growth, is important in spore formation (*Aspergillus fumigatus*), and prevents chlorosis (green algae).

Sodium. Sodium probably is more important in cellular processes than we realize. We are unaware of its function in the nutrition of bacteria.

Iron. Iron is essential as a catalyst in vital reactions and is the basis for Warburg's theory of biological oxidation. A deficiency of iron causes anemia in animals, chlorosis in plants, and poor growth and metabolism of many microorganisms. It is important in the growth of *Azotobacter* when both combined nitrogen and atmospheric nitrogen are used [Burk (1934)], and it is undoubtedly essential or stimulative for many other microorganisms. Specific examples are the studies by Reed and Rice (1928) of *Mycobacterium tuberculosis* and by McIntire, Riker, and Peterson (1941) of the crown-gall organism, *Phytomonas tumefaciens.* Another example which may be cited of the importance of iron in bacterial processes is toxin production by *Corynebacterium diphtheriae.* Strøm (1935), Pappenheimer and Johnson (1936), and others have noticed that toxin production by this organism is controlled to a large extent by the concentration of iron in the medium. Pappenheimer and Johnson reported that $2 \times 10^{-6}\ M$ is the optimum concentration of iron and that a sharp fall in toxin formation takes place on either side of this value. The inhibitory effect of increased concentrations is on toxin production and not on the growth of the organism. More recently Waring and Werkman (1943, 1944) have studied the iron requirements of several heterotrophic bacteria. They found that *Escherichia coli, Aerobacter aerogenes, Aerobacter indologenes,* and *Klebsiella pneumoniae* require an iron concentration of about 0.02 to 0.03 p.p.m. for maximal growth; *Pseudomonas aeruginosa* requires about four times this amount. *Serratia marcescens* has an even greater requirement, and the production of the pigment prodigiosin is associated with the iron concentration. A deficiency of iron in the medium suppresses the activity of catalase, peroxidase, formic hydrogenlyase, formic dehydrogenase, and hydrogenase of *Aerobacter indologenes*, and the cytochrome bands are not visible in the iron-deficient cells. Similar results have been reported by Young, Begg, and Pentz (1944), using *Escherichia coli.*

Yeasts apparently require iron for normal growth, and the element is essential for growth and spore formation of *Aspergillus niger* and other molds. Some fumaric acid- and citric acid-forming molds are stimulated by iron salts, whereas others are extremely sensitive to them.

Several organic iron complexes, such as hemin, catalase, and cytochrome, also play very important roles in the normal metabolism of bacteria and other cells. The iron bacteria are interesting in connection with this brief discussion. They derive their energy for cellular activities by oxidizing certain iron salts. The nutrition of these organisms will be discussed later.

Chlorine, Iodine, Bromine, and Fluorine. The role played by the halogens in the nutrition of bacteria is unknown. As a matter of fact, there is no definite information available to prove that they are even essential. Iodine, bromine, and fluorine are known to be present in quite large quantities in certain algae, but their function, if any, has not been established. However, it is known that small quantities [1 p.p.m. to 1 p.p.t. (part per trillion)] of iodine, either as elementary iodine or as the salts of sodium, potassium, or calcium accelerate yeast [Greaves, Zobell, and Greaves (1928)] and bacterial growth [Lewis (1942)]. It is of interest that Lewis (1942) demonstrated an interaction between copper and iodine in the early growth stages of *Azotobacter agile*. The presence of certain concentrations of copper in the medium lengthened the lag phase of the population cycle, but this effect was diminished in the presence of iodine. Powers (1939) has also found that the nodule organisms of legumes are beneficially affected by traces of iodine.

Silicon, Boron, and Lithium. There is no evidence available which indicates that these elements are essential to bacterial growth. They are known to be of importance in the nutrition of certain plants, but their metabolic function is unknown. Brenchley (1943) states that several workers have observed poor development of nodule bacteria on the roots of leguminous plants which were deficient in boron and thus deprived of their usual accessory supply of nitrogen. The function of boron in plants may therefore be concerned with the permeability of the root protoplasm. Boron has also been reported to be essential for normal growth of certain higher fungi (*Dothiorella* species). It has been reported [Lasnitzki and Szörényi (1934)] that lithium salts slightly increase the growth of some yeasts, but in certain concentrations they markedly deform the morphology of various bacteria.

Barium and Strontium. Although these elements are widely disseminated in nature and occur in plants and animals, their function is not well understood. For several years it was thought that strontium could replace calcium as an essential element in the nitrogen-fixation process by *Azotobacter*, but even the importance of calcium in this reaction has been questioned in the last few years. Both barium and strontium are far more toxic than calcium, and it is doubtful if either can replace calcium in cellular nutrition. With molds of the genus *Aspergillus* receiving optimum quantities of sulfur, small amounts of barium chloride increase the yield of mycelium and acidity in certain media, whereas large amounts decrease both [Steinberg (1936)]. Barium and strontium also decrease the elasticity of *Spirogyra* protoplasm.

Manganese, Copper, and Zinc. The function of these three elements in metabolic processes is probably catalytic. In fact, copper and zinc are known to be the prosthetic groups of certain oxidizing pigments, enzymes, and other substances.

Manganese stimulates the development of *Phytomonas tumefaciens* [McIntire, Riker, and Peterson (1941)] and the rate of growth of *Lactobacillus casei* but does not influence the extent of growth of the latter organism [Woolley (1941)]. For example, in *L. casei* growth and acid production are completed in 12 to 16 hours in the presence of manganese (1.3 to 2.6 μg.), but in its absence 40 hours' incubation is required to obtain the same results. Manganese salts in small amounts have been found to have a beneficial effect on ammonification and nitrification processes in the soil. The element also stimulates the growth and development of certain yeasts, conidia production by molds (*Aspergillus niger*), and color formation by some algae. The importance of manganese in the nutrition of plants and animals has been discussed by Brenchley (1943) and Forman (1943).

The part played by copper in bacterial processes is not very well understood. Mulder (1939) has shown that *Azotobacter chroococcum* cultures do not blacken on ageing in the absence of copper, and Lewis (1942) has found that certain concentrations of copper salts lengthen the lag phase of *Azotobacter agile.* Yeast development appears to be quite sensitive to copper; even small amounts decrease growth. Minute amounts of copper also influence the growth and pigment formation of certain molds (*Aspergillus niger*) and algae. In fact, the color of *Aspergillus niger* spores can be used as an indicator to test for the presence of copper in soils and other substances; as little copper as 0.06 μg. per milliliter of nutrient solution permits normal spore color. The importance of copper in the formation of hemoglobin from iron by animals and the role played by this element in plant nutrition have been discussed by Brenchley (1943) and Forman (1943).

Zinc is known to be essential in trace amounts for the normal development of certain plants, animals, and microorganisms. Most of the work on microorganisms has been done with molds and algae (*Chlorella* species). In molds zinc has been shown to be essential for the optimum growth of such species as *Phycomyces blakesleeanus,*

Aspergillus niger, and *Rhizopus nigricans*. Its role is catalytic, glucose being utilized more completely in its presence [Foster and Waksman (1939)].

Tin to Zirconium. The last twenty-six elements in the list on p. 620 have been isolated from plants and animals, but very little, if anything, is known about their function in such organisms. Even less is known about these elements in bacteria and other microorganisms. In fact, only a few studies have been carried out on these elements.

The effect of tin on the nutrition of microorganisms has not been studied, but it is considered nonnutritive. Aluminum is not needed by any known microorganism; in fact, concentrations above approximately 0.35 per cent hinder the growth of some molds, such as *Aspergillus niger*. Rubidium can partially replace potassium in the nutrition of certain organisms [Rahn (1936)], but its function is unknown. Even though cobalt deficiencies lead to anemia in certain animals and may cause chlorosis in plants, nothing is known about the effect of this element on the nutrition of fungi [Forman (1942)]. It is known, however, that cobalt markedly inhibits the formation of bacterial tumors (*Phytomonas tumefaciens*) in certain plants.

Lead, nickel, and mercury have been found in small amounts in certain living cells, although their function, if any, is not known. These elements are usually considered nonnutritive and toxic for most cells. Arsenic probably belongs to this same group of toxic elements, even though several workers have reported that low concentrations of arsenic salts stimulate the growth and activities of some plants and soil bacteria. It is also known that certain molds, such as *Penicillium* species, produce volatile arsenic substances when grown in the presence of stable arsenic compounds; nothing is known about the function of such reactions.

Certain bacteria can derive their energy by oxidizing selenium to selenic acid, and it has been reported that the germination of spores and the growth of certain molds are favored by very dilute concentrations of sodium selenate. The enrichment of growth of streptococci by thallium has been studied by McKenzie (1941), and Richards found that approximately 0.001 mg. of thallium per milliliter of medium increased the growth of yeast by about 80 per cent. Stapp (1942) has found that the virulence of *Phytomonas tumefaciens* for certain plants is increased by trace amounts (0.0001 to 0.001 per cent) of titanium sulfate. Silver is considered to be a nonnutritive and toxic element, although it has been demonstrated in certain cells in minute amounts.

Molybdenum is known to increase nitrogen fixation by certain species of *Azotobacter* and *Rhizobium* and by the blue-green algae of the genera *Anabaena* and *Nostoc* [see Wilson (1940), Horner, Burk, Allison, and Sherman (1942)]. In *Azotobacter* species, for example, 1 to 4 p.p.m. of molybdenum increases the amount of nitrogen fixed by 10 to 30 times. This element has also been reported to be essential for the optimum growth and development of certain molds (*Aspergillus niger*). Vanadium can replace molybdenum as an accelerator of nitrogen fixation by some *Azotobacter* species, but it produces a maximum effect of only about one-half to three-fourths that of molybdenum. A trace amount of vanadium also acts as a stimulant for *Aspergillus niger* [Bertrand (1941)].

It has been reported that radium in minute amounts increases the growth of certain microorganisms, but it is also known that larger amounts are harmful to protoplasm. The effect of germanium on microbial processes has not been studied very extensively; however, Geilmann and Brünger (1935) showed that *Aspergillus niger* takes up considerable amounts of this element from nutrient solutions and is unaffected by even large quantities (up to 100 mg. Ge_2O per 100 ml.). Gallium in a concentration of 0.01 to 0.02 mg. per liter, along with several other elements, is essential to the optimum growth and development of *Aspergillus niger* [Steinberg (1938)], but its need by other microorganisms is unknown.

The nutritional aspects of a few other elements which have not been mentioned have also been studied, but, in general, nothing is known about their function. For example, it has been observed that beryllium and cadmium can replace zinc in the nutrition of some molds, and that chromium salts stimulate the oxygen uptake by *Rhizobium meliloti* in a nitrate-mannitol medium. Cesium may increase slightly the growth of certain yeasts in a synthetic medium and stimulate the development of *Chlorella*. Cesium, as well as lithium, calcium, barium, and strontium, decreases the elasticity of the protoplasm of *Spirogyra*, whereas potassium and sodium increase it.

From the foregoing discussion it can be seen that not too much is known concerning the function of the various elements in the nutrition of bacteria. In this connection it is interesting to mention Thatcher's (1934) classification of the elements found in plants, since these elements probably act in a like manner in microorganisms. Thatcher classified the elements into the following eight groups on the basis of their similarity of function and chemical properties:

Group I: hydrogen and oxygen, energy-exchange elements.

Group II: carbon, nitrogen, sulfur, and phosphorus, energy storers.

Group III: sodium, potassium, calcium, and magnesium, translocation regulators.

Group IV: manganese, iron, (cobalt, nickel), copper, and zinc, oxidation-reduction regulators.

Group V: boron, aluminum, silicon, arsenic, and selenium, function unknown.

Group VI: chlorine, fluorine, bromine, and iodine, function unknown.

Group VII: cobalt and nickel, function unknown but probably those of IV.

Group VIII: germanium, gallium, and other rare elements, function unknown.

In spite of the fact that little is known concerning the mineral requirements of bacteria, their needs are usually satisfied by adding a few simple salts of ordinary purity to common bacteriological media. When chemically defined media are used, it is customary to include the ions sodium, potassium, magnesium, calcium, iron, chloride, sulfate, phosphate, and carbonate. Sometimes, however, certain specific ions may be needed before the bacteria will grow and exhibit their normal activities. For example, some intermediate strains of *Corynebacterium diphtheriae* grow only in the presence of a mixture of certain mineral salts in a chemically defined medium [Evans, Happold, and Handley (1939)].

THE ORGANIC REQUIREMENTS

Bacteria vary greatly in their carbon requirements, and the answer to the question of whether any given compound can serve as a source of carbon for any specific organism depends on several factors. For example, the organism must be able to decompose the compound, since it is unlikely that any constituent of ordinary culture media is sufficiently reactive to enter into the material of the cell without first undergoing some change. This change may occur aerobically or anaerobically, but it must yield energy for subsequent metabolic reactions, and it must produce compounds which can be built into cellular protoplasm.

As a matter of convenience, bacteria are usually divided into two groups on the basis of their ability to obtain energy by the oxido-reduction of different substances. One group, called the *autotrophic bacteria,* utilizes carbon dioxide or carbonates as a sole source of carbon, whereas the other group, called *heterotrophic bacteria,* requires a source of carbon more complex than CO_2. Until recently it was thought that the distinction between these two groups was quite sharp. However, the discovery by Wood and Werkman in 1935 that heterotrophic bacteria assimilate CO_2 has weakened the distinction between the two groups. This subject is discussed in more detail on pp. 633 to 635.

It is evident that the so-called autotrophic bacteria cannot secure energy by oxidizing carbon dioxide or carbonates. Instead they are reduced and built up into organic compounds. Since energy is required for this reduction, autotrophic bacteria may be divided into two groups on the basis of the source of this energy. The first group is termed *photosynthetic*, inasmuch as light energy is used for their reduction. Some of the sulfur bacteria (*Thiobacteriales*) possess coloring matter which apparently functions for these bacteria in much the same fashion as chlorophyll acts for the higher green plants. Thus such bacteria absorb certain of the sun's rays and build up organic carbon compounds from carbon dioxide in much the same manner as the green plant utilizes the energy of the sun's rays in the manufacture of starch. The second group of autotrophic bacteria is called *chemosynthetic*. These organisms build organic compounds from carbon dioxide by utilizing the energy from the oxidation of various inorganic compounds. Sulfur and its compounds, ammonia, nitrites, and probably ferrous and manganous salts are among the inorganic substances from which this energy is derived.

The heterotrophic bacteria obtain their energy by oxidation of organic matter. Such a process is sometimes termed dissimilation, or catabolism. All the organisms concerned in the production of disease, as well as other microorganisms which are most frequently studied in the laboratory, secure energy by the oxidation of organic carbon compounds. The range of organic compounds available to an organism varies greatly from species to species and probably forms the principal basis of its adaptation to environment. Although it is more convenient to mention the utilization of various carbon compounds by bacteria when the nutrition of the individual species is discussed, one or two examples from the study by den Dooren de Jong (1926) should be cited here. Using a group of 14 common bacteria and some 200 different substances, den Dooren de Jong found that carbohydrates and related compounds are the most generally utilized source of carbon; next come malic, citric, succinic, and lactic acids, followed by the fatty acids and then the monohydric alcohols. One species (*Pseudomonas putida*), for example, was able to supply its carbon requirements from 77 out of some 200 compounds examined, including 6 out of 7 carbohydrates, 10 out of 40 alcohols, 10 saturated and 3 unsaturated out of 68 fatty acids, 17 out of 28 amino acids, 9 out of 19 amides, and 7 out of 41 amines.

THE GASEOUS REQUIREMENTS

Bacteria show considerable variation in their gaseous requirements, especially for oxygen and carbon dioxide. Because of the importance of these two gases in the metabolic processes of bacteria, they will be discussed separately. Although other gases, such as hydrogen and nitrogen, may be of importance in certain individual bacteria, they do not appear to be of fundamental importance to all.

Although the proper gas relationship in bacterial nutrition is very important, this fact has not always been realized by many workers, and more work is seriously needed in this field.

Some bacteria will not grow in the absence of free oxygen; others will not develop in its presence; still others can adapt themselves to either condition. An organism which requires free oxygen is called *aerobic;* one whose growth is inhibited by free oxygen is *anaerobic;* one that grows under aerobic or anaerobic conditions is termed *facultative.* It is also known that certain organisms grow neither in contact with oxygen at atmospheric pressure nor in a medium totally devoid of oxygen. Such organisms are usually called *microaerophilic.* Although the distinctions among these four groups are not well marked, it is often convenient to use this classification in determining the oxygen requirements of an organism.

The technique used for the cultivation of bacteria under aerobic conditions is so common that it hardly needs comment. In general, little attention is given to the oxygen supply, providing the media employed are nutritionally adequate for the organism. Recent studies by Cahn-Bronner (1940) and Rahn and Richardson (1941), however, show that not enough attention has been given in the past to the oxygen supply when cultivating aerobic bacteria. On the other hand, there are several important factors which must be considered in the cultivation of anaerobic bacteria in nutritionally adequate media. Knight (1941) believes that the three main factors involved are the following.

1. The Exclusion of Oxygen of the Air from the Media. Most vegetative cells of the anaerobic bacteria are very sensitive to oxygen, and it has been assumed, since such organisms lack catalase, that peroxide accumulates in the media under aerobic conditions and kills the organisms. Other factors also seem to be involved, however, because it is possible to prepare liquid media free of dissolved oxygen (by deaeration with pure nitrogen gas) in which a small inoculum of washed and aerated cells will not grow. Usually such cells will grow, however, if a little cysteine is added to the deaerated media.

2. The Use of Media of Sufficient Reducing Capacity and Intensity. Most common bacteriological media consisting of meat extract, peptones, glucose, etc., contain reducing substances, such as reduced glutathione or cysteine, whose presence can be detected by the ability of the media, when thoroughly deaerated, to reduce certain oxidation-reduction indicator dyes like methylene blue and to impress a relatively negative potential on a noble electrode when measured with a potentiometer. Certain of these reduced substances in complex bacteriological media are oxidized only slowly in the presence of molecular oxygen, the rate depending upon the presence of catalysts and the *p*H. Therefore such media are often partially reduced for some time after their preparation. It has also been shown by Lepper and Martin (1929) that in broth media containing solid meat (the so-called deep-meat tubes) at least two reducing systems are in operation. One is due to the autooxidation of the unsaturated fatty acids, particularly linolenic, of the meat lipides catalyzed by the hematin of the muscle tissue. This process removes dissolved oxygen but does not reduce methylene blue. The second system consists of glutathione plus fixed thiol groups of the denatured muscle protein. This system reduces methylene blue and would show a negative (reducing) potential (E_h of about -0.2 volt) at an electrode by virtue of the reduced glutathione and other such compounds.

The reducing capacity of most common bacteriological media is not very great, since the presence of a small amount of an oxidizing agent or gaseous oxygen is sufficient to overcome their reducing activity. This point can be demonstrated by the reoxidation of a reduced oxidation-reduction indicator dye dissolved in the medium or by the rapid positive drift of an electrode. It is often advantageous to add suitable reducing agents to such media immediately before inoculation so as to increase their weak reducing capacity. Reducing agents which are capable of more or less general application include certain thiol compounds, such as glutathione, cysteine, and thioglycollic acid in a final concentration of about 0.002 *M;* ascorbic acid; and "glucose évolué," prepared by heating a 10 per cent solution of glucose in 0.1 *N* NaOH at 110°C. for 15 minutes.

3. The Condition of the Inoculum. It is well known that the vegetative cells of the Clostridia and other anaerobes are sensitive to oxygen and other oxidizing agents. In an actively growing culture anaerobic bacteria act as strong reducing agents and produce reducing substances such as cysteine from the ingredients in the medium. Similarly, other substances, such as coenzymes I and II, hematin, and riboflavin, which may be present in a medium containing tissue extracts will be reduced by the bacterial growth. Therefore an inoculum of a growing culture will carry with it some of its own reducing agents which will protect the cells from the oxygen of the air and add to the reducing capacity at the locality in the medium where the inoculum is placed. The effect of materials such as sand, kieselguhr, charcoal, and filter-pulp, which have sometimes been placed in media for anaerobic cultivation, is due to their providing a "nidus," where the proliferation of a few cells can take place without the reducing substances formed locally being rapidly dispersed or oxidized by inward-diffusing oxygen. Such substances also help to maintain the proper CO_2 concentration in the vicinity of the cells. The spores of the Clostridia are of course much more resistant to the effects of oxidation than are the vegetative cells, and as a rule they are not killed in the presence of oxygen. The aeration of a washed spore suspension, however, will make the spores more difficult to germinate than are unoxidized spores.

From this brief analysis of the factors involved in anaerobic cultivation of bacteria it can be seen that what happens when an inoculum of an anaerobic organism is placed in a medium is determined by the interaction of the three factors just discussed. There is competition between the reducing power of the medium and inoculum, on the one hand, and the oxidizing action of atmospheric oxygen on the other. The outcome of this competition determines whether continued proliferation of the bacteria will take place. The situation can be simplified by the total exclusion of gaseous oxygen, that is, by cultivating agar plates or other media in an atmosphere of purified nitrogen or hydrogen.

Carbon dioxide is another gas which plays a very important role in the nutrition of many bacteria. Although it has been known for a long time that autotrophic bacteria require or utilize carbon dioxide, the necessity for this gas in the culture medium of heterotrophic bacteria became apparent only in 1924 in *Brucella abortus*, and since then it has been shown that, in the complete absence of CO_2, growth and metabolism of diverse living systems are seriously impaired. For example, under experimental conditions which would insure (1) the initial presence of not more than traces of CO_2, and (2) the prompt removal of additional amounts formed during metabolism, the germination of spores and the growth of various microorganisms are greatly retarded, if not altogether prevented. Even such a respiratory activity as the reduction of methylene blue by resting cells has been shown to be dependent upon the presence of carbon dioxide [see Valley and Rettger (1927), Valley (1928), Gladstone, Fildes, and Richardson (1935), Longsworth and MacInnes (1936), and Hes (1938)]. Until recently, however, it has been impossible to interpret these results.

In 1935 Wood and Werkman presented the first experimental evidence that heterotrophic bacteria actually assimilate carbon dioxide. Although their proposals necessitated the acceptance of a new principle in the metabolism of bacteria, their work has now been so completely confirmed that there is no longer any doubt that their original theory was correct. Actual proof came, however, only when labeled CO_2($C^{11}O_2$ and $C^{13}O_2$) became available for biological studies; that is, when the assimilation of CO_2 could be traced.

One explanation of the role of carbon dioxide in cellular metabolism, therefore, is that the gas is assimilated or converted into organic substances. The available evidence [see Krampitz and Werkman (1941)] supports the following reaction:

$$CO_2 + \underset{\text{Pyruvic acid}}{CH_3 \cdot CO \cdot COOH} \rightleftarrows \underset{\text{Oxaloacetic acid}}{HOOC \cdot CH_2 \cdot CO \cdot COOH}$$

The oxaloacetic acid thus formed may then be reduced to malic, fumaric, and succinic acids and take part in the C_4-dicarboxylic acid cycle, the Krebs citric acid cycle, or some similar catalytic cycle concerned with the growth and respiration of cells. Although Wood and Werkman first postulated such a reaction for the propionic acid bacteria, it is now apparent that the mechanism is not limited to these bacteria. In fact, it seems to be quite widespread, since various types of living systems have been shown to produce malic, fumaric, succinic, and probably other acids from CO_2. For example, such a synthesis appears to be carried out by liver tissue [Krebs and Eggleston (1940), Krebs (1941), and others], plant tissues [Ruben and Kamen (1940)], *Staphylococcus aureus* [Smyth (1940)], *Escherichia coli*, and other bacteria [Elsden (1938), Wood *et al.* (1940–1941), Nisina, Endo, and Nakayama (1941)], *Micrococcus lysodeikticus* [Krampitz and Werkman (1941)], yeast [Kleinzeller (1941)], molds [Foster *et al.* (1941)], and protozoa [van Niel *et al.* (1942)].

The synthesis of oxaloacetic acid by the foregoing mechanism, however, is not the only way by which CO_2 enters into cellular metabolism. This fact is apparent, according to van Niel and his associates (1942), from a consideration of the following well-established facts:

1. The reduction of CO_2 to formic acid by *Escherichia coli* [Woods (1936)]
2. The participation of CO_2 in the formation of acetic acid by *Clostridium acidi-urici* [Barker, Ruben, and Beck (1940)]
3. The production of methane from CO_2 in methane fermentation by *Methanobacterium omelianskii* and *Methanomonas methanica* [Barker, Ruben, and Kamen (1940)]
4. The utilization of CO_2 in the formation of urea by animal tissues [Rittenberg and Waelsch (1940), Evans and Slotin (1940)]
5. The synthesis of all cell constituents from CO_2 as the only source of carbon by all obligate autotrophic and several facultative autotrophic bacteria, such as hydrogen-oxidizing bacteria

According to Werkman and Wood (1942), considerable misunderstanding has arisen concerning the relative significance of some of these investigations, because at least two distinct types of reactions are involved in the fixation of carbon dioxide in these experiments: (1) reduction with no creation of carbon-to-carbon linkage, and (2) creation of the carbon-to-carbon linkage. In the first type CO_2 functions only as a hydrogen acceptor, whereas in the second reaction CO_2 is actually assimilated to produce a compound containing one more carbon atom. These two types of reactions must, therefore, be differentiated to prevent confusion.

For further details on the importance of carbon dioxide in the metabolism of bacteria, Chapter 8 of this book, and more especially, the review articles by Krebs (1941), Werkman and Wood (1942), and van Niel, Ruben, Carson, Kamen, and Foster (1942) should be consulted.

NUTRITION OF THE INDIVIDUAL GROUPS OF BACTERIA

From the foregoing discussion it will be realized that the nutritional requirements of bacteria probably differ more profoundly from species to species than do those of any other class of organisms studied in biology. Although it is usually convenient for discussion purposes to classify the bacteria into different groups, depending upon their needs, it should be kept in mind that nature does not permit such a rigid classification. Nevertheless in Fig. 1 the bacteria have been allocated to twelve groups on the basis of their requirements in chemically defined media. Even though the groups appear to be distinct and quite well differentiated, there are many intermediate forms. Thus the bacteria should be visualized as a continuous spectrum in which one group blends gradually into the other.

Only a few representative species of each group will be mentioned in this discussion. For more details the references, especially the excellent monograph by Knight (1936), should be consulted.

Autotrophic Bacteria

The autotrophic bacteria have already been defined as those organisms which are able to derive their carbon from carbon dioxide or carbonates and their nitrogen from ammonium ions, nitrites, or nitrates. Since they cannot oxidize CO_2 or carbonates to secure energy for growth, they must obtain energy by other means. This requirement is usually met in one of two ways: (1) by utilizing radiant energy from the sun to reduce CO_2 in a manner similar to that of higher plants,

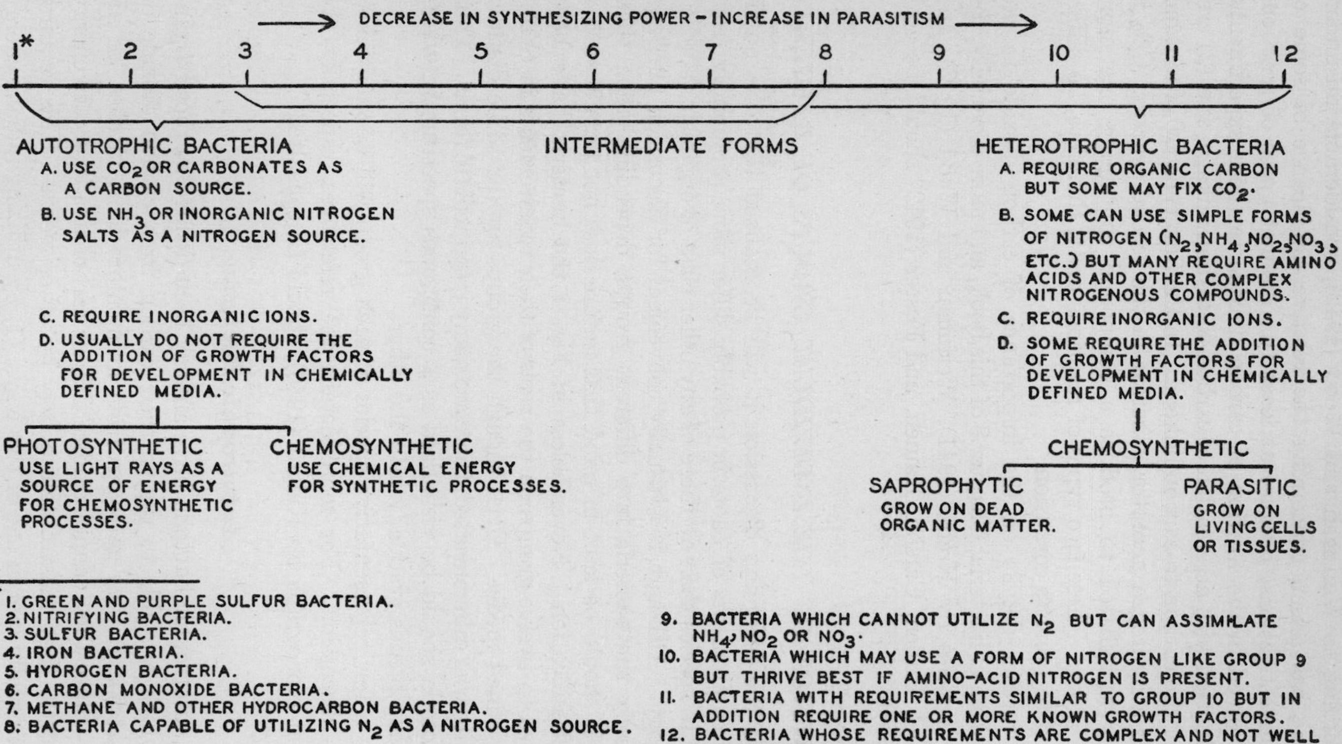

DECREASE IN SYNTHESIZING POWER - INCREASE IN PARASITISM
1* 2 3 4 5 6 7 8 9 10 11 12
AUTOTROPHIC BACTERIA
A. USE CO_2 OR CARBONATES AS A CARBON SOURCE.
B. USE NH_3 OR INORGANIC NITROGEN SALTS AS A NITROGEN SOURCE.
C. REQUIRE INORGANIC IONS.
D. USUALLY DO NOT REQUIRE THE ADDITION OF GROWTH FACTORS FOR DEVELOPMENT IN CHEMICALLY DEFINED MEDIA.
PHOTOSYNTHETIC
USE LIGHT RAYS AS A SOURCE OF ENERGY FOR CHEMOSYNTHETIC PROCESSES.
CHEMOSYNTHETIC
USE CHEMICAL ENERGY FOR SYNTHETIC PROCESSES.
INTERMEDIATE FORMS
HETEROTROPHIC BACTERIA
A. REQUIRE ORGANIC CARBON BUT SOME MAY FIX CO_2.
B. SOME CAN USE SIMPLE FORMS OF NITROGEN (N_2, NH_4, NO_2, NO_3, ETC.) BUT MANY REQUIRE AMINO ACIDS AND OTHER COMPLEX NITROGENOUS COMPOUNDS.
C. REQUIRE INORGANIC IONS.
D. SOME REQUIRE THE ADDITION OF GROWTH FACTORS FOR DEVELOPMENT IN CHEMICALLY DEFINED MEDIA.
CHEMOSYNTHETIC
SAPROPHYTIC
GROW ON DEAD ORGANIC MATTER.
PARASITIC
GROW ON LIVING CELLS OR TISSUES.
* 1. GREEN AND PURPLE SULFUR BACTERIA.
2. NITRIFYING BACTERIA.
3. SULFUR BACTERIA.
4. IRON BACTERIA.
5. HYDROGEN BACTERIA.
6. CARBON MONOXIDE BACTERIA.
7. METHANE AND OTHER HYDROCARBON BACTERIA.
8. BACTERIA CAPABLE OF UTILIZING N_2 AS A NITROGEN SOURCE.
9. BACTERIA WHICH CANNOT UTILIZE N_2 BUT CAN ASSIMILATE NH_4, NO_2 OR NO_3.
10. BACTERIA WHICH MAY USE A FORM OF NITROGEN LIKE GROUP 9 BUT THRIVE BEST IF AMINO-ACID NITROGEN IS PRESENT.
11. BACTERIA WITH REQUIREMENTS SIMILAR TO GROUP 10 BUT IN ADDITION REQUIRE ONE OR MORE KNOWN GROWTH FACTORS.
12. BACTERIA WHOSE REQUIREMENTS ARE COMPLEX AND NOT WELL UNDERSTOOD.

FIG. 1. A Hypothetical Bacterial Nutrition Spectrum.

and (2) by growing in the dark, but utilizing energy released from certain simple chemical reactions to assimilate carbon. Those organisms which assimilate CO_2 by the aid of radiant energy are usually called *photosynthetic* autotrophs, whereas those which reduce CO_2 by chemical energy are known as *chemosynthetic* autotrophs.

Since all the autotrophic bacteria grow in simple mineral salt media, it is believed by some that they are the most primitive of all bacteria and that other species with more exacting requirements have arisen from them as a result of altered environmental conditions. Furthermore, since the autotrophic bacteria contain cellular constituents very similar to those found in the ordinary bacteria studied in the laboratory, they must possess remarkable synthesizing powers in order to build up protoplasm from such simple raw materials as carbon dioxide and ammonia.

PHOTOSYNTHETIC AUTOTROPHS

The photosynthetic autotrophs comprise the first group of organisms to be considered. Not too much is known about the nutrition of these organisms, but in general it is convenient to separate the group into three subdivisions [van Niel (1941)]: (1) the so-called green bacteria, (2) the sulfur purple bacteria, and (3) the nonsulfur purple bacteria. The main characteristics of these three subgroups may be briefly summarized as follows:

1. Green bacteria	Green filamentous bacteria. Occur in H_2S media. Photosynthetic activity appears to be restricted to the reduction of CO_2. H_2S serves as the hydrogen donator and is oxidized only to free sulfur. Other sulfur compounds and organic substances not used as hydrogen donors.
2. Sulfur purple bacteria (*Thiorhodaceae* of Molish or *Chromatioideae* of Bergey)	Purple to red filamentous bacteria. Anaerobic. Contain sulfur granules. Occur primarily in sulfide-containing media. Oxidize various inorganic sulfur compounds to sulfate with the simultaneous photoreduction of CO_2. Some species can use lower fatty acids, certain hydroxy and dibasic acids, or molecular hydrogen rather than H_2S as hydrogen donors.

3. Nonsulfur purple bacteria (*Athiorhodaceae* of Molish or *Rhodobacterioideae* of Bergey) — Purple, red, or brown filamentous bacteria. Contain bacteriopurpurin or bacteriochlorophyll but no sulfur granules. Occur principally in media containing organic compounds. Growth is dependent on the presence of small amounts of organic materials. CO_2 reduced at the expense of organic substances, molecular hydrogen, or inorganic sulfur compounds.

Ever since 1883 the so-called purple bacteria have been suspected of having a photochemical metabolism similar to that of green plants. Much confusion existed in the early literature, however, because investigators used mixed cultures and because some of their observations led them to the viewpoint that the purple sulfur bacteria lacked photosynthetic functions, since there was no evolution of oxygen such as occurs as a result of photosynthesis in the higher green plants. Although a number of observations concerning these organisms have in the meantime been published [see reviews by van Niel (1941, 1944)], it has been only within the past 10 years or so that definite knowledge of their metabolism and nutrition has been obtained.

Van Niel has applied the ideas of Wieland and of Kluyver and Donker on biological oxidation as a hydrogen transfer to the explanation of the metabolism of the purple bacteria. Since it is generally assumed that the first stage of photosynthesis in the higher plants is of the following nature:

$$CO_2 + 2H_2O = (CH_2O)\,\text{[3]} + H_2O + O_2$$

Van Niel considered it a typical biological oxidation-reduction reaction, in which CO_2 is reduced by virtue of the fact that the hydrogen of the water molecules is sufficiently activated to be transferred to CO_2. Now, as he further pointed out, it is conceivable that in organisms other than typical green plants, water may not serve as the only hydrogen donator but may be replaced or complemented by some other molecule. In other words, the foregoing equation is only one of a number of possible photosynthetic reactions of the general type:

$$CO_2 + 2H_2A = (CH_2O) + H_2O + 2A$$

where H_2A represents the hydrogen donator. Thus, on the basis of

[3] The symbol (CH_2O) is used here to denote the conversion products of CO_2. In the past it has frequently been written as formaldehyde or formic acid, but since these names may not always be accurate, it seems better to use the empirical expression.

this equation, photosynthesis leads to oxygen production only when the function of the hydrogen donator is fulfilled by H_2O.

The experimental results of van Niel and others [see van Niel (1941)] tend to substantiate the following hypotheses. In green plants photosynthesis involves the photochemical splitting of water with the aid of chlorophyll and unknown enzyme systems: H_2O + Radiant energy $\rightarrow$ H + OH.[4] The liberated hydrogen then reduces the CO_2 in the atmosphere. The following simplified equations present van Niel's ideas of the reduction of CO_2 to its supposed final state:

$$\text{Green plants}\begin{cases} 4(H_2O + h\nu \rightarrow H + OH) \\ 4H + CO_2 \rightarrow (CH_2O) + H_2O \\ 2(2OH \rightarrow \text{Peroxide} \rightarrow H_2O + O_2) \end{cases}$$

Although there is no reason for assuming that the photochemical reaction in purple bacteria differs in principle from that in green plants, van Niel points out that the process with the purple bacteria may occur at longer wavelengths (including the infrared light up to 9,000 $m\mu$), and thus the energy available to the bacteria will be less. This fact may make it impossible for the "hydroxylated" system to become rearranged into a peroxide compound and thereby permit the spontaneous regeneration of oxygen and water (2OH $\rightarrow$ Peroxide $\rightarrow H_2O + O_2$). Under these circumstances the hydroxylated system could regenerate water only with the assistance of a reducing system, for example, $2OH + H_2S \rightarrow 2H_2O + S$. The dependence of bacterial photosynthesis on the presence of suitable hydrogen donators, such as H_2S, thus becomes understandable, and it explains why oxygen is not evolved during the process. Van Niel represents bacterial photosynthesis as follows:

$$\text{Purple bacteria}\begin{cases} 4(H_2O + h\nu \rightarrow H + OH) \\ 4H + CO_2 \rightarrow (CH_2O) + H_2O \\ 2(2OH + H_2A \rightarrow 2H_2O + A) \end{cases}$$

where $h\nu$ is radiant energy and H_2A is usually H_2S, although organic hydrogen donators, such as fatty acids, or sulfur oxides or molecular hydrogen may serve, depending upon the bacterial species being studied.

It is apparent from this brief consideration that H_2S does not replace H_2O in bacterial photosynthesis but rather complements it.

[4] This reaction does not imply that the water molecule is split into a hydrogen atom and a hydroxyl radical. The scheme represents merely the essence of the photochemical reaction.

The reduction of CO_2 is the same in both plant and bacterial photosynthesis; that is, it is accomplished by the hydrogen which has been released from water by the action of radiant energy in cooperation with plant or bacteriochlorophyll. Van Niel does not claim that the reduction of CO_2 yields only carbohydrate, as the foregoing reactions imply, but rather he favors the idea that the "final acceptor" enters into the system by enzymatically combining with an organic compound already present. The reaction discovered by Wood and Werkman in which a four-carbon organic acid is formed from a three-carbon compound and CO_2 may serve as a most interesting example of such reactions. The actual reduction process in photosynthesis, therefore, may well involve substances other than CO_2.

As we have already stated, not too much was known about the specific nutritional requirements of some of the photosynthetic bacteria until recently. What information we have on this subject is covered in some detail by van Niel (1931, 1936, 1941, 1944), Foster (1940), and Hutner (1944). Since these references are readily available, the student is referred to them for details. In brief, however, a few general statements may be made to illustrate the basic nutritional requirements of these bacteria.

In 1931 van Niel was able to isolate pure cultures of the green sulfur bacteria by using an aqueous medium of *p*H 7.5 which contained the following ingredients: NH_4Cl, 0.1 per cent; KH_2PO_4, 0.05 per cent; $MgCl_2$, 0.02 per cent; $NaHCO_3$, 0.1 per cent; $Na_2S \cdot 9H_2O$, 0.05 to 0.1 per cent. After inoculation with crude material this medium was incubated at 25° to 30°C. in completely filled, glass-stoppered bottles which were exposed in front of a north window or continuously illuminated by a 25- to 50-watt electric bulb placed at a distance of 20 to 30 cm. To obtain pure cultures of the green bacteria, it was necessary to make repeated transfers as soon as a green sediment appeared in the bottles. This procedure was necessary because after a time (3 to 4 weeks in a window or 4 to 5 days under continuous illumination) certain strains of the so-called purple bacteria also grew in this medium.

A basal medium very similar to the one just described has also been used by van Niel (1944) and others for the cultivation of the sulfur and nonsulfur purple bacteria. The nonsulfur purple organisms develop best, however, when the *p*H is adjusted to 6.4 to 7.0, and they also require the presence of a small amount of organic matter, such as yeast extract or peptone, before they will grow. It has been assumed in the past that this organic matter serves as a source of growth factors and amino acids for these bacteria. This assumption has recently been verified by Hutner (1944), who has shown that at least one species

(*Rhodospirillum rubrum*) of nonsulfur bacteria requires *d*-glutamic acid, *d*-arginine, cystine, and biotin for growth in a chemically defined medium.

Like some of the so-called heterotrophic bacteria, the nonsulfur purple bacteria can, after primary isolation, carry out a typically oxidative metabolism. A number of simple organic substances, such as alcohols, fatty acids, and hydroxy and dibasic acids, can be utilized as a substrate, providing oxygen, methylene blue, or nitrate is present to serve as a hydrogen acceptor. Thus the nonsulfur bacteria are physiologically related, on the one hand, to the green and purple sulfur bacteria by virtue of their photosynthetic metabolism and, on the other hand, to the various types of nonphotosynthetic organisms with a typically oxidative metabolism.

Already it can be seen that it is impossible to adhere too closely to a rigid allocation of bacteria to the various groups shown in the nutritional spectrum (Fig. 1).

CHEMOSYNTHETIC AUTOTROPHS

In general, the chemosynthetic autotrophs are able to use carbon as CO_2 or carbonates and to assimilate nitrogen from some inorganic source, such as ammonium salts, nitrites, or nitrates. Some species, however, are facultative in nature because they can assimilate more complex carbon and nitrogen compounds. Since these organisms cannot oxidize CO_2 and since they lack bacteriochlorophyll (the energy transformer of the photosynthetic autotrophs), they derive their energy for the reduction of CO_2 in the assimilation process from some characteristic oxidation of an inorganic compound, such as ammonia, nitrite, nitrate, sulfur compounds, or ferrous and manganous salts.

It can thus be seen that the chemosynthetic autotrophs are fairly distinct from the photosynthetic autotrophs, since they lack bacteriochlorophyll, and also from the true heterotrophs, which cannot live in such simple substrates but require more complex carbon compounds as a source of energy for the assimilation process. It should be pointed out, however, that these groups are not as distinct and unrelated as might be supposed but instead are connected by intermediate physiological types. Also, since every organism displays the faculty of chemical synthesis, the term chemosynthetic is not restricted to this group alone. It is only for our convenience that these distinctions are made.

In Table 3 have been listed several of the better-known chemosynthetic autotrophs. The different groups will now be briefly discussed. For additional information the book by Waksman (1927) and the excellent review by van Niel (1943) should be consulted.

TABLE 3

PROPERTIES OF SEVERAL REPRESENTATIVE CHEMOSYNTHETIC OBLIGATE AND FACULTATIVE AUTOTROPHIC BACTERIA

Group, Genus, and/or Species	Autotrophic Relationship	Carbon Source	Nitrogen Source	Energy Source		Oxygen Relationship
				Oxidation of	*Reduction of*	
Nitrifying bacteria *Nitrosomonas* species *Nitrosococcus* species *Nitrosocystis* species *Nitrosospira* species	Obligate	CO_2	NH_4 salts	NH_4	CO_2, O_2	Aerobic
Nitrobacter species *Bactoderma* species *Nitrosogloea* species	Obligate and facultative	CO_2 or organic carbon	NO_2	NO_2	CO_2, O_2	Aerobic
Sulfur bacteria *Thiothrix* species *Beggiatoa* species *Thioploca* species	Obligate?	CO_2	NH_4	H_2S	CO_2, O_2	Aerobic or microaerophilic
Thiobacillus thioparus	Obligate	CO_2	NH_4, NO_2, NO_3	H_2S, S_2O_3, S_4O_6	CO_2, O_2	Aerobic
Thiobacillus novellus	Facultative	CO_2 or organic carbon	NH_4	S_2O_3, S_4O_6	CO_2, O_2	Aerobic or facultative
Thiobacillus denitrificans	Obligate	Carbonates	NH_4 or NO_3	S, S_2O_3	CO_2, NO_3	Anaerobic
Thiobacillus thiooxidans	Obligate	CO_2	NH_4	S, S_2O_3	CO_2, O_2	Aerobic
Iron bacteria *Spherotilis* species *Clonothrix* species *Leptothrix* species *Crenothrix* species	Obligate, facultative, or intermediate	CO_2 or organic carbon	NH_4 or organic nitrogen	Fe^{++}, Mn^{++}	CO_2	Aerobic?
Hydrogen bacteria *Hydrogenomonas pantotropha*	Facultative or intermediate	CO_2 or organic carbon	NH_4	H_2	CO_2, O_2	Aerobic
Carbon monoxide bacteria *Carboxydomonas oligocarbophila*	Facultative or intermediate	CO_2 or organic carbon	NH_4, NO_3	CO, H_2	CO_2	
Methane and other hydrocarbon bacteria *Methanomonas methanica*	Facultative or intermediate	CO_2 or organic carbon	NH_4	CH_4	CO_2, O_2	Aerobic

The Nitrifying Bacteria. Although Pasteur in 1862 believed that microorganisms were responsible for the oxidation of ammonia to nitrates in the soil, it was not until 1877 that Schloesing and Muntz demonstrated quite conclusively the biological origin of the nitrification process. Many of the important factors governing nitrification were worked out by Schloesing and Muntz from 1877 to 1879 and by Warington from 1879 to 1888, but these workers were unable to obtain pure cultures of the organisms responsible for the process. However, in 1890 Winogradsky was able to isolate pure cultures of the organisms by plating soil samples on a silica gel medium which contained no organic matter. Workers previous to this time had failed to realize that organic matter was toxic or inhibitory to the growth of these organisms and had consequently taken no precautions to exclude it from the media they employed.

The task of obtaining pure cultures of the nitrifying bacteria has presented difficulties to many workers ever since the early work of Winogradsky. This problem has been studied again in some detail by Winogradsky and Winogradsky (1933), Boltjes (1935), Hanks and Weintraub (1936), Engel and Skallau (1937), and Bömeke (1939). These reports should be studied by anyone who attempts to isolate such organisms.

During the years 1890 to 1892 Winogradsky showed that the nitrification process actually took place in two steps: (1) the oxidation of ammonia to nitrite:

$$NH_4^+ + 1\tfrac{1}{2}O \rightarrow NO_2^- + H_2O + 2H^+$$

or

$$(NH_4)_2CO_3 + 3O_2 \rightarrow 2HNO_2 + CO_2 + 3H_2O$$

and then (2) the oxidation of nitrite to nitrate:

$$NO_2^- + \tfrac{1}{2}O_2 \rightarrow NO_3^-$$

$$2HNO_2 + O_2 \rightarrow 2HNO_3$$

Two different groups of organisms were shown to be responsible for the first step. One group consisted of motile rods to which Winogradsky assigned the generic name, *Nitrosomonas;* the other was a large, spherical organism to which he gave the name *Nitrosococcus nitrosus.* The second reaction was found to be due to a group of short, nonmotile bacilli to which the generic name *Nitrobacter* was given. More recently Winogradsky and Winogradsky (1933) and H. Winogradsky (1935) have shown that other organisms also are capable of performing these two reactions. As a result they have named several new genera and species.

The nitrifying bacteria, in common with many other autotrophic organisms, display a strict specificity towards the material which they oxidize. For example, not only are the *Nitrobacter* species inactive toward ammonia and *Nitrosomonas* inactive toward nitrite, but neither is able to utilize sulfite or phosphite or any carbon compound as a source of energy. The mechanism by which the energy derived from the oxidation of ammonia or nitrite is employed in the reduction of CO_2 is unknown. Some workers have maintained that formaldehyde is an intermediate in the reduction process, whereas others have suggested that hydroxylamine and hyponitrous acid may be intermediate products. However, as yet there are no sound experimental data to support these views.

Although little information is available concerning the mechanism involved in the nitrification process or concerning the fundamental nutritional requirements of the nitrifying bacteria, several factors are known which influence the activities of the organisms. The four most important will be mentioned.

1. Effect of Concentration of Substrate. For the maximum rate of nitrification Meyerhof (1916) found that the optimum concentration of ammonia for *Nitrosomonas* was approximately 0.005 *M*, and of nitrite for *Nitrobacter* about 0.015 *M*. When concentrations above or below these values were used, the rate of the processes decreased very rapidly.

2. Effect of *p*H. Most species of nitrifying bacteria have a rather narrow *p*H range through which the rate of oxidation is at a maximum. Meyerhof (1916) observed, for example, that the optimum *p*H for the oxidation of ammonia lies between 8.5 and 8.8 and that for nitrite oxidation between 8.4 and 9.3. These high optimum *p*H figures, however, do not apply to all strains, because Meek and Lipman (1922) have found that nitrifying bacteria are active in acid peat soils of *p*H 4.6 or below. Also Winogradsky and Winogradsky (1933) have observed that nitrification may take place between a *p*H of 6.0 and 9.2, depending upon the species involved.

3. Effect of Inorganic Ions. Several early workers demonstrated that carbonates of calcium or magnesium favored the rate of nitrification. Likewise, Boltjes (1935) found that calcium ($CaCl_2$ or $CaCO_3$) plays a very important function in the activities of *Nitrosomonas* species; in fact, he found that a concentration of at least 0.000025 *M* was required for optimum nitrification, although the process proceeded slowly even without added calcium.

4. Effect of Organic Matter. It has been known for a long time that, when the nitrifying organisms (*Nitrosomonas* and *Nitrobacter* species) are cultured in artificial inorganic media, they are paralyzed

by the addition of very minute quantities of organic matter. This point may be illustrated with figures compiled by Meyerhof (1916) on the effect of glucose, urea, and asparagine on the growth and rate of nitrite oxidation by a *Nitrobacter* species (Table 4). Similar results

TABLE 4

EFFECT OF CERTAIN ORGANIC COMPOUNDS ON THE GROWTH AND RATE OF NITRITE OXIDATION BY *Nitrobacter*

[From Meyerhof (1916)]

Compound	Concentration	Effect on Growth	Concentration	Effect on Oxidation
Glucose	0.0025 *M*	Delayed	0.3 *M*	No effect
	0.015 *M*	Prevented	0.6 *M*	10% inhibition
			0.8 *M*	25–30% inhibition
Urea	0.15 *M*	Delayed	0.15 *M*	No effect
	0.30 *M*	Prevented	0.50 *M*	30% inhibition
Asparagine	0.15 *M*	Delayed	0.15 *M*	10–20% inhibition
	0.30 *M*	Prevented	0.80 *M*	25–30% inhibition

have been reported by other workers with a variety of compounds. On the other hand, nitrification in nature, especially in soil and sewage, proceeds in the presence of fairly large quantities of organic matter. Pandalai (1936) believes that this incompatibility of behavior of the nitrifying organisms in artificial cultures and in their natural environments may be explained as due to one or more of the following causes: (1) the nitrifying bacteria function in association with the saprophytes of the soil; (2) there are in soil several strains of organism other than the classical nitrifiers which can tolerate fairly large quantities of organic matter and still nitrify ammonia; and (3) all nitrifiers are heterotrophic at some stage in their life. After conducting personal researches on nitrification in the presence of organic matter, Pandalai found that, although organic matter tended to depress nitrification when *Nitrosomonas* was present by itself, the adverse effect was completely removed in the presence of other organisms, such as *Azotobacter* or *Bacillus mycoides;* in fact, nitrification was usually increased in the presence of such organisms. These observations tend to support the first of the causes just listed; they show that, by utilizing the interfering organic matter in some way, the associated saprophytes assist *Nitrosomonas* in its function. Boltjes (1935) also studied the effects of organic compounds on the growth and respiration of nitrifying bacteria. Most of the organic materials which he studied were toxic, except the salts of certain fatty acids, which were nontoxic at low concentrations, and "Nährstoff-Heyden" (an incomplete acid-digest of egg albumin), which stimulated the growth of both types of nitrifiers when added to an inorganic medium. As a result of these studies we can state that the inhibitory effect of organic matter on the nitrifying bacteria is not general. Some compounds are decidedly toxic, some are inhibitory only at a given concentration, and others appear to stimulate growth but are not essential. For further reading on the nitrifying bacteria the general review by Bömeke (1939) should be consulted.

The Sulfur Bacteria. The so-called sulfur bacteria are a very heterogeneous group of organisms which are widely distributed in nature. Not all of them are strictly autotrophic in nature, as can be seen in Table 3. They include a variety of morphological types which may be aerobic or anaerobic, and they vary profoundly in their biochemical activities.

If we were to list here all the organisms which are capable of effecting a change in sulfur or its compounds, this discussion would become extremely involved. Therefore the photosynthesizing sulfur bacteria and the organisms which break down proteins with the liberation of hydrogen sulfide will not be included in this brief discussion. Only those specialized organisms in whose metabolism sulfur plays an essential and leading part will be mentioned here. They include microorganisms whose metabolism results in the formation of either (a) oxidation products of sulfur and sulfur compounds, or (b) reduction products of sulfur and sulfur compounds. Most of the organisms which can be allocated to the first group are obligate or facultative autotrophs and therefore fit into the nutrition spectrum under the heading of chemosynthetic autotrophs. Probably none of the second group is autotrophic, but they will be mentioned here to complete the discussion of the sulfur bacteria.

a. Microorganisms Whose Metabolism Results in the Formation of Oxidation Products of Sulfur and Sulfur Compounds. The organisms which are usually placed in this group cover a wide range of morphological types and vary profoundly in their biochemical activities. For convenience they may be divided into the following three classes: (1) bacteria which oxidize hydrogen sulfide and deposit elementary sulfur inside their cells; (2) bacteria which oxidize not only hydrogen sulfide but also thiosulfate and tetrathionate and in many cases deposit sulfur outside their cells; (3) bacteria which oxidize elementary sulfur and thiosulfate directly to sulfate. Some of the outstanding features of several of the organisms in these three classes will now be mentioned.

1. Bacteria Which Oxidize H_2S and Deposit Elementary Sulfur Inside Their Cells (Beggiatoa, Thiothrix, and Thioploca). From a biochemical standpoint this group includes the purple sulfur bacteria as well as a number of colorless forms. However, since the purple sulfur bacteria are photosynthetic, it is usually more convenient to group them separately, and they have already been considered.

The recorded observations of the colorless sulfur bacteria appear to date back in one instance as far as 1817 [see Bunker (1936)], but little was actually known about them until Cramer showed in 1870 that the granules in their cells were elementary sulfur and could be extracted with carbon disulfide. There is no point in cataloging here the various species of this group of the sulfur bacteria. Their morphology has been studied in some detail by Ellis (1932), and *Bergey's Manual* (1939) differentiates the three most important genera [5] as follows:

I. Filamentous, nonmotile, with a contrast to base and tip, attached.
 Thiothrix (Type species: *Thiothrix nivea*).
II. Filamentous, motile (oscillating), not attached, no differentiation into base and tip.
 A. Filaments not in bundles nor surrounded by a gelatinous sheath.
  Beggiatoa (Type species: *Beggiatoa alba*).
 B. Filaments in bundles, surrounded by a gelatinous sheath.
  Thioploca (Type species: *Thioploca schmidlee*).

The first and the outstanding contribution to the study of the physiology of these organisms was made by Winogradsky from 1887 to 1888. Working with *Beggiatoa*, he showed that, when the organism was cultivated in the presence of hydrogen sulfide and air, granules of sulfur were deposited within the cells but that, when the supply of H_2S was removed, the sulfur granules disappeared and sulfates appeared in the culture medium. Furthermore, when all the intracellular sulfur disappeared, the organisms died. Although Winogradsky showed that carbon dioxide was essential for the growth of the organisms and that they develop best in the presence of a minimum supply of organic matter, he could not prove that the organisms were completely autotrophic because his cultures were not pure.

Keil (1912), however, obtained pure cultures of *Beggiatoa* and *Thiothrix* and showed that his strains would grow in the complete absence of organic carbon. The composition of the simplest inorganic medium

[5] Kolkwitz (1938) names a new genus (*Thionema*) which is closely related to *Thiothrix* and oxidizes H_2S to S.

employed by Keil was based on an analysis of sulfur spring water and contained ammonium salts as a source of nitrogen, carbonate as a source of carbon, and several mineral constituents, including phosphate, which was found to be essential. In this basal medium optimum growth occurred in an atmosphere containing H_2S and O_2 at 0.8 mm. and 15 mm. pressure, respectively. Peptone, asparagine, leucine, and nitrate were not used as a sole source of nitrogen. Later Cataldi (1940) isolated pure cultures of *Beggiatoa alba*. Since the organism can be grown on several organic media but not in an absolutely mineral medium, there is some question as to whether this particular species is an obligate autotroph.

It is assumed by most workers that the energy requirements of these sulfur organisms are met by the oxidation, or dehydrogenation, of hydrogen sulfide, thus:

$$H_2S + \tfrac{1}{2}O_2 \rightarrow H_2O + S$$

or

$$H_2S + H_2CO_3 \rightarrow HCOOH + S + H_2O$$

It has also been stated that these organisms can oxidize as much as four times their weight of H_2S every 24 hours and that from 8 to 19 g. of sulfur are consumed for every gram of carbon assimilated.

When the H_2S is withdrawn from the medium, the elementary sulfur granules are thought to be transformed directly to sulfate, thus:

$$S + 1\tfrac{1}{2}O_2 + H_2O \rightarrow H_2SO_4$$

Under experimental conditions, however, the medium does not become acid; this phenomenon is believed to be due to the neutralization effected by carbonates present in the medium.

2. Bacteria Which Oxidize Not Only H_2S but also Thiosulfate and Tetrathionate and in Many Cases Deposit Sulfur outside Their Cells (Thiobacillus thioparus, Thiobacillus novellus, Thiobacillus denitrificans). Although the organisms of this group of sulfur bacteria differ in many ways from the group just discussed, it is usually convenient to differentiate them on the basis that they deposit sulfur outside their cells. However, it should be mentioned that this characteristic may not always be constant, because on several occasions workers have observed sulfur both inside and outside the cells. Morphologically the members of this group are true bacteria; that is, they are not filamentous or thread-like and they contain no photosynthetic pigment. They may be either aerobic or anaerobic, and some are obligate autotrophs whereas others are facultative autotrophs.

The best-known bacterium of this group is *Thiobacillus thioparus*, which was first isolated by Nathansohn from sea water about 1902 but was named later by Beijerinck (1904), who demonstrated its presence in water, soil, and canal mud. It is an aerobic obligatory autotroph, and it grows at or near a neutral reaction, a feature distinguishing it sharply from *Thiobacillus thiooxidans*, which will be considered later. The organism can apparently obtain its energy by oxidizing sulfur, sulfide, thiosulfate, and tetrathionate. Beijerinck suggested that tetrathionate is oxidized in accordance with the following reaction:

$$Na_2S_4O_6 + Na_2CO_3 + \tfrac{1}{2}O_2 \rightarrow 2Na_2SO_4 + CO_2 + 2S$$

but the results of Starkey (1934) indicate that thiosulfate is oxidized with the formation of sulfate and elementary sulfur in the proportion of 60 per cent and 40 per cent, respectively, from 100 parts of thiosulfate. The following medium was found to be suitable for studies of thiosulfate decomposition:

K_2HPO_4	2 g.	$FeCl_3 \cdot 6H_2O$	0.02 g.
$MgSO_4 \cdot 7H_2O$	0.1 g.	$(NH_4)_2SO_4$	0.1 g.
$CaCl_2$	0.1 g.	$Na_2S_2O_3 \cdot 5H_2O$	10 g.
$MnSO_4 \cdot 2H_2O$	0.02 g.	Tap water	1,000 g.

The reaction proposed by Starkey to account for the oxidation was:

$$5Na_2S_2O_3 + H_2O + 4O_2 \rightarrow 5Na_2SO_4 + H_2SO_4 + 4S$$

The organism assimilates about 1 g. of carbon from HCO_3^- for every 125 g. of thiosulfate sulfur oxidized, and about 4.8 per cent of the energy released is used for the synthesis of cellular material.

Another organism (*Thiobacillus novellus*), which closely resembles *Thiobacillus thioparus* in many features, has been described by Starkey (1934, 1935). The organism is only a facultative autotroph, because it will develop on various organic media with no thiosulfate, as well as on mineral media containing thiosulfate. Its optimum *p*H for growth is between 7.8 and 9.0, and it cannot tolerate an acidity below *p*H 5.5 to 5.0, a feature which differentiates it from *Thiobacillus thiooxidans*. It oxidizes thiosulfate to sulfate, with no precipitation of elementary sulfur and without the accumulation of any other sulfur compound:

$$Na_2S_2O_3 + H_2O + 2O_2 \rightarrow Na_2SO_4 + H_2SO_4$$

According to Starkey, more energy is liberated per unit of thiosulfate oxidized by *Thiobacillus novellus* than by *Thiobacillus thioparus;* consequently the ratio of thiosulfate oxidized to carbon assimilated is less, namely, 48 to 1 instead of 125 to 1. This fact means that approximately 5.7 per cent of the available energy is used for cellular synthesis. Closely related to *Thiobacillus novellus* is *Thiobacillus coproliticus*, a new species discovered by Lipman and McLees (1940) in coprolite from Triassic in Arizona.

The fourth organism to be considered in this group is the anaerobic bacterium, *Thiobacillus denitrificans*, first isolated by Beijerinck in 1904 but studied in more detail by Lieske (1912) and later by Beijerinck (1920). It is a strict autotroph, since it will not grow on organic media. The organism supposedly obtains its energy for the assimilation of CO_2 from carbonate or bicarbonate by oxidizing sulfur, hydrogen sulfide, thiosulfate, or tetrathionate to sulfate and at the same time reducing (denitrifying) nitrates in the medium. It has been stated that free CO_2 cannot be utilized by this organism because its use leads to the accumulation of free sulfuric acid, and that the organism is intolerant of low *p*H values. The energy reaction with elementary sulfur may be illustrated by the following equations:

$$5S + 6KNO_3 + 2CaCO_3 \rightarrow 3K_2SO_4 + 2CaSO_4 + 2CO_2 + 3N_2$$

or

$$5S + 6KNO_3 + 2H_2O \rightarrow K_2SO_4 + 4KHSO_4 + 3N_2$$

However, since it has been found by several workers that the quantitative yield of sulfate is only about one-half of what would have been expected from the amount of nitrate reduced, it seems that the denitrification cannot entirely account for the oxidation of the elementary sulfur. Lieske (1912) observed that *Thiobacillus denitrificans* oxidized thiosulfate in accordance with the following equation:

$$5Na_2S_2O_3 + 8KNO_3 + 2NaHCO_3 \rightarrow 6Na_2SO_4 + 4K_2SO_4 + 4N_2 + 2CO_2 + H_2O$$

but, since he detected the presence of ephemeral intermediate compounds, it is doubtful if the reaction proceeds directly to sulfate; free nitrogen, however, is evolved. Furthermore, it was found that the organism fixed 1 g. of carbon for every 100 g. of thiosulfate decomposed, an indication of a free energy efficiency of about 8.7 per cent. This figure is somewhat higher than the corresponding values for the other *Thiobacillus* species thus far studied.

A number of other autotrophic and heterotrophic organisms are known which can oxidize thiosulfate to sulfate. Since their functions have been discussed in some detail by Bunker (1936), we shall say only that all these sulfur-oxidizing bacteria play important roles in the transformation of sulfur in the soil.

3. Bacteria Which Oxidize Elementary Sulfur and Thiosulfate Directly to Sulfate (*Thiobacillus thiooxidans*). The third group of sulfur-oxidizing bacteria which may be mentioned briefly is the one which oxidizes elementary sulfur or thiosulfate directly to sulfate. This group is restricted in that only one well-described species, *Thiobacillus thiooxidans*, is known. This organism was first described by Waksman and Joffe (1922), who isolated it from soils containing free sulfur and rock phosphate. Its physiological behavior has since been studied in some detail by Starkey (1935, 1937), Vogler and Umbreit (1941, 1942), Umbreit, Vogel, and Vogler (1942), and Vogler (1942).

Thiobacillus thiooxidans is an interesting organism, especially since its optimum *p*H for growth lies between 3 and 4 but it can survive a concentration of acid, which it produces, equivalent to a *p*H value between 0.2 and 0.6 (this acid corresponds to a solution of approximately 5 to 10 per cent H_2SO_4). The organism is a strict aerobic, obligate autotroph, since it is able to grow in the following mineral medium and to utilize CO_2 in the gas phase as a source of carbon and $(NH_4)_2SO_4$ as a source of nitrogen:

$(NH_4)_2SO_4$	0.2 g.	KH_2PO_4	3–5 g.
$MgSO_4 \cdot 7H_2O$	0.1–0.5 g.	Powdered sulfur	10 g.
$FeSO_4$	0.01 g.	Water	1,000 ml.
$CaCl_2$	0.25 g.		

The response of the organism to organic substances is also of interest; even though it is a strict autotroph, the presence of substances such as glucose, mannitol, and glycerol increases the rate of sulfur oxidation, and they must therefore be utilized in some manner. Nitrates are injurious, only small concentrations of nitrites are tolerated, and peptones are distinctly deleterious; in fact, ammonium salts are the only satisfactory source of nitrogen for the organism. Phosphate ions are indispensable for growth.

It has been generally assumed in the past that the organism acquires all its energy by oxidizing sulfur or thiosulfate directly to sulfate, thus:

$$S + 1\tfrac{1}{2}O_2 + H_2O \rightarrow H_2SO_4$$

or

$$2S + 3O_2 + 2H_2O \rightarrow 2H_2SO_4$$

or

$$Na_2S_2O_3 + 2O_2 + H_2O \rightarrow Na_2SO_4 + H_2SO_4$$

A recent study by Vogler (1942), however, shows that there exists in the organism a measurable oxygen uptake in the absence of the specific nutrient (sulfur). This respiration has been shown to be due to the utilization of organic material which has been previously synthesized by the chemosynthetic process. Therefore, *Thiobacillus thiooxidans* must also possess an endogenous respiration which involves the utilization of previously synthesized organic materials.

Since it is probable that a cell can derive energy from oxidations carried on only within its boundaries, one of the most interesting physiological problems in connection with the sulfur-oxidizing bacteria is the nature of the mechanism by which insoluble elementary sulfur outside the cell is rendered soluble and then taken into the cell, where it undergoes oxidation. In the past several hypotheses have been advanced to explain this mechanism in connection with *Thiobacillus thiooxidans*, but there have been few experimental data on the subject. Recently, however, Vogler and Umbreit (1941, 1942) and Umbreit, Vogel, and Vogler (1942) showed that the cells of *Thiobacillus thiooxidans* must be in direct contact with the sulfur particles before the oxidation can take place. This phenomenon was thought to be due to one of at least two possibilities: either sulfur was oxidized at the surface of the cell, or sulfur was dissolved in some component of the cell wall. Upon further investigation the same workers were able to show that *Thiobacillus thiooxidans* oxidizes insoluble sulfur by first dissolving it in a fat globule located at the ends of the cell, after which the sulfur is taken into the cell for oxidation. The actual sulfur-oxidation process (energy input) within the cell appears to be coupled with phosphate esterification, whereas the CO_2-fixation process (energy utilization) is connected with phosphate release [Vogler and Umbreit (1942)].

b. Microorganisms Whose Metabolism Results in the Reduction of Sulfur Compounds (*Vibrio desulfuricans*, etc.). It has been known for a long time that microorganisms can reduce various inorganic sulfur-containing compounds to hydrogen sulfide; in fact, as early as 1889 it was reported that certain bacteria reduce thiosulfate to H_2S, and later Neuberg and Welde (1914) found that various yeasts reduce thiosulfate in accordance with the following reaction:

$$Na_2S_2O_3 + H_2 \rightarrow H_2S + Na_2SO_3$$

The first important studies of the sulfate-reducing bacteria were carried out by the Dutch microbiologists Beijerinck (1895), van Delden (1903), and Elion (1924). The organisms (*Vibrio* [6] *desulfuricans, Vibrio estuarii,* and *Vibrio thermodesulfuricans*) which they isolated and described are anaerobic, motile, curved rods containing no spores. However, in a more recent study by Starkey (1938) strains were isolated which form spores.

All these workers found that the organisms were capable of growing in a medium containing sulfate, asparagine, lactate, or other organic

[6] These organisms have also been allocated to the genera *Spirillum* and *Microspira* by various workers.

carbon substances and various inorganic salts. The composition of the substrate employed by Starkey (1938) was as follows:

K_2HPO_4	0.5 g.
NH_4Cl	1 g.
$MgSO_4 \cdot 7H_2O$	2 g.
$CaSO_4 \cdot 2H_2O$	1 g.
or	
{ Na_2SO_4	1 g.
{ $CaCl_2 \cdot 2H_2O$	0.1 g.
$CH_3 \cdot CHOH \cdot COONa$	3.5 g.
Mohr's salt (ferrous ammonium sulfate)	Trace
H_2O (tap)	1,000 ml.

This medium had a *p*H of 7.0. The iron salt which served as an indicator of sulfide formation was not incorporated in the solution medium; a small crystal was sterilized in a flame and added to each culture flask before inoculation. The reduction of sulfate was found to be accompanied by a concurrent oxidation of the organic compound present in the medium:

$$2C_3H_5O_3Na + 3MgSO_4 \rightarrow 3MgCO_3 + Na_2CO_3 + 2CO_2 + 2H_2O + 3H_2S$$

or

$$3CaSO_4 + 2C_2H_5OH \rightarrow 3CaCO_3 + 3H_2S + CO_2 + 3H_2O$$

Quantitative proof for these general reactions has been presented by Baars (1930) in his comprehensive study of sulfate-reducing bacteria. Although much of Baars's investigation was concerned with the ability of numerous organic compounds to act as hydrogen donators in the sulfate reduction, he showed that *Vibrio estuarii* was capable of producing a much higher maximum yield of H_2S per liter than the other species, for example:

Vibrio thermodesulfuricans	566 mg.
Vibrio desulfuricans	794 mg.
Vibrio estuarii	1,448 mg.

Furthermore Baars postulated that the reduction of sulfate took place in several steps:

$$\text{Sulfate } (H_2SO_4) + 2H \rightarrow H_4SO_4 \xrightarrow{-H_2O}$$

$$\text{Sulfurous acid } (H_2SO_3) + 2H \rightarrow H_4SO_3 \xrightarrow{-H_2O}$$

$$\text{Sulfoxylic acid } (H_2SO_2) + 2H \rightarrow H_4SO_2 \xrightarrow{-H_2O}$$

$$\text{Sulfur hydrate } (H_2SO) + 2H \rightarrow H_4SO \xrightarrow{-H_2O}$$

$$\text{Hydrogen sulfide } (H_2S)$$

with the hydrogen for the reduction coming from a variety of organic compounds, such as acids, sugars, and alcohols.

Another interesting point in connection with the reduction of sulfates by the sulfur-reducing bacteria has been raised by the studies of Stephenson and Stickland (1931). These investigators found that certain sulfate-reducing organisms contain an enzyme, hydrogenase, which activates molecular hydrogen and renders them capable of reducing sulfate quantitatively to sulfide by means of molecular hydrogen, thus:

$$H_2SO_4 + 4H_2 \rightarrow H_2S + 4H_2O$$

Sulfite and thiosulfate were found to be similarly reduced.

Ever since the sulfate-reducing bacteria were first isolated from canal mud and soil by Beijerinck in 1895, they have been repeatedly recovered by numerous workers [see Bunker (1936) and Starkey (1938)] from these habitats and also found in ocean mud, bottom (800 fathoms deep) deposits of the Black Sea, sewage, brine of oil wells varying in depth from 450 to 3,090 ft., and water at the bottom of gasoline storage tanks. The black color of muds and clay caused by the precipitation of iron sulfide, the deposition of chalk in tropical seas [Bavendamm (1932)], the corrosion of iron conduits under anaerobic conditions in grounds containing considerable amounts of sulfate, the corrosion of concrete, and the periodic destruction of large numbers of fish in the waters off the South African coast have all been attributed to the activities of these organisms. It is even possible that some deposits of mineral sulfides have been formed through the activity of the sulfate-reducing bacteria [Bastin (1926)].

At this point mention should be made of the biological oxidation of ammonium thiocyanate by *Bacterium thiocyanoxidans*. This organism is a slender, Gram-negative, motile bacillus, growing best at 22°C. on nutrient agar, where it produces a water-soluble, canary-yellow pigment. Practically nothing is known about the nutrition of this organism, except that it is a heterotroph. In the absence of organic matter, however, it can, through an adaptive enzyme, attack ammonium thiocyanate as a sole carbon and nitrogen source. The energy reaction is thought to be as follows:

$$NH_4CNS + 2H_2O + 2O_2 \rightarrow (NH_4)_2SO_4 + CO_2$$

Bacterium thiocyanoxidans is an interesting organism, because we usually assume that the CNS ion is one of the more toxic anions for bacteria. This organism, however, can actually oxidize it to obtain energy for growth.

The Iron Bacteria. The so-called iron bacteria consist largely of a group of filamentous or thread-like organisms whose morphology closely resembles a spiral ribbon or a twisted hairpin. They grow best at low temperatures (0° to 20°C.), and they are normally found in cool springs and brooks, especially those rich in iron salts. *Bergey's Manual* (1939) characterizes the four most important genera of iron bacteria (*Chlamydobacteriales*) as follows:

I. Bacteria showing typical false branching.
  A. Sheaths entirely organic, not impregnated with iron.
    Spherotilus (Type species: *Spherotilus nantans*).
  B. Sheaths impregnated with iron.
    Clonothrix (Type species: *Clonothrix fusca*).
II. Bacteria unbranched or showing true branching.
  A. Cells of the filaments divide transversely.
    Leptothrix (Type species: *Leptothrix ochracea*).
  B. Cells of the filaments divide in three planes.
    Crenothrix (Type species: *Crenothrix polyspora*).

Closely related physiologically to these forms are the nonfilamentous stalk bacteria of the genus *Gallionella* (Type species: *Gallionella ferruginea*), first described by Ehrenberg in 1838 and studied more recently by Cholodny (1926) and Henrici and Johnson (1935). The organisms of this genus are kidney-shaped bacteria, 1.2 to 1.5 μ in length and 0.5 to 0.6 μ in thickness, which secrete colloidal ferric hydroxide from the concave portion of the cell, forming band-like stalks. They are not filamentous or ensheathed. Thus, according to Cholodny, early workers were wrong about the morphology of *Gallionella ferruginea* because they observed only the inert ferric hydroxide stalk and based their conclusions entirely on it.

The morphological and physiological characteristics and the geological significance of the iron bacteria have been extensively studied by Winogradsky (1888), Ellis (1907), Molisch (1910), Lieske (1911), Harder (1919), Cholodny (1926), Starkey and Halvorson (1927), Naumann (1928, 1929), Halvorson (1931), Beger (1935), Schorr (1939), Cataldi (1939), and others. These references should be consulted for further details.

The literature on the iron bacteria is full of many conflicting hypotheses, particularly concerning the physiology of the organisms. For instance, some early workers, especially Winogradsky, have maintained that all the so-called iron bacteria are obligate autotrophs whose development depends on the assimilation of carbon dioxide by means of the energy liberated from the oxidation of ferrous to ferric iron and, furthermore, that the insoluble ferric material formed by the oxidation is deposited in the sheaths of the organisms. Certain other early investigators, especially Molisch, have believed that the organisms are not strictly autotrophic because they can be cultivated on peptone media with or without iron. Ellis and Molisch have concluded that iron plays no essential part in the metabolism of the iron bacteria but that its presence in the sheaths of the organisms is due to physical adsorption or to positive chemotaxis. Still others, particularly Lieske, have believed that the organisms are probably autotrophic and that in certain species the iron can be replaced by manganese, but in other species iron is specific and cannot be replaced by other metallic ions, such as those of manganese, lead, bismuth, cadmium, copper, zinc, or magnesium. It is difficult to reconcile these various opinions. Certain of the discrepancies can probably be explained by the fact that different species were worked with and different conditions prevailed, but others seem to be due to faulty observations with impure cultures. For example, in 1910 Molisch worked with *Leptothrix* and found that it needed organic matter but did not require iron in solution. Lieske (1911), on the other hand, did much of his work with *Gallionella* (*Spirophyllum*) and observed that it required ferrous carbonate in solution but that it could live in the absence of organic matter. Here are two different organisms that clearly show entirely different characteristics. Such an explanation, however, does not apply to the discrepancies between the observations of Molisch and Winogradsky. Both these investigators were working with *Leptothrix*, but their findings concerning the need for iron and organic matter differed radically.

After surveying the literature and carrying out extensive researches of his own, Harder (1919) concluded that the iron bacteria can be placed in three physiological groups:

1. Those, such as *Gallionella ferruginea*, that precipitate ferric hydroxide from solutions of ferrous carbonate and use the CO_2 liberated and the energy produced by the oxidation of the iron for their life processes (obligate autotrophs).
2. Those, such as *Leptothrix ochracea*, that do not require iron compounds for growth but, if these compounds (or other ions such as manganese) are present, cause the deposition of insoluble salts in their sheath (facultative autotrophs).
3. Those, such as certain lower bacteria (sulfate-reducing, hydrogen sulfide-forming), that attack specified soluble organic iron salts, using the organic radical as food and precipitating ferric hydroxide

or basic ferric salts which are gradually changed to ferric hydroxide, but that cannot utilize any inorganic iron salts or CO_2 (heterotrophs).

Naumann (1928, 1929) has also classified the iron bacteria on a physiological basis. He prefers to limit the term iron bacteria to those organisms which oxidize ferrous compounds and show chemosynthetic nutrition.

Lieske (1911), Naumann (1929), and others offer the following equations to indicate the reactions which probably take place during the process of oxidation by the iron bacteria (*Gallionella ferruginea*):

$$2FeCO_3 + 3H_2O + \frac{1}{2}O_2 \rightarrow Fe_2(OH)_6 + 2CO_2$$

or

$$4FeCO_3 + 6H_2O + O_2 \rightarrow 4Fe(OH)_3 + 4CO_2$$

The iron bacteria sometimes grow in the pipes of certain public water supplies rich in iron salts, where they form brownish-red, flocculent masses which often lead to a complete stoppage of the pipes [Beger (1937, 1938)]. Many persons [see Harder (1919)] believe that these bacteria have played an important part also in the formation of natural iron ore deposits. However, as Starkey and Halvorson (1927) have pointed out, so many agencies are active in the precipitation of iron that biologically it appears to be of little significance unless the reactions responsible for the change are understood. Halvorson (1931) believes that the importance of the true iron bacteria has been overemphasized, whereas the importance of the heterotrophic bacteria in the transformations of iron in nature has not been fully appreciated.

The Hydrogen Bacteria. Another interesting group of bacteria which are usually classified as autotrophs obtains its energy for growth by oxidizing molecular hydrogen to water. Like some of the other bacteria which we have already mentioned, however, these organisms are probably facultative autotrophs and thus are intermediate between the obligate autotrophs and the true heterotrophs. These bacteria occur in canal mud, swamps, and soils where large amounts of hydrogen are formed as a result of anaerobic processes. Most of the species are short rods, and several of them are known to produce spores. Some are aerobic; others are microaerophilic or anaerobic.

According to Baas-Becking and Parks (1927), the various hydrogen-oxidizing bacteria can catalyze the following reactions:

(1) $$H_2 + \frac{1}{2}O_2 \rightarrow H_2O$$

(2) $$H_2 + N_2O \rightarrow N_2 + H_2O$$

(3) $$5H_2 + 2NO_3^- \rightarrow N_2 + 4H_2O + 2OH^-$$

(4) $$H_2 + \frac{1}{4}SO_4^{--} \rightarrow \frac{1}{4}S^{--} + H_2O$$

(5) $$H_2 + \frac{1}{4}CO_2 \rightarrow \frac{1}{4}CH_4 + \frac{1}{2}H_2O$$

(6) $$H_2 + S \rightarrow H_2S$$

No organism is definitely known which can catalyze reaction 6, and those which produce 3, 4, and 5 have been described but studied very little. Beijerinck and Minkman (1909) have cultured the bacterium responsible for reaction 2, but little is known concerning its properties. The nutrition of the organisms responsible for reaction 1 is better known and will be briefly summarized.

The first member of this group (*Hydrogenomonas pantotropha*) was described by Kaserer (1906), who found that it would grow in the following inorganic medium in the presence of a gaseous mixture consisting of air, CO_2, and H_2:

KH_2PO_4	0.5 g.	$NaHCO_3$	0.5 g.
$MgSO_4$	0.2 g.	$FeCl_3$	Trace
NH_4Cl	1 g.	H_2O	1,000 ml.

The organism also grew as a heterotroph on ordinary laboratory media.

After the discovery of *Hydrogenomonas pantotropha* other aerobic, microaerophilic, and anaerobic organisms of this group were described by Niklewski (1908), Grohmann (1924), Ruhland (1924), and others. Ruhland did most of his work with an organism which he named *Hydrogenomonas pycnotica,* and most of our information concerning the metabolism of the hydrogen oxidizers will be found in his excellent paper. The organism grew in the following inorganic medium in a gaseous environment consisting of O_2, H_2, and CO_2:

$NaHCO_3$	1 g.	$MgSO_4$	0.1 g.
NH_4Cl	1 g.	NaCl	0.1 g.
KH_2PO_4	0.5 g.	H_2O (glass-distilled)	1,000 ml.

The relative pressures of hydrogen and oxygen had little effect on the rate of oxidation, and the optimum *p*H for the process was between 6.8 and 8.1, the reaction ceasing outside the limits *p*H 5.2 and 9.1.

It has been shown by several workers that the oxidation of hydrogen, $H_2 + \frac{1}{2}O_2 \rightarrow H_2O$, yields relatively large amounts of energy (34.2 cal. per gram as contrasted with about 4.1 cal. per gram of starch) and that the free energy efficiency of these organisms is 10 to 20 per cent higher than that of other autotrophs. It has also been suggested that all the hydrogen is not burned directly by these organisms but that part of it is converted to carbohydrate, which may in turn be either oxidized or used for cellular syntheses.

$$2H_2 + CO_2 \rightarrow (CH_2O) + H_2O$$

$$(CH_2O) + O_2 \rightarrow H_2O + CO_2$$

The oxidation of hydrogen, like that of sulfur and iron, is not restricted to a group of obligate or even facultative autotrophs. Work by Stephenson and Stickland (1931) and others has shown that several common heterotrophic bacteria are able to activate gaseous hydrogen; with one bacterium the hydrogen was oxidized at the expense of sulfate.

The Carbon Monoxide Bacteria. The oxidation of carbon monoxide by soil bacteria was first reported by Beijerinck and van Delden (1903), who also isolated and named the organism (*Carboxydomonas oligocarbophila*) responsible for the reaction. Although Beijerinck and van Delden observed that *Carboxydomonas oligocarbophila* is an autotrophic, rod-shaped bacterium capable of obtaining its nitrogen from ammonia, nitrite, or nitrate in an otherwise inorganic medium, they did not demonstrate how the organism derives its energy for growth. Later, however, Kaserer (1906) showed that a pure culture of the organism secures its energy by the oxidation of carbon monoxide to carbon dioxide:

$$CO + \tfrac{1}{2}O_2 \rightarrow CO_2$$

Or in symbioses with other bacteria it oxidizes hydrogen to H_2O by catalytically reducing CO_2 to CO; the CO may then be utilized as food and again oxidized to CO_2.

The morphology and physiology of this bacterium have also been studied by Lantzsch (1922), who believes that it is really an *Actinomyces* rather than a true bacterium. He cultivated the organism under autotrophic conditions in the following inorganic medium:

K_2HPO_4	0.1 g.	$MgSO_4$	Trace
$NaNO_3$	0.1 g.	$FeCl_3$	Trace
$CaCl_2$	0.05 g.	H_2O (distilled)	1,000 ml.

When the supernatant atmosphere was saturated with CO or vapors from formic acid, the resulting growth was very filamentous, or *Actinomyces*-like in form. On the other hand, normal morphology was observed when the organism was cultivated on the same medium plus formaldehyde, methyl alcohol, or acetic acid or on common bacteriological media.

The Methane- and Other Hydrocarbon-Oxidizing Bacteria. Like the hydrogen-oxidizing organisms and some of the iron and sulfur bacteria, this group is generally considered to be intermediate between the obligate autotrophs and the true heterotrophs.

The best-known member of this group is *Methanomonas methanica*, which was first described by Söhngen (1906, 1910, 1913). This organism is a short, motile rod which grows best at about 30°C. in an inorganic medium with the gas phase above it composed of approximately one-third methane and two-thirds air. To illustrate the utilization of methane by this bacterium one of Söhngen's experiments may be cited. To a closed flask containing about 100 ml. of media he added 225 parts of CH_4 and 320 parts of O_2. After the flask had been inoculated with the organism, it was incubated for 2 weeks. The gas phase of the culture was then analyzed and found to contain the following:

CO_2	78 parts
CH_4	0 parts
O_2	172 parts

Other hydrocarbons are also attacked by this organism (see Table 5). Energy for its growth is apparently derived from the following reaction [Orla-Jensen (1909)]:

$$CH_4 + 2O_2 \rightarrow CO_2 + 2H_2O$$

Many other hydrocarbon-oxidizing bacteria have also been described, including such well-known species as *Pseudomonas aeruginosa* [Bushnell and Haas (1941), Johnson, Goodale, and Turkevich (1942)]. Tausz and Peter (1919) and Tausz and Donath (1930) isolated from soil three interesting organisms (*Bacterium aliphaticum*, *Bacterium aliphaticum-liquefaciens*, and a large, spore-forming bacillus which they called Paraffin Bakterien). The species grew aerobically at 30°C. in a mineral medium with ammonia as a source of nitrogen and utilized added hydrocarbons for energy and carbon. These bacteria also grew as heterotrophs on ordinary laboratory media. The Paraffin Bakterien exhibited little effect on naphthenes, benzoid hydrocarbons, and some paraffins, such as *n*-hexane and *n*-octane, but they attacked higher paraffins like hexadecane, tricontane, and tetratricontane. The other two organisms utilized a number of compounds, as will be seen in Table 5, where some comparative data on *Methanomonas methanica* are also given.

More recently Bushnell and Haas (1941) and Johnson, Goodale, and Turkevich (1942) have studied the utilization of hydrocarbons by microorganisms and have reported some interesting results. For example, they found that many organisms are capable of using petroleum fractions such as Skelly-solve, gasoline, kerosene, light and heavy mineral oils, paraffin wax, and related hydrocarbons as the source of carbon and energy for their metabolism. The technique employed for testing these compounds was only slightly modified from that

TABLE 5

Oxidation of Various Compounds by *Bacterium aliphaticum-liquefaciens* and *Methanomonas methanica*

[From Tausz and Donath (1930)]

Compound	*Bacterium aliphaticum-liquefaciens*	*Methanomonas methanica*
Hydrogen	+	+
Methane	−	+
Ethane	−	+
Propane	−	+
Butane	−	+
Pentane	+	
Hexane	+	+
Heptane	+	
Octane	+	
Decane	+	
Ethylene	−	?
Propylene	−	+
Butylene	−	+
Benzol	−	−
Methylbenzol	−	
Propylbenzol	−	Cyclohexane −
Butylbenzol	−	Paraffin oil +
Cetylbenzol	+	

\+ = compound used as carbon and energy source.
− = compound not utilized.

used by Söhngen and others. The following basal medium proved to be satisfactory [Bushnell and Haas (1941)]:

NH_4NO_3 or $(NH_4)_2SO_4$	1 g.	KH_2PO_4	1 g.
$MgSO_4$	0.2 g.	K_2HPO_4	1 g.
$CaCl_2$	0.02 g.	$FeCl_3$ (conc. sol.)	2 drops
H_2O (distilled)	1,000 ml.		

The final *p*H was adjusted to 7.0 to 7.2. The hydrocarbon to be tested was sterilized separately and added to the extent of about 5 per cent.

Certain of these species, such as *Bacterium aliphaticum*, can also utilize a great many carbohydrates as a source of carbon [Johnson and Schwarz (1944)].

Heterotrophic Bacteria

Most of the bacteria which we know today are heterotrophs, since in general they require a more complex (reduced) source of carbon than CO_2. It should be mentioned again, however, that a sharp distinction does not exist between the autotrophic and heterotrophic bacteria; rather there is a gradual blending of metabolic activity between the two groups. Evidence for this statement is found in certain groups of bacteria which have just been discussed and in the fact that certain heterotrophic cells can fix carbon dioxide. It is likely that true heterotrophism consists in the loss of ability by an organism to synthesize from CO_2 certain molecular structures that are necessary in metabolism. This fact does not mean, however, that heterotrophic bacteria are unable to carry out syntheses impossible to autotrophic forms. The fixation of atmospheric nitrogen by *Azotobacter* and *Rhizobium* species is a good example of a metabolic activity which is lacking in autotrophs. Both these genera are heterotrophic, since they require complex carbon compounds, such as glucose or mannitol, but they can still use inorganic nitrogen (N_2, NO_3, or NH_4).

For purposes of discussion it is convenient to classify the heterotrophic bacteria into arbitrary groups on the basis of the complexity of the simplest nitrogen source which they can utilize and their need for growth factors, or vitamins, when cultivated in chemically defined media (see Fig. 1, p. 636). There are many exceptions, however, to such classification. For example, in one medium an organism may use ammonium salts as a source of nitrogen, whereas in another substrate the same organism may fail to utilize these salts for this purpose. Thus the specialization of bacteria with each step in differentiation must be visualized, and it must be realized that, as they become generally more fastidious or parasitic, they may lose their ability to synthesize certain required protoplasmic components or growth factors. In a medium devoid of these substances the nitrogen in ammonium salts may not be utilized by the organism, whereas in a substrate in which these components have been supplied growth will occur. Also certain bacteria may be "trained" to use a simpler form of nitrogen than that to which they are generally accustomed. Still another phenomenon of some bacteria which precludes the possibility of rigid grouping by the foregoing scheme is growth and multiplication through the use of nitrogen or growth factors liberated from dead cells. In spite of these inherent disadvantages of allocating heterotrophic bacteria to certain more or less fixed groups on the basis of their nitrogen and growth-factor requirements, however, this classification is convenient in discussing the nutrition of these organisms and will be followed here.

BACTERIA CAPABLE OF UTILIZING GASEOUS NITROGEN AS A SOURCE OF NITROGEN

The first type of true heterotrophs whose nutrition we will consider is the so-called nitrogen-fixing group. So far as we know at the present time, a few species of microorganisms are the only forms of life which possess the property of using molecular nitrogen in their metabolism. A few remarks concerning the nutrition of these nitrogen-fixing bacteria will be made here; further details of the fixation process are presented in Chapter 9.

The bacteria which are capable of fixing or assimilating atmospheric nitrogen, that is, of bringing it into combination with other elements to form compounds which are utilized by the organisms in building organic compounds, may conveniently be classified into two groups: (1) those which live freely (nonsymbiotically) in soil or water; and (2) those which grow symbiotically with certain plants.

Let us briefly consider the nutrition of the bacteria in each of these groups.

Nonsymbiotic (Free-Living) Nitrogen-Fixing Bacteria. The bacteria of this group are of two kinds, aerobic and anaerobic. The aerobic forms are, for the most part, included in the genus *Azotobacter*, and several species have been described, such as *Azotobacter chroococcum, Azotobacter agilis, Azotobacter vinelandii*, and *Azotobacter beijerinckii*. These forms are rather large rod-shaped or coccobacillary bacteria which never produce spores but are sometimes motile. They often contain vacuoles and a slimy capsule of variable thickness. *Azotobacter* species are quite abundant in many fertile soils where the acidity is not less than *p*H 6.0, and they are probably in a measure responsible for the accumulation of many nitrogenous substances in the soil. They were first isolated by Beijerinck (1901) and have since been studied in some detail by many workers because of their importance in soil fertility. The organisms may be easily isolated from the soil by using Ashby's mannitol phosphate solution (*p*H 7.2 to 8.0):

Mannitol	10 g.	$CaSO_4 \cdot 2H_2O$	0.1 g.
KH_2PO_4	0.2 g.	$CaCO_3$	5 g.
$MgSO_4 \cdot 7H_2O$	0.2 g.	H_2O (distilled)	1,000 ml.
NaCl	0.2 g.		

or by plating soil samples on the same basal medium containing 2.0 per cent agar. Quite similar media for isolation purposes have been proposed by other workers, especially Horner and his associates [see Horner and Burk (1934), Horner, Burk, Allison, and Sherman (1942)], who have extensively studied the essential inorganic requirements of *Azotobacter*.

The carbon and nitrogen requirements of *Azotobacter* may be briefly summarized. Carbon compounds, such as mannitol, propionate, malate, succinate, or glucose, can be oxidized as a source of energy for the metabolic activities of *Azotobacter* species. *Azotobacter chroococcum* decomposes glucose mainly to CO_2, but ethyl alcohol and formic, acetic, and lactic acids have been observed occasionally in old cultures [Kostytschew, Ryskaltschuk, and Schwezowa (1926)]. In addition to atmospheric nitrogen such nitrogenous substances as ammonium salts, nitrites, nitrates, and urea are readily assimilated by *Azotobacter* species. Aspartic acid, asparagine, adenine, glutamic acid, guanine, allantoin, cytosine, and uramil are also utilized, but not as readily. Leucine, phenylalanine, uracil, acetamide, hydroxylamine, hydrazine, unhydrolyzed gelatin, and other compounds cannot be used [Burk and Horner (1935), Horner and Allison (1944)]. When a nitrogenous compound is readily available, as a rule the *Azotobacter* species do not assimilate or fix gaseous nitrogen. However, when such a compound is absent from the medium, nitrogen gas is used to synthesize bacterial protoplasm; the amount of nitrogen fixed is generally in direct proportion to the amount of cellular synthesis. The mechanism involved in the nonsymbiotic fixation of nitrogen is not well understood. It is known that the end products of nitrogen synthesis are proteins (protoplasm), but the specific reactions concerned in the transformation of free nitrogen to protein are not known [see Burk (1934)].

The relationship of accessory growth factors to the development of *Azotobacter* species has been studied by several workers [see Jones and Greaves (1943)]. In general the organisms do not need an external source of the following substances for normal growth and metabolism in simple substrates: ascorbic acid, biotin, carotene, indole-3-acetic acid, inositol, nicotinamide, pantothenic acid, pimelic acid, thiamin, riboflavin, and pyridoxine. When grown in synthetic media devoid of accessory factors, however, *Azotobacter* species synthesize fairly large quantities of biotin, inositol, nicotinic acid, pantothenic acid, pyridoxine, riboflavin, thiamin, and other vitamins.

The nonsymbiotic, anaerobic, nitrogen-fixing bacteria belong to the genus *Clostridium*. The most important species is *Clostridium pasteurianum*, which is closely related to the butyric acid bacteria. This organism is widely distributed in soil; but, since it is a strict anaerobe, it is doubtful if conditions are optimum for its growth in well-aerated normal soil. However, in boggy, acid (*p*H 6.0 or below) soils it may serve an important function, since *Azotobacter* species are inactive in such an environment. When studied in the laboratory, *Cl. pasteurianum* fixes considerable nitrogen. Winogradsky (1902) studied this species in some detail and found that it grows at 28° to 30°C. in the following nitrogen-free medium (optimum *p*H 6.9 to 7.3):

Glucose	20 g.
K_2HPO_4	1.0 g.
$MgSO_4 \cdot 7H_2O$	0.2 g.
NaCl, $FeSO_4$, $MnSO_4$	Trace
H_2O (distilled, ammonia-free)	1,000 ml.
$CaCO_3$ was added sometimes.	

It has been assumed that in such a medium nitrogen is fixed by means of the energy liberated from the anaerobic breakdown of the glucose. The chief products of the fermentation of glucose are acetic and butyric acids, carbon dioxide, and hydrogen. As a source of carbon *Cl. pasteurianum* utilizes glucose, maltose, lactose, levulose, sucrose, dextrin, inulin, glycerol, mannitol, and lactate. Winogradsky found that the greater is the concentration of sugar, the lower is its economic utilization, 3.2 mg. of nitrogen being fixed per gram of glucose in 0.5 per cent solution, 2.0 mg. in 2.0 per cent solution, and 1.2 mg. in 4.0 per cent solution. Apparently no systematic study has been made of the various types of nitrogen compounds which can be assimilated by this organism, although Winogradsky observed that, when combined nitrogenous substances, such as ammonium salts, are present in the medium, the fixation of elementary nitrogen is inhibited. This inhibition can, however, be counteracted by increasing the concentration of glucose in the medium.

The nutrition of *Cl. pasteurianum* has not been studied in recent years. For a review of the available information on the nutrition of this and related species up to 1927 the book by Waksman and the reviews mentioned early in this chapter should be consulted.

Symbiotic Nitrogen-Fixing Bacteria. Two types of microorganisms are known to live in symbiotic relationship to higher plants: certain fungi and certain bacteria. In this discussion we shall mention only the bacteria.

Two genera (*Rhizobium* and *Mycobacterium*) of rod-shaped bacteria are known definitely to contain species which grow in symbiosis with higher plants. Members of the genus *Rhizobium* occur upon or in the roots of all leguminous plants, such as peas, beans, alfalfa, and sweet clover; *Mycobacterium rubiacearum*, on the other hand, occurs in the nodules of leaves of certain tropical plants of the family *Rubiaceae*. These bacteria may be discussed here with the free-living nitrogen fixers, because their gross nutritional requirements are the same: they fix nitrogen, and they use organic carbon compounds as a carbon source to derive energy for the fixation process or for inorganic nitrogen (NH_4, NO_3) assimilation. However, as we shall point out shortly, most of the legume bacteria are nutritionally more complex than the other members of this group, since they require certain factors for optimum growth in chemically defined media. It may be that this requirement is partly responsible for their symbiotic existence in nature.

The nutritional requirements of the various species of the genus *Rhizobium* have been reviewed by West and Wilson (1939), Wilson (1940), and Wilson and Wilson (1942). Therefore only a brief summary will be presented here; these references should be consulted for more complete details. Since Beijerinck first isolated pure cultures in 1888, a number of organic and inorganic media have been proposed by various workers for the cultivation of the bacteria causing nodules on leguminous plants. Although several early workers observed that rhizobia would grow in synthetic media, it was found that the addition of extracts of plants, such as yeast, potato, sauerkraut, and straw greatly stimulated their growth. For several years it was thought that one of the more important roles played by such extracts was the control of the physico-chemical properties of the substrate, for example, providing a suitable oxidation-reduction environment for the bacteria. In 1933 Allison, Hoover, and Burk showed that the growth of rhizobia in synthetic media depends on other factors besides proper physico-chemical environment. They found that the bacteria from alfalfa, clover, and peas were unable to grow to any extent in a purified mineral-sugar medium; but, if commercial cane sugar was used as the carbon source, good growth occurred. The active impurity of the cane sugar, which was extracted with absolute ethyl alcohol, was readily dialyzable, was organic in character, and, when added in a small amount to the purified mineral-sugar medium, resulted in good growth. Since these results could not be explained on the basis of merely altering the physico-chemical environment, Allison and his associates concluded that the function of the stimulating substance was to furnish a coenzyme for respiration; hence they proposed that it be called coenzyme R.[7] This study suggested, therefore, that the various extracts which are needed for the optimum growth of rhizobia in synthetic media contain one or more specific growth factors.

After the study by Allison, Hoover, and Burk (1933) several investigators [see Wilson (1940)] tested a number of known substances

[7] Since this substance is in all probability identical with biotin, the term coenzyme R should be abandoned.

for their growth-promoting property for rhizobia. The following compounds were found to have little or no effect: cysteine, glutathione, pimelic acid, nicotinic acid, β-alanine, pantothenic acid, pyruvic acid, indoleacetic acid, indolepropionic acid, indolebutyric acid, numerous amino acids, and uracil. Variable results were at first obtained by several workers with thiamin (B_1) and riboflavin (B_2), but West and

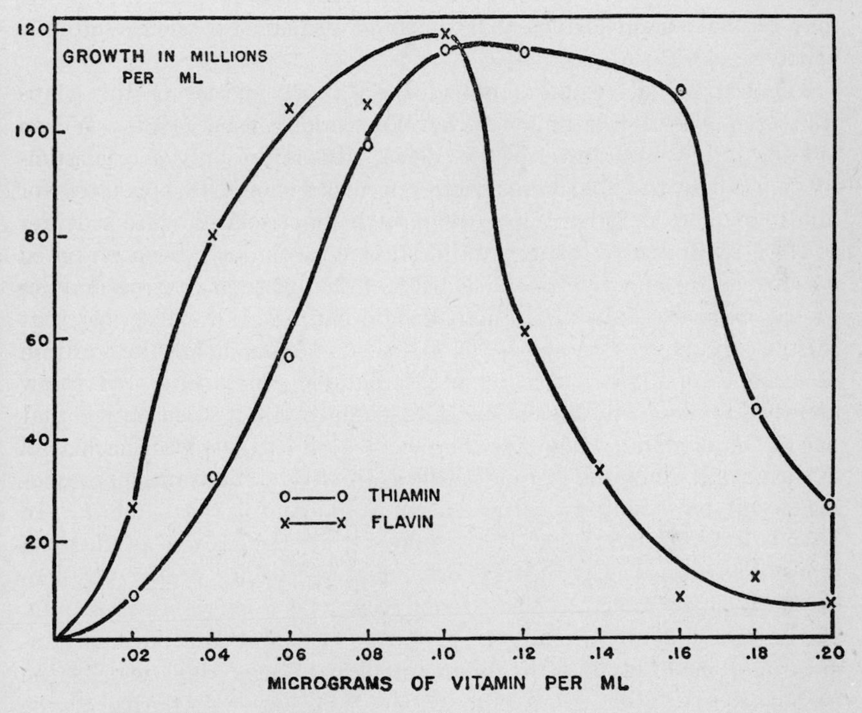

FIG. 2. The Influence of Thiamin and Riboflavin on the Growth of *Rhizobium trifolii*. (From West and Wilson, 1939.)

Wilson (1939) were able to solve this phase of the problem. They found that the method in which the inoculum was prepared greatly influenced the initiation of growth by the legume bacteria in chemically defined media. For instance, if the cells of the inoculum were washed free of their metabolic products, no growth occurred when they were subsequently added to certain synthetic media. However, if before the inoculation the cells were suspended in a filtrate from a growing culture or an autolysate of rhizobia cells and this was used as the inoculum, growth was readily initiated. Further study showed that the rhizobia filtrates could be replaced by thiamin or riboflavin, but that the pure vitamins exhibited a very narrow optimum range (Fig. 2). From this study West and Wilson concluded that thiamin (and/or riboflavin) is an essential growth factor for at least one rhizobium (*Rhizobium trifolii* 205), in that small amounts must be provided for the initiation of growth in a chemically defined medium, either directly in the preparation of the medium or indirectly in the inoculum. Once growth is started, the organisms synthesize enough of the factor to meet their need and to make continuous transfer possible. Even under such conditions, however, maximum populations are not reached unless other factors in yeast extract and similar substances are also present.

A search for the major factors in plant extracts which stimulate rhizobia has been undertaken by several workers, especially Dr. Perry Wilson and his associates at Wisconsin, Allison and his coworkers in the United States Department of Agriculture, and Nilsson, Bjälfve, and Burström (1938, 1939) in Sweden. Although considerable progress has been made in the elucidation of the essential growth factors for rhizobia, additional work is needed before any definite conclusions can be reached concerning their exact requirements. The distribution and properties of these plant-extract factors definitely suggest that they are members of the so-called bios complex. Biotin has been identified [West and Wilson (1940)] as one of these factors required by certain strains of rhizobia when cultivated in the following highly purified basal medium [Wilson and Wilson (1942)]:

K_2HPO_4	0.5 g.	$NaCl$	0.1 g.
NH_4Cl	0.376 g.	$FeCl_3$	Trace
$MgSO_4$	0.2 g.	H_2O	1,000 ml.
$CaSO_4$	0.2 g.		

In fact, Wilson and Wilson (1942) concluded that strains of rhizobia can be allocated to three groups on the basis of their biotin requirements in the above medium: (1) those (the majority) which grow on continuous transfer in the absence of biotin but reach a population of only about one-tenth of the maximum (when yeast extract is present in the medium); (2) those (a few) which attain practically maximum growth in the absence of biotin; and (3) those (a few) which are unable to grow unless biotin is supplied.

The carbon and nitrogen requirements of the root-nodule bacteria can be briefly summarized. Carbon in the form of carbohydrates is easily utilized by the rhizobia as a source of energy. The various species, however, do not exhibit identical degrees of activity. For example, *Rhizobium leguminosarum* and *Rhizobium trifolii* usually ferment dextrose, galactose, mannose, lactose, and maltose with slight acid production; whereas the soya bean organism, *Rhizobium japoni-*

cum, forms little if any acid from carbohydrates other than xylose and arabinose, which are attacked slowly. The chief end products of carbohydrate metabolism by the rhizobia are carbon dioxide, water, and bacterial cells, although several strains produce in addition traces of organic acids and a gum composed of glucuronic acid and glucose [Hoover and Allison (1940), Wilson (1940)]. Most of the work on the nitrogen metabolism of the rhizobia has been qualitative in the sense that many investigators have merely determined whether growth took place in the presence of a given source of nitrogen. Quantitative studies involving a measurement of the changes induced in the nitrogen source are few, in spite of the fact that such information might help in determining the intermediate steps in the fixation reaction. The root-nodule bacteria hydrolyze only slightly such proteins as gelatin and casein but are able to attack certain peptides, especially the dipeptides. A number of amino acids, for example, glycine, alanine, and glutamic acid, are capable of serving as a nitrogen source [Pohlman (1931)], and most if not all of the species of rhizobia use asparagine, urea, ammonium salts, or nitrates. Nitrites are assimilated to only a small extent.

The nutrition of *Mycobacterium rubiacearum* has not been studied recently. Faber (1912, 1914) used an organic medium to isolate first the species from the nodules of the leaves of certain tropical plants, but he also demonstrated that the organism could grow in a nitrogen-free medium and could fix atmospheric nitrogen. Plants free of bacteria grew poorly in nitrogen-free soil (sand cultures), but those containing the bacteria thrived. From these experiments Faber concluded that the organism is of advantage to the plant because of its ability to fix nitrogen. The organic carbon and combined nitrogen requirements so far known may be summarized briefly. The organism was cultivated in a basal medium containing these compounds.

KH_2PO_4	5 g.	$NaCl$	0.1 g.
$CaCl_2$	0.1 g.	Fe_2Cl_6	0.01 g.
$MgSO_4 \cdot 7H_2O$	0.3 g.	H_2O	100 g. plus

The following results were obtained:

2 Per Cent	0.5 Per Cent	Growth after 10 Days at 28°–30°C.
Gum arabic	Asparagine	Good growth
	Peptone	Slight growth
	NH_4Cl	Luxuriant growth
	KNO_3	Luxuriant growth

2 Per Cent	0.5 Per Cent	Growth after 10 Days at 28°–30°C.
Dextrose	Asparagine	Slight growth
	Peptone	No growth
	NH_4Cl	Slight growth
	KNO_3	Slight growth
Sucrose	Asparagine	Slight growth
	Peptone	No growth
	NH_4Cl	Moderate growth
	KNO_3	Slight growth
Starch	Asparagine	Good growth
	Peptone	Good growth
	NH_4Cl	Luxuriant growth
	KNO_3	Good growth
Inulin	Asparagine	Good growth
	Peptone	No growth
	NH_4Cl	No growth
	KNO_3	No growth
Lactose, cellulose, or glycerol	Asparagine	No growth
	Peptone	No growth
	NH_4Cl	No growth
	KNO_3	No growth

BACTERIA WHICH CANNOT UTILIZE GASEOUS NITROGEN BUT CAN ASSIMILATE NH_4, NO_2, OR NO_3

To the second (ninth in the nutritional spectrum, Fig. 1) arbitrary group of heterotrophic bacteria we may allocate many saprophytic bacteria commonly studied in the laboratory, as well as several animal and plant pathogens. In general, the organisms of this group derive their energy from the oxidation of sugars, organic acids, and related compounds and utilize either the ammonium ion or simple nitrogenous salts (nitrites or nitrates) as a sole source of nitrogen; they do not require the addition of growth factors to chemically defined media in order to grow. Several more fastidious heterotrophs may utilize the ammonium ion or other simple nitrogenous substances, providing certain growth factors are present. These organisms are discussed on pp. 686 to 715.

A few remarks concerning several representative species will serve to illustrate the general characteristics of the group.

Bacterium radiobacter. Since *Bacterium radiobacter* is a common soil saprophyte frequently associated with the legume-nodule bacteria, it will be discussed first in this group. The exact characterization of this organism presents a problem, inasmuch as it is similar in many respects not only to the species of the genus *Rhizobium* but also to certain plant pathogens of the genus *Phytomonas*. Since this phase of the problem has been discussed in some detail by Hofer (1941), we will consider here only the nutritional requirements of the species. The organism grows well on most common laboratory media, as well as on the following medium [Hofer (1941)]:

NH_4NO_3	1 g.	$CaCl_2 \cdot 2H_2O$	0.1 g.
K_2HPO_4	0.5 g.	Carbon source	1.5 g.
$MgSO_4 \cdot 7H_2O$	0.1 g.	H_2O (distilled)	1,000 ml.
NaCl	0.1 g.		

The organism has a *p*H range between 5 and 11 to 12 and exhibits slight growth at 1°C. and 45°C. The organism is well known for its ability to assimilate nitrate nitrogen; it also utilizes ammonium sulfate, ammonium citrate, and ferrous ammonium citrate, but not potassium nitrite. Organic nitrogen compounds, such as acetamide, oxamide, succinimide, asparagine, urea, glycine, alanine, aspartic acid, and glutamic acid, will also serve as a nitrogen source [Sagen, Riker, and Baldwin (1934)]. The species has long been thought to fix atmospheric nitrogen, but investigations by Wilson, Hopkins, and Fred (1932) have shown that there is no basis for this belief, whether the organism is grown in pure culture or in association with *Rhizobia*. A number of sugars, alcohols, organic acids, and related compounds can serve as a source of carbon and energy for *B. radiobacter*. For example, Sagen, Riker, and Baldwin (1934), Smith and Brown (1935), and Hofer (1941) found that the following compounds permitted abundant growth: arabinose, xylose, rhamnose, dextrose, galactose, mannose, lactose, sucrose, trehalose, raffinose, salicin, glycerol, arabitol, adonitol, dulcitol, mannitol, sodium propionate, calcium gluconate, sodium succinate, lactic acid, and malic acid. Lactose, methyl alcohol, ethyl alcohol, propyl alcohol, butyl alcohol, sodium formate, sodium acetate, butyric acid, stearic acid, sodium malonate, and tartaric acid permitted a trace to moderate growth. Amygdalin and sodium oxalate were not utilized. The chief end products of the fermentation of the above sugars appeared to be carbon dioxide and gum, since Hofer (1941) could not detect the presence of volatile acids or alcohols.

***Alcaligenes fecalis* and *Alcaligenes viscosus*.** These organisms are quite common and may be briefly mentioned. They both grow well on common laboratory media, but their fundamental nutritional requirements have not been studied very extensively. They differ principally from the other members of their group in that they seldom ferment any of the sugars; and, when they do, the reaction is always reversed to the alkaline side of neutrality. Although several early workers [see Braun and Cahn-Bronner (1921)] found that *Alcaligenes* *fecalis* would grow in simple media containing only ammonium lactate as a source of nitrogen and carbon, the most complete study of the nutrition of this organism is that of Berthelot and Amoureux (1938). These workers found that the organism grew very well in the following medium (*p*H 7.8):

NH_4NO_3	0.25 g.	Asparagine	2 g.
NaCl	8 g.	Cysteine	0.02 g.
K_2HPO_4	1.5 g.	Sodium pyruvate	2.5 g.
$MgSO_4$	0.5 g.	H_2O	1,000 ml.

No studies are available on the types of nitrogen which can be used by this species.

We have mentioned that this species does not ferment any of the sugars; however, it is known to be able to oxidize formic acid and acetic acid [Kendall and Ishikawa (1929)], as well as phosphorylated hexose (hexose mono- or diphosphate), saturated fatty acids, hydroxy acids, keto acids, amino acids, and alcohols [Barron and Friedemann (1941)]. Barron and Friedemann concluded that the organism's failure to oxidize glucose is due to lack of phosphorylation. *Alcaligenes viscosus* is similar in many respects to *Alcaligenes fecalis*, except that it usually produces a very ropy condition in milk. The organism has been studied by Long and Hammer (1936), but information on its basal nutrition is still lacking.

Pseudomonas aeruginosa. Several early workers, including Koser and Rettger (1919), observed that *Pseudomonas aeruginosa* and related species would grow in simple media containing the usual inorganic salts with ammonium phosphate or chloride as a source of nitrogen, and glycerol and dextrose or other compounds as a source of carbon and energy. More recently Robinson (1932), Sandiford (1937), and Pandalai and Rao (1942) extended our information on the nutrition of this species. For example, Robinson found that any of the following three media stimulated satisfactory growth between *p*H 6.0 and 9.0 under aerobic conditions:

1. Citric acid, 0.5 g.; ammonium hydrate, 0.5 ml.; saturated magnesium hydrogen phosphate solution, to 100 ml.
2. Sodium lactate, 0.5 g.; ammonium dihydrogen phosphate, 0.2 per cent solution neutralized by excess magnesium oxide and filtered, then diluted to 100 ml.
3. Succinic acid, 0.5 per cent solution, neutralized by excess $MgNH_4PO_4 \cdot 6H_2O$, and filtered.

The following medium supported growth at *p*H 7.6 under anaerobic conditions:

Sodium citrate, 1.0 g.; sodium nitrate, 0.5 g.; $MgSO_4$, 0.05 g.; phosphate buffer (0.05 *M*), to 100 ml.

Phosphate and probably magnesium were essential inorganic constituents of the media. Available nitrogen sources for growth were ammonium salts, nitrates, and amino acids, but not nitrites, urea, monoethylamine, betaine, guanidine, aniline, picric acid, or pyocyanin. Available carbon sources and energy sources were carbamate, acetate, lactate, pyruvate, succinate, butyrate, citrate, glycerol, dextrose, amino acids, ethyl alcohol, and *n*-butyl alcohol, but not carbonate, urea, acetaldehyde, acetone, *n*-propyl alcohol, guanidine, glycerophosphate, betaine, and many sugars and aromatic compounds, including pyocyanin. Oxalates supported anaerobic growth but not aerobic growth. Robinson also worked out the optimum concentrations of several constituents in his media, a point which is very important in nutritional studies but is frequently ignored even today. He found that the optimum ranges of concentrations were generally wide for aerobic growth, whereas those for anaerobic growth and pigmentary activity tended to be more limited regions within these broad ranges. The following data illustrate this point:

	Minimal Range, per cent	Optimal Range, per cent	Pigmentary Optimum, per cent	Anaerobic Optimum, per cent
Na, K, Cl, SO_4	0.0	0.0	0.0	0.0
$MgSO_4 \cdot 7H_2O$	0.0001–0.0005	0.0005–0.5	0.05	0.05
KH_2PO_4	0.001–0.0025	0.0025–2.0	0.05	0.50
NH_4Cl	0.0025–0.05	0.05–0.25	0.10	....
$NaNO_3$	0.01	0.1–2.0	....	0.5
$Na_3C_6H_5O_7 \cdot 5\frac{1}{2}H_2O$	0.01–0.25	0.25–2.0	1.0	1.0
$NaC_2H_3O_2 \cdot 3H_2O$	0.01–0.05	0.1–0.25	0.25	0.1

Pandalai and Rao (1942) studied the nutritional requirements of ten strains of *Ps. aeruginosa* and showed that in a simple substrate phosphate was essential for growth, and that sulfur (sulfate) improved pigment formation. Lactic acid was also found to be essential for good pigment production. Magnesium ions, on the other hand, were not considered necessary for either pigmentation or growth.

***Achromobacter mobile* (*Termobacterium mobile, Pseudomonas lindneri*).** This interesting organism is one of the few bacteria which can produce large amounts (40 to 47 per cent) of ethyl alcohol from dextrose. It apparently has a zymase complex very similar to that of certain yeasts. Although the organism grows best in the presence of yeast extract, it will grow in the following medium

[Kluyver and Hoppenbrouwers (1931), Schreder, Brunner, and Hampe (1934)]:

K_2HPO_4	1 g.	$MgSO_4$	0.5 g.
$(NH_4)_2SO_4$	1 g.	Tap water	1,000 ml.
Dextrose	20 g.		

Only dextrose, levulose, and sucrose are fermented, the sucrose enzyme being adaptive. Little is known about the forms of nitrogen that can be utilized.

***Bacillus* and *Clostridium* species.** Several aerobic spore-forming bacilli will grow in inorganic salt media containing ammonium salts, or nitrates, as the sole source of nitrogen, and sugars, or organic acids, as a source of carbon and energy. For example, Bredemann and his associates, Werner (1933), Stührk (1935), and Heigener (1935) have described several aerobic species of the *Bacillus subtilis* group which will grow in a medium composed of:

NH_4Cl or KNO_3	10 g.	$MgSO_4$	1 g.
Dextrose or other carbon sources, such as calcium *n*-butyrate	10 g.	$FeSO_4$	Trace
		$CaCl_2$	0.1 g.
		NaCl	0.1 g.
K_2HPO_4	1 g.	H_2O (distilled)	1,000 ml.

Some other *Bacillus* species are more fastidious; their nutritional requirements are discussed later in the chapter.

Acetobacter aceti. The species of the genus *Acetobacter*, with the exception of *Acetobacter aceti*, will not grow in media containing ammonium salts as a sole source of nitrogen. Vaughn (1942) believes that this fact can be used as a reliable criterion to differentiate *A. aceti* from other closely related species. Little is known concerning the fundamental nutritional requirements of this organism, although it will grow on many common laboratory media, as well as that prepared by Henneberg [see Vaughn (1942)], which consisted of the following ingredients:

$(NH_4)_2SO_4$	3 g.	H_2O	1,000 ml.
KH_2PO_4	3 g.	Sterile ethyl alcohol (final concentration of 2 per cent) is added just before use.	
$MgSO_4$	2 g.		
Glucose	20 g.		

Glucose, ethyl alcohol, propyl alcohol, and glycerol are oxidized by this species with the production of acid; but arabinose, levulose, galactose, maltose, lactose, dextrin, and several alcohols, including mannitol and dulcitol, are not attacked.

Erwinia amylovora. The pear-blight or fire-blight organism, *Erwinia amylovora*, and some of the related plant pathogens may be placed in this nutritional group. Although this organism can be cultivated on most common laboratory media, it will also grow in synthetic media, such as the one used by Ark (1937):

$(NH_4)_2HPO_4$	6 g.	Carbon source	10 g.
K_2HPO_4	2 g.	H_2O	1,000 ml.
$MgSO_4$	0.3 g.		

The optimum *p*H is 6.8, although growth will occur from *p*H 4.8 to 8.8. Available nitrogen sources are ammonium salts, asparagine, and for some strains alanine, leucine, and proline; but glycine, valine, isoleucine, glutamic acid, tyrosine, tryptophan, cystine, or urea are not used as a sole source of nitrogen. All the strains studied by Ark (1937) produced acid from arabinose, mannose, glucose, levulose, maltose, cellobiose, sucrose, raffinose, dextrin, arbutin, salicin, amygdalin, citrate, and malic acid. Some strains fermented lactose, glycerol, mannitol, lactate, and succinate; but xylose, rhamnose, starch, dulcitol, oxalate, tartrate, and valerate were not used as a source of carbon.

Serratia marcescens. Several early workers found that this species grew aerobically and anaerobically in simple inorganic salt media, with ammonium salts, nitrates, urea, asparagine, or uric acid as a nitrogen source and with glucose, sucrose, lactose, glycerol, mannitol, ethyl alcohol, succinate, fumarate, maleate, lactate, citrate, or malonate as a carbon and energy source [Robertson (1924), Pederson and Breed (1928), Knight (1936)]. Several early workers also observed that magnesium, phosphate, and sulfate were essential inorganic ingredients of the media. More recently Kost (1942) has studied the effect of temperature, inorganic salts, and amino acids on the morphology and pigment production of *Serratia marcescens*. He found, for example, that many minerals in varying concentrations favored pigment production; calcium chloride in concentrations of 1.0 per cent or more suppressed pigmentation and growth, whereas lower concentrations aided them. Glucose favored growth but reduced pigmentation; lactose stimulated both growth and pigmentation. Bunting [see Bunting and Ingraham (1942), Bunting (1942)] has studied the factors affecting pigmentation of *S. marcescens* when cultivated in the following medium:

Ammonium citrate	5 g.	NaCl	0.5 g.
Glycerol	10 g.	Ferric ammonium citrate	0.05 g.
$K_2HPO_4 \cdot 3H_2O$	10 g.	H_2O (distilled)	1,000 ml.
$MgSO_4$	0.5 g.		

The metabolic end products from the fermentation of glucose by members of the genus *Serratia* were determined by Pederson and Breed (1928). *Serratia marcescens* produced the following substances: acetic, formic, succinic, and *l*-lactic acids, ethyl alcohol, acetylmethylcarbinol, 2,3-butylene glycol, CO_2, and a trace of H_2.

***Spirillum* and *Vibrio* Species.** The nutritive requirements of various saprophytic species of the genera *Spirillum* and *Vibrio* have been studied by Giesberger (1936), Myers (1940), and others. The basal medium (*p*H 7.0 to 7.2) employed by Myers may be cited to illustrate the requirements of most of these organisms:

$MgSO_4$	0.5 g.	Nitrogen source	1 g.
K_2HPO_4	0.5 g.	Carbon source	5 or 10 g.
$CaCl_2$	0.5 g.	H_2O	1,000 ml.

Asparagine, NH_4Cl, KNO_2, or KNO_3 served as a source of nitrogen, but, since ammonium chloride was utilized by most strains, it was employed in the greater part of the work. Lactate and pyruvate were generally used as a source of carbon, and glucose, levulose, glycerol, and ethyl alcohol served for some strains. Giesberger employed some twenty-three other carbon compounds in his study, but Myers found that the six just listed were the only ones of differential importance.

Probably most of the saprophytic species of the genus *Spirillum* have simple nutritional requirements, but Dimitroff (1926) reported that *Spirillum virginianum* grew abundantly only in Uschinsky's protein-free media and other more complex substrates. The ingredients of Uschinsky's medium are:

Sodium aspartate [8] (natrium asparaginicum)	3.4 g.	K_2HPO_4	2–2.5 g.
		$MgSO_4 \cdot 7H_2O$	0.2–0.4 g.
		$CaCl_2$	0.1 g.
Ammonium lactate	6–7 g.	NaCl	5–7 g.
Glycerol	30–40 g.	H_2O	1,000 ml.

Although abundant growth occurred in this medium, Dimitroff stated that inocula of three drops from a young beef-extract broth culture or from egg cube media were necessary to obtain good growth. This statement and the fact that Dimitroff did not carry out successive subcultures in the medium cast some doubt on whether Uschinsky's medium is adequate for the growth of this species. Little or nothing is known about the carbon and nitrogen requirements of the organism, except that it does not produce acid or gas in sugar-containing media.

[8] According to Mueller (1940), it is often incorrectly stated that the amide of aspartic acid, asparagine, was used by Uschinsky.

***Escherichia-Aerobacter-Klebsiella* Species.** The literature dealing with the nutrition of the species of these genera is large. Since many of the early studies are summarized by Knight (1936), they will not be discussed in these notes.

The best-known species of these three genera are *Escherichia coli*, *Aerobacter aerogenes*, and *Klebsiella pneumoniae*. *Escherichia coli* grows well on ordinary laboratory media, as well as in simple synthetic media such as the one (*p*H 6.8) used by Koser (1923):

$NH_4H_2PO_4$	1 g.	$MgSO_4 \cdot 7H_2O$	0.2 g.
Carbon source	2 g.	K_2HPO_4	1 g.
NaCl	5 g.	H_2O	1,000 ml.

Besides ammonium phosphate other, more complex substances, such as commercial peptones, amino acids, and uracil, may serve as a sole source of nitrogen for *E. coli;* but such compounds as yeast nucleic acid, uric acid, allantoin, hydantoin, and urea are not utilized [Koser (1918), Koser and Rettger (1919), Mitchell and Levine (1938)]. As a source of carbon and energy this species ferments a great variety of sugars, organic acids, and related compounds. For example, the organism produces acid and gas from arabinose, xylose, rhamnose, glucose, levulose, galactose, lactose, maltose, and mannitol. Sucrose, raffinose, salicin, esculin, dulcitol, and glycerol may or may not be attacked. Adonitol, inulin, and pectin are rarely utilized, and cellobiose and α-methylglucoside are not fermented. Several unusual glucosides [Twort (1907)], sugar alcohols and their anhydrides [Dozois *et al.* (1935, 1936, 1938)], and rare sugars [Poe and Klemme (1935), Field and Poe (1940)] are fermented by *E. coli*. The sodium salts of such organic acids as acetic, succinic, malic, lactic, mucic, and glyceric serve as a carbon and energy source for *E. coli* and *Aerobacter aerogenes;* but *n*-valeric, isovaleric, *n*-caproic, oxalic, salicylic, and *o*-phthalic are not utilized. Several organic acids support the growth of some but not all of the *coli-aerogenes* group. Koser (1923) found, for example, that propionic acid permitted a slight or moderate growth of many of the fecal *E. coli* strains, whereas *A. aerogenes* cultures, with few exceptions, were negative; tartaric acid was readily utilized by a few of the *A. aerogenes* strains, but not by *E. coli*. The most striking results were obtained with citric acid, on which all the *A. aerogenes* strains grew, whereas none of the *E. coli* did. A great deal has been written about some of the citrate-utilizing strains of the *A. aerogenes* group since Koser made his observation in 1923. Since many of them show characteristics which in the past were thought to be restricted to the better-known members of the *coli-aerogenes* group, they are now often termed intermediates or placed in a separate genus (*Citrobacter*). Mitchell and Levine (1938) constructed the following dichotomous chart, based on the utilization of various nitrogenous substances and on metabolic end products, to differentiate the colon group of bacteria:

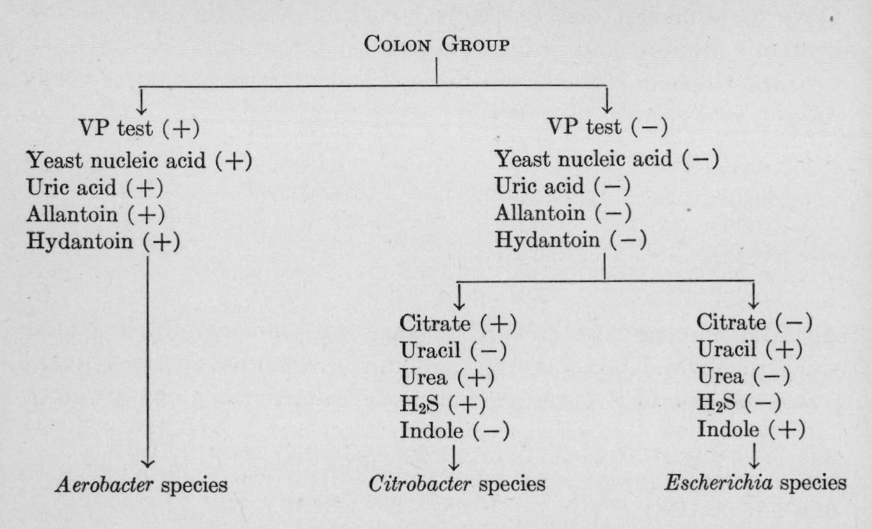

Although *Aerobacter aerogenes* is very similar in many respects to *E. coli*, it differs in several ways, as can be seen from the dichotomous chart. The following substances serve as a sole source of nitrogen for this species: ammonium salts, commercial peptones, amino acids, yeast nucleic acid, uric acid, allantoin, and hydantoin; uracil and urea do not. As a source of carbon and energy many sugars, organic acids, and related compounds are attacked. For example, acid and gas are formed from arabinose, levulose, glucose, galactose, lactose, maltose, raffinose, cellobiose, glycerol, sorbitol, inositol, salicin, esculin, starch, and dextrin; α-methylglucoside is usually fermented. Variable results are obtained with sucrose, mannitol, dulcitol, adonitol, inulin, and pectin; the organic acids attacked have been discussed.

Klebsiella pneumoniae has many characteristics in common with *A. aerogenes*. A study of the nutrition of this organism was made by Lévy-Bruhl and Legrand (1930), who found that it would grow in the following synthetic medium (pH 7.8 to 8.0):

$NH_4H_2PO_4$	0.75–1.0 g.	Na_2SO_4	0.03 g.
Carbon source	0.5–2.2 g.	H_2O (distilled)	100 ml.

Phosphate was found to be essential, and sulfate greatly favored growth. As a source of nitrogen, ammonium salts, urea, and amines (mono-, di-, tri-, and tetraamines, proline, phenylalanine, and glucosamine) were utilized. As carbon and energy sources the organism used lactate, succinate, and tartrate especially well, and certain strains utilized ethyl alcohol and butyric acid. Some did not use lactose. Growth, virulence, and antigenic structure were the same in the synthetic medium as in ordinary laboratory media.

Staphylococcus flavus. O'Kane (1941) found that *Staphylococcus flavus* would grow in the following substrate (*p*H 7.0):

$NaNH_4HPO_4$	1 g.	NaCl	0.01 g.
Glucose	10 g.	$FeSO_4 \cdot 7H_2O$	0.01 g.
K_2HPO_4	0.5 g.	$MnSO_4 \cdot 4H_2O$	0.01 g.
KH_2PO_4	0.5 g.	H_2O	1,000 ml.
$MgSO_4 \cdot 7H_2O$	0.2 g.		

Although the organism grew rather poorly in this medium, it synthesized riboflavin. As a source of carbon and energy this species usually fermented glucose and lactose, but not sucrose, glycerol, and mannitol.

BACTERIA WHICH MAY USE A FORM OF NITROGEN LIKE THAT EMPLOYED BY THE PREVIOUS GROUP, BUT THRIVE BEST IF AMINO ACIDS, AMIDES, OR PURINES ARE PRESENT

A great many saprophytic organisms and several disease-producing bacteria can be allocated to this group. Since it is possible to discuss here the nutritional requirements of only a few of the species, the monograph by Knight (1936) should be consulted for complete details.

The nutritional characteristics of certain species of this class are not very distinct from those of some of the last group. In fact, many of these species will grow in simple media containing ammonium salts as a source of nitrogen, although they are usually stimulated by the presence of one or more amino acids or related substances. Another factor which prevents a rigid separation of this class from the preceding one is that certain strains of a given species in this group may utilize ammonium salts as a sole source of nitrogen, whereas others, which are indistinguishable by ordinary tests, must be supplied with a more complex source of nitrogen, such as tryptophan. Knight (1936) applied the term nonexacting to those strains of a given species which can utilize a simple nitrogen source, such as ammonium salts, and the term exacting to those which require a more complex nitrogen source. Finally it should be mentioned that certain exacting strains of a given species can be trained to grow in an ammonium salt medium by continued subculture in substrates containing suboptimal amounts of amino acids.

Sarcina lutea. The recorded findings on the nutrition of *Sarcina lutea* serve very well to illustrate the points which we have just mentioned, and probably the phenomenon of training can be used to explain some of the discrepancies which occur in the literature on the nutrition of this organism. The strain of *S. lutea* studied by Koser and Rettger (1919) did not grow in media containing ammonium salts or a single amino acid as a sole source of nitrogen, with glycerol or glucose as a carbon and energy source; however, it grew when a group of amino acids was employed as a nitrogen source. The strains used by Robertson (1924) grew for fifty subcultures in a synthetic medium consisting of asparagine, glucose, and inorganic salts. On the other hand, the strains employed by Rubenstein (1933) grew well on a simple inorganic salt medium (*p*H 6.8) containing the following ingredients:

NH_4Cl or ammonium lactate	1.9 g.	$NaHCO_3$	1.3 g.
Glucose	18 g.	KCl	0.5 g.
NaCl	0.6 g.	$CaHPO_4$	0.3 g.
		H_2O	1,000 ml.

In addition to glucose the following compounds served as a source of carbon and energy: lactate, pyruvate, succinate, malate, tartrate, glycerol, and glyceric aldehyde. The following substances failed to support growth: acetate, formate, propionate, oxalate, butyrate, ethylene glycol, ethyl alcohol, methyl alcohol, acetaldehyde, and formaldehyde. More recently Barron and Friedemann (1941) have shown that a strain of *S. lutea* is able to oxidize glucose, pyruvate, and several other related compounds, but that the organisms will not utilize these compounds under anaerobic conditions. Their experiments demonstrate clearly the distinction between aerobic and anaerobic metabolism (oxidation versus fermentation) by bacteria.

***Bacillus* and *Clostridium* Species.** Some of the species of the genus *Bacillus* grow very well in simple media containing ammonium salts or nitrates as a source of nitrogen. Other members of this group, however, thrive best in media containing one or more amino acids. For example, Glinka-Tschernorutzky (1933) found that *Bacillus mycoides* grew fairly well in a mineral solution [9] with several ammonium salts as a source of nitrogen, and glucose as a source of carbon and energy; twelve amino acids also served as a source of nitrogen, but three (cystine, phenylalanine, and tyrosine) were unable to do so. However, better growth was obtained in the mineral solution containing a mixture of the following fifteen amino acids: glycine, *dl*-alanine,

[9] Composition: $MgSO_4 \cdot 7H_2O$, 0.5 g.; K_2HPO_4, 1.0 g.; NaCl, 0.1 g.; $FeSO_4$ 0.02 g.; $CaCl_2$, 0.1 g.; distilled water, 1,000 ml.

dl-phenylalanine, *d*-glutamic acid, *l*-aspartic acid, *l*-leucine, *d*-arginine, and *dl*-valine, all at 0.05 per cent; and *l*-cystine, *l*-tryptophan, *l*-tyrosine, *l*-proline, *l*-histidine·HCl, *d*-lysine·2HCl, and *dl*-serine, all at 0.025 per cent. Evidently the amino acids served as a source of nitrogen, carbon, and energy, because the addition of glucose to the medium did not improve the mass of growth (see Table 6). The quantitative data in Table 6 show that the amino acid medium produced a slightly greater mass of growth than did peptone media when cultivated under the same conditions (10 ml. of media, pH 7.8, in 50-ml. Erlenmeyer flasks, at 30°C. for 7 days).

TABLE 6

EFFECT OF MEDIUM ON THE GROWTH OF *Bacillus mycoides*

[From Glinka-Tschernorutzky (1933)]

Medium	Growth Measured as Milligrams of Bacterial Nitrogen (Kjeldahl) per 10 ml. of Media
Peptone (Witte) broth (0.5%)	0.865
Peptone (Witte) broth (0.5%) + 0.5% glucose	0.878
Mineral solution + 15 amino acids	0.901
Mineral solution + 15 amino acids + 0.5% glucose	0.906
Mineral solution + 0.2% K_2HPO_4 + 0.1% NH_4Cl + 0.5% glucose	0.354
Mineral solution + 0.1% ammonium phosphate + 0.5% glucose	0.380

Heigener (1935) has described several new species of the genus *Bacillus* which grow well in an amino acid medium:

K_2HPO_4	1 g.	$MnSO_4$	0.01 g.
$MgSO_4$	0.2 g.	Agar	16 g.
NaCl	0.02 g.	H_2O	1,000 ml.
$FeSO_4$	0.01 g.		

The following amino acids were present in concentrations of 0.02 *M*: *dl*-valine, glycine, betaine (basic), betaine·HCl, *dl*-alanine, *dl*-phenylalanine, *dl*-leucine, *dl*-aspartic acid, and *d*-glutamic acid, as was the amide, asparagine. The reaction was adjusted to pH 7.5. The amino acids served as a nitrogen, carbon, and energy source for these organisms.

Bacillus anthracis is more exacting in its amino acid requirements than are most species of the genus *Bacillus*. Gladstone (1939) found that this species grew very well in a glucose-inorganic salt medium containing the following seventeen amino acids: *dl*-aspartic acid, *dl*-

valine, *dl*-leucine, *dl*-alanine, *dl*-glutamic acid, *dl*-isoleucine, *dl*-phenylalanine, *dl*-lysine·HCl, glycine, *l*-proline, *l*-hydroxyproline, *l*-tyrosine, *l*-arginine·HCl, *l*-histidine·HCl, *l*-cystine, *dl*-methionine, and *l*-tryptophan. However, Gladstone found that an interrelationship exists between certain amino acids of similar chemical configuration, and this fact had a marked effect on the growth of *B. anthracis*. When valine, leucine, or isoleucine was added singly to a mixture of amino acids able to support growth without it, it completely prevented development. When the three were added together, however, growth was improved and accelerated. The toxic effect of valine could be counteracted by leucine and vice versa, but that of isoleucine could not be neutralized by the presence of either valine or leucine. Norleucine was similar to isoleucine in its action. Similar interrelationships were found between valine and threonine, valine and α-aminobutyric acid, and threonine and serine. The toxic effect of serine could also be neutralized by a combination of valine and leucine, but not by either amino acid alone. Gladstone's results are very interesting and have a certain practical application. In investigations of the amino acid growth requirements of animals and bacteria the general procedure is to omit a single amino acid from a balanced diet and then note the effect on growth. An amino acid is regarded as indispensable if growth is impaired when it is omitted from the diet. Gladstone's results suggest that, before such statements are made, the effect of omitting two or more of the indispensable amino acids at one time should be investigated. With such a procedure it is possible that some may be found to be indispensable only in combination with others.

Very few of the anaerobic bacilli of the genus *Clostridium* are known which can grow in simple amino acid media without the addition of growth factors. Barker and Peterson (1944), for example, have shown that *Clostridium acidi-urici* will grow in a simple mineral salt medium containing uric acid and thioglycolate as the only organic constituents. However, this organism is one of the few known examples of an anaerobic spore-former with such simple nutritional requirements.

***Phytomonas* and Other Phytopathogenic Species.** Certain plant pathogens of the genera *Phytomonas*, *Corynebacterium*, and others probably belong to this nutritional group, although many of the species will grow in simpler media and therefore actually fit into the last class mentioned, whereas some are even more fastidious in their requirements. For example, McCulloch (1929) found that certain strains of *Phytomonas campestris*, the organism which causes a vascular disease in rutabagas and cabbage, grew poorly in Uschinsky's medium, which contains nitrogen in the form of sodium aspartate and ammonium lactate. Furthermore the gall-forming bacterium, *Phytomonas tumefaciens*, will grow in mineral media with nitrogen in the form of KNO_3, NH_4HSO_4, NH_4NO_3, or ferric ammonium citrate [Sagen, Riker, and Baldwin (1934)]. However, the nutrition of *P. tumefaciens* has been studied in some detail by McIntire, Riker, and Peterson (1941), and they have shown that amino acids, and even the vitamins riboflavin, thiamin, and pantothenic acid, stimulate growth in simple media. Certain inorganic substances, especially iron, manganese, and zinc, were also found to favor growth in a synthetic medium consisting of nutrient salts, glutamic acid, sucrose, and phosphate buffer of *p*H 7.0. Many organic nitrogen compounds will supply the nitrogen requirements of *P. tumefaciens*. For instance, Sagen, Riker, and Baldwin (1934) found that acetamide, oxamide, succinimide, dicyandiamide, asparagine, urea, uric acid, and a number of amino acids, such as glycine, alanine, aspartic acid, and glutamic acid, serve as a sole source of nitrogen; but methylamine is not utilized. For carbon and energy the following compounds are utilized: arabinose, xylose, glucose, sucrose, maltose, raffinose, glycerol, mannitol, sodium citrate, and sodium tartrate [Patel (1928–1929), Sagen, Riker, and Baldwin (1934)].

Starr and Weiss (1934) found that certain phytopathogenic bacteria of the genus *Corynebacterium*, such as *Corynebacterium fascians*, will grow in a chemically defined medium containing inorganic salts and asparagine. Many other closely related species, however, will not, and it is assumed that they require growth factors or other nutrients for development in a simple medium.

Luminous Bacteria. Many of the so-called luminous bacteria, such as *Photobacterium fischeri* and *Achromobacter harveyi*, will develop in inorganic media with simple organic compounds as a sole source of carbon. These species thus belong to the nutritional group last mentioned. It is of interest, however, that certain other species, such as *Photobacterium phosphoreum*, will not grow unless methionine is added as an accessory factor [Doudoroff (1942)].

Enteric Group. Certain strains of the species which belong to the genera *Proteus*, *Salmonella*, *Eberthella*, *Shigella*, and *Vibrio* are capable of growing in simple media where ammonium salts serve as the sole source of nitrogen; in Knight's terminology these are nonexacting strains. Most of the strains which belong to these genera, however, need one or more amino acids for growth in simple media, and some even require growth factors; such strains, according to Knight (1936), are exacting in their requirements. Some of these exacting strains can be trained to do without the required amino acids by subculturing them in media containing suboptimal amounts of the acids. A good example of such an experiment will be found in the paper by Fildes, Gladstone, and Knight (1933).

In this section on the nutrition of the enteric group only one representative species, *Eberthella typhosa*, will be discussed. The nutritive requirements of the other members of the enteric group have been treated in detail by Knight (1936), whose monograph should be consulted for many interesting facts. In general, however, all the species have requirements very similar to those of the typhoid bacillus, except for the more exacting species which require growth factors for development in simple media. These species, which include some of the *Salmonella* and *Proteus* and many of the dysentery bacilli, will be mentioned on pp. 701 to 703.

Eberthella typhosa. Certain strains of *Eberthella typhosa* will grow in a simple glucose-ammonium salt medium; many will grow in a similar substrate containing a single amino acid; and all of them can be grown without difficulty in an aqueous mixture consisting of several common amino acids, nutritive salts, and glucose. The one essential amino acid is usually tryptophan [Fildes, Gladstone, and Knight (1933), Knight (1936), Johnson and Rettger (1943)], but Burrows (1939, 1942) has studied one strain which will grow with either arginine or glutamic acid but not with tryptophan, and another that will grow with either tryptophan or lysine. Cystine and several other amino acids stimulate the growth rate of certain strains, but they cannot be considered essential, since development will occur in their absence. Recently Burrows (1942) has studied the effect of variation in the source of carbon and energy on the amino acid requirements of eleven strains of *Eberthella typhosa.* The basal medium to which amino acids and carbon compounds were added consisted of $(NH_4)_2SO_4$, 0.5 per cent; NaCl, 0.05 per cent; and KH_2PO_4, 0.2 per cent. The compounds used as a source of carbon and energy consisted of glucose, glycerol, lactic acid, pyruvic acid, and succinic acid; they were added in amounts of 0.1 per cent. The eighteen amino acids employed were added in quantities of 0.05 per cent, with the exception of cystine and tyrosine, which were added in amounts of 0.001 per cent and 0.02 per cent, respectively.

From Burrows' results (see Table 7) it is apparent that the amino acid requirements of the typhoid bacillus are by no means limited to tryptophan. In the glucose-containing media, which served as a control, there were three strains which grew neither in the glucose-ammonium salt solution alone nor in this solution with tryptophan added. One of these strains (no. 2) required either arginine or glutamic acid but not trytophan. One (no. 22) would not grow in any of the

TABLE 7

GROWTH OF *Eberthella typhosa* STRAINS IN MEDIA CONTAINING VARIOUS AMINO ACIDS AND CARBON SUBSTANCES

[From Burrows (1942)]

Carbon Source	Strain Number	Tryptophan	Alanine	Aspartic Acid	Glycine	Cystine	Arginine	Glutamic Acid	Histidine	Hydroxyproline	Leucine	Lysine	Methionine	Phenylalanine	Proline	Serine	Valine	β-Alanine	Threonine
Glucose	1	+	+	+	+	+	+	+	+	+	+	+	+	+	+	+	+	+	+
	2						+	+											
	3	+	+	+	+	+	+	+	+	+	+	+	+	+	+	+	+	+	+
	22																		
	28																		
	29	+																	
	30	+																	
	34	+																	
	39	+																	
	42	+										+							
	44	+																	
Glycerol	1	+	+		+	+	+	+	+	+	+	+	+	+	+	+	+	+	+
	2						+	+											
	3	+	+	+	+	+	+	+	+	+	+	+	+	+	+	+	+	+	+
	22																		
	28																		
	29	+						+		+									
	30	+																	
	34																		
	39	+					+	+		+									
	42	+	+		+	+	+						+						
	44	+																	
Lactic acid	1	+	+		+	+	+		+	+	+	+	+	+	+	+	+	+	+
	2						+												
	3	+	+		+	+	+		+	+	+		+	+	+		+	+	+
	22																		
	28	+																	
	29	+																+	
	30	+																	
	34	+																	
	39	+					+								+				
	42	+	+								+				+		+	+	+
	44	+																	
Pyruvic acid	1	+	+	+	+	+		+	+	+	+	+	+	+	+	+	+	+	+
	2							+				+							
	3	+	+	+	+	+		+	+	+	+	+	+	+	+	+	+	+	+
	22																		
	28																		
	29	+																	
	30	+																	
	34	+																	
	39	+						+											
	42	+						+											
	44	+																	
Succinic acid	1	+	+	+	+		+	+	+	+	+	+	+	+	+	+	+	+	+
	2							+				+							
	3								+	+					+				
	22																		
	28																		
	29	+																	
	30																		
	34																		
	39	+																	
	42																		
	44																		

+ = growth for five subcultures; blanks indicate no growth in 6 to 8 days.

media employed. The third one (no. 28) would not grow in the presence of glucose and tryptophan but grew when lactic acid was substituted for glucose, although only in the presence of tryptophan. For strain no. 42 lysine could be substituted for tryptophan when glucose was present. Of the eleven strains used in this investigation four, or approximately one-third, differ from the so-called nutritive typical strains, which usually require tryptophan for growth in synthetic media containing glucose. Burrows also observed that the presence of different carbon compounds in the basal solution altered the amino acid requirements of these bacteria. Of the compounds tested, glycerol appeared to be the most favorable for growth, because more amino acids supported growth in combination with this compound than with any other substance. Lactic acid also appeared to be relatively favorable, but pyruvic acid and succinic acid were inferior to glycerol. Some of Burrows' data are presented in Table 7 to illustrate the points which have just been mentioned.

In addition to the carbon compounds employed by Burrows levulose, galactose, xylose, maltose, raffinose, dextrin, glycerol, mannitol, and sorbitol are usually fermented with acid production by the typhoid bacillus; but lactose, sucrose, inulin, rhamnose, inositol, salicin, and usually arabinose and dulcitol are not attacked.

In summary, we can say that the amino acid requirements of the typhoid bacillus are variable rather than fixed and that these requirements may be made to differ for strains by alteration of the carbon compounds included in the chemically defined media. Although tryptophan is required by most strains of *Eberthella typhosa*, it can sometimes be replaced by other amino acids.

BACTERIA WHICH HAVE REQUIREMENTS SIMILAR TO THOSE OF THE PREVIOUS GROUP BUT IN ADDITION NEED ONE OR MORE KNOWN GROWTH FACTORS

Several of the bacterial species which are allocated to this nutritional group actually have simple nitrogen and carbon requirements, but they differ from the bacteria which have been discussed in that they require an external supply of one or more growth factors before they will develop in simple media. This characteristic clearly suggests a loss of synthetic power on the part of these bacteria and means that they must find certain "ready-made" substances in their environment which are capable of taking part in cellular metabolism. A simple example of this group is *Proteus vulgaris*, which can carry out all its activities in an inorganic salt medium containing lactate and ammonium salts, providing nicotinic acid is also present. Other species of this group, such as *Proteus morganii*, are slightly more deficient in their synthetic powers, since they require one growth factor and one amino acid in ready-made form for growth in a mineral substrate containing glucose and ammonium salts. Still other species are more fastidious and require several growth factors and a mixture of amino acids.

Acid-fast Bacilli: Genus *Mycobacterium*. The nutrition of several of the acid-fast bacilli of the genus *Mycobacterium* has been studied by various investigators. A brief discussion of three species will be given here.

Mycobacterium tuberculosis is, of course, the best-known member of the acid-fast group. In primary isolation of this organism from infectious material complex media, such as a glycerol-potato medium or a glycerol-egg medium, must be employed. However, after primary isolation the bacterium can be grown on a simple synthetic medium such as Long's (*p*H 7.0):

Asparagine	5 g.	$MgSO_4$	1 g.
Ammonium citrate	5 g.	Ferric ammonium citrate	0.05 g.
KH_2PO_4	3 g.	Glycerol	25–50 g.
Na_2CO_3	3 g.	H_2O	1,000 ml.
NaCl	2 g.		

Comparatively large inocula (1.0 mg. or about five billion cells) must be used for each milliliter of medium. On the other hand, if subcultures are made on egg media, growth occurs regularly after plantings of 0.001 mg. of cells per milliliter of culture medium are used; and, if a potato medium is employed, growth takes place when an inoculum containing as little as 0.000000001 mg. is used [Uyei (1930)]. It is thus evident that the organism requires some additional factor for growth in simple media.

Uyei (1927, 1930) tested the effect of several vitamins on tubercle bacilli in an effort to improve the growth of the organism in synthetic media. Cod-liver oil (rich in vitamins A and D) had little effect, but other vitamin-containing substances, such as Harris' yeast preparation (1 : 1,000 dilution), orange juice (1 : 100), tomato juice (1 : 100), and cabbage juice (1 : 20), exerted a pronounced stimulatory effect. In a second report Uyei discussed the nature of the growth-promoting principles of the potato and stated that the proteins or salts in potato would not stimulate growth, but that the active ingredients remained in the residue after extraction with common organic solvents, such as acetone, alcohol, or ether. Investigation of the various components known to be present in the potato revealed two classes of stimulants

One was represented by inositol, maltose, and glucose, which were called *metabolic stimulants,* because the members of this group stimulated the growth of tubercle bacilli only when the inoculum consisted of a large number of cells. The second class of stimulants was represented by soluble starch and dextrin, which were termed *reproductive stimulants,* because they promoted growth regardless of whether the inoculum contained a large number of cells or only a few. Later Boissevain and Schultz (1938) demonstrated a lipoid growth factor for the tubercle bacillus in extracts from egg yolk and from the liver and spleen of guinea pigs and rats. This factor was soluble in alcohol and insoluble in cold acetone. The addition of 0.3 per cent of the extract from egg yolk to a modified Long's medium permitted growth of tubercle bacilli after plantings of 0.000001 mg. In contrast, growth occurred only after seeding of 0.1 mg. of cells per milliliter on synthetic media without the egg yolk extract. The factor could not be replaced by lecithin, thiamin, nicotinic acid, uracil, inositol, riboflavin, indole-3-acetic acid, or a watery extract from egg yolk containing biotin and pantothenic acid. Heise and Steenken (1941) also found that thiamin, riboflavin, and pyridoxine did not stimulate the growth of the tubercle bacillus.

Very little is known about the nitrogen and carbon requirements or the metabolism of *Mycobacterium tuberculosis.* A few amino acids, such as alanine, can usually serve as a sole source of nitrogen, and the organism can generally produce acid from glucose, maltose, lactose, sucrose, glycerol, and trehalose. Growth takes place between *p*H 4.5 and 8.0, with an optimum between 7.0 and 7.6. Growth occurs best at 37°C. in an atmosphere of 40 to 50 per cent oxygen; little growth takes place under 30°C. or under strictly anaerobic conditions.

The second acid-fast bacterium which may be mentioned is *Mycobacterium leprae.* According to Loving (1943), this species can be cultivated on a special medium having as a base alkaline nutrient agar, to which is added 1.0 per cent aqueous solutions of cysteine and cholesterol, 0.1 per cent tryptophan, sterile unheated rabbit serum, and 0.1 to 1.0 per cent thiamin. Since the specific nutrients contained in the rabbit serum have not yet been determined, it is probable that the requirements of this species are still pretty much unknown.

Mycobacterium paratuberculosis (Johne's bacillus) was one of the first bacteria of which the growth-factor requirements were studied. Twort and Ingram (1912), Boquet (1939), and others have showed that certain other acid-fast bacteria, including the tubercle bacillus, contain a necessary growth factor for the primary isolation of Johne's bacillus from infectious material. Crude concentrates of the active substance have been prepared from *Mycobacterium phlei* by precipitation with barium salts. More recently Woolley and McCarter (1940) have studied the nutrition of this organism and have shown that two antihemorrhagic compounds are growth factors. They grew the organism on the following basal medium:

Glycerol	70 ml.	$MgSO_4 \cdot 7H_2O$	1 g.
Asparagine	5 g.	$FeC_6H_5O_7 \cdot 3H_2O$	0.063 g.
$Na_3C_6H_5O_7$	0.5 g.	H_2O to	1,000 ml.
K_2HPO_4	1 g.		

The growth in this medium was very poor but was improved by adding dried cells or a filtrate of *M. phlei*, or the antihemorrhagic compounds, phthiocol and 2-methylnaphthoquinone (see Table 8). It is possible that future studies with bacteria may be useful in the elucidation of the role of vitamin K in cell physiology.

TABLE 8

GROWTH OF JOHNE'S BACILLUS IN MEDIA CONTAINING ANTIHEMORRHAGIC COMPOUNDS

[From Woolley and McCarter (1940)]

Culture Medium	Dry Weight of Johne's Bacilli Produced per 20 ml. of Media after 3 Months' Growth, milligrams
Assay 1	
Basal medium	120
" " + dried *Mycobacterium phlei* cells (40 mg./ml.)	260
" " + phthiocol (10 μg./ml.)	207
" " + " (1 μg./ml.)	250
" " + " (0.1 μg./ml.)	227
" " + " (0.01 μg./ml.)	147
Assay 2	
Basal medium	139
" " + *M. phlei* filtrate * (0.05 ml./ml.)	195
" " + 2-methylnaphthoquinone (1 μg./ml.)	167
" " + " (0.15 μg./ml.)	206
" " + " (0.1 μg./ml.)	212
" " + " (0.01 μg./ml.)	152

* The filtrate from a culture of *M. phlei* grown on a synthetic medium was concentrated by heat to about one-thirtieth of its original volume.

Corynebacterium diphtheriae. The nutritional requirements of *Corynebacterium diphtheriae* and related species have been studied by many workers. Since the early literature on this subject has been reviewed in some detail by Mueller (1940), we shall say here merely that, even though some early workers claimed that the diphtheria bacillus would grow in simple media, we now know that most strains refuse to develop in chemically defined media unless certain vitamins or an extract from fresh animal tissue, such as liver, is added. It is difficult to evaluate some of the early studies because of their lack of details concerning the purity of the materials employed, the size and nature of the inoculum used, the number of subcultures made, and the amount of growth observed.

From 1933 to 1935 Mueller and his associates began a series of investigations to determine the additional substances needed by the diphtheria bacillus for growth in chemically defined media. Since that time they have published an interesting series of papers on the separation and identification of the growth factors needed by this organism. Starting with a basal medium composed of acid-hydrolyzed casein fortified with cystine and glutamic acid, inorganic salts, and lactic acid, Mueller and Subbarow (1937) observed that certain components of liver extract (or meat extract) were essential for good growth of a strain of *Corynebacterium diphtheriae*. That there were at least two substances involved, which could be separated by ether extraction, was also demonstrated. The ether-extractable substance from liver could be replaced by concentrates of cow or horse urine, and on further investigation of these concentrates an active substance was isolated and identified as pimelic acid, $HOOC(CH_2)_5 \cdot COOH$ [Mueller (1937)]. Quantitative determinations of bacterial nitrogen showed that the stimulating effect of pimelic acid became evident at a concentration of about 0.005 μg. per milliliter of medium and reached a maximum in five times this concentration. Other dibasic acids of the same series, from oxalic, $HOOC \cdot COOH$, to azelaic, $HOOC \cdot (CH_2)_7 \cdot COOH$, exerted no growth-stimulating effect. The other fraction, that is, the ether-insoluble fraction, was subsequently shown to contain two active substances which were in turn identified as nicotinic acid [Mueller (1937)] and β-alanine [Mueller and Cohen (1937)]; these compounds were active in amounts of approximately 1 μg. and 2 μg. per milliliter of medium, respectively.

Although these results were soon confirmed by Evans and his associates (1939) for a number of strains of diphtheria bacilli, other strains were shown to require certain inorganic "trace" elements and pantothenic acid. Previously Mueller and Klotz (1938) had found that pantothenic acid could replace β-alanine for their test strain, and it was suggested that β-alanine was used by the organism to synthesize pantothenic acid. From the results of Evans and his coworkers, however, it appears that not all strains are capable of carrying out this synthesis. McIlwain (1943) has also carried out an interesting study in this connection. It has been known for a few years that pantoyltaurine, a compound structurally related to pantothenic acid, prevents or antagonizes the utilization of pantothenate. Furthermore it is known that certain strains of diphtheria bacilli are pantoyltaurine-resistant. McIlwain, however, has shown that the presence of the drug (pantoyltaurine) is not necessary for resistant strains to develop. He proved this point after deriving very resistant strains by serial subculture of susceptible strains in media containing large amounts of β-alanine and no pantothenate, or little β-alanine and decreasing amounts of pantothenate.

Studies by Mueller and others indicate that the nutritional requirements of *C. diphtheriae* are complicated by many factors. In 1939 Mueller investigated the possibility of obtaining an agar medium which could be used for diagnostic purposes. He believed that, since his medium contained no vitamin B_1, riboflavin, or other growth accessories required by streptococci and pneumococci, it would be more or less selective for the diphtheria bacillus. Preliminary experiments with cultures from known cases of diphtheria showed that some cultures grew, but frequently no growth was obtained. Further investigation showed that the *size of the inoculum* was the controlling factor; when plates were streaked, even with strains which grew well in the liquid medium, growth was slow in starting, and on the more lightly inoculated areas of the plate individual colonies did not develop at all or developed only after two to three days. The indication was clear that a heavy inoculum introduced enough of some still unidentified factor to initiate growth, after which the growing organisms were able to elaborate the material and permit its diffusion into the surrounding medium. This deficiency of the agar medium could be corrected by adding small amounts of horse and beef serum or cows' milk, but human and hog serum possessed little activity. Subsequently Cohen and Mueller (1940) and Cohen, Snyder, and Mueller (1941) showed that the active substance in milk could be separated by extraction of the acid-precipitated casein with hot alcohol or cold acetone, and this substance has been identified by them as oleic acid, $C_{17}H_{33}COOH$. The maximal effect was obtained with about 1 mg. in 15 to 18 ml. of the basal agar medium. Later du Vigneaud, Dittmer, Hague, and Long (1942) presented evidence to show that pimelic acid was utilized by the diphtheria bacillus for the synthesis of biotin. In fact, pimelic acid could be eliminated from the medium, providing it was replaced by biotin. It is of interest in this connection that pimelic acid is unable to replace biotin in its growth-stimulating effect on yeast. Apparently yeast lacks the ability to synthesize the other component or to condense the necessary components into a molecule of biotin. Chattaway, Happold, Sandford, Lythgoe, and Todd (1943) have shown that certain strains of *C. diphtheriae* require other factors besides the ones just mentioned.

Numerous attempts have been made by various workers to increase the potency of the toxin produced by the diphtheria bacillus by altering the medium on which the organism was cultivated, but relatively few workers have employed chemically defined media. One study in which success was obtained with a medium of known composition, however, was that by Pappenheimer, Mueller, and Cohen (1937). Using the Park no. 8 strain of *C. diphtheriae*, they obtained a toxin of the following potency: M.L.D. = 0.00075 ml.; L_+ dose = 0.05 ml.; and L_f units = 36 per milliliter. The constituents of the medium employed in this study (medium II) are listed below. Recently Mueller and Miller (1941) have improved the medium for toxin production still further by reducing the NaCl and potassium-ion concentrations and by using shallower layers of media in the flasks. Using the improved formula, 5,000 M.L.D. or 100 L_f per milliliter of toxin may be routinely produced [see also Pappenheimer (1942)].

To summarize our information on the nutrition of the diphtheria bacillus, the composition of two media may be given. One (I) is the medium employed by Mueller (1938), which supported normal growth of a strain of *C. diphtheriae*, and the other (II) is the medium proposed by Pappenheimer, Mueller, and Cohen for toxin production. For complete details of the methods of preparation the original papers should be consulted.

	Medium I *	Medium II *
l-Cystine	70 mg.	20 mg.
dl-Valine	200 mg.	100 mg.
dl-Methionine	60 mg.	20 mg.
l-Tyrosine	50 mg.	10 mg.
l-Proline	75 mg.	
l-Aspartic acid	500 mg.	
d-Glutamic acid·HCl	750 mg.	500 mg.
Glycine		50 mg.
dl-Leucine		50 mg.
Ethyl alcohol	0.7 ml.	
d-Lactic acid	1.75 ml.	
Sodium lactate		740 mg.
Maltose		300 mg.
Glucose		150 mg.

	Medium I	Medium II
Pimelic acid	0.015 mg.	0.1 mg.
Nicotinic acid	0.23 mg.	0.2 mg.
β-Alanine	0.2 mg.	0.1 mg.
KCl	40 mg.	
NaCl		500 mg.
K_2HPO_4		200 mg.
Na_2HPO_4	300 mg.	
$MgSO_4 \cdot 7H_2O$	100 mg.	30 mg.
$CuSO_4 \cdot 5H_2O$	0.25 mg.	0.25 mg.
$CaCO_3$ (in HCl)	20 mg.	
$CaCl_2$		6 mg.
$FeSO_4 \cdot 7H_2O$	0.5 mg.	
$MnCl_2 \cdot 4H_2O$	0.25 mg.	
ZnO (in HCl)	0.25 mg.	
H_2O to	100 ml.	100 ml.

* Medium I gave normal growth; Medium II yielded good toxin.

A few facts are available concerning the exact carbon, nitrogen (amino acids), sulfur, and inorganic requirements of the diphtheria bacillus and have been reviewed recently by Mueller (1940).

Streptococci and Pneumococci. With very few exceptions the streptococci and pneumococci fail to grow in chemically defined media containing various salts, amino acids, and sugars unless infusions from animal tissues are supplied. In the past few years, however, considerable progress has been made in determining the exact nutritional requirements of these bacteria; in fact, media of essentially defined chemical composition can now be prepared which will permit massive growth of group A hemolytic streptococci [Bernheimer and Pappenheimer (1942), Bernheimer, Gillman, Hottle, and Pappenheimer (1942)]. This fact does not mean, though, that all streptococci and pneumococci can be cultivated in media of known composition, because it has been pointed out by several workers that additional factors are required by certain strains.

The factors essential for the growth of beta-hemolytic streptococci have been investigated recently by a number of workers [see Hutner (1938), Rane and Subbarow (1938), Subbarow and Rane (1938), McIlwain and associates (1939), Woolley and Hutchings (1939), Pappenheimer and Hottle (1940), Hottle *et al.* (1941), Woolley (1941), Bass, Berkman, and Saunders (1941), Bernheimer and associates (1942), Sprince and Woolley (1944), and others]. As a result of these studies the growth-factor requirements of certain strains of hemolytic streptococci have been pretty well established. The composition of the medium used by Pappenheimer and Hottle (1940) may be cited to give the student some idea of the complex requirements of the hemolytic streptococci of the Lancefield group A (*Streptococcus pyogenes*). Although this medium has now been improved by Bernheimer and Pappenheimer (1942) and others, its original formula still serves to illustrate the basal requirements of the group. It should be mentioned also that many of the workers listed above helped Pappenheimer and his associates in one way or another to work out some of the ingredients of their medium. This statement is not meant to imply that Pappenheimer and Hottle's work was not original, but rather that some progress had been made before their study. For example, Subbarow and Rane (1939), McIlwain (1939), and Woolley and Hutchings (1939) had already shown that pantothenic acid was an essential factor for the growth of these organisms; McIlwain, Fildes, Gladstone, and Knight (1939) had established the necessity for glutamine under certain conditions; Woolley and Hutchings (1939) had observed that riboflavin was an essential factor; and McIlwain (1940) had shown the need for vitamin B_6. The complete medium employed by Pappenheimer and Hottle (1940) is made up as follows:

I. Forty milliliters of a stock solution of acid-hydrolyzed gelatin equivalent to 25 per cent gelatin is diluted with distilled H_2O to 500 ml.; and 500 mg. of cystine dissolved in a few milliliters of dilute HCl, 3 g. of KH_2PO_4, 1 g. of anhydrous Na_2HPO_4, and enough 5 *N* NaOH to bring the *p*H to 7.4 to 7.6 are added. The solution is boiled gently for 5 minutes and filtered.

II. To the filtrate from I are added 50 mg. of tryptophan, 100 mg. of tyrosine, 15 mg. of adenine sulfate, 10 mg. of uracil, 0.2 mg. of nicotinic acid, 2 mg. of vitamin B_6, 0.1 mg. of biotin concentrate, and 2 ml. of salt mixture.[10] The volume is made up to 900 ml.; the *p*H readjusted to 7.4 to 7.6; and the mixture tubed in 9-ml. amounts and autoclaved.

III. To each tube add 0.1 ml. of the following solutions which have been sterilized separately: vitamin B_1, 0.1 mg. per milliliter; riboflavin, 0.05 mg. per milliliter; calcium pantothenate, 0.1 mg. per milliliter; neutralized thioglycolic acid, 1 per cent, containing glutathione, 0.2 mg. per milliliter, and glutamine, 5 mg. per milliliter. The last three solutions are sterilized by filtration. Finally, add 0.5 ml. of 5 per cent glucose containing 0.04 per cent $CaCl_2 \cdot 2H_2O$.

The hemolytic streptococcus strain (C2O3S) employed by Pappenheimer and Hottle grew very well in this complete medium, as can be seen in Table 9; in fact, the amount of growth, measured as bacterial nitrogen, was approximately equal to that in glucose broth. All the substances listed in Table 9 are essential for rapid growth with the exception of uracil, which, while not required, improved growth slightly. The effect of omitting each of the factors from the complete medium of Pappenheimer and Hottle is also indicated in Table 9; the figures listed in the second column of the table indicate the minimum amount of each substance necessary for optimum growth in 10 ml. of media.

The nutrition of Lancefield group B streptococci (*Streptococcus agalactiae* or *Streptococcus mastitidis*) of human and animal origin has been studied by Niven (1943). All the strains employed required biotin, nicotinic acid, pantothenic acid, thiamin, and pyridoxine for development in a chemically defined medium consisting of twenty amino acids, glucose, sodium thioglycolate, and inorganic salts. A few strains also required riboflavin and an additional factor for op-

[10] $MgSO_4 \cdot 7H_2O$, 25 g.; $MnCl_2 \cdot 4H_2O$, 20 mg.; $CuSO_4$, 5 mg.; $FeSO_4 \cdot 7H_2O$, 2 mg.; and $ZnSO_4 \cdot 7H_2O$, 2 mg., made up to 100 ml. with H_2O slightly acidified with HCl.

timum growth. Of the twenty amino acids employed, the following nine were shown to be essential: valine, leucine, isoleucine, phenylalanine, glutamic acid, arginine, lysine, histidine, and tryptophan; threonine, cystine, methionine, and tyrosine stimulated growth.

Additional data on the growth of group C hemolytic streptococci (*Streptococcus equi*, "human C," etc.) in simplified media have been presented by Rogers (1944). Optimum growth occurred only when

TABLE 9

GROWTH OF A HEMOLYTIC STREPTOCOCCUS STRAIN IN GLUCOSE BROTH AND A CHEMICALLY DEFINED MEDIUM AND THE EFFECT OF OMITTING CERTAIN FACTORS FROM THE CHEMICALLY DEFINED MEDIUM

[From Pappenheimer and Hottle (1940)]

Medium	Amount Necessary for Optimum Growth	Bacterial Nitrogen after 40 Hours' Incubation from 10 ml. × 50, milligrams
1. Chemically defined medium		10–13
" " " minus glucose	25,000 μg.	0.1
" " " " glutamine	500 μg.	Variable *
" " " " tyrosine	1,000 μg.	3.9
" " " " tryptophan	500 μg.	0.8
" " " " uracil	100 μg.	9.9
" " " " adenylic acid (0.4 mm. CO_2 tension)	100 μg.	0.7
" " " " CO_2(CO_2—free air)	8 mm.	2.2
" " " " thioglycolic acid	1,000 μg.	0.1
" " " " glutathione	4 μg.	0.1
" " " " thiamin	0.01 μg.	3.1
" " " " nicotinic acid	1 μg.	1.9
" " " " pantothenate	10 μg.	0.2
" " " " riboflavin	0.04 μg.	0.8
" " " " vitamin B_6	20 μg.	5.9–7.1 †
" " " " biotin concentrate	1 μg.	1.8
2. Broth (25 mg. glucose per 10 ml.)		10–17

* No significant growth in 20 hours without glutamine; growth after 40 hours at 8 mm. CO_2 tension was variable.

† No significant growth at atmospheric CO_2 tension without vitamin B_6.

uracil, or orotic acid, was present in the medium. The two pyrimidine derivatives were equally effective in increasing both the rate and the mass of growth of this group of streptococci.

The nutritional requirements of the so-called enterococci belonging to the Lancefield serological group D have been studied by several workers [see Woolley and Hutchings (1940), Woolley (1941), Schuman and Farrell (1941), Niven and Sherman (1944), McIlwain and Hughes (1944), Hutchings, Stokstad, Bohonos, and Slobodkin (1944)]. The four major varieties or species within this group are: *Streptococcus zymogenes*, *Streptococcus durans*, *Streptococcus fecalis*, and *Streptococcus liquefaciens*. The organism called *Streptococcus lactis* R, which is used in the microbiological assay of folic acid, is actually a strain of *S. fecalis* [Gunsalus, Niven, and Sherman (1944)]. Of the reports mentioned above, the one by Niven and Sherman may be briefly summarized to show the requirements of this group. All of the nineteen cultures studied required pantothenic acid, nicotinic acid, pyridoxine, and biotin. Seventeen strains needed riboflavin; seven required folic acid. All the organisms grew in the absence of purine (adenine, guanine, xanthine) and pyrimidine (uracil) bases; but, when these substances were included in the basal medium, the growth rate of most strains was enhanced. When the hydrolyzed casein in the basal medium was replaced by thirteen amino acids, fourteen of the nineteen cultures were able to grow.

The alpha-hemolytic streptococci, or the so-called *viridans group*, have recently been studied from a nutritional standpoint by Smiley, Niven, and Sherman (1943). A typical species (*Streptococcus salivarius*) was used for these experiments. It was found that the simplest medium which would support growth contained, in addition to inorganic salts, glucose, and sodium thioglycolate, the following substances: glutamic acid, leucine, arginine, isoleucine, lysine, methionine, riboflavin, nicotinic acid, pantothenic acid, biotin, thiamin, and uracil. No other streptococci (groups A to H) were found to be capable of initiating growth in this medium except a few cultures of other species within the viridans group.

The nutritive requirements of certain nonhemolytic streptococci, such as *Streptococcus lactis*, *Streptococcus cremoris*, and *Streptococcus fecalis*, have also received some attention. Orla-Jensen, Otte, and Snog-Kjaer (1936) and Wood, Andersen, and Werkman (1937) found that the growth of certain strains of lactic acid-producing streptococci was improved by the addition of riboflavin; but the strains of *S. lactis* employed by Snell and Strong (1939) grew as luxuriantly in a medium containing no riboflavin as they did in its presence. These early studies of the lactic acid streptococci have been greatly extended by Smith (1943), Niven (1943), and Wright and Skeggs (1944). For example, twenty-one strains of *S. lactis* were used in the study by Niven. All cultures required pantothenic acid, nicotinic acid, and biotin for growth in a basal medium containing salts, glucose, hydrolyzed casein, purine, and pyrimidine bases. Eighteen of the twenty-one strains tested required thiamin, whereas only one-third of the cultures required riboflavin. All strains were able to grow without added folic acid and pyridoxine; however, pyridoxine stimulated growth. Glutamine and asparagine were necessary for the initiation of growth in all cultures tested. When the hydrolyzed casein was replaced by amino acids, it was observed that the demands by various strains were complex. At least fourteen amino acids were necessary before prompt growth occurred. *Streptococcus fecalis*, a nonhemolytic group D streptococcus, was cultivated in a chemically defined medium consisting of pantothenic acid, vitamin B_6, riboflavin, glucose, a salt mixture, and six amino acids (arginine, glutamic acid, methionine, tryptophan, tyrosine, and valine) by Schuman and Farrell (1941). The addition of other substances, such as glutathione, nicotinic acid, betaine, glucosamine, uracil, xanthine, hypoxanthine, glutamine, sodium sulfide, and reduced iron, described by other workers as stimulating for certain hemolytic streptococci, did not measurably increase the growth of this streptococcus.

The nutritional requirements of pneumococci of types I, II, V, VII, and VIII were studied by Rane and Subbarow (1940), who found that types I, II, V, and VIII grew in a medium consisting of gelatin hydrolysate, certain additional amino acids (*d*-glutamic acid and cystine), inorganic salts, glucose, choline, nicotinic acid, pantothenic acid, and thioglycolic acid; the addition of riboflavin gave slightly increased growth but was not essential. It was also observed that the following amino acid medium could be substituted for the hydrolyzed gelatin substrate with types II, V, and VIII but was deficient for the growth of type I:

Amino Acid Medium * for Pneumococci

d-Glutamic acid	1	g.	*l*-Phenylalanine	0.01	g.
Glycine	0.25	g.	*l*-Oxyproline	0.01	g.
l-Asparagine	0.20	g.	KH_2PO_4	5	g.
dl-Leucine	0.15	g.	NaCl	2.5	g.
d-Arginine carbonate	0.075	g.	$MgSO_4$	1	g.
dl-Alanine	0.05	g.	Glucose	5	g.
dl-Lysine·2HCl	0.05	g.	Pantothenic acid	1	mg.
dl-Methionine	0.05	g.	Choline	2.5	mg.
l-Cystine	0.05	g.	Nicotinic acid	50	mg.
dl-Histidine·HCl	0.025	g.	Riboflavin	0.1	mg.
l-Tryptophan	0.025	g.	Thioglycolic acid	50	mg.
β-Alanine	0.025	g.	H_2O (distilled)	1,000	ml.
Norleucine	0.015	g.			

* For the details of preparation the original paper by Rane and Subbarow (1940) should be consulted.

No growth was observed with type VII pneumococcus in either the hydrolyzed gelatin medium or the amino acid substrate. The addition of purines, pyrimidines, vitamin B_1, vitamin B_6, thiochrome, and glucosamine did not alter the situation.

More recently Bohonos and Subbarow (1943) have shown that biotin is an essential growth factor for twenty-six types of pneumococci. Badger (1944) and Gibert (1944) have also studied the nutrition and the structural specificity of choline for the growth of types I, II, and III pneumococci. In general, their results on the nutrition of the pneumococci confirm those of Rane and Subbarow. However, ascorbic acid was found to be a better reducing agent than thioglycolic acid, and the addition of asparagine, creatine, purine and pyrimidine bases, and thiamin to the basal medium increased the rate of growth, although they were not essential. When some thirty-five compounds chemically related to choline [$(CH_3)_3N(Cl)$—CH_2—CH_2OH] were tested for their ability to replace choline in the nutrition of pneumococcus type III, it was found that the active compounds all contained a N—C—C—OH or a N—C—C—C—OH linkage. Substitution of ethyl or methyl groups on the nitrogen or α-carbon atoms usually increased the activity, but the addition of a phenyl group to the nitrogen atom or a carboxyl group to either carbon atom inactivated the molecule. Furthermore the hydroxyl group had to remain free, since any substitution of or through this group resulted in the loss of activity. The fact that ethanolamine, but not acetylcholine, methionine, or betaine, can replace choline suggests the formation of phospholipides as the most likely explanation of the action of choline in pneumococcal metabolism.

Staphylococci. Information on the exact growth-factor requirements of the staphylococci begins with a paper by Hughes in 1932. He obtained a fraction from meat extract which permitted multiplication of *Staphylococcus aureus* in substrates, such as Uschinsky's medium or a hydrolyzed casein medium, which normally are incapable of supporting continued growth. The active material was concentrated to a point where the addition of 0.02 μg. per milliliter of hydrolyzed casein medium supported growth. It was soluble in water, alcohol, and acetone but insoluble in ether and benzene; it was thermostable at pH 7.0 and was dialyzable. Knight (1935) obtained a similar fraction from yeast extract (marmite) which allowed growth of certain strains of staphylococci to take place when as little as 0.004 μg. per milliliter was present in a deficient basal medium consisting of acid-hydrolyzed gelatin, glucose, and salts. Subsequently it was found possible [Fildes, Richardson, Knight, and Gladstone (1936), Gladstone (1937)] to replace the gelatin hydrolysate in the basal medium with a mixture of sixteen amino acids.[11] Later Knight (1937) resolved the active marmite fraction into three parts, two being the pyrimidine and thiazole components of vitamin B_1 and the third being nicotinamide. Vitamin B_1 was adequate in 0.002 μg. per milliliter, and nicotinic acid or its amide in 0.2 μg. per milliliter of the amino acid-glucose medium.

The specificity of the components of vitamin B_1 and related derivatives, as well as of several pyridine compounds closely related to nicotinic acid or its amide, was the subject of a careful study by Knight and McIlwain (1938). Their results emphasize that vitamin B_1 and nicotinamide are quite highly specific for the growth of staphylococci. Only very limited departures from these structures are permissible if growth activity is to be maintained. For the anaerobic growth of *S. aureus* Richardson (1936) has demonstrated that uracil must be added to the medium in addition to the above compounds.

After these reports a study was undertaken by Porter and Pelczar (1941) to determine whether the quantity of growth produced by *S. aureus* in the chemically defined medium [11] of Gladstone (1937) was equal to that obtainable in standard glucose-meat-infusion broth. The results revealed that the chemically defined medium was inferior to the broth. When the basal chemically defined medium was fortified with the following growth factors and related substances, there was no demonstrable influence on growth: riboflavin, pimelic acid, glutamine, vitamin B_6, inositol, pantothenic acid, cocarboxylase, cozymase, glutathione, uracil, guanine, adenine, adenylic acid, adenosine triphosphate, and several additional amino acids. Evidently some other unidentified factor is still needed for the optimum growth of staphylococci in synthetic media. Another interesting point in connection with the study by Porter and Pelczar (1941) was that two strains which they employed could not initiate growth on continued subculture in the chemically defined medium. A study of these strains revealed that a biotin concentrate was required for growth.

Kögl and van Wagtendonk (1938) previously showed that as little as 5×10^{-6} μg. of the pure methyl ester of biotin stimulated the growth of *S. aureus* in the medium described by Knight (1937), but

[11] Briefly, the medium contained the following sixteen amino acids: *dl*-alanine, *dl*-valine, glycine, *dl*-leucine, *l*-proline, *l*-oxyproline, *l*-aspartic acid, and *dl*-glutamic acid, each in a final concentration of 0.0006 *M*; *dl*-phenylalanine, *l*-tyrosine, *d*-arginine·HCl, *l*-histidine·HCl, and *dl*-lysine, each in a final concentration of 0.00025 *M*; *l*-tryptophan (0.00005 *M*), *l*-cystine (0.0001 *M*), and *dl*-methionine (0.00002 *M*). In addition to the amino acids the medium contained nicotinamide (10^{-5} *M*), thiamin (vitamin B_1) (10^{-7} *M*), glucose (0.5 per cent), and inorganic salts (KH_2PO_4, $MgSO_4 \cdot 7H_2O$, $FeSO_4$, and $(NH_4)_2SO_4 \cdot 6H_2O$). The *p*H was 7.2 to 7.4.

apparently the growth factor was not essential for their strain, because it was able to grow in the basal medium without biotin. Similar results were obtained by Sartory, Meyer, and Netter (1939).

The effect of various factors, including shaking of cultures, amino acids, sugars, polyhydric alcohols, organic and inorganic salts, oxygen, and CO_2, on the production of staphylococcus α-hemolysin in chemically defined media has been studied by Gladstone (1938) [see also Casman (1940)].

Koser, Finkle, Dorfman, Gordon, and Saunders (1938) observed that a strain of *Staphylococcus albus* developed in a medium of known composition containing thiamin and nicotinic acid, but growth was considerably slower than that secured in broth or after the addition of fractions of spleen preparation to the chemically defined medium. Evidently something else was needed by this strain for optimum growth. This factor may have been vitamin B_6, since Vilter and Spies (1940) have shown that pyridoxine, 0.3 to 1.2 μg. per milliliter of medium, serves as an accessory growth factor for *S. albus*.

***Hemophilus influenzae* and *Hemophilus pertussis*.** In 1917 Davis demonstrated that Pfeiffer's bacillus (*Hemophilus influenzae*) required two factors for growth in peptone broth: one a thermostable compound contained in or derived from hemoglobin; the other a thermolabile substance present in the tissues of various plants and animals and synthesized by many bacteria other than *H. influenzae*. In the next few years after the report by Davis numerous studies [see Olsen (1920), Thjötta and Avery (1921), Fildes (1921 to 1924), and Rivers (1922)] appeared on the nutrition of the *Hemophilus* group of bacteria. In general these reports confirmed and extended Davis' work. One point which should be mentioned, however, is that Thjötta and Avery (1921) suggested the terms *X-factor* for the growth substance contained in blood pigments and *V-factor* for the substance present in tissue extracts; this V-factor was likened to a vitamin.

Later Lwoff and Lwoff (1937), Bass, Berkman, Saunders, and Koser (1941), Hoagland, Ward, Gilder, and Shank (1942), Gingrich and Schlenk (1944), and others reinvestigated the nutrition of certain *Hemophilus* species. The Lwoffs discovered that the so-called V-factor needed by certain *Hemophilus* species was actually the coenzyme, di- or triphosphopyridine nucleotide. Using a culture medium consisting of proteose-peptone (Difco) 20 g., NaCl 6 g., distilled water 1,000 ml., and NaOH to bring it to pH 7.5, they found that *H. parainfluenzae* would multiply only if the coenzyme was added and, furthermore, that the organism was unable to synthesize the factor when it was supplied with the coenzyme components (Adenine + Pentose + Phosphoric acid + Nicotinamide). More recently, however, Schlenk and Gingrich

(1942) and Gingrich and Schlenk (1944) have observed that both nicotinamide nucleoside (consisting of nicotinamide and pentose) and desaminocozymase (a derivative in which the adenylic acid portion of the molecule is replaced by inosinic acid) can serve as V-factor. This fact indicates that the adenylic acid portion of the coenzyme molecule is of minor importance in the growth of this organism. Although the Lwoffs found that optimum growth occurred when 0.004 μg. of di- or triphosphopyridine nucleotide was present per milliliter of medium, the maximum dilution compatible with the development of a bacterial cloudiness visible to the naked eye was about 1/270,000,000 to 1/600,000,000 (dry weight of coenzyme). Using a basal medium consisting of veal infusion-peptone broth plus 0.2 per cent dextrose and 0.15 μg. of diphosphopyridine nucleotide per milliliter, Bass, Berkman, Saunders, and Koser (1941) found that highly purified preparations of catalase were capable of replacing both hemin (the X-factor) and coenzyme I (the V-factor) in the nutrition of *H. influenzae.* They observed also that, in addition to X- and V-factors, the influenza bacilli appeared to require one or more other factors which could not be replaced by pantothenic acid, cocarboxylase, riboflavin, ascorbic acid, vitamin B_6, or inositol.

Hornibrook (1940) reported that nicotinic acid or its amide (0.5 to 0.001 μg. per milliliter) favored the growth of *Hemophilus pertussis* in a medium consisting of amino acids, soluble starch, and salts.

***Proteus vulgaris* and *Proteus morganii*.** The early literature on the growth requirements of the various *Proteus* species is conflicting [see Knight (1936)]. Some workers have asserted that all nitrogen requirements can be satisfied by ammonium salts or amino acids, whereas others have failed to obtain continued growth under these conditions. Probably both groups were partly correct, but they failed to realize the possibility of nonexacting and exacting strains.

In 1938 Fildes studied the nutritional requirements of ten strains of *Proteus vulgaris* and *Proteus X19* and found that nicotinic acid was the only nitrogenous substance required in their metabolism which could not be synthesized from ammonium salts. The medium employed by Fildes (1938) had a *p*H of 7.6 and contained the following ingredients, the mixture being tubed in 4.5 ml. quantities and autoclaved:

KH_2PO_4	4.5 g.	Lactate (0.5 *M*)	50 ml.
$(NH_4)_2SO_4$	0.5 g.	H_2O (distilled) to	900 ml.
NH_4Cl	0.5 g.		

Prior to inoculation with the test organism, each tube of this medium was fortified with the following materials from sterile stock solutions:

$FeSO_4(NH_4)_2 \cdot SO_4 \cdot 6H_2O$ (0.002 *M* in 0.02 *M* HCl)	0.12 ml.
$MgSO_4 \cdot 7H_2O$ (0.4 per cent in H_2O)	0.05 ml.
Nicotinic acid (10^{-3} *M* in H_2O, final concentration 2×10^{-5} *M*)	0.10 ml.
H_2O (distilled) to a final volume of	5 ml.

Lwoff and Querido (1939) soon confirmed the results of Fildes and, in addition, tested the ability of various pyridine compounds to replace nicotinic acid. After these reports Pelczar and Porter (1940) studied 189 strains of *Proteus vulgaris* and related species from the standpoint of their ability to grow on continued subculture in Fildes' medium containing nicotinic acid or one of 13 other related pyridine compounds. Their results showed that several pyridine compounds were biologically active besides nicotinic acid or its amide; further details on this subject will be found on pp. 730 to 731 on the growth factors and their physiological role in microorganisms. Pelczar and Porter also showed that the nutritional requirements of strains allocated to the genus *Proteus* were not uniform, since some strains were capable of growing in the absence of the pyridine compounds, whereas others failed to grow even when such compounds were present. All 37 strains of Morgan's bacillus (*Proteus morganii*) employed were unable to grow in Fildes' medium, but in later reports Pelczar and Porter (1940, 1941, 1943) announced that, when pantothenic acid and cystine were added to the medium, the strains of *Proteus morganii* grew very well.

***Salmonella* and *Shigella* Species.** Certain species of *Salmonella* have nutritional requirements very similar to those of *Eberthella typhosa*, which has been discussed. Other species, however, are more fastidious in their requirements. For example, all the strains of *Salmonella gallinarum* studied by Johnson and Rettger (1943) were found to require thiamin for growth in a chemically defined medium containing amino acids, glucose, and inorganic salts, and some strains of *Salmonella pullorum* needed nicotinic acid.

Most strains of *Shigella dysenteriae* will not grow on continued subculture in the usual chemically defined media consisting of amino acids, glucose, and salts which support the growth of other enteric organisms. However, if a small quantity of extract from liver, spleen, or yeast is added to such media, luxuriant growth takes place. Until recently the nature of the active substance in such extracts was unknown. After considerable work several investigators [see Koser, Dorfman, and Saunders (1938, 1940), Dorfman, Koser, Reames, Swingle, and Saunders (1939), Koser and Wright (1943)] at the University of Chicago showed that the factor in extracts from spleen tissues was nicotinic acid. Here is the final medium (*p*H 6.8 to 7.0) they proposed for the cultivation of these organisms:

K_2HPO_4	1 g.
$MgSO_4 \cdot 7H_2O$	0.1 g.
l-Glutamic acid and *l*-alanine, each	0.5 g.
Glycine, *l*-lysine·2HCl, *l*-tryptophan, and *l*-histidine·2HCl, each	0.2 g.
l-Tyrosine	0.05 g.
dl-Valine, *l*-leucine, *dl*-phenylalanine, *l*-cystine, *l*-proline, *l*-hydroxyproline, *dl*-methionine, and *l*-arginine, each	0.1 g.
Glucose	2 g.
Nicotinic acid or amide	0.1–0.004 g.
H_2O (redistilled)	1,000 ml.

Other known growth factors, with the exception of di- or triphosphopyridine nucleotide (coenzyme I or II), were not capable of replacing, either partially or completely, nicotinic acid or its amide. Nicotinamide was at least ten times as potent as nicotinic acid when cultural development was compared 24 hours after inoculation. The activities of twenty-four compounds structurally related to nicotinic acid were studied also; the results of this phase of the work are discussed on page 730 on bacterial growth factors and their physiological role in microorganisms.

Several other workers have also studied the vitamin requirements of certain dysentery bacilli. For example, Bovarnick (1943) recorded an interesting observation in connection with the nicotinamide requirements of this organism and other species of bacteria. After heating a neutral solution of glutamic acid and asparagine for several days at 100°C., she found that it could be substituted for nicotinamide as a growth factor for several strains of dysentery bacilli, staphylococci, and certain lactic acid bacilli. The explanation of this phenomenon is unknown, although others have observed that heating certain ingredients of media improves growth [see Snell (1942), Smiley, Niven, and Sherman (1943)]. Weil and Black (1944) observed that with *Shigella paradysenteriae* Flexner cultures, pantothenate, in addition to nicotinic acid, is needed by some strains, whereas other cultures require still another factor.

Little is known about the carbon and nitrogen requirements of the dysentery bacilli. They ferment a few sugars, such as glucose, with acid production, but with very few exceptions they never form gas from carbohydrates. Although most strains require amino acids in the medium for growth, some, such as *Shigella paradysenteriae*-Sonne, which was employed by Isbell, Wooley, Butler, and Sebrell (1941), can utilize ammonium salts as a source of nitrogen. Therefore, in *Shigella*, as in many other organisms of the enteric group, exacting and nonexacting strains are known to exist.

***Brucella* and *Pasteurella* Species.** In the past several workers reported that certain strains of *Brucella* would develop in media of known composition without the addition of growth factors but that fairly large inocula were necessary before growth occurred [Zobell and Meyer (1932)]. The failure of *Brucella* species to grow on continued subculture in chemically defined media composed solely of amino acids, salts, and a nonnitrogenous source of energy presents a decided contrast to the prompt growth in media containing infusions of meat, liver, or yeast. Although these substances contain some factor necessary for growth, their exact nature has remained obscure until recently. Preliminary reports by Kerby (1939) and others shed some light on the subject, but, since the basal media employed usually supported growth by themselves, it was not clear whether the accessory substances used were actually essential.

Later Koser, Breslove, and Dorfman (1941) studied the growth-factor requirements of representative species of the *Brucella* group. They found that seven out of eight strains grew on continued subculture in a medium consisting of seventeen amino acids, glucose, and inorganic salts. The significant accessory factors required were thiamin, nicotinamide, pantothenic acid, and probably biotin; however, not all these factors were actually required by all strains. Thiamin and nicotinamide supported the growth of four cultures, although the development was slow for some strains. The presence of pantothenic acid accelerated growth, and the further addition of a biotin concentrate permitted the growth of three of the remaining four strains. Other factors, such as riboflavin, vitamin B_6, adenine, inositol, and glutamine, did not substitute for the required factors and, when supplied along with those needed for growth, did not accelerate cell multiplication. Diphosphothiamin (cocarboxylase) and diphosphopyridine nucleotide (coenzyme I) were of no greater value than thiamin and nicotinamide, respectively. Although a biotin concentrate was required by some cultures, it produced no marked stimulation of several other cultures which were able to develop without it. Growth of some, but not all, strains was facilitated by thioglycolic acid. On the assumption that the effect of the thioglycolic acid was due to lowering of the oxidation-reduction potential, it was concluded that different strains varied in their potential requirements. Of considerable interest and importance was the fact that the presence of certain concentrations of salt in the basal medium proved to be important, the optimum amount of NaCl being from 0.6 to 1.0 per cent. With decreasing amounts of NaCl in the complete medium, progressively slower growth occurred until with 0.1 per cent or less most cultures failed to grow. The effect of NaCl was apparently to provide the proper osmotic relationship, since other salts could be substituted for sodium chloride. These results have since been confirmed and extended by McCullough and Dick (1942, 1943).

The nutritional requirements of the plague bacillus (*Pasteurella pestis*) have been studied in some detail by Rao (1939 to 1940). Several strains of this species grew very well in the following amino acid medium:

dl-Proline	140 mg.	*dl*-Leucine	180 mg.
dl-Phenylalanine	214 mg.	*dl*-Methionine	150 mg.
l-Cystine	80 mg.	*dl*-Valine	130 mg.
dl-Alanine	120 mg.	Bacterial ash	
d-Glutamic acid	100 mg.	equivalent to	50 mg.
Glycine	100 mg.		of bacteria
l-Tyrosine	128 mg.	0.033 *M* Phosphate	
dl-Serine	140 mg.	buffer at *p*H 7.4	50 ml.
dl-Isoleucine	130 mg.	H_2O to	1,000 ml.

The amino acids proline, phenylalanine, and cystine were found to be indispensable; although glycine and several other amino acids were not essential, they were stimulatory. It was also observed that the plague bacillus oxidized carbohydrates more easily than it did organic acids or amino acids. Those substances which underwent pronounced oxidation fell into the following series of relative oxidation rates:

Carbohydrates: mannose > glucose > fructose > galactose > hexose diphosphate > maltose > mannitol > arabinose > lactose > rhamnose > xylose > sucrose > dulcitol.

Organic acids. lactate > pyruvate > acetate > formate > malate > succinate > citrate > tartrate.

Amino acids: serine > alanine > proline > cystine > glutamate > glycine > phenylalanine > tyrosine > methionine.

From these results it was concluded that the best energy and carbon sources with which to fortify media are glucose and lactate. The effect of hematin, cozymase (diphosphopyridine nucleotide), thiamin, nicotinic acid, alloxazine-adenine dinucleotide, and β-alanine on the growth and metabolism of *Pasteurella pestis* was also studied. Hematin (20 μg./ml.) was found to be highly active in reducing the lag in the growth of the bacillus in the foregoing amino acid medium. Cozymase (10 μg./ml.), thiamin (10 μg./ml.), nicotinic acid (20 μg./ml.), and β-alanine (20 μg./ml.) possessed similar but less marked activity; the flavin (0.02 mg./ml.) had little or no effect. Hematin, thiamin, and nicotinic acid, when combined, had a greater effect on growth than when tested separately. Hematin, cozymase, thiamin, and nicotinic acid stimulated the respiration (O_2 uptake) of actively growing cultures of *P. pestis.* Doudoroff (1943) has also showed that cystine, phenylalanine, and proline are required by *P. pestis,* but he was unable to demonstrate any growth-stimulating effect by hematin, biotin, pantothenic acid, *p*-aminobenzoic acid, riboflavin, nicotinic acid, thiamin, or pyridoxine for the strains he used.

Berkman, Saunders, and Koser (1940) studied the growth-factor requirements of *Pasteurella avicida* and *Pasteurella boviseptica* in a chemically defined medium consisting of several amino acids, glucose, and salts. Thirteen of the seventeen strains that they used grew well in the basal medium, providing nicotinamide (0.1 μg./ml.) and pantothenic acid (0.1 μg./ml.) were present. None of the growth factors alone was effective, and pantothenic acid could not be replaced by β-alanine. The other four cultures produced a scantier, though still distinct, growth in the basal medium containing nicotinamide and pantothenic acid; but, when the so-called butyl factor (probably biotin) was added, prompt and vigorous growth of three of the four cultures resulted. Other substances, such as riboflavin, vitamin B_6, inositol, and glutamine, apparently had no effect on the growth of these organisms.

The cultivation of *Pasteurella tularensis* in simplified media was reported by Tamura and Gibby (1943) and Steinhaus, Parker, and McKee (1944). Tamura and Gibby, for example, obtained slight growth in a basal medium containing cystine and thirteen other amino acids, glucose, inorganic salts, pantothenate, pimelic acid, nicotinic acid, and liver concentrate. The nature of the growth factors in the liver concentrate was not determined, but the concentrate could not be replaced by various combinations of known substances, such as biotin, adenine, guanine, and uracil.

***Acetobacter* Species (*Acetobacter suboxydans*).** It was mentioned earlier in this chapter that only a few acetic acid bacteria (*Acetobacter aceti*) will grow on simple substrates without the addition of yeast extract or other similar substances. The nature of the compounds in yeast extract required by *A. suboxydans* has been determined by Lampen, Underkofler, and Peterson (1942), Underkofler, Bantz, and Peterson (1943), and Landy and Streightoff (1943). In addition to a suitable carbon source, organic nitrogen, and mineral salts the medium must contain pantothenic acid, *p*-aminobenzoic acid, and nicotinic acid for the growth of this species. Certain purine bases also favor development.

***Lactobacillus* and *Propionibacterium* Species (Lactic and Propionic Acid Bacteria).** The true lactic and propionic acid bacteria are quite fastidious in their growth requirements; in fact, they grow very poorly, if at all, on common laboratory media unless milk, yeast extracts, or other tissue extracts are added. The early work on the nutrition of these organisms is adequately covered in several of the reviews mentioned earlier in the chapter.

In the past few years a great many studies have been published on the nutrition of the various species of lactic acid bacteria [see Wood, Anderson, and Werkman (1937), Snell, Tatum, and Peterson (1937), Snell, Strong, and Peterson (1937, 1939), Möller (1938, 1939, 1940), Snell and Strong (1939), Wood, Geiger, and Werkman (1940), Snell and Peterson (1940), Pennington, Snell, and Williams (1940), Snell and Mitchell (1941), Stokstad (1941, 1943), Hutchings, Bohonos, and Peterson (1941), Mitchell, Snell, and Williams (1941), Clarke, Lechycka, and Light (1942), Feeney and Strong (1942), Pollack and Lindner (1942), Hutchings and Peterson (1942), Landy and Dicken (1942), Hill and Kniesner (1942), Keresztesy, Rickes, and Stokes (1943), Snell and Guirard (1943), Shankman (1943), Hutchings, Stokstad, Bohonos, and Slobodkin (1944), Hegsted (1944)]. As a result of these studies our information has increased to such an extent that several lactic acid bacteria, such as *Lactobacillus arabinosus*, *Lactobacillus casei*, and *Lactobacillus delbrückii*, can now be cultivated on media of essentially known composition. The medium (*p*H 6.7 to 6.8) employed by Pollack and Lindner (1942) may be cited as an example of a substrate which supports the growth of lactic acid bacteria:

Glucose	20	g.
Sodium acetate	12	g.
Glycine, *dl*-alanine, *l*-leucine, *dl*-isoleucine, *l*-aspartic acid, *dl*-valine, *l*-histidine, *l*-tryptophan, *l*-proline, *l*-hydroxyproline, *dl*-serine, *dl*-threonine, *l*-tyrosine, *l*-cystine, *dl*-methionine, *dl*-β-phenylalanine, *l*-lysine, *l*-arginine, *l*-asparagine, each	10	mg.
Adenine, guanine, uracil, thymine, and xanthine, each	10	mg.
Thiamin, vitamin B_6, calcium pantothenate, riboflavin, and nicotinic acid, each	200	μg.
Inositol	5	mg.
Biotin	0.4	μg.
Folic acid concentrate	5	μg.
Glutamine	0.6	μg.
K_2HPO_4	1	g.
KH_2PO_4	1	g.
$MgSO_4 \cdot 7H_2O$	0.4	g.
NaCl, $FeSO_4 \cdot 7H_2O$, $MnSO_4 \cdot H_2O$, each	0.02	g.
H_2O to	1,000	ml.

Although this medium of Pollack and Lindner will support the growth of many species of lactic acid bacteria, additional factors seem to be required for the optimum growth of some strains. For example, Stokstad (1941) has described an active substance, probably a nucleotide, which stimulates the growth of certain lactobacilli; Hutchings, Bohonos, and Peterson (1941), Pfiffner *et al.* (1943), Stokstad (1943), Keresztesy *et al.* (1943), Chattaway *et al.* (1943), and Hutchings, Stokstad, Bohonos, and Slobodkin (1944) have prepared active factors from liver or yeast; Clarke *et al.* (1942) have demonstrated a substance in rice polishings; and Feeney and Strong (1942) have observed another factor in blood.

The nutritional requirements of the propionic acid bacteria (genus *Propionibacterium*) are variable and have not been investigated so thoroughly as those of the lactic acid bacteria [Tatum, Peterson, and Fred (1936), Tatum, Wood, and Peterson (1936), Wood, Tatum, and Peterson (1937), Wood, Andersen, and Werkman (1938), and Thompson (1943)]. The propionic acid bacteria are able to utilize ammonium salts as a source of nitrogen and in general are less fastidious in their requirements than the lactic acid bacteria. The medium (*p*H 7.0) employed by Wood, Andersen, and Werkman (1938) may be cited to illustrate the basal requirements of these organisms; it contained the following ingredients:

Glucose	10	g.
Sodium acetate	6	g.
$(NH_4)_2SO_4$	3	g.
Speakman's salts in $\frac{1}{2}$ concentration		
Ether extract of 30 g. of Difco yeast extract (amino acid-free)		
Vitamin B_1	0.01	mg.
Riboflavin	1.0	mg.
H_2O (distilled) to	1,000	ml.

A mixture of seventeen amino acids was found to be beneficial but not essential to the propionic acid bacteria; certain cultures grew with difficulty in their absence, but others thrived. Riboflavin stimulated growth in the ammonium sulfate medium but could be dispensed with by most strains. Vitamin B_1 was found to be an effective stimulant, although some cultures could be trained to grow vigorously without it. The ether extract of yeast extract was essential for all cultures. It could not be replaced by a mixture of nicotinic acid, vitamin B_1, riboflavin, pimelic acid, uracil, β-alanine, and pantothenic acid. More recently Thompson (1943) has studied the vitamin requirements of the propionic acid bacteria. He concluded that yeast extract owes part of its growth-promoting activity to its pantothenic acid and biotin content. With certain species, however, other unknown factors in yeast extract appear to be required. Thiamin and *p*-aminobenzoic acid also seemed to be necessary for the continued growth of some strains.

***Clostridium* Species.** The chemical nature of the substances concerned in the nutrition of the anerobic spore-formers has received less attention from the bacteriologist than have those required for aerobic bacteria. Nevertheless, considerable information is available on the subject, and the work on a few representative species will be discussed briefly. For additional information the references at the end of the chapter and the general reviews mentioned earlier should be consulted.

Clostridium sporogenes was probably the first anaerobic spore-former, except for the nitrogen-fixing bacterium *Clostridium pasteurianum*, whose nutritional requirements were systematically studied. In a series of papers from the Department of Bacterial Chemistry at Middlesex Hospital in London it was shown that *Cl. sporogenes* and certain other obligate anaerobes can be grown in media containing salts, a source of carbon, and known amino acids only when an unknown ether-soluble acid, which has been called the sporogenes vitamin, is present [Knight and Fildes (1933), Fildes (1935), Fildes and Richardson (1935), Pappenheimer (1935)]. The exact composition of the medium that was adequate for the growth of *Cl. sporogenes* was as follows:

s *-Alanine	0.12	g.
s-Valine	0.15	g.
s-Leucine	0.17	g.
s-Glycine	0.20	g.
l-Proline	0.15	g.
s-Aspartic acid	0.18	g.
s-Serine	0.14	g.
s-Methionine	0.07	g.
l-Cystine	0.06	g.
s-Phenylalanine	0.08	g.
l-Tyrosine	0.05	g.
l-Histidine	0.05	g.
s-Lysine·2HCl	0.09	g.
d-Arginine·HCl	0.05	g.
l-Tryptophan	0.02	g.
$MgSO_4 \cdot 7H_2O$ (4% solution)	10	ml.
Ash solution †	10	ml.
Thioglycolic acid (1% solution in *N* HCl)	20	ml.
Sporogenes vitamin ‡	10	ml.
NaOH solution to *p*H 7.6		
H_2O to	1,000	ml.

* The prefix s- denotes a synthetic substance.

† A neutralized HCl extract of incinerated hay, diluted equivalent to 1 kg. hay per 10 liters of H_2O.

‡ A nitrogen- and sulfur-free preparation from mare's urine.

The chemical properties of the sporogenes vitamin were studied in some detail by Pappenheimer (1935), but he was unable to obtain the substance in crystalline form. Starting with 10 liters of mare's urine concentrate (concentrated from 1,300 liters), he separated and partially purified the sporogenes vitamin. The total yield of the substance in the form of redistilled esters from these 10 liters of mare's urine concentrate was about 7.0 g., of which 0.001 to 0.005 μg. was sufficient to activate 1 ml. of gelatin hydrolysate medium so that *Cl. sporogenes* would grow; in the foregoing amino acid medium 0.04 μg./ml. was sufficient. The methyl ester failed to crystallize even when kept at the temperature of solid CO_2 for two days. It was very soluble in ether, alcohol, and benzene but only slightly soluble in water. Repeated analyses of different preparations of the methyl ester showed a constant elementary composition suggesting a formula of $C_{11}H_{14}O_4$ or $C_{11}H_{16}O_4$. Later Peterson, McDaniel, and McCoy (1940) and Lampen and Peterson (1943) observed that the addition of biotin (0.00001 μg. /ml.) to a synthetic medium (glucose, asparagine, and salts) produced good growth of *Cl. sporogenes.* These results indicate that at least one constituent of the so-called sporogenes vitamin is biotin.

Clostridium acetobutylicum is another anaerobic, spore-forming bacillus whose nutrition has been studied in some detail by several workers. In 1938 Brown, Wood, and Werkman showed that an acidic ether-soluble extract of Difco yeast extract was essential for vigorous growth of this organism in a medium of known chemical constitution. Later McDaniel, Woolley, and Peterson (1939) partially purified the ether-soluble factor, and Brown and his associates (1939) showed that the known growth factors, thiamin, riboflavin, nicotinic acid, pimelic acid, pantothenic acid, β-alanine, and uracil, did not stimulate growth in simplified media. Weizmann and Rosenfeld (1939) found that, in order to bring the nutritive level of a synthetic medium up to 70 per cent of that represented by Maize mash, both asparagine and biotin had to be present; the remaining 30 per cent of the full requirements could be supplied by a third factor, which was found to be present in the first dialyzates of autolyzed yeast. Subsequently Oxford, Lampen, and Peterson (1940) studied the nutritional requirements of *Cl. acetobutylicum* in a medium of known constitution [12] and observed that two factors were required for development, that is, biotin and another

[12] Basal medium employed by Oxford, Lampen, and Peterson (1940): glucose, 2 per cent; asparagine, 0.1 per cent; $(NH_4)_2SO_4$, 0.1 per cent; Speakman's salt mixture (KH_2PO_4, K_2HPO_4, Mg, Mn, and ferrous sulfates); reduced iron at the bottom of each tube. The medium used by Rubbo and his associates (1941) differed only in that it contained NaCl and no $(NH_4)_2SO_4$ or reduced iron.

factor. This other factor, the so-called BY-factor, was not identical with any known growth factor for microorganisms but was present in yeast extract and had the properties of a weak acid whose activity was destroyed by nitrous acid. Soon afterward Rubbo and his coworkers (1940, 1941) isolated *p*-aminobenzoic acid from brewers' yeast and found that the naturally occurring acid, a synthetic sample of the same acid, and several structurally related compounds were able to stimulate the growth of the bacterium in a medium of known chemical constitution;[13] but biotin was not found to be essential. They reconciled their findings with those of other workers by tentatively assuming that Weizmann's biotin preparation and the BY-factor are crude extracts containing a trace of *p*-aminobenzoic acid. Since *p*-aminobenzoic acid stimulates growth in concentrations as low as 1.46×10^{-10} M, this reconciliation seems well founded.

Rubbo and his associates (1941) then extended their study to a comparison of the yields of solvents formed in the synthetic medium with those obtained in wheat mash containing the same amount of fermentable carbohydrate and incubated under the same environment. Their results show that in a chemically defined medium containing *p*-aminobenzoic acid normal yields of butyl alcohol are formed, but the production of acetone is suppressed, even after prolonged fermentation. A full explanation of this interesting but atypical form of fermentation cannot be given at present, but certain observations by Rubbo and his coworkers offer a partial explanation. It appears that the fermentation of glucose under these conditions is diverted through the absence in the medium of a second factor, termed an acetone factor, which is primarily concerned with the formation of acetic acid from acetaldehyde and secondarily with its conversion to acetone by way of acetoacetic acid. This contention is partially substantiated by the following facts:

1. The acetone factor can be isolated from yeast, cereals, and potatoes, and, when it is added to a chemically defined medium containing *p*-amino-benzoic acid, normal fermentation is restored.
2. The acetone factor alone does not support growth; it is heat stable, is precipitated by phosphotungstic acid, and is probably a coenzyme related to the nitrogenous bases.
3. The addition of sodium acetate to the synthetic medium does not yield acetone.

[13] Basal medium employed by Oxford, Lampen, and Peterson (1940): glucose, 2 per cent; asparagine, 0.1 per cent; $(NH_4)_2SO_4$, 0.1 per cent; Speakman's salt mixture (KH_2PO_4, K_2HPO_4, Mg, Mn, and ferrous sulfates); reduced iron at the bottom of each tube. The medium used by Rubbo and his associates (1941) differed only in that it contained NaCl and no $(NH_4)_2SO_4$ or reduced iron.

4. The titratable acidity in synthetic media is abnormally low but is raised in the presence of the acetone factor.

In view of these findings Rubbo and his associates concluded that two factors are required for normal fermentation of glucose by *Cl. acetobutylicum:* (1) *p*-aminobenzoic acid, which acts as a growth stimulant, and (2) the acetone factor, which is essential for the production of acetone.

Lampen and Peterson (1941, 1943) confirmed the work of Rubbo and his associates concerning the essential nature of *p*-aminobenzoic acid for *Cl. acetobutylicum*, but they insisted that biotin is also required. They believed that the natural constituents of Rubbo and his associates' medium may have contained traces of biotin, and for this reason they were not able to rule it out as an essential factor. Lampen and Peterson also showed that *p*-aminobenzoic acid would replace the yeast factor described by Oxford, Lampen, and Peterson. Davies and Stephenson (1941) also studied the nutritional factors necessary for *Cl. acetobutylicum* to produce acetone and other solvents in simplified media.

Clostridium butylicum is an organism closely related to *Cl. acetobutylicum*, but it differs in certain cultural and physiological characteristics. The ability of the organism to ferment glucose and other substrates (see Chapter 10) has been studied in some detail by several workers. Also the nutrition and growth-factor requirements of the species have been investigated by McDaniel, Woolley, and Peterson (1939), Woolley, McDaniel, and Peterson (1939), Snell and Williams (1939), and Lampen and Peterson (1943). Peterson and his associates obtained an active substance from a commercial extract of cereal grains known as Vitab, which they called the butyl factor (BY-factor). The most active preparations were detectable when 0.001 μg./ml. was added to an otherwise chemically defined substrate. Subsequently Snell and Williams found that biotin was the only essential growth factor needed by *Cl. butylicum* for development in a medium of known composition containing asparagine, glucose, and Speakman's inorganic salts. As little as 0.0000133 μg./ml. of pure biotin permitted growth, although larger amounts stimulated better development.

The growth-factor requirements of three strains of saccharolytic butyl alcohol-acetone bacteria have also been studied by Reyes-Teodoro and Mickelson (1944). Two of the strains require biotin (0.001 μg./ml.) for growth in a chemically defined medium, while the other requires *p*-aminobenzoic acid (0.2 μg./ml.) in addition to biotin.

Clostridium perfringens (*Clostridium welchii*) is another anaerobic spore-forming bacillus whose nutritional requirements have been studied in simplified media. Tamura, Tytell, Boyd, and Logan (1941) employed the following basal medium (pH 7.9) in their study:

$MgSO_4$	0.02 g.	Glucose	2 g.
$Na_2HPO_4 \cdot 12H_2O$	5.76 g.	Casein acid hydrolysate (0.28% total N)	1,000 ml.
KH_2PO_4	0.24 g.		
l-Tryptophan	0.1 g.		
Glucosamine	1 g.		

No growth occurred in the basal medium alone, but on addition of 0.1 per cent of mother-liquor from alcohol-precipitated liver extract good development resulted. Equally good growth was obtained by substituting pantothenic acid (2 μg./ml.) and pimelic acid (2 μg./ml.) for the liver-extract preparation. Addition of riboflavin (0.2 μg./ml.) and nicotinic acid (5 μg./ml.) was found necessary for toxin production by *Cl. perfringens.* According to Tamura, Tytell, Boyd, and Logan, toxins were consistently produced which were equal to those formed in glucose peptone meat-infusion broth or were more potent.

Clostridium botulinum strains have been cultivated in media containing only amino acids, inorganic salts, and glucose by Burrows (1933) and Ehrismann (1937); but other workers [see Fildes (1935), Knight (1936), Elberg and Meyer (1939), Clifton (1940)] have been unable to confirm these observations with other strains. Even though all workers are not in agreement on the nutritional requirements of *Cl. botulinum,* it seems safe to draw the following conclusions from their studies:

1. Many strains of *Cl. botulinum* can be grown in media containing amino acids, inorganic salts, and sugar, providing tryptophan and certain acidic fractions from yeast or urine (the so-called sporogenes vitamin) are present.

2. In general the nutritional requirements of *Cl. botulinum* resemble those of *Clostridium sporogenes* with respect to the amino acids required for growth, but there are qualitative differences in their needs. Certain amino acids can serve as a source of energy.

3. Glucose can serve as a source of energy, the chief products of fermentation being ethyl alcohol and CO_2.

4. Some strains of *Cl. botulinum* are not able to develop in simple media, having more complex requirements.

For further details on the nutrition of this organism the foregoing references and the monograph by Knight (1936) should be consulted.

Clostridium tetani is another anaerobic spore-former whose nutritional requirements have been investigated in the past few years. Although Ehrismann (1937) reported that a strain of this organism grew in an amino acid medium containing glucose, inorganic salts, and ascorbic acid, we know that most strains are more fastidious. Recently Mueller and Miller (1941, 1942) and Feeney, Mueller, and Miller (1943) studied the growth requirements of *Cl. tetani*. Their results may be summarized by the statement that the strains which they used apparently required the following materials for growth in a medium containing glucose, salts, and an acid hydrolysate of protein (casein) or a mixture of fifteen amino acids: adenine or hypoxanthine (5 μg./ml.), uracil (2.5 μg./ml.), pantothenic acid (0.25 μg./ml.), thiamin (0.01 μg./ml.), pyridoxine (1 μg./ml.), riboflavin (0.01 μg./ml.), nicotinic acid (1 μg./ml.), folic acid (0.0025 μg./ml.), biotin (0.001 μg./ml.), oleic acid (2.5 μg./ml.), and perhaps one or more additional compounds. A high grade of toxin (60,000 M.L.D./ml.) has been produced with a medium having these ingredients.

The nutritional requirements and factors affecting the production of toxin of *Clostridium septicum* have been studied by Bernheimer (1944). The basal medium employed consisted of hydrolyzed casein, glucose, inorganic salts, cystine, tryptophan, and a reducing agent, such as thioglycolic acid. The growth accessory substances required were thiamin, pyridoxine, nicotinic acid, and biotin. Glutamine was not indispensable for growth, but it shortened the lag period. Other known vitamins had no effect on growth or toxin formation by this organism. The quantity of toxin produced (400 to 700 $L.D._{50}$/ml.) in the medium was found to be as great as that usually reported in media containing more complex materials or even greater.

Clostridium thermosaccharolyticum required thiamin, biotin, and *p*-aminobenzoic acid for growth in a chemically defined medium [Clark and Mitchell (1944)]. Nicotinic acid and pantothenate also slightly increased growth.

The growth-factor requirements of several other *Clostridium* species, such as *Clostridium felsineum* and *Clostridium saccharobutyricus*, have also been studied by Lampen and Peterson (1943). Biotin was found to be essential for all the clostridia used, and *p*-aminobenzoic acid was required by certain strains.

***Neisseria intracellularis* and *Neisseria gonorrhoeae*.** Although *Neisseria intracellularis* has been thought of as fastidious in its nutritional requirements, little information has been reported concerning its growth in chemically defined media. Frantz (1942) has observed that fourteen out of fifteen strains of this species can be cultivated in a medium containing inorganic salts, glucose, *d*-glutamic acid, and *l*-cystine. Therefore this organism may actually belong to group 10 in the nutritional spectrum (Fig. 1). Until further data are available on freshly isolated strains, however, the species may be placed here provisionally.

The cultivation of *Neisseria gonorrhoeae* in various types of media has been studied rather extensively in the past few years [see Mueller, Hinton, and Miller (1942), Gould (1943), Lankford and Snell (1943), Gould, Kane, and Mueller (1944), Welton, Stokinger, and Carpenter (1944), Morton and Leberman (1944)]. To illustrate the basal requirements of most strains, the medium employed by Welton, Stokinger, and Carpenter may be mentioned. They found that many cultures would grow in a medium composed of glucose, inorganic salts, indole-3-acetic acid, and the following eight amino acids: *d*-glutamic acid, *dl*-leucine, *l*-arginine, *l*-histidine, *dl*-methionine, *l*-proline, glycine, and *l*-cystine. Some strains would not grow in this medium, and it was presumed that other factors were essential. Lankford and Snell previously showed that glutamine is required by some strains of the gonococcus. Thus, when glutamine and choline were incorporated in the foregoing medium, it was found that additional strains would grow. Gould (1943) also pointed out that glutathione is essential for the growth of certain stock strains of *N. gonorrhoeae*, although most freshly isolated cultures do not require this compound.

Mueller and his associates are of the opinion that much of the difficulty encountered in the past in the cultivation of the *Neisseria* species was due to the presence of an inhibitory substance rather than to the absence of essential nutrilites in the media. For example, they have presented evidence to show that the function of starch, which is commonly used in media for gonococci, is a protection against the inhibitory effect of certain samples of agar.

BACTERIA WHOSE REQUIREMENTS ARE COMPLEX AND NOT WELL UNDERSTOOD

The last group of organisms which will be considered consists of bacteria whose nutritional requirements are not well understood at this time. Future studies will undoubtedly provide us with information concerning the vitamin requirements of these organisms; in fact, considerable progress has already been made for certain species, and these studies will be cited. Since this group contains many bacteria, especially pathogenic species, it will be possible to mention only a few representative organisms.

Probably more success has been obtained in the study of the requirements of a group of nonsporulating anaerobes than with any of the other organisms [see West, Lewis, and Militzer (1942)]; in fact, it has been observed that the addition of a mixture of known growth factors to a chemically defined medium allows the development of the majority of strains. Pyruvic acid, pantothenic acid, and riboflavin appear to be of special importance in the nutrition of these organisms in amino acid media.

The nutrition of *Listerella monocytogenes* and *Erysipelothrix rhusiopathiae* has recently been studied by Porter and Pelczar (1941) and Hutner (1942), but the studies need to be extended before any definite conclusions can be drawn. Riboflavin and possibly biotin have been definitely characterized as necessary for the growth of *L. monocytogenes* in simplified media, and oleic acid and riboflavin have been identified as essential for *Erysipelothrix*, but additional factors are needed for both bacterial species.

Organisms with even more complex requirements include such species as *Streptobacillus moniliformis* [Dienes (1939)], *Bartonella bacilliformis* [Jiménez (1940), Geiman (1941)], and many others. The spirochetes, rickettsia, and viruses may also be included provisionally in this group, in spite of the fact that most of them at the present time require living tissue for growth. However, as our information concerning vitamins, enzymes, and proteins increases, it is not unlikely that some progress will be made in determining the requirements of some of these fastidious organisms. In fact, some progress has already been made by Spizizen (1943), who studied the influence of numerous compounds on the multiplication of a coli-bacteriophage in the presence of nonproliferating bacterial cells. He found that glycine anhydride, certain phosphorylated compounds, and the 4-carbon dicarboxylic acids stimulated phage multiplication, whereas a sulfonic acid analog of glycine inhibited it.

THE GROWTH FACTORS, OR VITAMINS,[14] AND THEIR PHYSIOLOGICAL ROLE IN MICROORGANISMS

So far the discussion in this chapter has centered around the groups of bacteria which have common nutritional requirements. In this section we propose to discuss the problem from the standpoint of the individual growth factors, or vitamins. Such an approach will help in correlating some of the data discussed for groups 11 and 12 (see Fig. 1) of the bacterial nutrition spectrum. Although certain species in the other groups may be stimulated by some of these growth factors or actually require them, most of them can initiate growth in simple media without any external supply of the vitamins.

[14] For an interesting discussion of the relationship between microbial growth factors and vitamins the papers by Peterson (1941) and by Peterson and Peterson (1945) should be consulted.

HEMIN (X-FACTOR)

Hemin, which occurs in the form of characteristic microscopic, reddish-brown crystals, has been synthesized by Fischer, who ascribed to it the following formula:

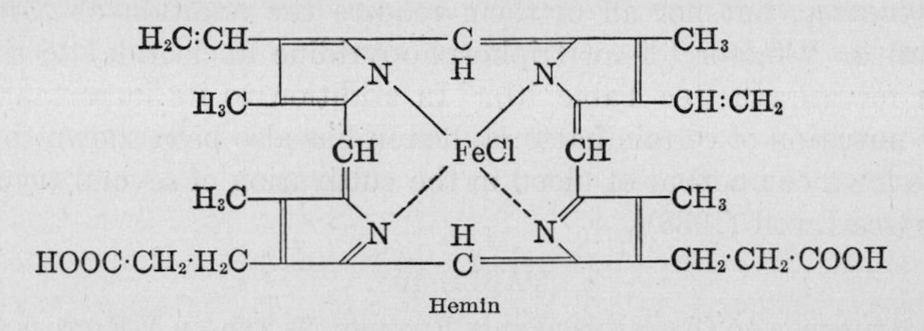

Hemin

It is not known definitely which pair of nitrogen atoms are attached to the iron atom. The system of conjugated double bonds accounts for the color of the compound. When hemin ($C_{34}H_{32}O_4N_4FeCl$) is reduced by hydrogen in the presence of a catalyst, such as colloidal palladium, it takes up to four hydrogen atoms and becomes mesohemin ($C_{34}H_{36}O_4N_4FeCl$). When treated with NaOH, hemin yields the corresponding base ($C_{34}H_{32}N_4O_4FeOH$), which is known as *heme* or *hematin*.

Hemin was probably the first of the so-called growth factors for microorganisms to be definitely identified. In fact, as early as 1917 Davis demonstrated that Pfeiffer's bacillus (*Hemophilus influenzae*) required the addition of at least two distinct substances for its growth in peptone broth: (1) a thermostable compound contained in or derived from hemoglobin, and (2) a thermolabile substance present in the tissues of various plants and animals and synthesized by many bacteria other than *H. influenzae*. In 1921 Thjötta and Avery suggested the terms *X-factor* for the growth-accessory substance contained in blood pigments and *V-factor* for the substance contained in tissue extracts; this second factor was likened to a vitamin and will be mentioned more in detail on pp. 728 to 732 on nicotinic acid and its derivatives. Since both of these factors are now known to be distinct chemical entities, that is, X-factor = hemin, and V-factor = di- or triphosphopyridine nucleotide, it is no longer necessary to refer to them merely as X- and V-factors. However, for convenience this terminology is still used generally in bacteriology.

The so-called X-factor, as we have just stated, was first demonstrated in blood pigments. It was also observed by several of the early workers that the factor was more active under aerobic conditions when supplied in the form of an iron-containing derivative of hemoglobin—methemoglobin, carboxyhemoglobin, hematin, or hemin—

than as unaltered hemoglobin. In fact, pure crystallized hemoglobin was found to be almost inactive, and hemocyanin, bilirubin, chlorophyll, and similar metalloproteins were completely inactive.

Several other species are included in the genus *Hemophilus* besides *H. influenzae*, but not all of them require the addition of X-factor (hemin) or V-factor (di- or triphosphopyridine nucleotide) to simple media for growth (see Table 10). In addition to its important role in the nutrition of certain bacteria, hemin has also been shown to substitute for a component of blood in the cultivation of several trypanosomes [see Lwoff (1938)].

TABLE 10

THE HEMOTROPHIC ORGANISMS WHICH REQUIRE X- AND/OR V-FACTORS FOR GROWTH IN SIMPLE MEDIA

[From Rivers (1922), Fildes (1923), Lwoff (1938), and Jiménez (1940)]

Organisms	Growth in Peptone Broth Containing			
	No factors	X-Factor	V-Factor	X-Factor + V-Factor
Hemophilus influenzae	−	−	−	+
Hemophilus suis	−	−	−	+
Hemophilus conjunctivitidis (Koch-Weeks bacillus)	−	−	−	+
Hemophilus parainfluenzae	−	−	+	+
Hemophilus canis	−	+	−	+
Hemophilus ducreyi	−	+	−	+
Hemophilus pertussis	+	+	+	+
Bartonella bacilliformis *	−	+	−	+
Several trypanosomes *	−	+	−	+

* The medium used by Lwoff (1938) and Jiménez (1940) to cultivate these organisms was more complex than peptone broth.

Since hemin is active for the *Hemophilus* species in very small amounts (about 0.001 μg./ml. of medium) an obvious suggestion is that it functions as a respiratory catalyst. Early observations [Olsen (1920), Fildes (1921)] suggested that its growth-promoting property was correlated with peroxidase activity, but more recent studies have not entirely supported this view, because certain compounds have been shown to possess peroxidase activity without promoting the growth of *H. influenzae*, and some have been shown to function as X-factor but to be devoid of peroxidase activity. Many of the iron compounds that promote the growth of *H. influenzae*, however, show catalase activity, and Bass, Berkman, Saunders, and Koser (1941) have even observed that highly purified catalase preparations will replace hemin, as well as V-factor compounds, in the growth of certain *Hemophilus* strains.

Heme (20 μg./ml.) accelerates the growth of *Pasteurella pestis* in an amino acid medium containing all the essentials for growth [Rao (1940)], and the same substance is an essential growth factor for *Bartonella bacilliformis* [Jiménez (1940)].

Lwoff (1936) studied the function of hemin in the metabolism of certain protozoa and *Hemophilus* species and came to the conclusion that the substance is used for the synthesis of the prosthetic groups of several components of the catalytic system of Warburg and Keilin, for example, the cytochromes and cytochrome oxidase. In this connection it is also of interest to mention a study concerned with the anaerobic growth of *Hemophilus* species. Such species are usually regarded as aerobic, but Anderson (1931) and others have recorded the anaerobic growth of certain strains. Moreover, under these conditions the organisms grow in the absence of X-factor. This phenomenon clearly suggests the possibility that under aerobic conditions the hemin functions as part of a protective catalyst to shield the growing organisms from the injurious action of peroxide. Therefore we can say in conclusion that hemin is required as a growth factor for certain microorganisms under aerobic conditions and that it probably functions by being synthesized into several enzymes (catalase, peroxidase, cytochrome oxidase) or carrier substances (cytochromes).

THIAMIN (VITAMIN B_1 OR ANEURIN)

Thiamin (also called vitamin B_1, aneurin, or the antiberiberi vitamin), which is widely distributed in nature, is a definite and specific organic compound of known structure. The thiamin (thiamin chloride) which is available on the market is termed 2-methyl-5-(4-methyl-5-β-hydroxyethyl thiazonium chloride) methyl-6-aminopyrimidine hydrochloride; it has the following structure:

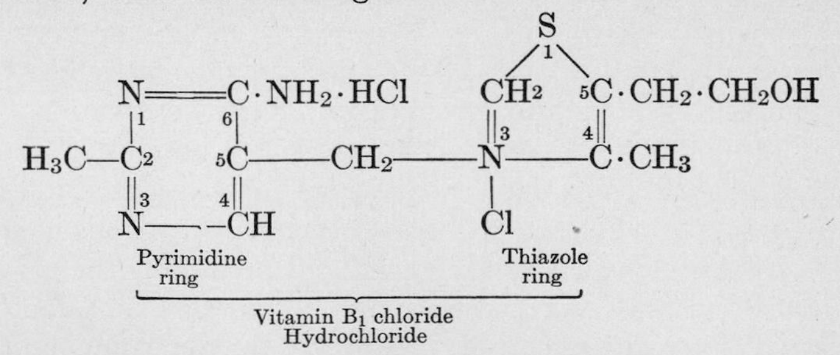

Vitamin B_1 chloride Hydrochloride

Thiamin is soluble in water (1 g. in 1 ml.) and alcohols (1 g. in 100 ml. of 95 per cent alcohol or 18 ml. of glycerol) but is insoluble in ether, acetone, chloroform, and benzene. In the dry form the vitamin is stable to heat, but in solution prolonged heat above 100°C. should be avoided. Although it is not sensitive to atmospheric oxidation, it can be easily oxidized or reduced by certain chemicals and is believed to undergo reversible oxidation and reduction in some biological reactions.

TABLE 11

Several Organisms Which Require or Are Stimulated by Thiamin (Vitamin B_1) or Its Products (Pyrimidine and/or Thiazole Components or Cocarboxylase) in Simple Media

Organism	Quantity Used per Milliliter of Medium	Reference *
Staphylococcus aureus	4×10^{-10}–10^{-7} *M*	Knight (1937)
	3 or 4×10^{-9} *M*	Hills (1938)
	10^{-7} *M*	Knight and McIlwain (1938)
Staphylococcus albus	0.8–4 μg.	Koser, Finkle, Dorfman, Gordon, and Saunders (1938), Vilter and Spies (1940)
Sarcina flava	0.05 μg.	Sartory, Sartory, and Meyer (1938)
Hemolytic streptococci of groups A, B, C, etc.	0.001–1 μg.	Pappenheimer and Hottle (1940); (*see discussion*)
Streptococcus salivarius	0.001–0.1 μg.	Niven and Smiley (1943)
Streptococcus lactis	0.1 μg.	Niven (1944)
Rhizobium trifolii and other soil bacteria		Nilsson, Bjälfve, and Burström (1938)
	0.006 μg.	Bjälfve, Nilsson, and Burström (1938)
	0.1 μg.	West and Wilson (1939), West and Lochhead (1940)
Salmonella gallinarum	1 mg.	Johnson and Rettger (1943)
Brucella species	25 μg.	Kerby (1939)
	0.2–0.5 μg.	Koser, Breslove, and Dorfman (1941)
	0.2 μg.	McCullough and Dick (1943)
Pasteurella pestis	10 μg.	Rao (1940)
Propionic acid bacteria	0.005–0.05 μg.	Tatum, Wood, and Peterson (1936)
	0.01 μg.	Wood, Andersen, and Werkman (1938)
	0.25 μg.	Silverman and Werkman (1938)
	10^{-7} *M*	Quastel and Webley (1939, 1941)
	0.1 μg.	Thompson (1943)
Lactic acid bacteria of the genera *Lactobacillus* and *Leuconostoc*	0.0005–0.2 μg.	Wood, Anderson, and Werkman (1937)
		Wood, Geiger, and Werkman (1940)
		Pollack and Lindner (1942)
		Gaines and Stahly (1943)
Acetic acid bacteria	0.5 μg.	Paleĭ (1938)
Clostridium tetani	0.01 μg.	Mueller and Miller (1942)
Clostridium thermosaccharolyticum	0.1 μg.	Clark and Mitchell (1944)
Clostridium septicum	1 μg.	Bernheimer (1944)
Phytomonas tumefaciens	0.2 μg.	McIntire, Riker, and Peterson (1941)
Mycobacterium tuberculosis	0.875–3.5 mg.	Leitner (1937)
Mycobacterium leprae	100–1,000 mg.	Loving (1943)
Leptospira canicola	1–3 μg.	Rosenfeld and Greene (1941)
Porphyrin formation by several common bacteria	20 μg.	Mallinckrodt-Haupt (1938)
Certain strains of *Saccharomyces cerevisiae*	0.01–5 μg.	Williams and Roehm (1930), Kögl and Fries (1937), Schultz, Atkin, and Frey (1937), Williams, Eakin, and Snell (1940), Williams (1941), Schopfer (1943), Burkholder and Moyer (1943), Rogosa (1944)
Torula utilis	10–15 μg.	Odintsova (1940)
Torula cremoris	0.2 μg.	Koser and Wright (1943)
Certain molds and related filamentous fungi (136 species)	0.0004–0.25 μg.	Schopfer (1938, 1943), Robbins (1938, 1939), Robbins and Kavanagh (1941, 1942), Fries (1943)
Algae (14 species)	0.1–1 mg.	VanOverbeek (1940), Ondratschek (1940), Schopfer (1943)
Protozoa and other invertebrates	0.001–0.8 μg.	Lwoff (1938), Trager (1941), Dewey (1941)

* For other studies in which thiamin has been used these references and those cited in the review articles mentioned at the beginning of the chapter should be consulted.

Microorganisms can be allocated to four groups on the basis of their thiamin requirements in simple media:

1. Those which can synthesize all they need;
2. Those which must be supplied with the vitamin or its components;

3. Those which are stimulated by an external supply but can synthesize enough to initiate growth;

4. Those which are inhibited by the presence of the vitamin in the medium.

Among those microorganisms which can synthesize the vitamin from the more elementary constituents of a medium are such species as *Bacillus subtilis*, *Escherichia coli*, *Pseudomonas aeruginosa*, *Absidia repens*, and *Aspergillus niger*. Several organisms which require an external supply of thiamin or are stimulated by its presence in simple media are listed in Table 11. These organisms differ considerably in their synthetic power. For example, some are able to construct the pyrimidine but not the thiazole portion of the molecule; these must be furnished with thiamin thiazole. Very few organisms of this kind are known; certain molds of the genus *Mucor* are examples. Other organisms can make the thiazole but not the pyrimidine portion of the molecule; these are more common. Still others are unable to construct either the thiazole or pyrimidine component of thiamin but can combine the two into the complete molecule. Other microorganisms require the intact molecule.

Some species of molds of the genus *Rhizopus* may be cited as examples of the group which is inhibited by thiamin. These organisms require no external supply of the vitamin, and their growth is partially retarded by adding it to the medium. To demonstrate this inhibition, however, certain factors, such as temperature and age of culture, have to be controlled [Robbins (1939), Schopfer (1943)].

The vitamin action of thiamin seems to be associated with the specific structure of the molecule. The different vitamin salts, such as the hydrochloride, hydrobromide, and sulfate, and the pyrophosphoric acid ester, cocarboxylase, all have about the same corresponding activity. Structural alterations, however, cause a decrease or disappearance of this activity. For example, thiochrome, an oxidation product of thiamin in which the nitrogen atom of the 6-amino group of the pyrimidine is linked to the 2-carbon atom of the thiazole ring, can substitute only very imperfectly or not at all for thiamin in the growth of *Staphylococcus aureus* [Knight (1937)] and *Phycomyces* and *Rhodotorula* [Schopfer (1938)]. Several substitution products of both the pyrimidine and the thiazole components of the thiamin molecule have also been tested (see Tables 12, 13, 14, and 15). In so far as the pyrimidine ring is concerned, the groups attached to the ring which appear essential for activity are a methyl group at position 2, an amino group at position 4 or 6, and a methyl group substituted in certain ways at position 5. Substitutions in the thiazole component have

TABLE 12

THE INFLUENCE OF SUBSTITUTIONS IN POSITION 5 ON THE ACTIVITY OF 2-METHYL-4 OR 6-AMINO-5-AMINOMETHYLPYRIMIDINE FOR BACTERIA, PROTOZOA, AND MOLDS

Substitution in Position 5	*Staphylococcus aureus* [1]	Protozoa (*Leucophytes*) [2]	Molds (*Phycomyces*) [3]
Amino ethyl	+	+	+
Hydroxymethyl	+	+	
Bromomethyl			+
Ethyoxymethyl			+
Thioformylaminomethyl	+	+	±
Methyl	−	−	±
Acetamide	−	−	±
Hydrogen			−

+ = growth; − = no growth; ± = questionable growth.

[1] Knight (1937), Knight and McIlwain (1938).

[2] Lwoff and Dusi (1938).

[3] Schopfer (1938), Robbins and Kavanagh (1938, 1942).

TABLE 13

THE INFLUENCE OF VARIOUS SUBSTITUTED PYRIMIDINES ON THE GROWTH OF BACTERIA, PROTOZOA, AND MOLDS

Position of Groups in the Pyrimidine Ring	*Staphylococcus aureus* [1]	Protozoa (*Leucophytes*) [2]	Molds (*Phycomyces*) [3]
2-Methyl-4-hydroxy-5-methyl	−	−	±
2-Methyl-4-hydroxy-5-amino-6-methyl	−	−	
2-Methyl-4-hydroxy-6-amino	−	−	±
2-Methyl-4-mercapto	−		±
2-Hydroxy-4-amino-(cytosine)	−	−	
2,5-Dimethyl-4-amino	−		
2,6-Dimethyl-4-hydroxy-5-amino	−		
2-Methyl-4-hydroxy-5-hydroxymethyl	−		−
2,4-Dihydroxy-(uracil)			−
2,4-Dichloro-5-chloromethyl-6-methyl			−
2,4-Dihydroxy-5-hydroxymethyl-6-methyl			−
2,6-Dichloro-4-methyl-5-chloromethyl			−
2,6-dimethyl-4-amino			−
2,4,6-Trimethyl			−
5-Hydroxymethyl-6-methyl uracil			−
2-Thio-6-methyl uracil			−

+ = growth; − = no growth; ± = questionable growth.

[1] Knight (1937), Knight and McIlwain (1938).

[2] Lwoff and Dusi (1938).

[3] Schopfer (1938), Robbins and Kavanagh (1938, 1942), Bonner and Erickson (1938).

TABLE 14

THE INFLUENCE OF VARIOUS SUBSTITUTIONS IN POSITIONS 2 AND 5 ON THE ACTIVITY OF 4-METHYL THIAZOLE FOR BACTERIA, PROTOZOA, AND MOLDS

Substitution in		*Staphylococcus aureus* [1]	Protozoa (*Leucophytes*) [2]	Molds (*Phycomyces*) [3]
Position 2	*Position 5*			
Hydrogen: H	β-hydroxyethyl: CH_2CH_2OH	+	+	+
Methyl: CH_3	β-hydroxyethyl: CH_2CH_2OH	−	+	−
Hydroxy: OH	Acetoxyethyl: $CH_2CH_2O \cdot CO \cdot CH_3$	−	−	
Amine: NH_2	β-hydroxyethyl: CH_2CH_2OH	−	−	

+ = growth; − = no growth; ± = questionable growth.

[1] Knight (1937), Knight and McIlwain (1938).

[2] Lwoff and Dusi (1938).

[3] Schopfer (1938), Robbins and Kavanagh (1938, 1941, 1942), Bonner and Erickson (1938).

TABLE 15

THE INFLUENCE OF VARIOUS SUBSTITUTIONS IN POSITION 5 ON THE ACTIVITY OF 4-METHYL-5-β-HYDROXYETHYL THIAZOLE FOR BACTERIA, PROTOZOA, AND MOLDS

Substitution in Position 5	*Staphylococcus aureus* [1]	Protozoa (*Leucophytes*) [2]	Molds (*Phycomyces*) [3]
Hydrogen: H	−	−	−
Methyl: CH_3	−	−	−
Ethyl: CH_2CH_3	−	−	−
α-Hydroxyethyl: $CHOHCH_3$	−	−	−
β-Hydroxyethyl: CH_2CH_2OH	+	+	+
β-Aminoethyl (picrate): $CH_2CH_2NH_2$ (picrate)	−	+	±
β-Chloroethyl (picrate): CH_2CH_2Cl (picrate)			+
β-Ethoxyethyl (picrate): $CH_2CH_2OC_2H_5$ (picrate)			±
β-Carbethoxyethyl: $CH_2CH_2O \cdot COO \cdot C_2H_5$			−
Acetoxyethyl: $CH_2CH_2O \cdot CO \cdot CH_3$	+	+	+
β-Hydroxypropyl: $CH_2CHOHCH_3$	+	+	+
γ-Hydroxypropyl: $CH_2CH_2CH_2OH$	+	+	+
β-Aminopropionic acid: CH_2CHNH_2COOH	−	+	±
Vinyl: $CH{=}CH_2$	+	+	±
Acetamide: CH_2CONH_2			−

+ = growth; − = no growth; ± = questionable growth.

[1] Knight (1937), Knight and McIlwain (1938).

[2] Lwoff and Dusi (1938).

[3] Schopfer (1938, 1943), Robbins and Kavanagh (1938, 1941, 1942), Bonner and Erickson (1938).

demonstrated a similar high degree of specificity. In fact, the data in Tables 14 and 15 show that even a slight alteration of 4-methyl-5-hydroxyethyl thiazole makes the compound inactive or greatly reduces its activity. Many other substitutions of the thiazole- and sulfur-containing compounds have been tested for their ability to replace the thiamin thiazole [see Robbins and Kavanagh (1942)], but, since they are ineffective, they will not be mentioned.

It should be mentioned also that Woolley and White (1943) have found that many microbial species are inhibited by pyrithiamin, 1-[(4-amino-2-methyl)-5-pyrimidylmethyl]-2-methyl-3-(β-hydroxyethyl) pyridinium bromide. The more exacting a given species is in its requirements for thiamin, the more susceptible it is to the action of pyrithiamin. In all instances the inhibition of growth by these substances is overcome by adding thiamin to the medium. It is also of interest that Sarett and Cheldelin (1944) found pyrithiamin to be more inhibitory to the utilization of diphosphothiamin (cocarboxylase) than of thiamin in the growth of *Lactobacillus fermentum.*

Although required in small amounts for growth, thiamin is not to be regarded merely as a stimulant for this activity. It plays a definite and significant role in the metabolism of carbohydrates by organisms and may also take part in other metabolic processes. In the discussion of coenzymes in Chapter 6 we mentioned that thiamin combines with phosphoric acid to form thiamin pyrophosphate or cocarboxylase, which in association with a specific protein is concerned in the decarboxylation and oxidation of pyruvic acid, an important intermediate in the metabolism of glucose. Also, there is some evidence that thiamin (or cocarboxylase) is oxidized to thiochrome and that this thiochrome is ineffective or is much less effective than thiamin or cocarboxylase, probably because the change of thiamin to thiochrome is not readily reversible. It appears, therefore, that at least one of the functions of thiamin is to serve as a precursor of a part of an enzyme system involved in respiration and that it is eventually rendered inactive, possibly by its oxidation to thiochrome or by some other reaction.

RIBOFLAVIN (VITAMIN B_2 OR G)

Riboflavin, also called vitamin B_2 or G and lactoflavin, is widely distributed in nature; in fact, every plant and animal cell seems to contain some. The compound belongs to a subdivision, called flavins, of a class of colored, water-soluble, naturally occurring substances known as lyochromes. The members of the subdivision are usually named according to their source, for example, lactoflavin from milk, ovoflavin from eggs, and uroflavin from urine. With few exceptions, however, all the naturally occurring flavins appear to be identical with riboflavin. Riboflavin can be prepared commercially from natural sources, such as whey or yeast, or as a by-product of butyl alcohol fermentation, or it can be synthesized from *o*-xylene, *d*-ribose, and alloxan. The compound has the following formula:

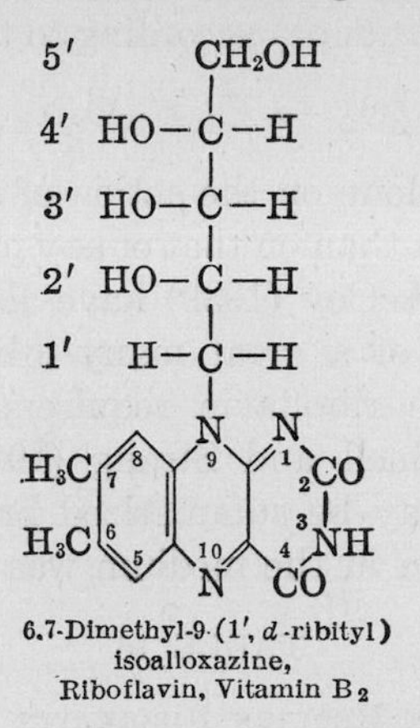

6.7-Dimethyl-9-(1′, *d*-ribityl) isoalloxazine, Riboflavin, Vitamin B_2

Riboflavin occurs as fine orange-yellow needles and is slightly soluble in water (12 mg. in 100 ml. at 27.5°C., 19 mg. at 40°C.), ethyl alcohol (4.5 mg. at 27.5°C.), amyl alcohol, and phenol and in alkali solutions, but is insoluble in chloroform, ether, acetone, and benzene. When protected against light, it is quite stable in acid solutions, but it decomposes in alkalies. It is rather thermostable, since it will stand autoclaving at 120°C. for over an hour.

Many bacteria [see Warburg and Christian (1933), Boissevain, Drea, and Schultz (1938), Snell and Strong (1939), Krauskopf, Snell, and McCoy (1939), O'Kane (1941), Peterson and Peterson (1945)], molds [Lavollay and Laborey (1938)], and related fungi [Raffy (1939), Schopfer (1943)] are capable of synthesizing riboflavin and therefore do not need an external supply of this vitamin for growth in chemically defined media. For example, Boissevain, Drea, and Schultz (1938) found that the synthetic culture medium in which they had cultivated four strains of *Mycobacterium tuberculosis* for 6 weeks contained 0.5–2.86 μg./ml. of riboflavin, and others [Rohner and Roulet (1939), Street and Reeves (1940)] have calculated that tubercle bacilli themselves contain 12.5 to 36.6 mg. of flavin per kilogram of dry organisms.

A number of bacteria have been studied which require an external supply of riboflavin for growth in chemically defined media or are stimulated by its presence in such media. A few examples of these organisms are listed in Table 16. It also seems probable that riboflavin or some derivative of it is associated with one of the enzymes involved in the luminescence of bacteria [Doudoroff (1938)].

It is of interest that Foster (1944) has described a new bacterial species, *Pseudomonas riboflavinus*, which oxidizes riboflavin to lumichrome (6,7-dimethylalloxazine) according to the following reaction:

$$C_{17}H_{20}O_6N_4 + 5\frac{1}{2}O_2 \rightarrow C_{12}H_{10}O_2N_4 + 5CO_2 + 5H_2O$$

More work has been done on the action of riboflavin on the growth of the lactic acid bacteria than on that of any other organisms, although Krauskopf, Snell, and McCoy (1939) have also made a survey of the riboflavin requirements of a great many other bacteria. The most complete studies of the riboflavin requirements of the lactic acid bacteria are those of Snell and Strong (1939) and Möller (1940). Some of their results may be summarized briefly. They found that the presence of riboflavin in the medium was required for the growth

TABLE 16

SEVERAL ORGANISMS WHICH REQUIRE RIBOFLAVIN IN SIMPLE MEDIA OR ARE STIMULATED BY IT

Organism	Quantity Used per Milliliter of Medium	Reference *
Many lactic acid bacteria of the genera *Lactobacillus*, *Leuconostoc*, and *Streptococcus*	0.1 μg.	Orla-Jensen, Otte, and Snog-Kjaer (1936)
	0.05–0.1 μg.	Snell and Strong (1939)
	0.1 μg.	Krauskopf, Snell, and McCoy (1939)
	0.05–0.1 μg.	Möller (1940)
	0.2 μg.	Pollack and Lindner (1942)
	0.002–0.02 μg.	Campbell and Hucker (1944)
Several propionic acid bacteria of the genus *Propionibacterium*	0.1–1 μg.	Wood, Anderson, and Werkman (1938), Krauskopf, Snell, and McCoy (1939), Thompson (1943)
Hemolytic streptococci of Groups A, B, C, D, etc.	0.004–1 μg.	Woolley and Hutchings (1939), Pappenheimer and Hottle (1940), Woolley (1941), Bernheimer, *et al.* (1942); see discussion for other references.
Streptococcus fecalis	0.1–2.5 μg.	Schuman and Farrell (1941), Niven, and Sherman (1944)
Streptococcus paracitrovorus	0.1–2 μg.	Wood, Anderson, and Werkman (1937)
Streptococcus lactis	1 μg.	Niven (1944)
Diplococcus pneumoniae, types II, V, VIII	0.1 μg.	Rane and Subbarow (1940)
Sarcina flava	0.05 μg.	Sartory, Sartory, and Meyer (1938)
Erysipelothrix rhusiopathiae	0.05–0.5 μg.	Hutner (1942)
Listerella monocytogenes	0.05–1 μg.	Porter and Pelczar (1941), Hutner (1942)
Achromobacter phosphoricum	0.02–10 μg.	Doudoroff (1938)
Clostridium perfringens (toxin formation)	0.2 μg.	Tamura, Tytell, Boyd, and Logan (1941)
Clostridium tetani	0.01 μg.	Mueller and Miller (1942), Feeney, Mueller, and Miller (1943)
Nonsporulating, anaerobic bacilli	40 μg.	West, Lewis, and Militzer (1942)
Leptospira canicola	0.001 μg.	Rosenfeld and Greene (1941)
Molds and filamentous fungi (3 species)	0.02–1 μg.	Robbins and Kavanagh (1942)
Protozoa	....	Dewey (1941)

* For other studies where riboflavin has been used these references, the review by Peterson and Peterson (1945), and the discussion earlier in the chapter should be consulted.

of *Lactobacillus delbrückii*, *Lactobacillus gayonii*, *Lactobacillus casei*, and *Bacterium lactis-acidi*, whereas the growth of *Lactobacillus arabinosus*, *Lactobacillus pentosus*, *Lactobacillus plantarum* (*Bacillus brassicae*), *Lactobacillus pentoaceticus*, *Lactobacillus mannitopoeus*, *Leuconostoc mesenteroides*, and *Streptococcus lactis* was as luxuriant in the absence of riboflavin as in its presence. It is therefore apparent that preformed riboflavin is not an indispensable nutrient for all species of lactic acid bacteria. The indispensability of riboflavin for *Lactobacillus casei* and *Bacterium lactis-acidi* afforded an opportunity for securing data on the biological activity of various synthetic flavins, and Snell and Strong tested the following compounds for their specificity for these bacteria:

		Approximate Growth Response for		
		Lactobacillus casei	*Bacterium lactis-acidi*	Rat
I.	6,7-Dimethyl-9-(1′,*d*-ribityl)-isoalloxazine (riboflavin)	++++	++++	++++
II.	6-Methyl-9-(1′,*d*-ribityl)-isoalloxazine	+	+	++++
III.	7-Methyl-9-(1′,*d*-ribityl)-isoalloxazine	++	++	++++
IV.	6-Ethyl-7-methyl-9-(1′,*d*-ribityl)-isoalloxazine	+++	+++	++++
V.	6,7-Dimethyl-9-(1′,*d*-arabityl)-isoalloxazine	0	0	++?
VI.	6,7-Dimethyl-9-(1′,*l*-arabityl)-isoalloxazine	0	+?	+
VII.	6-Ethyl-7-methyl-9-(1′,*l*-arabityl)-isoalloxazine	?	?	+
VIII.	6,7-Dimethyl-9-(1′-sorbityl)-isoalloxazine	0	0	0
IX.	9-(1′,*l*-Arabityl)-isoalloxazine	?	?	0
X.	5,6-Benzo-9-(1′,*d*-ribityl)-isoalloxazine	?	?	0
XI.	6,7,9-Trimethylisoalloxazine (lumiflavin)	0	0	0
XII.	6,7-Dimethylalloxazine (lumichrome)	0	0	0
XIII.	Riboflavin tetraacetate	0	0	+++

A survey of the action of these flavins showed that besides riboflavin only compounds II, III, and IV, all derivatives of ribose, exhibited appreciable activity when tested in amounts of 0.05–0.1 μg./ml. of medium; flavin IV was approximately equal in action to I (riboflavin), and the potencies of III and II were less, II being the least active. *Bacterium lactis-acidi* also showed a slight response to 10 μg. of VI, but this reaction was not consistent; and in the presence of suboptimal amounts of riboflavin compounds V, VI, VII, and X exhibited detectable activity. On the other hand, compounds VIII, XI, XII, and XIII showed no activity under any conditions. With few exceptions these results with bacteria compare with those of experiments in which the rat was used as the test organism [see Möller (1940)].

The physiological role of riboflavin in microorganisms has not been studied very extensively. It is, however, reasonable to assume that practically the same reactions are carried out by riboflavin, especially as part of enzyme systems in microorganisms as in animals. Since the reactions catalyzed by the flavin enzymes are discussed in Chapter 6, they will not be mentioned here.

NICOTINIC ACID AND NICOTINAMIDE AND THEIR DERIVATIVES (PYRIDINE COENZYMES, ETC.)

The chemical constitution and natural occurrence of nicotinic acid have been known for a long time, but it has only been within the past ten years that its importance in cellular metabolism has been realized. In 1935 Warburg and Christian and von Euler and his associates found that nicotinamide was a component of certain coenzymes (cozymase, or di- and triphosphopyridine nucleotide) responsible for the transfer of hydrogen in biological oxidations. This discovery showed that nicotinamide played an important role in the cellular metabolism of both plants and animals and led to renewed interest in nicotinic acid and its derivatives.

Nicotinic acid (or its amide) is a white crystalline powder and is readily soluble in water and several other solvents; it is quite stable to heat, acids, and alkalies.

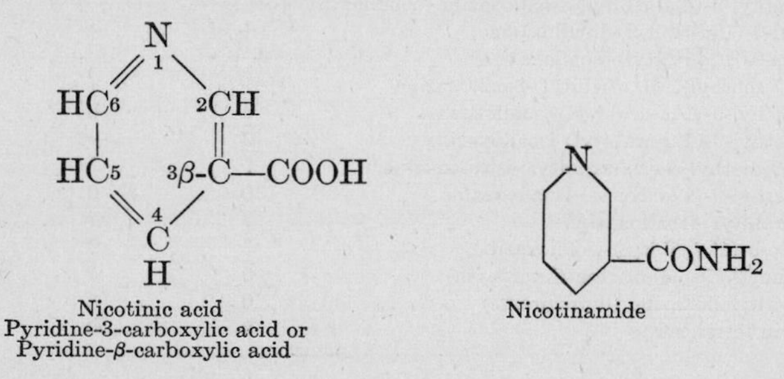

Nicotinic acid
Pyridine-3-carboxylic acid or
Pyridine-β-carboxylic acid

Nicotinamide

Nicotinic acid, or its derivatives, apparently occurs in all living cells. Many bacteria can synthesize the substance because they do not require an external source for growth in simple media. Other organisms are unable to effect this synthesis, however, and therefore must be supplied with nicotinic acid for cultivation in an otherwise deficient medium. A few bacteria which must be supplied with nicotinic acid are listed in Table 17. Growth of many of these organisms is not dependent entirely upon the utilization of nicotinic acid or its amide, however, because certain other pyridine derivatives will function in their place. This point is illustrated in Table 18, where it will also be seen that there is a good correlation between the compounds which function in bacterial metabolism and those which cure blacktongue in dogs and improve human pellagra. More parasitic organisms, such as some of the *Hemophilus* species, cannot utilize nicotinic acid or its simple derivatives but require one of the more complex derivatives of nicotinic acid (di- or triphosphopyridine nucleotide); this group will be discussed in detail under the phosphopyridine nucleotides, pp. 718 and 731 to 732.

TABLE 17

SEVERAL ORGANISMS WHICH REQUIRE OR ARE STIMULATED BY NICOTINIC ACID OR ITS DERIVATIVES (COENZYME I OR II) IN SIMPLE MEDIA

Organism	Quantity Used per Milliliter of Medium	References *
Staphylococcus aureus	2.5 × 10^{-8}–10^{-5} *M*	Knight (1937)
	10^{-5} *M*	Knight and McIlwain (1938)
	0.001–2 μg.	Landy (1938)
Staphylococcus albus	0.8–4 μg.	Koser, Finkle, Dorfman, Gordon, and Saunders (1938), Vilter and Spies (1940)
Hemolytic streptococci of groups A, B, C, D, etc.	40–200 μg.	Rane and Subbarow (1938)
	0.1 μg.	Pappenheimer and Hottle (1940)
	5 μg.	Woolley (1941)
Streptococcus salivarius	1 μg.	Smiley, Niven, and Sherman (1943)
Streptococcus lactis	1 μg.	Niven (1944)
Pneumococci, several types	50 μg.	Rane and Subbarow (1940)
Corynebacterium diphtheriae	0.1–1 μg.	Mueller (1937, 1938)
	1 μg.	Evans, Happold, and Handley (1939)
Proteus vulgaris, X19 and related strains	7.8 × 10^{-8}–2 × 10^{-5} *M*	Fildes (1938), Lwoff and Querido (1938, 1939)
	2 × 10^{-5} *M*	Pelczar and Porter (1940)
	0.02–0.033 μg.	Morel (1941, 1943)
Proteus morganii	10^{-5} *M*	Pelczar and Porter (1940)
Salmonella paratyphi A and other colon-typhoid-dysentery species	0.0003–100 μg.	Kligler and Grosowitz (1939), Kligler and Grossowicz (1941)
Salmonella gallinarum	10 mg.	Johnson and Rettger (1943)
Shigella dysenteriae, several strains	0.01–0.4 μg.	Koser, Dorfman, and Saunders (1938)
	0.0006–10,000 μg.	Dorfman, Koser, Reames, Swingle, and Saunders (1939)
	1 × 10^{-8}–1 × 10^{-6} *M*	Koser, Dorfman, and Saunders (1940), Weil and Black (1944)
Brucella species	30 μg.	Kerby (1939)
	0.2–0.5 μg.	Koser, Breslove, and Dorfman (1941)
	0.2 μg.	McCullough and Dick (1943)
Pasteurella pestis	20 μg.	Rao (1940)
Pasteurella species	0.1 μg.	Berkman, Saunders, and Koser (1940)
Pasteurella tularensis	0.1–1 μg.	Tamura and Gibby (1943)
Hemophilus parainfluenzae (requires coenzyme I or II)	0.004 μg.	Lwoff and Lwoff (1937)
	0.004–4 μg.	Bass, Berkman, Saunders, and Koser (1941)
Hemophilus pertussis	0.001–0.5 μg.	Hornibrook (1940)
Lactic acid bacteria (certain species)	0.1–0.3 μg.	Snell, Strong, and Peterson (1938, 1939)
	0.2 μg.	Pollack and Lindner (1942)
Propionibacterium species	0.01–0.3 μg.	Snell, Strong, and Peterson (1939)
Clostridium perfringens	5 μg.	Tamura, Tytell, Boyd, and Logan (1941)
Clostridium tetani	1 μg.	Feeney, Mueller, and Miller (1943)
Clostridium septicum	1 μg.	Bernheimer (1944)
Leptospira canicola	1 μg.	Rosenfeld and Greene (1941)
Leptospira icterohemorrhagiae	100 μg.	Ward and Starbuck (1941)

* For additional studies the discussion on the individual species and the review by Peterson and Peterson (1945) should be consulted.

It is generally assumed that the main activity of nicotinic acid in cellular metabolism is to act as a component of certain coenzymes, which in turn function in oxidation-reduction systems. However, some evidence has been presented recently which indicates that nicotinic acid or its amide may have an additional function outside the coenzyme linkages. For example, certain symptoms of blacktongue in dogs can be cured by nicotinic acid, but little or no change occurs when cozymase is injected intravenously in an amount corresponding to a large dose of nicotinic acid. McIlwain (1940) studied the action of pyridine-3-sulfonic acid and its amide as inhibitors of bacterial growth and reported that pyridine-3-sulfonic acid inhibited the growth of *Proteus* promoted by nicotinamide less strongly than it inhibited that promoted by diphosphopyridine nucleotide. On the basis of these results he postulated that nicotinamide must have some function

TABLE 18

THE ABILITY OF VARIOUS PYRIDINE DERIVATIVES TO SERVE AS GROWTH FACTORS FOR BACTERIA AND TO ALLEVIATE CANINE BLACKTONGUE AND HUMAN PELLAGRA

	Staphylococcus aureus[1]	*Shigella dysenteriae*[2]	*Proteus vulgaris*[3]	*Lactobacillus arabinosus*[4,5]	Cure for Blacktongue[5]	Cure for Human Pellagra[5]
Pyridine		−	−		−	
Pyridine-2-carboxylic acid (picolinic acid)	−	−	−		−	−
Pyridine-3-carboxylic acid (nicotinic acid)	+	+	+	+	+*	+
Pyridine-4-carboxylic acid (isonicotinic acid)	−	−	±		−	
1-Hydropyridine-3-carboxylic acid (nipecotic acid)		−			−	
Pyridine-2,3-dicarboxylic acid (quinolinic acid)	−	+	±		−	±
Pyridine-3,4-dicarboxylic acid (cinchomeronic acid)		−				
Pyridine-3,5-dicarboxylic acid (dinicotinic acid)		−				
2,4-Dimethyl pyridine-3,5-dicarboxylic acid	−					
2,4,6-Trimethyl pyridine-3,5-dicarboxylic acid	−		−			
Nicotinuric acid	+	+	+	+	+	
Pyridine-3-carboxylic amide (nicotinamide)	+	+	+	+	+	+
N-Methyl pyridine-3-carboxylic amide (nicotinic acid-N-methyl amide)		+			+	
Pyridine-3-carboxylic ethyl amide	+		+			
Pyridine-3-carboxylic diethyl amide (coramine)	−	+	+		+	+
Sodium pyridine-3-carboxylate	+		+			
Ammonium pyridine-3-carboxylate	+		+			
Methyl pyridine-3-carboxylate (methyl nicotinate)	+	+				
Ethyl pyridine-3-carboxylate (ethyl nicotinate)	+	+	+	−	+*	
Propyl pyridine-3-carboxylate (propyl nicotinate)		+		−	*	
Butyl pyridine-3-carboxylate (butyl nicotinate)		+		+	*	
2-Methyl pyridine (β-methyl pyridine)	−					
3-Methyl pyridine (β-picoline)	−	−	+		+	+
3-Acetyl pyridine (β-acetyl pyridine)		−			−	
4-Methyl pyridine	−					
6-Methyl nicotinic acid		−	±		−	
Pyridine-3-sulfonic acid		−	+		−	
Pyridine-3-nitrile (nicotinonitrile)	−	−	+		−	
Pyridine-3-amide (β-aminopyridine)		−			−	−
Ethyl nicotinoacetate		−			−	
Trigonelline	−	−	−	−	−	−
1-Methylmethyl pyridine-3-carboxylate (arecoline)		−				
1-Methyl pyridine-3-carboxylic acid			−			

+ = growth or active; − = no growth or nonactive; ± = variable results.

* Also active for chicks.

[1] Knight and McIlwain (1938), Landy (1938).

[2] Dorfman, Koser, Reames, Swingle, and Saunders (1939), Koser, Dorfman, and Saunders (1940).

[3] Lwoff and Querido (1939), Pelczar and Porter (1940).

[4] Snell and Wright (1941), Möller and Birkofer (1942).

[5] Data from Elvehjem and Teply (1943).

other than acting as a building stone for di- or triphosphopyridine nucleotide, or both. Finally, it has been shown that growth and respiration of dysentery bacilli are much more favorably influenced by nicotinic acid or its amide than by the coenzymes and that the efficacy of the action of the coenzymes can be increased markedly by hydrolysis under conditions which free the nicotinamide [Saunders, Dorfman, and Koser (1941)].

The Pyridine Nucleotides (V-Factor). The so-called V-factor was briefly mentioned in connection with hemin but will now be discussed in more detail. The substance was first demonstrated in fresh animal and plant tissues, yeast, and many bacterial cultures by early workers [see the references under hemin, pp. 717 to 718, and Meyer (1934)], who also observed that it was water-soluble, sensitive to heat in alkaline solutions, filterable, and partially adsorbed by bone charcoal. Although Thjötta and Avery in 1921 considered it an essential vitamin for *Hemophilus influenzae* and called it V-factor, it was not until 1937 that the factor was definitely identified. In that year Lwoff and Lwoff published their classical papers on the nutrition of *Hemophilus parainfluenzae* and showed that the V-factor was identical with Harden and Young's cozymase and Warburg and Christian's coenzymes (di- or triphosphopyridine nucleotide). Since the chemical properties and function of these coenzymes were discussed under the pyridine coenzymes in Chapter 6, pp. 466 to 473, they will not be repeated here.

It has been generally assumed that bacteria can be allocated to three groups on the basis of their need for the phosphopyridine nucleotides (coenzyme I and II):

1. Organisms which can synthesize coenzyme I or II in a medium containing ammonium salts or other simple nitrogenous substances and a simple carbon source. Example: *Escherichia coli.*

2. Organisms which can synthesize the pyridine nucleotides providing one or more of the components (nicotinamide, adenylic acid, pentose) of the coenzymes are added. Examples: *Staphylococcus aureus, Corynebacterium diphtheriae, Proteus* species, dysentery bacilli.

3. Organisms which can neither synthesize the pyridine coenzymes in a simple medium nor couple the various components together, but require the addition of the intact coenzymes for growth. Examples: Certain *Hemophilus* species.

It should be pointed out, however, that the requirements of this third group of bacteria may not be as specific for the intact coenzymes as we once thought. Recent studies by Schlenk and Gingrich (1942) and Gingrich and Schlenk (1944) have shown that *Hemophilus parain-*

fluenzae and *Hemophilus influenzae* can proceed with the synthesis of the pyridine coenzymes if the first step, the linkage between nicotinamide and pentose (nicotinamide riboside), is accomplished (see Table 19). Furthermore, the fact that the nicotinamide riboside and desaminocoenzyme I (a derivative in which the adenylic acid portion of the molecule is replaced by inosinic acid) support growth indicates that the adenylic acid portion of the molecule is not entirely important in the activity of the pyridine coenzymes. The intact coenzymes are more active, however, and coenzyme I is the most active of all. Finally it should be mentioned that Bass, Berkman, Saunders, and Koser (1941) have observed that highly purified catalase preparations will supply the coenzyme I or II requirements of certain *Hemophilus* strains in simplified media.

TABLE 19

Compounds Which Exhibit Growth-Promoting Activity with *Hemophilus parainfluenzae*

[From Schlenk and Gingrich (1942)]

Compound	Minimum Concentration for Detectable Growth, μg. mole/ml. medium
Coenzyme I (Cozymase, DPN)	0.2×10^{-5} (0.001326 μg.)
Dihydrocoenzyme I (reduced coenzyme I)	0.3×10^{-5}
Acid-treated dihydrocoenzyme I	0.5×10^{-4}
Desaminocoenzyme I	0.5×10^{-5}
Coenzyme II (codehydrogenase II, TPN)	0.5×10^{-5}
Nicotinamide riboside	0.1×10^{-4}
Nicotinamide + *d*-ribose + adenylic acid	No growth with 1 μg. each

In summary we can say that the phosphopyridine nucleotides are important factors in the metabolism of bacteria, since they apparently function as hydrogen-transporting substances, or coenzymes, in biological oxidations. Certain organisms can synthesize these coenzymes from simple substances; others can couple the components together and form the intact molecules. Other bacteria appear to require the intact molecules for growth, although some doubt has been cast on this point in the past few years.

PYRIDOXINE (VITAMIN B_6 OR ADERMIN)

Vitamin B_6 was first clearly recognized as a substance preventing dermatitis in rats by György in 1934. Its isolation in crystalline form was announced independently by five different groups of workers in 1938, and its chemical structure and synthesis were reported simultaneously by two groups of investigators in 1939. It has the following structure:

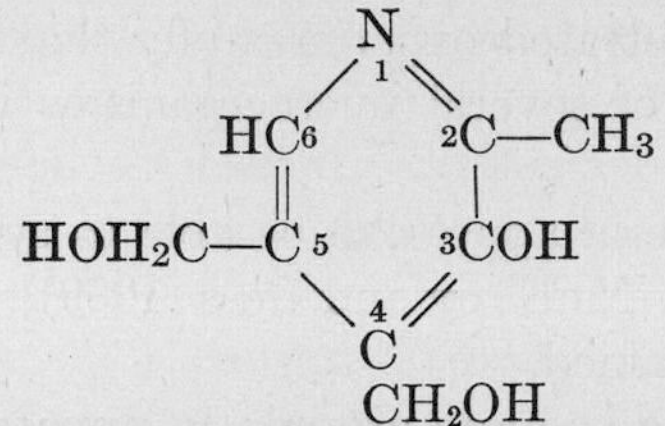

2-Methyl-3-hydroxy-4,5-bis(hydroxymethyl) pyridine
Vitamin B_6 or Pyridoxine

Vitamin B_6 is manufactured in the form of the hydrochloride. It is colorless, readily soluble in water (22.5 g./100 ml. at 26.5°C.), acetone, and alcohol. An aqueous solution of the vitamin hydrochloride is quite acid (*p*H about 3.2). Such a solution is quite stable, but less acid solutions (above *p*H 5.0) decompose, especially on heating. No-

TABLE 20

Several Microorganisms Which Require or Are Stimulated by the Presence of Vitamin B_6 in Simple Media

Organism	Quantity Used per Milliliter of Medium	Reference *
Many lactic acid bacteria	0.5–1 μg.	Möller (1938, 1940), Pollack and Lindner (1942), Bohonos, Hutchings, and Peterson (1942), Snell and Guirard (1943)
Hemolytic streptococci	0.5 μg.	Hutchings and Woolley (1939)
of Groups A, B, C, etc.	0.5 μg.	Woolley and Hutchings (1939, 1940)
	$0.2–2.5 \times 10^{-5}$ *M*	McIlwain (1940)
	2 μg.	Pappenheimer and Hottle (1940)
	1 μg.	Woolley (1941)
Streptococcus fecalis	0.1–2.5 μg.	Schuman and Farrell (1941), Niven and Sherman (1944)
Staphylococcus albus	0.3–1.2 μg.	Vilter and Spies (1940)
Yeast	0.01 μg.	Möller (1938)
	1.6 μg.	Schultz, Atkin, and Frey (1939)
	0.0001–0.004 μg.	Eakin and Williams (1939), Stokes, Gunness, and Foster (1944)
Molds and filamentous fungi (6 species)	0.5–5 μg.	Robbins and Kavanagh (1942), Fries (1943)
Graphium ulmi	0.00001–0.0005 μg.	Burkholder and McVeigh (1942)

* For other studies where vitamin B_6 has been used, consult these references, the discussion under the nutrition of the individual species, and the review by Peterson and Peterson (1945).

ticeable decomposition also occurs when dilute solutions are exposed to light.

It has been demonstrated experimentally that vitamin B_6 is necessary for the growth of several microorganisms in simple media (see Table 20).

Certain other bacteria appear to be able to synthesize the vitamin in the rumen of sheep [McElroy and Goss (1939)], but the exact species have not been determined.

In certain lactic acid bacteria vitamin B_6 apparently owes its physiological action to the molecule as an entity, because compounds of very similar structure and most derivatives of the vitamin are inactive. This point may be illustrated by citing the following results of Bohonos, Hutchings, and Peterson (1942), who studied the activity of pyridoxine derivatives for *Lactobacillus casei:*

Compound	*Comparative Activity * of Pyridoxine (Vitamin B_6) Derivatives*
2-Methyl-3-hydroxy-4:5-bis (hydroxymethyl) pyridine (pyridoxine)	1.0
Derivatives of 2-methyl pyridine:	
3-Hydroxy-4:5-bis (acetoxymethyl)-	0.8–1.0
3-Acetoxy-4:5-bis (acetoxymethyl)-	0.0
3-Hydroxy-4:5-bis (bromomethyl)-	0.6–0.8
3-Amino-4-bromomethyl-5-aminomethyl-	0.0
3-Amino-4-hydroxymethyl-5-aminoethyl-	0.0
3-Hydroxy-4-ethoxymethyl-5-hydroxymethyl-	0.3
3-Hydroxy-4-methoxymethyl-5-hydroxymethyl-	0.3–0.4
3-Hydroxy-4:5-epoxydimethyl-	0.2–0.3
3-Hydroxy-4-methyl-5-hydroxymethyl-	0.03 (?)
3-Hydroxy-4:5-dimethyl-	0.0
Lactone of 3-hydroxy-4-hydroxymethyl-5-carboxy-	0.0
Lactone of 3-amino-4-hydroxymethyl-5-carboxy-	0.0

* Activity based on the amount of acid produced when the various derivatives of the same molarity were substituted for pyridoxine. Somewhat similar results have been recorded by Möller (1940) for *Lactobacillus arabinosus* and the rat.

The activity of compounds similar to pyridoxine has also been studied in some detail by Snell and Rannefeld (1945). They found that pyridoxine,

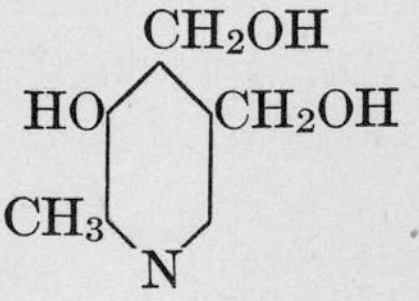

pyridoxal,

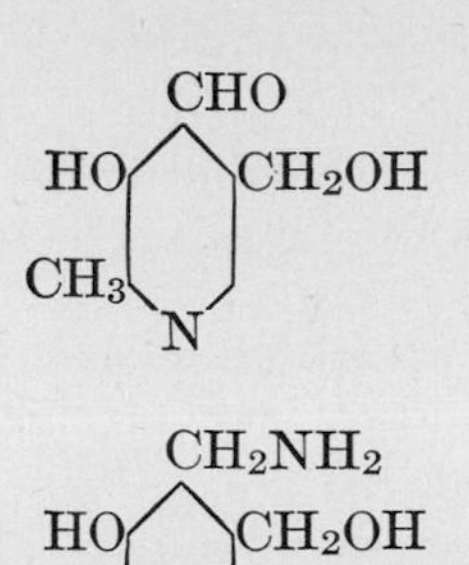

and pyridoxamine,

CH_2NH_2
HO CH_2OH
CH_3
N

have approximately the same activity for one group of organisms represented by certain yeasts, molds, and the rat. For some yeasts pyridoxamine and pyridoxal were somewhat less active than pyridoxine, but for a large group of lactic acid bacteria pyridoxine was a fewfold to several thousandfold more active than pyridoxal or pyridoxamine.

The exact functions of pyridoxine, pyridoxal, and pyridoxamine have not been fully elucidated. However, Gunsalus and Bellamy (1944) showed that pyridoxal stimulated the tyrosine decarboxylase system of *Streptococcus fecalis* R, whereas pyridoxamine did not. The exact role of pyridoxal in this enzymatic reaction is still to be determined. Snell (1945) has also observed that pyridoxal and pyridoxamine function in transamination reactions. For example, pyridoxal was found to react with glutamic acid to produce pyridoxamine and α-ketoglutaric acid. The reaction was demonstrated to be reversible, since it could be driven to completion in either direction if sufficient glutamic acid or α-ketoglutaric acid was employed. Pyridoxamine (or pyridoxal) is also needed in the synthesis of lysine, threonine, and alanine by certain lactobacilli [Stokes and Gunness (1945)].

Snell (1945*a*) has shown that pyridoxine, pyridoxal, and pyridoxamine are widely distributed in nature and that the proportions in which the three compounds occur differ markedly with various materials. The presence of pyridoxal and pyridoxamine in nature appears to explain "pseudopyridoxine" activity, as first described by Snell, Guirard, and Williams (1942). Snell and Guirard (1943) have found also that certain concentrations of alanine will replace pyridoxine in the nutrition of some streptococci. In this function it is believed that alanine serves as a direct precursor for the vitamin.

PANTOTHENIC [15] ACID

The first indication of the existence of pantothenic acid is found in the early publications on yeast nutrition by R. J. Williams and his associates in 1931, but it was 1938 before these workers determined the chemical nature of the compound [see Williams (1941)]. Subsequently R. J. Williams and Major (1940) and Stiller, Harris, Finkelstein, Keresztesy, and Folkers (1940) synthesized pantothenic acid and gave it the following structure and chemical name:

$$HOH_2C \cdot \overset{\displaystyle CH_3}{\underset{\displaystyle CH_3}{\overset{|}{\underset{|}{C}}}} \cdot CHOH \cdot CO \cdot NH \cdot CH_2 \cdot CH_2 \cdot COOH$$

(+)-α,γ-Dihydroxy-β,β-dimethylbutyryl-β′-alanide
Pantothenic acid

Pantothenic acid is made up of two components, the amino group of β-alanine being bound to the carboxyl group of a dihydroxy acid to form an acid-amide group. This acid is marketed as the calcium salt. It is readily soluble in water (1.0 g./6.9 ml.), dioxane, and several other solvents but is practically insoluble in benzene and chloroform. The vitamin is sensitive toward strong acids, bases, and heat. It can be adsorbed on charcoal but not on Fuller's earth. *l*-Pantothenate has less than 1.0 per cent of the activity of the *d*-form as measured by bacterial assay [see Williams (1943)].

Microorganisms may be allocated to two groups with respect to their pantothenic acid requirements: (1) those which synthesize the vitamin, and (2) those which need an external supply for growth in simple media. The second group may be further subdivided into those organisms which need the entire pantothenic acid molecule, such as the lactic acid bacteria, the propionic acid bacteria, pneumococci, *Proteus morganii*, and certain strains of *Corynebacterium diphtheriae;* those which need only the β-alanine portion of the molecule, such as yeasts, certain strains of *Corynebacterium diphtheriae* and the *Brucella* species; and those bacteria, such as certain hemolytic streptococci, *Brucella* species, and *Acetobacter suboxydans,* which need only the aliphatic dihydroxycarboxylic acid part of the pantothenic acid molecule for growth in simple media. A few examples of organisms which require, or whose growth is stimulated by, the addition of pantothenic acid or its components to simple media are listed in Table 21. Certain molds and related fungi synthesize pantothenic acid readily during growth; in some other fungi pantothenic acid serves as a growth stim-

[15] Name derived from the Greek, meaning "from everywhere."

ulant without being an indispensable constituent. Certain protozoa are also stimulated by the addition of pantothenic acid to their substrate [see Williams (1941)].

TABLE 21

SEVERAL ORGANISMS WHICH REQUIRE OR ARE STIMULATED BY PANTOTHENIC ACID OR ITS COMPONENTS (β-ALANINE AND/OR α-HYDROXY-β,β-DIMETHYL-γ-BUTYROLACTONE) IN SIMPLE MEDIA

Organism	Quantity Used per Milliliter of Medium	References *
Many lactic acid bacteria of the genera *Lactobacillus*, *Leuconostoc*, and *Streptococcus*	0.005–0.05 μg.	Snell, Strong, and Peterson (1938)
	0.5 μg.	Krauskopf, Snell, and McCoy (1939)
	0.2 μg.	Pollack and Lindner (1942)
Several propionic acid bacteria of the genus *Propionibacterium*	0.5 μg.	Krauskopf, Snell, and McCoy (1939)
	0.1 μg.	Thompson (1943)
Hemolytic streptococci, groups A, B, C, etc.	0.05–10 μg.	Subbarow and Rane (1939)
	0.004–0.1 μg.	McIlwain (1939)
	0.01–1 μg.	Woolley and Hutchings (1939)
	0.5 μg.	Krauskopf, Snell, and McCoy (1939)
	10 μg.	Pappenheimer and Hottle (1940)
	0.1–1 μg.	Woolley (1939, 1940)
Streptococcus salivarius, *Streptococcus fecalis*, *Streptococcus lactis*	1 μg.	Smiley *et al.* (1943), Niven and Sherman (1944), Niven (1944)
Pneumococci, types II, V, VIII	1 μg.	Rane and Subbarow (1940)
Certain strains of *Corynebacterium diphtheriae*	0.031–12.5 μg.	Mueller and Klotz (1938)
	0.1 μg.	Evans *et al.* (1939)
Proteus morganii	0.0002–1 μg.	Pelczar and Porter (1940, 1941)
	0.0003 μg.	Dorfman, Berkman, and Koser (1942)
Acetobacter suboxydans	1 μg.	Lampen, Underkofler, and Peterson (1942)
	0.1–1 μg.	Underkofler *et al.* (1943)
	2 μg.	Karabinos and Dicken (1944)
Brucella species	0.2–0.5 μg.	Koser, Breslove, and Dorfman (1941)
	0.04	McCullough and Dick (1943)
Pasteurella avicida, *Pasteurella boviseptica*	0.1 μg.	Berkman, Saunders, and Koser (1940)
Pasteurella tularensis	1–4 μg.	Tamura and Gibby (1943)
Clostridium perfringens	2 μg.	Tamura, Tytell, Boyd, and Logan (1941)
Clostridium tetani	0.25 μg.	Mueller and Miller (1941, 1942)
Clostridium thermosaccharolyticum	0.1 μg.	Clark and Mitchell (1944)
Nonsporulating anaerobes	2 μg.	West, Lewis, and Militzer (1942)
Yeast	0.006 μg.	Williams, Eakin, and Snell (1940), Williams (1941)
Torula cremoris	0.2 μg.	Koser and Wright (1943)
Molds and filamentous fungi (2 species)	0.1–1 μg.	Robbins and Kavanagh (1942)
Colpodium striatum	....	Elliott (1935); see Williams (1941)

* For additional studies these references, the discussions on the individual species, and the review by Peterson and Peterson (1945) should be consulted.

Very little is known about the physiology of pantothenic acid and its metabolism in animals, plants, and microorganisms, even though it is probably required by all living matter. The compound exhibits considerable specificity, because even the optical isomer, the (−) pantothenic acid, is inactive. Certain salts of the acid are active, but the benzoate, acetate, and diphosphate are inactive. Hydroxypantothenic acid,

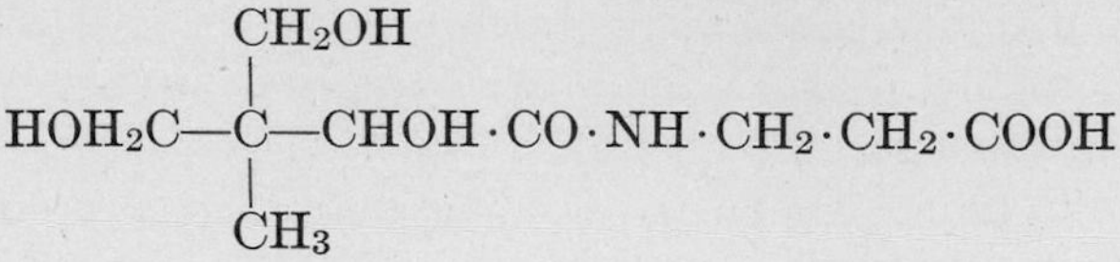

$$
\begin{array}{c}
\quad CH_2OH \\
| \\
HOH_2C\text{—}C\text{—}CHOH \cdot CO \cdot NH \cdot CH_2 \cdot CH_2 \cdot COOH \\
| \\
CH_3
\end{array}
$$

which contains a β-methyl and a β-hydroxymethyl group, rather than the β, β-dimethyl groups of normal pantothenic acid, is less than 25 per cent as active biologically as the normal acid [Mitchell, Snell, and Williams (1940)], and α-methyl pantothenate is active only to a limited extent for certain lactic acid bacteria and for yeast [Pollack (1943)].

Dorfman, Berkman, and Koser (1942) and Hills (1943) have presented evidence which indicates that pantothenic acid is concerned with the metabolism of pyruvic acid, such as the conversion of pyruvic acid to lactic acid or to acetic acid, by *Proteus morganii*, but the mechanism is unknown. Teague and Williams (1942) have also observed that added pantothenic acid has no appreciable effect on the fermentation of glucose, the rate of phosphorylation of glucose, or the rate of decarboxylation of pyruvic acid by yeast maceration juice, but fermentation by pantothenate-deficient yeast cells is accelerated by added pantothenic acid and is accompanied by a "binding" of pantothenic acid by the yeast cells. Since added pantothenic acid has no effect on the rate of glycolysis of homogenized pantothenate-deficient chick tissues, Teague and Williams concluded that the compound does not serve as a dissociable coenzyme for the glycolytic system [see McIlwain and Hughes (1944)]. More recently Sevag and Green (1944) have found that pantothenic acid is required for the building of tryptophan by certain strains of *Staphylococcus aureus*. Thus it appears that pantothenic acid functions in several metabolic processes.

Bacteria which require intact pantothenic acid for growth are inhibited by N-(α,γ-dihydroxy-β,β-dimethylbutyryl)-taurine [Snell (1941)] and pantoyltaurine,

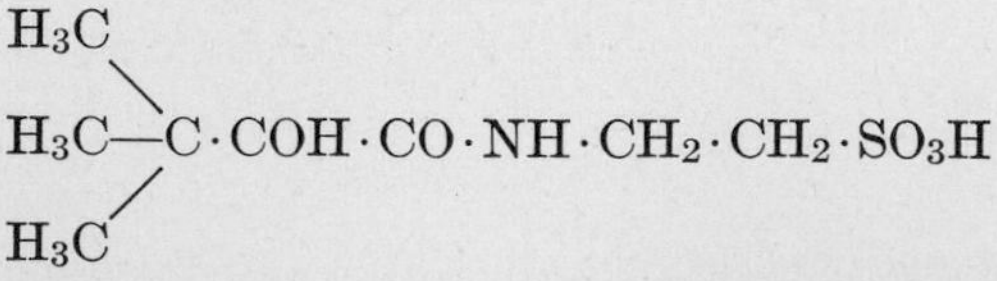

$$
\begin{array}{l}
H_3C \\
\quad\quad \diagdown \\
H_3C\text{—}C \cdot COH \cdot CO \cdot NH \cdot CH_2 \cdot CH_2 \cdot SO_3H \\
\quad\quad \diagup \\
H_3C
\end{array}
$$

[McIlwain (1942)], which are chemically related to pantothenic acid. The compounds appear to act in the same way that sulfanilamide acts on *p*-aminobenzoic acid; that is, they become attached to the bacteria at enzymes where pantothenate must react for normal growth. Pantoyltaurine has about $\frac{1}{100}$ to $\frac{1}{500}$ of the affinity of pantothenate for the enzymes concerned. In concentrations greater than 100 to 500 times that of the pantothenate present, pantoyltaurine apparently blocks the majority of the active centers of the enzymes where pantothenate normally reacts. Since pantoyltaurine cannot functionally replace pantothenate, the essential process ceases, and the organisms are unable to grow. Organisms needing pantothenate are not equally susceptible to the action of N-(α,γ-dihydroxy-β,β-dimethylbutyryl)-taurine and pantoyltaurine, and it appears that those organisms which synthesize their own pantothenic acid, either completely or from added β-alanine, are not inhibited [see McIlwain (1943)].

BIOTIN (VITAMIN H, COENZYME R, BIOS II_B, ETC.) [16]

Biotin was first recognized as a growth factor for yeast by Kögl in 1935. Later it was isolated as the pure crystalline methyl ester by Kögl and Tönnis (1936), who obtained only 1.1 mg. from 250 kg. of dried Chinese duck egg yolks by several ingenious chemical techniques. As the result of studies by several workers, especially West and Wilson (1940) and György, Melville, Burk, and duVigneaud (1940), we now know that biotin is identical with vitamin H (the so-called anti-egg-white-injury factor), coenzyme R, bios II_B, and probably several other factors which have already been described in the literature; however, the name biotin is now quite generally used for all these factors.

Biotin is 2′-keto-3:4-imidazolido-thiopane-(2)-*n*-valeric acid. The formula for biotin methyl ester [duVigneaud, Hofmann, and Melville (1942), duVigneaud (1942), Hofmann (1943)] is as follows:

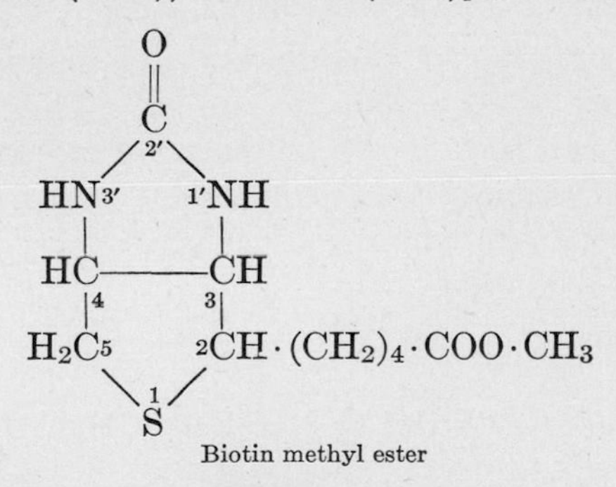

Biotin methyl ester

Biotin (free acid) is insoluble in water and several other ordinary solvents but is quite soluble in basic solutions; the methyl ester, on the other hand, is soluble in alcohol and chloroform and sparingly soluble in benzene, but insoluble in ether and water. It is quite heat-

[16] For a review of the literature on vitamin H, biotin, and coeznyme R see Landy (1941), Hofmann (1943), and Peterson and Peterson (1945).

stable, readily dialyzable, and resistant to treatment with acid, except nitrous acid, or alkali. It is adsorbed on charcoal and is optically active. Synthetic biotin has the same potency as natural biotin, but *dl*-biotin is only about 50 per cent as active, and *l*-biotin and *dl*-allobiotin are almost inactive [Stokes and Gunness (1945*a*)]. The free acid and the methyl ester possess about the same biological activity; however, some lactic acid bacteria exhibit better growth and fermentation with the free biotin [Stokes and Gunness (1943)].

Biotin has been found widely distributed in the plant and animal kingdoms. It is necessary to add the vitamin to simple media before certain microorganisms will grow (see Table 22), but a number of other

TABLE 22

SEVERAL ORGANISMS WHICH REQUIRE BIOTIN IN SIMPLE MEDIA OR ARE STIMULATED BY IT

Organism	Quantity Used per Milliliter of Medium, μg.	References *
Staphylococcus aureus	0.000005–0.005	Kögl and van Wagtendonk (1938)
	0.098	Sartory, Meyer, and Netter (1939)
	0.005–0.1	Porter and Pelczar (1940, 1941)
Pneumococci, 26 types	0.0002	Bohonos and Subbarow (1943)
Hemolytic streptococci of groups A, B, C, D, etc.; viridans streptococci, etc.	0.00002–0.001	Hottle, Lampen, and Pappenheimer (1941); see discussion
Streptococcus thermophilus	....	Pray (1941)
Root-nodule bacteria of the genus *Rhizobium*	Trace	Allison, Hoover, and Burk (1933)
	0.0005	Nilsson, Bjälfve, and Burström (1939)
	0.06–50	West and Wilson (1942)
	0.00002	Wilson and Wilson (1942)
Shigella paradysenteriae (Flexner) (some strains)	0.2	Weil and Black (1944)
Corynebacterium diphtheriae (Allen strain)	0.15	duVigneaud, Dittmer, Hague, and Long (1942)
Lactic acid bacteria of the genus *Lactobacillus*	0.0004–0.004	Snell and Wright (1941), Pollack and Lindner (1942), Stokes and Gunness (1943)
Propionibacterium species	0.01	Thompson (1943)
Brucella species	0.5	Koser, Breslove, and Dorfman (1941)
	0.001	McCullough and Dick (1943)
Clostridium butylicum	0.0000133–0.00066	Snell and Williams (1939)
Clostridium septicum	0.001	Bernheimer (1944)
Clostridium acetobutylicum	0.00025	Weizmann and Rosenfeld (1939)
	0.0000055–0.00023	Oxford, Lampen, and Peterson (1940)
Clostridium sporogenes and related *Clostridia*	0.00001–0.001	Peterson, McDaniel, and McCoy (1940), Lampen and Peterson (1943)
Several *Clostridium* and *Lactobacillus* species, *Bacillus brevis*	....	Landy, Dicken, Bicking, and Mitchell (1942)
Rhodospirillum rubrum	0.001–0.002	Hutner (1944)
Yeast	0.167	Kögl (1935)
	0.000025	Kögl and Tönnis (1936)
	0.0001	Williams, Eakin, and Snell (1940), Leonian and Lilly (1942), Lochhead and Landerkin (1942)
Torula cremoris	0.002	Koser and Wright (1943)
Ashbya gossypii, *Fusarium avenaceum*, and related fungi	0.002–0.05	Kögl and Fries (1937)
	0.00012–0.012	Robbins and Schmidt (1939), Robbins and Ma (1941), Robbins and Kavanagh (1942), Fries (1943)

* For additional studies these references, the discussions on the individual species, and the review by Peterson and Peterson (1945) should be consulted.

bacteria, molds, and related fungi synthesize this vitamin in chemically defined biotin-free media in amounts ranging from approximately 0.33 millimicrograms (or 0.00033 μg.) for *Monilia albicans* to 30.3 millimicrograms for *Escherichia coli* per milliliter of culture medium [Landy and Dicken (1941), Eakin and Eakin (1942)]. In *Aspergillus niger* biotin synthesis appears to be associated with the presence of pimelic acid in the medium, and it has been postulated that the pimelic acid serves as one of the precursors of biotin [Eakin and Eakin (1942)]. Biotin is also synthesized by the microorganisms in the rumen of cattle [Wegner, Booth, Elvehjem, and Hart (1940)].

The role which biotin plays in microorganisms may be that of a true growth stimulant, but it also appears to function in other ways. For example, it has been observed that in yeast biotin increases fermentation more directly than respiration, and respiration again more directly than growth [Burk, Winzler, and duVigneaud (1941)]. It has also been shown for the root-nodule bacteria that their respiration can be markedly increased without concomitant growth by the addition of biotin to the culture medium [Allison, Hoover, and Burk (1933)]. It is of interest that biotin will replace pimelic acid in the nutrition of *Corynebacterium diphtheriae* [duVigneaud, Dittmer, Hague, and Long (1942)]. This fact suggests that pimelic acid may be a precursor of biotin. Furthermore biotin can be partially replaced by *dl*- or *l*-aspartic acid for *Torula cremoris*, but nothing is known about this relationship. A close connection between this vitamin and fat metabolism in animals has also been postulated.

Desthiobiotin methyl ester has the following formula:

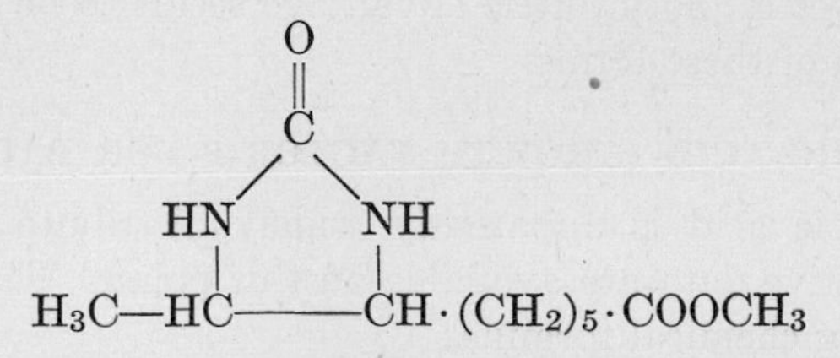

It can be formed from biotin methyl ester by replacement of the sulfur atom in the molecule by two hydrogen atoms [Melville, Dittmer, Brown, and duVigneaud (1943)]. This compound can replace biotin in the nutrition of yeast, but not of some other fungi, including the bacteria, *Lactobacillus casei*, *Lactobacillus arabinosus*, and *Rhizobium trifolii*. In the presence of an exogenous supply of biotin, desthiobiotin does not show any inhibitory effect for yeast or some bacteria, but it exhibits an antibiotin action with *Lactobacillus casei* and some higher fungi [Dittmer *et al.* (1944), Lilly and Leonian (1944)].

Biotin is made unavailable to the living organisms (rats, chicks, yeasts, and bacteria) by the formation of a complex with a protein constituent of raw egg white, and the typical syndromes of a biotin deficiency occur (or in certain microorganisms no growth takes place) when, instead of the free biotin, the protein-complex is administered or is placed in the medium [see Eakin, Snell, and Williams (1940), Pennington, Snell, and Eakin (1942), Landy, Dicken, Bicking, and Mitchell (1942)]. In general those microorganisms which have been found to require biotin (see Table 22) are inhibited by the protein-biotin complex, whereas those organisms, such as *Escherichia coli* and *Serratia marcescens,* which synthesize biotin are unaffected [Landy, Dicken, Bicking, and Mitchell (1942)]. The combination of biotin with the protein appears to be rather firm because the biotin cannot be recovered by dialysis. The protein which has the peculiar capacity of binding biotin is called avidin and has been obtained in crystalline form by Pennington, Snell, and Eakin (1942). It is of interest in connection with the discussion of avidin to mention the work of Dittmer and duVigneaud (1944). They found that a number of compounds with a urea ring and a carboxylic acid side chain of five or six carbon atoms are able to combine with avidin, whereas other substances without a cyclic urea structure are unable to do so.

Burk and Winzler (1943) have obtained biotin-like products from urine and vitab hydrolysates which they have designated as miotin, tiotin, and rhiotin, depending on their reaction to heat, avidin, yeast, and root-nodule bacteria. Since these products have not been identified chemically, and since many of their properties are possessed by known derivatives of biotin, little advantage seems to be gained from the introduction of these terms.

p-AMINOBENZOIC ACID (GROWTH FACTOR-P FOR BACTERIA)[17]

p-Aminobenzoic acid is apparently widely distributed in nature, but no quantitative data are available on this point. The compound has the following chemical formula:

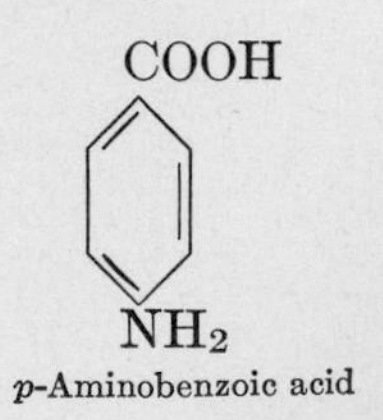

p-Aminobenzoic acid

[17] H. N. Green (1940) found that bacterial extracts contain an antisulfanilamide factor which powerfully stimulates the reproduction of many bacteria. The factor was termed provisionally P-factor (proliferation or pullulation factor), but was not isolated in pure form.

It is soluble in water (0.33 per cent at 10°C.), alcohol (11.3 per cent at 10°C.), and ether (6.11 per cent at 10°C.). It is an interesting compound because it acts both as an acid and a base, that is, it is amphoteric.

The discovery that *p*-aminobenzoic acid is a growth factor for bacteria and a vitamin for higher animals was made rather indirectly. In 1940 Woods and Fildes were studying the mode of action of sulfanilamide and made the interesting observation that *p*-aminobenzoic acid acts as an antisulfanilamide agent. Subsequently Woods (1940) found that yeast extracts contain a factor which counteracts sulfanilamide activity and suggested that this factor was identical with *p*-aminobenzoic acid; at the same time Green (1940) reported that bacterial extracts contain an antisulfanilamide factor (termed provisionally P-factor), but he did not realize that it was *p*-aminobenzoic acid. In the same issue of the journal in which Green and Woods published their work Selbie (1940) reported that he was able to inhibit by means of *p*-aminobenzoic acid the protective action of sulfanilamide in mice infected with fatal doses of hemolytic streptococci. In December, 1940, Rubbo and Gillespie recovered *p*-aminobenzoic acid as the benzoyl derivative from yeast and noted that it is not only an antisulfanilamide agent but also a growth factor for *Clostridium acetobutylicum.* About the same time Fildes (1940) concluded that *p*-aminobenzoic acid is an essential metabolite for many bacteria, and Ansbacher (1941) presented evidence to show that the compound is a vitamin, namely, a chromotrichia factor for the rat and a growth-promoting factor for the chick.

Little is known about the physiological action of *p*-aminobenzoic acid, except that it does not function as a source of carbon and energy [Saz and Bernheim (1942)]. It is known to be synthesized by many bacteria in media containing no *p*-aminobenzoic acid [Landy, Larkum, and Oswald (1943)]. It is also required as a growth factor for certain bacteria [Fildes (1940)], such as *Clostridium acetobutylicum, Clostridium butylicum,* and *Clostridium felsineum* [Rubbo and Gillespie (1940, 1942), Rubbo *et al.* (1941), Lampen and Peterson (1941, 1943), Park and Wood (1942), Clark and Mitchell (1944)], *Brucella abortus* [Green (1940)], hemolytic streptococci [Selbie (1940)], some strains or species of lactic acid bacilli [Möller and Schwarz (1941), Kuhn and Schwarz (1941)], and *Acetobacter suboxydans* [Lampen *et al.* (1942)]. It is also required by some filamentous fungi, such as *Ceratostomella piceaperda* and *Neurospora crassa* [see Robbins and Kavanagh (1942), Wyss, Lilly, and Leonian (1944)]. The needs of the microorganisms which require this vitamin are satisfied by about 0.05 to 1.0 μg./ml. of medium. Wyss and his associates have shown, however, that the effectiveness of *p*-aminobenzoic acid as a growth factor decreases with an increase in *p*H. For example, at *p*H 4.0 the presence of 0.01 μg. of *p*-aminobenzoic acid in 25 ml. of media produced 8 mg. of *Neurospora* mycelia, whereas at *p*H 6.0 0.1 μg. and at *p*H 7.0 over 0.4 μg. was required to produce the same weight of mold tissue. The addition of the vitamin (5 mg./100 ml.) to all routine culture media has been recommended by Janeway (1941).

The therapeutic action of some sulfonamide drugs is inhibited or completely neutralized by *p*-aminobenzoic acid in mice infected with hemolytic streptococci, pneumococci, and staphylococci [Selbie (1940), Landy and Wyeno (1941), McCarty (1941), and others]. *In vitro* *p*-aminobenzoic acid has a pronounced influence on tyrosinase activity [Wisansky, Martin, and Ansbacher (1941)], inhibits the oxidation of adrenaline, and appears to function in certain other enzymatic processes [Martin, Ichniowski, Wisansky, and Ansbacher (1942)]. Experimental evidence for Woods's hypothesis that *p*-aminobenzoic acid and sulfonamides have a common point of attack on some enzyme system or systems is presented clearly in the paper by Rubbo and Gillespie (1942). Their findings reveal that a remarkably small amount of the growth factor is necessary to remove the inhibitory action of the drug for *Clostridium acetobutylicum*. As will be seen in Table 23, 0.001 μg. of *p*-aminobenzoic acid antagonizes 26 μg. of sulfanilamide, that is, one part by weight neutralizes 26,000 parts of drug. Similarly, if the concentration of inhibitor is increased twofold or fourfold, a proportionate increase of growth factor is necessary to permit growth. Quite similar results were reported by Woods (1940) with hemolytic streptococci and *Escherichia coli*. He found that a final concentration of

TABLE 23

THE NEUTRALIZING OR INHIBITORY ACTION OF *p*-AMINOBENZOIC ACID ON SULFANILAMIDE INHIBITION OF *Clostridium acetobutylicum*

[From Rubbo and Gillespie (1942)]

Concentration of Sulfanilamide		Amount of *p*-Aminobenzoic Acid per Milliliter of Basal Medium, μg.					Ratio of Sulfanilamide to *p*-Aminobenzoic Acid by Weight
Molarity	μg./ml.	0.0005	0.001	0.002	0.003	0.004	
M/6600	26	−	+	+	+	+	26,000
M/3300	52	−	−	+	+	+	26,000
M/1650	104	−	−	−	−	+	26,000

− = no growth; + = growth

1.2 to 5.8 × 10^{-8} *M* *p*-aminobenzoic acid was sufficient to reverse the inhibition of 3.03 × 10^{-4} *M* sulfanilamide, that is, 0.02 to 0.1 μg. in 11 ml. of media, as compared with 570 μg. of sulfanilamide.

After the discovery of the growth-stimulating activity of *p*-aminobenzoic acid for *Clostridium acetobutylicum*, Rubbo, Maxwell, Fairbridge, and Gillespie (1941) tested a series of more than twenty-five organic chemicals to determine the connection between molecular pattern and growth stimulation. Their results (see Table 24) show

TABLE 24

GROWTH-FACTOR ACTIVITY OF SUBSTANCES STRUCTURALLY RELATED TO *p*-AMINOBENZOIC ACID

[From Rubbo, Maxwell, Fairbridge, and Gillespie (1941)]

Substance	Growth	Growth-Factor Activity,* 1 unit in
1. *p*-Aminophenyl acetic acid	+	0.00001 μg.
2. *p*-Aminobenzoic acid	+	0.0001 μg.
3. *p*-Aminobenzoic acid (Na^+ salt)	+	0.0001 μg.
4. *p*-Aminobenzoic acid (ethyl ester)	+	0.0001 μg.
5. *p*-Aminobenzaldehyde	+	0.0001 μg.
6. *p*-Aminobenzoic acid (benzoyl derivative)	+	0.001 μg.
7. *p*-Aminobenzoic acid (diethylaminoethyl ester)	+	0.001 μg.
8. *p*-Nitrobenzoic acid	+	0.001 μg.
9. *p*-Nitrobenzaldehyde	+	0.01 μg.
10. *p*-Methylbenzoic acid	+	1.0 μg.
11. *o*-Aminobenzoic acid	+	10.0 μg.
12. *m*-Aminobenzoic acid	+	10.0 μg.
13. *p*-Aminobenzamide	+	10.0 μg.
14. *p*-Aminobenzyl alcohol	−	−
15. *p*-Hydroxybenzoic acid	−	−
16. *p*-Aminophenol	−	−
17. *p*-Dimethylaminobenzaldehyde	−	−
18. *p*-Aminobenzene sulfonamide	−	−
19. Benzene	−	−
20. Benzoic acid	−	−
21. Inositol	−	−
22. Nicotinic acid	−	−
23. Thiamin	−	−
24. Tryptophan	−	−
25. Tyrosine	−	−
26. Cholesterol	−	−

* "The unit of growth-factor activity" (G.F.A.) is the smallest amount of material necessary to stimulate visible growth of *Clostridium acetobutylicum* in 5 ml. of basal medium under anaerobic conditions at 37°C. for 48 hours.

that substances conforming to the structural configuration of *p*-aminobenzoic acid are biologically active. These findings are of particular interest in view of the antisulfanilamide properties assigned to a similar series of compounds by Woods (1940). The compounds which Woods found to be antisulfanilamide in action were demonstrated to be active as growth factors by Rubbo and his associates, whereas those found to be inactive as antisulfanilamide agents were incapable of supporting the growth of *Cl. acetobutylicum.*

From the information obtained by Rubbo and his associates several general conclusions are permissible in regard to the relationship of chemical structure to growth-factor activity:

1. Compounds possessing growth-stimulating properties are aromatic compounds containing a di-substituted benzene ring in which the substituents occupy 1:4 positions. The orientation is probably of fundamental importance, and any departures from it considerably reduce the activity of the new compound. For instance, *p*-aminobenzoic acid (2) is ten thousand times more active than *o*- (11) or *m*- (12) isomers.

2. In regard to the type of substituents it appears that greatest activity is shown when one of the two is an amino group and the other a carboxyl or carboxymethyl group. Derivatives of these chemical types or any compound possessing substituents which yield amino and carboxyl groups would be included in this category (compounds 5, 8, and 9, Table 24). It is of interest that the formation of an amide of *p*-aminobenzoic acid effects a significant reduction in activity (compare compounds 2 and 13, Table 24); this phenomenon is in striking contrast to the behavior of nicotinic acid and its amide. The importance of the amino and carboxyl substituents is best illustrated by comparing compounds in the inactive group (compounds 14 to 26, Table 24). Thus the replacement of —COOH in the 1:4 substituted ring of *p*-aminobenzoic acid by $—CH_2OH$ (14) or by —OH (15) or the replacement of $—NH_2$ by $—N(CH_3)_2$ (17) or —OH (16) results in complete inactivation of the new derivative.

INOSITOL

Inositol is widely distributed in nature, where it occurs in a number of different forms. For example, in many animal tissues it is mostly in combination with large molecules, probably proteins; in plants the majority appears in the form of hexaphosphate (phytic acid); in the tubercle bacillus inositol is bound in the phosphatide fraction as a glucoside [Anderson and Roberts (1930)].

Inositol has the following formula:

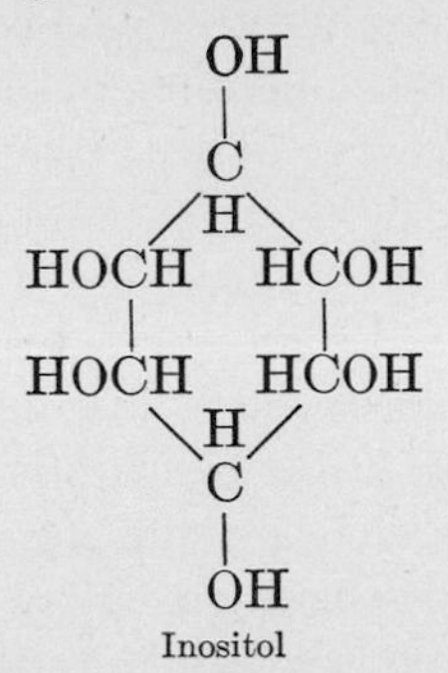

Inositol

It is soluble in water (17.5 g. in 100 ml. at 24°C.) but is insoluble in absolute alcohol and ether. From its formula it is evident that inositol can exist in eight isomeric forms; only one is optically inactive (meso- or *i*-inositol).

i-Inositol was first demonstrated to be a growth factor for yeast by Eastcott (1928), who showed that it was the same as Lucas' (1924) bios I. Since that time it has been observed that certain strains of yeast and higher fungi require an external supply of inositol for optimum growth in chemically defined media, whereas other strains are apparently able to synthesize it and are not stimulated when the substance is added to media [Miller, Eastcott, and Maconachei (1933), Kögl and van Hasselt (1936), Kögl and Fries (1937), Lesh, Underkofler, and Fulmer (1938)]. In concentrations of 0.01 to 1 per cent inositol also stimulates the growth of tubercle bacilli in Long's synthetic medium, providing large inocula of the bacilli are used [Uyei (1930)]. More recently Woolley (1940) has shown that inositol functions as a vitamin in mice by preventing alopecia; and Gavin and McHenry (1941) have observed that inositol prevents a fatty liver condition in rats. Thus it seems established that inositol possesses growth factor or vitamin properties.

Very little is known about the physiological action of *i*-inositol. The compound is fairly specific for yeast, because only *i*-inositol and methyl inositol (mytilitol) are fully active, and inositol hexaacetate, *d*-inositol, *l*-inositol, phytin, Na-phytate, and several other derivatives are less than one-tenth as active as *i*-inositol. Mice, however, respond to most of the esters of inositol [Woolley (1941)]. The following two properties distinguish inositol from the other growth factors so far mentioned:

1. Relatively high concentrations of inositol are required. For example, workers have reported that 10 to 50 μg. is required by certain

strains of yeast, and Uyei (1930) found that at least 100 μg./ml. is necessary to stimulate the growth of the tubercle bacillus.

2. When inositol is added by itself to synthetic media, it has practically no effect. In other words, it becomes a limiting factor for growth only when other nutrilites are supplied.

CHOLINE

Choline (trimethyl-β-hydroxyethyl ammonium hydroxide) is a very interesting compound from a biological standpoint. For information concerning its importance in the nutrition of animals the review by Griffith (1941) should be consulted. It is present in many cellular phosphatides and most phospholipides and is also concerned with the regulation of certain metabolic processes.

Choline is a colorless, hygroscopic base, readily soluble in water and alcohol but insoluble in ether; it forms such salts as chlorides and borates very easily, and the solutions of such salts are practically neutral. Choline has the following formula:

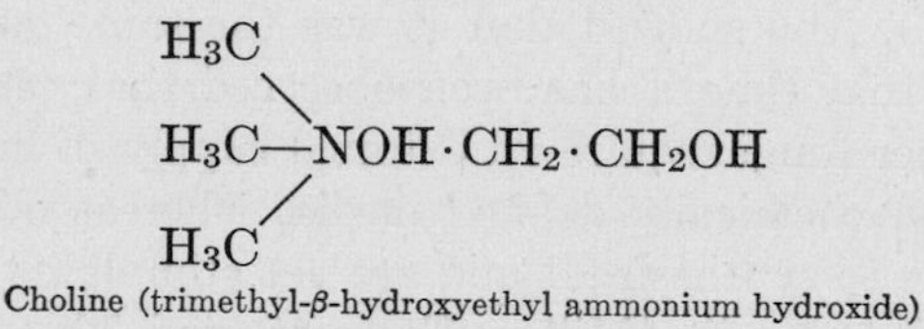

Choline (trimethyl-β-hydroxyethyl ammonium hydroxide)

Choline is apparently required by all animals, because a deficiency of it in the diet causes a variety of physiological abnormalities, such as the deposition of excess fat in the liver and a hemorrhagic degeneration of the kidneys. Because of the ability of choline to cure such conditions it has been classified as a vitamin [György and Goldblatt (1940)]. It should also be remembered that choline is a constituent of the important humoral substance, acetylcholine.

Choline is also an essential growth factor for several types of *Diplococcus pneumoniae*, which require approximately 2.5 to 5 μg./ml. of medium for optimum growth [Rane and Subbarow (1940), Badger (1944)]. The structural specificity of choline for the growth of the pneumococcus has been studied by Badger (1944). She tested some thirty-five different compounds related to choline and found that all the active substances contained a N—C—C—OH or a N—C—C—C—OH linkage. Substitution of or through the hydroxyl group resulted in complete inactivation of the molecule. Of all the naturally occuring compounds examined only ethanol amine was able to support growth in the absence of choline, but a concentration ten times that of choline was required for maximum growth.

One of the most interesting physiological processes in animals in which choline functions is methyl group transfer. The number of naturally occurring compounds which may serve, among other purposes, as suppliers of the essential transferable methyl group is not known; but, besides choline, methionine, $CH_3 \cdot S \cdot CH_2 \cdot CH_2 \cdot CHNH_2 \cdot COOH$, and betaine, $(CH_3)_3 \cdot N \cdot CH_2 \cdot CO$ (with N and CO joined through O), are known to act in this capacity, especially in the absence of choline. Important physiological processes in which these substances serve as methylating agents are, for example, the synthesis of creatine from guanidineacetic acid and the synthesis of methionine from homocysteine and choline [duVigneaud *et al.* (1939)]. On the other hand, choline and homocysteine can be built up from methionine and ethanolamine. This series of reactions may be shown in the following scheme:

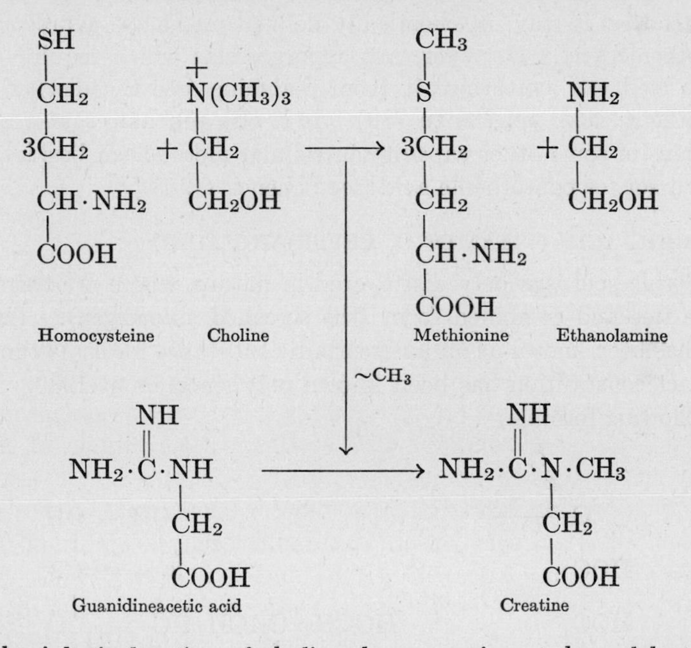

The physiological action of choline, however, is not due solely to the available methyl groups, because ethyl derivatives of choline, which are devoid of methyl groups, are unable to support the growth of rats on a choline- and methionine-free diet in the presence of homocysteine. The ethyl derivatives of choline, however, prevent the hemorrhagic kidney condition and the other syndromes associated with choline deficiency in animals.

Whether choline functions in the transfer of methyl groups in bacterial synthesis is not known. Badger (1944) concluded from her study of the need for choline in the growth of pneumococci that this function seems unlikely. She believes that choline is used for the synthesis of phospholipides in pneumococci.

β-ALANINE

Little is known about the distribution of β-alanine ($CH_2NH_2 \cdot CH_2 \cdot COOH$) in nature. It is very soluble in water, slightly soluble in alcohol, and insoluble in ether and acetone. β-Alanine was first demonstrated to be a growth stimulant for yeast about 1936 [see Williams (1941, 1943)]. Soon afterward Mueller and Cohen (1937) reported that it was a growth accessory for certain strains of *Corynebacterium diphtheriae*, the optimum amount being about 1 μg./ml. of medium [see Schenck (1943)]. The importance of β-alanine lies primarily in the fact that it may, in chemically defined media, be a precursor of pantothenic acid. However, not all organisms which require pantothenic acid can synthesize it from β-alanine (see the discussion on pantothenic acid, pp. 736 to 739). It is also probable that β-alanine functions in some other capacity in cellular metabolism besides being a precursor for pantothenic acid [see Schenck (1943)].

ASCORBIC ACID (VITAMIN C, CEVITAMIC ACID)

Ascorbic acid is widely distributed in nature, where it occurs both in the free and combined form (the so-called ascorbigen). The free form has been known as an antiscorbutic substance for some time, but its exact constitution has been known only since about 1933. It has the following formula:

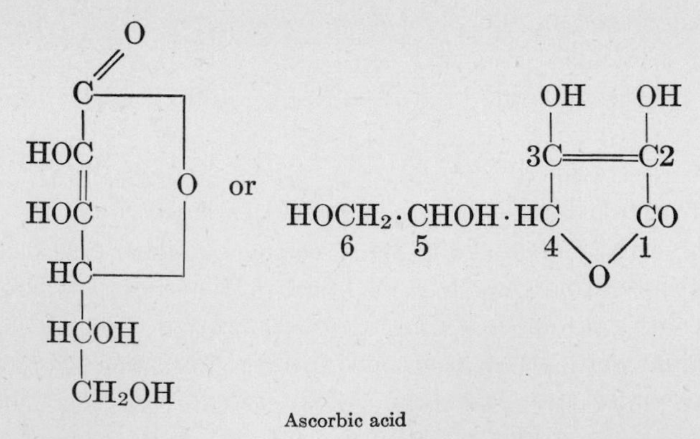

Ascorbic acid

Ascorbic acid is quite soluble in water (1.0 g. in 3 ml.), less soluble in ethyl alcohol (1.0 g. in 50 ml. absolute alcohol), and insoluble in benzene, ether, and chloroform. It is stable in the dry crystalline form but deteriorates rapidly in solution, especially in the presence of air, light, and traces of such metals as copper and iron. An outstanding property of ascorbic acid is its strong reducing action in solution and the ease of its oxidation. Its oxidation-reduction potential at *p*H 4.0 and 35°C. is +0.166 volt.

Very little is known about the physiology of vitamin C in microorganisms. Some species of higher fungi [Bourne and Allen (1935)] and bacteria, such as *Serratia marcescens* [Büsing and Peters (1940)], apparently need ascorbic acid and are able to synthesize it. The addition of 0.02 per cent ascorbic acid to the culture medium stimulates the lactic acid fermentation of *Streptococcus lactis* [Rahn and Hegarty (1938)], and a concentration of 0.05 μg./ml. accelerates the growth of *Sarcina flava* [Sartory, Sartory, and Meyer (1938)]. The presence of ascorbic acid in the substrate is known also to favor the growth of molds (*Aspergillus* species), certain green algae (*Hematococcus pluvialis*), and flagellated protozoa (*Trichomonas* species) [see Cailleau (1939), Ondratschek (1940), Gupta and Guha (1941)]. The presence of 0.02 and 0.1 per cent vitamin C in liquid culture media permits the growth of certain anaerobes, such as *Clostridium tetani* and *Clostridium perfringens*, in the presence of air [Ehrismann (1936), Kligler and Guggenheim (1938), Büsing (1941)]. Under such circumstances it seems to operate as an oxidation-reduction compound and can usually be replaced by other substances, such as cysteine, that regulate the O—R potential of the medium.

GLUTAMINE

Glutamine ($HOOC \cdot CHNH_2 \cdot CH_2 \cdot CH_2 \cdot CONH_2$) is apparently widely distributed in the plant and animal kingdoms, but little information is available on this point. It is soluble in water (3.5 to 4 g./100 ml.), less soluble in alcohol (5 mg./100 ml.), and insoluble in ether.

In 1939 McIlwain, Fildes, Gladstone, and Knight showed that the growth of certain hemolytic streptococci depended upon the addition of glutamine to their medium, the presence of as little as 0.1 μg./ml. producing noticeable growth in 24 hours. It was further shown that growth would take place, though less actively, if glutamate, instead of glutamine, were added in a concentration 100 times greater. Subsequently, Fildes and Gladstone (1939) noted that other organisms, especially certain strains of *Bacillus anthracis* and *Diplococcus pneumoniae*, were also stimulated by 0.001 *M* to 0.0002 *M* glutamine and concluded that it probably was associated with the metabolism of many bacteria. After these studies McIlwain (1939) reported that glutamine was highly specific for hemolytic streptococci, since a number of related compounds and derivatives had no effect on the growth of this organism. Still later Pollack and Lindner (1942) studied the effect of glutamine and glutamic acid on the growth of several lactic acid bacteria. The striking growth effects produced by the addition of glutamine to a medium containing most other growth essentials are shown in Table 25. In every case there was practically no growth

TABLE 25

THE EFFECT OF GLUTAMINE ON THE GROWTH OF LACTIC ACID BACTERIA
[From Pollack and Lindner (1942)]

Glutamine, μg./ml. of Medium *	Amount of Bacteria Formed, μg. of wet cell/ml.			
	Streptococcus lactis	*Lactobacillus pentosus*	*Lactobacillus arabinosus*	*Lactobacillus casei*
0.0	50	25	15	20
0.2	70	35	20	25
0.6	100	50	35	30
1.0	120	70	50	75
2.0	260	110	90	75
3.0	380	140	135	70
4.0	500	190	165	70
5.0	600	210	185	70
10.0	650	280	275	75

* The basal medium employed is listed on p. 707 on the discussion of the nutrition of the lactic acid bacteria.

without glutamine, but a definite response to 0.2 to 0.6 μg./ml. occurred in 13 hours. This low limit of effectiveness is in essential agreement with the results of McIlwain and his associates for hemolytic streptococci and suggests a similarity of function for all organisms. Pollack and Lindner also found that certain lactic acid bacteria responded as well to glutamic acid as to glutamine, but others required at least eleven times as much acid as amide to produce the same effect. Glutamine was also required by certain strains of *Neisseria gonorrhoeae* [Lankford and Snell (1943)].

Leuthardt (1938) and McIlwain and his associates (1939) suggested that glutamine functions in cellular metabolism as an ammonia-transfer agent and works in a cycle, but Pollack and Lindner (1942) believed that the most likely explanation is that the bacteria require glutamine or glutamic acid simply for the construction of cell proteins, particularly in view of the fact that the requirements of these amino acids are of the order of magnitude which would be expected for this function.

PIMELIC ACID

Pimelic acid, $HOOC \cdot (CH_2)_5 \cdot COOH$, is a dicarboxylic acid of the oxalic acid series and appears to be present in several animal tissues. It is soluble in water (5 g. in 100 ml. at 20°C.) and is very soluble in alcohol and ether.

So far pimelic acid has only been shown to be a growth stimulant for *Corynebacterium diphtheriae* [Mueller (1937)]. In this organism its effect becomes evident at concentrations of about 0.005 μg./ml. of medium and reaches a maximum at about five times this amount. Further increase up to 1.0 per cent has no additional effect and produces no inhibition of growth. None of the other simple dibasic acids, from oxalic to azelaic, has any effect on the growth of this organism (see Table 26).

TABLE 26

THE SPECIFICITY OF PIMELIC ACID FOR THE DIPHTHERIA BACILLUS

[Data from Mueller (1937)]

Dibasic Acid	Solubility in 100 ml. of H_2O at 15°–20°C.	Effect on Growth
Oxalic, $HOOC \cdot COOH$	Slightly soluble	−
Malonic, $HOOC \cdot CH_2 \cdot COOH$	73.5	−
Succinic, $HOOC \cdot (CH_2)_2 \cdot COOH$	6.8	−
Glutaric, $HOOC \cdot (CH_2)_3 \cdot COOH$	64.0	−
Adipic, $HOOC \cdot (CH_2)_4 \cdot COOH$	1.5	−
Pimelic, $HOOC \cdot (CH_2)_5 \cdot COOH$	5.0	+
Suberic, $HOOC \cdot (CH_2)_6 \cdot COOH$	0.14	−
Azelaic, $HOOC \cdot (CH_2)_7 \cdot COOH$	0.24	−

− = no effect on growth; + = stimulates growth.

Little is known about the function of pimelic acid in the metabolism of bacteria, and up to the present time it has not been shown to be essential for other forms of life. It is of interest that duVigneaud, Dittmer, Hague, and Long (1942) have shown that pimelic acid can be replaced by biotin in the nutrition of the Allen strain of *Corynebacterium diphtheriae* and that biotin synthesis by *Aspergillus niger* is stimulated by the addition of pimelic acid to the medium [Eakin and Eakin (1942)]. This fact suggests that pimelic acid may be synthesized into biotin by these organisms; but, on the other hand, such organisms as *Lactobacillus casei*, which require biotin, do not seem to be able to use pimelic acid in its place [Wright (1942)].

PURINE AND PYRIMIDINE BASES

Several purines (adenine, guanine, xanthine, and hypoxanthine) and pyrimidines (cytosine, thymine, uracil, and orotic acid) are required by microorganisms for growth in simple chemically defined media, but as yet they have not found a place in the list of vitamins for higher forms of life.

Richardson (1936) was the first to demonstrate that the hydrolytic products of nucleic acids may be factors limiting growth of various organisms under certain conditions. Working with *Staphylococcus aureus,* he showed that uracil (2,6-dihydroxypyrimidine) in a concentration of 0.00005 *M* was essential for anaerobic growth within 24 hours, but not for aerobic growth, in a mixed amino acid medium containing pyruvic acid and other necessary nutrients. Twenty-one related compounds, including the better-known purine and pyrimidine bases, were tested, but none had a comparable effect in permitting growth in 24 hours. Rahn and Hegarty (1938) reported that adenine (0.02 to 0.6 per cent) may increase the lactic acid fermentation of *Streptococcus lactis* in combination with other factors but not by itself, and Möller (1939) showed that adenine or guanine, but not xanthine or hypoxanthine, favored the growth of *Lactobacillus plantarum.* Pappenheimer and Hottle (1940) also found that adenine (15 μg./ml.) was necessary for the growth of a strain of hemolytic streptococcus under certain conditions; it could be replaced by adenosine or adenylic acid, by guanine, guanosine, or guanylic acid, and by xanthine and hypoxanthine, but not by uric acid, caffeine, theophylline, or the pyrimidines uracil and cytosine. They also made the interesting observation that adenine was unnecessary for the growth of this organism if the carbon dioxide tension in the gas space above the medium was maintained at a sufficiently high level. Stokstad (1941) isolated from liver a dinucleotide containing guanine but no adenine which promoted the growth of *Lactobacillus casei* in an amount of 0.02 μg./ml. of medium. Guanine and thymine partially replaced it. Adenine, xanthine, and hypoxanthine were as active as guanine, but uracil or cytosine did not replace thymine. Mueller and Miller (1941, 1942) found adenine and Stokstad's dinucleotide essential for the growth of *Clostridium tetani.* Adenine could be replaced by hypoxanthine, but not by guanine, xanthine, and uric acid.

Snell and Mitchell (1941) believe that each of the purine and pyrimidine bases of nucleic acid may, under certain conditions, become limiting factors for the growth of certain lactic acid bacteria. For example, adenine was found to stimulate the growth of *Lactobacillus arabinosus* and *Lactobacillus pentosus* and to be essential for the growth of *Streptococcus lactis*. Uracil stimulated the growth of *L. arabinosus* and of *Leuconostoc mesenteroides*. Guanine was found to be essential for *L. mesenteroides* and thymine for *S. lactis*. They also observed that in general the purine and pyrimidine bases were replaceable by the corresponding oxy-derivatives. Thus cytosine and uracil were interchangeable, as were guanine and xanthine. Chattaway (1944) found that orotic acid (uracil-4-carboxylic acid) possesses growth-promoting activity for *Lactobacillus casei*.

Certain higher fungi (*Phycomyces*) are quite specific in their requirements for guanine and hypoxanthine. Robbins and Kavanagh (1942) and Robbins (1943), for instance, observed that guanine and hypoxanthine in amounts of 0.004 to 4 μg./ml. of a basal medium containing minerals, sugar, asparagine, and vitamin B_1 increased spore germination and the mass of growth of a *Phycomyces* culture. Adenine, xanthine, thymine, uracil, and cytosine were ineffective. Loring and Pierce (1944) have also observed that certain pyrimidine compounds are essential for the normal development of two mutant strains of the ascomycete *Neurospora* in a simple chemically defined medium. The pyrimidine nucleosides, uridine and cytidine, and the nucleotides, uridylic acid and cytidylic acid, were found to be from ten to sixty times as active in promoting growth as the free pyrimidines, uracil and orotic acid. Cytosine and thymine were inactive for one strain but permitted some growth of the other.

The exact function of the purines and pyrimidines in the metabolism of these microorganisms is unknown; but, since most of them are components of the nucleic acids and certain vitamins, it is reasonable to assume that they are used by the organisms to synthesize certain essential protoplasmic units. In this connection it is of interest that Stokes (1944) has shown that thymine or its nucleoside, thymidine, can be substituted for folic acid in the growth of *Streptococcus fecalis* (*Streptococcus lactis* R); however, at least five thousand times more thymine is required than folic acid. It was concluded that folic acid probably participates directly or indirectly in the synthesis of thymine and related compounds in cells. However, this may not be the only function of folic acid and the purine and pyrimidine compounds, because it will be recalled that certain known coenzymes active in various phases of hexose metabolism contain these ring structures as part of their molecules, for example, riboflavin and thiamin.

FAT-SOLUBLE FACTORS (VITAMINS A, D, E, AND K, AUXINS, AND ESSENTIAL FATTY ACIDS)

Little is known about the various fat-soluble factors in microbial nutrition, but it can probably be said that they are a great deal less important as growth factors for microorganisms than as vitamins and hormones for higher forms of life. On the other hand, certain of these factors must have some function in microorganisms, since they have been repeatedly isolated from such organisms, and in a few instances they have been shown actually to stimulate growth when added to culture media.

Vitamin A (Epithelium-Protecting and Antixerophthalmic Vitamin). In general, microorganisms like plants contain only provitamins A, that is, compounds which may be activated to yield vitamin A. The presence of vitamin A has never been demonstrated in microorganisms; and, whatever its function is in animals, either microorganisms do not need this function or they take care of it by some other means. There are nine different naturally occurring compounds known as provitamins A, namely, α-, β-, and γ-carotene, cryptoxanthene, echinenone, myxoxanthin, leprotene, aphanin, and aphanicin [Rosenberg (1942)]. These substances are soluble in fats, chloroform, carbon disulfide, and benzene but are practically insoluble in alcohol and completely insoluble in water. α-, β-, and γ-carotene and cryptoxanthene have been isolated from several different microorganisms (see pp. 421 to 439 on microbial pigments in Chapter 5), and it thus appears that they have a definite function in microorganisms. What this function is, however, has not been elucidated.

Vitamin D (Antirachitic Vitamin). Actually there are several members of this group, but, since the individual substances are difficult to isolate and characterize, they have not been properly named as yet. For convenience they are all usually called simply vitamin D and are given subnumbers such as D_1, D_2, and D_3 for differentiation. Compounds possessing the physiological property of vitamin D occur only in the animal organism, although plants and microorganisms contain materials (provitamins) which can be converted into vitamin D. Thus today we have the following members of the vitamin D group with their corresponding provitamins:

Vitamin D	*Provitamin*
Vitamin D_1 (a molecular compound containing D_2 and lumisterol$_2$)	Ergosterol
Vitamin D_2 (also called calciferol in England and viosterol in America)	Ergosterol
Vitamin D_3 (also referred to as dimethyldihydrocalciferol)	7-Dehydrocholesterol
Vitamin D_4	22-Dihydroergosterol
Vitamin D_5	7-Dehydrositosterol

Vitamin D occurs only in small amounts in most members of the animal kingdom, but abundant quantities are present in the livers of certain fish. The provitamins D, on the other hand, are widely distributed in nature. It appears that the most prevalent provitamin D in higher animals and in man is 7-dehydrocholesterol, whereas plants, molds, and yeast contain predominantly ergosterol. The best sources of ergosterol are yeasts and certain molds, some of which contain this provitamin as practically the only sterol. All the known vitamins D and provitamins D have similar solubility characteristics. They are insoluble in water but soluble in the typical fat solvents, such as ether.

Nothing is known about the function of the provitamins D in microorganisms. However, Devloo (1938) reported that the addition of 3 to 10 μg. of ergosterol per milliliter of medium stimulated the growth of certain yeasts, and Cailleau (1938) [also see Lwoff (1938)] has observed that some protozoa require cholesterol for growth in peptone media. The activity of some seventy-one sterols was also tested by Cailleau; besides cholesterol, eighteen other sterols, including ergosterol, sitosterol, and 22-dihydroergosterol, were active, but the remainder, including vitamin D_2 and testosterone, were inactive.

Vitamin E (Fertility Vitamin). Three different but closely related compounds have been isolated which produce the physiological effects of vitamin E in animals. They are called α-tocopherol ($C_{29}H_{50}O_2$), β-tocopherol ($C_{28}H_{48}O_2$), and γ-tocopherol ($C_{28}H_{48}O_2$) and occur predominantly in vegetable oils, such as wheat-germ oil. They have also been synthesized, but they are oils and have not been obtained in crystalline form. Some of the esters, however, are crystallizable. The vitamins E are soluble in lipoid solvents but insoluble in water; they are quite sensitive to oxidation, which destroys the biological activity.

It is not known whether the tocopherols play any role in microorganisms. Certain molds (*Phycomyces*) do not seem to contain any tocopherols [Schopfer and Blumer (1939)], but whether this fact means that all microorganisms lack vitamin E is unknown.

Vitamin K (Antihemorrhagic Vitamin). Vitamin K, like the other fat-soluble vitamins, has now expanded into an extensive group of biologically active compounds. The existence of two naturally occurring vitamins K of high activity, namely, vitamin K_1 (2-methyl-3-phytyl-1,4-naphthoquinone) and vitamin K_2 (2-methyl-3-difarnesyl??-1,4-naphthoquinone), has been proved with certainty [Rosenberg (1942)]. Phthiocol (2-methyl-3-hydroxy-1,4-naphthoquinone), a compound occurring naturally in the tubercle bacillus, is also somewhat active but in considerably higher amounts. Phthiocol is of special historic interest in this field, however, because it was the first pure, natural antihemorrhagic compound of known structure to be discovered and used, and its activity confirmed the suggestion of a naphthoquinoid structure for vitamin K [see Almquist (1941)].

In general, vitamin K occurs only in plants and microorganisms although small amounts are contained in certain animal tissues. Which one of the group of vitamins K is present in each source is largely unknown, but it is assumed that green leaves of plants, such as alfalfa or spinach, contain predominantly or solely vitamin K_1, whereas the microorganisms contain vitamin K_2. In Table 27 is a list of several microorganisms, together with their antihemorrhagic activity as com-

TABLE 27

ANTIHEMORRHAGIC ACTIVITIES OF CERTAIN MICROORGANISMS

[From Almquist, Pentler, and Mecchi (1938), Almquist (1941)]

Preparation	Comparative Potency *
Alfalfa standard	1
Bacillus subtilis	38
Bacillus mycoides	31
Bacillus cereus	23
Sarcina lutea	20
Proteus vulgaris	15
Staphylococcus aureus	12
Mycobacterium tuberculosis	11
Serratia marcescens (*Erythrobacillus prodigiosus*)	4
Aerobacter aerogenes	4
Escherichia coli	3
Eberthella typhosa	3
Pseudomonas aeruginosa	Nil
Staphylococcus albus	Nil
Streptococcus lactis	Nil
Monilia albicans and *Monilia candida*	Nil
Mucor and *Penicillium* species	Nil

* Comparative potency was measured by feeding dried bacteria to vitamin K-deficient chicks and then measuring their blood-clotting time.

pared with that of alfalfa as a standard [see also Orla-Jensen, Orla-Jensen, Dam, and Glavind (1941)].

Nothing is known about the physiological function of the anti-hemorrhagic compounds which are present in microorganisms. Woolley and McCarter (1940) have shown that phthiocol (0.01 to 10 μg./ml.) and 2-methyl-naphthoquinone (0.01 to 1 μg./ml.) function as growth factors for Johne's bacillus (*Mycobacterium paratuberculosis*), but it is not known whether these compounds stimulate the growth of other bacteria in a similar manner.

Auxins (Plant Hormones). The term auxin was first used to designate the plant hormones which regulate the process of cellular elongation. We now know, however, that the function of auxins in plants is not limited to cell elongation, because botanical investigations have shown that they also play a role in phototropism, root development, and premature outgrowth of axillary buds. Auxins therefore regulate plant growth in many ways [Kögl (1937), Thimann and Bonner (1938)].

Isolation of the auxins was first carried out successfully about 1931 by Kögl and his associates in Utrecht. They obtained these substances in crystalline form from various sources, such as urine, maize oil, malt, yeasts, and molds [Thimann (1935)]; all are insoluble in water but are ether-soluble, unsaturated organic acids or their salts or esters. There are two well-known groups of auxins, entirely unrelated chemically. To the first group belong auxin a ($C_{18}H_{32}O_5$, a cyclopentene derivative of trihydroxyvaleric acid) and auxin b ($C_{18}H_{30}O_4$, a keto-hydroxy derivative of auxin a). The second type is called heteroauxin and is now known to be identical with β-indoleacetic acid. Other compounds are also known to have heteroauxin-like properties. The amounts of auxins causing growth responses in plants are extremely low; about 10^{-8} mg. suffices to cause a one-degree curvature in oat seedlings (*Avena test*), and a 10^{-10} *M* solution produces a detectable increase in the growth rate of corn roots.

Very few studies have been undertaken to determine the effects of the auxins on bacteria. Ball (1938) and Beckwith and Geary (1940) have observed that, when β-indoleacetic acid is added to media in dilutions of 1:50,000 to 1:30,000,000, the growth of *Escherichia coli* and *Eberthella typhosa* is stimulated. However, nothing is known about the function of this compound in the metabolism of these organisms.

Essential Fatty Acids. That certain fatty acids are essential for the proper development of rats on a simple diet is well established. However, some controversy has arisen as to whether these substances should be classified as vitamins. It is true that they are needed only in small quantities and that they contribute to the mechanism of the transformation of energy in the animal, but, on the other hand, they also serve as building units of the phospholipides. In this respect the essential fatty acids are similar to the purine and pyrimidine bases, which probably serve as building stones for nucleic acid, and to glutamine, which may serve as a unit in protein synthesis by microorganisms. Provisionally we can place all these acids in the realm of growth factors, but probably as more information becomes available this classification will have to be altered.

The fatty acids which have been shown to be essential in the rat are linoleic acid [$CH_3 \cdot (CH_2)_4 \cdot CH{=}CH \cdot CH_2 \cdot CH{=}CH \cdot (CH_2)_7 \cdot COOH$], linolenic acid [$CH_3 \cdot (CH_2 \cdot CH = CH)_3 \cdot (CH_2)_7 \cdot COOH$], and arachidonic acid [$CH_3(CH = CH \cdot CH_2 \cdot CH_2)_4(CH_2)_2 \cdot COOH$]. All these acids are insoluble in water but soluble in alkali and in organic solvents. They occur naturally in both plants and animals, although linolenic acid is usually absent from animal fats and arachidonic acid occurs predominantly in animal rather than plant tissues.

Although none of these three fatty acids has been reported as useful to bacteria or other microorganisms, a closely related compound, oleic acid, $C_8H_{17} \cdot CH = CH \cdot (CH_2)_7 \cdot COOH$, has been shown to be required for the growth of *Corynebacterium diphtheriae* on agar media containing other known ingredients when small inocula are used [Cohen and Mueller (1940), Cohen, Snyder, and Mueller (1941)]. *Clostridium tetani* also requires oleic acid (1 μg./ml.) for growth [Feeney, Mueller, and Miller (1943)], and this acid favors the growth of the fungus *Pityrosporum ovale* in concentrations of 0.01 to 1 per cent [Benham (1941)]. Nothing is known about the function of oleic acid in the metabolism of these organisms.

MISCELLANEOUS GROWTH FACTORS[18] (GLUTATHIONE, FOLIC ACID, STREPOGENIN, ETC.)

There still remain many unidentified growth factors for bacteria,[18] yeasts [see Williams (1941)], molds [see Robbins and Kavanagh (1942)], and protozoa [see Trager (1941)]. Although most of these factors have not been characterized, enough work has been done on their properties to indicate that they are not any of the known growth-promoting compounds. Some of these substances have properties similar to those of unidentified animal factors, and it is highly probable that many of them will eventually merge identities [Peterson (1941)]. Space does not permit a discussion of the many unidentified factors required by certain bacteria. Therefore only brief mention will be made of a few of the better-known factors.[18]

[18] For an extensive discussion on the miscellaneous growth factors required by bacteria the review by Peterson and Peterson (1945) should be consulted.

Glutathione. Several unknown factors appear to be required by certain strains of *Neisseria gonorrhoeae;* one of these is glutathione [Gould (1943)]. Of the many other compounds tested only two, aspartathione and isoglutathione, were capable of replacing glutathione.

Folic Acid.[19] A substance called folic acid (Latin, *folium* = leaf) has been isolated in relatively pure form and studied chemically and physiologically by Snell and Williams (1941), Mitchell *et al.* (1944), Frieden *et al.* (1944), and others. Folic acid is widespread in nature, being present in the green leaves of plants, such as spinach, in animal tissues, such as liver and kidney, and in mushrooms and yeast. The substance is quite unstable, being partially or completely inactivated by oxidation, reduction, acids, alkalies, light, heat, esterification, and methylation. A summation of analyses indicates that the compound has a molecular weight of 400 to 500 and an approximate empirical formula of $C_{15}H_{15}O_8N_5$. Absorption spectra data indicate the presence of a structural unit similar to xanthopterin:

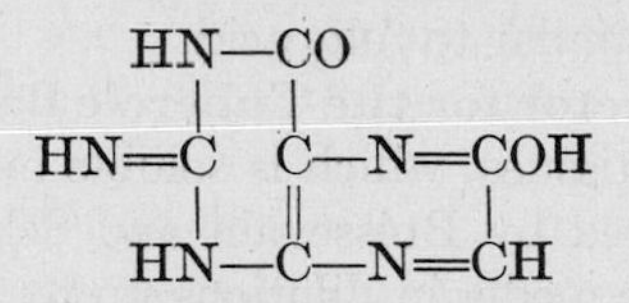

Side chains or other rings of an unknown nature which lack nitrogen or sugar residues are also indicated.

Folic acid is required for the growth of *Streptococcus fecalis* (*Streptococcus lactis* R), *Lactobacillus casei*, *Lactobacillus delbrückii* [Mitchell, Snell, and Williams (1941), Lindner and Pollack (1942)], *Clostridium tetani* [Mueller and Miller (1942)], and other bacteria. The quantity required for these bacteria is quite low. For example, in one experiment with *S. lactis* R, half of the maximum growth was obtained when only 0.00012 μg. of crude folic acid was present per milliliter of an otherwise chemically defined medium [Mitchell *et al.* (1941)]. Folic acid also appears to be necessary for the normal development of several other organisms, such as chick, rat, and trout.

Several other growth factors seem to be closely related to folic acid, but the exact relationship is not yet clear. The dinucleotide described by Stokstad (1941), the eluate factor studied by Hutchings, Bohonos, and Peterson (1941), and the antianemia factor (vitamin Bc) of Pfiffner *et al.* (1943) appear to have much in common with folic acid.

[19] The synthesis of the *Lactobacillus casei* factor by Angier *et al.* (1945) and the isolation of the antianemia factor (vitamin Bc conjugate) by Pfiffner *et al.* (1945) will help to demonstrate the relationship between folic acid, norite eluate factor, *L. casei* factor, vitamin Bc, *S. lactis* factor, strepogenin, and some of the other unknown growth factors which have been described in the literature.

Dinucleotide of Stokstad. In 1941 Stokstad isolated from liver a substance which he characterized as a dinucleotide. The substance contained guanine but no adenine, and the pentose present was not desoxyribose. It stimulated the growth of certain lactobacilli in an amount of 0.02 μg./ml. of medium. For a discussion of the relationship of the active principle in this substance to folic acid and the eluate factor the papers by Mitchell, Snell, and Williams (1941) and Hutchings, Bohonos, and Peterson (1941) should be consulted.

Eluate Factor Required by Certain Lactobacilli.[20] A factor required by certain lactobacilli, and probably the chick, has been studied in some detail by Hutchings, Bohonos, and Peterson (1941). On a dry basis this eluate has one unit (amount of material which must be added to 10 ml. of medium to produce half of the maximum fermentation) in from 0.09 to 0.1 μg. The active principle is an acid and probably contains an amino group; it is very labile to acid and reducing agents but somewhat more stable to alkali and oxidizing agents. This substance appears to be similar to folic acid.

Lipoid Growth Factor for the Tubercle Bacillus. A factor from egg yolk and animal tissues, which is soluble in an ether-alcohol mixture, has been reported by Boissevain and Schultz (1938). Growth appeared on synthetic media in dilutions up to 10^{-1} mg. of cells when the egg-yolk lipoid was absent, but in its presence the inoculum could be reduced to 10^{-6} mg. of cells. Very little is known about the properties of this factor.

Hemolytic Streptococcus Growth Factors (Strepogenin).[20] A new factor essential for the growth of hemolytic streptococci of Lancefield's group A has been demonstrated by Woolley (1941) and Sprince and Woolley (1944). At first it was not possible to identify this substance with any other known vitamin or with several of the unidentified factors, such as the eluate factors. More recently, however, Sprince and Woolley (1944) have found that this substance (now called strepogenin) is very similar to or identical with the factors required by *Lactobacillus casei* [see Hutchings, Stokstad, Bohonos, and Slobodkin (1944)] and *Streptococcus lactis* [see Smith (1943), Wright and Skeggs (1944)]. Strepogenin occurs in liver as a water-soluble, alcohol-insoluble, nondialyzable substance and is not adsorbed on norite or Fuller's earth. The most active concentrates prepared gave a maximal effect when approximately 10 μg./ml. was added to a chemically defined medium.

[20] The synthesis of the *Lactobacillus casei* factor by Angier *et al.* (1945) and the isolation of the antianemia factor (vitamin Bc conjugate) by Pfiffner *et al.* (1945) will help to demonstrate the relationship between folic acid, norite eluate factor, *L. casei* factor, vitamin Bc, *S. lactis* factor, strepogenin, and some of the other unknown growth factors which have been described in the literature.

A somewhat similar factor has been described by Bass, Berkman, and Saunders (1941). The best source of their factor is yeast, although it also occurs in spleen, liver, and fresh tomato juice. It is soluble in water and glacial acetic acid but only slightly soluble in alcohol (concentrations greater than 60 per cent) and practically insoluble in the fat solvents. It is not adsorbed on Fuller's earth, talc, aluminum oxide, or barium sulfate but is adsorbed on norite. The activity of the factor for hemolytic streptococci varied somewhat from batch to batch, but growth could be detected when amounts ranging from 1.5 to 4.0 μg./ml. of medium were present.

Lactobacillus Factor in Blood. Eckardt, György, and Johnson (1941) have described a substance in human blood which enhances the growth-promoting activity of riboflavin on *Lactobacillus casei;* however, few data were given on the chemical composition of this factor. Later Feeney and Strong (1942) concentrated the substance in blood which stimulates the growth of this organism. The substance is stable to autoclaving for 20 minutes in weak alkali and acid but is destroyed by the same treatment if strong acid is used. It is soluble in ether and alcohol.

Other Factors for Lactic Acid Bacteria.[21] Several other extremely active growth factors required by certain lactic acid bacteria have been isolated and described in recent years. The original reports by Keresztesy, Rickes, and Stokes (1943), Stokstad (1943), Chattaway, Happold, Sandford, Lythgoe, and Todd (1943), Hutchings, Stokstad, Bohonos, and Slobodkin (1944), and Sprince and Woolley (1944) should be consulted. Some of these factors appear to be very similar to folic acid and strepogenin, but more work is required before their exact relationship is known.

Acetone Factor. Rubbo, Maxwell, Fairbridge, and Gillespie (1941) described a factor which they called the acetone factor because it is required by *Clostridium acetobutylicum* before the organism can produce acetone in chemically defined media. It is a heat-stable, acid-resistant factor which appears to be a nitrogenous base soluble in butyl alcohol and precipitated by phosphotungstic acid.

Other Substances. A number of other microbial growth factors have been described, but few of them have been characterized even as well as the ones mentioned. Reference to several such factors is made under the discussion of the nutrition of the individual species; conse-

[21] The synthesis of the *Lactobacillus casei* factor by Angier *et al.* (1945) and the isolation of the antianemia factor (vitamin Bc conjugate) by Pfiffner *et al.* (1945) will help to demonstrate the relationship between folic acid, norite eluate factor, *L. casei* factor, vitamin Bc, *S. lactis* factor, strepogenin, and some of the other unknown growth factors which have been described in the literature.

quently pp. 686 to 716 should be consulted for further details. Additional information will be found in several reviews mentioned at the beginning of the chapter, especially the review by Peterson and Peterson (1945).

ESSENTIAL AMINO ACIDS

That certain species of bacteria require the presence of amino acids in order to grow in media containing ammonium salts, glucose, and

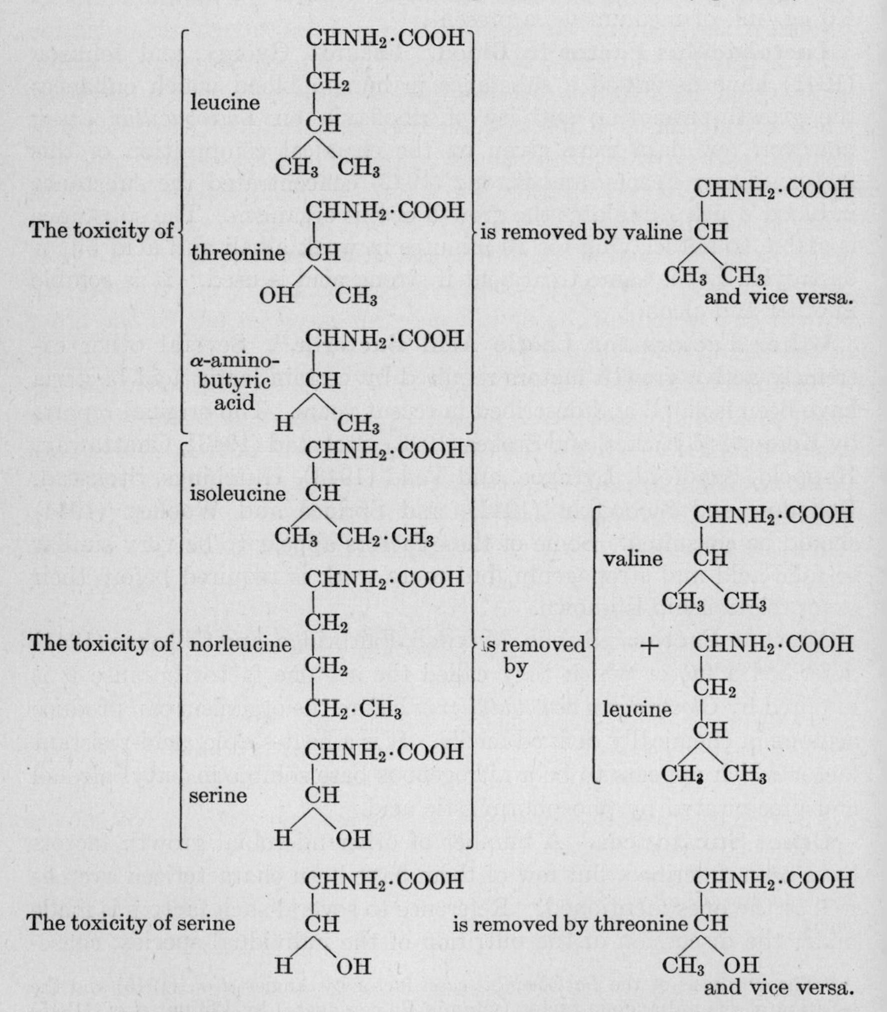

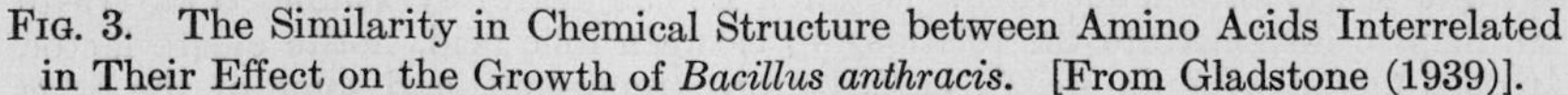

FIG. 3. The Similarity in Chemical Structure between Amino Acids Interrelated in Their Effect on the Growth of *Bacillus anthracis*. [From Gladstone (1939)].

inorganic ions is well established. The function of these required or essential amino acids in the growth of bacteria is usually that of serving as molecular units which the bacterium is unable to synthesize but which are necessary building stones in the synthesis of cellular protoplasm. On the other hand, it is quite possible that the amino acids have other important functions in the metabolism of cells. For example, Gladstone (1939) has found that the amino acid requirements of the anthrax bacillus are to some degree variable in that the necessity for a given acid is dependent upon what other amino acids are present in the medium. In this case it appears as though certain amino acids neutralize the toxicity of others (Fig. 3). Moreover, the amino acids which are able to neutralize the toxic effect are themselves toxic when added singly. Thus we have the interesting fact that two substances, each of which is toxic singly, when added together not only allow growth to occur but in most cases actually improve it. The particular amino acids which appear to be associated in this way have a similarity in chemical structure, as will be seen in Fig. 3; this likeness is suggestive of some common reaction which is necessary for growth and which can be inhibited by an excess of one or the other of the amino acids taking part.

Among the twenty-two or twenty-three amino acids which are recognized as normal constituents of dietary proteins ten are known to be essential for animals (rat), and the others can apparently be synthesized in the animal organism. Proof has come largely from the work of Rose and his associates [see Rose (1937, 1938), Rose and Rice (1939)]. Their list of essential and nonessential amino acids may be cited as follows:

Essential		*Nonessential*	
l-Lysine	*l*-Leucine	Glycine	Hydroxyglutamic acid
*d**- or *l*-Tryptophan	*l*-Isoleucine	Alanine	Proline
	l-Threonine	Serine	Hydroxyproline
d- or *l*-Histidine	*d*- or *l*-Methionine	Norleucine	Citrulline
d- or *l*-Phenylalanine	*l*-Valine	Aspartic acid	Tyrosine
	Arginine †	Glutamic acid	Cystine

* Both isomers promote growth, but in some cases the *d*-form is not quite as effective as the natural isomer.

† Can be synthesized by the rat but not at a rate sufficiently rapid to meet the needs for normal growth; it is not needed by the adult dog but is necessary for the chick.

When we attempt to compare the needs of certain bacteria with those of higher animals, distinct differences, as well as similarities, become apparent. A few examples are given in Table 28. From these

TABLE 28

AMINO ACIDS REQUIRED FOR OPTIMUM GROWTH BY CERTAIN BACTERIA *

Clostridium sporogenes [1]	*Corynebacterium diphtheriae* [2]		Lactic acid bacteria [3]	*Eberthella typhosa* [4]	*Streptococcus zymogenes* [5]	*Proteus morganii* [6]	*Neisseria intracellularis* [7]	*Acetobacter suboxydans* [8]
	P.-W. No. 8 strain	H.Y. strain						
			Alanine					Alanine
Arginine			Arginine		Arginine			
			Aspartic acid					
Cystine	Cystine	Cystine	Cystine		Cystine	Cystine	Cystine	Cystine
	Glutamic acid	Glutamic acid	Glutamic acid		Glutamic acid		Glutamic acid	
		Glycine						
		Histidine	Histidine					Histidine
Leucine	Leucine		Leucine or isoleucine					
					Isoleucine			Isoleucine
			Lysine		Lysine			
Methionine	Methionine	Methionine	Methionine					
Phenylalanine		Phenylalanine	Phenylalanine					
			Serine					
			Threonine					
Tryptophan		Tryptophan	Tryptophan	Tryptophan †	Tryptophan			
Tyrosine			Tyrosine		Tyrosine			
Valine	Valine	Valine	Valine					Valine
								Proline

* For the requirements of other bacteria the discussion of the nutrition of the individual species should be consulted.

† For strains which can utilize other amino acids the discussion of the nutrition of *Eberthella typhosa*, pp. 683 to 686, should be consulted.

[1] Fildes and Richardson (1935).

[2] Mueller and Kapnick (1935).

[3] Wood, Geiger, and Werkman (1940), Hutchings and Peterson (1942), Shankman (1943), Hegsted (1944).

[4] Fildes, Gladstone, and Knight (1933), Burrows (1942).

[5] Woolley and Hutchings (1940).

[6] Pelczar and Porter [(1943) and unpublished data].

[7] Frantz (1942).

[8] Stokes and Larsen (1945).

data it will be seen that methionine, cystine, glutamic acid, tryptophan, and valine are the amino acids most commonly required by these representative species; others, such as threonine, are needed only by certain bacteria. For additional information on the amino acid requirements of various bacterial species, the discussion of the nutrition of the individual species and the references cited there should be consulted.

In studies of the amino acid requirements of bacteria the concentrations of the various acids employed may be a limiting factor for growth. Therefore the concentration of the individual amino acids may have to be varied to suit the requirements of the particular organism being studied. In other compounds the optical activity, the structure, the solubility, or other factors may have to be taken into account.

Many compounds which inhibit the growth of microorganisms appear to do so by interfering with substances essential in reactions involved in growth. To determine whether such an inhibition is possible with certain necessary amino acids, McIlwain (1941) prepared a series of α-aminosulfonic acid analogs of some naturally occurring α-aminocarboxylic acids, such as glycine, alanine, valine, and leucine, and tested their abilities to interfere with the growth of several microorganisms in amino acid media. In every case the α-aminosulfonic acids delayed or prevented growth, but the inhibition could be reduced or removed by the further addition of an excess of α-aminocarboxylic acids. These results are considered to afford further instances of the blocking of enzyme reactions essential to growth by inhibitors which act on account of their structural similarity to normal substrates of the enzymes concerned. In other words, the α-aminosulfonic acids appear to compete with the natural α-aminocarboxylic acids in a manner similar to that in which sulfanilamide interferes with *p*-aminobenzoic acid and pyridine-3-sulfonic acid blocks nicotinic acid.

THE USE OF MICROORGANISMS TO ASSAY VITAMINS

In the past a number of different physical, chemical, and biological methods have been developed for the assay of substances for their vitamin content. Although the physical and chemical methods are very useful, they are incontestable only if their results can be correlated with biological potency. Therefore, the biological methods, which have been an important tool in the discovery of the vitamins, must still be used today as the final criteria for qualitative and quantitative vitamin assays and for the standardization and evaluation of the accuracy of other methods. Biological methods using animals,

TABLE 29

A SUMMARY OF THE MICROBIOLOGICAL METHODS FOR THE QUANTITATIVE ASSAY OF SEVERAL VITAMINS OF THE B-COMPLEX *

Vitamin or Its Derivative	Microorganism Employed	Principle of the Test	Sensitivity or Smallest Quantity Detectable (Approximately) per Milliliter of Medium, μg.	Reference
Thiamin (vitamin B_1)	Yeast	Fermentation test in which CO_2 production is measured	1	Schultz, Atkin, and Frey (1937, 1938, 1942), Deutsch (1944)
			0.2	Ochoa and Peters (1938)
	Yeast	Turbidity of culture	0.0002–0.001	Williams and associates (1941, 1942)
	Phycomyces blakesleeanus	Growth or weight of mycelium or CO_2 production	0.01–0.025	Schopfer and Jung (1936), Sinclair (1938), Bonner and Erickson (1938), Heyns (1939), Hamner, Stewart, and Matrone (1943)
	Lactobacillus fermentum	Turbidity of culture	0.0–0.005	Sarett and Cheldelin (1944)
	Leuconostoc mesenteroides	Turbidity and acid production	0.0–0.003	Gaines and Stahly (1943)
	Streptococcus salivarius	Turbidity of culture	0.00001–0.0002	Niven and Smiley (1943)
Cocarboxylase	Yeast	Measurement of CO_2 produced by decarboxylation of pyruvic acid	0.1	Ochoa and Peters (1938)

Riboflavin and its coenzymes and enzymes	*Lactobacillus casei* ε	Acid production or turbidity of culture	0.005–0.025	Snell and Strong (1939), † Arnold, Lipsius, and Greene (1941), Strong, Feeney, Moore, and Parsons (1941), Landy and Dicken (1942), Bauernfeind *et al.* (1942), Greene and Black, 1943; Chattaway, Happold, and Sandford (1943), Lowry and Bessey (1944)
Nicotinic acid or its amide (niacin)	*Proteus* species	Turbidity of culture	0.002–0.012	Lwoff and Querido (1938), Querido, Lwoff, and Lataste (1939)
	Dysentery bacilli	Acid production	0.002–0.006	Dorfman, Koser, Horwitt, Berkman, and Saunders (1940)
	Shigella paradysenteriae (Sonne)	Turbidity of culture	0.05	Fraser, Topping, and Sebrell (1938), Isbell, Wooley, Butler, and Sebrell (1941)
	L. mesenteroides	Turbidity or acid production	0.0–0.1	Gaines and Stahly (1943)
	Lactobacillus arabinosus	Acid production	0.05–0.3	Snell and Wright (1941),† Isbell (1942), Atkin, Schultz, Williams, and Frey (1943), Krehl, Strong, and Elvehjem (1943), Sarett, Pederson, and Cheldelin (1945)
	L. casei ε	Acid production	0.005	Landy and Dicken (1942)
Di- or triphosphopyridine nucleotide (cozymase)	*Hemophilus parainfluenzae*	Turbidity of culture	0.004	Lwoff and Lwoff (1937), Kohn (1938), Vilter, Koch, and Spies (1940)
	Hemophilus influenzae	Nitrite production from nitrate	0.001–0.003	Hoagland and Ward (1942)

* For more complete details consult the references; see also Sandford (1943), Stokes, Gunness, and Foster (1944), and Spitzer, Biddison, Bergeron, and Caldwell (1944).

† For more complete details of these techniques and their practical application see "Studies on the Vitamin Content of Tissues. I and II," by R. J. Williams and associates in *University of Texas Publication No.* 4137 (1941), pp. 1–87, and *Publication No.* 4237 (1942), pp. 1–145.

TABLE 29 (*Continued*)

A SUMMARY OF THE MICROBIOLOGICAL METHODS FOR THE QUANTITATIVE ASSAY OF SEVERAL VITAMINS OF THE B-COMPLEX *

Vitamin or Its Derivative	Microorganism Employed	Principle of the Test	Sensitivity or Smallest Quantity Detectable (Approximately) per Milliliter of Medium, μg.	Reference
Pyridoxine (vitamin B_6)	Yeast	Fermentation test or turbidity of culture	0.0005–0.01	Schultz, Atkin, and Frey (1939), Eakin and Williams (1939) †
	Saccharomyces carlsbergensis	Turbidity of culture	0.0005–0.004	Atkin, Schultz, Williams, and Frey (1943)
	Neurospora sitophila mutant	Weight of mycelium	0.01–0.1	Stokes, Larsen, Woodward, and Foster (1943)
	Lactobacillus plantarum	Turbidity or acidity of culture	0.125–1	Moller (1938), Moller, Zima, Jung, and Moll (1939)
	L. casei ε	Acid production	0.005–0.01	Landy and Dicken (1942)
Pantothenic acid	Yeast	Turbidity of culture	0.0005	Williams, Truesdail, Weinstock, Rohrmann, Lyman, and McBurney (1938)
	L. mesenteroides	Turbidity or acid production	0.0–0.01	Gaines and Stahly (1943)
	L. plantarum	Turbidity of culture	0.5	Kuhn and Wieland (1940)
	L. casei ε	Acid production or turbidity of culture	0.004–0.09	Pennington, Snell, and Williams (1940),† Stanbery, Snell, and Spies (1940), Strong, Feeney, and Earle (1941), Neal and Strong (1943)
		Acid production	0.0025	Landy and Dicken (1942)

	L. arabinosus	Turbidity or acid production	0.01–0.08	Skeggs and Wright (1944), Hoag, Sarett, and Cheldelin (1945)
	Proteus morganii	Turbidity of culture	0.0002	Pelczar and Porter (1941)
Biotin	Yeast	Turbidity and moist weight of cells	0.00002–0.001	Snell, Eakin, and Williams (1940),† Nielsen and Hartelius (1942), Hertz (1943)
	Rhizobium trifolii	Turbidity of culture	0.01	West and Wilson (1940)
	Clostridium butylicum	Turbidity of culture	0.0000133	Peterson, McDaniel, and McCoy (1940), Lampen, Klein, and Peterson (1941), Snell and Williams (1939)
	L. mesenteroides	Turbidity or acid production	0.0–0.001	Gaines and Stahly (1943)
	L. arabinosus	Acid production	0.0004	Snell and Wright (1941), Wright and Skeggs (1944*a*)
	L. casei ε	Acid production	0.04	Shull, Hutchings, and Peterson (1942), Shull and Peterson (1943), Tomlinson and Peterson (1944), Williams and Fieger (1945)
			0.000025	Landy and Dicken (1942)
	Ashbya gossypii	Weight of mycelium	0.0002	Robbins and Schmidt (1939)
Folic acid	*Streptococcus fecalis* (*Streptococcus lactis* R)	Turbidity of culture	0.0005 or less	Mitchell and Snell (1941); see Williams and associates (1941) †
	L. casei ε	Acid production	0.0001 or less	Landy and Dicken (1942)

* For more complete details consult the references; see also Sandford (1943), Stokes, Gunness, and Foster (1944), and Spitzer, Biddison, Bergeron, and Caldwell (1944).

† For more complete details of these techniques and their practical application see "Studies on the Vitamin Content of Tissues. I and II," by R. J. Williams and associates in *University of Texas Publication No.* 4137 (1941), pp. 1–87, and *Publication No.* 4237 (1942), pp. 1–145.

TABLE 29 (*Continued*)

A SUMMARY OF THE MICROBIOLOGICAL METHODS FOR THE QUANTITATIVE ASSAY OF SEVERAL VITAMINS OF THE B-COMPLEX *

Vitamin or Its Derivative	Microorganism Employed	Principle of the Test	Sensitivity or Smallest Quantity Detectable (Approximately) per Milliliter of Medium, μg.	Reference
p-Aminobenzoic acid	*Acetobacter suboxydans*	Turbidity of culture	0.001–0.003	Landy and Dicken (1942*a*), Landy and Streightoff (1943)
	L. arabinosus	Acid production	0.0002–0.005	Lewis (1942)
	Neurospora crassa mutant	Area of growth	0.0003–0.001	Thompson, Isbell, and Mitchell (1943)
	Clostridium acetobutylicum	Turbidity of culture	0.00003–0.0002	Lampen and Peterson (1944)
Inositol	Yeast	Turbidity	0.1 or less	Williams and associates (1941) †
	N. crassa mutant	Weight of dry mycelium	0.2–2.5	Beadle (1944)
Choline	*N. crassa* mutant	Weight of dry mycelium	0.02	Horowitz and Beadle (1943), Luecke and Pearson (1944)

* For more complete details consult the references; see also Sandford (1943), Stokes, Gunness, and Foster (1944), and Spitzer, Biddison, Bergeron, and Caldwell (1944).

† For more complete details of these techniques and their practical application see "Studies on the Vitamin Content of Tissues. I and II," by R. J. Williams and associates in *University of Texas Publication No.* 4137 (1941), pp. 1–87, and *Publication No.* 4237 (1942), pp. 1–145.

such as the rat, are usually costly and time-consuming and cannot be employed when only small amounts of material are available, but in general they are statistically valid.

The discovery that microorganisms require certain vitamins for growth has provided a new, rapid, and frequently specific and quantitative method of vitamin assay. In the past few years the determination of vitamins by microbiological methods has found wide application. Like the physical and chemical methods, however, such techniques must be investigated thoroughly in order to determine the types of compounds which interfere with the assay, the specificity afforded by them, and their sensitivity. Several of the special microbiological assay techniques for some of the members of the vitamin B-complex are listed in Table 29; the original papers should be consulted for details of the procedures employed in these tests. The choice of a test will depend upon several factors. For example, a test which involves the measurement of acid production may be used for colored or turbid solutions, whereas one in which turbidity measurements are made would be impossible.

Although the microbiological methods are rapidly gaining favor, their use is at the present time restricted to certain B vitamins. As time goes on, special tests will undoubtedly be developed for all the members of the vitamin B-complex and possibly other vitamins as well.

USE OF MICROORGANISMS TO ASSAY AMINO ACIDS

Within the past few years it has been observed by several workers that certain microorganisms can be used to assay amino acids. The techniques employed are very similar to those used for the microbiological assay of vitamins. For example, an organism which requires a given amino acid is used, and all other factors necessary for growth are kept constant in the medium. A standard curve is then obtained by varying the concentration of the amino acid in question and plotting the turbidity or acid production in the culture medium against the various concentrations of the amino acid. The amount of a given amino acid in an unknown substance can then be determined by using this material in the medium in place of the known amino acid.

Amino acids can be detected in 1-mg. amounts of protein or even less, and extensive pretreatment of protein hydrolyzates is not necessary. The organisms used so far are capable of detecting about 1 to 10 μg. of amino acid, and errors of not over 5 to 10 per cent are commonly reported.

With *Lactobacillus arabinosus* or *Lactobacillus casei* these nine amino acids can be assayed with no more than 10 per cent error: *l*-cystine, *dl*-methionine, *dl*-isoleucine, *l*-leucine, *dl*-valine, *l*-arginine, *l*-glutamic acid, *dl*-threonine, and *l*-tryptophan. For the technical details of the methods used, the original reports should be consulted [see Shankman, Dunn, and Rubin (1943), Kuiken, Norman, Lyman, Hale, and Blotter (1943), McMahan and Snell (1944), Baumgarten, Garey, Olsen, Stone, and Boruff (1944)].

An accurate and specific microbiological method for the determination of *dl*-aspartic acid and *dl*-serine in purified proteins has been developed by Stokes and Gunness (1945*b*). The method is based on the quantitative response of *Lactobacillus delbrückii* to the two amino acids as measured by the lactic acid formed.

Dunn and his associates (1944) have employed *Leuconostoc mesenteroides* for the quantitative determination of *l*-lysine. A straight-line standard exists between about 8 and 200 μg. of lysine, when plotted against acid-titration values using milliliters of 0.1 *N* NaOH. From the appearance of the curves it seems likely that twelve other amino acids can be quantitatively determined with this organism.

Schenck (1943) has proposed a microbiological assay for β-alanine, employing the diphtheria bacillus, which requires about 2.5 to 5 μg. of this amino acid for optimum growth.

INTERPRETATION OF CHEMOTHERAPY THROUGH NUTRITIONAL STUDIES OF MICROORGANISMS

A great many theories have been advanced in the past to explain the mode of action of chemotherapeutic agents. Within the past few years numerous studies have been carried out with bacteria in an effort to explain the mode of action of various types of drugs, and a few examples may be mentioned in this discussion. It should also be pointed out that, although the activity *in vivo* of the better-known chemotherapeutic agents, such as sulfanilamide, appears to be directed against the invading microorganism, the recovery of the infected host seems to entail two factors: the drug and the host. In other words, although the drug may be able to bring the infection under control, it requires the cooperation of the host's defense mechanism to dispose of the infectious agent. We shall concern ourselves here with the drug factor only, that is, with the ability of chemical compounds to inhibit the growth of susceptible bacteria or possibly actually to kill them.

In 1940 Woods concluded that sulfanilamide acts by competing with *p*-aminobenzoic acid, by virtue of its similarity in structure, for enzymes whose functions are essential for growth. The essential nature of *p*-aminobenzoic acid in normal organisms has been confirmed by its isolation from yeast [Rubbo and his associates (1940, 1941)], and sulfanilamide inhibition of the metabolism of *p*-aminobenzoic acid by an enzyme system has been observed by Lipmann (1941). It is known also that inhibitors can act by interfering, not with the substrate of an enzyme, but with an essential part of the enzyme itself, or in other ways. This has been suggested by Fildes (1940) to be true of mercuric salts, which appear to act by combining with thiol groups essential to the cell. Fildes also observed that the action of mercuric salts *in vitro* could be prevented or neutralized by the further addition of thiol compounds. Acriflavin appears to act by combining with nucleotides which are essential to the enzymes of the inhibited organisms [McIlwain (1941, 1942)], but the inhibition can be reversed by supplying not only nucleotides but also amino acids, which appear to be the normal products of the enzymes which are being inhibited. Higher concentrations of acriflavin seem to affect hydrogen-transporting systems, and inhibitions due to such concentrations can be reversed by artificial carriers, such as methylene blue. There is also considerable evidence that the following inhibitors act as described: certain dyes, by preventing oxidized substances which must be reduced from functioning normally [Fildes (1940)]; pyridine-3-sulfonic acid and amide, by competitive and noncompetitive inhibition with enzymes concerned with nicotinic acid and derivatives [McIlwain (1940)]; α-aminosulfonic acids, by interfering with the metabolism of α-aminocarboxylic acids [McIlwain (1941)]; gramicidin by affecting glucose metabolism [Dubos (1939)]; styryl 430 (2-*p*-aminostyryl-6-*p*-aminobenzoylaminoquinoline) and rivanol, by mechanisms similar to that of acriflavin [see Pourbaix (1939) and McIlwain (1942), respectively]. Additional examples of these types will be found in Chapter 4.

It has been noted frequently that the activities of substances inhibitory to bacterial growth vary with the media employed in their testing, and such observations have received exact interpretation in a similar manner. A few examples are given in Table 30, and others will be found in papers by Rubbo and Gillespie (1940, 1942), Snell (1941), and others. The most suitable media for such experiments are those of the simplest constitution which support optimum growth of the organism being studied.

Fildes (1940), writing in the journal *Lancet*, suggested that future research in chemotherapy should be directed to making such modifications of known essential metabolites as to inhibit growth by one of the following methods: (1) by molecular combination with the essential metabolite to form an inactive product, (2) by oxidation of a substance which requires to be reduced, or (3) by competition for an enzyme associated with the essential metabolite. Several compounds so prepared (see Fig. 4 and Table 30) have been found inhibitory to bacterial growth.

TABLE 30

THE EFFECT OF REVERSING AGENTS ON CERTAIN MICROBIAL INHIBITORS

[From McIlwain (1942) and others]

Organism	Main Constituents of the Basal Medium	Inhibitor	Reversing Agent	Growth
Streptococcus pyogenes [1]	Bacto-peptone, glucose, glutamine and other growth factors, and phosphate buffer	None	None	+
		Sulfanilamide	None	−
		Sulfanilamide	Yeast extract	+
		Sulfanilamide	Yeast concentrates	+
		Sulfanilamide	*p*-Aminobenzoic acid	+
Clostridium acetobutylicum [2]	Asparagine, glucose, inorganic salts, and *p*-aminobenzoic acid	None	None	+
		Sulfanilamide	None	−
		Sulfanilamide	Yeast extract	+
		Sulfanilamide	Excess of *p*-aminobenzoic acid	+
Staphylococcus aureus [3]	Amino acids, vitamin B_1, nicotinamide, and salts	None	None	+
		Pyridine-3-sulfonic acid	None	−
		Pyridine-3-sulfonic acid	Excess of nicotinamide	+
Proteus vulgaris [4]	Ammonium lactate, nicotinamide, and salts	None	None	+
		α-NH_2-sulfonic acids	None	−
		α-NH_2-sulfonic acids	α-NH_2-carboxylic acids	+
Yeast [5]	Asparagine-inorganic salt medium plus pantothenic acid	None	None	+
		N-(α, γ-dihydroxy-β, β-dimethyl butyryl)-taurine	None	−
		N-(α, γ-dihydroxy-β, β-dimethyl butyryl)-taurine	Excess of pantothenate	+
Lactic acid bacteria [5]	Amino acids, glucose purines and pyrimidines, and growth factors, including pantothenic acid	None	None	+
		N-(α, γ-dihydroxy-β, β-dimethyl-butyryl)-taurine	None	−
		N-(α, γ-dihydroxy-β, β-dimethyl-butyryl)-taurine	Excess of pantothenate	+
Diplococcus pneumoniae [6]	Yeast extract or filtered plasma plus pantothenic acid	None	None	+
		Pantoyltaurine	None	−
		Pantoyltaurine	Excess of pantothenate	+
Streptococcus pyogenes [6]	Amino acids and growth factors, including pantothenic acid	None	None	+
		Pantoyltaurine	None	−
		Pantoyltaurine	Excess of pantothenate	+
Escherichia coli [7]	Ammonium lactate and inorganic salts	None	None	+
		Acriflavin components	None	−
		Acriflavin components	Yeast extract or tryptic casein	+
		Acriflavin components	Nucleate or amino acids	+

[1] Woods (1940).
[2] Rubbo and Gillespie (1940, 1942).
[3] McIlwain (1940, 1942*a*).
[4] McIlwain (1941).
[5] Snell (1941).
[6] McIlwain (1942).
[7] McIlwain (1941*a*, 1942*a*).

Future work in this same field will undoubtedly produce other compounds which function in much the same manner. For additional reading on this interesting subject the articles by McIlwain (1942–1944), Rubbo and Gillespie (1942), and others (see Chapter 4) should be consulted.

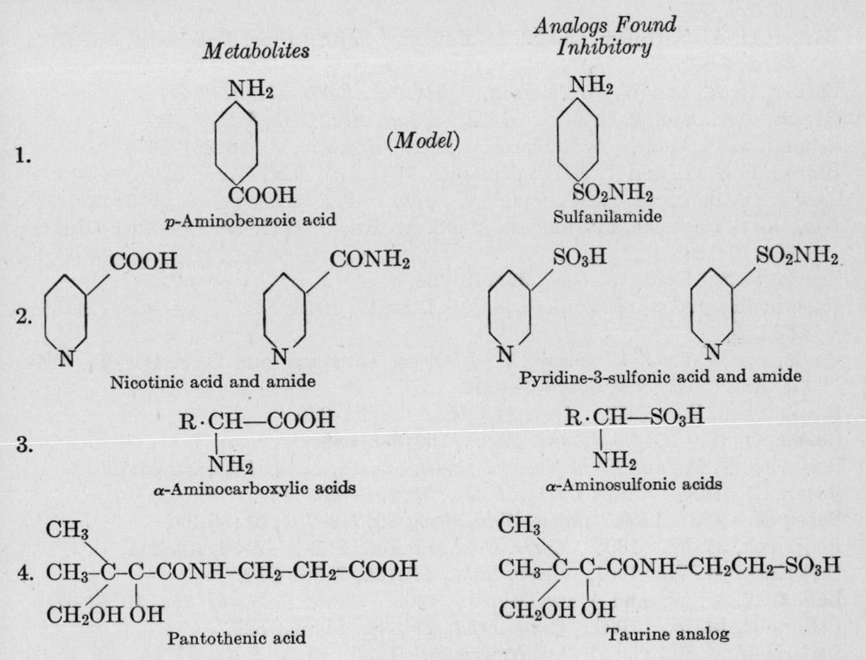

FIG. 4. The Relationship between Essential Metabolites and Inhibitory Analogs [From McIlwain (1942); for references see Table 30].

REFERENCES

Adolph, E. F. 1933. *Physiol. Rev.*, **13**:336–371.
Allison, F. E., S. R. Hoover, and D. Burk. 1933. *Science*, **78**:217–218.
Almquist, H. J., C. F. Pentler, and E. Mecchi. 1938. *Proc. Soc. Exptl. Biol. Med.*, **38**:336–338.
Almquist, H. J. 1941. *Physiol. Rev.*, **21**:194–216.
Anderson, L. R. 1931. *Am. J. Hyg.*, **13**:164–200.
Anderson, R. J., and E. G. Roberts. 1930. *J. Biol. Chem.*, **89**:599–610, 611–617.
Angier, R. B., J. H. Boothe, B. L. Hutchings, J. H. Mowat, J. Semb, E. L. R. Stokstad, Y. SubbaRow, C. W. Waller, D. B. Cosulich, M. J. Fahrenbach, M. E. Hultquist, E. Kuh, E. H. Northey, D. R. Seeger, J. P. Sickels, and J. M. Smith, Jr. 1945. *Science*, **102**:227–228.
Ansbacher, S. 1941. *Science*, **93**:164–165.
Ark, P. A. 1937. *Phytopathology*, **27**:1–28.
Arnold, A., S. T. Lipsius, and D. J. Greene. 1941. *Food Research*, **6**:39–43.
Atkin, L., A. S. Schultz, W. L. Williams, and C. N. Frey. 1943. *Ind. Eng. Chem., Anal. Ed.*, **15**:141–144; *J. Am. Chem. Soc.*, **65**:992.

Baars, J. K. 1930. "Over Sulfaatreductie door Bacterien." Dissertation, Delft. 164 pp.

Baas-Becking, L. G. M., and G. S. Parks. 1927. *Physiol. Rev.*, **7**:85–106.

Badger, E. 1944. *J. Biol. Chem.*, **153**:183–191; *J. Bact.*, **47**:509–518.

Ball, E. 1938. *J. Bact.*, **36**:559–565.

Barker, H. A., S. Ruben, and J. V. Beck. 1940. *Proc. Natl. Acad. Sci. U. S.*, **26**:477–482.

Barker, H. A., S. Ruben, and M. D. Kamen. 1940. *Proc. Natl. Acad. Sci. U. S.*, **26**:426–430.

Barker, H. A., and W. H. Peterson. 1944. *J. Bact.*, **47**:307–308.

Barnes, T. C., and T. L. Jahn. 1934. *Quart. Rev. Biol.*, **9**:292–341.

Barnett, J. W., and F. A. Robinson. 1942. *Biochem. J.*, **36**:364–367.

Barron, E. S. G., and T. E. Friedemann. 1941. *J. Biol. Chem.*, **137**:593–610.

Bass, A., S. Berkman, and F. Saunders. 1941. *J. Infectious Diseases*, **68**:220–225.

Bass, A., S. Berkman, F. Saunders, and S. A. Koser. 1941. *J. Infectious Diseases*, **68**:175–183.

Bastin, E. S. 1926. *J. Geol.*, **34**:773–792.

Bauernfeind, J. C., A. L. Sotier, and C. S. Boruff. 1942. *Ind. Eng. Chem.*, **14**:666–671.

Baumgarten, W., J. C. Garey, M. J. Olsen, L. Stone, and C. S. Boruff. 1944. *J. Am. Chem. Soc.*, **66**:1607–1609.

Bavendamm, W. 1932. *Arch. Mikrobiol.*, **3**:205–276.

Beadle, G. W. 1944. *J. Biol. Chem.*, **156**:683–689.

Beckwith, T. D., and E. M. Geary. 1940. *J. Infectious Diseases*, **66**:78–79.

Beger, H. 1935. *Centr. Bakt., II Abt.*, **92**:401–406.

Beger, H. 1937, 1938. *Gas-u. Wasserfach*, **80**:779–784; **81**:35–39.

Beijerinck, M. W. 1895. *Centr. Bakt., II Abt.*, **1**:1–9, 49–59, 104–114.

Beijerinck, M. W. 1901. *Centr. Bakt., II Abt.*, **7**:561–582.

Beijerinck, M. W., and A. vanDelden. 1903. *Centr. Bakt., II Abt.*, **10**:33–47.

Beijerinck, M. W. 1904. *Centr. Bakt., II Abt.*, **11**:593–599.

Beijerinck, M. W., and D. C. J. Minkman. 1909. *Centr. Bakt., II Abt.*, **25**:30–63.

Beijerinck, M. W. 1920. *Proc. Konink. Akad. Wetenschappen Amsterdam*, **22**:899–908.

Benham, R. W. 1941. *Proc. Soc. Exptl. Biol. Med.*, **46**:176–178.

Bergey, D. H., R. S. Breed, E. G. D. Murray, and A. P. Hitchens. 1939. *Bergey's Manual of Determinative Bacteriology.* Williams & Wilkins Co., Baltimore.

Berkman, S., F. Saunders, and S. A. Koser. 1940. *Proc. Soc. Exptl. Biol. Med.*, **44**:68–70.

Bernheimer, A. W., W. Gillman, G. A. Hottle, and A. M. Pappenheimer, Jr. 1942. *J. Bact.*, **43**:495–498.

Bernheimer, A. W., and A. M. Pappenheimer, Jr. 1942. *J. Bact.*, **43**:481–494.

Bernheimer, A. W. 1944. *J. Exptl. Med.*, **80**:321–331.

Berthelot, A., and G. Amoureux. 1938. *Compt. rend. soc. biol.*, **128**:980–981.

Bertrand, D. 1941. *Bull. soc. chim. biol.*, **23**:467–471.

Bjälfve, G., R. Nilsson, and D. Burström. 1938. *Naturwissenschaften*, **26**:840.

Bohonos, N., B. L. Hutchings, and W. H. Peterson. 1942. *J. Bact.*, **44**:479–485.

Bohonos, N., and Y. SubbaRow. 1943. *Arch. Biochem.*, **3**:257–259.

Boissevain, C. H., W. F. Drea, and H. W. Schultz. 1938. *Proc. Soc. Exptl. Biol Med.*, **39**:481–483.

Boissevain, C. H., and H. W. Schultz. 1938. *Am. Rev. Tuberc.*, **38**:624–628.

Boltjes, T. Y. K. 1935. *Arch. Mikrobiol.*, **6**:79–138.
Bömeke, H. 1939. *Arch. Mikrobiol.*, **10**:385–445.
Bonner, J., and J. Erickson. 1938. *Am. J. Botany*, **25**:685–692.
Boquet, A. 1939. *Compt. rend. soc. biol.*, **130**:200–202.
Bourne, G., and R. Allen. 1935. *Australian J. Exptl. Biol. Med. Sci.*, **13**:165–174.
Bovarnick, M. R. 1943. *J. Biol. Chem.*, **148**:151–161; **149**:301–302; **151**:467–475.
Braun, H., and C. E. Cahn-Bronner. 1921. *Centr. Bakt., I Abt. Orig.*, **86**:196–211.
Braun, H., and F. Mündel. 1929. *Centr. Bakt., I Abt. Orig.*, **112**:347–354.
Brenchley, W. E. 1943. *Biol. Rev. Cambridge Phil. Soc.*, **18**:159–171.
Brown, R. W., H. G. Wood, and C. H. Werkman. 1939. *J. Bact.*, **38**:631–640.
Bunker, H. J. 1936. "A Review of the Physiology and Biochemistry of the Sulphur Bacteria." Dept. Sci. Ind. Research, Chem. Research, Spec. Rept. No. 3. 48 pp.
Bunting, M. I., and L. J. Ingraham. 1942. *J. Bact.*, **43**:585–591.
Bunting, M. I. 1942. *J. Bact.*, **43**:593–606.
Burk, D. 1934. *Ergeb. Enzymforsch.*, **3**:23–56.
Burk, D., and C. K. Horner. 1935. *Naturwissenschaften*, **23**:259–260.
Burk, D., R. J. Winzler, and V. duVigneaud. 1941. *J. Biol. Chem.*, **140**: xxi–xxii.
Burk, D., and R. J. Winzler. 1943. *Science*, **97**:57–60.
Burkholder, P. R., and I. McVeigh. 1942. *Science*, **95**:127–128.
Burkholder, P. R., and D. Moyer. 1943. *Bull. Torrey Botan. Club*, **70**:372–377.
Burrows, W. 1933. *J. Infectious Diseases*, **52**:126–137.
Burrows, W. 1936. *Quart. Rev. Biol.*, **11**:406–424.
Burrows, W. 1939. *J. Infectious Diseases*, **64**:145–156.
Burrows, W. 1942. *J. Infectious Diseases*, **70**:126–130.
Bushnell, L. D., and H. F. Haas. 1941. *J. Bact.*, **41**:653–673.
Büsing, K.-H., and F. Peters. 1940. *Biochem. Z.*, **304**:134–136.
Büsing, K.-H. 1941. *Centr. Bakt., II Abt.*, **103**:70–72.
Cahn-Bronner, C. E. 1940. *Proc. Soc. Exptl. Biol. Med.*, **45**:454–456.
Cailleau, R. 1938, 1939. *Compt. rend. soc. biol.*, **127**:861–863, 1421–1423; **130**:319.
Calvery, H. O. 1942. *Food Research*, **7**:313–331.
Campbell, T. E., and G. J. Hucker. 1944. *Food Research*, **9**:197–205.
Casman, E. P. 1940. *J. Bact.*, **40**:601–617.
Cataldi, M. S. 1939, 1940. *Rev. inst. bacteriol. dept. nacl. hig.* (*Buenos Aires*), **9**:1–96; **9**:393–423.
Chattaway, F. W., F. C. Happold, and M. Sandford. 1943, 1944. *Biochem. J.*, **37**:298–302; **38**:111–115.
Chattaway, F. W., F. C. Happold, M. Sandford, B. Lythgoe, and A. R. Todd. 1943. *Nature*, **151**:559.
Chattaway, F. W. 1944. *Nature*, **153**:250–251.
Chilean Nitrate Educational Bureau, Inc. 1939–1944. "Bibliography of References to the Literature on the Minor Elements and their Relation to Plant and Animal Nutrition." New York. (Originally compiled by L. G. Willis.)
Cholodny, N. 1926. *Die Eisenbakterien. Beiträge zu einer Monographie.* Gustav Fischer, Jena. 162 pp.
Clark, F. M., and W. R. Mitchell. 1944. *Arch. Biochem.*, **3**:459–466.
Clarke, M. F., M. Lechycka, and A. E. Light. 1942. *J. Biol. Chem.*, **142**:957–958.
Clifton, C. E. 1940. *J. Bact.*, **39**:485–497.
Cohen, S., and J. H. Mueller. 1940. *Proc. Soc. Exptl. Biol. Med.*, **45**:244–245.
Cohen, S., J. C. Snyder, and J. H. Mueller. 1941. *J. Bact.*, **41**:581–591.

Davies, R., and M. Stephenson. 1941. *Biochem. J.*, **35**:1320–1331.
Davies, R. 1942. *Biochem. J.*, **36**:582–599.
Davis, D. J. 1917, 1921. *J. Infectious Diseases*, **21**:392–403; **29**:178–186, 187–189.
den Dooren de Jong, L. E. 1926. "Bijdrage tot de Kennis van het Mineralisatieproces." Thesis, Rotterdam.
Deutsch, H. F. 1944. *J. Biol. Chem.*, **152**:431–443.
Devloo, R. 1938. *Arch. intern. physiol.*, **46**:157–188.
Dewey, V. C. 1941. *Proc. Soc. Exptl. Biol. Med.*, **46**:482–484.
Dienes, L. 1939. *J. Infectious Diseases*, **65**:24–42.
Dimitroff, V. T. 1926. *J. Bact.*, **12**:19–49.
Dittmer, K., D. B. Melville, and V. duVigneaud. 1944. *Science*, **99**:203–205.
Dittmer, K., and V. duVigneaud. 1944. *Science*, **100**:129–131.
Dorfman, A., S. A. Koser, H. R. Reames, K. F. Swingle, and F. Saunders. 1939. *J. Infectious Diseases*, **65**:163–182.
Dorfman, A., S. A. Koser, M. K. Horwitt, S. Berkman, and F. Saunders. 1940. *Proc. Soc. Exptl. Biol. Med.*, **43**:434–438.
Dorfman, A., S. Berkman, and S. A. Koser. 1942. *J. Biol. Chem.*, **144**:393–400.
Doudoroff, M. 1938. *Enzymologia*, **5**:239–243.
Doudoroff, M. 1942, 1943. *J. Bact.*, **44**:451–459; *Proc. Soc. Exptl. Biol. Med.*, **53**:73–75.
Dozois, K. P., F. Hachtel, C. J. Carr, and J. C. Krantz, Jr. 1935. *J. Bact.*, **30**:189–192.
Dozois, K. P., C. J. Carr, J. C. Krantz, Jr., F. Hachtel, and F. E. Beck. 1936. *J. Bact.*, **32**:499–503.
Dozois, K. P., C. J. Carr, and J. C. Krantz, Jr. 1938. *J. Bact.*, **36**:599–604.
Dubos, R. J. 1939. *J. Exptl. Med.*, **70**:1–10.
Dunn, M. S., M. N. Camien, S. Shankman, W. Frankl, and L. B. Rockland. 1944. *J. Biol. Chem.*, **156**:715–724.
Dunn, M. S., S. Shankman, M. N. Camien, W. Frankl, and L. B. Rockland. 1944. *J. Biol. Chem.*, **156**:703–713.
duVigneaud, V., J. P. Chandler, A. W. Moyer, and D. M. Keppel. 1939. *J. Biol. Chem.*, **131**:57–76.
duVigneaud, V. 1942. *Science*, **96**:455–461.
duVigneaud, V., K. Dittmer, E. Hague, and B. Long. 1942. *Science*, **96**:186–187.
duVigneaud, V., K. Hofmann, and D. B. Melville. 1942. *J. Am. Chem. Soc.*, **64**:188–189.
Eakin, R. E., and R. J. Williams. 1939. *J. Am. Chem. Soc.*, **61**:1932.
Eakin, R. E., E. E. Snell, and R. J. Williams. 1940. *J. Biol. Chem.*, **136**:801–802.
Eakin, R. E., and E. Eakin. 1942. *Science*, **96**:187–188.
Eastcott, E. V. 1928. *J. Phys. Chem.*, **32**:1094–1111.
Eckhardt, R. E., P. György, and L. V. Johnson. 1941. *Proc. Soc. Exptl. Biol. Med.*, **46**:405–409.
Ehrismann, O. 1936. *Z. Hyg. Infektionskrankh.*, **118**:544–554.
Ehrismann, O. 1937. *Centr. Bakt., I Abt. Orig.*, **140**:273–280.
Elberg, S. S., and K. F. Meyer. 1939. *J. Bact.*, **37**:429–445.
Elion, L. 1924. *Centr. Bakt., II Abt.*, **63**:58–67.
Ellis, D. 1907. *Centr. Bakt., II Abt.*, **19**:502–518.
Ellis, D. 1932. *Sulphur Bacteria.* Longmans, Green and Co., New York.
Elsden, S. R. 1938. *Biochem. J.*, **32**:187–193.
Elvehjem, C. A., and L. J. Teply. 1943. *Chem. Rev.*, **33**:185–208.

Engel, H., and W. Skallau. 1937. *Centr. Bakt., II Abt.*, **97**:305–311.
Evans, E. A., Jr., and L. Slotin. 1940. *J. Biol. Chem.*, **136**:805–806.
Evans, W. C., W. R. C. Handley, and F. C. Happold. 1939. *Brit. J. Exptl. Path.*, **20**:396–408.
Evans, W. C., F. C. Happold, and W. R. C. Handley. 1939. *Brit. J. Exptl. Path.*, **20**:41–48.
Faber, F. C. von. 1912, 1914. *Jahrb. wiss. Botan.*, **51**:285–375; **54**:243–264.
Feeney, R. E., and F. M. Strong. 1942. *J. Biol. Chem.*, **142**:961–962.
Feeney, R. E., J. H. Mueller, and P. A. Miller. 1943. *J. Bact.*, **46**:559–562, 563–571.
Field, J. T., and C. F. Poe. 1940. *J. Biol. Chem.*, **132**:473–476.
Fildes, P. 1921, 1922, 1923, 1924. *Brit. J. Exptl. Path.*, **2**:16–25; **3**:210–214; **4**:265–271; **5**:69–74.
Fildes, P., G. P. Gladstone, and B. C. J. G. Knight. 1933. *Brit. J. Exptl. Path.*, **14**:189–196.
Fildes, P. 1935. *Brit. J. Exptl. Path.*, **16**:309–314.
Fildes, P., and G. M. Richardson. 1935. *Brit. J. Exptl. Path.*, **16**:326–335.
Fildes, P., G. M. Richardson, B. C. J. G. Knight, and G. P. Gladstone. 1936. *Brit. J. Exptl. Path.*, **17**:481–484.
Fildes, P. 1938. *Brit. J. Exptl. Path.*, **19**:239–244.
Fildes, P., and G. P. Gladstone. 1939. *Brit. J. Exptl. Path.*, **20**:334–341.
Fildes, P. 1940. *Lancet*, **1940** (i):955–957.
Forman, J. 1942, 1943. *Ohio State Med. J.*, **38**:1131–1132; **39**:48–49, 145–146, 553–554, 651.
Foster, J. W. 1939. *Botan. Rev.*, **5**:207–239.
Foster, J. W., and S. A. Waksman. 1939. *J. Bact.*, **37**:599–617.
Foster, J. W. 1940. *J. Gen. Physiol.*, **24**:123–134.
Foster, J. W., S. F. Carson, S. Ruben, and M. D. Kamen. 1941. *Proc. Natl. Acad. Sci. U. S.*, **27**:590–596.
Foster, J. W. 1944. *J. Bact.*, **47**:27–41.
Frantz, I. D. 1942. *J. Bact.*, **43**:757–761.
Fraser, H. F., N. H. Topping, and W. H. Sebrell. 1938. *U. S. Pub. Health Repts.*, **53**:1836–1842.
Frieden, E. H., H. K. Mitchell, and R. J. Williams. 1944. *J. Am. Chem. Soc.*, **66**:269–271.
Fries, N. 1943. *Nature*, **152**:105.
Gaines, S., and G. L. Stahly. 1943. *J. Bact.*, **46**:441–449.
Gavin, G., and E. W. McHenry. 1941. *J. Biol. Chem.*, **139**:485.
Geilmann, W., and K. Brünger. 1935. *Biochem. Z.*, **275**:387–395.
Geiman, Q. M. 1941. *Proc. Soc. Exptl. Biol. Med.*, **47**:329–332.
Gibert, E. B. 1944. *Proc. Soc. Exptl. Biol. Med.*, **57**:363–366.
Giesberger, G. 1936. "Beiträge zur Kenntnis der Gattung *Spirillum* Ehrenberg." Dissertation, Delft.
Gingrich, W., and F. Schlenk. 1944. *J. Bact.*, **47**:535–550.
Gladstone, G. P., P. Fildes, and G. M. Richardson. 1935. *Brit. J. Exptl. Path.*, **16**:335–348.
Gladstone, G. P. 1937, 1938, 1939. *Brit. J. Exptl. Path.*, **18**:322–333: **19**:208–226; **20**:189–200.
Glinka-Tschernorutzky, E. 1933. *Biochem. Z.*, **263**:144–148.
Gortner, R. A. 1932, 1934. *Ann. Rev. Biochem.*, **1**:21–54; **3**:1–22.

Gould, R. G. 1943. *J. Biol. Chem.*, **153**:143–150.
Gould, R. G., L. W. Kane, and J. H. Mueller. 1944. *J. Bact.*, **47**:287–292.
Greaves, J. E., C. E. Zobell, and J. D. Greaves. 1928. *J. Bact.*, **16**:409–430.
Green, H. N. 1940. *Brit. J. Exptl. Path.*, **21**:38–64.
Greene, R. D., and A. Black. 1943. *J. Am. Pharm. Assoc., Sci. Ed.*, **32**:217–220.
Griffith, W. H. 1941. *J. Nutrition*, **22**:239–253.
Grohmann, G. 1924. *Centr. Bakt., II Abt.*, **61**:256–271.
Grossowicz, N. 1942. *Proc. Soc. Exptl. Biol. Med.*, **49**:8–11.
Gunsalus, I. C., and W. D. Bellamy. 1944. *J. Biol. Chem.*, **155**:357–358, 557–563.
Gunsalus, I. C., C. F. Niven, Jr., and J. M. Sherman. 1944. *J. Bact.*, **48**:611.
Gupta, G. C. D., and B. C. Guha. 1941. *Ann. Biochem. Exptl. Med.*, **1**:14–26.
György, P., and H. Goldblatt. 1940. *J. Exptl. Med.*, **72**:1–9.
György, P., D. B. Melville, D. Burk, and V. duVigneaud. 1940. *Science*, **91**:243–245.
Haines, R. B. 1932, 1933. *Biochem. J.*, **26**:323–336; **27**:466–473.
Halvorson, H. O. 1931. *Soil Sci.*, **32**:141–165.
Hamner, K. C., W. S. Stewart, and G. Matrone. 1943. *Food Research*, **8**:444–452.
Hanks, J. H., and R. L. Weintraub. 1936. *J. Bact.*, **32**:653–670.
Happold, F. C., and A. Key. 1937. *Biochem. J.*, **31**:1323–1329.
Harder, E. C. 1919. *U. S. Geol. Survey Professional Paper* 113. 89 pp.
Hegarty, C. P., and O. Rahn. 1934. *J. Bact.*, **28**:21–30.
Hegsted, D. M. 1944. *J. Biol. Chem.*, **152**:193–200.
Heigener, H. 1935. *Centr. Bakt., II Abt.*, **93**:81–113.
Heise, F. H., and W. Steenken, Jr. 1941. *Am. Rev. Tuberc.*, **44**:635–636.
Henrici, A. T., and D. E. Johnson. 1935. *J. Bact.*, **30**:83–93.
Hertz, R. 1943. *Proc. Soc. Exptl. Biol. Med.*, **52**:15–17.
Hes, J. W. 1938. *Ann. fermentations*, **4**:547–558.
Heyns, K. 1939. *Z. physiol. Chem.*, **258**:219–237.
Hill, T. J., and A. H. Kniesner. 1942. *J. Dental Research*, **21**:467–471.
Hills, G. M. 1938, 1943. *Biochem. J.*, **32**:383–391; **37**:418–425.
Hoag, E. H., H. P. Sarett, and V. H. Cheldelin. 1945. *Ind. Eng. Chem., Anal. Ed.*, **17**:60–62.
Hoagland, C. L., and S. M. Ward. 1942. *J. Biol. Chem.*, **146**:115–122.
Hoagland, C. L., S. M. Ward, H. Gilder, and R. E. Shank. 1942. *J. Exptl. Med.*, **76**:241–252.
Hofer, A. W. 1941. *J. Bact.*, **41**:193–224.
Hofmann, K. 1943. *Advances in Enzymol.*, **3**:289–313.
Hoover, S. R., and F. E. Allison. 1940. *J. Biol. Chem.*, **134**:181–192.
Horner, C. K., and D. Burk. 1934. *J. Agr. Research*, **48**:981–995.
Horner, C. K., D. Burk, F. E. Allison, and M. S. Sherman. 1942. *J. Agr. Research*, **65**:173–193.
Horner, C. K., and F. E. Allison. 1944. *J. Bact.*, **47**:1–14.
Hornibrook, J. W. 1940. *Proc. Soc. Exptl. Biol. Med.*, **45**:598–599.
Horowitz, N. H., and G. W. Beadle. 1943. *J. Biol. Chem.*, **150**:325–333.
Horster, H. 1930. *Centr. Bakt., I Abt. Orig.*, **118**:283–297.
Hottle, G. A., J. O. Lampen, and A. M. Pappenheimer, Jr. 1941. *J. Biol. Chem.* **137**:457–458.
Hughes, T. P. 1932. *J. Bact.*, **23**:437–447.
Hutchings, B. L., and D. W. Woolley. 1939. *Science*, **90**:41–42.

Hutchings, B. L., N. Bohonos, and W. H. Peterson. 1941. *J. Biol. Chem.*, **141**:521–528.
Hutchings, B. L., and W. H. Peterson. 1942. *Proc. Soc. Exptl. Biol. Med.*, **52**:36–38.
Hutchings, B. L., E. L. R. Stokstad, N. Bohonos, and N. H. Slobodkin. 1944. *Science*, **99**:371.
Hutner, S. H. 1938. *J. Bact.*, **35**:429–440.
Hutner, S. H. 1942. *J. Bact.*, **43**:629–640.
Hutner, S. H. 1944. *Arch. Biochem.*, **3**:439–444.
Isbell, H., J. G. Wooley, R. E. Butler, and W. H. Sebrell. 1941. *J. Biol. Chem.*, **139**:499–510.
Isbell, H. 1942. *J. Biol. Chem.*, **144**:567–568.
Janeway, C. A. 1941. *J. Am. Med. Assoc.*, **116**:941–942.
Janke, A. 1939. *Centr. Bakt., II Abt.*, **100**:409–459.
Jiménez, J. F. 1940. *Proc. Soc. Exptl. Biol. Med.*, **45**:402–405.
Johnson, E. A., and L. F. Rettger. 1943. *J. Bact.*, **45**:127–135.
Johnson, F. H., W. T. Goodale, and J. Turkevich. 1942. *J. Cellular Comp. Physiol.*, **19**:163–172.
Johnson, F. H., and H. W. Schwarz. 1944. *J. Bact.*, **47**:373–378.
Jones, L. W., and J. E. Greaves. 1943. *Soil Sci.*, **55**:393–404.
Karabinos, J. V., and D. M. Dicken. 1944. *Arch. Biochem.*, **4**:211–215.
Kaserer, H. 1906. *Centr. Bakt., II Abt.*, **16**:681–696.
Katznelson, H. 1944. *J. Bact.*, **48**:495.
Keil, F. 1912. *Beitr. Biol. Pflanz.*, **11**:335–372.
Kendall, A. I., and M. Ishikawa. 1929. *J. Infectious Diseases*, **44**:282–291.
Kerby, G. P. 1939. *J. Bact.*, **37**:495–499.
Keresztesy, J. C., E. L. Rickes, and J. L. Stokes. 1943. *Science*, **97**:465.
Kleinzeller, A. 1941. *Biochem. J.*, **35**:495–501.
Kligler, I. J., and K. Guggenheim. 1938. *J. Bact.*, **35**:141–156.
Kligler, I. J., and N. Grosowitz. 1939. *J. Bact.*, **38**:309–320.
Kligler, I. J., and N. Grossowicz. 1941. *J. Bact.*, **42**:173–192.
Kluyver, A. J., and W. J. Hoppenbrouwers. 1931. *Arch. Mikrobiol.*, **2**:245–260.
Knight, B. C. J. G., and P. Fildes. 1933. *J. Physiol., Proc. Physiol. Soc.*, **78**:6P–8P; *Brit. J. Exptl. Path.*, **14**:112–124.
Knight, B. C. J. G. 1935. *Brit. J. Exptl. Path.*, **16**:315–326.
Knight, B. C. J. G. 1936. "Bacterial Nutrition." *Med. Research Council (Brit.) Special Rept. Series* 210. London. 182 pp.
Knight, B. C. J. G. 1937. *Biochem. J.*, **31**:731–737, 966–973.
Knight, B. C. J. G., and H. McIlwain. 1938. *Biochem. J.*, **32**:1241–1251.
Knight, B. C. J. G. 1941. *Chemistry & Industry*, **60**:369–371.
Knorr, M. 1925. *Ergeb. Hyg. Bakt., Immunitätsforch. Exptl. Therap.*, **7**:641–706.
Kögl, F. 1935. *Ber. deut. chem. Ges.*, **68**:16–28.
Kögl, F., and B. Tönnis. 1936. *Z. physiol. Chem.*, **242**:43–73.
Kögl, F., and W. van Hasselt. 1936. *Z. physiol. Chem.*, **242**:74–80.
Kögl, F. 1937. *Proc. Roy. Soc. London, B*, **124**:1–4.
Kögl, F., and N. Fries. 1937. *Z. physiol. Chem.*, **249**:93–110.
Kögl, F., and W. J. van Wagtendonk. 1938. *Rec. trav. chim.*, **57**:747–754.
Kohn, H. I. 1938. *Biochem. J.*, **32**:2075–2083.
Kolkwitz, R. 1938. *Ber. deut. botan. Ges.*, **56**:11–15.
Koser, S. A. 1918, 1923. *J. Infectious Diseases*, **23**:377–379; *J. Bact.*, **8**:493–520

Koser, S. A., and L. F. Rettger. 1919. *J. Infectious Diseases,* **24**:301–321.
Koser, S. A., A. Dorfman, and F. Saunders. 1938, 1940. *Proc. Soc. Exptl. Biol. Med.,* **38**:311–313; **43**:391–394.
Koser, S. A., R. D. Finkle, A. Dorfman, M. V. Gordon, and F. Saunders. 1938. *J. Infectious Diseases,* **62**:209–218.
Koser, S. A., and F. Saunders. 1938. *Bact. Rev.,* **2**:99–160.
Koser, S. A., B. B. Breslove, and A. Dorfman. 1941. *J. Infectious Diseases,* **69**:114–124.
Koser, S. A., M. H. Wright, and A. Dorfman. 1942. *Proc. Soc. Exptl. Biol. Med.,* **51**:204–205.
Koser, S. A., and M. H. Wright. 1943. *Proc. Soc. Exptl. Biol. Med.,* **53**:249–251; *J. Bact.,* **46**:239–249.
Kost, P. F. 1942. *Bull. Pittsburgh Univ.,* **38**:258–265.
Kostytschew, S., A. Ryskaltschuk, and O. Schwezowa. 1926. *Z. physiol. Chem.,* **154**:1–17.
Krampitz, L. O., and C. H. Werkman. 1941. *Biochem. J.,* **35**:595–602.
Krauskopf, E. J., E. E. Snell, and E. McCoy. 1939. *Enzymologia,* **7**:327–330.
Krebs, H. A., and L. V. Eggleston. 1940. *Biochem. J.,* **34**:1383–1395.
Krebs, H. A. 1941. *Nature,* **147**:560–570.
Krehl, W. A., F. M. Strong, and C. A. Elvehjem. 1943. *Ind. Eng. Chem., Anal. Ed.,* **15**:471–475.
Kuhn, R., and T. Wieland. 1940. *Ber. deut. chem. Ges.,* **73**:962–971, 971–975.
Kuhn, R., and K. Schwarz. 1941. *Ber. deut. chem. Ges.,* **74**(2):1617–1624.
Kuiken, K. A., W. H. Norman, C. M. Lyman, F. Hale, and L. Blotter. 1943. *J. Biol. Chem.,* **151**:615–626.
Lampen, J. O., A. A. Klein, and W. H. Peterson. 1941. *J. Biol. Chem.,* **140**:LXXIV.
Lampen, J. O., and W. H. Peterson. 1941, 1943, 1944. *J. Am. Chem. Soc.,* **63**:2283; *Arch. Biochem.,* **2**:443–449; *J. Biol. Chem.,* **153**:193–202.
Lampen, J. O., L. A. Underkofler, and W. H. Peterson. 1942. *J. Biol. Chem.,* **146**:277–278.
Landy, M. 1938. *Proc. Soc. Exptl. Biol. Med.,* **38**:504–506.
Landy, M. 1941. "Vitamin H, Biotin and Coenzyme R. A Brief Review of the Literature." Publication from the Research Laboratories of S. M. A. Corporation, Chagrin Falls, Ohio.
Landy, M., and D. M. Dicken. 1941. *Proc. Soc. Exptl. Biol. Med.,* **46**:449–452.
Landy, M., and J. Wyeno. 1941. *Proc. Soc. Exptl. Biol. Med.,* **46**:59–62.
Landy, M., and D. M. Dicken. 1942, 1942*a*. *J. Lab. Clin. Med.,* **27**:1086–1092; *J. Biol. Chem.,* **146**:109–114.
Landy, M., D. M. Dicken, M. M. Bicking, and W. R. Mitchell. 1942. *Proc. Soc. Exptl. Biol. Med.,* **49**:441–444.
Landy, M., N. W. Larkum, and E. J. Oswald. 1943. *Proc. Soc. Exptl. Biol. Med.,* **52**:338–341.
Landy, M., and F. Streightoff. 1943. *Proc. Soc. Exptl. Biol. Med.,* **52**:127–128
Lankford, C. E., and E. E. Snell. 1943. *J. Bact.,* **45**:410–411.
Lantzsch, K. 1922. *Centr. Bakt., II Abt.,* **57**:309–319.
Lasnitzki, A., and E. Szörényi. 1934. *Biochem. J.,* **28**:1678–1683.
Lavollay, J., and F. Laborey. 1938. *Compt. rend.,* **206**:1055–1056.
Leitner, J. 1937. *Klin. Wochschr.,* **16**:1423–1425.
Leonian, L. H., and V. G. Lilly. 1942. *J. Bact.,* **43**:17–18.

Lepper, E., and C. J. Martin. 1929. *Brit. J. Exptl. Path.*, **10**:327–334.
Lesh, J. B., L. A. Underkofler, and E. I. Fulmer. 1938. *J. Am. Chem. Soc.*, **60**:2505–2507.
Leuthardt, F. 1938. *Z. physiol. Chem.*, **252**:238–260.
Levine, M., and H. W. Schoenlein. 1930. *A Compilation of Culture Media for the Cultivation of Microorganisms.* Williams & Wilkins Co., Baltimore.
Lévy-Bruhl, M., and M. Legrand. 1930. *Compt. rend. soc. biol.*, **103**:1070–1072.
Lewis, J. C. 1942. *Am. J. Bot.*, **29**:207–210; *J. Biol. Chem.*, **146**:441–450.
Lieske, R. 1911, 1912. *Jahrb. wiss. Bot.*, **49**:91–127; *Ber. deut. botan. Ges.*, **30**:(12)–(22).
Lilly, V. G., and L. H. Leonian. 1944. *Science*, **99**:205–206.
Lipman, C. B., and E. McLees. 1940. *Soil Sci.*, **50**:429–433.
Lipmann, F. 1941. *J. Biol. Chem.*, **139**:977–978.
Lochhead, A. G., and G. B. Landerkin. 1942. *J. Bact.*, **43**:18.
Long, H. F., and B. W. Hammer. 1936. *Iowa State College J. Sci.*, **10**:261–265.
Longsworth, L. G., and D. A. MacInnes. 1936. *J. Bact.*, **31**:287–300; **32**:567–585.
Loring, H. S., and J. G. Pierce. 1944. *J. Biol. Chem.*, **153**:61–69.
Loving, W. L. 1943. *Am. J. Trop. Med.*, **23**:593–596.
Lowry, O. H., and O. A. Bessey. 1944. *J. Biol. Chem.*, **155**:71–77.
Lucas, G. H. W. 1924. *J. Phys. Chem.*, **28**:1180–1200.
Luecke, R. W., and P. B. Pearson. 1944. *J. Biol. Chem.*, **153**:259–263.
Lwoff, A. 1936. *Compt. rend. soc. biol.*, **122**:1041–1042.
Lwoff, A., and M. Lwoff. 1937. *Proc. Roy. Soc. London, B*, **122**:352–359, 360–373.
Lwoff, A. 1938. *Ann. inst. Pasteur*, **61**:580–617.
Lwoff, A., and H. Dusi. 1938. *Compt. rend. soc. biol.*, **127**:53–56, 1408–1411; **128**:238–241.
Lwoff, A., and A. Querido. 1938, 1939. *Compt. rend. soc. biol.*, **129**:1039–1043; **130**:1569–1573.
Mallinckrodt-Haupt, A. St. von. 1938. *Z. Vitaminforsch.*, **7**:303–311.
Mann, T. 1943. *Nature*, **151**:619–620.
Martin, G. J., C. T. Ichniowski, W. A. Wisansky, and S. Ansbacher. 1942. *Am. J. Physiol.*, **136**:66–69.
McCarty, M. 1941. *Proc. Soc. Exptl. Biol. Med.*, **46**:133–136.
McCulloch, L. 1929. *J. Agr. Research*, **38**:269–287.
McCullough, N. B., and L. A. Dick. 1942. *J. Infectious Diseases*, **71**:193–197, 198–200.
McCullough, N. B., and L. A. Dick. 1943. *Proc. Soc. Exptl. Biol. Med.*, **52**:310–311.
McDaniel, L. E., D. W. Woolley, and W. H. Peterson. 1939. *J. Bact.*, **37**:259–268.
McElroy, L. W., and H. Goss. 1939. *J. Biol. Chem.*, **130**:437–438.
McIlwain, H. 1939, 1940, 1941, 1942, 1943. *Brit. J. Exptl. Path.*, **20**:330–333; **21**:25–38, 136–147; **22**:148–155; **23**:95–102; **24**:203–212, 212–217.
McIlwain, H. 1939*a*, 1941*a*. *Biochem. J.*, **33**:1942–1946; **35**:1311–1319.
McIlwain, H., P. Fildes, G. P. Gladstone, and B. C. J. G. Knight. 1939. *Biochem. J.*, **33**:223–229.
McIlwain, H. 1942*a*. *Lancet*, **1942**(i):412–415.
McIlwain, H., and D. E. Hughes. 1944. *Biochem. J.*, **38**:187–195.
McIntire, F. C., A. J. Riker, and W. H. Peterson. 1941. *J. Bact.*, **42**:1–13.
McKenzie, D. A. 1941. *Proc. Soc. Agr. Bact.*, **1941**:45–46.

McMahan, J. R., and E. E. Snell. 1944. *J. Biol. Chem.*, **152**:83–95.
Meek, C. S., and C. B. Lipman. 1922. *J. Gen. Physiol.*, **5**:195–204.
Melville, D. B., K. Dittmer, G. B. Brown, and V. duVigneaud. 1943. *Science*, **98**:497–499.
Merrill, A. T., and W. M. Clark. 1928. *J. Bact.*, **15**:267–296.
Meyer, K. 1934. *Centr. Bakt., I Abt. Orig.*, **131**:289–290, 291–300.
Meyerhof, O. 1916. *Pflügers Arch. ges. Physiol.*, **164**:353–427; **165**:229–284.
Miller, W. L., E. V. Eastcott, and J. E. Maconachie. 1933. *J. Am. Chem. Soc.*, **55**:1502–1517.
Mitchell, H. K., E. E. Snell, and R. J. Williams. 1940, 1941, 1944. *J. Am. Chem. Soc.*, **62**:1791–1792; **63**:2284; **66**:267–268.
Mitchell, H. K. 1944. *J. Am. Chem. Soc.*, **66**:274–278.
Mitchell, H. K., and R. J. Williams. 1944. *J. Am. Chem. Soc.*, **66**:271–274.
Mitchell, N. B., and M. Levine. 1938. *J. Bact.*, **36**:587–598.
Molisch, H. 1910. *Die Eisenbakterien.* Gustav Fischer, Jena. 83 pp.
Möller, E. F. 1938, 1939. *Z. physiol. Chem.*, **254**:285–286; **260**:246–256.
Möller, E. F., O. Zima, F. Jung, and T. Moll. 1939. *Naturwissenschaften*, **27**:228–229.
Möller, E. F. 1940. *Angew. Chem.*, **53**:204–209.
Möller, E. F., and K. Schwarz. 1941. *Ber. deut. chem. Ges.*, **74**(2):1612–1616.
Möller, E. F., and L. Birkofer. 1942. *Ber. deut. chem. Ges.*, **75**(2):1108–1118.
Morel, M. 1941. *Ann. inst. Pasteur*, **67**:285–298.
Morton, H. E., and P. R. Leberman. 1944. *U. S. Naval Med. Bull.*, **43**:409–419.
Mueller, J. H. 1935. *J. Bact.*, **30**:513–524.
Mueller, J. H., and I. Kapnick. 1935. *J. Bact.*, **30**:525–534.
Mueller, J. H. 1937. *J. Bact.*, **34**:163–178, 429–441.
Mueller, J. H. 1937. *J. Biol. Chem.*, **119**:121–131.
Mueller, J. H., and S. Cohen. 1937. *J. Bact.*, **34**:381–386.
Mueller, J. H., and Y. Subbarow. 1937. *J. Bact.*, **34**:153–161.
Mueller, J. H. 1938. *J. Bact.*, **36**:499–515.
Mueller, J. H., and A. W. Klotz. 1938. *J. Am. Chem. Soc.*, **60**:3086–3087.
Mueller, J. H. 1940. *Bact. Rev.*, **4**:97–134.
Mueller, J. H., and P. A. Miller. 1941. *J. Biol. Chem.*, **140**:933–934.
Mueller, J. H., and P. A. Miller. 1941. *J. Immunol.*, **40**:21–32.
Mueller, J. H., J. Hinton, and P. A. Miller. 1942. *J. Bact.*, **43**:100.
Mueller, J. H., and P. A. Miller. 1942. *J. Bact.*, **43**:763–772.
Mueller, J. H., and P. A. Miller. 1942. *Proc. Soc. Exptl. Biol. Med.*, **49**:211–212.
Mulder, E. G. 1939. *Arch. Mikrobiol.*, **10**:72–86.
Myers, J. 1940. *J. Bact.*, **40**:705–719.
Naumann, E. 1928, 1929. *Ber. deut. bot. Ges.*, **46**:135–140; **47**:262–265.
Neal, A. L., and F. M. Strong. 1943. *Ind. Eng. Chem., Anal. Ed.*, **15**:654–657.
Neuberg, C., and E. Welde. 1914. *Biochem. Z.*, **67**:111–118.
Nielsen, N., and V. Hartelius. 1942. *Biochem. Z.*, **311**:317–328.
Niklewski, B. 1908. *Centr. Bakt., II Abt.*, **20**:469–473.
Nilsson, R., G. Bjälfve, and D. Burström. 1938–1939. *Ann. Landw. Hochschule Swedens.*, **5**:291–322; **6**:299–326; **7**:51–61, 301–331.
Nilsson, R., G. Bjälfve, and D. Burström. 1938, 1939. *Naturwissenschaften*, **26**:284–661; **27**:389.
Nisina, Y., S. Endo, H. Nakayama. 1941. *Sci. Papers Inst. Phys. Chem. Research (Tokyo)*, **38**:341–346.

Niven, C. F., Jr. 1943, 1944. *J. Bact.*, **46**:573–576; **47**:343–350.
Niven, C. F., Jr., and K. L. Smiley. 1943. *J. Biol. Chem.*, **150**:1–9.
Niven, C. F., Jr., and J. M. Sherman. 1944. *J. Bact.*, **47**:335–342.
Ochoa, S., and R. A. Peters. 1938. *Biochem. J.*, **32**:1501–1515.
Odintsova, E. N. 1940. *Microbiology (U.S.S.R.)*, **9**:253–265.
O'Kane, D. J. 1941. *J. Bact.*, **41**:441–446.
Olsen, O. 1920. *Centr. Bakt., I Abt. Orig.*, **85**:12–27.
Ondratschek, K. 1940. *Arch. Mikrobiol.*, **11**:89–117, 219–226, 228–238, 239–263.
Orla-Jensen, S. 1909. *Centr. Bakt., II Abt.*, **22**:305–346.
Orla-Jensen, S., N. C. Otte, and A. Snog-Kjaer. 1936. *Centr. Bakt., II Abt.*, **94**:434–477.
Orla-Jensen, S., A. D. Orla-Jensen, H. Dam, and J. Glavind. 1941. *Centr. Bakt., II Abt.*, **104**:202–204.
Oxford, A. E., J. O. Lampen, and W. H. Peterson. 1940. *Biochem. J.*, **34**:1588–1597.
Paleĭ, T. Ya. 1938. *Microbiology (U.S.S.R.)*, **7**:841–849.
Pandalai, K. M. 1936. *Science*, **84**:440–441.
Pandalai, N. G., and K. R. Rao. 1942. *Indian J. Med. Research*, **30**:381–389.
Pappenheimer, A. M., Jr. 1935. *Biochem. J.*, **29**:2057–2063.
Pappenheimer, A. M., Jr., and S. J. Johnson. 1936. *Brit. J. Exptl. Path.*, **17**:335–341.
Pappenheimer, A. M., Jr., J. H. Mueller, and S. Cohen. 1937. *Proc. Soc. Exptl. Biol. Med.*, **36**:795–796.
Pappenheimer, A. M., Jr., and G. A. Hottle. 1940. *Proc. Soc. Exptl. Biol. Med.*, **44**:645–649.
Pappenheimer, A. M., Jr. 1942. *J. Bact.*, **43**:273–289.
Park, C. R., and W. B. Wood, Jr. 1942. *Bull. Johns Hopkins Hosp.*, **70**:19–25.
Patel, M. K. 1928–1929. *Iowa State College J. Sci.*, **3**:271–298.
Pederson, C. S., and R. S. Breed. 1928. *J. Bact.*, **16**:163–185.
Pelczar, M. J., Jr., and J. R. Porter. 1940. *J. Bact.*, **39**:429–435.
Pelczar, M. J., Jr., and J. R. Porter. 1941. *J. Biol. Chem.*, **139**:111–119.
Pelczar, M. J., Jr., and J. R. Porter. 1941. *Proc. Soc. Exptl. Biol. Med.*, **43**:151–154.
Pelczar, M. J., Jr., and J. R. Porter. 1943. *Arch. Biochem.*, **2**:323–332.
Pennington, D., E. E. Snell, and R. J. Williams. 1940. *J. Biol. Chem.*, **135**:213–222.
Pennington, D., E. E. Snell, and R. E. Eakin. 1942. *J. Am. Chem. Soc.*, **64**:469.
Peskett, G. L. 1933. *Biol. Rev.*, **8**:1–45.
Peterson, W. H., L. E. McDaniel, and E. McCoy. 1940. *J. Biol. Chem.*, **133**: LXXV–LXXVI.
Peterson, W. H. 1941. *Biol. Symposia*, **5**:31–43.
Peterson, W. H., and M. S. Peterson. 1945. *Bact. Revs.*, **9**:49–109.
Pfiffner, J. J., S. B. Binkley, E. S. Bloom, R. A. Brown, O. D. Bird, A. D. Emmett, A. G. Hogan, and B. L. O'Dell. 1943. *Science*, **97**:404–405.
Pfiffner, J. J., D. G. Calkins, B. L. O'Dell, E. S. Bloom, R. A. Brown, C. J. Campbell, and O. D. Bird. 1945. *Science*, **102**:228–230.
Poe, C. E., and D. E. Klemme. 1935. *J. Biol. Chem.*, **109**:43–46.
Pohlman, G. G. 1931. *Soil Sci.*, **31**:385–406.
Pollack, M. A., and M. Lindner. 1942. *J. Biol. Chem.*, **143**:655–661.
Pollack, M. A. 1943. *J. Am. Chem. Soc.*, **65**:1335–1339.

Porter, J. R., and M. J. Pelczar, Jr. 1940. *Science*, **91**:576–577.
Porter, J. R., and M. J. Pelczar, Jr. 1941. *J. Bact.*, **41**:173–192; **42**:141.
Pourbaix, Y. 1939. *Compt. rend. soc. biol.*, **131**:1306–1309.
Powers, W. L. 1939. *Science*, **89**:434–435.
Pray, E. G. 1941. *J. Bact.*, **42**:291.
Quastel, J. H., and D. M. Webley. 1939. *Nature*, **144**:633–634.
Quastel, J. H., and D. M. Webley. 1941, 1942. *Biochem. J.*, **35**:192–206; **36**:8–33.
Querido, A., A. Lwoff, and C. Lataste. 1939. *Compt. rend. soc. biol.*, **130**:1580–1584.
Raffy, A. 1939. *Compt. rend.*, **209**:900–902.
Rahn, O. 1936. *J. Bact.*, **32**:393–399.
Rahn, O., and C. P. Hegarty. 1938. *Proc. Soc. Exptl. Biol. Med.*, **38**:218–222.
Rahn, O., and G. L. Richardson. 1941. *J. Bact.*, **41**:225–249.
Rane, L., and Y. Subbarow. 1938. *Proc. Soc. Exptl. Biol. Med.*, **38**:837–839.
Rane, L., and Y. Subbarow. 1940. *J. Bact.*, **40**:695–704.
Rane, L., and Y. Subbarow. 1940. *J. Biol. Chem.*, **134**:455–456.
Rao, M. S. 1939–1940. *Ind. J. Med. Research*, **27**:75–89, 617–626, 833–846.
Reed, G. B., and C. E. Rice. 1928. *J. Bact.*, **16**:97–107.
Reyes-Teodoro, R., and M. N. Mickelson. 1944. *Arch. Biochem.*, **4**:291–292.
Richards, O. W. 1932. *J. Biol. Chem.*, **96**:405–418.
Richards, O. W., and M. C. Troutman. 1940. *J. Bact.*, **39**:739–746.
Richardson, G. M. 1936. *Biochem. J.*, **30**:2184–2190.
Rittenberg, D., and H. Waelsch. 1940. *J. Biol. Chem.*, **136**:799–800.
Rivers, T. M. 1922. *J. Bact.*, **7**:579–581.
Robbins, W. J. 1938, 1943. *Proc. Natl. Acad. Sci. U. S.*, **24**:53–56; **29**:201–202.
Robbins, W. J., and F. Kavanagh. 1938. *Proc. Natl. Acad. Sci. U. S.*, **24**:141–145, 145–147; *Am. J. Botany*, **25**:229–236.
Robbins, W. J. 1939. *Science*, **89**:303–307.
Robbins, W. J., and M. B. Schmidt. 1939. *Bull. Torrey Botan. Club*, **66**:139–150.
Robbins, W. J., and F. Kavanagh. 1941, 1942. *Proc. Natl. Acad. Sci. U. S.*, **27**:423–427; **28**:4–7.
Robbins, W. J., and R. Ma. 1941. *Bull. Torrey Botan. Club*, **68**:446–462.
Robbins, W. J., and V. Kavanagh. 1942. *Botan. Rev.*, **8**:411–471.
Robertson, R. C. 1924. *J. Infectious Diseases*, **35**:311–314.
Robinson, G. L. 1932. *Brit. J. Exptl. Path.*, **13**:310–317.
Rogers, H. J. 1944. *Nature*, **153**:251.
Rogosa, M. 1944. *J. Bact.*, **47**:159–170.
Rohner, F., and F. Roulet. 1939. *Biochem. Z.*, **300**:148–152.
Rose, W. C. 1937. *Science*, **86**:298–300.
Rose, W. C. 1938. *Physiol. Rev.*, **18**:109–136.
Rose, W. C., and E. E. Rice. 1939. *Science*, **90**:186–187.
Rosenberg, H. R. 1942. *Chemistry and Physiology of Vitamins.* Interscience Publishers, Inc., New York.
Rosenfeld, W. D., and M. R. Greene. 1941. *J. Bact.*, **42**:165–172.
Rubbo, S. D., and J. M. Gillespie. 1940. *Nature*, **146**:838–839.
Rubbo, S. D., M. Maxwell, R. A. Fairbridge, and J. M. Gillepsie. 1941. *Australian J. Exptl. Biol. Med. Sci.*, **19**:185–198.
Rubbo, S. D., and J. M. Gillespie. 1942. *Lancet*, **1942**(i):36–38.
Ruben, S., and M. D. Kamen. 1940. *Proc. Natl. Acad. Sci. U. S.*, **26**:418–422.
Rubenstein, B. B. 1933. *J. Cellular Comp. Physiol.*, **3**:247–260.

Ruhland, W. 1924. *Jahrb. wiss. Botan.*, **63**:321–389.
Sagen, H. E., A. J. Riker, and I. L. Baldwin. 1934. *J. Bact.*, **28**:571–595.
Sandford, M. 1943. *Nature*, **152**:374–376.
Sandiford, B. R. 1937. *J. Path. Bact.*, **44**:567–572.
Sarett, H. P., and V. H. Cheldelin. 1944. *J. Biol. Chem.*, **155**:153–160; **156**:91–100.
Sarett, H. P., R. L. Pederson, and V. H. Cheldelin. 1945. *Arch. Biochem.*, **7**:77–85.
Sartory, A., R. Sartory, and J. Meyer. 1938. *Compt. rend.*, **206**:1414–1416.
Sartory, A., J. Meyer, and A. Netter. 1939. *Bull. acad. Méd.*, **121**:815–819; *Compt. rend.*, **209**:1931–1933.
Saunders, F., A. Dorfman, and S. A. Koser. 1941. *J. Biol. Chem.*, **138**:69–82.
Saz, A. K., and F. Bernheim. 1942. *J. Bact.*, **44**:385–386.
Schenck, J. R. 1943. *J. Biol. Chem.*, **149**:111–115.
Schlenk, F., and W. Gingrich. 1942. *J. Biol. Chem.*, **143**:295–296.
Schopfer, W. H., and A. Jung. 1936. *Compt. rend. soc. biol.*, **122**:249–251.
Schopfer, W. H. 1938. *Arch. Mikrobiol.*, **9**:116–128.
Schopfer, W. H., and S. Blumer. 1939. *Z. Vitaminforsch.*, **9**:344–349.
Schopfer, W. H. 1943. *Plants and Vitamins.* (Translated by N. L. Noecker.) Cronica Botanica Co., Waltham, Mass.
Schorr, L. 1939. *Centr. Bakt., II Abt.*, **100**:146–154.
Schreder, K., R. Brunner, and R. Hampe. 1934. *Biochem. Z.*, **273**:223–242.
Schultz, A. S., L. Atkin, and C. N. Frey. 1937, 1938, 1939. *J. Am. Chem. Soc.*, **59**:948–949, 2457–2460; **60**:1514–1515; **61**:1931.
Schultz, A. S., L. Atkin, and C. N. Frey. 1942. *Ind. Eng. Chem., Anal. Ed.*, **14**:35–39.
Schuman, R. L., and M. A. Farrell. 1941. *J. Infectious Diseases*, **69**:81–86.
Selbie, F. R. 1940. *Brit. J. Exptl. Path.*, **21**:90–93.
Sergent, A.-L. 1928. *Les facteurs de croissance de microbes sur milieux artificiels.* Doin et Cie, Paris.
Sevag, M. G., and M. N. Green. 1944. *J. Biol. Chem.*, **154**:719–720.
Shankman, S. 1943. *J. Biol. Chem.*, **150**:305–310.
Shankman, S., M. S. Dunn, and L. B. Rubin. 1943. *J. Biol. Chem.*, **150**:477–478; **151**:511–514.
Shull, G. M., B. L. Hutchings, and W. H. Peterson. 1942. *J. Biol. Chem.*, **142**:913–920.
Shull, G. M., and W. H. Peterson. 1943. *J. Biol. Chem.*, **151**:201–202.
Silverman, M., and C. H. Werkman. 1938. *Proc. Soc. Exptl. Biol. Med.*, **38**:823–827.
Sinclair, H. M. 1938. *Biochem. J.*, **32**:2185–2199.
Skeggs, H. R., and L. D. Wright. 1944. *J. Biol. Chem.*, **156**:21–26.
Smiley, K. L., C. F. Niven, Jr., and J. M. Sherman. 1943. *J. Bact.*, **45**:445–454.
Smith, F. B., and P. E. Brown. 1935. *Iowa State College J. Sci.*, **10**:17–25.
Smith, F. R. 1943. *J. Bact.*, **46**:369–371.
Smyth, D. H. 1940. *Biochem. J.*, **34**:1598–1604.
Snell, E. E., F. M. Strong, and W. H. Peterson. 1937. *Biochem. J.*, **31**:1789–1799.
Snell, E. E., E. L. Tatum, and W. H. Peterson. 1937. *J. Bact.*, **33**:207–225.
Snell, E. E., F. M. Strong, and W. H. Peterson. 1938. *J. Am. Chem. Soc.*, **60**:2825.
Snell, E. E., and F. M. Strong. 1939. *Enzymologia*, **6**:186–193.
Snell, E. E., and F. M. Strong. 1939. *Ind. Eng. Chem., Anal. Ed.*, **11**:346–350.

Snell, E. E., F. M. Strong, and W. H. Peterson. 1939. *J. Bact.*, **38**:293–308.
Snell, E. E., and R. J. Williams. 1939. *J. Am. Chem. Soc.*, **61**:3594.
Snell, E. E., R. E. Eakin, and R. J. Williams. 1940. *J. Am. Chem. Soc.*, **62**:175–178.
Snell, E. E., and W. H. Peterson. 1940. *J. Bact.*, **39**:273–285.
Snell, E. E. 1941. *J. Biol. Chem.*, **141**:121–128.
Snell, E. E., and H. K. Mitchell. 1941. *Proc. Natl. Acad. Sci. U. S.*, **27**:1–7.
Snell, E. E., and L. D. Wright. 1941. *J. Biol. Chem.*, **139**:675–686.
Snell, E. E. 1942. *Proc. Soc. Exptl. Biol. Med.*, **51**:356–358.
Snell, E. E., B. M. Guirard, and R. J. Williams. 1942. *J. Biol. Chem.*, **143**:519–530.
Snell, E. E., and B. M. Guirard. 1943. *Proc. Natl. Acad. Sci. U. S.*, **29**:66–73.
Snell, E. E. 1945, 1945*a*. *J. Am. Chem. Soc.*, **67**:194–197; *J. Biol. Chem.*, **157**:491–505.
Snell, E. E., and A. N. Rannefeld. 1945. *J. Biol. Chem.*, **157**:475–489.
Söhngen, N. L. 1906. *Centr. Bakt.*, *II Abt.*, **15**:513–517.
Söhngen, N. L. 1910. *Rec. trav. chim.*, **29**:238–274.
Söhngen, N. L. 1913. *Centr. Bakt.*, *II Abt.*, **37**:595–609.
Spitzer, E. H., E. A. Biddison, C. Bergeron, and J. E. Caldwell. 1944. *Science*, **100**:555–556.
Spizizen, J. 1943. *J. Infectious Diseases*, **73**:212–221, 222–228.
Sprince, H., and D. W. Woolley. 1944. *J. Exptl. Med.*, **80**:213–217.
Stanbery, S. R., E. E. Snell, and T. D. Spies. 1940. *J. Biol. Chem.*, **135**:353–354.
Stapp, C. 1942. *Centr. Bakt.*, *II Abt.*, **104**:395–401.
Starkey, R. L., and H. O. Halvorson. 1927. *Soil Sci.*, **24**:381–402.
Starkey, R. L. 1934. *J. Bact.*, **28**:365–386, 387–400.
Starkey, R. L. 1935. *J. Gen. Physiol.*, **18**:325–349.
Starkey, R. L. 1935. *Soil Sci.*, **39**:197–219.
Starkey, R. L. 1937. *J. Bact.*, **33**:545–571.
Starkey, R. L. 1938. *Arch. Mikrobiol.*, **9**:268–304.
Starr, M. P., and J. E. Weiss. 1943. *Phytopathology*, **33**:314–318.
Stavely, H. 1936. *Iowa State College J. Sci.*, **10**:99–101.
Steinberg, R. A. 1935, 1936, 1938, 1941. *J. Agr. Research*, **51**:413–424; **52**:439–448; **57**:461–476; **63**:109–127.
Steinhaus, E. A., R. R. Parker, and M. T. McKee. 1944. *U. S. Pub. Health Repts.*, **59**:78–79.
Stephenson, M., and L. H. Stickland. 1931, 1933. *Biochem. J.*, **25**:205–214, 215–220; **27**:1517–1527.
Stiller, E. T., S. A. Harris, J. Finkelstein, J. C. Keresztesy, and K. Folkers. 1940. *J. Am. Chem. Soc.*, **62**:1785–1790.
Stokes, J. L., and M. Gunness. 1943. *Proc. Soc. Exptl. Biol. Med.*, **54**:28–31.
Stokes, J. L., A. Larsen, C. R. Woodward, Jr., and J. W. Foster. 1943. *J. Biol. Chem.*, **150**:17–24.
Stokes, J. L. 1944. *J. Bact.*, **48**:201–209.
Stokes, J. L., M. Gunness, and J. W. Foster. 1944. *J. Bact.*, **47**:293–299.
Stokes, J. L., and M. Gunness. 1945. *Science*, **101**:43–44.
Stokes, J. L., and M. Gunness. 1945*a*, *b*. *J. Biol. Chem.*, **157**:121–126, 651–659.
Stokes, J. L., and A. Larsen. 1945. *J. Bact.*, **49**:495–501.
Stokstad, E. L. R. 1941, 1943. *J. Biol. Chem.*, **139**:475–476; **149**:573–574.
Street, H. R., and R. E. Reeves. 1940. *Proc. Soc. Exptl. Biol. Med.*, **44**:641–644.

Strøm, A. 1935. *The Production of Diphtheria Toxin.* A. s. Haakensen and Co., Oslo, Norway. 151 pp.
Strong, F. M., R. E. Feeney, and A. Earle. 1941. *Ind. Eng. Chem., Anal. Ed.*, **13**:566–570.
Strong, F. M., R. E. Feeney, B. Moore, and H. T. Parsons. 1941. *J. Biol. Chem.*, **137**:363–372.
Stührk, A. 1935. *Centr. Bakt., II Abt.*, **93**:161–198.
Subbarow, Y., and L. Rane. 1939. *J. Am. Chem. Soc.*, **61**:1616.
Tamura, J. T., A. A. Tytell, M. J. Boyd, and M. A. Logan. 1941. *Proc. Soc. Exptl. Biol. Med.*, **47**:284–287.
Tamura, J. T., and I. W. Gibby. 1943. *J. Bact.*, **45**:361–371.
Tatum, E. L., W. H. Peterson, and E. B. Fred. 1936. *J. Bact.*, **32**:157–166.
Tatum, E. L., H. G. Wood, and W. H. Peterson. 1936. *J. Bact.*, **32**:167–174; *Biochem. J.*, **30**:1898–1904.
Tausz, J., and M. Peter. 1919. *Centr. Bakt., II Abt.*, **49**:497–554.
Tausz, J., and P. Donath. 1930. *Z. physiol. Chem.*, **190**:141–168.
Teague, P. C., and R. J. Williams. 1942. *J. Gen. Physiol.*, **25**:777–783.
Thatcher, R. W. 1934. *Science*, **79**:464–466.
Thimann, K. V. 1935. *J. Biol. Chem.*, **109**:279–291.
Thimann, K. V., and J. Bonner. 1938. *Physiol. Rev.*, **18**:524–553.
Thjötta, T., and O. T. Avery. 1921. *J. Exptl. Med.*, **34**:97–114, 455–466; *Proc. Soc. Exptl. Biol. Med.*, **18**:197–199.
Thompson, R. C. 1943. *J. Bact.*, **46**:99–104.
Thompson, R. C., E. R. Isbell, and H. K. Mitchell. 1943. *J. Biol. Chem.*, **148**: 281–287.
Tomlinson, F. F., and W. H. Peterson. 1944. *Arch. Biochem.*, **5**:221–231.
Trager, W. 1941. *Physiol. Rev.*, **21**:1–35.
Twort, F. W. 1907. *Proc. Roy. Soc. London, B*, **79**:329–336.
Twort, F. W., and G. L. Y. Ingram. 1912. *Proc. Roy. Soc. London, B*, **84**:517–542.
Umbreit, W. W., H. R. Vogel, and K. G. Vogler. 1942. *J. Bact.*, **43**:141–148.
Underkofler, L. A., A. C. Bantz, and W. H. Peterson. 1943. *J. Bact.*, **45**:183–190.
Utter, M. F., and C. H. Werkman. 1942. *J. Biol. Chem.*, **146**:289–300.
Uyei, N. 1927. *J. Infectious Diseases*, **40**:425–432, 433–437.
Uyei, N. 1930. *Am. Rev. Tuberc.*, **22**:203–217.
Valley, G., and L. F. Rettger. 1927. *J. Bact.*, **14**:101–137.
Valley, G. 1928. *Quart. Rev. Biol.*, **3**:209–224.
van Delden, A. H. 1903. *Centr. Bakt., II Abt.*, **11**:81–94, 113–119.
van Niel, C. B. 1931, 1936. *Arch. Mikrobiol.*, **3**:1–112; **7**:323–358.
van Niel, C. B. 1941. *Advances in Enzymol.*, **1**:263–328.
van Niel, C. B., S. Ruben, S. F. Carson, M. D. Kamen, and J. W. Foster. 1942. *Proc. Natl. Acad. Sci. U. S.*, **28**:8–15.
van Niel, C. B. 1943. *Physiol. Rev.*, **23**:338–354.
van Niel, C. B. 1944. *Bact. Rev.*, **8**:1–118.
Van Overbeek, J. 1940. *Proc. Natl. Acad. Sci. U. S.*, **26**:441–443.
Vaughn, R. H. 1942. *Wallerstein Labs. Commun.*, **5**:5–26.
Vilter, S. P., and T. D. Spies. 1940. *Science*, **91**:200–201.
Vilter, S. P., M. B. Koch, and T. D. Spies. 1940. *J. Lab. Clin. Med.*, **26**:31–44.
Vogler, K. G., and W. W. Umbreit. 1941. *Soil Sci.*, **51**:331–337.
Vogler, K. G. 1942. *J. Gen. Physiol.*, **25**:617–622.

Vogler, K. G., and W. W. Umbreit. 1942. *J. Gen. Physiol.*, **26**:157–167.
Waksman, S. A., and J. S. Joffe. 1922. *J. Bact.*, **7**:239–256.
Waksman, S. A. 1927. *Principles of Soil Microbiology.* Williams & Wilkins Co., Baltimore.
Warburg, O., and W. Christian. 1933. *Biochem. Z.*, **266**:377–411.
Ward, T. G., and E. B. Starbuck. 1941. *Proc. Soc. Exptl. Biol. Med.*, **48**:19–21.
Waring, W. S., and C. H. Werkman. 1943, 1944. *Arch. Biochem.*, **1**:425–433; **4**:75–87.
Wegner, M. I., A. N. Booth, C. A. Elvehjem, and E. B. Hart. 1940. *Proc. Soc. Exptl. Biol. Med.*, **45**:769–771.
Weil, A. J., and J. Black. 1944. *Proc. Soc. Exptl. Biol. Med.*, **55**:24–26.
Weizmann, Ch., and B. Rosenfeld. 1939. *Biochem. J.*, **33**:1376–1389.
Welton, J. P., H. E. Stokinger, and C. M. Carpenter. 1944. *Science*, **99**:372.
Werkman, C. H., and H. G. Wood. 1942. *Botan. Rev.*, **8**:1–68.
Werner, W. E. G. 1933. Dissertation, University of Hamburg, and *Centr. Bakt., II Abt.*, **87**:446–475.
West, P. M., and P. W. Wilson. 1939. *J. Bact.*, **37**:161–185.
West, P. M., and A. G. Lochhead. 1940. *Soil Sci.*, **50**:409–420.
West, P. M., and P. W. Wilson. 1940. *Enzymologia*, **8**:152–162.
West, R. A., Jr., K. H. Lewis, and W. E. Militzer. 1942. *J. Bact.*, **43**:155–169.
Williams, R. J., and R. R. Roehm. 1930. *J. Biol. Chem.*, **87**:581–590.
Williams, R. J., J. H. Truesdail, H. Weinstock, Jr., E. Rohrmann, C. M. Lyman, and C. H. McBurney. 1938. *J. Am. Chem. Soc.*, **60**:2719–2723.
Williams, R. J., R. E. Eakin, and E. E. Snell. 1940. *J. Am. Chem. Soc.*, **62**:1204–1207.
Williams, R. J., and R. T. Major. 1940. *Science*, **91**:246.
Williams, R. J. 1941. *Biol. Rev.*, **16**:49–80.
Williams, R. J., and associates. 1941–1942. "Studies on the Vitamin Content of Tissues, I and II." *Univ. Texas Publication* 4137, pp. 1–87, Oct. 1, 1941; and 4237, pp. 1–145, Oct. 1, 1942.
Williams, R. J. 1943. *Advances in Enzymol.*, **3**:253–287.
Williams, V. R., and E. A. Fieger. 1945. *Ind. Eng. Chem. Anal. Ed.*, **17**:127–130.
Wilson, J. B., and P. W. Wilson. 1942. *J. Bact.*, **43**:329–341.
Wilson, P. W., E. W. Hopkins, and E. B. Fred. 1932. *Arch. Mikrobiol.*, **3**:322–340.
Wilson, P. W. 1940. *The Biochemistry of Symbiotic Nitrogen Fixation.* University of Wisconsin Press, Madison.
Winogradsky, H. 1935. *Compt. rend.*, **200**:1886–1888.
Winogradsky, S. 1888. *Botan. Zeitung*, **46**:262–270.
Winogradsky, S. 1902. *Centr. Bakt., II Abt.*, **9**:43–54.
Winogradsky, S., and H. Winogradsky. 1933. *Ann. inst. Pasteur*, **50**:350–432.
Wisansky, W. A., G. J. Martin, and S. Ansbacher. 1941. *J. Am. Chem. Soc.*, **63**:1771–1772.
Wood, H. G., and C. H. Werkman. 1935. *J. Bact.*, **30**:332.
Wood, H. G., A. A. Anderson, and C. H. Werkman. 1937. *Proc. Soc. Exptl. Biol. Med.*, **36**:217–219.
Wood, H. G., E. L. Tatum, and W. H. Peterson. 1937. *J. Bact.*, **33**:227–242.
Wood, H. G., A. A. Andersen, and C. H. Werkman. 1938. *J. Bact.*, **36**:201–214.
Wood, H. G., C. Geiger, and C. H. Werkman. 1940. *Iowa State Coll. J. Sci.*, **14**:367–378.

Wood, H. G., C. H. Werkman, A. Hemingway, and A. O. Nier. 1940, 1941. *J. Biol. Chem.*, **135**:789–790; **139**:377–381.
Woods, D. D. 1936. *Biochem. J.*, **30**:515–527.
Woods, D. D. 1940. *Brit. J. Exptl. Path.*, **21**:74–90.
Woods, D. D., and P. Fildes. 1940. 207th Meeting Biochem. Soc. Univ. Sheffield, Febr. 17, 1940; through *Chem. Ind.*, **59**:133.
Woolley, D. W. 1939. *J. Biol. Chem.*, **130**:417–419.
Woolley, D. W., and B. L. Hutchings. 1939. *J. Bact.*, **38**:285–292.
Woolley, D. W., L. E. McDaniel, and W. H. Peterson. 1939. *J. Biol. Chem.*, **131**:381–385.
Woolley, D. W. 1940. *Science*, **92**:384–385.
Woolley, D. W., and B. L. Hutchings. 1940. *J. Bact.*, **39**:287–296.
Woolley, D. W., and J. R. McCarter. 1940. *Proc. Soc. Exptl. Biol. Med.*, **45**:357–360.
Woolley, D. W. 1941. *J. Biol. Chem.*, **140**:311–312; *J. Exptl. Med.*, **73**:487–492.
Woolley, D. W. 1941. *J. Nutrition* (Suppl.), **21**:17.
Woolley, D. W., and A. G. C. White. 1943. *J. Exptl. Med.*, **78**:489–497.
Wright, L. D. 1942. *Proc. Soc. Exptl. Biol. Med.*, **51**:27.
Wright, L. D., and H. R. Skeggs. 1944. *J. Bact.*, **48**:117–118.
Wright, L. D., and H. R. Skeggs. 1944*a*. *Proc. Soc. Exptl. Biol. Med.*, **56**:95–98.
Wyss, O., V. G. Lilly, and L. H. Leonian. 1944. *Science*, **99**:18–19.
Young, E. G., R. W. Begg, and E. I. Pentz. 1944. *Arch. Biochem.*, **5**:121–136.
Zobell, C. E., and K. F. Meyer. 1932. *J. Infectious Diseases*, **51**:344–360, 361–381.

8

METABOLISM OF CARBON COMPOUNDS BY MICROORGANISMS

The metabolism of microorganisms, like that of higher forms of life, can be conveniently considered under the transformation of carbon, of nitrogen, and of mineral compounds. Actually, all these metabolic processes overlap, and for a complete understanding of the resulting dynamic phenomena the metabolism of any organism should always be considered as a whole. However, it is often more convenient to study these transformations separately. This chapter will therefore be devoted principally to the metabolism of nonnitrogenous carbon compounds, and in Chapter 9 the utilization of nitrogenous substances will be discussed. What little information is available concerning the transformation of minerals by microorganisms was mentioned briefly in Chapter 7 and will not be repeated here.

Werkman (1939) and Werkman and Wood (1942) used the following scheme to depict the metabolism of microorganisms:

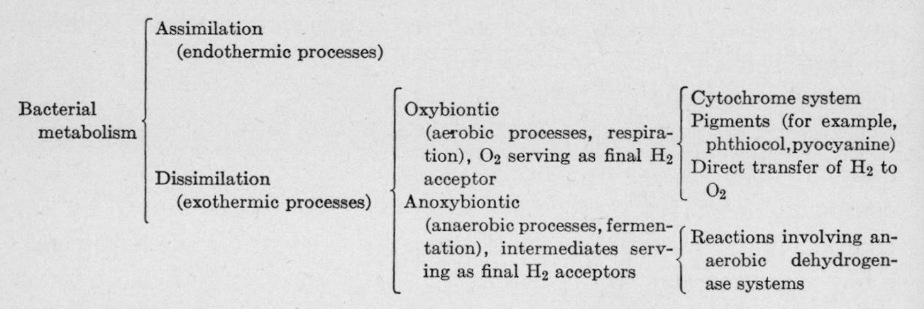

Dissimilation may be defined in general terms as the decomposition or transformation of the substrate to yield energy for the use of the organism. *Assimilation,* on the other hand, consists of the processes whereby the cells of microorganisms are built up out of the substances previously broken down by other cells. Dissimilation may be further subdivided into two processes: oxybiontic (aerobic processes, respiration) and anoxybiontic (anaerobic processes, fermentation). Both are true oxidative processes, but in oxybiontic dissimilation the substrate undergoes transformations in which oxygen serves as the final hydrogen acceptor, and water is formed; whereas in anoxybiontic dissimilation intermediate products serve as final hydrogen acceptors rather than oxygen (for example, ethyl alcohol may be formed from acetaldehyde, or lactic acid from pyruvic acid). *Metabolism* is the sum of dissimilation and assimilation, or the chemical changes in living cells by which energy is provided for vital processes and activities, and new material is assimilated to repair damage.

The metabolism of autotrophic bacteria consists primarily of the synthesizing stage, so far as organic compounds are concerned. The autotrophic organisms utilize for their synthesis the products of dissimilation of the heterotrophic organisms, such as the various minerals, nitrogen compounds, and even energy sources like hydrogen sulfide and ammonia. On the other hand, the heterotrophic organisms utilize for their dissimilation the products of assimilation of the autotrophic forms, namely, the complex organic substances synthesized by these cells.

KINDS OF CARBON COMPOUNDS METABOLIZED BY MICROORGANISMS

The major portion of the metabolism of any cell is concerned with the utilization of carbon compounds, particularly nonnitrogenous carbon compounds. Organisms oxidize such substances mainly as a source of energy; in fact, it is generally believed that only a small proportion of the products resulting from such dissimilations is transformed into cellular protoplasms.

It has been stated on several occasions by various workers that microorganisms probably exist which can attack every known carbon compound. Although we will not attempt to list all the known carbon compounds which can serve as a source of energy to microorganisms, a few representative substances may be cited as examples of the types of compounds which can be utilized. Since the early literature on this subject is reviewed completely in Volume III of *Physiology and Biochemistry of Bacteria* by Buchanan and Fulmer (1930) and in *An Index to the Chemical Action of Microorganisms on the Nonnitrogenous Organic Compounds* by Fulmer and Werkman (1930), only a brief outline of the compounds, together with a few representative studies which illustrate their end-products, will be presented here. Additional data on this subject will be found in Chapter 10.

The classification of compounds which we will use here is essentially that proposed by Buchanan and Fulmer (1930); it includes:

I. Elementary carbon.
II. Compounds consisting of only carbon and oxygen: carbon monoxide and carbon dioxide.
III. Compounds containing only carbon and hydrogen: methane and other hydrocarbons.
IV. Compounds consisting of carbon, hydrogen, and oxygen, but never nitrogen:
 Aliphatic monohydric and polyhydric alcohols.
 Aliphatic aldehydes and ketones.
 Aliphatic monobasic, dibasic, and polybasic acids.
 Carbohydrates, glycosides, and related substances.
 Cyclic or aromatic compounds.
 Fats and waxes.
V. Compounds containing nitrogen or carbon and nitrogen and usually oxygen and hydrogen:
 Molecular nitrogen.
 Ammonia, hydroxylamine, nitrous acid, nitric acid, and their salts.
 Cyanogen compounds.
 Amines and related compounds.
 Amides, imides, and related compounds.
 Urea, guanidine, purine, pyrimidine, and their derivatives.
 Amino acids.
 Peptides.
 Peptones and proteoses.
 Proteins.

The next few pages will be devoted to a discussion of the first four of these groups of compounds and their utilization as a source of carbon for microorganisms. Compounds which can be placed in the fifth group will be considered in Chapter 9.

ELEMENTARY CARBON

In 1908 Potter observed that aerobic soil bacteria, especially a coccus which was obtained in pure culture, slowly oxidized amorphous carbon in the form of charcoal, lampblack, coal, and peat. He found that, when these substances were subjected to bacterial action, CO_2 was given off. The amount of gas evolved increased in proportion to the rise of temperature until supravital temperatures were reached, and no CO_2 was formed under perfectly dry conditions such as preclude the possibility of bacterial life.

COMPOUNDS CONSISTING OF ONLY CARBON AND OXYGEN

The utilization of carbon monoxide, carbon dioxide, and the carbonates by the autotrophic bacteria was discussed in Chapter 7 and will be only briefly summarized here. Carbon monoxide is apparently used by only a few bacteria (genus *Carboxydomonas*), but this is not true of carbon dioxide.

Before 1924 it was assumed that only the autotrophic bacteria consumed carbon dioxide as a metabolite. However, in that year Theobald Smith demonstrated that CO_2 was essential for the isolation and growth of *Brucella abortus*, and since then it has been observed by several workers that in the complete absence of CO_2 growth and metabolism of diverse living systems are seriously impaired. Until recently, however, there has been no indication of the function of CO_2 in such cellular processes. In 1935 Wood and Werkman [see the review by Werkman and Wood (1942*a*)] presented the first experimental evidence of the function of CO_2 in heterotrophic cellular systems. Using propionic acid bacteria, they showed that in the fermentation of glycerol there is a net uptake of CO_2 and that the carbon of the CO_2 can be accounted for in the metabolic products—acetic, propionic, and succinic acids. It thus became clear that nonphotosynthetic systems can actually assimilate CO_2. Subsequently other investigators found that CO_2 was reactive in the metabolism of heterotrophic bacteria. For example, Woods (1936) demonstrated that *Escherichia coli* reduces CO_2 to formic acid in the presence of gaseous hydrogen, and Barker (1936) proved that CO_2 is a hydrogen acceptor, being converted to methane by the methane bacteria (see also the discussion on CO_2, pp. 633 to 635, in Chapter 7).

As a result of the above investigations considerable confusion has arisen concerning the role of CO_2 in the metabolism of heterotrophic cells. Obviously at least two distinct types of reactions are involved in the utilization or "fixation" of CO_2 in these experiments: (1) a reduction of CO_2 without the formation of carbon-to-carbon linkages, and (2) a creation of carbon-to-carbon linkages. In the first type CO_2 functions only as a hydrogen acceptor, whereas in the second new compounds are formed containing additional carbon atoms. Since the first reaction does not require the acceptance of new principles, it needs no further attention. On the other hand, when Wood and Werkman first proposed the second reaction, it required the acceptance of an entirely new principle in the metabolism of bacteria. However, their work has now been so completely confirmed that there is no longer any doubt that their original proposals were correct [see reviews by Krebs (1941), Solomon *et al.* (1941), Evans and Slotin (1941), van Niel, Ruben, Carson, Kamen, and Foster (1942), Werkman and Wood (1942, 1942*a*)].

Although this subject is reviewed in some detail by Wood and Werkman (1942*a*), a few remarks may be presented here concerning some of the facts that are now available on the role of CO_2 in bacterial metabolism. In 1938 Wood and Werkman presented evidence to show that there is a direct equimolar relationship between the amount of CO_2 fixed and the amount of succinic acid formed during the fermentation of glycerol by the propionic acid bacteria. In view of these results they suggested that the succinic acid may be synthesized by a union of 3-carbon and 1-carbon compounds, and that CO_2 is "fixed" by this mechanism. Pyruvic acid was thought to be the 3-carbon compound involved in the reaction. Although during the next two years Wood and Werkman and others presented additional evidence to show that CO_2 is fixed by union with a 3-carbon compound, it was not until 1940, when the isotopes of carbon (radioactive carbon, atomic weight 11; and the stable isotope, atomic weight 13) became available for use as tracers of fixed CO_2, that proof of the fixation of CO_2 to form succinic acid was obtained [Carson and Ruben (1940), Wood, Werkman, Hemingway, and Nier (1940, 1941)]. Wood, Werkman, and their associates furthermore showed that, if fixation of CO_2 occurs by the union of 3-carbon and 1-carbon compounds, the fixed carbon in the succinic acid will be located in the carboxyl group. The following reactions indicate the probable mechanism for such a synthesis; the stable isotope of carbon was used by these workers and is designated as $C^{13}O_2$.

$$\underset{\text{Stable isotope of carbon (dioxide)}}{C^{13}O_2} + \underset{\text{Pyruvic acid}}{HCH_2 \cdot CO \cdot COOH} \rightarrow \underset{\text{Oxaloacetic acid}}{HOOC^{13} \cdot CH_2 \cdot CO \cdot COOH}$$

$$\underset{\text{Oxaloacetic acid}}{HOOC^{13} \cdot CH_2 \cdot CO \cdot COOH} + 4H \rightarrow \underset{\text{Succinic acid}}{HOOC^{13} \cdot CH_2 \cdot CH_2 \cdot COOH} + H_2O$$

The reaction of CO_2 fixation in nonphotosynthetic systems can certainly be included among the more important discoveries in biology during the past decade. As van Niel, Ruben, Carson, Kamen, and Foster (1942) have pointed out, fixation of CO_2 is not restricted to bacterial processes but has been observed with many other systems, including liver tissue, yeasts, molds and protozoa, barley roots, and plants in the absence of light. Furthermore, these workers have shown that CO_2 may enter into cellular metabolic processes by other routes than through the synthesis of oxaloacetic or succinic acids (see Chapter 7). For additional reading on this subject the foregoing references should be consulted.

COMPOUNDS CONTAINING ONLY CARBON AND HYDROGEN

The ability of methane, ethylene, acetylene, benzene, xylene, crude oil, gasoline, and other related compounds to serve as a source of carbon for microorganisms was briefly discussed in Chapter 7 in the section on methane- and other hydrocarbon-oxidizing bacteria. More recently Stone, Fenske, and White (1942), Grant and Zobell (1942), and Johnson and Schwarz (1944) have presented additional data on this subject.

COMPOUNDS CONSISTING OF CARBON, HYDROGEN, AND OXYGEN, BUT NEVER NITROGEN

The compounds which can be allocated to this group are very numerous, and only a few will be listed here. Some attention has already been given to some of these compounds in Chapter 6 on bacterial enzymes and Chapter 7 on bacterial nutrition.

Aliphatic Monohydric and Polyhydric Alcohols. Several microorganisms are able to utilize such monohydric saturated alcohols ($C_nH_{2n+1}OH$) as methyl, ethyl, propyl, and butyl alcohols as a source of carbon, but not the higher members of this series. For example, Visser't Hooft (1925) found that certain acetic acid bacteria (genus *Acetobacter*) oxidized the alcohols in this series up to isobutyl alcohol, but not tertiary butyl alcohol, $(CH_3)_3 \cdot COH$, nor amyl alcohol, $CH_3 \cdot (CH_2)_3 \cdot CH_2OH$. Den Dooren de Jong (1926) reported similar results with *Mycobacterium phlei* but found that several other common bacteria were unable to oxidize such alcohols as a source of energy. Little is known about the ability of the monohydric unsaturated alcohols, such as allyl, $CH_2{:}CH \cdot CH_2OH$, to serve as a source of energy for microorganisms. Den Dooren de Jong (1926) found that none of thirteen common bacterial species was able to oxidize allyl alcohol in a simple inorganic medium, but possibly other microorganisms can attack such a compound.

Certain of the polyhydric alcohols are very easily attacked by certain microorganisms, and a few representative examples may be cited. Several bacteria, especially certain acetic acid bacteria, are able to oxidize ethylene glycol ($CH_2OH \cdot CH_2OH$), α-propylene glycol ($CH_3 \cdot CHOH \cdot CH_2OH$), 2,3-butylene glycol ($CH_3 \cdot CHOH \cdot CHOH \cdot CH_3$), and related dihydric alcohols [see Visser't Hooft (1925), den Dooren de Jong (1926)]. The trihydric alcohol *glycerol* ($CH_2OH \cdot CHOH \cdot$

CH_2OH) is easily oxidized by many bacteria, yeasts, and molds [see Braak (1928), Buchanan and Fulmer (1930), Peppler (1942), Gunsalus and Sherman (1943)]. It has been employed frequently in studies where the products of metabolism of various microorganisms have been determined, and Braak (1928) noted that the following twenty-three compounds have been reported in the literature as produced by the action of microorganisms upon glycerol: methyl, ethyl, propyl, butyl, amyl, and hexyl alcohols, trimethylene glycol and 2,3-butylene glycol, acetaldehyde, acrolein, 1,3-propanaldehyde, and phoron (?), formic, acetic, propionic, butyric, caproic, caprylic, lactic, succinic, and acrylic acids, and carbon dioxide and hydrogen. Den Dooren de Jong (1926) found that twelve out of thirteen common bacterial species tested were able to utilize glycerol as a source of carbon and energy.

Reynolds, Hoehn, and Werkman (1939) and Mickelson and Werkman (1940) have studied the dissimilation of glycerol by certain coli-aerogenes intermediates. Trimethylene glycol was the principal metabolic product, constituting 30 to 60 per cent of the end products; formic, acetic, lactic, and succinic acids, ethyl alcohol, CO_2, and H_2 were also formed. Acrolein appeared during the fermentation as an intermediate product. *Erythritol* ($CH_2OH \cdot CHOH \cdot CHOH \cdot CH_2OH$) is metabolized by certain bacteria, although den Dooren de Jong (1926) could not demonstrate oxidation by twelve of the thirteen bacteria he used in his study. Similar results have been reported by various workers who have employed *arabitol*, $CH_2OH \cdot (CHOH)_3 \cdot CH_2OH$, *adonitol*, $CH_2OH \cdot (CHOH)_3 \cdot CH_2OH$, *sorbitol*, $CH_2OH \cdot (CHOH)_4 \cdot CH_2OH$, and *dulcitol*, $CH_2OH \cdot (CHOH)_4 \cdot CH_2OH$. *Mannitol*, $CH_2OH \cdot (CHOH)_4 \cdot CH_2OH$, is extensively used in bacteriology to differentiate various microorganisms by physiological tests. Several workers have also studied the metabolic end products of microorganisms which oxidize mannitol. Buchanan and Fulmer (1930) list the following compounds as produced by the action of various organisms upon mannitol: formic, acetic, lactic, succinic, oxalic, and citric acids, ethyl and butyl alcohols, levulose, mannose, 2,3-butylene glycol, acetone, acetaldehyde, CO_2, and H_2.

Aliphatic Aldehydes and Ketones. The aldehydes and ketones are seldom employed as substrates for microorganisms, although it is known that several organisms can utilize such compounds as a source of carbon [see Buchanan and Fulmer (1930)]. The aldehydes, such as acetaldehyde ($CH_3 \cdot CHO$), however, are important intermediate products in the metabolism of other carbon substances. For example, the principal changes produced by microbial enzymes acting upon acetaldehyde are as follows:

1. Oxidation to acetic acid

$$CH_3 \cdot CHO + \tfrac{1}{2}O_2 \rightarrow CH_3 \cdot COOH$$

2. Reduction to ethyl alcohol

$$CH_3 \cdot CHO + 2H \rightarrow CH_3 \cdot CH_2OH$$

or

$$\text{Diphosphoglyceraldehyde} + CH_3 \cdot CHO \rightarrow C_2H_5OH + \text{Diphosphoglycerate}$$

3. Synthesis to acetylmethylcarbinol (acetoin)

$$CH_3 \cdot CHO + OHC \cdot CH_3 \rightarrow CH_3 \cdot CHOH \cdot CO \cdot CH_3$$

4. Condensation to aldol

$$CH_3 \cdot CHO + CH_3 \cdot CHO \rightarrow CH_3 \cdot CHOH \cdot CH_2 \cdot CHO$$

The aldehydes are not usually found as end products of fermentation processes because they are easily converted to other products by one of the foregoing reactions. On the other hand, some of the ketones, such as acetone ($CH_3 \cdot CO \cdot CH_3$), are important metabolic end products of certain bacteria, for example, *Clostridium acetobutylicum*.

Aliphatic Monobasic, Dibasic, and Polybasic Acids. Some of the organic acids are utilized by certain microorganisms as a source of carbon. Usually such compounds are added to media in the form of salts rather than as free acids. Their decomposition results in the formation of alkali carbonates, which in turn produce an alkaline reaction of the medium, for example, the decomposition of sodium formate:

$$2HCOONa + 2H_2O \rightarrow Na_2CO_3 + H_2O + CO_2 + 2H_2$$

Extensive studies of the utilization of organic acids by bacteria have been made by Koser (1923) and den Dooren de Jong (1926); the early literature on the subject has been reviewed by these workers and Buchanan and Fulmer (1930).

These acids will be discussed briefly under the following headings: (1) monobasic saturated acids; (2) monobasic unsaturated acids; (3) monohydroxy monobasic acids; (4) dihydroxy and polyhydroxy monobasic acids; (5) monobasic ketonic acids; (6) dibasic saturated acids; (7) dibasic and tribasic unsaturated acids; (8) mono- and polyhydroxy polybasic acids; (9) miscellaneous acids.

1. MONOBASIC SATURATED ACIDS. The acids belonging to this class have been studied by a number of workers who have used a variety of microorganisms. Space does not permit a discussion of the types of changes, such as oxidation, reduction, and decarboxylation, which have been observed as the result of microorganisms acting on these acids. One example (see Table 1), taken from the study by den Dooren de Jong (1926), will be cited to illustrate the ability of these compounds to serve as a source of carbon for bacteria. From these data it will

TABLE 1

UTILIZATION OF MONOBASIC SATURATED ACIDS BY BACTERIA

[From den Dooren de Jong (1926)]

Basal Medium * plus 0.5 Per Cent of the Undermentioned Compounds	*Bacillus vulgatus*	*Bacillus mycoides*	*Bacillus polymyxa*	*Aerobacter aerogenes*	*Escherichia coli*	*Serratia marcescens*	*Bacterium herbicola*	*Proteus vulgaris*	*Mycobacterium phlei*	*Staphylococcus albus*	*Sarcina lutea*	*Pseudomonas fluorescens*	*Spirillum tenue*
Formic acid, $HCOOH$	−	−	−	−	−	−	−	(−)	−	−	−	(−)	−
Acetic acid, CH_3COOH	(−)	(−)	−	+	(−)	(+)	(−)	(−)	+	−	+	+	(−)
Propionic acid, C_2H_5COOH	(−)	(−)	−	−	−	−	(−)	+	+	−	+	+	(−)
Butyric acid, C_3H_7COOH	(−)	(−)	−	(−)	−	−	−	(−)	+	−	+	(+)	(−)
Isobutyric acid, C_3H_7COOH	(−)	(−)	−	−	−	−	−	(−)	+	−	+	(+)	(−)
Valeric acid, C_4H_9COOH	(−)	(−)	−	−	−	−	−	(−)	+	−	+	−	(−)
Caproic acid, $C_5H_{11}COOH$	(−)	(−)	−	(−)	−	+	−	(+)	+	−	+	+	(−)
Heptylic acid, $C_6H_{13}COOH$	(−)	−	−	−	−	(+)	−	(+)	+	−	+	+	−
Caprylic acid, $C_7H_{15}COOH$	−	−	−	−	−	+	−	−	+	−	+	+	−
Nonylic acid, $C_8H_{17}COOH$	−	−	−	−	−	+	−	−	(+)	−	+	+	−
Capric acid, $C_9H_{19}COOH$	−	(−)	−	−	−	+	−	−	(+)	−	(−)	+	−
Lauric acid, $C_{11}H_{23}COOH$	−	−	−	−	−	−	−	−	−	(−)	−	−	−
Palmitic acid, $C_{15}H_{31}COOH$	−	−	−	−	−	−	−	−	−	−	−	−	−
Stearic acid, $C_{17}H_{35}COOH$	−	−	−	−	−	−	−	−	−	(−)	−	−	−

+ = heavy to good growth; (+) = very good to moderate growth; (−) = feeble growth but somewhat better than control; − = extremely feeble growth or equal to control. Only + and (+) signs indicate that the compounds were attacked.

* Basal medium: Tapwater with 2% agar, 0.1% $(NH_4)_2SO_4$, 0.1% K_2HPO_4, and 1% $CaCO_3$. Incubation: 5 days at 30°C.

be seen that *Mycobacterium phlei*, *Sarcina lutea*, and *Pseudomonas fluorescens* are able to use a number of these acids as a source of carbon, whereas other bacteria are unable to attack any of them.

2. MONOBASIC UNSATURATED ACIDS. The utilization of the monobasic unsaturated acids by microorganisms has been studied very little by the bacteriologist. Den Dooren de Jong (1926) observed that a few bacteria were able to use certain acids of this group as a source of carbon (see Table 2), but nothing is known concerning the nature

TABLE 2

UTILIZATION OF MONOBASIC UNSATURATED ACIDS BY BACTERIA

[From den Dooren de Jong (1926)]

Basal Medium * plus 0.5 Per Cent of the Undermentioned Compounds	*Bacillus vulgatus*	*Bacillus mycoides*	*Bacillus polymyxa*	*Aerobacter aerogenes*	*Escherichia coli*	*Serratia marcescens*	*Bacterium herbicola*	*Proteus vulgaris*	*Mycobacterium phlei*	*Staphylococcus albus*	*Sarcina lutea*	*Pseudomonas fluorescens*	*Spirillum tenue*
Acrylic acid, $CH_2{:}CH{\cdot}COOH$	–	–	–	(–)	–	–	–	–	–	–	–	–	–
α-Crotonic acid, $CH_3{\cdot}CH{:}CH{\cdot}COOH$	–	–	–	–	–	–	–	–	+	–	+	–	(–)
Undecylic acid, $CH_2{:}CH{\cdot}(CH_2)_8{\cdot}COOH$	–	–	–	–	–	–	–	(–)	(+)	–	(+)	(–)	–
Oleic acid, $C_{17}H_{33}{\cdot}COOH$	(–)	(–)	–	–	–	(+)	–	–	(+)	–	(+)	(+)	–
Elaidic acid, $C_{17}H_{33}{\cdot}COOH$	–	–	–	–	–	–	–	–	(–)	–	–	–	–

+ = heavy to good growth; (+) = very good to moderate growth; (–) = feeble growth but somewhat better than control; – = extremely feeble growth or equal to control. Only + and (+) signs indicate that the compounds were attacked.

* Basal medium: Tapwater with 2% agar, 0.1% $(NH_4)_2SO_4$, 0.1% K_2HPO_4, and 1% $CaCO_3$. Incubation: 5 days at 30°C.

of the end products produced from their metabolism. Oleic acid is known to function in the metabolism of the diphtheria bacillus, although no information is available concerning its physiological role (see the discussion of the nutrition of the diphtheria bacillus in Chapter 7).

3. MONOHYDROXY MONOBASIC ACIDS. The best-known organic acids which belong to this class are shown in Table 3. Several workers have reported that the salts of glycolic acid are attacked by bacteria, but den Dooren de Jong (1926) and others have been unable to confirm these results. Lactic acid and its salts, on the other hand, are dissimilated by a great many aerobic, facultative, and anaerobic bacteria. Although the end products of the aerobic dissimilation of lactic acid have not been studied, considerable information is available concerning the anaerobic dissimilation. Buchanan and Fulmer (1930) reviewed the literature on this subject and found that the following fourteen compounds have been reported as being formed by various microorganisms which attack lactic acid: formic, acetic, propionic, butyric, caproic, caprylic, lactic, and succinic acids, 2,3-butylene glycol, acetone, acetaldehyde, ethyl and butyl alcohols, and CO_2.

4. Dihydroxy and Polyhydroxy Monobasic Acids. Probably the best known acids of this class are glyceric acid, $CH_2OH \cdot CHOH \cdot COOH$, and gluconic acid, $CH_2OH \cdot (CHOH)_4 \cdot COOH$. Both of these compounds can be utilized by certain microorganisms; with other organisms they appear as intermediates or as end products when other carbon compounds are metabolized.

TABLE 3

Utilization of Monohydroxy Monobasic Acids

[From den Dooren de Jong (1926)]

Basal Medium * plus 0.5 Per Cent of the Undermentioned Compounds	*Bacillus vulgatus*	*Bacillus mycoides*	*Bacillus polymyxa*	*Aerobacter aerogenes*	*Escherichia coli*	*Serratia marcescens*	*Bacterium herbicola*	*Proteus vulgaris*	*Mycobacterium phlei*	*Staphylococcus albus*	*Sarcina lutea*	*Pseudomonas fluorescens*	*Spirillum tenue*
Glycolic acid, $CH_2(OH) \cdot COOH$	−	−	−	−	−	−	−	−	−	−	−	−	−
Lactic acid, $CH_3 \cdot CHOH \cdot COOH$	(+)	−	−	+	+	+	+	−	+	−	+	+	−
α-Hydroxybutyric acid, $CH_3 \cdot CH_2 \cdot CHOH \cdot COOH$	(−)	−	−	−	−	−	−	−	(−)	−	−	−	−
β-Hydroxybutyric acid, $CH_3 \cdot CHOH \cdot CH_2 \cdot COOH$	−	−	−	−	−	(+)	−	−	+	−	(−)	(+)	(+)
Hydroxyisobutyric acid, $(CH_3)_2 \cdot C(OH) \cdot COOH$	−	−	−	−	−	−	−	−	−	−	−	−	−

+ = heavy to good growth; (+) = very good to moderate growth; (−) = feeble growth but somewhat better than control; − = extremely feeble growth or equal to control. Only + and (+) signs indicate that the compounds were attacked.

* Basal medium: Tapwater with 2% agar, 0.1% $(NH_4)_2SO_4$, 0.1% K_2HPO_4, and 1% $CaCO_3$. Incubation: 5 days at 30°C.

5. Monobasic Ketonic Acids. Several of the keto acids are dissimilated by microorganisms. Pyruvic acid ($CH_3 \cdot CO \cdot COOH$) has assumed considerable importance in recent years in metabolism studies because of its demonstration as an intermediate product and because of the ease with which it is fermented by many organisms. Buchanan and Fulmer (1930) found that the following thirteen compounds have been reported as dissimilation products of pyruvic acid by bacteria, yeasts, or molds: formic, acetic, propionic, lactic, fumaric, glycolic, and oxalic acids, acetylmethylcarbinol, acetaldehyde, aldol (α-hydroxybutyric aldehyde), fat, H_2, and CO_2. Other ketonic acids, such as

α-ketobutyric acid, $CH_3 \cdot CH_2 \cdot CO \cdot COOH$, acetoacetic acid, $CH_3 \cdot CO \cdot CH_2 \cdot COOH$, and levulinic acid, $CH_3 \cdot CO \cdot (CH_2)_2 \cdot COOH$, are known to be dissimilated by certain microorganisms, but little is known about their metabolism.

6. Dibasic Saturated Acids. The most important dibasic saturated acids are listed in Table 4. Certain of these acids are utilized easily as a source of carbon by a few microorganisms, whereas others

TABLE 4

Utilization of Dibasic Saturated Acids

[From den Dooren de Jong (1926)]

Basal Medium * plus 0.5 Per Cent of the Undermentioned Compounds	*Bacillus vulgatus*	*Bacillus mycoides*	*Bacillus polymyxa*	*Aerobacter aerogenes*	*Escherichia coli*	*Serratia marcescens*	*Bacterium herbicola*	*Proteus vulgaris*	*Mycobacterium phlei*	*Staphylococcus albus*	*Sarcina lutea*	*Pseudomonas fluorescens*	*Spirillum tenue*
Oxalic acid, $HOOC \cdot COOH$	−	−	−	−	−	−	−	−	−	−	−	−	−
Malonic acid, $HOOC \cdot CH_2 \cdot COOH$	(−)	−	−	−	−	−	−	−	(−)	−	−	+	+
Ethyl malonic acid, $HOOC \cdot CH(C_2H_5) \cdot COOH$	−	−	−	−	−	−	−	−	(−)	−	+	−	−
Dimethylmalonic acid, $HOOC \cdot C(CH_3)_2 \cdot COOH$	−	−	−	−	−	−	−	−	−	−	−	−	−
Diethylmalonic acid, $HOOC \cdot C(C_2H_5)_2 \cdot COOH$	−	−	−	−	−	−	−	−	−	−	−	−	−
Succinic acid, $HOOC \cdot (CH_2)_2 \cdot COOH$	(+)	−	−	+	+	+	+	(−)	+	−	(−)	+	+
Methyl succinic acid, $HOOC \cdot CH_2 \cdot CH(CH_3) \cdot COOH$	−	−	−	−	−	−	−	−	−	−	−	−	−
Glutaric acid, $HOOC \cdot (CH_2)_3 \cdot COOH$	−	−	−	−	−	(−)	−	−	−	−	−	(+)	−
Adipic acid, $HOOC \cdot (CH_2)_4 \cdot COOH$	−	−	−	−	−	−	−	−	(−)	−	−	−	−
Pimelic acid, $HOOC \cdot (CH_2)_5 \cdot COOH$	−	−	−	−	−	−	−	−	−	−	−	−	−
Suberic acid, $HOOC \cdot (CH_2)_6 \cdot COOH$	−	−	−	−	−	−	−	−	(+)	−	−	−	(−)
Azelaic acid, $HOOC \cdot (CH_2)_7 \cdot COOH$	−	−	−	−	−	−	−	−	(+)	−	−	−	(−)
Sebacic acid, $HOOC \cdot (CH_2)_8 \cdot COOH$	−	(−)	−	−	−	(−)	−	−	(+)	−	(−)	(−)	−

+ = heavy to good growth; (+) = very good to moderate growth; (−) = feeble growth but somewhat better than control; − = extremely feeble growth or equal to control. Only + and (+) signs indicate that the compounds were attacked.

* Basal medium: Tapwater with 2% agar, 0.1% $(NH_4)_2SO_4$, 0.1% K_2HPO_4, and 1% $CaCO_3$. Incubation: 5 days at 30°C.

are relatively refractory. Some appear as important intermediate products or end products in the dissimilation of carbohydrates by bacteria, yeasts, or molds [see Buchanan and Fulmer (1930)]. Pimelic acid plays an important, but yet unknown, role in the nutrition of *Corynebacterium diphtheriae.*

7. Dibasic and Tribasic Unsaturated Acids. Several acids which belong to this class are utilized as a source of carbon by microorganisms, or they appear as intermediate or end products when carbohydrates are dissimilated by such organisms. The data in Table 5 may be cited as an example of the utilization of certain of these compounds by bacteria. For additional reading Buchanan and Fulmer (1930) and Chapter 6, Bacterial Enzymes and Bacterial Respiration, and Chapter 7, Bacterial Nutrition, in this book should be consulted.

TABLE 5

Utilization of Dibasic and Tribasic Acids by Bacteria

[From den Dooren de Jong (1926)]

Basal Medium * plus 0.5 Per Cent of the Undermentioned Compounds	*Bacillus vulgatus*	*Bacillus mycoides*	*Bacillus polymyxa*	*Aerobacter aerogenes*	*Escherichia coli*	*Serratia marcescens*	*Bacterium herbicola*	*Proteus vulgaris*	*Mycobacterium phlei*	*Staphylococcus albus*	*Sarcina lutea*	*Pseudomonas fluorescens*	*Spirillum tenue*
Maleic acid, HOOC·CH:CH·COOH (*cis*)	—	—	—	—	—	—	—	—	—	—	—	—	—
Fumaric acid, HOOC·CH:CH·COOH (*trans*)	—	—	—	—	—	(—)	(+)	—	+	—	(—)	(+)	(+)
Citraconic acid, HOOC·C(CH_3):CH·COOH (*cis*)	—	—	—	—	—	—	—	—	—	—	—	(+)	—
Mesaconic acid, HOOC·C(CH_3):CH·COOH (*trans*)	—	—	—	—	—	—	—	—	—	—	—	—	—
Aconitic acid, HOOC·CH_2·C(COOH):CH·COOH)	(—)	—	—	—	—	(+)	+	—	(—)	—	—	(+)	—

+ = heavy to good growth; (+) = very good to moderate growth; (—) = feeble growth but somewhat better than control; — = extremely feeble growth or equal to control. Only + and (+) signs indicate that the compounds were attacked.

* Basal medium: Tapwater with 2% agar, 0.1% $(NH_4)_2SO_4$, 0.1% K_2HPO_4, and 1% $CaCO_3$. Incubation: 5 days at 30°C.

8. Mono- and Polyhydroxy Polybasic Acids. A number of acids may be allocated to this class of compounds. Some of the better-known members are included in Table 6.

9. Miscellaneous Acids. Several derivatives of some of the acids mentioned above, as well as other acids, have also been studied for

their ability to serve as a source of carbon to bacteria. One example (see Table 7) will be cited.

It should be mentioned again that the examples which have been cited in this discussion are valid only under the conditions of the experiments. If different basal media containing various growth factors had been employed, for example, the results might have been entirely different. The data cited, however, serve very well to illustrate the types of compounds which have been studied.

TABLE 6

Utilization of Mono- and Polyhydroxy Polybasic Acids

[From den Dooren de Jong (1926)]

Basal Medium * plus 0.5 Per Cent of the Undermentioned Compounds	*Bacillus vulgatus*	*Bacillus mycoides*	*Bacillus polymyxa*	*Aerobacter aerogenes*	*Escherichia coli*	*Serratia marcescens*	*Bacterium herbicola*	*Proteus vulgaris*	*Mycobacterium phlei*	*Staphylococcus albus*	*Sarcina lutea*	*Pseudomonas fluorescens*	*Spirillum tenue*
Malic acid, HOOC·CH_2·CHOH·COOH	+	−	−	+	+	+	+	(−)	+	(−)	(+)	+	+
Tartaric acid, HOOC·CHOH·CHOH·COOH (*d*)	−	−	−	−	−	−	−	+	(−)	−	−	−	−
Racemic acid, HOOC·CHOH·CHOH·COOH (*dl*)	−	−	−	−	−	−	−	−	−	−	−	−	−
Saccharic acid, HOOC·$(CHOH)_4$·COOH	+	−	−	+	+	(+)	+	(−)	+	−	+	+	−
Mucic acid, HOOC·$(CHOH)_4$·COOH	+	−	−	(−)	(+)	−	(+)	(−)	(−)	−	−	(+)	(−)
Citric acid, HOOC·CH_2·COH(COOH)·CH_2·COOH	(+)	−	−	+	−	+	+	+	+	−	+	+	+

+ = heavy to good growth; (+) = very good to moderate growth; (−) = feeble growth but somewhat better than control; — = extremely feeble growth or equal to control. Only + and (+) signs indicate that the compounds were attacked.

* Basal medium: Tapwater with 2% agar, 0.1% $(NH_4)_2SO_4$, 0.1% K_2HPO_4, and 1% $CaCO_3$. Incubation: 5 days at 30°C.

Carbohydrates. Many of the compounds which are classified as carbohydrates are easily utilized as a source of carbon by microorganisms, but others are quite resistant to attack. The literature on this topic is large. Some attention was given to the subject in Chapters 6 and 7, and for additional reading the books by Waksman (1932), Thaysen and Bunker (1927), Thaysen and Galloway (1930), and Buchanan and Fulmer (1930) should be consulted.

TABLE 7

Utilization of Miscellaneous Acids by Bacteria

[From den Dooren de Jong (1926)]

Basal Medium * plus 0.5 Per Cent of the Undermentioned Compounds	*Bacillus vulgatus*	*Bacillus mycoides*	*Bacillus polymyxa*	*Aerobacter aerogenes*	*Escherichia coli*	*Serratia marcescens*	*Bacterium herbicola*	*Proteus vulgaris*	*Mycobacterium phlei*	*Staphylococcus albus*	*Sarcina lutea*	*Pseudomonas fluorescens*	*Spirillum tenue*
Phenylacetic acid, $C_6H_5 \cdot CH_2 \cdot COOH$	−	−	−	+	−	+	−	−	−	−	−	−	−
β-Phenylpropionic acid, $C_6H_5 \cdot CH_2 \cdot CH_2 \cdot COOH$	−	−	−	−	−	−	−	−	−	−	−	−	−
Phenylglycolic acid, $C_6H_5 \cdot CHOH \cdot COOH$	−	−	−	−	−	−	−	−	(−)	−	(−)	−	−
β-Phenylacrylic acid, $C_6H_5 \cdot CH{:}CH \cdot COOH$	−	−	−	−	−	−	−	−	+	−	(−)	−	−
o-Cumaric acid, $HO \cdot C_6H_5 \cdot CH{:}CH \cdot COOH$ (*trans*)	−	−	−	−	−	−	−	−	−	−	−	−	−
Cyclohexanecarbonic acid, $C_6H_{11} \cdot COOH$	−	(−)	−	−	−	−	−	−	(−)	−	(−)	−	−
Quinic acid, $C_6H_7 \cdot (OH)_4 \cdot COOH$	−	−	−	+	−	−	−	(+)	(+)	−	(−)	+	−
Thioacetic acid, $CH_3 \cdot COSH$	−	−	−	−	−	−	−	−	−	−	−	−	−
Thioglycolic acid, $CH_2(SH) \cdot COOH$	−	−	−	−	−	−	−	−	−	−	−	−	−
Thiolactic acid, $CH_3 \cdot CH(SH) \cdot COOH$	−	−	−	−	−	−	−	−	−	−	−	−	−
Trichloracetic acid, $CCl_3 \cdot COOH$	−	−	−	−	−	−	−	−	(−)	−	(−)	−	−
Bromoacetic acid, $CH_2Br \cdot COOH$	−	−	−	−	−	−	−	−	−	−	−	−	−
α-Bromopropionic acid, $CH_3 \cdot CHBr \cdot COOH$	−	−	−	−	−	+	−	−	+	−	−	−	−
β-Bromopropionic acid, $CH_2Br \cdot CH_2 \cdot COOH$	−	(−)	−	−	−	−	−	+	(−)	−	(−)	+	−
Trichlorobutyric acid, $C_3H_4Cl_3 \cdot COOH$	−	−	−	−	−	−	−	−	−	−	−	−	−
α-Bromobutyric acid, $CH_3 \cdot CH_2 \cdot CHBr \cdot COOH$	−	−	−	−	−	−	−	−	−	−	−	−	−
α-Bromoisobutyric acid, $(CH_3)_2 \cdot CBr \cdot COOH$	−	−	−	−	−	−	−	−	(−)	−	(−)	−	−
Bromosuccinic acid, $HOOC \cdot CHBr \cdot CH_2 \cdot COOH$	(−)	(−)	−	(+)	(+)	(+)	(+)	−	+	−	(−)	+	+
Benzoic acid, $C_6H_5 \cdot COOH$	−	−	−	+	−	−	−	+	+	−	(+)	−	−
p-Hydroxybenzoic acid, $HO \cdot C_6H_4 \cdot COOH$	−	−	−	+	−	(−)	−	+	+	−	(−)	+	−
Salicylic acid, $HO \cdot C_6H_4 \cdot COOH(1{:}2)$	−	−	−	−	−	−	−	−	(−)	−	(−)	−	−

+ = heavy to good growth; (+) = very good to moderate growth; (−) = feeble growth but somewhat better than control; − = extremely feeble growth or equal to control. Only + and (+) signs indicate that the compounds were attacked.

* Basal medium: Tapwater with 2% agar, 0.1% $(NH_4)_2SO_4$, 0.1% K_2HPO_4, and 1% $CaCO_3$. Incubation: 5 days at 30°C.

The compounds which we will consider here may be classified as follows:

I. Monosaccharides.

Pentose sugars:
- Aldopentoses, $CH_2OH \cdot (CHOH)_3 \cdot CHO$: arabinose, xylose, ribose, and lyxose.
- Ketopentoses, $CH_2OH \cdot (CHOH)_2 \cdot CO \cdot CH_2OH$: xyloketose, etc.
- Methylpentoses, $H_3C \cdot (CHOH)_4 \cdot CHO$: rhamnose, fucose.

Hexose sugars:
- Aldohexoses, $CH_2OH \cdot (CHOH)_4 \cdot CHO$: glucose, mannose, galactose.
- Ketohexoses, $CH_2OH \cdot CO \cdot (CHOH)_3 \cdot CH_2OH$: fructose (levulose).

Heptose, octose, and nonose sugars: glucoheptose, glucooctose, glucononose.

II. Disaccharides, $C_{12}H_{22}O_{11}$.

Linked through reducing group of each component: sucrose and trehalose.

Linked to carbon four of the alcohol portion,[1] or the C_4-disaccharides: maltose, cellobiose, and lactose.

Linked to carbon six of the alcohol portion,[1] or the C_6-disaccharides: gentiobiose and melibiose.

III. Trisaccharides, $C_{18}H_{32}O_{16}$.

Raffinose, melezitose, and gentianose.

IV. Tetrasaccharides, $C_{24}H_{42}O_{21}$.

Stachyose.

V. Polysaccharides, $(C_6H_{10}O_5)_x$.

Dextrins, starch, glycogen, and inulin.

Gums, pectins, and hemicelluloses.

Cellulose and lignins.

Arabinose. Both the *l*- and *d*-forms of arabinose have been used by the bacteriologist to differentiate organisms on the basis of their fermentative characteristics [Sternfeld and Saunders (1937)]. In several studies some of the dissimilation products of arabinose have been reported, and a few examples are cited in Table 8. For additional reading on this subject Buchanan and Fulmer (1930) and Fulmer and Werkman (1930) should be consulted.

Xylose. The fermentation of *d*-xylose by microorganisms has been studied rather extensively by Koser and Saunders (1933), Sternfeld

[1] *d*-Glucose is the alcohol portion of each.

TABLE 8

PRODUCTS OF ARABINOSE DISSIMILATION BY MICROORGANISMS *

Organism	Products of Arabinose Dissimilation	Reference
Escherichia coli	Acetic, lactic, and succinic acids, ethyl alcohol, CO_2, H_2	Harden (1901)
Aerobacter aerogenes	Acetylmethylcarbinol, 2,3-butylene glycol	Harden and Norris (1912)
Acetobacter suboxydans	Arobonic acid	Visser't Hooft (1925)
Lactobacillus arabinosus	Acetic and lactic acids, CO_2	Fred, Peterson, and Anderson (1921)
Propionibacterium pentosaceum	Acetic and propionic acids, CO_2	Werkman, Hixon, Fulmer, and Rayburn (1929)
Bacillus acetoethylicus	Acetone, ethyl alcohol, formic acid	Northrop, Ashe, and Morgan (1919)
Clostridium acetobutylicum	Butyl alcohol, ethyl alcohol, acetone	Underkofler and Hunter (1938)
Saccharomyces cerevisiae	Ethyl alcohol, CO_2, glyceraldehyde (?)	Abbott (1926)
Aspergillus niger	Citric acid, oxalic and gluconic acids	Amelung (1927), Bernhauer (1928), Allsopp (1937)

* See Chapter 10 for other organisms which utilize arabinose and for the products formed.

and Saunders (1937), and Lechner (1940). This substance is commonly used in the differentiation of bacteria on a physiological basis, but in only a few studies have the products of dissimilation of various organisms been determined (see Table 9).

RIBOSE AND LYXOSE. These two pentose sugars have not been used very extensively in metabolic studies of microorganisms. Sternfeld and Saunders (1937) found that a number of common pathogenic and nonpathogenic bacteria ferment *d*- and *l*-ribose and *d*-lyxose, whereas the yeasts *Saccharomyces cerevisiae* and *Torula cremoris* were unable to attack any compounds.

RHAMNOSE AND FUCOSE. Fermentation of *l*-rhamnose by bacteria is frequently used to differentiate certain species, but little is known concerning their metabolic products. Kluyver and Schnellen (1937) found that *Bacterium rhamnosifermentans* produced formic, acetic, and succinic acids, ethyl alcohol, CO_2, and H_2 from rhamnose, but no other studies have appeared on the fermentation products of other

TABLE 9

PRODUCTS OF XYLOSE DISSIMILATION BY MICROORGANISMS *

Organism	Products of Xylose Dissimilation	Reference
Aerobacter aerogenes	Formic, acetic, butyric, lactic, and succinic acids, ethyl alcohol	Peterson and Fred (1920)
Aerobacter feni	Formic, acetic, lactic, and succinic acids, ethyl alcohol, acetylmethylcarbinol, 2,3-butylene glycol, CO_2, H_2	Breden, Fulmer, Werkman, and Hixon (1930)
Aerobacter indologenes	Formic, acetic, and succinic acids, ethyl alcohol, acetylmethylcarbinol, 2,3-butylene glycol, CO_2, H_2	Reynolds and Werkman (1937)
Serratia marcescens	Ascorbic acid	Berencsi and Illényi (1938)
Lactobacillus pentosus	Acetic and lactic acids	Fred, Peterson, and Anderson (1921)
Propionibacterium pentosaceum	Acetic and propionic acids	Werkman, Hixon, Fulmer, and Rayburn (1929)
Bacillus acetoethylicum	Formic, acetic, and lactic acids, ethyl alcohol, acetone, CO_2	Arzberger, Peterson, and Fred (1920)
Bacillus polymyxa	Formic, lactic, and succinic acids, ethyl alcohol, acetylmethylcarbinol, 2,3-butylene glycol, CO_2, H_2	Stahly (1936)
Clostridium acetobutylicum	Acetone, butyl alcohol, ethyl alcohol	Underkofler, Christensen, and Fulmer (1936), Underkofler and Hunter (1938); see Chapter 10
Saccharomyces cerevisiae	Ethyl alcohol, glyceric aldehyde (?), CO_2	Abbott (1926); see Chapter 10
Aspergillus niger	Citric and oxalic acids	Bernhauer (1928), Allsopp (1937); see Chapter 10
Aspergillus flavus, *Aspergillus tamarii*	Kojic acid	Barham and Smits (1936), Gould (1938); see Chapter 10

* See Chapter 10 for other organisms which utilize xylose and for the products formed.

bacteria which attack this sugar. Fucose is fermented by coli-aerogenes bacteria with acid and gas production [Koser and Saunders (1933), Field and Poe (1940)], lactic, succinic, and acetic acids are formed by both bacteria, and acetylmethylcarbinol is produced by the aerogenes strains. Tadokoro (1936) studied the fermentation of fucose by *Asper-*

TABLE 10

PRODUCTS OF GLUCOSE DISSIMILATION BY MICROORGANISMS *

Organism	Products of Glucose Dissimilation	Reference
Escherichia coli	Formic, acetic, lactic, and succinic acids, ethyl alcohol, CO_2, H_2	Harden (1901), Grey and Young (1921), Tikka (1935), Krebs (1937), Friedemann (1938)
Aerobacter aerogenes	Formic, acetic, lactic, and succinic acids, ethyl alcohol, acetylmethylcarbinol, 2,3-butylene glycol, CO_2, H_2	Harden and Walpole (1906), Scheffer (1928), Fosdick and Dodds (1945); see Chapter 10
Aerobacter indologenes	Formic and acetic acids, ethyl alcohol, acetylmethylcarbinol, 2,3-butylene glycol, CO_2, H_2	Reynolds and Werkman (1937)
Proteus hydrophilus	Similar to *Aerobacter* species	Stanier and Adams (1944)
Eberthella typhosa	Formic, acetic, lactic, and succinic acids, ethyl alcohol	Harden (1901), Friedemann (1938)
Salmonella, *Shigella*, and *Vibrio* species	Formic, acetic, lactic, and succinic acids, ethyl alcohol	Friedemann (1938)
Pasteurella pestis	Formic, acetic, lactic, pyruvic, and succinic acids, ethyl alcohol, CO_2	Doudoroff (1943)
Vibrio comma } *Vibrio ElTor* }	Formic, acetic, lactic, and succinic acids, ethyl alcohol, acetylmethylcarbinol, 2,3-butylene glycol, CO_2	Baars (1940)
Neisseria gonorrheae	Acetic, pyruvic, and lactic acids, CO_2	Barron and Miller (1932)
Pneumococcus types, *Streptococcus* and *Staphylococcus* species	Formic, acetic, lactic, and unidentified nonvolatile acids, ethyl alcohol	Friedemann (1938)
Staphylococcus albus	Lactic and α-keto-γ-hydroxyvaleric acids; α-keto-γ-hydroxyvaleraldehyde; etc.	Fosdick and Rapp (1943)
Sarcina ventriculi, *Sarcina maxima*	Formic, acetic, butyric, lactic, and succinic acids, ethyl alcohol, CO_2, and H_2	Smit (1928)
Sarcina lutea	Lactic and acetic acids	Fosdick and Calandra (1945)
Serratia marcescens, *Serratia indica*	Formic, acetic, lactic, and succinic acids, ethyl alcohol, acetylmethylcarbinol, 2,3-butylene glycol, CO_2	Pederson and Breed (1928)
Acetobacter suboxydans	2- and 5-Ketogluconic acid	Kluyver and Boezaardt (1938), Bernhauer and Knobloch (1938), Stubbs, Lockwood, Roe, Tabenkin, and Ward (1940); see Chapter 10
Pseudomonas aeruginosa	Formic and acetic acids, ethyl alcohol	Aubel (1921)
Pseudomonas mucidolens, *Phytomonas stewartii*, and related species	2-Ketogluconic acid	Lockwood, Tabenkin, and Ward (1941)
Photobacterium phosphoreum	Formic, acetic, lactic, and succinic acids, ethyl alcohol, 2, 3-butylene glycol, H_2, CO_2, trace of acetylmethylcarbinol }	Doudoroff (1942)
Photobacterium fischeri	Similar to *Photobacterium phosphoreum*, but no H_2 or 2,3-butylene glycol }	
Pseudomonas lindneri	Ethyl alcohol, CO_2, traces of acetic, lactic, and succinic acids, glycerol, acetaldehyde, and esters	Schreder, Brunner, and Hampe (1934)
Lactobacillus lycopersici, *Leuconostoc dextranicum*	Acetic and lactic acids, glycerol, ethyl alcohol, CO_2	Nelson and Werkman (1940)
Lactobacillus leichmannii	*l*-Lactic acid }	Allgeier and Peterson (1930)
Streptococcus lactis	*d*-Lactic acid }	
Propionibacterium species	Propionic, acetic, and succinic acids, CO_2	van Niel (1928), Wood and Werkman (1936)

* See Chapter 10 for other organisms which utilize glucose and for the products formed.

TABLE 10 (*Continued*)

PRODUCTS OF GLUCOSE DISSIMILATION BY MICROORGANISMS

Organism	Products of Glucose Dissimilation	Reference
Bacillus acetoethylicum	Acetone, ethyl alcohol, formic acid, CO_2, H_2	Northrop, Ashe, and Morgan (1919), Peterson and Fred (1920)
Bacillus polymyxa	Formic, acetic, lactic, and succinic acids, ethyl alcohol, acetylmethylcarbinol, 2,3-butylene glycol, CO_2, H_2	Patrick (1932), Stahly (1936)
Lactobacillus lycopersici, Lactobacillus mannitopoeus	Acetic and lactic acids, ethyl alcohol, glycerol, CO_2	Nelson and Werkman (1935)
Corynebacterium diphtheriae	Formic, acetic, propionic, lactic, and succinic acids, ethyl alcohol, CO_2	Tasman and Brandwijk (1938)
Bacillus dextrolacticus	*d*-Lactic acid, traces of 2,3-butylene glycol, acetylmethylcarbinol, diacetyl, acetic acid, and ethyl alcohol	Andersen and Werkman (1940)
Clostridium thermosaccharolyticum	Acetic, butyric, and lactic acids, CO_2, H_2	Sjolander, McCoy, and McClung (1937)
Clostridium tetani	Acetic, butyric, and lactic acids, methyl, ethyl, and butyl alcohols, CO_2, trace of H_2	Boorsma, Prévot, and Veillon (1939)
Clostridium botulinum	Ethyl alcohol, CO_2, trace of acetic and lactic acids, and H_2	Clifton (1940)
Clostridium perfringens, Clostridium septicum, Clostridium sporogenes	Ethyl alcohol, formic, acetic, butyric, and lactic acids	Friedemann and Kmieciak (1941)
Clostridium tetani, Clostridium botulinum	Ethyl alcohol, formic, acetic, and butyric acids	Friedemann and Kmieciak (1941)
Clostridium butylicum	Butyl and isopropyl alcohol, CO_2, H_2, small amounts of acetic and butyric acids, and ethyl alcohol	Osburn, Brown, and Werkman (1938)
Clostridium thermoaceticum	Acetic acid	Fontaine, Peterson, McCoy, Johnson, and Ritter (1942)
Yeasts, especially *Saccharomyces* species	Ethyl alcohol, CO_2, glycerol, lactic acid, and traces of other products	Numerous workers [see Guillemet (1939), Hohl and Joslyn (1941), and references in Chapter 10]
Zygosaccharomyces acidifaciens	Ethyl alcohol, acetic and lactic acids, glycerol, CO_2	Nickerson and Carroll (1945)
Aspergillus tamarii	Kojic acid	Gould (1938)
Aspergillus niger	Gluconic acid	Porges, Clark, and Gastrock (1940), Porges, Clark, and Aronovsky (1941)

gillus oryzae and reported that the metabolic products consisted of formic, kojic, glycolic, lactic, succinic, and oxalic acids.

GLUCOSE (DEXTROSE). The literature dealing with the fermentation of glucose by microorganisms is so extensive that it will be impossible to review it even briefly here. *d*-Glucose is utilized readily as a source of carbon and energy by many microorganisms and is therefore the most commonly used sugar in the bacteriology laboratory. *l*-Glucose, on the other hand, is apparently not utilized by bacteria [Rudney (1940)]. A few studies in which the products of metabolism of glucose by microorganisms have been determined are cited in Table 10; additional studies will be found in the references and in Chapter 10.

MANNOSE. The hexose *d*-mannose is widely used in studies dealing with the physiological characteristics of microorganisms. The products of fermentation are in general the same as those from glucose and fructose, and many organisms are capable of fermenting all these sugars. Wedum and Golden (1937), however, have observed that a number of bacteria utilize glucose and fructose, but not mannose.

GALACTOSE. This aldohexose is fermented by many bacteria, yeasts, and molds. It is apparently not utilized by all yeasts [Amadio (1936)], and in some cases it is attacked more slowly than glucose. The products of fermentation are in general the same as those from glucose. The study by Takahashi and Asai (1934), however, is of special interest, because they reported for the first time the production of galactonic acid and comenic acid ($C_6H_4O_5$) from galactose by a strain of acetic acid bacteria.

FRUCTOSE (*d*-FRUCTOSE, LEVULOSE). This ketohexose is utilized as a source of carbon and energy by a number of microorganisms, and the consensus is that organisms which ferment glucose are able also to ferment fructose [Wedum and Golden (1937)]. Usually the same products of fermentation are produced from both fructose and glucose, although only a few studies have been carried out in which the two sugars were compared. For example, Nelson and Werkman (1940) studied the dissimilation of glucose and fructose by two heterofermentative lactic acid bacteria (*Lactobacillus lycopersici*, *Leuconostoc dextranicum*) and found that both sugars yielded glycerol, acetic and lactic acids, ethyl alcohol, and CO_2; however, mannitol was also formed from fructose. Pervozvanskiĭ (1939) found that the chief product of the fermentation of *d*-fructose by *Pseudomonas fluorescens* was *d*-mannonic acid.

SORBOSE AND TAGATOSE. These two ketohexoses have been studied very little as a source of carbon and energy for microorganisms. It is generally assumed that organisms which ferment fructose also attack these sugars, but this assumption is probably not valid, because Koser and Saunders (1933) found *d*-sorbose to be quite resistant to bacterial attack. Only a few strains of *Aerobacter aerogenes* and *Klebsiella pneumoniae*, out of some twenty-five different species of microorganisms tested, were able to ferment this sugar. Dozois, Carr, and Krantz (1938), on the other hand, observed that *l*-sorbose was used by certain strains of *Escherichia coli* and *Aerobacter aerogenes*, but not by strains of typhoid or paratyphoid.

GLUCOHEPTOSE, GLUCOOCTOSE, AND GLUCONONOSE. The 5- and 6-carbon sugars are quite easily attacked by many microorganisms, the pentoses being attacked by fewer organisms than the hexoses.

The 7-, 8-, and 9-carbon sugars, on the other hand, are apparently quite resistant to attack by microorganisms, since Koser and Saunders (1933) and Sternfeld and Saunders (1937) found that none of twenty-three bacterial and yeast species utilized heptoses or octoses, and only three species (*Proteus vulgaris*, *Staphylococcus albus*, and *Torula cremoris*) fermented gluconononose with acid production. Johnson and

TABLE 11

PRODUCTS OF SUCROSE DISSIMILATION BY MICROORGANISMS *

Organism	Products of Sucrose Dissimilation	Reference
Aerobacter feni	Formic, acetic, lactic, and succinic acids, ethyl alcohol, acetylmethylcarbinol, 2,3-butylene glycol, CO_2, H_2	Breden, Fulmer, Werkman, and Hixon (1930)
Shigella paradysenteriae-Sonnei	Formic, acetic, lactic, and succinic acids, ethyl alcohol, CO_2	Reynolds, McCleskey, and Werkman (1934)
Lactobacillus casei	*l*-Lactic acid	Virtanen, Wichmann, and Lindström (1927)
Streptococcus lactis	*d*-Lactic acid	
Lactobacilli	Acetic and lactic acids, mannitol	Stiles, Peterson, and Fred (1925)
Leuconostoc mesenteroides	Dextran	Peat, Schlüchterer, and Stacey (1939), Hassid and Barker (1940)
Leuconostoc vermiforme	Dextran	Daker and Stacey (1939)
Thermobacillus tarbellicus	Formic, acetic, valeric, and lactic acids	Guittonneau, DeLaval, and Bejambes (1930)
Bacillus subtilis	Acetylmethylcarbinol	Lafon (1932)
Bacillus acetoethylicum	Acetone, ethyl alcohol, formic acid	Northrop, Ashe, and Morgan (1919)
Yeast	Ethyl alcohol, CO_2, traces of acetic acid, acetaldehyde, glycerol	Neuberg and Hirsch (1919); see Chapter 10
Saccharomyces sake, *Zygosaccharomyces major*, *Zygosaccharomyces salsus*	Ethyl alcohol, CO_2, acetic acid, acetaldehyde, glycerol	Kumagawa (1922)
Torula cremoris, *Torula sphericus*	Ethyl alcohol, CO_2	Hammer and Cordes (1920)
Aspergillus niger and other molds	Citric, gluconic, and oxalic acids	Amelung (1927), Bernhauer (1928); see Chapter 10

* See Chapter 10 for other organisms which utilize sucrose and for the products formed.

Schwarz (1944), however, reported that heptose sugars can be utilized by *Bacterium aliphaticum*.

Sucrose. The disaccharide sucrose is a nonreducing sugar, and upon hydrolysis by dilute acids or by its specific enzyme (invertase) one mole of glucose and one of fructose are formed. It is used as a source of carbon and energy by many bacteria, yeasts, and molds and is employed to differentiate certain closely related species of bacteria, especially members of the colon-typhoid group. In general, the products of fermentation of sucrose by microorganisms are the same as those from glucose and fructose. A few examples of the products of dissimilation of sucrose by microorganisms are cited in Table 11; for additional data on this subject the books by Buchanan and Fulmer (1930), Fulmer and Werkman (1930), and the discussion in Chapter 10 should be consulted.

Trehalose. This disaccharide is used as a source of carbon by a number of microorganisms. Such organisms probably produce the same dissimilation products from trehalose as from glucose, since trehalose is composed of two glucose units. For example, Kluyver and van Roosmalen (1932) found that *Saccharomyces cerevisiae* and *Torula dattila* ferment trehalose to ethyl alcohol and CO_2; *Fusarium lini* also ferments this sugar [O'Connor (1940)]; and Poe and Field (1932) observed that *Escherichia coli* and *Aerobacter aerogenes* strains form acetic, lactic, and succinic acids, ethyl alcohol, CO_2, and H_2 from this disaccharide.

Maltose. This reducing disaccharide is easily fermented by a number of bacteria, yeasts, and molds. Although its linkage of carbon atoms is different from that of trehalose, the products of dissimilation of the two sugars are approximately the same; both yield two moles of glucose upon hydrolysis.

Cellobiose. Cellobiose differs from maltose only in its glucosidic configuration; it is reducing and is hydrolyzed by acid or by emulsin into two moles of glucose. Like certain other sugars, cellobiose is utilized as a source of carbon and energy by several microorganisms. For a while it was thought that the sugar could be used to differentiate coli-aerogenes and related forms, but this theory is now doubted in view of the work of Skinner and Brudnoy (1932), Tittsler and Sandholzer (1935), and Poe and Klemme (1935). It is fermented by yeast, although somewhat more slowly than is glucose [Myrbäck (1940)]; it is also utilized by certain molds. The fermentation products appear to be approximately the same from cellobiose as from glucose and other sugars [Poe and Klemme (1935)].

Lactose (Milk Sugar). Lactose is one of the most common of the disaccharides. It produces one mole of glucose and one mole of galactose on acid hydrolysis and is a reducing sugar. Certain bacteria, yeasts, and molds can utilize lactose as a source of carbon; its fermentation is of special importance in the differentiation of members of the colon-typhoid group of bacteria. The products of dissimilation of lactose by microorganisms are in general the same as those from glucose and galactose.

Gentiobiose. This reducing sugar produces two moles of glucose on hydrolysis. It has been studied very little in bacteriology, but it is known to be utilized by molds and bacteria.

Melibiose. The reducing disaccharide melibiose is composed of one mole of glucose and one mole of galactose. It is fermented by certain microorganisms. Although very little is known concerning its degradation products, it is generally assumed that they are the same as those from glucose and galactose.

Raffinose. Raffinose is the most important of the trisaccharides and is composed of one mole each of fructose, glucose, and galactose. It is fermented by certain bacteria, but little is known about its products. Yeasts utilize raffinose, but, according to Amadio (1936), *Saccharomyces cerevisiae* yields only about 10 per cent as much alcohol from raffinose as from glucose. *Aspergillus niger* produces citric acid from raffinose [Amelung (1930)].

Melezitose. This is a nonreducing sugar, and mild acid hydrolysis produces one mole of glucose and one mole of turanose (an isomer of sucrose); the turanose yields one mole each of glucose and fructose on further hydrolysis. It is utilized by certain bacteria, yeasts, and molds.

Gentianose. The trisaccharide gentianose yields one mole of fructose and one mole of gentiobiose on mild acid hydrolysis; the gentiobiose produces two moles of glucose on further hydrolysis. The sugar is fermented by certain bacteria, yeasts [Guillemet (1935)], and other microorganisms, although little is known concerning its dissimilation products.

Stachyose. The nonreducing tetrasaccharide stachyose is composed of one mole of fructose, one of glucose, and two of galactose. Little is known concerning the action of bacteria and molds [Thaysen and Galloway (1930)] on this sugar, but it is slowly attacked by certain yeasts [Chaudun (1933), Guillemet (1935)].

Dextrins. The dextrins are intermediate in complexity between the starches and maltose and are not readily prepared in pure form. According to Buchanan and Fulmer (1930), a number of microorganisms ferment dextrins. In one genus the fermentation is usually regarded as differential; that is, *Corynebacterium diphtheriae* ferments dextrins, whereas *Corynebacterium xerosis* and *Corynebacterium hoffmannii* do not. *Vibrio amylocella* is an interesting bacterium because it attacks cellulose, starch, and dextrins; with starch and dextrins glucose accumulates in the medium when NH_4Cl is used as a nitrogen source [Gray (1939)]. Certain yeasts cannot ferment dextrins [Haehn, Glaubitz, and Gross (1937)], and others, such as *Schizosaccharomyces pombe*, can attack potato dextrin but not rice dextrin [Skaguti and Otani (1939)]. Several molds are known which can attack dextrins.

STARCH. A number of microorganisms are known to attack starch [Buchanan and Fulmer (1930)]. It is usually assumed that the organisms hydrolyze the starch through dextrins to maltose and glucose, the glucose then being oxidatively or fermentatively dissimilated to other products. Usually there is little evidence of any accumulation of intermediate products, particularly those of hydrolysis. On the other hand, Tarr (1934) has reported that the endospores of certain bacteria hydrolyze starch to maltose only; Gray (1939) found that under certain conditions *Vibrio amylocella* hydrolyzed starch and dextrins to glucose only; and Doudoroff (1940) observed that the extracellular enzymes of *Pseudomonas saccharophila* produced only disaccharides from starch. Certain products of bacterial action upon starch have been found to be of some commercial significance; such products as acetone, isopropyl alcohol, and butyl alcohol are produced in considerable quantities by certain species of the genera *Bacillus* and *Clostridium*. Fermentation of starch is not a general property of yeast, but a few reports have appeared stating that certain yeasts ferment starch. Many molds possess the power to attack starch, and cell-free enzyme preparations have been extracted from some of them for industrial uses.

GLYCOGEN. This polysaccharide is very closely related to starch and is utilized by several microorganisms. Certain organisms produce only hydrolytic products such as maltose [Tarr (1934), Doudoroff (1940)]; in other instances the hydrolytic products are further dissimilated to other substances.

INULIN. This carbohydrate differs from starch in that it appears to be built up of fructose units rather than glucose. In general, however, little is known concerning the intermediate products of hydrolysis and the products of dissimilation. It is attacked by several microorganisms and is useful in differentiating pneumococci from streptococci and in separating certain species of the colon-typhoid group. According to Finkle (1936), it is not oxidized or fermented by washed cells of pneumococci; thus the fermentation as ordinarily determined seems to be associated with cell growth and division. Certain yeasts, which do not ferment fructose, slowly attack inulin and form ethyl alcohol, CO_2, glycerol, and other products [Guillemet and Leroux (1938, 1939)]. Some molds are also known to attack inulin.

GUMS. The name gum is given to a group of complicated substances, most of them mixtures, which contain carbohydrates and form sticky or colloidal solutions when mixed with water. On hydrolysis the gums yield a pentose or hexose and compounds of an acid nature. Probably the best known of the gums are gum arabic, gum tragacanth, and cherry-tree gum. Bacteria and other fungi have been described which utilize the gums as a source of carbohydrate; they appear to be widely distributed in nature [Thaysen and Bunker (1927)], but little is known concerning their properties.

PECTINS. Pectins occur in considerable quantities in the cell walls of many fruits and fleshy roots. They are complex carbohydrates, but little information is available concerning their exact chemical constitution. A number of aerobic, facultative, and anaerobic microorganisms are known to attack the pectins, and the early literature on this subject is fully reviewed by Thaysen and Bunker (1927); their book should be consulted for further details. Later Makrinov (1932) and Werch, Day, Jung, and Ivy (1941) studied the fermentation of pectins by bacteria. Makrinov reported that pectin fermentation by *Clostridium pectinovorum* does not yield fully oxidized compounds, but rather butyric acid and small amounts of acetic acid, CO_2, and H_2. The aerobe *Pectinobacter amylophilum*, on the other hand, forms more highly oxidized products, such as CO_2 and H_2, with about 25 per cent of the fermented carbohydrates being in the form of ethyl alcohol and formic acid. It is also of interest to note here that Funck (1937) has substituted pectins for agar in bacteriological media with good results.

HEMICELLULOSES. The plant cell-wall substances known as hemicelluloses do not contain cellulose but instead are complex carbohydrates containing such monoses as galactose, mannose, arabinose, and xylose in association with inorganic ions and other substances. Agar, xylan (wood gum), and related materials belong to this group of substances.

The information available concerning the utilization of hemicelluloses by microorganisms is scanty [see the review by Thaysen and

Bunker (1927)]. The various kinds of agar, which are widely used in the bacteriological laboratory, have the following compositions:

	Japanese Agar [Itano (1933)]	Agar [Waksman and Bavendamm (1931)]	American Agar *
Moisture	23%	15.29–16.57%	17–23%
Ash	2.4–3.8%	3.85–4.23%	2.1–3.5%
Crude protein	1.4–2.0%		0.8–1.3%
Crude fiber	16.1–25.1%	0.80–0.89%	0.1–0.3%
Soluble N-free compounds	53.0–73.0% †	76.15–77.34%	75.0–78.0%

* Courtesy of American Agar and Chemical Co., San Diego, California.
† About one-third is galactose.

Several bacterial species have been described which decompose agar [Thaysen and Bunker (1927), Waksman and Bavendamm (1931), Goresline (1933)]. The species studied by Goresline belong to the genera *Achromobacter* and *Pseudomonas*. It is also of interest to note that agar contains a substance which can be partially extracted by methyl alcohol or pyridine and which favors the growth of molds [Robbins (1939)]. The information available on the microbial decomposition of the pentosan xylan, sometimes called wood gum, is more extensive than that on some of the other hemicelluloses [see the review by Thaysen and Bunker (1927) for a discussion of the early literature]. Patrick and Werkman (1933) described eleven species of the genus *Bacillus* and two of the genus *Achromobacter* which ferment xylan with acid production, and Werkman (1936) reported that *Bacillus polymyxa* and *Bacillus macerans* convert xylan into acetone, 2,3-butylene glycol, acetylmethylcarbinol, ethyl alcohol, CO_2, H_2, and formic, acetic, lactic, and succinic acids. Iwata (1937) also found that certain species of the genus *Bacillus* utilize xylan, forming xylose and small amounts of formic, acetic, and lactic acids and CO_2.

Cellulose. Cellulose constitutes from 30 to 50 per cent of the dry weight of seed or flowering plants, and in substances such as cotton it represents about 90 per cent of the total weight of the air-dry material. Among the lower plants cellulose is found in the tissues of ferns and mosses, and it is probably present in certain of the higher algae. Its presence in the cells of lower algae, fungi, and bacteria is still problematical. Thus it can be seen that its decomposition in nature is of great importance.

True cellulose is characterized by well-defined botanical and chemical properties and by a characteristic crystalline structure. Although resistant to ordinary mild chemical reagents and the digestive juices of higher animals, it is readily decomposed by a great variety of microorganisms; as a result it does not tend to accumulate in nature. Some microorganisms capable of decomposing cellulose, notably certain bacteria, are highly specialized in their activities and depend upon cellulose as the exclusive source of energy. Other organisms, including certain bacteria, fungi, and actinomycetes, depend only partially upon cellulose as their nutrient. Frequently, several different organisms collaborate in the digestion of the cellulose molecule, and the products of decomposition by one organism may become sources of carbon and energy for the activities of another.

The literature dealing with the utilization of cellulose by microorganisms is very large, and only two phases of the problem will be outlined here: (1) a classification of the cellulose-decomposing organisms, and (2) the chemistry of cellulose decomposition by such organisms. The entire subject has been reviewed in some detail by Thaysen and Bunker (1927), Khouvine (1934), Gray (1939), Waksman (1940), and Boswell (1941), and these references should be consulted for additional reading.

Khouvine (1934) divided the cellulose bacteria into the following groups:

I. Cellulose-decomposing bacteria.
    A. Aerobic bacteria. Examples: *Bacillus cellare-solvens*, *Pseudomonas perlurida*, *Micrococcus cytophagus*, *Spirocheta cytophaga*, *Cellvibrio ochracea*.
    B. Anaerobic bacteria. Examples: *Clostridium cellulosae-dissolvens*, *Clostridium cellulosolvens*, *Clostridium cellulolyticum*.
    C. Thermophilic bacteria. Examples: *Clostridium thermocellum*, *Bacillus thermocellolyticus*.
II. Cellulose-synthesizing bacteria. Example: *Acetobacter xylinum*.

Although such a classification has its merit, the one proposed by Waksman (1940) seems more logical because it takes into consideration the habitat of organisms. Waksman's classification is as follows:

1. Microorganisms concerned in cellulose decomposition in growing plants, comprising a number of plant pathogens, primarily among the lower or filamentous fungi and the higher or fleshy fungi.

2. Microorganisms assisting in the decomposition of cellulose in the digestive tracts of insects and higher animals; these may be considered primarily as symbiotic organisms and comprise certain anaerobic bac-

teria and protozoa; aerobic bacteria belonging to the *Cytophaga* and *Cellvibrio* groups may also participate.

3. Microorganisms bringing about the digestion of cellulose in the purification of sewage and the disposal of garbage; the first function is carried out by various aerobic and anaerobic bacteria and to a lesser extent by actinomycetes and lower fungi; in the second process a number of fungi and bacteria, including thermophilic groups, are largely concerned.

4. Microorganisms concerned in cellulose decomposition of soils and composts; a great many fungi, bacteria, actinomycetes, and possibly also invertebrate animals are responsible for these processes.

5. Microorganisms active in cellulose decomposition in peat bogs, leading to the formation of various peats and coal; anaerobic bacteria and some aerobic forms are active under these conditions.

6. Microorganisms bringing about the decomposition of cellulose in oceans, rivers, and other flowing water systems; these comprise mostly anaerobic bacteria.

7. Microorganisms decomposing cellulose in timbers, paper pulp, textiles, manufactured paper, and books; a great variety of lower and higher fungi, actinomycetes, and aerobic bacteria, as well as certain invertebrate animals such as termites and shipworms, belong to this group.

8. Microorganisms utilized in the fermentation of cellulose in certain industries, as well as in the preparation of certain foodstuffs (for example, the production of edible mushrooms and animal feeds); here belong anaerobic bacteria and a number of fungi. The use of microorganisms for industrial purposes offers great possibilities, because certain anaerobic bacteria are able to convert cellulose into butyric and acetic acids, ethyl and other alcohols, methane, CO_2, and H_2 [see the paper by Fulmer (1936)]. Aerobic bacteria and fungi usually bring about complete destruction of cellulose, without leaving much in the form of intermediate products; hence they have little to offer for the production of industrially valuable products.

A great deal has been written about the chemistry of cellulose decomposition by various microorganisms. It is usually assumed that cellulose is hydrolyzed in two stages; the first is to the disaccharide cellobiose and the second to glucose; the glucose may then be oxidatively or fermentatively dissimilated to other products. In anaerobic bacteria the products of hydrolysis and fermentation may be represented by the following reactions [see Viljoen, Fred, and Peterson (1926), Khouvine (1934), Waksman (1940)]:

$$(C_6H_{10}O_5)x + H_2O \rightarrow x(C_{12}H_{22}O_{11})$$

$$C_{12}H_{22}O_{11} + H_2O \rightarrow 2(C_6H_{12}O_6)$$

$$2(C_6H_{12}O_6) + H_2O \rightarrow 2CH_3 \cdot CHOH \cdot COOH + CH_3 \cdot COOH + CH_3 \cdot CH_2 \cdot OH + 2CO_2 + 2H_2$$

$$2CH_3 \cdot CH_2 \cdot OH \rightarrow CH_3 \cdot COOH + 2CH_4$$

$$2CH_3 \cdot CHOH \cdot COOH \rightarrow CH_3 \cdot CH_2 \cdot CH_2 \cdot COOH + 2CO_2 + 2H_2$$

$$CO_2 + 4H_2 \rightarrow CH_4 + 2H_2O$$

As Waksman (1940) pointed out, these reactions are largely hypothetical, but they serve nevertheless to explain the processes involved in the formation of various acids, alcohols, and gases in the anaerobic decomposition of cellulose. Less is known of the mechanism of cellulose decomposition by aerobic bacteria and fungi, since only seldom have intermediary substances been isolated by various investigators. Simola (1930) reported, however, that an obligate, aerobic, sporulating bacterium attacked cellulose and produced CO_2, formic acid, ethyl alcohol, and an unknown acid.

LIGNINS. The composition of the lignins is complex and still largely unknown. However, since they are closely associated with the pectins and cellulose in nature, they may be considered at this point in the discussion. Under aerobic conditions lignins are quite stable, although certain fungi, such as *Polyporus abietinus*, very slowly attack them [Norman (1936), Garren (1938)]. On the other hand, under anaerobic conditions lignins are decomposed by mesophilic and thermophilic organisms, but to a lesser extent than are other plant constituents [see Boruff and Buswell (1934), Levine, Nelson, Anderson, and Jacobs (1935), Waksman and Hutchings (1936), Berl and Koerber (1938)]. Little is known concerning the fermentation products of the lignins. For the most part they are fermented slowly and incompletely, with only a small amount of CO_2 and methane being evolved.

Glycosides. A great variety of glycosides are found in the plant world. They are composed of alcohols or phenols in glycosidic combination with a sugar. On hydrolysis by acids or enzymes the glycosides produce one or more sugars, chiefly *d*-glucose, and a nonsugar portion, which is termed the aglucon; these aglucons are of a very diversified nature. The function of the glycosides in nature is rather obscure, although the physiological actions of many are well established. A few of the great number of naturally occurring glycosides are cited below:

Glycoside	*Sugar*	*Aglucon*
Salicin	Glucose	*o*-Hydroxybenzyl alcohol
Esculin	Glucose	6,7-Dihydroxycoumarin
Coniferin	Glucose	Coniferyl alcohol
Amygdalin	Glucose (2 moles)	Benzoic oxynitrile
Scopolin	Glucose (2 moles)	6-Methylesculetin
Hesperidin	Glucose + rhamnose	Hesperitin
Lotusin	Gentiobiose	Lotoflavin
Digitoxin	Digitoxose (3 moles)	Digitoxigenin

The most complete study published on the utilization of glycosides by bacteria is that of Twort (1907). He tested the ability of eighteen species, including *Escherichia coli*, *Aerobacter aerogenes*, *Klebsiella pneumoniae*, *Eberthella typhosa*, *Shigella dysenteriae*, and *Alcaligenes fecalis*, to ferment forty-nine glycosides. The following twenty-two glycosides were not attacked by any of the bacteria tested:

Ononin	Jalapin	Convallarin
Ericolin	Scammonin	Quabin
Digitalein	Colocynthin	Scopolin
Helleborein	Plumierid	Frangulic acid
Cyclamin	Absynthin	Smilacin
Apiin	Quercitrin	Condurangin
Hederaglucoside	Hesperidin	Convolvulin
Tannin		

However, the following twenty-seven glycosides were attacked by one or more of the eighteen test species, with the production of either acid or acid and gas:

Euonymin green	Periplocin	Populin
Euonymin brown	Cathartinic acid	Camellin
Iridin	Amygdalin	Globularin
Senegin	Sapotoxin	Cerberid
Coniferin	Saponin	Baptisin
Arbutin	Bryonin	Coronillin
Salicin	Convallamarin	Gratiolin
Syringin	Digitalin	Adonidin
Quillajinic acid	Strophanthin	Phloridizin

The *Aerobacter* species and *Klebsiella pneumoniae* fermented the greatest number of compounds; *Alcaligenes fecalis* was the only species which did not attack any of the glycosides. Many other studies have appeared in the literature in which a few of the common glycosides were employed.

Cyclic Compounds. So far in this chapter we have dealt mainly with the so-called aliphatic or open-chain carbon compounds which serve as a source of carbon and energy for microorganisms. At this point a few remarks should be made concerning the utilization of the closed-chain compounds. Although such compounds have not been investigated as thoroughly as have the open-chain compounds, it is well recognized that they are relatively poor sources of carbon for microorganisms. In fact, only a few organisms are known to be able to attack such compounds. For example, Gray and Thornton (1928) isolated several types of soil bacteria which could decompose phenol ($C_6H_5 \cdot OH$),*o*-, *m*-, and *p*-cresol [$CH_3 \cdot C_6H_4 \cdot OH$], naphthalene [$C_{10}H_8$], phloroglucinol [$C_6H_3(OH)_3$], resorcinol [$C_6H_4(OH)_2$], and toluene [$C_6H_5 \cdot CH_3$]. Den Dooren de Jong (1926) likewise found that several pure cultures of bacteria could dissimilate certain cyclic compounds, such as quinic acid, $C_6H_7(OH)_4 \cdot COOH$, and benzoic acid, $C_6H_5 \cdot COOH$ (see Table 7); inositol, $C_6H_6(OH)_6$, is also fermented by by several microorganisms. According to Saz and Bernheim (1942), benzoic acid and the hydroxybenzoic acids are readily oxidized by the mycobacteria, but they will not serve as a sole source of carbon for such organisms.

Fats and Waxes. In general, the fats and waxes are not a ready source of carbon for microorganisms. However, a number of organisms are known to be capable of hydrolyzing such compounds by secreting specific lipases; examples of microorganisms which form lipases are discussed in Chapter 6.

REFERENCES

Abbott, O. D. 1926. *Missouri Agr. Expt. Sta. Res. Bull.* 85. 29 pp.

Allgeier, R. J., and W. H. Peterson. 1930. *J. Bact.*, **19**:18–19.

Allsopp, A. 1937. *New Phytologist*, **36**:327–356.

Amadio, G. 1936. *Ann. chim. applicata*, **26**:258–262 (1936. *Chem. Abstr.*, **30**: 7775).

Amelung, H. 1927, 1930. *Z. physiol. Chem.*, **166**:161–209; **187**:171–172.

Andersen, A. A., and C. H. Werkman. 1940. *Iowa State College J. Sci.*, **14**:187–194.

Arzberger, C. F., W. H. Peterson, and E. B. Fred. 1920. *J. Biol. Chem.*, **44**:465–479.

Aubel, E. 1921. *Compt. rend.*, **173**:1493–1495.

Baars, J. K. 1940. *Geneeskund. Tijdschr. Nederland.-Indië*, **80**:334–346.

Barham, H. N., and B. L. Smits. 1936. *Ind. Eng. Chem.*, **28**:567–570.

Barker, H. A. 1936. *Arch. Mikrobiol.*, **7**:404–419.

Barron, E. S. G., and C. P. Miller, Jr. 1932. *J. Biol. Chem.*, **97**:691–715.

Berencsi, G., and A. Illényi. 1938. *Biochem. Z.*, **298**:298–300.

Berl, E., and W. Koerber. 1938. *J. Am. Chem. Soc.*, **60**:1596–1598.

Bernhauer, K. 1928. *Biochem. Z.*, **197**:278–286, 287–308.

Bernhauer, K., and H. Knobloch. 1938. *Naturwissenschaften*, **26**:819.

Boorsma, H. J., A. R. Prévot, and R. Veillon. 1939. *Compt. rend. soc. biol.*, **131**:1137–1140.

Boruff, C. S., and A. M. Buswell. 1934. *J. Am. Chem. Soc.*, **56**:886–888.

Boswell, J. G. 1941. *New Phytologist*, **40**:20–33.

Braak, H. R. 1928. "Onderzoekingen over Vergisting van Glycerine." Dissertation, W. D. Meinema, Delft, Holland.

Breden, C. R., E. I. Fulmer, C. H. Werkman, and R. M. Hixon. 1930. *J. Bact.*, **19**:41.

Buchanan, R. E., and E. I. Fulmer. 1930. *Physiology and Biochemistry of Bacteria*, vol. III. Williams & Wilkins Co., Baltimore.

Carson, S. F., and S. Ruben. 1940. *Proc. Natl. Acad. Sci. U. S.*, **26**:422–426.

Chaudun, A. 1933. *Bull. soc. chim. biol.*, **15**:1117–1120.

Clifton, C. E. 1940. *J. Bact.*, **39**:485–497.

Daker, W. D., and M. Stacey. 1939. *J. Chem. Soc.*, **1939**:585–587.

den Dooren de Jong, L. E. 1926. "Bijdrage tot de Kennis van het Mineralisatieproces." Dissertation, Nijgh & VanDitmar's, Rotterdam. 200 pp.

Doudoroff, M. 1940. *Enzymologia*, **9**:59–72.

Doudoroff, M. 1942. *J. Bact.*, **44**:461–467.

Doudoroff, M. 1943. *Proc. Soc. Exptl. Biol. Med.*, **53**:73–75.

Dozois, K. P., C. J. Carr, and J. C. Krantz, Jr. 1938. *J. Bact.*, **36**:599–604.

Evans, E. A., Jr., and L. Slotin. 1941. *J. Biol. Chem.*, **141**:439–450.

Field, J. T., and C. F. Poe. 1940. *J. Biol. Chem.*, **132**:473–476.

Finkle, P. 1936. *J. Bact.*, **32**:473–483.

Fontaine, F. E., W. H. Peterson, E. McCoy, M. J. Johnson, and G. J. Ritter. 1942. *J. Bact.*, **43**:701–715.

Fosdick, L. S., and G. W. Rapp. 1943. *Arch. Biochem.*, **1**:379–389.

Fosdick, L. S., and J. C. Calandra. 1945. *Arch. Biochem.*, **6**:9–13.

Fosdick, L. S., and A. F. Dodds. 1945. *Arch. Biochem.*, **6**:1–8.

Fred, E. B., W. H. Peterson, and J. A. Anderson. 1921. *J. Biol. Chem.*, **48**:385–412.

Friedemann, T. E. 1938. *J. Bact.*, **35**:527–546.

Friedemann, T. E., and T. C. Kmieciak. 1941. *Proc. Soc. Exptl. Biol. Med.*, **47**:84–87.

Fulmer, E. I., and C. H. Werkman. 1930. *An Index to the Chemical Action of Microorganisms on the Non-nitrogenous Organic Compounds.* Charles C. Thomas, Springfield, Ill.

Fulmer, E. I. 1936. *Ind. Eng. Chem.*, **28**:778–782.

Funck, E. 1937. *Klin. Wochschr.*, **16**:1546.

Garren, K. H. 1938. *Phytopathology*, **28**:839–845, 875–878.

Goresline, H. E. 1933. *J. Bact.*, **26**:435–457.

Gould, B. S. 1938. *Biochem. J.*, **32**:797–802.

Grant, C. W., and C. E. Zobell. 1942. *Proc. Soc. Exptl. Biol. Med.*, **51**:266–267.

Gray, P. H. H., and H. G. Thornton. 1928. *Centr. Bakt.*, *II Abt.*, **73**:74–96.

Gray, P. H. H. 1939. *Canadian J. Research*, **17** (c):154–169.

Grey, E. C., and E. G. Young. 1921. *Proc. Roy. Soc. London, B*, **92**:135–150.

Guillemet, R. 1935. *Compt. rend.*, **201**:1517–1519.

Guillemet, R., and H. Leroux. 1938, 1939. *Compt. rend. soc. biol.*, **127**:1307–1308; *Bull. soc. chim. biol.*, **21**:1217–1241.
Guillemet, R. 1939. *Compt. rend. soc. biol.*, **130**:1402–1404.
Guittonneau, G., H. DeLaval, and M. Bejambes. 1930. *Compt. rend.*, **191**:82–84.
Gunsalus, I. C., and J. M. Sherman. 1943. *J. Bact.*, **45**:155–162.
Haehn, H., M. Glaubitz, and W. Gross. 1937. *Brennerei-Ztg.*, **54**:142 (1938. *Chem. Abstr.*, **32**:3896).
Hammer, B. W., and W. A. Cordes. 1920. *Iowa State College Agr. Expt. Sta. Res. Bull.* 61.
Harden, A. 1901. *J. Chem. Soc.*, **79**:610–628.
Harden, A., and G. S. Walpole. 1906. *Proc. Roy. Soc. London, B*, **77**:399–405.
Harden, A., and D. Norris. 1912. *Proc. Roy. Soc. London, B*, **84**:492–499.
Hassid, W. Z., and H. A. Barker. 1940. *J. Biol. Chem.*, **134**:163–170.
Hohl, L. A., and M. A. Joslyn. 1941. *Plant Physiol.*, **16**:343–360.
Itano, A. 1933. *Ber. Ohara Inst. landw. Forsch. Japan*, **6**:59–72 (1934. *Chem. Abstr.*, **28**:3846).
Iwata, H. 1937. *J. Agr. Chem. Soc. Japan*, **13**:978–988.
Johnson, F. H., and H. W. Schwarz. 1944. *J. Bact.*, **47**:373–378.
Khouvine, Y. 1934. "Cellulose et bactéries. Décomposition et synthèse." *Actualités Sci. et Ind. No.* 164. Hermann et Cie, Paris.
Kluyver, A. J., and F. L. W. van Roosmalen. 1932. *Biochem. Z.*, **245**:13–24.
Kluyver, A. J., and C. Schnellen. 1937. *Enzymologia*, **4**:7–12.
Kluyver, A. J., and A. G. J. Boezaardt. 1938. *Rec. trav. chim.*, **57**:609–615.
Koser, S. A. 1923. *J. Bact.*, **8**:493–520.
Koser, S. A., and F. Saunders. 1933. *J. Bact.*, **26**:475–488.
Krebs, H. A. 1937. *Biochem. J.*, **31**:2095–2124.
Krebs, H. A. 1941. *Nature*, **147**:560–563.
Kumagawa, H. 1922. *Biochem. Z.*, **131**:148–156, 157–160.
Lafon, M. 1932. *Bull. soc. chim. biol.*, **14**:263–271.
Lechner, R. 1940. *Biochem. Z.*, **304**:84–89; *Angew. Chem.*, **53**:163–167.
Levine, M., G. H. Nelson, D. Q. Anderson, and P. B. Jacobs. 1935. *Ind. Eng. Chem.*, **27**:195–200.
Lockwood, L. B., B. Tabenkin, and G. E. Ward. 1941. *J. Bact.*, **42**:51–61.
Makrinov, I. A. 1932. *Centr. Bakt., II Abt.*, **85**:339–348.
Mickelson, M. N., and C. H. Werkman. 1940. *J. Bact.*, **39**:709–715.
Myrbäck, K. 1940. *Svensk Kem. Tid.*, **52**:101–103 (1940. *Chem. Abstr.*, **34**: 6405).
Nelson, M. E., and C. H. Werkman. 1935. *J. Bact.*, **30**:547–557.
Nelson, M. E., and C. H. Werkman. 1940. *Iowa State College J. Sci.*, **14**:359–365.
Neuberg, C., and J. Hirsch. 1919. *Biochem. Z.*, **96**:175–202.
Nickerson, W. J., and W. R. Carroll. 1945. *Arch. Biochem.*, **7**:257–271.
Norman, A. G. 1936. *Science Progress*, **30**:442–456.
Northrop, J. H., L. H. Ashe, and R. R. Morgan. 1919. *Ind. Eng. Chem.*, **11**: 723–727.
O'Connor, R. C. 1940. *Biochem. J.*, **34**:1008–1011.
Osburn, O. L., R. W. Brown, and C. H. Werkman. 1938. *Iowa State College J. Sci.*, **12**:275–284.
Patrick, R. 1932. *Iowa State College J. Sci.*, **6**:457–461.
Patrick, R., and C. H. Werkman. 1933. *Iowa State College J. Sci.*, **7**:407–418.

Peat, S., E. Schlüchterer, and M. Stacey. 1939. *J. Chem. Soc.*, **1939**:581–585.
Pederson, C. S., and R. S. Breed. 1928. *J. Bact.*, **16**:163–185.
Peppler, H. J. 1942. *J. Bact.*, **44**:233–236.
Pervozvanskiĭ, V. V. 1939. *Microbiology (U.S.S.R.)*, **8**:915–930 (1941. *Chem. Abstr.*, **35**:3673).
Peterson, W. H., and E. B. Fred. 1920. *J. Biol. Chem.*, **44**:29–45.
Poe, C. F., and J. T. Field. 1932. *J. Biol. Chem.*, **99**:283–287.
Poe, C. F., and D. E. Klemme. 1935. *J. Biol. Chem.*, **109**:43–46.
Porges, N., T. F. Clark, and G. A. Gastrock. 1940. *Ind. Eng. Chem.*, **32**:107–111.
Porges, N., T. F. Clark, and S. I. Aronovsky. 1941. *Ind. Eng. Chem.*, **33**:1065–1067.
Potter, M. C. 1908. *Proc. Roy. Soc. London, B.*, **80**:239–259.
Reynolds, H., C. S. McCleskey, and C. H. Werkman. 1934. *J. Infectious Diseases*, **55**:207–219.
Reynolds, H., and C. H. Werkman. 1937. *Iowa State College J. Sci.*, **11**:373–378; *J. Bact.*, **33**:603–614.
Reynolds, H., W. M. Hoehn, and C. H. Werkman. 1939. *Iowa State College J. Sci.*, **13**:275–277.
Robbins, W. J. 1939. *Am. J. Botany*, **26**:772–778.
Rudney, H. 1940. *Science*, **92**:112–113.
Saz, A. K., and F. Bernheim. 1942. *J. Bact.*, **44**:385–386.
Scheffer, M. A. 1928. "De Suikervergisting door Bacteriën der Coli-groep." Dissertation, W. D. Meinema, Delft. 163 pp.
Schreder, K., R. Brunner, and R. Hampe. 1934. *Biochem. Z.*, **273**:223–242.
Simola, P. E. 1930. *Acta Chem. Fennica*, **3**:45–48.
Sjolander, N. O., E. McCoy, and L. S. McClung. 1937. *J. Bact.*, **33**:102–103.
Skaguti, K., and Y. Otani. 1939. *J. Agr. Chem. Soc. Japan*, **15**:11–17.
Skinner, C. E., and H. G. Brudnoy. 1932. *J. Hyg.*, **32**:529–534.
Smit, J. 1928. *Proc. Acad. Sci. Amsterdam*, **31**:421–432.
Solomon, A. K., B. Vennesland, F. W. Klemperer, J. M. Buchanan, and A. B. Hastings. 1941. *J. Biol. Chem.*, **140**:171–182.
Stahly, G. L. 1936. *Iowa State College J. Sci.*, **11**:110–112.
Stanier, R. Y., and G. A. Adams. 1944. *J. Bact.*, **47**:411–412.
Sternfeld, L., and F. Saunders. 1937. *J. Am. Chem. Soc.*, **59**:2653–2658.
Stiles, H. R., W. H. Peterson, and E. B. Fred. 1925. *J. Biol. Chem.*, **64**:643–654.
Stone, R. W., M. R. Fenske, and A. G. C. White. 1942. *J. Bact.*, **44**:169–178.
Stubbs, J. J., L. B. Lockwood, E. T. Roe, B. Tabenkin, and G. E. Ward. 1940. *Ind. Eng. Chem.*, **32**:1626–1631.
Tadokoro, T. 1936. *Bull. Chem. Soc. Japan*, **11**:239–247.
Takahashi, T., and T. Asai. 1934. *J. Agr. Chem. Soc. Japan*, **10**:604–607.
Tarr, H. L. A. 1934. *Biochem. J.*, **28**:391–393.
Tasman, A., and A. C. Brandwijk. 1938. *J. Infectious Diseases*, **63**:10–20.
Thaysen, A. C., and H. J. Bunker. 1927. *The Microbiology of Cellulose, Hemicelluloses, Pectin and Gums.* Oxford University Press, London.
Thaysen, A. C., and L. D. Galloway. 1930. *The Microbiology of Starch and Sugars.* Oxford University Press, London.
Tikka, J. 1935. *Biochem. Z.*, **279**:264–288.
Tittsler, R. P., and L. A. Sandholzer. 1935. *J. Bact.*, **29**:20–21.
Twort, F. W. 1907. *Proc. Roy. Soc. London, B*, **79**:329–336.

Underkofler, L. A., L. M. Christensen, and E. I. Fulmer. 1936. *Ind. Eng. Chem.*, **28**:350–354.

Underkofler, L. A., and J. E. Hunter, Jr. 1938. *Ind. Eng. Chem.*, **30**:480–481.

van Niel, C. B. 1928. *The Propionic Acid Bacteria.* J. W. Boissevain and Co., Haarlem. 187 pp.

van Niel, C. B., S. Ruben, S. F. Carson, M. D. Kamen, and J. W. Foster. 1942. *Proc. Natl. Acad. Sci. U. S.*, **28**:8–15.

Viljoen, J. A., E. B. Fred, and W. H. Peterson. 1926. *J. Agr. Sci.* (*England*), **16**:1–17.

Virtanen, A. I., E. Wichmann, and B. Lindström. 1927. *Z. physiol. Chem.*, **166**: 21–38.

Visser't Hooft, F. 1925. "Biochemische Onderzoekingen over het Geslacht *Acetobacter.*" Dissertation, Delft.

Waksman, S. A., and W. Bavendamm. 1931. *J. Bact.*, **22**:91–102.

Waksman, S. A. 1932. *Principles of Soil Microbiology*, 2nd Ed. Williams & Wilkins Co., Baltimore.

Waksman, S. A., and I. J. Hutchings. 1936. *Soil Sci.*, **42**:119–130.

Waksman, S. A. 1940. *Botan. Rev.*, **6**:637–665.

Wedum, A. G., and B. L. Golden. 1937. *J. Infectious Diseases*, **60**:94–98.

Werch, S. C., A. A. Day, R. W. Jung, and A. C. Ivy. 1941. *Proc. Soc. Exptl. Biol. Med.*, **46**:569–572.

Werkman, C. H., R. M. Hixon, E. I. Fulmer, and C. H. Rayburn. 1929. *Proc. Iowa Acad. Sci.*, **36**:111.

Werkman, C. H. 1936. *Iowa Agr. Expt. Sta. Ann. Rept.* 1936, pt. II. p. 57.

Werkman, C. H. 1939. *Bact. Rev.*, **3**:187–227.

Werkman, C. H., and H. G. Wood. 1942, 1942*a*. *Bot. Rev.*, **8**:1–68; *Advances in Enzymol.*, **2**:135–182.

Wood, H. G., and C. H. Werkman. 1936. *Biochem. J.*, **30**:618–623.

Wood, H. G., C. H. Werkman, A. Hemingway, and A. O. Nier. 1940, 1941. *J. Biol. Chem.*, **135**:789–790; **139**:365–376.

Woods, D. D. 1936. *Biochem. J.*, **30**:515–527.

9

METABOLISM OF NITROGEN COMPOUNDS BY MICROORGANISMS

About 70 per cent of the dry protoplasmic constituents of microbial cells are nitrogenous compounds of varying degrees of complexity. Thus, if such cells are to carry out their normal activities, they must find a utilizable source of nitrogen, as well as other substances, in their environment so that they can synthesize new protoplasm and repair the damage done to old. Probably no other group of organisms studied in biology use as diversified nitrogenous substances for protoplasmic synthesis as do the bacteria, since, for example, some are capable of building their nitrogenous cell constituents with molecular nitrogen as a beginning; others utilize nitrates, nitrites, or ammonium salts; and still others, which are more deficient in synthetic ability, must find substances, such as amino acids, in their environment which are already partly advanced in the synthesis leading to protoplasm.

In this chapter we will consider briefly a few of the nitrogenous substances which are known to be utilized as a source of nitrogen by certain microorganisms and, in so far as possible, list some of the changes which are thought to occur when the compounds are attacked and then assimilated by microorganisms. For additional reading on this subject the books by Buchanan and Fulmer (1930, Vol. III), Waksman (1932), and Stephenson (1939), and the articles cited under the various substances discussed in this chapter should be consulted.

KINDS OF NITROGEN COMPOUNDS METABOLIZED BY MICROORGANISMS

The arbitrary order in which the various nitrogenous substances which are utilized by microorganisms will be discussed is as follows:

Molecular Nitrogen (Nitrogen Fixation).
Ammonia, Hydroxylamine, Nitrous Acid, Nitric Acid, and Their Salts.
Cyanogen Compounds (Cyanic Acid, Thiocyanic Acid, Cyanamide, etc.).
Amines and Related Compounds.
Amides, Imides, and Their Compounds.

Urea, Guanidine and Creatine, Purine, Pyrimidine, and Their Derivatives.
Amino Acids.
Peptides.
Peptones, Proteoses, Metaproteins, and Proteins.

MOLECULAR NITROGEN (NITROGEN FIXATION)

The ability of various microorganisms to use atmospheric nitrogen for the synthesis of cellular material has been known for a number of years, but even now definite information is lacking on many phases of the process. Apparently the faculty of nitrogen fixation is not shared by very many higher forms of life,[1] and even among microorganisms only a few species are known definitely to possess this property.

Because of the economic importance of nitrogen fixation in agriculture a great amount of fundamental and practical research has been done on this subject. It will be impossible here to discuss even briefly the various ramifications of the problem; for such information the books by Waksman (1932) and Wilson (1940) and the reviews by Burk (1934) and Burk and Burris (1941) should be consulted.

The most important bacteria capable of fixing atmospheric nitrogen belong to the genera *Rhizobium* (symbiotic root-nodule bacteria) and *Azotobacter* (nonsymbiotic bacteria), although *Clostridium pasteurianum* and a few other anaerobes, *Mycobacterium rubiacearum*, and several other species of bacteria are known to fix some nitrogen. Pure cultures of blue-green algae of the genera *Anabena* and *Nostoc* are known to exhibit considerable nitrogen-fixing properties [Bortels (1940)], and small amounts of nitrogen appear to be fixed by certain molds and yeast [Fulmer and Christensen (1925)]. However, in certain bacteria, the yeasts, and the molds, the growths reported are so slow and the increase in nitrogen so small that the availability of gaseous nitrogen cannot be considered of practical importance.

Numerous factors have been shown to affect the fixation of nitrogen by bacteria under experimental conditions. A few examples may be cited.

1. Effect of Gaseous Pressure. It has been shown that gaseous pressure affects the fixation of nitrogen by various bacteria under experimental conditions. With *Azotobacter* species it has been observed by Meyerhof and Burk (1928), Lineweaver (1932), and others that the respiration rate is greatest at oxygen pressures below that of air,

[1] Using radioactive nitrogen for the study of nitrogen fixation by nonleguminous plants, Ruben, Hassid, and Kamen (1940) observed that barley plants assimilate N_2. Future studies along this line [see also Burris and Miller (1941) and Burris and Wilson (1942)] may reveal that nitrogen-fixation in nature is more general than has been supposed.

the maximum being at 10 to 15 per cent of O_2 and falling off sharply at lower and more gradually at higher pressures. In pure O_2 the respiration of *Azotobacter* was found to be only one-third to one-half that in air. However, maximum nitrogen fixation does not occur at this point but rather at 4 to 5 per cent of O_2. Burk (1930) has shown also with *Azotobacter* that at 0.2 atm. of O_2 appreciable respiration and growth occur when the N_2 pressure reaches 0.05 atm. and attain a maximum between 0.5 and 1.0 atm.; between 0.05 and 0.5 atm. respiration and growth are approximately proportional to the N_2 pressure. The fixation of nitrogen by *Azotobacter vinelandii* in culture is definitely inhibited by 0.2 per cent CO in air and is almost completely suppressed by 0.5 to 0.6 per cent. In the same range of CO concentration the assimilation of nitrogen supplied in the form of urea, ammonium, or nitrate ions, asparagine, aspartate, and glutaminate is not inhibited [Lind and Wilson (1942)].

A number of similar interesting experiments are available on the effect of gaseous pressure on symbiotic nitrogen-fixation processes [see Wilson, Umbreit, and Lee (1938), Wilson (1940)]. One of the most interesting points in this connection is that Wilson and his associates have shown that the partial pressure of N_2 can be lowered to about 0.1 to 0.15 atm. without a decrease in the quantity of N_2 fixed by nodulated red clover plants inoculated with *Rhizobium trifolii*, provided that the nitrogen removed either is unreplaced or is replaced with helium or argon. If the N_2 is replaced with H_2, however, the total quantity of N_2 fixed decreases linearly with the partial pressure of the N_2 of the atmosphere. Similar results are now also available with *Azotobacter* [Wyss and Wilson (1941)], Wyss, Lind, Wilson, and Wilson (1941)]. These results suggest that hydrogen may not be an inert gas in so far as nitrogen fixation is concerned, but rather may act as a specific inhibitor. This is apparently the first instance in which hydrogen has been shown to be a specific inhibitor for biological reactions.

2. Effect of *p*H. Although the maximum respiration of most *Azotobacter* species, in the presence of either free or fixed nitrogen, lies between *p*H 7.2 and 7.5 and falls to about 0 to 5 per cent of the optimum value at about *p*H 5.0 and 9.0 [Burk, Lineweaver, and Horner (1934)], other species have been described by Starkey (1939) which fix nitrogen at a *p*H as low as 2.9. The ability of *Rhizobium* species in symbiosis with legumes to fix nitrogen in soil solutions of different *p*H values varies with the species, but in general a reaction near neutrality is optimum with little nodulation or fixation occurring below *p*H 5.0 or above 8.0 [Wilson (1940)].

3. Effect of Fixed Nitrogen. Nitrogen fixation by *Clostridium pasteurianum* and *Azotobacter* species is inhibited by the presence of fixed forms of nitrogen, such as ammonium or nitrate salts. In *Azotobacter*, for example, inhibition is complete at concentrations above 0.5 mg. of nitrogen per 100 ml. of medium [Burk and Lineweaver (1930)]. Certain concentrations of nitrate also interfere with nodule formation and depress nitrogen fixation in leguminous plants; however, the inhibitory effects can be partially, but not completely, overcome by increasing the concentration of CO_2 in the air [Georgi (1935), Wilson (1940)].

4. Effect of Inorganic Elements. Besides sources of energy and nitrogen *Rhizobium* and *Azotobacter* species are known to require potassium, phosphorus, magnesium, sulfur, iron, calcium, and molybdenum for growth and optimum N_2 fixation. Various claims also have been made regarding the necessity of other elements, including copper, zinc, manganese, tungsten, silicon, vanadium, strontium, and iodine. Some information on the subject is presented in Chapter 7, and several excellent reviews are available [see Burk (1934), Steinberg (1938), Wilson (1940), Bortels (1940), Horner, Burk, Allison, and Sherman (1942)].

5. Effect of Other Factors. Numerous other factors have been found to influence the rate and extent of N_2 fixation. For example, Wilson and Wilson (1941) observed that such factors as purity of culture, size of inoculum, aeration, surface of medium, concentration of carbohydrate, and species all influence fixation by *Azotobacter*. Various growth factors are also known to be needed by the *Rhizobium* species; this phase of the subject is discussed in Chapter 7.

A great deal has been written in the past about the mechanism of nitrogen fixation by bacteria, but it has been only within the last few years that proposed schemes have been supported by carefully controlled experimental work. Although fixation by the root-nodule bacteria involves a system much more difficult to control than that of the nonsymbiotic nitrogen fixers, it is nevertheless the nodule system which has yielded the most information on the intermediate steps in the fixation process. However, as Virtanen and Laine (1939) and Wyss and Wilson (1941) have brought out, the mechanism of fixation by the symbiotic system is similar to, if not identical with, that of the fixation system in the free-living *Azotobacter*. A complete discussion of the work on this subject is not possible, but a few of Virtanen, Laine, and von Hausen's results may be briefly summarized because they are supported by considerable experimental work [see Wilson (1940), Burk and Burris (1941)]. Virtanen and his associates observed that, when cultures of legumes (pea) inoculated with the appropriate rhizobia were grown in sterile nitrogen-free media, the nodules excreted considerable amounts of soluble nitrogenous products. Furthermore, it was found that over 90 per cent of the excreted nitrogen consisted of *l*-aspartic acid and β-alanine, the β-alanine arising from the *l*-aspartic acid by decarboxylation;[2] in addition to the two amino acids 1 to 2 per cent of the excreted nitrogen was found to be in the form of oximinosuccinic acid. On the basis of these experiments and others not mentioned here the course of biological nitrogen fixation occurring in legume root nodules was expressed as follows:

$$N_2 \longrightarrow \underset{\text{intermediates}}{\text{Unknown}} \longrightarrow \underset{\text{Hydroxylamine}}{NH_2OH}$$

$$\longrightarrow \underset{\text{Oximinosuccinic acid}}{HOOC\cdot C(NOH)\cdot CH_2\cdot COOH} \longrightarrow \underset{l\text{-Aspartic acid}}{HOOC\cdot CH(NH_2)\cdot CH_2COOH}$$

$$\underset{\text{Carbohydrate}}{C_6H_{12}O_6} \longrightarrow \underset{\text{Oxaloacetic acid}}{HOOC\cdot CO\cdot CH_2\cdot COOH}$$

How hydroxylamine is formed from atmospheric nitrogen has not been experimentally proved, but Virtanen and his associates put forth the hypothesis that a diimide is formed as a primary reduction product ($N_2 \rightarrow HN:NH$), which then forms hydroxylamine by the addition of two water molecules. The reduction of the nitrogen molecule, nitrogen fixation in a stricter sense, requires a specific enzyme which is found in the nitrogen-fixing bacteria. The reaction of hydroxylamine with oxaloacetic acid (arising from carbohydrate metabolism), however, has been shown to be a nonenzymatic process. On the other hand, the reduction of oximinosuccinic acid to *l*-aspartic acid is known to be an enzymatic reaction. It has not been discovered yet which compounds in the plant liberate the hydrogen required for the reduction reactions or which enzymes act in the reduction process.

There is also considerable evidence that ammonia is an intermediate in the nitrogen-fixation reaction, although Virtanen and his associates do not believe it is of primary importance. However, as Wilson (1940) brought out, possibly both hydroxylamine and ammonia function as intermediates, depending upon the products of the respiratory metabolism of the organism involved.

AMMONIA, HYDROXYLAMINE, NITROUS ACID, NITRIC ACID, AND THEIR SALTS

Ammonia. Ammonia frequently appears as an end product of microbial metabolism, arising from the deamination of amino acids and other compounds or from the reduction of nitrates and nitrites

[2] In young cultures up to 75 per cent of the excreted nitrogen consisted of *l*-aspartic acid, whereas in older plants only 20 to 30 per cent of the nitrogen was aspartic acid; the remainder of the 90 per cent under each set of conditions consisted of β-alanine.

[Woods (1938)], but in general ammonia is too toxic and too reactive a metabolite to remain in the cells of organisms in a free form. Microorganisms produce at least two types of chemical changes in ammonia: (1) the oxidation of ammonia either to nitrite by such autotrophic bacteria as those of the genera *Nitrosomonas* and *Nitrosococcus* (see Chapter 7) or possibly directly to nitrogen gas or to nitrate by other bacteria; and (2) the assimilation of ammonia by microorganisms, synthesizing it into amino acids and other complex nitrogenous substances. All microorganisms probably make use of this second reaction to synthesize cellular constituents. Many bacteria, yeasts, molds, and green algae are capable of using ammonium salts as a starting material for cellular syntheses, whereas in other organisms, which are more fastidious in their nitrogen requirements, the ammonia may arise from the deaminization of such compounds as the amino acids and purines and then be synthesized into new compounds, possibly through transamination reactions. Ammonia may take part also in certain biochemical cycles, such as the so-called ornithine cycle.

Various reactions have been proposed to explain the mechanism of oxidation of ammonia to nitrite by the nitrifying bacteria. The overall reaction for the process is usually written as follows:

$$2NH_3 + 3O_2 \rightarrow 2HNO_2 + 2H_2O$$

However, it is quite probable that several intermediates, such as hydroxylamine (NH_2OH) and hyponitrous acid $(HNO)_2$, are formed during the course of the oxidation process [Kluyver and Donker (1926)].

The assimilation of ammonia by microorganisms may follow several alternate routes. One example may be similar to the reactions suggested by Fearon (1926) for the synthesis of amino acids:

$$CO_2 + NH_3 \rightarrow \underset{\text{Cyanic acid}}{HN{:}CO} + H_2O$$

Cyanic acid may then unite with an aldehyde, and by a reduction process the corresponding amino acid may be formed:

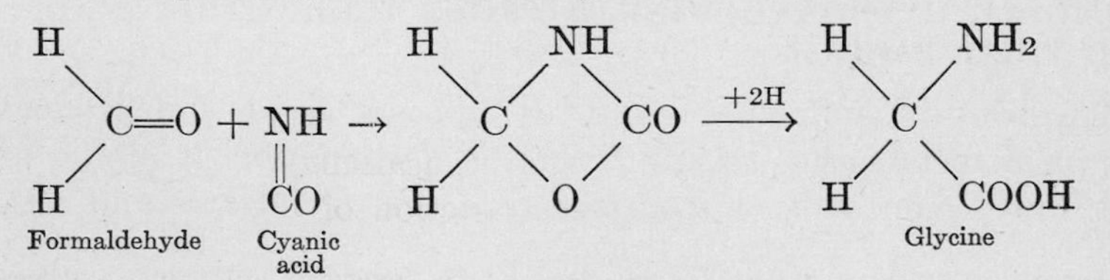

Certain organisms, such as coli-aerogenes forms, utilize ammonia salts, such as NH_4Cl, when they are supplied as a sole source of nitrogen; but, when peptone nitrogen is also present, little or no ammonium chloride is consumed [Carpenter (1939)].

In general, ammonium chloride, ammonium sulfate, ammonium lactate, ammonium phosphate, and ammonium carbonate are good sources of nitrogen for green algae; in fact, Ludwig (1938) found that inorganic and organic ammonium salts were superior to nitrate as a source of nitrogen for *Chlorella*.

Hydroxylamine (NH_2OH). Hydroxylamine appears to play an important intermediate role in several metabolic reactions, but little is known concerning its ability to serve as a source of nitrogen for microorganisms. It has already been stated that it is a likely intermediate in the nitrogen-fixation process by the root-nodule bacteria, and it has been detected on several occasions by various workers [see Lindsey and Rhines (1932), Aubel (1938), Woods (1938)] as an intermediate in the reduction of nitrates and nitrites to ammonia by *Escherichia coli*, *Clostridium welchii*, and other bacteria. It does not appear to be utilized as a source of nitrogen by green algae; in fact, several workers have found it to be highly toxic for such organisms [see Ludwig (1938)].

Nitrous Acid and Its Salts. Microorganisms may reduce the nitrite ion to free nitrogen gas or to ammonia, or they may oxidize it to nitrate; both types of reactions are known to occur in nature and are of considerable importance in maintaining soil fertility. In general, the nitrite ion is utilized by the same organisms which assimilate nitrate; but it appears to be toxic at a much lower concentration than is nitrate [Ludwig (1938), Burk and Horner (1939), Tarr (1941)].

The mechanism involved in the reduction of nitrite to nitrogen gas has not been elucidated, but it has been postulated that it may occur by an interaction with amino compounds:

$$HNO_2 + R\cdot NH_2 \rightarrow R\cdot OH + H_2O + N_2$$

or by a process in which the nitrous acid is reduced through hyponitrous acid to nitrous oxide and then to nitrogen gas:

$$2HNO_2 \rightarrow (HNO)_2 \rightarrow N_2O \rightarrow N_2$$

The steps in the process of reducing the nitrite ion to ammonia are not very well understood, but it appears probable that hydroxylamine is one of the intermediate products [Aubel (1938), Woods (1938)] and that the reaction is just the converse of that discussed for the oxidation of ammonia to nitrite.

The oxidation of nitrous acid, or the nitrite ion, to nitrate by bacteria of the genus *Nitrobacter* takes place according to the following reaction:

$$NaNO_2 + \tfrac{1}{2}O_2 \rightarrow NaNO_3$$

The system capable of catalyzing this reaction is apparently not present in very many microorganisms.

Nitric Acid and Its Salts. The nitrate ion is utilized by many species of bacteria, molds, and green algae as a source of nitrogen but is usually very unsatisfactory for the growth of yeasts. It is known also that certain bacteria, such as *Azotobacter vinelandii* [Lind and Wilson (1942)], require a period of adaptation before they can readily use nitrate nitrogen. In the presence of sufficient energy material bacteria and molds may utilize nitrate as a sole source of nitrogen, probably first reducing it to nitrite, then to hydroxylamine, and finally to ammonia in the process of assimilation. The ability of bacteria to reduce the nitrate ion to nitrite or to ammonia is commonly measured in the laboratory as one of the physiological characteristics for differentiating bacteria, and the factors governing the process have been studied by several workers [see Zobell (1932), Lindsey and Rhines (1932), Conn (1936), Yamagata (1938), Woods (1938), Randall and Reedy (1939)].

Certain autotrophic bacteria (*Thiobacillus denitrificans*) reduce nitrates to free nitrogen gas and oxidize sulfur to sulfate under anaerobic conditions. The reaction for the process is usually written as follows:

$$6KNO_3 + 5S + 2CaCO_3 \rightarrow 3K_2SO_4 + 2CaSO_4 + 2CO_2 + 3N_2$$

CYANOGEN COMPOUNDS (CYANIC ACID, THIOCYANIC ACID, CYANAMIDE, ETC.)

The so-called cyanogen compounds have not been studied very extensively as a source of nitrogen for microorganisms; a few compounds will be mentioned here.

Hydrocyanic Acid (HCN). This compound is not used by very many organisms as a source of nitrogen. In fact, only a few organisms are known to be able to alter this acid. For example, *Aspergillus niger* in a nitrogen-free sugar medium will oxidize HCN, sometimes 100 per cent being utilized if the mold is sufficiently starved for nitrogen:

$$HCN + \tfrac{1}{2}O_2 \rightarrow HCNO$$ [Iwanoff and Zwetkoff (1936)]

Powdered sulfur and sodium thiosulfate promote this conversion; in the presence of sulfur the formation of thiocyanate from the cyanide is also possible.

Cyanic Acid (NC·OH). Cyanic acid is a very unstable compound and has not been studied as a source of nitrogen for microorganisms. However, it has been postulated as an intermediate in the breakdown of urea to ammonia by certain organisms [see Fearon (1940)].

Thiocyanic Acid (NC·SH) and Its Derivatives. Several early workers found that thiocyanates could be used as a source of sulfur and nitrogen, but not as a source of carbon for microorganisms. For example, Tanner (1918) found that ten out of thirty cultures of yeast-like fungi produced H_2S from potassium thiocyanate. Later Happold and Key (1937) described an organism (*Bacterium thiocyanoxidans*) which is capable of using ammonium thiocyanate and nitrate as a sole source of carbon and nitrogen; the following reaction was given for the oxidation of thiocyanate:

$$NH_4CNS + 2O_2 + 2H_2O \rightarrow (NH_4)_2SO_4 + CO_2$$

This oxidation is thought to be due to an adaptive enzyme system.

Cyanamide ($NC \cdot NH_2$ or HN═C═NH) and Its Derivatives. Several microorganisms have been described which can utilize cyanamide (or calcium cyanamide) as a source of nitrogen [Perotti (1908), Löhnis and Sabaschnikoff (1908), Cowie (1920)]. It is assumed that the compound is first broken down to ammonia, which is then assimilated by the organisms. The polymer of cyanamide, dicyanodiamide ($C_2N_4H_4$), is also used by certain bacteria as a source of nitrogen, but it is decomposed very slowly and no ammonia is formed.

AMINES AND RELATED COMPOUNDS

Although several early workers reported that certain bacteria utilize amines as a source of nitrogen, the first extensive study on this subject was made by den Dooren de Jong (1926, 1927), who employed forty-one amines and thirteen different bacterial species in his work. Den Dooren de Jong studied not the dissimilation products of the various amines, but rather their ability to support growth. Certain of his data are summarized in Table 1, pp. 840–841.

Later Gale (1942) studied the oxidation of several amines by washed cells of *Pseudomonas aeruginosa*. The oxidation of putrescine, cadaverine, agmatine, and benzylamine was complete; therefore the breakdown of these molecules corresponds to the equations:

$$\underset{\text{Putrescine}}{C_4H_{12}N_2} + 5.5O_2 \rightarrow 2NH_3 + 4CO_2 + 3H_2O$$

$$\underset{\text{Cadaverine}}{C_5H_{14}N_2} + 7O_2 \rightarrow 2NH_3 + 5CO_2 + 4H_2O$$

$$\underset{\text{Agmatine}}{C_5H_{14}N_4} + 5.5O_2 \rightarrow 4NH_3 + 5CO_2 + H_2O$$

$$\underset{\text{Benzylamine}}{C_7H_9N} + 8.5O_2 \rightarrow NH_3 + 7CO_2 + 3H_2O$$

Each of these oxidations was inhibited by 0.01 *M* semicarbazide or by 0.0001 *M* cyanide. Histamine and tyramine were not oxidized to completion like these amines; rather they were oxidized incompletely by adaptive enzymes to ammonia and other products.

Several common bacteria are known to be able to ferment *glucosamine* with ammonia, acid, or acid and gas production [Meyer (1913), Lutwak-Mann (1941)]; however, it is not used as a source of nitrogen by *Chlorella* but is assimilated by certain other green algae [see Ludwig (1938)]. *Chitin*, a polymer consisting of at least four acetyl glucosamine ($CH_3 \cdot CO \cdot NH \cdot C_6H_{11}O_5$) units, is also decomposed by such bacteria as *Bacillus chitinovorus*, *Bacillus chitinobacter*, *Bacterium chitinophilum*, and *Bacterium chitinophagum*, which are distributed widely in nature [see Benton (1935), Bucherer (1935), Stuart (1936), Zobell and Rittenberg (1938), Hock (1940, 1941)]. Certain of the chitinoclastic bacteria can derive their complete carbon or energy and nitrogen requirements from chitin. Some require supplementary carbon compounds but can utilize nitrogen from chitin, whereas still others attack chitin only in the presence of simple carbon and nitrogen sources. Among the readily demonstrable products resulting from the decomposition of purified chitin by pure cultures of bacteria are ammonia and acetic acid; the formation of butyric acid and reducing substances by certain strains has also been reported. Zobell and Rittenberg (1938) suggest that ammonia and acetic acid are formed as the result of the bacteria hydrolyzing the acetylated amino groups of the chitin molecule:

$$-\overset{|}{\underset{|}{C}}-NH-CO \cdot CH_3 + 2H_2O \rightarrow -\overset{|}{\underset{|}{C}}-OH + NH_3 + CH_3COOH$$

The reaction probably takes place in two steps with acetic acid first being liberated, after which deaminization occurs; or it is possible that the carbon-nitrogen linkage is hydrolyzed first, thereby liberating acetamide ($CH_3CO \cdot NH_2$), which upon hydrolysis gives ammonia and acetic acid. The liberated ammonia is then probably assimilated by the bacteria.

Indole. In 1921 Raistrick and Clark found that *Pseudomonas aeruginosa* and other bacteria can decompose the indole ring, and since then their observation has been confirmed with other bacteria [see Happold and Hoyle (1936)]. Also, Fildes (1940) observed that certain bacteria (*Eberthella typhosa*, *Corynebacterium diphtheriae*) which have been shown to require tryptophan for growth are capable of using indole in a concentration as low as 10^{-6} *M*. From this fact he deduced that

TABLE 1

The Assimilation of Amines by Bacteria *

[From den Dooren de Jong (1926, 1927)]

Amines	*Bacillus vulgatus*	*Bacillus mycoides*	*Bacillus polymyxa*	*Aerobacter aerogenes*	*Escherichia coli*	*Serratia marcescens*	*Bacterium herbicola*	*Proteus vulgaris*	*Mycobacterium phlei*	*Staphylococcus albus*	*Sarcina lutea*	*Pseudomonas fluorescens*	*Spirillum tenue*
Methylamine, $CH_3 \cdot NH_2$	(−)	(−)	(−)	+	(+)	(+)	+	(+)	+	−	+	(+)	−
Dimethylamine, $(CH_3)_2 \cdot NH$	(−)	(−)	(−)	+	(−)	(−)	+	(−)	(+)	−	(−)	(−)	−
Trimethylamine, $(CH_3)_3 \cdot N$	(−)	−	(+)	+	(−)	(−)	+	(−)	(+)	−	(−)	(−)	−
Tetramethylamine ammonium hydroxide, $(CH_3)_4N \cdot OH$	(−)	−	+	+	(−)	(−)	+	(−)	(+)	−	−	(−)	−
Ethylamine, $C_2H_5 \cdot NH_2$	+	(−)	+	+	(+)	+	+	+	+	−	(−)	(+)	−
Diethylamine, $(C_2H_5)_2 \cdot NH$	−	−	+	+	−	(+)	(+)	(−)	(+)	−	(−)	(−)	(−)
Triethylamine, $(C_2H_5)_3 \cdot N$	−	−	+	+	(−)	(−)	+	(−)	(−)	−	(−)	(−)	(−)
Tetraethylamine ammonium hydroxide, $(C_2H_5)_4N \cdot OH$	−	−	+	+	(−)	(−)	+	(−)	(−)	−	(−)	(−)	(−)
Propylamine, $CH_3 \cdot CH_2 \cdot CH_2 \cdot NH_2$	(−)	(−)	+	+	(−)	(+)	+	(−)	(+)	−	(−)	(−)	−
Isopropylamine, $(CH_3)_2 \cdot CH \cdot NH_2$	(−)	−	+	+	(−)	(−)	+	(−)	(+)	−	(−)	(−)	−
Dipropylamine, $(C_3H_7)_2 \cdot NH$	−	−	+	+	−	(+)	+	(−)	(+)	−	(−)	−	−
Tripropylamine, $(C_3H_7)_3 \cdot N$	−	−	+	+	(−)	(−)	+	(−)	(+)	−	(−)	(−)	−
Tetrapropylamine ammonium hydroxide, $(C_3H_7)_4N \cdot OH$	−	−	+	+	(−)	(−)	+	(−)	(+)	−	−	−	−
Butylamine, $CH_3 \cdot CH_2 \cdot CH_2 \cdot CH_2 \cdot NH_2$	−	−	+	+	(+)	(+)	+	(−)	+	−	−	(−)	−
Isobutylamine, $(CH_3)_2 \cdot CH \cdot CH_2 \cdot NH_2$	−	(−)	+	+	(+)	(+)	+	(−)	(+)	−	(−)	(−)	−
Diisobutylamine, $(C_4H_9)_2 \cdot NH$	−	−	+	+	(−)	(−)	+	(−)	(+)	−	(−)	(−)	−
Triisobutylamine, $(C_4H_9)_3 \cdot N$	−	−	+	+	−	(−)	+	(−)	(−)	−	(−)	(−)	−
Amylamine, $C_5H_{11} \cdot NH_2$	(−)	(−)	+	+	(+)	(−)	+	(−)	(+)	−	(−)	(−)	−
Diamylamine, $(C_5H_{11})_2 \cdot NH$	−	−	(+)	+	(−)	(−)	+	(−)	(−)	−	(−)	(−)	−
Triamylamine, $(C_5H_{11})_3 \cdot N$	−	−	+	+	(−)	(−)	+	(−)	(−)	−	(−)	(−)	−
Hexylamine, $C_6H_{13} \cdot NH_2$	−	−	−	−	−	−	−	−	−	−	−	−	−

+ = heavy to good growth; (+) = very good to moderate growth; (−) = feeble growth but somewhat better than control; − = extremely feeble growth or equal to control. Only + and (+) signs indicate that the compounds were attacked.

* Basal medium: Tap water with 2.0% agar, 0.1% K_2HPO_4, 1.0% glucose, 1.0% $CaCO_3$, plus 0.1% of the listed compounds as the hydrochloride or chloride. Incubation: 5 days at 30°C.

TABLE 1 (*Continued*)

THE ASSIMILATION OF AMINES BY BACTERIA *

[From den Dooren de Jong (1926, 1927)]

Amines	*Bacillus vulgatus*	*Bacillus mycoides*	*Bacillus polymyxa*	*Aerobacter aerogenes*	*Escherichia coli*	*Serratia marcescens*	*Bacterium herbicola*	*Proteus vulgaris*	*Mycobacterium phlei*	*Staphylococcus albus*	*Sarcina lutea*	*Pseudomonas fluorescens*	*Spirillum tenue*
Heptylamine, $C_7H_{15} \cdot NH_2$	–	–	–	–	–	–	–	–	–	–	–	–	–
Ethanolamine, $HO \cdot CH_2 \cdot CH_2 \cdot NH_2$	+	(+)	+	+	+	+	+	(–)	+	–	+	+	–
Diethanolamine, $(HO \cdot CH_2 \cdot CH_2)_2 \cdot NH$	–	–	+	+	–	(–)	+	–	(+)	–	(–)	(–)	–
Triethanolamine, $(HO \cdot CH_2 \cdot CH_2)_3 \cdot N$	(–)	–	+	+	(–)	(–)	+	(–)	(–)	–	(–)	(–)	–
Choline, $HO \cdot CH_2 \cdot CH_2 \cdot N(CH_3)_3 \cdot OH$	(–)	–	(+)	+	–	(+)	+	(–)	(+)	–	(–)	(–)	–
Glucosamine, $CH_2OH \cdot (CHOH)_3 \cdot CHNH_2 \cdot CHO$	+	(–)	+	+	(+)	(+)	+	(+)	(+)	–	(+)	(+)	(+)
Neurine, $H_2C{:}CH \cdot N(CH_3)_3 \cdot OH$	–	–	+	+	+	(+)	+	(+)	(+)	–	(+)	(–)	–
Allylamine, $H_2C{:}CH \cdot CH_2 \cdot NH_2$	(–)	–	(+)	+	(–)	(+)	+	(–)	(+)	–	(–)	(–)	–
Ethylenediamine, $H_2N \cdot CH_2 \cdot CH_2 \cdot NH_2$	(–)	–	+	+	(+)	(+)	(+)	(+)	(+)	–	(+)	(–)	–
Pentamethylenediamine (cadaverine), $H_2N \cdot (CH_2)_5 \cdot NH_2$	(–)	(–)	+	+	+	(+)	+	+	+	–	–	+	–
Hexamethylenetetramine, $N(CH_2 \cdot N{:}CH_2)_3$	–	–	+	–	(+)	(+)	–	(+)	(+)	–	(+)	(–)	–
Benzylamine, $C_6H_5 \cdot CH_2 \cdot NH_2$	(–)	–	(–)	+	(–)	(–)	+	(–)	+	–	–	(–)	–
α-Phenylethylamine, $CH_3 \cdot CH(C_6H_5) \cdot NH_2$	(–)	–	(+)	+	(+)	(+)	+	–	–	–	–	–	–
β-Phenylethylamine, $C_6H_5 \cdot CH_2 \cdot CH_2 \cdot NH_2$	–	(–)	+	+	+	(+)	+	–	(–)	–	–	–	–
Histamine, HC<(NH—CH=)(N——C)·$CH_2 \cdot CH_2 \cdot NH_2$ (ring)	–	–	+	+	(+)	(+)	+	(+)	+	(+)	(–)	(+)	+
Piperidine, $(CH_2)_5NH$	–	–	+	(+)	(+)	(+)	+	(+)	(–)	–	(–)	–	–
Piperazine, $(CH_2)_4(NH_2)$	–	–	+	+	(–)	(+)	+	(–)	(–)	–	–	–	–
Pyrrol, $(CH)_4NH$	–	–	–	+	(+)	+	+	–	–	–	–	(–)	–
Pyridine, HC<(CH=CH)(CH—CH)>N (ring)	(–)	–	(–)	+	(–)	(+)	+	(–)	(–)	–	–	(–)	–
Hydrazine, $H_2N \cdot NH_2$	–	–	(+)	–	–	(+)	–	–	–	–	–	–	–

+ = heavy to good growth; (+) = very good to moderate growth; (–) = feeble growth but somewhat better than control; – = extremely feeble growth or equal to control. Only + and (+) signs indicate that the compounds were attacked.

* Basal medium: Tap water with 2.0% agar, 0.1% K_2HPO_4, 1.0% glucose, 1.0% $CaCO_3$, plus 0.1% of the listed compounds as the hydrochloride or chloride. Incubation: 5 days at 30°C.

tryptophan is synthesized by bacteria from ammonia in stages, one of which is indole.

Another example of the utilization of indole is found in the study by Gray (1928). He discovered that, when various soil bacteria (*Pseudomonas indoloxidans, Mycobacterium globerulum, Micrococcus piltonensis*) are cultivated in broth or on agar media containing indole, the indole is oxidized to indigotin:

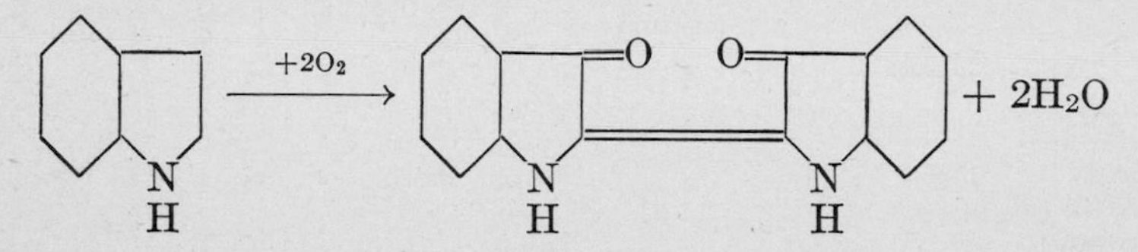

These indole-oxidizing organisms are unable to produce indole from tryptophan, and indole does not serve as a source of energy for the growth. Indoxyl,

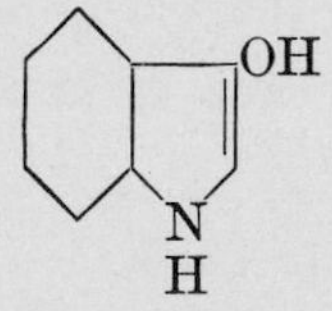

does not appear to be an intermediate in the oxidation of indole to indigotin; and the indigotin is not oxidized further to isatin,

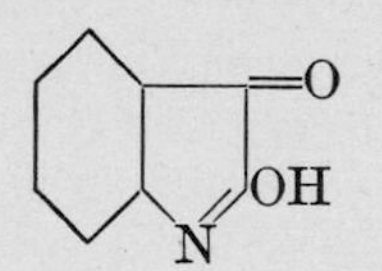

Glutamine and *choline* possess marked growth-promoting properties for certain bacteria. They have been discussed in Chapter 7.

Amines are frequently formed as the result of the decarboxylation of amino acids, and this phase of the subject is discussed on pp. 854 to 880 on the utilization of amino acids.

AMIDES, IMIDES, AND THEIR COMPOUNDS

Some of the amides[3] and imides serve as a source of nitrogen for certain bacteria (see Table 2). Utzino, Imaizumi, and Nakayama (1938) demonstrated that *Bacillus subtilis, Proteus vulgaris, Serratia marcescens, Staphylococcus aureus*, and several other bacteria attacked acetamide, benzamide, and oxamide. Very little is known concerning the mechanism of the metabolism of these compounds; it is probable that they are first hydrolyzed, and then the ammonia is assimilated.

[3] See discussion on urea, pp. 844 to 845.

TABLE 2

THE ASSIMILATION OF AMIDES AND IMIDES BY BACTERIA *

[From den Dooren de Jong (1926)]

Amides and Imides	*Bacillus vulgatus*	*Bacillus mycoides*	*Bacillus polymyxa*	*Aerobacter aerogenes*	*Escherichia coli*	*Serratia marcescens*	*Bacterium herbicola*	*Proteus vulgaris*	*Mycobacterium phlei*	*Staphylococcus albus*	*Sarcina lutea*	*Pseudomonas fluorescens*	*Spirillum tenue*
Formamide, $H\cdot CO\cdot NH_2$	+	−	+	(+)	+	+	+	−	−	(−)	(−)	+	−
Acetamide, $CH_3\cdot CO\cdot NH_2$	(−)	(+)	(−)	+	+	(−)	+	−	+	−	(−)	−	+
Propionamide, $CH_3\cdot CH_2\cdot CO\cdot NH_2$	(+)	(−)	+	(−)	+	(−)	+	−	+	(−)	+	(−)	+
Butyramide, $CH_3(CH_2)_2\cdot CO\cdot NH_2$	(+)	−	+	+	(−)	+	+	−	+	−	(−)	(−)	(+)
Isobutyramide, $(CH_3)_2\cdot CH\cdot CO\cdot NH_2$	(−)	−	(+)	(+)	(−)	(+)	+	−	+	−	+	(+)	(+)
Valeramide, $C_4H_9\cdot CO\cdot NH_2$	(+)	−	+	(−)	−	(−)	+	−	+	−	+	(−)	(−)
Capronamide, $C_5H_{11}\cdot CO\cdot NH_2$	(+)	−	+	−	(−)	−	+	−	+	−	+	−	(−)
Palmitamide, $C_{15}H_{31}\cdot CO\cdot NH_2$	(−)	−	−	−	−	−	+	−	(−)	−	−	(−)	..
Stearamide, $C_{17}H_{35}\cdot CO\cdot NH_2$	(−)	(−)	−	−	(−)	−	+	−	+	−	(+)	−	(−)
Lactamide, $CH_3\cdot CHOH\cdot CO\cdot NH_2$	(−)	−	+	+	−	+	+	−	+	−	+	+	(−)
Oxamide, $H_2N\cdot OC\cdot CO\cdot NH_2$	(+)	(−)	+	−	(−)	(−)	+	−	+	(−)	(−)	(−)	(−)
Methyloxamide, $CH_3\cdot NH\cdot OC\cdot CO\cdot NH_2$	(−)	−	+	+	(+)	(−)	+	(−)	(−)	−	(−)	(−)	(+)
Malonamide, $CH_2(CO\cdot NH_2)_2$	(−)	(−)	+	−	(−)	(−)	+	−	(+)	−	(−)	(−)	(−)
Succinamide, $H_2N\cdot CO\cdot CH_2\cdot CH_2\cdot CO\cdot NH_2$	(+)	−	(+)	+	(−)	+	+	(+)	+	−	(−)	(+)	(+)
Fumaramide, $H_2N\cdot CO\cdot CH:CH\cdot CO\cdot NH_2$	(−)	−	(−)	+	−	(−)	+	−	+	−	+	+	−
Succinimide, CH_2—CO | >NH CH_2—CO	+	−	+	+	(−)	(+)	+	(+)	(+)	−	(+)	+	(−)
Glutarimide, CH_2—CO | \\ CH_2 NH | / CH_2—CO	(−)	−	(+)	+	(−)	(+)	+	(+)	+	−	(−)	+	+
Asparagine, $HOOC\cdot CH(NH_2)\cdot CH_2\cdot CO\cdot NH_2$	+	(+)	+	+	+	+	+	+	+	+	(−)	+	+
Thioacetamide, $CH_3\cdot CS\cdot NH_2$	(−)	−	+	+	(+)	(+)	+	(+)	+	−	(−)	(+)	−

+ = heavy to good growth; (+) = very good to moderate growth; (−) = feeble growth but somewhat better than control; − = extremely feeble growth or equal to control. Only + and (+) signs indicate that the compounds were attacked.

* Basal medium: Tap water with 2.0% agar, 0.1% K_2HPO_4, 1.0% glucose, 1.0% $CaCO_3$, plus 0.1% of the listed compounds. Incubation: 5 days at 30°C.

With the exception of asparagine and urea, the amides, imides, and amines are not readily utilized as a source of nitrogen by yeasts [Burk and Horner (1939)]. Certain amides such as acetamide are a good source of nitrogen for *Chlorella* and other green algae, but they are not assimilated by some of the blue-green algae [see Ludwig (1938)].

UREA, GUANIDINE AND CREATINE, PURINE, PYRIMIDINE, AND THEIR DERIVATIVES

A number of biologically important compounds can be allocated to this general class of substances. For example, urea is one of the most widely distributed of the biological nitrogen compounds; creatine and its derivatives are also widely distributed and play very important roles in several metabolic processes; and the purines and pyrimidines are constituents of the nuclear material of every living cell.

Urea and Its Derivatives. Quite a number of microorganisms are capable of utilizing urea as a source of nitrogen (see Table 3); in fact, they are chiefly responsible for the decomposition of urea in nature. The literature dealing with the decomposition of urea by microorganisms is rather extensive and has been reviewed by several workers during the past several years [see Rubentschik (1925–1926), Mischoustin (1932), Gibson (1934–1935), Sakayuchi and Shizume (1937), Wohlfeil and Weiland (1937), Utzino, Imaizumi, and Nakayama (1938), Ludwig (1938), Burk and Horner (1939), Rustigian and Stuart (1941), Schulte and Thompson (1941), White and Hill (1941)]. Even though many species of bacteria, yeasts (*Torula* and *Schizosaccharomyces*), and green algae (*Chlorella*) utilize urea as a source of nitrogen, one group of bacteria, sometimes called the urobacteria, exhibit strong uroclastic abilities. Both cocci and rod-shaped bacteria belong to this group, and they are quite widespread in nature.

The ability of various bacteria and other microorganisms to attack the many urea derivatives has not been studied very extensively. Utzino, Imaizumi, and Nakayama (1938), however, found that ethyl- and dimethylurea were very slowly attacked by *Bacillus subtilis*, *Proteus vulgaris*, *Serratia marcescens*, and *Pseudomonas aeruginosa*, but that thiourea and bromural were not utilized by these or other organisms as a source of nitrogen. Biuret was used by *P. vulgaris*, *E. coli*, and *Staphylococcus aureus* and cyanuric acid by *B. subtilis* and *E. coli;* allantoin was attacked by all these species as well as by *S. marcescens* and *Ps. aeruginosa*. Mitchell and Levine (1938) observed that species of the genus *Aerobacter* utilize allantoin and hydantoin as a source of nitrogen and that this fact can be used to help separate such species from those of the genus *Escherichia* and from the intermediates.

Very little is known concerning the mechanism of urea breakdown by bacteria, except that ammonia is liberated in the process. It may be that the changes occurring in the urea-bacteria urease system are the same as those described by Fearon (1936) or others for urease from other sources; but this hypothesis remains to be proved.

A study on this subject in which bacteria are used is needed before we can actually say that bacterial urease is the same as the enzyme from other sources.

Guanidine and Creatine. Several bacteria [see Table 3 and Bierema (1909)], molds of the genera *Aspergillus*, *Penicillium*, *Mucor*, and *Rhizopus* [Iwanoff and Awetissowa (1931), Chrzaszcz and Zakomorny (1934)], and green algae (*Chlorella*) are known to use guanidine as a source of nitrogen; but it has been reported to be toxic for species of *Spirogyra* [see Ludwig (1938)]. It is thought that certain of these organisms convert the guanidine to urea and NH_3:

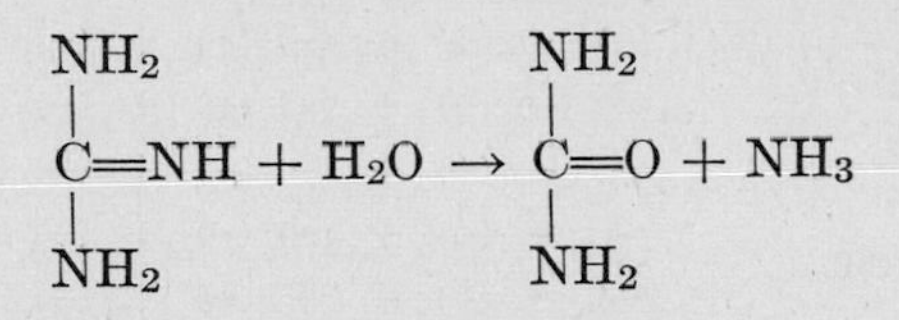

and that the urea accumulates while the ammonia is assimilated, whereas in other organisms the urea is further decomposed.

Several bacteria are known to be able to utilize creatine or creatinine as a source of nitrogen in their metabolism or to decompose it under various conditions [see Table 3 and Ackermann (1913–1914), Linneweh (1930), Dubos and Miller (1937), Miller, Allinson, and Baker (1939), Allinson (1940), Krebs and Eggleston (1940), and Bodansky, Duff, and McKinney (1941)]. The best-known organism which is capable of attacking creatine and creatinine is *Corynebacterium ureafaciens*,[4] and, according to Krebs and Eggleston (1940), these compounds are almost quantitatively converted to urea, with a very small amount of the nitrogen being used for growth of the bacterium. Linneweh (1930) has also studied the breakdown of creatinine by bacteria. He believes that certain putrefactive bacteria change creatinine first to methyl hydantoin with the elimination of ammonia and then, by prolonged putrefaction, to sarcosine (methylglycine).

Purine and Pyrimidine Derivatives. Certain purine and pyrimidine derivatives are extremely important biological compounds, but they have not been studied very extensively from the standpoint of microbial metabolism.

[4] This organism is listed as *Corynebacterium creatinovorans* by the American Type Culture Collection.

TABLE 3

THE ASSIMILATION OF UREA, GUANIDINE, AND PURINE DERIVATIVES BY BACTERIA *

[From den Dooren de Jong (1926)

Urea, Guanidine, and Purine Derivatives	*Bacillus vulgatus*	*Bacillus mycoides*	*Bacillus polymyxa*	*Aerobacter aerogenes*	*Escherichia coli*	*Serratia marcescens*	*Bacterium herbicola*	*Proteus vulgaris*	*Mycobacterium phlei*	*Staphylococcus albus*	*Sarcina lutea*	*Pseudomonas fluorescens*	*Spirillum tenue*
Urea, $H_2N \cdot CO \cdot NH_2$	+	(+)	+	+	+	+	+	(+)	+	−	+	+	+
Methylurea, $H_2N \cdot CO \cdot NH(CH_3)$	(−)	−	+	+	(−)	(+)	+	(−)	(+)	−	(+)	(+)	−
Ethylurea, $H_2N \cdot CO \cdot NH(C_2H_5)$	−	−	+	+	(−)	(+)	+	(+)	(+)	−	(−)	(−)	(−)
Diethylurea, *sym*-$(C_2H_5)HN \cdot CO \cdot NH(C_2H_5)$	(−)	(−)	+	+	(−)	(−)	+	(−)	(+)	−	(+)	(−)	(−)
Diethylurea, *asym*-$H_2N \cdot CO \cdot N(C_2H_5)_2$	(+)	(−)	(−)	+	(+)	(−)	(+)	(−)	+	−	+	(+)	(−)
Tetraethylurea, $(C_2H_5)_2N \cdot CO \cdot N(C_2H_5)_2$	(−)	(−)	(+)	+	(+)	(+)	+	(−)	(−)	−	(+)	(−)	−
Diphenylurea, *sym*-$(C_6H_5)HN \cdot CO \cdot NH(C_6H_5)$	(−)	−	+	+	(−)	(+)	+	(−)	(+)	−	(−)	(+)	(−)
Diphenylurea, *asym*-$H_2N \cdot CO \cdot N(C_6H_5)_2$	(−)	(−)	(+)	+	(−)	(+)	+	(−)	(+)	−	(−)	(+)	(−)
Thiourea, $H_2N \cdot CS \cdot NH_2$	−	−	(+)	+	−	(−)	+	(−)	(+)	−	(−)	(−)	(−)
Diethylthiourea, *sym*-$(C_2H_5)HN \cdot CS \cdot NH(C_2H_5)$	−	−	(+)	+	(−)	(−)	+	(+)	(+)	−	−	−	(−)
Biuret, $H_2N \cdot CO \cdot NH \cdot CO \cdot NH_2$	(+)	−	(−)	+	+	(−)	+	(−)	+	(+)	(−)	(−)	+
Guanidine, $HN{:}C(NH_2)_2$	−	(−)	+	+	(−)	(+)	+	(−)	+	−	−	(+)	−
Aminoguanidine, $HN{:}C(NH_2)NH \cdot NH_2$	(−)	(−)	−	+	(−)	+	+	(−)	(+)	(−)	−	−	−
Creatine, $HN{:}C(NH_2) \cdot N(CH_3) \cdot CH_2 \cdot COOH$	(−)	−	+	+	(−)	+	+	(−)	(+)	−	(−)	(−)	(−)
Creatinine, $HN{:}C\langle NH—CO ; N(CH_3) \cdot CH_2 \cdot CO \rangle$ (ring)	(−)	(−)	+	+	(−)	+	+	(+)	(−)	−	(+)	+	(−)
Arginine, $(HN)(H_2N)C \cdot NH \cdot (CH_2)_3 \cdot CH(NH_2) \cdot COOH$	+	+	+	+	+	+	+	+	+	−	+	+	+
Parabanic acid, $OC\langle NH—CO ; NH—CO \rangle$ (ring)	+	−	+	+	+	(+)	+	+	+	(+)	+	+	+
Alloxan, $OC\langle NH—CO ; NH—CO \rangle CO$ (ring)	(+)	(−)	+	+	+	+	+	(+)	+	(−)	+	+	+
Alloxantine, $OC\langle NH—CO ; NH—CO \rangle C—OH$, linked by O to $OC\langle NH—C(OH) ; NH—CO \rangle C$	+	(−)	+	+	+	+	+	(−)	+	−	+	+	+

+ = heavy to good growth; (+) = very good to moderate growth; (−) = feeble growth but somewhat better than control; − = extremely feeble growth or equal to control. Only + and (+) signs indicate that the compounds were attacked.

* Basal medium: Tap water with 2.0% agar, 0.1% K_2HPO_4, 1.0% glucose, 1.0% $CaCO_3$, plus 0.1% of the listed compounds. Incubation: 5 days at 30°C.

TABLE 3 (*Continued*)

THE ASSIMILATION OF UREA, GUANIDINE, AND PURINE DERIVATIVES BY BACTERIA *

[From den Dooren de Jong (1926)]

Urea, Guanidine, and Purine Derivatives	*Bacillus vulgatus*	*Bacillus mycoides*	*Bacillus polymyxa*	*Aerobacter aerogenes*	*Escherichia coli*	*Serratia marcescens*	*Bacterium herbicola*	*Proteus vulgaris*	*Mycobacterium phlei*	*Staphylococcus albus*	*Sarcina lutea*	*Pseudomonas fluorescens*	*Spirillum tenue*
Barbituric acid, OC<(NH—CO)(NH—CO)>CH_2	(−)	(−)	+	+	(−)	+	+	(+)	(+)	−	(+)	(+)	(−)
Thiobarbituric acid, SC<(NH—CO)(NH—CO)>CH_2	+	−	(+)	+	(−)	(+)	+	(−)	(−)	−	(−)	(−)	−
Violuric acid, OC<(NH—CO)(NH—CO)>C:NOH	−	−	−	−	(−)	+	−	−	−	−	−	−	−
Allantoin, OC<(NH—CH—N·CO·NH_2)(NH—CO)	+	(−)	+	+	(+)	+	+	(−)	+	(+)	+	(−)	+
Guanine (2-amino-6-oxy-purine)	+	(−)	(+)	+	(+)	(+)	+	(−)	(+)	−	+	(−)	+
Xanthine (2,6-dioxypurine)	+	(−)	+	+	+	+	+	+	(+)	(−)	(+)	+	(+)
Uric acid (2,6,8-trioxypurine)	(+)	(−)	(+)	+	(+)	+	+	(−)	(+)	−	(+)	(+)	(+)
Theobromine (3,7-dimethyl-2,6-dioxypurine)	−	−	+	+	(+)	(+)	+	(+)	(+)	−	(−)	(−)	(−)
Theophylline (1,3-dimethyl-2,6-dioxypurine)	−	−	(−)	(+)	(−)	(−)	(+)	(−)	(+)	−	(−)	(−)	(−)
Caffeine (1,3,7-trimethyl-2,6-dioxypurine)	−	−	(+)	+	(−)	(−)	+	(+)	(−)	−	(−)	(−)	−

(Purine ring structure printed beside Guanine–Caffeine, labelled "Purine".)

\+ = heavy to good growth; (+) = very good to moderate growth; (−) = feeble growth but somewhat better than control; − = extremely feeble growth or equal to control. Only + and (+) signs indicate that the compounds were attacked.

* Basal medium: Tap water with 2.0% agar, 0.1% K_2HPO_4, 1.0% glucose, 1.0% $CaCO_3$, plus 0.1% of the listed compounds. Incubation: 5 days at 30°C.

The biological purines are simple amino, hydroxy, or methyl derivatives of a parent purine ring:

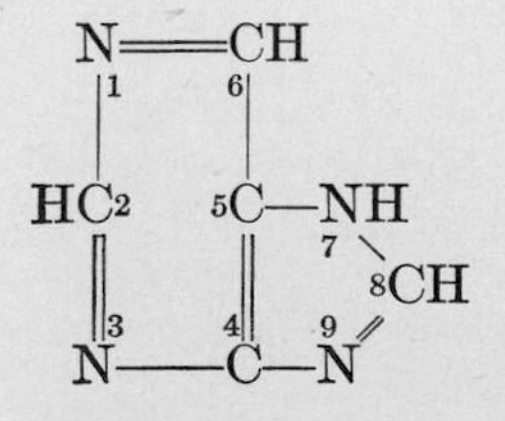

This ring does not occur free in nature. The amino purines, represented by *adenine* (6-aminopurine) and *guanine* (2-amino-6-oxypurine), are components of cellular nucleic acids and nucleosides. The hydroxy purines, *hypoxanthine* (6-oxypurine) and *xanthine* (2,6-dioxypurine), occur in the tissues of many plants and animals; *uric acid* (2,6,8-trioxypurine) is also widely distributed in nature, especially as a nitrogenous excretory product of birds and snakes. The methyl purines, such as caffeine (1,3,7-trimethyl-2,6-dioxypurine), are the characteristic alkaloids of tea, coffee, and cocoa.

The decomposition of *adenine* compounds by several bacterial species was studied in some detail by Lutwak-Mann (1936). The following compounds were utilized in either an aerobic or anaerobic environment: adenosine triphosphoric acid, adenylic acid, adenosine, and adenine. The first and second compounds were both deaminated and dephosphorylated, whereas the third and fourth were only deaminated; one of the end products of decomposition was hypoxanthine. *Guanine* is utilized aerobically by some species of yeasts and certain bacteria (see Table 3); xanthine is usually formed, but it may also be broken down into smaller units by certain organisms. The anaerobic decomposition of guanine has been studied by Barker and Beck (1941), using the anaerobes *Clostridium acidi-urici* and *Clostridium cylindrosporum*. Their data show that the intermediate compounds known to be involved in the breakdown of guanine by animal and plant tissues and by aerobic microorganisms are not included in the dissimilation processes of these anaerobic bacteria which produce acetic acid, ammonia, and carbon dioxide. *Xanthine* is utilized as a source of nitrogen by certain bacteria (see Table 3), but little is known about the mechanism of its breakdown. *Uric acid* serves as a source of nitrogen for certain bacteria, and this fact can be used to differentiate between *Aerobacter aerogenes* and *Escherichia coli*, since most strains of *A. aerogenes* can use the compound, whereas *E. coli* cannot [Koser (1918), Mitchell and Levine (1938)]. Uric acid and some of its derivatives are very poor sources of nitrogen for most yeasts [Burk and Horner (1939)], but such compounds serve as a ready source of nitrogen for many, but not all, green algae [Ludwig (1938)]. Nothing is known, however, about the reactions involved in the metabolism of these compounds by algae.

At least four pyrimidine bases are known to be components of nucleoproteins; each is derived from a parent pyrimidine ring:

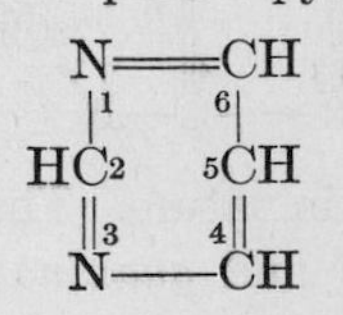

This ring is not found free in nature. *Uracil* (2,6-dioxypyrimidine), *thymine* (5-methyl-2,6-dioxypyrimidine), *cytosine* (2-oxy-6-amino-pyrimidine), and *5-methylcytosine* are the best-known biological pyrimidine bases. The various pyrimidine bases do not occur only as essential components in nucleoproteins; the pyrimidine ring is also a part of the structure of vitamin B_1 (thiamin) and the coenzyme, co-carboxylase. Concerning the fate of the pyrimidine bases in microbial metabolism very little is known. However, since the pyrimidines are quite reactive and readily undergo reversible oxidation, it is probable that they participate in the intense metabolism that is characteristic of nuclear material. The role the pyrimidine bases play in microbial nutrition was discussed in Chapter 7.

AMINO ACIDS

The broad definition of an amino acid as any organic acid which has one or more substituent amino groups covers a large number of compounds. However, the term amino acid is used today in a limited sense and usually includes only those substances which are constituents of proteins. The number of amino acids so far isolated from proteins is about fifty, but of these only about eighteen to twenty-five are accepted generally to be structural units of any given protein.

Chemically, the majority of the biologically important amino acids are α-amino acids; that is, the $—NH_2$ group is attached to the carbon atom adjacent to the terminal carboxyl group, $R \cdot \underset{\displaystyle NH_2}{\underset{|}{C}} \cdot COOH$, where R represents an aliphatic, aromatic, or heterocyclic radical. According to Vickery (1941), the amino acids may be classified into four groups on the basis of our present chemical knowledge concerning their presence in proteins:

I. Amino acids which are known to be present in variable amounts in the hydrolysates of most proteins.

1. Glycine	10. Arginine *
2. Leucine *	11. Histidine *
3. Tyrosine	12. Valine *
4. Serine	13. Proline
5. Glutamic acid	14. Tryptophan *
6. Aspartic acid	15. Hydroxyproline
7. Phenylalanine *	16. Isoleucine *
8. Alanine	17. Methionine *
9. Lysine *	18. Threonine *

II. Amino acids that occupy a special position because of their narrow range of distribution or for other reasons.

1. Thyroxine (thyroid-gland protein)
2. Diiodotyrosine or iodogorgoic acid (thyroid-gland protein and skeleton protein of certain marine organisms)
3. Dibromotyrosine (skeleton of *Primnoa lepodifera*)
4. Norleucine (spinal-cord protein)
5. Cystine (universally distributed)
6. Cysteine (some evidence for its presence in a few proteins)
7. Hydroxyglutamic acid (existence in proteins doubted by some workers)
8. Lanthionine (wool) †
9. β-Alanine †

III. Amino acids known as plant constituents that may possibly be expected to be found in proteins.

1. Thiolhistidine (in ergot as betaine ergothioneine; in blood)
2. Dihydroxyphenylalanine (in bean seedlings; probably widely distributed)
3. Citrulline (watermelon tissue; probably of metabolic significance in urea formation in animals)
4. Canavanine (certain beans)
5. Djenkolic acid (Djenkol bean)

IV. Amino acids for which claims have not been substantiated.

1. Aminobutyric acid
2. Hydroxyvaline
3. Hydroxylysine
4. Norvaline
5. Diaminoglutaric acid
6. Diaminoadipic acid
7. Hydroxyaspartic acid
8. Dihydroxydiaminosuberic acid
9. "Caseianic acid"
10. "Caseinic acid"
11. Prolysine (α-amino-ε-hydantoincaproic acid)
12. Hyphasamine ($C_{16}H_{24}O_5N_2$)
13. Dodecandiaminodicarboxylic acid
14. Base ($C_4H_{11}O_3N$)
15. Protoctine ($C_8H_{15}O_3N_3$)
16. Diaminotrihydroxydodecanic acid
17. Hydroxytryptophan

* Essential amino acids for animals.
† Lanthionine and β-alanine are placed here provisionally.

It is quite probable that microorganisms are in existence which are capable of breaking down all the amino acids in this classification, but, since some of these compounds are of doubtful nature or are unavailable, they have not been tested. Of the twenty-five more common amino acids, however, several have been studied rather extensively from the standpoint of microbial decomposition, and much of our present information concerning the organisms which utilize them and their decomposition products is summarized in Table 4.

Several factors govern the ability of microorganisms to attack amino acids. For example, the chemical nature of the group represented by R in the general amino acid formula $R \cdot CHNH_2 \cdot COOH$ may determine to what extent an amino acid is decomposed; the *p*H, oxygen supply, carbohydrate content, presence of coenzymes, buffering capacity, and the time and temperature of incubation of the inoculated medium may markedly influence the process; the species or sometimes even the strain of microorganism and the quantity of the inoculum are also important governing factors.

The method by which an amino acid is attacked by the enzymes of microorganisms may vary considerably; in general, however, the chemical reaction involved may be allocated to one of the four following groups [Gale (1940)]:

A. *Deamination*, or removal of the amino group from the α-position.

B. *Decarboxylation*, or removal of the carboxyl group.

C. *Deamination* accompanied by *decarboxylation*.

D. *Breakdown* of the amino acid into smaller units by routes other than deamination and decarboxylation, or by unspecified or unknown mechanisms.

These groups will now be discussed separately in more detail.

A. Deamination, or Removal of the Amino Group from the α-Position of the Amino Acid

Many bacteria possess an enzyme system (deaminase) which catalyzes the deamination of various amino acids; in some bacteria this system may actually consist of more than one enzyme, because it is known that in certain instances the deamination takes place in two steps, and a separate enzyme may be responsible for each.

Several factors influence the deaminase activity of bacteria. For example, Gale (see 1940 review) has shown that the period of maximum activity of various bacteria coincides with the cessation of active cell division during the population cycle, that the gaseous environment is important, and that most organisms exhibit optimum deaminase activity between *p*H 7.5 and 8.0. It is also known that deamination may be accomplished in several ways, with each resulting in a different product and in ammonia. The six most important of these ways will now be outlined:

1. Oxidative Deamination to Form a Keto Acid and Ammonia

$$R \cdot CHNH_2 \cdot COOH + \tfrac{1}{2}O_2 \rightarrow R \cdot CO \cdot COOH + NH_3$$

Examples of bacteria which deaminate amino acids by a reaction of this type are shown in Table 4, together with references and some other pertinent data. Certain of the bacterial deaminases which catalyze reactions of this type are known to require one of the pyridine coenzymes for their activity; this fact suggests that the enzyme involved is a dehydrogenase. For example, Adler and his associates (1938) extracted an enzyme from *Escherichia coli* which reduced methylene blue in the presence of glutamic acid and coenzyme II (TPN); they believed that the oxidation occurred in two steps, both of which were reversible:

$$\text{Glutamic acid} + \text{Coenzyme II} \rightleftarrows \text{Iminoglutaric acid} + \text{Reduced coenzyme II}$$

$$\text{Iminoglutaric acid} + H_2O \rightleftarrows \text{Ketoglutaric acid} + NH_3$$

$$\text{Reduced coenzyme II} + \tfrac{1}{2}O_2 \rightarrow \text{Coenzyme II} + H_2O$$

These equations may also represent one way in which amino acids are synthesized by various cells from nonamino compounds. Klein (1940) has shown that washed suspensions of *Hemophilus parainfluenzae* oxidize aspartic acid and glutamic acid with the liberation of ammonia and carbon dioxide and the formation of acetic acid. The course of the oxidation of aspartic acid was thought to be as follows:

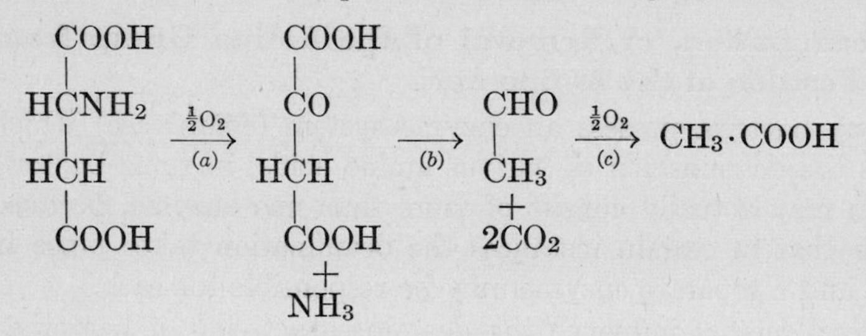

Reactions (*a*) and (*c*) required the presence of coenzyme I or II (the exact requirement not being established) and suggested that the first step in the breakdown of this dicarboxylic amino acid by *H. parainfluenzae* was an oxidative deamination probably proceeding in stages similar to those elucidated by Adler and his coworkers.

2. Hydrolytic Deamination to Give a Hydroxy Acid and Ammonia

$$R \cdot CHNH_2 \cdot COOH + H_2O \rightarrow R \cdot CHOH \cdot COOH + NH_3$$

The literature contains several references (see Table 4) to hydroxy acids being isolated from bacterial growth experiments involving certain amino acids. However, according to Gale (1940), the only positive demonstration of a cell-free hydrolytic deaminase in bacteria has been accomplished by Virtanen and Erkama (1938).

3. Reductive Deamination to Yield a Saturated Fatty Acid and Ammonia

$$R \cdot CHNH_2COOH + 2H \rightarrow R \cdot CH_2 \cdot COOH + NH_3$$

The microbial production of saturated fatty acids from corresponding amino acids in culture media has been reported by various workers (see Table 4), but the process has not been studied very extensively.

4. Desaturation Deamination at the α-, β-Positions to Give an Unsaturated Fatty Acid and Ammonia

$$R \cdot CHNH_2 \cdot COOH \rightarrow R \cdot CH{:}CH \cdot COOH + NH_3$$

Several bacteria have been studied which are capable of catalyzing this type of reaction, either when they are grown in media containing the amino acids or in cell-free extracts [Gale (1940)]. Examples of bacteria will be found in Table 4. It is of interest to note that the rate of the desaturation deamination reaction of aspartic acid by *Escherichia coli* is greatly increased by the presence of small amounts of adenosine or inosine [Gale (1938)].

5. Mutual Oxidation-Reduction between Pairs of Amino Acids to Form a Keto Acid, a Fatty Acid, and Ammonia

$$R_1 \cdot CHNH_2 \cdot COOH + R_2 \cdot CHNH_2 \cdot COOH + H_2O \rightarrow R_1 \cdot CO \cdot COOH + R_2 \cdot CH_2 \cdot COOH + 2NH_3$$

This type of transformation is sometimes spoken of as the Stickland reaction, and it apparently plays a very important role in the normal metabolism of certain anaerobic bacteria where oxygen is not utilized as a hydrogen acceptor. In such a reaction certain amino acids are activated and serve as hydrogen donators, and others as hydrogen acceptors, so that coupled reactions take place between pairs of them, resulting in their deamination. As a result of studies by Stickland (1934–1935), Woods (1936), Hoogerheide and Kocholaty (1938), Clifton (1940), and others, it has been found that the following amino acids act as hydrogen donators for various bacteria: the natural isomers of alanine, valine, leucine, phenylalanine, cysteine, serine, histidine, aspartic acid, and glutamic acid; the following act as hydrogen acceptors: glycine, proline, hydroxyproline, ornithine, and arginine.

6. Unclassified Deamination Processes Which Yield Ammonia and Other Unidentified Products

Several reports have appeared in the literature which state merely that various bacteria produce ammonia and other products from amino acids. Although a deaminase is undoubtedly involved in such breakdowns, it is difficult to assign these studies to one of the foregoing groups. Thus they will be listed provisionally under this general heading until further studies are available so that they can be properly classified.

B. Decarboxylation, or Removal of the Carboxyl Group from the Amino Acid

The ability of bacteria to form amines during putrefaction has been known for a number of years, but it has been only comparatively recently that quantitative methods and the factors governing the process have been studied [see Eggerth (1939), Gale (1940), Gale and Epps (1944), Epps (1944)]. Examples of bacteria which are capable of decarboxylation or elimination of CO_2 from amino acids are listed in Table 4; the general reaction involved may be written as follows:

$$R \cdot CHNH_2 \cdot COOH \rightarrow R \cdot CH_2NH_2 + CO_2$$

where R has its usual significance. The process has usually been studied by isolating the amine, by measuring the production of CO_2, or by both methods.

Several early workers reported that amine production by microorganisms is influenced by a variety of conditions, such as the presence of the proper medium, the *p*H of the substrate, and the temperature of incubation of the culture. Later Gale (1940) studied in some detail the factors influencing the bacterial decarboxylation of amino acids and observed the following:

a. The decarboxylase activity of a washed suspension of bacteria toward any given amino acid varies with the *age of the culture* from which the suspension is prepared; young cultures have little activity, but activity increases during active cell division and reaches a maximum as growth ceases.

b. The decarboxylases are formed in response to *acid growth conditions;* the lower the *p*H during growth, the more active the washed suspensions obtained; the fact that the optimum *p*H is below 5.5 in every case and below 4.5 in most cases indicates that the amino acid can be attacked only when it possesses an undissociated carboxyl group.

c. *Oxygen has no effect* on the decarboxylation reaction, with the exception of the glutamic acid decarboxylase of *Clostridium perfringens*, which is partially inhibited by the presence of oxygen.

d. There is evidence that the decarboxylases require a coenzyme or coenzymes for their action, but these have not been fully identified; the coenzyme is not cocarboxylase [see Gale and Epps (1944), Epps (1944)].

At present it is difficult to assign any function to the amino acid decarboxylases of microorganisms, but, as Hanke and Koessler (1924) and Gale (1940) have pointed out, the decarboxylation mechanism may serve as a protective mechanism or "buffer," in that the organism resorts to it when the accumulation of H ions within the organism's protoplasm is incompatible with its normal life functions. Instead, since microbial deaminases are inactive and carbohydrates are only slowly attacked at *p*H values lower than 5, the production of decarboxylases may be a method by which the organism extends its range of existence, that is, by utilizing amino acid decarboxylation when other substrates and methods of attack are no longer available. A third possibility is that the decarboxylases may serve the purpose of providing CO_2, which is essential for the growth of many bacteria.

C. Deamination Accompanied by Decarboxylation

In several reports it has been stated that deamination and decarboxylation of amino acids by microorganisms may take place simultaneously, following one of these three chemical reactions:

1. Hydrolytic deamination and decarboxylation resulting in the formation of a primary alcohol, NH_3, and CO_2:

$$R\cdot CHNH_2\cdot COOH + H_2O \rightarrow R\cdot CH_2OH + NH_3 + CO_2$$

2. Reductive deamination and decarboxylation with the formation of a hydrocarbon, NH_3, and CO_2:

$$R\cdot CHNH_2\cdot COOH + 3H \rightarrow R\cdot CH_3 + NH_3 + CO_2$$

3. Oxidative deamination and decarboxylation yielding a fatty acid, NH_3, and CO_2:

$$R\cdot CHNH_2\cdot COOH + H_2O + 2O \rightarrow R\cdot COOH + NH_3 + CO_2 + H_2O$$

However, it has been pointed out by Gale (1940), who determined the *p*H activity values of *Escherichia coli* glutamic acid deaminase and decarboxylase, that the optimum *p*H values for these two enzymes from the same organism are widely separated and on opposite sides of neutrality. Furthermore, the decarboxylase is active over such a restricted range that there is no *p*H at which both enzymes are effectively active together. It is not possible to say whether this case, the only one for which complete data are available at present, is representative of deaminases and decarboxylases in general. It is significant, however, that all the deaminases so far studied exhibit optimum activity at *p*H 7.5 to 8.0, whereas all the decarboxylases have optimal *p*H values at or below 5.0; this fact may mean that for decarboxylation to occur the —COOH group must be undissociated, and for deamination the $—NH_3^+$ group must be undissociated. Therefore it seems quite probable that bacteria cannot attack amino acids by both deamination and decarboxylation simultaneously. Those experiments on record, in which yeast and a few bacterial species were used and deamination and decarboxylation occurred, usually lasted over several days and were carried out in culture media in which considerable changes in *p*H could occur because of the metabolic activities of the growing organisms. Thus it is quite possible that deamination and decarboxylation occur at separate times during incubation rather than simultaneously.

D. Breakdown of the Amino Acid into Smaller Units by Routes Other Than Deamination and Decarboxylation or by Unknown Mechanisms

A number of studies have appeared in the literature in which the authors state merely that, when various individual amino acids are incorporated in media, they are attacked or that gas (NH_3, CO_2, or H_2) is formed from them by the action of microorganisms; in many of these experiments no attempt was made to isolate and identify the important end products formed after the incubation period. Also several workers have showed that because of the nature of the amino acid breakdown the course of the process cannot be allocated to one of the three main groups (A, B, and C) just described, especially when the decomposition is primarily concerned with a rupture of the ring structure of such amino acids as tryptophan and tyrosine. Thus all such studies cited in Table 4 have been grouped under this general heading until more information is available so that they can be properly classified.

Metabolism of the Individual Amino Acids. Each amino acid listed in Table 4 has its own metabolic history in so far as microorganisms and other cells are concerned, but few of these are known in more than outline form. It is generally assumed that the essential amino acids are in some way synthesized into cellular proteins and other constituents. Since many of these compounds, however, can be converted to glucose and other carbohydrate units in higher animals, it is probable that similar conversions also occur in microorganisms under various conditions; such a change provides a link between protein and carbohydrate metabolism in the organism.

The metabolic outline of a few amino acids will now be discussed.

GLYCINE. With few exceptions it is not necessary to supply bacteria with this amino acid for optimum growth, and it is likewise nonessential to higher animals; therefore such organisms as require glycine can synthesize it. As Fig. 1 indicates, it is possible for glycine to be converted into several different compounds by bacteria and other types of cells; it may therefore have considerable metabolic significance.

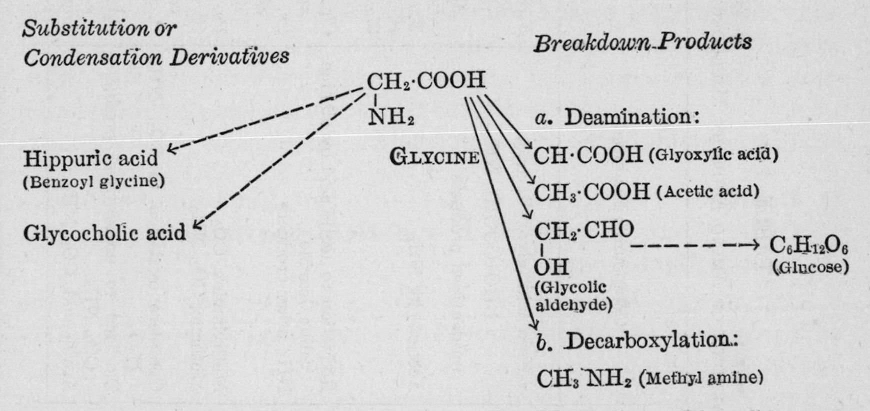

FIG. 1. Some Possible Changes in Glycine during Metabolism. The solid arrows are reactions known to be produced by microorganisms and other types of cells; the dotted arrows are reactions which are thought to occur in higher animals or are hypothetical. (From Fearon, 1940.)

Other less well-established breakdown products of glycine will be found in Table 4.

ALANINE. This amino acid has been shown to be nonessential for several higher animals and for many microorganisms. It has considerable significance, however, in that it can be converted to carbohydrate units in animals, that it is related in structure but not necessarily in biological derivation to many more complex and important amino acids, and that it readily "transaminates" with ketoglutaric acid. See Fig. 2, p. 874.

TABLE 4

THE BREAKDOWN OF AMINO ACIDS BY MICROORGANISMS

Amino Acid	Type of Reaction (see pp. 851–856)	Compounds Produced	Organism	Reference
Glycine or glycocoll (aminoacetic acid) $CH_2 \cdot COOH$ with NH_2	A1	α-Keto acid (glyoxylic acid, $CHO \cdot COOH$), NH_3, unidentified products	*Escherichia coli* *Proteus vulgaris*, *Pseudomonas fluorescens*, *Bacillus mycoides*	Janke and Tayenthal (1937)
	A3	Acetic acid, NH_3	*E. coli*	Stephenson and Gale (1937)
			P. vulgaris	Nawiasky (1908)
			Clostridium lentoputrescens	Brasch (1909)
	A5	Reduction to acetic acid by alanine, valine, leucine	*Clostridium sporogenes*	Stickland (1934, 1935)
	A6	NH_3, other products	*Ps. fluorescens*, *Trichoderma* and *Actinomyces* species	Waksman and Lomanitz (1925)
	B	Methylamine, CO_2	*Ps. fluorescens*	Emerling and Reiser (1902)
	C	Methane, CO_2, NH_3	*Clostridium carnofetidis*	McCrudden (1910)
	D	Complete oxidation to CO_2, NH_3, H_2O	*P. vulgaris*	Bernheim, Bernheim, and Webster (1935)
	D	Oxidized to unidentified products, CO_2, NH_3	*Pseudomonas aeruginosa*	Webster and Bernheim (1936)
	D	Acetic acid, CO_2, NH_3	Anaerobic coccus	Cardon (1942)

Alanine (α-aminopropionic acid) $CH_3 \cdot CH(NH_2) \cdot COOH$	A1	α-Keto acid, NH_3, unidentified products	Unidentified soil bacterium	Aubel and Egami (1936)
			E. coli	Stephenson and Gale (1937)
	A1	Pyruvic acid, NH_3	*Fusarium lini*	Wirth and Nord (1943)
	A2	Lactic acid, NH_3	*Oidium lactis*	Otani and Ichihara (1925)
	A3	Propionic acid, NH_3	*Cl. lentoputrescens*	Brasch (1909)
	A5	Reduction to acetic acid, NH_3, CO_2 by glycine, proline, etc.	*Cl. sporogenes*	Stickland (1934, 1935)
			Cl. botulinum	Clifton (1940)
	A6	Acetic acid, NH_3, other products	*P. vulgaris*	Nawiasky (1908)
			Ps. fluorescens, *Trichoderma* and *Actinomyces* species	Waksman and Lomanitz (1925)
	B	Ethylamine, CO_2	Mixed culture	Sullivan (1858)
	C	Propionic acid, acetic acid, NH_3, CO_2	Gram-negative, spore-forming rod	Cardon (1942)
	D	Oxidation to unidentified products, NH_3, CO_2	*E. coli*, *P. vulgaris*	Bernheim, Bernheim, and Webster (1935)
			Ps. aeruginosa	Webster and Bernheim (1936)
	D	Acetic acid and unidentified products	*Mycobacterium tuberculosis*	Campbell (1925)
Serine (β-hydroxyalanine or β-hydroxy-α-aminopropionic acid) $HOCH_2 \cdot CH(NH_2) \cdot COOH$	A1	Pyruvic acid, NH_3	*E. coli*	Chargaff and Sprinson (1943)
	A5	Oxidation to unknown products by glycine, etc.	*Cl. sporogenes*	Stickland (1934)
	A6	Propionic acid, formic acid, NH_3, unidentified products	*Cl. lentoputrescens*	Brasch (1909)
	A6	Unidentified products, NH_3	*E. coli*	Gale and Stephenson (1939)
			Staphylococcus aureus, *Eberthella typhosa*	Hills (1940)
	B	Aminoethyl alcohol or cholamine, $CH_2 \cdot NH_2 \cdot CH_2OH$	Putrefactive bacteria	Nord (1919)
	C	Propionic acid, acetic acid, NH_3, CO_2	Gram-negative, spore-forming rod	Cardon (1942)

TABLE 4 (*Continued*)

THE BREAKDOWN OF AMINO ACIDS BY MICROORGANISMS

Amino Acid	Type of Reaction (see pp. 851–856)	Compounds Produced	Organism	Reference
	C	Ethylene glycol, CH_2OH–CH_2OH, but not definitely identified	Yeast	Ehrlich (1908)
	D	Oxidation to unidentified products, NH_3, CO_2	*P. vulgaris*	Bernheim, Bernheim, and Webster (1935)
			Ps. aeruginosa	Webster and Bernheim (1936)
	D	Unidentified volatile acids, NH_3, CO_2	*Clostridium tetanomorphum*	Woods and Clifton (1937)
Valine (β-dimethyl-α-aminopropionic acid) $(CH_3)_2{>}CH \cdot CH(NH_2) \cdot COOH$	A1	Isovaleric acid, NH_3	Mixed culture	Neuberg and Karczag (1909)
	A5	Oxidation to unidentified products and NH_3 by glycine, proline, etc.	*Cl. sporogenes*	Stickland (1934), Woods (1936)
	A6	Isobutyric acid, NH_3, acetic acid, formic acid, unidentified products	*P. vulgaris*	Nawiasky (1908)
	B	Isobutylamine, CO_2	Putrefactive bacteria	Neuberg and Karczag (1909)
	C	Isobutyl alcohol, NH_2, CO_2	Yeast	Ehrlich (1906)
	D	Oxidized to unidentified products, NH_3, CO_2	*P. vulgaris*	Bernheim, Bernheim, and Webster (1935)
			Ps. aeruginosa	Webster and Bernheim (1936)

Threonine (α-amino-β-hydroxy-*n*-butyric acid) $CH_3 \cdot CHOH \cdot CH(NH_2) \cdot COOH$	A6	Unidentified products, NH_3	*S. aureus*, *E. typhosa*	Hills (1940)
	C	Butyric acid, acetic acid, NH_3, CO_2	Gram-negative, spore-forming rod	Cardon (1942)
	D	Unidentified products, NH_3, CO_2, H_2	*Clostridium perfringens*	Woods and Trim (1942)
Leucine (α-aminoisocaproic acid) $(CH_3)_2 > CH \cdot CH_2 \cdot CH(NH_2) \cdot COOH$	A1	α-Keto acid, NH_3, unidentified products	*Aspergillus oryzae*	Uemura (1937)
	A2	Leucinic acid, $(CH_3)_2 > CH \cdot CH_2 \cdot CHOH \cdot COOH$, and NH_3	*P. vulgaris*, *Bacillus subtilis*	Arai (1921)
			Clostridium acetobutylicum	Schmidt, Peterson, and Fred (1924)
	A5	Unidentified products and NH_3 by glycine, proline, or ornithine	*Cl. sporogenes*	Stickland (1934), Woods (1936)
	B	Isoamylamine, CO_2, unidentified products	Mixed culture	Barger and Walpole (1909)
			Yeast	Müller (1857)
			Boletus edulis	Reuter (1912)
			P. vulgaris	Virtanen, Laine, and Rintala (1940)
	C	Isoamyl alcohol, NH_3, CO_2	Yeast	Ehrlich (1906)
			Mucor, *Rhizopus*, *Monilia*, and *Torula* species	Pringsheim (1908)
	D	Oxidation to unidentified products, NH_3	*P. vulgaris*	Bernheim, Bernheim, and Webster (1935)
			Ps. aeruginosa	Webster and Bernheim (1936)
Isoleucine (β-methyl-β-ethyl-α-aminopropionic acid) $(CH_3)(C_2H_5) > CH \cdot CH(NH_2) \cdot COOH$	A1	Methylethylpyruvic acid, NH_3	Yeast	Neuberg and Peterson (1914)
	A3	Methylethylpropionic acid (isocaproic acid), NH_3	Mixed culture	Neuberg (1911)
	A6	Methylethylacetic acid, NH_3, unidentified products	Mixed culture	Neuberg (1911)
	B	Amylamine, CO_2	Yeast autolysate	Iwanoff (1913)
	D	Oxidized to unidentified products, NH_3	*P. vulgaris*	Bernheim, Bernheim, and Webster (1935)
			Ps. aeruginosa	Webster and Bernheim (1936)

TABLE 4 (*Continued*)

THE BREAKDOWN OF AMINO ACIDS BY MICROORGANISMS

Amino Acid	Type of Reaction (see pp. 851–856)	Compounds Produced	Organism	Reference
Norleucine (α-amino-*n*-caproic acid) $CH_3 \cdot (CH_2)_3 \cdot CH(NH_2) \cdot COOH$	C	*n*-Amyl alcohol, NH_3, CO_2	Yeast	Neuberg and Nord (1914), Janke (1930)
Aspartic acid (aminosuccinic acid) $HOOC \cdot CH_2 \cdot CH(NH_2) \cdot COOH$	A2	Malic acid, $HOOC \cdot CH_2 \cdot CHOH \cdot COOH$, and NH_3	*E. coli*	Woolf (1929), Gale (1938)
			Ps. fluorescens	Virtanen and Erkama (1938)
	A3	Succinic acid, $HOOC \cdot CH_2 \cdot CH_2 \cdot COOH$, and NH_3	*P. vulgaris*	Nawiasky (1908)
			Cl. lentoputrescens	Brasch (1909)
			Ps. fluorescens	Blanchétière (1916)
			B. subtilis, B. megatherium, Mycobacterium phlei, Ps. aeruginosa, Serratia marcescens, P. vulgaris, Cl. sporogenes, Cl. tertium, Cl. histolyticum	Cook and Woolf (1928)
	A4	Fumaric acid, $HOOC \cdot CH{:}CH \cdot COOH$, and NH_3	*E. coli*	Quastel and Woolf (1926), Cook and Woolf (1928), Gale (1938)
			Ps. fluorescens	Cook and Woolf (1928), Virtanen and Tarnanen (1932)

			Ps. aeruginosa, *S. marcescens*, *P. vulgaris*	Cook and Woolf (1928)
	A5	Unidentified products, NH_3 by glycine, etc.	*Cl. sporogenes*	Stickland (1934)
	A6	Unidentified products, NH_3	*E. typhosa*, *Corynebacterium diphtheriae*	Hills (1940)
	B	β-Alanine, $CH_2NH_2 \cdot CH_2 \cdot COOH$, and CO_2	*Rhizobium leguminosarum*	Virtanen and Laine (1937), Virtanen, Laine, and Rintala (1940)
	C	Propionic acid, $CH_3 \cdot CH_2 \cdot COOH$, and NH_3, CO_2	*Cl. lentoputrescens*	Brasch (1909)
	D	Acetic acid, unidentified products	*P. vulgaris*	Nawiasky (1908)
	D	*n*-Propyl alcohol and unidentified products	Yeast	Ehrlich (1914)
	D	Unidentified products, H_2, CO_2	*Cl. tetanomorphum*	Woods and Clifton (1937)
	D or A1 + B	Acetic acid, NH_3, CO_2	*Hemophilus parainfluenzae*	Klein (1940)
Glutamic acid (α-aminoglutaric acid) $HOOC \cdot CH_2 \cdot CH_2 \cdot CH(NH_2) \cdot COOH$	A1	α-Ketoglutaric acid, $HOOC \cdot CH_2 \cdot CH_2 \cdot CO \cdot COOH$, and NH_3	Yeast	Neuberg and Ringer (1918)
			E. coli	Adler, Hellström, Günther, and Euler (1938)
	A3	Glutaric acid, $HOOC \cdot CH_2 \cdot CH_2 \cdot CH_2 \cdot COOH$, and NH_3	Mixed culture	Ackermann and Mey (1906)
	A5	Unidentified products and NH_3 by glycine, etc.	*Cl. sporogenes*	Stickland (1934)
	A6	NH_3 and other products	*Ps. fluorescens*, *Zygorhynchus* and *Trichoderma* species	Waksman and Lomanitz (1925)
	B	Unidentified products, CO_2	Washed cells of *E. coli*, *Proteus* species, *Cl. perfringens*, and *Cl. aerofetidum*	Gale (1940)

TABLE 4 (*Continued*)

THE BREAKDOWN OF AMINO ACIDS BY MICROORGANISMS

Amino Acid	Type of Reaction (see pp. 851–856)	Compounds Produced	Organism	Reference
	D	Succinic acid, $HOOC\cdot CH_2\cdot CH_2\cdot COOH$, and unidentified products	*P. vulgaris* Yeast *Acetobacter aceti*	Nawiasky (1908) Ehrlich (1914), Thorne (1937) Miyaji (1925)
	D	Acetic acid, butyric acid, NH_3, CO_2, H_2	*Cl. tetanomorphum* *Clostridium* species	Woods and Clifton (1937, 1938) Barker (1937)
	D or A1 + B	Acetic acid, NH_3, CO_2	*H. parainfluenzae*	Klein (1940)
	D	Unidentified products	*Brucella abortus*	Mannozzi-Torini and Vendramini (1941)
Phenylalanine (β-phenyl alanine or α-amino-β-phenylpropionic acid) $CH_2\cdot CH(NH_2)\cdot COOH$ (with CH_2 attached to benzene ring)	A1	Phenylpyruvic acid, $CH_2\cdot CO\cdot COOH$, | C_6H_5 and NH_3	*Aspergillus oryzae*	Uemura (1937)
	A2	Phenyllactic acid, $CH_2\cdot CHOH\cdot COOH$, | C_6H_5 and NH_3	*Oidium lactis* *B. subtilis*, *P. vulgaris* *Acetobacter xylinoides*	Ehrlich and Jacobsen (1911) Sasaki and Otsuka (1921) Miyaji (1925)
	A3	Phenylpropionic acid, $CH_2\cdot CH_2\cdot COOH$, | C_6H_5 and NH_3	Mixed culture	Salkowski and Salkowski (1879), Nawiasky (1908)

	A5	Unidentified products and NH_3 by glycine	*Cl. sporogenes*	Stickland (1934)
	A6	NH_3, other products	*Ps. fluorescens* and *Trichoderma* species	Waksman and Lomanitz (1925)
	B	Phenylethylamine, $CH_2 \cdot CH_2NH_2$ (with C_6H_5 on CH_2), and CO_2	*Streptococcus longus* Mixed culture *Boletus edulis*	Emmerling (1897) Barger and Walpole (1909) Reuter (1912)
	C	Phenylethyl alcohol, $CH_2 \cdot CH_2OH$; (with C_6H_5 on CH_2) NH_3 and CO_2	Yeast	Ehrlich (1907), Thorne (1937)
	D	Oxidation to phenylacetic acid and unidentified products	Mixed culture	Salkcwski and Salkowski (1879)
	D	Oxidation to unidentified products, NH_3, CO_2	*P. vulgaris* *Ps. aeruginosa*	Bernheim, Bernheim, and Webster (1935) Webster and Bernheim (1936)
Tyrosine (*p*-hydroxyphenylalanine) $CH_2 \cdot CH(NH_2) \cdot COOH$ on benzene ring with para-OH	A2	*p*-Hydroxyphenyllactic acid, $CH_2 \cdot CHOH \cdot COOH$, (with C_6H_4OH on CH_2) and NH_3	*P. vulgaris* *B. subtilis* *E. coli* *Oidium lactis* *Monilia* and *Mycoderma* species	Barger and Walpole (1909) Sasaki (1914) Sasaki and Otsuka (1921) Ehrlich and Jacobsen (1911) (Yukawa) Janke (1930)
	A3	*p*-Hydroxyphenylpropionic acid, $CH_2 \cdot CH_2 \cdot COOH$, (with C_6H_4OH on CH_2) and NH_3	*Cl. lentoputrescens* *Ps. aeruginosa* *Acetobacter xylinoides*, *A. rancens*	Brasch (1909) Traetta Mosca (1910) Miyaji (1925)
	A4	*p*-Hydroxyphenylacrylic acid, $CH{:}CH \cdot COOH$, (with $C_6H_4 \cdot OH$ on CH) and NH_3	*P. vulgaris*	Hirai (1921)

TABLE 4 (*Continued*)

THE BREAKDOWN OF AMINO ACIDS BY MICROORGANISMS

Amino Acid	Type of Reaction (see pp. 851–856)	Compounds Produced	Organism	Reference
	B	*p*-Hydroxyphenylethylamine (tyramine), $CH_2 \cdot CH_2NH_2$, | $C_6H_4 \cdot OH$ and CO_2	Mixed culture *E. coli* *Aerobacter aerogenes* *Streptococcus fecalis*, *Cl. aerofetidum*	Barger and Walpole (1909) Hanke and Koessler (1924), Virtanen, Laine, and Rintala (1940) Hirai (1939) Gale (1940, 1941), Epps (1944)
	C	*p*-Hydroxyphenylethyl alcohol (tyrosol), $CH_2 \cdot CH_2OH$, | $C_6H_4 \cdot OH$ and NH_3, CO_2	Yeast of the genera *Saccharomyces*, *Willia*, *Monilia*, etc.	Ehrlich (1911), Janke (1930), Thorne (1937)
	D	*p*-Hydroxyphenylacetic acid, $CH_2 \cdot COOH$, | $C_6H_4 \cdot OH$ and unidentified products	*P. vulgaris*	Hirai (1921)
	D	*p*-Hydroxybenzoic acid, $HO \cdot C_6H_4 \cdot COOH$, and unidentified products	*Ps. aeruginosa* (?) *Escherichia phenologenes*	Traetta Mosca (1910) Rhein (1918)
	D	*p*-Cresol, $HO \cdot C_6H_4 \cdot CH_3$, and unidentified products	*Ps. aeruginosa* (?) *Clostridium cresologenes*	Traetta Mosca (1910) Rhein (1922), Janke (1930)

	D	Phenol, $HO \cdot C_6H_4$, and unidentified products	*E. phenologenes* and other coliform bacteria	Berthelot (1917), Rhein (1918), Hanke and Koessler (1924)
			Cl. tetani and *Cl. pseudotetani*	Rhein (1922)
	D	Oxidation to unidentified products, NH_3, CO_2	*P. vulgaris*	Bernheim, Bernheim, and Webster (1935)
			Ps. aeruginosa	Webster and Bernheim (1936)
	D	Unidentified products formed by the rupture of the benzene ring or removal of the OH group	*Ps. fluorescens*, *Ps. aeruginosa*	Raistrick and Clark (1921)
Iodogorgoic acid (3:5-diiodotyrosine) $I_2(OH)C_6H_2 \cdot CH_2 \cdot CH(NH_2) \cdot COOH$	D	Tyrosine and iodine	*E. coli*	Habild (1939)
Tryptophan (α-amino-β-indolepropionic acid) $C_8H_5NH \cdot CH_2 \cdot CH(NH_2) \cdot COOH$	A2	β-indolelactic acid, $CH_2 \cdot CHOH \cdot COOH$ | $C_8H_5 \cdot NH$, and NH_3	*P. vulgaris*	Sasaki and Otsuka (1921)
			Oidium lactis	Ehrlich and Jacobsen (1911)
	A3	β-indolepropionic acid, $CH_2 \cdot CH_2 \cdot COOH$ | $C_8H_5 \cdot NH$, and NH_3	*E. coli*	Hopkins and Cole (1903), Woods (1935), Majima (1936)

TABLE 4 (*Continued*)

THE BREAKDOWN OF AMINO ACIDS BY MICROORGANISMS

Amino Acid	Type of Reaction (see pp. 851–856)	Compounds Produced	Organism	Reference
	B	β-Indoleethylamine or tryptamine, $CH_2 \cdot CH_2 \cdot NH_2$, | $C_8H_5 \cdot NH$ and CO_2	*Bacterium aminophilis-intestinalis*	Berthelot and Bertrand (1911)
	C	β-Indoleethyl alcohol or tryptophol, $CH_2 \cdot CH_2OH$, | $C_8H_5 \cdot NH$ and NH_3, CO_2	Yeast	Ehrlich (1912), Thorne (1937)
	D	Indoleacetic acid, $CH_2 \cdot COOH$ | $C_8H_5 \cdot NH$	*E. coli*	Hopkins and Cole (1903)
	D	β-Methylindole (skatol)	Mixed culture	Nencki (1880)
			E. coli	Hopkins and Cole (1903)
	D	Indole	*E. coli*	Hopkins and Cole (1903), Woods (1935), Majima (1936), Vaughan (1939), Krebs, Hafez, and Eggleston (1942)
			E. coli culture filtrate	Happold and Hoyle (1935, 1936), Evans, Handley, and Happold (1942)
			Eberthella typhosa	Burrows (1939)

	A6 or D	Oxidation to unidentified products, NH_3	*P. vulgaris*	Bernheim, Bernheim, and Webster (1935)
	A6 or D	Unidentified products and NH_3, formed by the rupture of the indole ring	*S. marcescens*, *Ps. fluorescens*, *Ps. aeruginosa*	Raistrick and Clark (1921)
	D	Kynurenine, $C_6H_4(NH_2)\cdot C{:}CH\cdot CHNH_2\cdot COOH$ (with COOH attached to C), kynurenic acid, $C_9H_5N(OH)\cdot COOH$, and anthranilic acid, $C_6H_4(NH_2)\cdot(COOH)$	*B. subtilis*	Kotake and associates (1931, 1933)
Cystine (β-dicysteine) $CH_2-S-S-CH_2$ / $CHNH_2$ $CHNH_2$ / COOH COOH	D	Methyl mercaptan, $CH_3\cdot SH$, ethyl sulfide, $(C_2H_5)_2S$, and H_2S	Mixed cultures Twenty species *P. vulgaris*	Wohlgemuth (1905) Sasaki and Otsuka (1912) Kondo (1923)
	D	Reduction by an unknown agent to H_2S, acetic acid, formic acid, NH_3, CO_2, H_2	*P. vulgaris*	Tarr (1933)
	D	Unidentified products, H_2S, CO_2, NH_3	*Cl. tetanomorphum*	Woods and Clifton (1937)
	D	Reduction to cysteine and then to unidentified products, H_2S, NH_3	*E. coli* *Propionibacterium pentosaceum*	Desnuelle (1939) Desnuelle, Wookey, and Fromageot (1940)
	D	H_2S, unidentified products	*Proteus vulgaris*, *Proteus morganii*	Meyers and Porter (1944)
Cysteine (β-thioalanine) CH_2SH / $CHNH_2$ / COOH	A5	Oxidation to unidentified products, H_2S by glycine and proline	*Cl. sporogenes*	Woods (1936)
	D	Unidentified products, H_2S, CO_2, H_2	*Cl. tetanomorphum*	Woods and Clifton (1937)
	D	Unidentified products, H_2S, NH_3	*E. coli*	Desnuelle and Fromageot (1939), Desnuelle (1939)
	D	Unidentified products, H_2S, NH_3	*Propionibacterium pentosaceum* *E. coli*	Desnuelle, Wookey, and Fromageot (1940) Binkley (1943)

TABLE 4 (*Continued*)

THE BREAKDOWN OF AMINO ACIDS BY MICROORGANISMS

Amino Acid	Type of Reaction (see pp. 851–856)	Compounds Produced	Organism	Reference
Methionine (γ-methylthiol-α-amino-n-butyric acid) $CH_3 \cdot S \cdot (CH_2)_2 \cdot CH(NH_2) \cdot COOH$	A2	α-Hydroxy-γ-methiobutyric acid, NH_3	*Oidium lactis*, *B. subtilis*	Akobe (1936)
	D	Unidentified products, NH_3	*P. vulgaris*	Bernheim, Bernheim, and Webster (1935)
	D	Unidentified products, CO_2, H_2	*Cl. tetanomorphum*	Woods and Clifton (1937)
	D	Unidentified products	*P. morganii*	Meyers and Porter (1944)
Lanthionine (β-amino-β-carboxyethyl sulfide) $H_2C(CHNH_2 \cdot COOH)$—S—$CH_2(CHNH_2 \cdot COOH)$	D	Unidentified products	*P. morganii*	Meyers and Porter (1943)
Lysine (α-ϵ-diaminocaproic acid) $CH_2(NH_2) \cdot CH_2 \cdot CH_2 \cdot CH_2 \cdot CH(NH_2) \cdot COOH$	A3	ϵ-Aminocaproic acid, but not definitely identified	Mixed culture	Ackermann (1910)
	B	Pentamethylenediamine (cadaverine), $CH_2(NH_2) \cdot CH_2 \cdot CH_2 \cdot CH_2 \cdot CH_2(NH_2)$	Mixed culture	Ellinger (1900), Ackermann (1910)
			E. coli	Virtanen and Laine (1937), Gale (1940)
			A. aerogenes	Hirai (1939)
			Klebsiella pneumoniae	Gale (1940)
			Bact. cadaveris	Gale and Epps (1944)

Histidine (β-imidazole-α-aminopropionic acid or β-imidazolealanine) $HC{=}C(CH_2 \cdot CH(NH_2) \cdot COOH)-N{=}CH-NH$ (ring)	A2	β-Imidazolelactic acid, $CH_2 \cdot CHOH \cdot COOH$, $C_3H_3N_2$ and NH_3	*P. vulgaris* *Acetobacter xylinoides*	Hirai (1919) Miyaji (1925)
	A3	β-Imidazolepropionic acid, $CH_2 \cdot CH_2 \cdot COOH$, $C_3H_3N_2$ and NH_3	*E. coli* *Oidium lactis*	Koessler and Hanke (1919) Kiyokawa (1933)
	A4	β-Imidazoleacrylic acid (urocanic acid), $CH{:}CH \cdot COOH$, $C_3H_3N_2$ and NH_3	*E. coli*, *Salmonella paratyphi*, *Salmonella schottmuelleri*, *Shigella dysenteriae*	Raistrick (1917, 1919), Darby and Lewis (1942)
	A5	Unidentified products and NH_3 by glycine	*Cl. sporogenes*	Stickland (1934)
	B	α-Imidazoleethylamine (histamine) $CH_2 \cdot CH_2 \cdot NH_2$, $C_3H_3N_2$ and CO_2	*E. coli*	Koessler and Hanke (1919), Hanke and Koessler (1924), Eggerth (1939), Gale (1940, 1941), Virtanen, Laine, and Rintala (1940), Geiger (1944)
			Cl. perfringens	Kendall and Gebauer (1930)
			Eberthella, *Salmonella*, and *Shigella* species, *Cl. perfringens* and other bacteria	Eggerth (1939)
			Vibrio comma and other cholera vibrios	Chatterjee (1939)
			Clostridium fallax, *Cl. perfringens*, *Clostridium bifermentans*	Gale (1940, 1941)

TABLE 4 (*Continued*)

THE BREAKDOWN OF AMINO ACIDS BY MICROORGANISMS

Amino Acid	Type of Reaction (see pp. 851–856)	Compounds Produced	Organism	Reference
	C	β-Imidazoleethyl alcohol (histidol), $CH_2 \cdot CH_2OH$, $C_3H_3N_2$ (attached to CH_2) and NH_3, CO_2	Yeast	Ehrlich (1911, 1912, 1914)
	D	β-Imidazoleacetic acid, unidentified products	*M. tuberculosis*	Campbell (1925)
	D	Unidentified volatile acids, CO_2, H_2	*Cl. tetanomorphum*	Woods and Clifton (1937)
	D	Unidentified products formed by the rupture of the ring	*Ps. aeruginosa* and other bacteria	Raistrick (1919)
			Cl. tetani	Pickett (1943)
Arginine (δ-guanidine-α-aminovaleric acid) $(NH)(NH_2)C \cdot NH \cdot CH_2 \cdot CH_2 \cdot CH_2 \cdot CH(NH_2) \cdot COOH$	A5	Reduction to unidentified products by alanine	*Cl. sporogenes*	Woods (1936)
	A6	Unidentified products, NH_3	Streptococci of Lancefield serological groups A to G	Niven, Smiley, and Sherman (1942)
			E. typhosa	Hills (1940)
	B	Agmatine, $(HN)(H_2N)C \cdot NH \cdot (CH_2)_3 \cdot CH_2(NH_2)$, and CO_2	*E. coli*	Gale (1940)
	D	Unidentified products, NH_3, CO_2, ornithine, $H_2N \cdot CH_2 \cdot (CH_2)_2 \cdot CH(NH_2) \cdot COOH$	Mixed culture	Ackermann (1908)
			Lactobacillus acidophilus	Gale (1940)
			Streptococcus pyogenes, other streptococci	Hills (1940)

	D	Unidentified products, citrulline, $H_2N \cdot CO \cdot NH \cdot (CH_2)_3 \cdot CH(NH_2) \cdot COOH$	*Ps. aeruginosa*	Horn (1933)
	D	Succinic acid, γ-butylene glycol, unidentified products	Yeast	Thorne (1937)
Ornithine (α-δ-diaminovaleric acid) $CH_2(NH_2) \cdot CH_2 \cdot CH_2 \cdot CH(NH_2) \cdot COOH$	A3	δ-Aminovaleric acid (putridin), $CH_2(NH_2) \cdot CH_2 \cdot CH_2 \cdot CH_2 \cdot COOH$, and NH_3	Mixed culture *Cl. sporogenes*	Ackermann (1908) Woods (1936)
	B	Tetramethylenediamine (putrescine), $CH_2(NH_2) \cdot CH_2 \cdot CH_2 \cdot CH_2(NH_2)$, and CO_2	Mixed culture *Cl. septicum*, *E. coli* and *Proteus* strains *E. coli*	Ellinger (1899), Ackermann (1910) Gale (1940, 1941) Virtanen, Laine, and Rintala (1940)
Proline (α-pyrrolidine carboxylic acid) H_2C—CH_2, H_2C—$CH \cdot COOH$, ring closed by NH	A5	Reduction to δ-aminovaleric acid, $H_2N \cdot CH_2 \cdot CH_2 \cdot CH_2 \cdot CH_2 \cdot COOH$, by alanine, valine, leucine, and cysteine	*Cl. sporogenes* *Cl. botulinum*	Stickland (1934, 1935) Clifton (1940)
	D	Unidentified products, NH_3, CO_2	*P. vulgaris* *Ps. aeruginosa*	Bernheim, Bernheim, and Webster (1935) Webster and Bernheim (1936)
Hydroxyproline (β-hydroxyproline) $HC(OH)$—CH_2, H_2C—$CH \cdot COOH$, ring closed by NH	A5	Reduction to unidentified products by alanine, valine or leucine	*Cl. sporogenes*	Stickland (1934, 1935)
	D	Unidentified products, NH_3, CO_2	*Ps. aeruginosa*	Webster and Bernheim (1936)

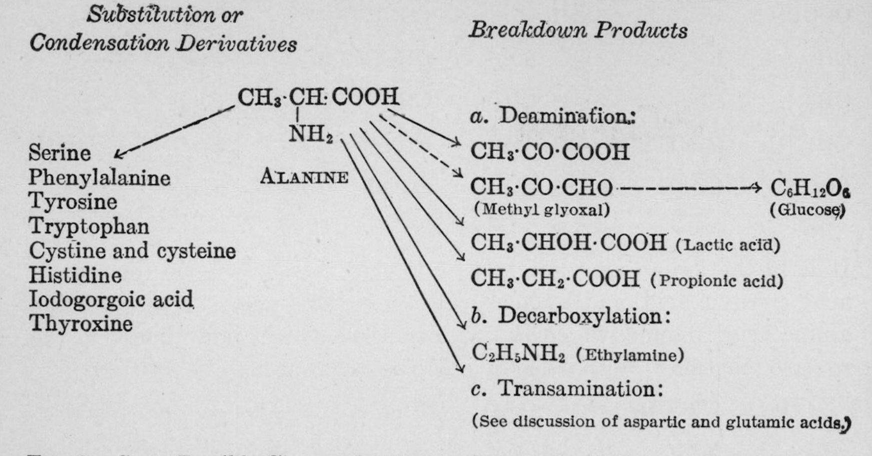

FIG. 2. Some Possible Changes in Alanine during Metabolism. The solid arrows are reactions known to be produced by microorganisms and other types of cells; the broken arrows are reactions which are thought to occur in higher animals or are hypothetical. (From Fearon, 1940.)

ASPARTIC ACID AND GLUTAMIC ACID AND THE "GLUTAMINE CYCLE." These two amino acids are considered nonessential for the development of higher animals, but they are required for the optimum growth of certain bacteria in chemically defined media (see Chapter 7); and, as is shown in Table 4, they are broken down to several compounds by various microorganisms. Probably the most interesting metabolic function in which these amino acids take part is the process known as "transamination." This process has not been studied very extensively with microorganisms,[5] although it is known to occur in muscle, liver, and many other tissues [see Braunstein and Kritzmann (1937), Braunstein (1939), Schoenheimer (1942)]. Transamination consists of the biological transfer of nitrogen among amino acids without the occurrence of ammonia as an intermediate. The enzyme systems, called *aminopherases*, involved are highly specific in that they require a particular amino donor, glutamic acid or aspartic acid, or a particular amino acceptor, α-ketoglutaric acid or oxaloacetic acid, depending upon the direction of the reaction. The transamination process with glutamic acid is thought to occur as follows:

[5] In 1945 Lichstein and Cohen established the presence of a potent transaminase system in several bacteria (*Escherichia coli, Proteus vulgaris, Azotobacter vinelandii, Staphylococcus aureus, Clostridium perfringens*, streptococci, and pneumococci). The system catalyzes the following reaction:

$l(+)$-Glutamic acid + Oxaloacetic acid $\rightarrow$ α-Ketoglutaric acid + $l(-)$-Aspartic acid.

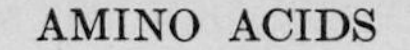

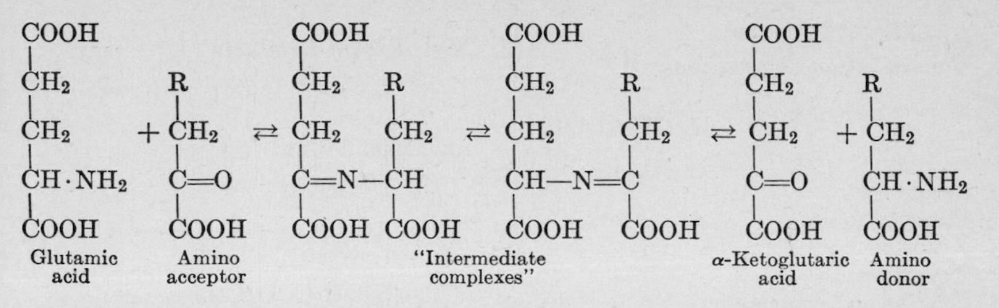

If R in the amino acceptor is a hydrogen, then it will be the α-keto acid, pyruvic acid, and by accepting the $—NH_2$ group it becomes the amino acid, alanine, which in turn can serve as an amino donor in the reverse reaction. With aspartic acid the reaction may be written:

$$\underset{\text{Aspartic acid}}{HOOC\cdot \underset{|\atop NH_2}{CH}\cdot CH_2\cdot COOH} + \underset{\text{Amino acceptor}}{AO} \rightleftarrows \underset{\text{Oxaloacetic acid}}{HOOC\cdot \underset{\|\atop O}{C}\cdot CH_2\cdot COOH} + \underset{\text{Amino donor}}{AH\cdot NH_2}$$

where AO represents a specific amino acceptor, such as an α-keto acid, and $AH\cdot NH_2$ a suitable amino donor, which may be a natural amino acid. In other words, the specific enzymes (aminopherase system), working in one direction, convert monocarboxyketo acids, such as pyruvic acid, into amino acids by the transfer of $—NH_2$; working in the reverse direction, this enzyme system deaminates amino acids and transfers the $—NH_2$ to keto acids. Such a system appears to be of considerable importance in the natural synthesis of amino acids from carbohydrate residues and products.

Glutamine, the amide of glutamic acid, is thought to play a cyclic role in ureagenesis in animals [Leuthardt (1938)], and it has been shown to be required for the optimum growth of certain bacteria in chemically defined media. It is not known, however, whether glutamine functions in bacteria in a manner similar to that in animals. In animals (cat, rat, or guinea pig) Leuthardt believes that glutamine reacts with carbonic acid to form urea and pyrrolidine-2-carboxylic acid, which undergoes successive transformation to proline and glutamic acid, which on subsequent amination to glutamine completes the so-called "glutamine cycle." Krebs (1942) has criticized the work of Leuthardt and believes that, although glutamine may have a stimulating effect on the ornithine cycle, a glutamine cycle as such does not exist.

PHENYLALANINE AND TYROSINE. These two aromatic amino acids are supposedly the chief source of the benzene ring for higher animals, and they seem to be interchangeable in animal nutrition; apparently phenylalanine is transformed into tyrosine before metabolism. Aromatic amino acids are also essential for the optimum growth of several bacteria when they are cultivated in chemically defined media (see Chapter 7). Some of the reactions involved in the metabolism of tyrosine are shown in Fig. 3.

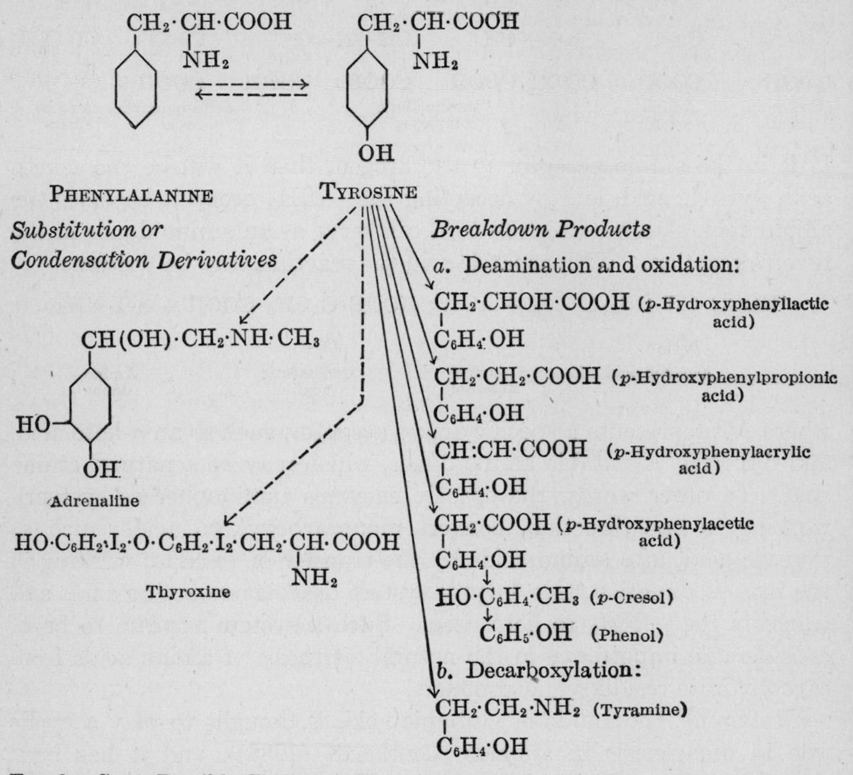

FIG. 3. Some Possible Changes in Tyrosine during Metabolism. The solid arrows are reactions known to be produced by microorganisms and other types of cells; the broken arrows are reactions which are thought to occur in higher animals or are hypothetical. (From Fearon, 1940.)

Tyrosine is also oxidized by the enzyme tyrosinase to a red indole compound formed by the closure of the side chain; this red compound is then reduced spontaneously to an indole base, *melanogen,* which by oxidative polymerization forms the dark brown pigment called *melanin.* This series of reactions may be of importance in establishing a relationship between tryptophan and tyrosine. The melanin pigments impart the characteristic color to brown or black hair, the fur of animals, and the racial pigment of skin and are thought to be responsible for the pigmentation of the colonies of several microorganisms (see Chapter 5).

TRYPTOPHAN. Tryptophan is an essential amino acid for higher animals and many microorganisms; it serves as the chief source of the indole nucleus. It is also probable that tryptophan supplies pyrrol nuclei for the synthesis of cellular porphyrins, including the cytochromes and hematin. The products formed by the microbial breakdown of tryptophan vary, depending upon the organism, the nature of the medium, and other factors (see Table 4).

The general physiological interest in tryptophan and the fact that certain bacteria and other microorganisms convert tryptophan into indole—a reaction which has long been employed as a diagnostic test in systematic bacteriology—have resulted in a large literature on this subject [see Raistrick and Clark (1921), Woods (1935), Happold and Hoyle (1935), Thorne (1937), Burrows (1939), Baker and Happold (1940), Fildes (1940, 1941), Evans, Handley, and Happold (1942), Krebs, Hafez, and Eggleston (1942), Snell (1943)].

It is also of interest that Tatum and Bonner (1943) have presented evidence to show that serine is concerned in the synthesis of tryptophan by the ascomycete *Neurospora crassa*, apparently through a direct reaction with indole. Likewise, Fildes (1940) and Snell (1943) have observed that certain bacteria which require tryptophan for growth can use indole, but the reaction between indole and serine was not established. Snell also found that anthranilic acid will replace tryptophan in the nutrition of some lactic acid bacteria.

In 1903 Hopkins and Cole showed that tryptophan is the parent substance of the indole formed by bacteria, and soon afterward several workers proposed the reactions shown in Fig. 4 to account for the processes whereby tryptophan is converted to indole.

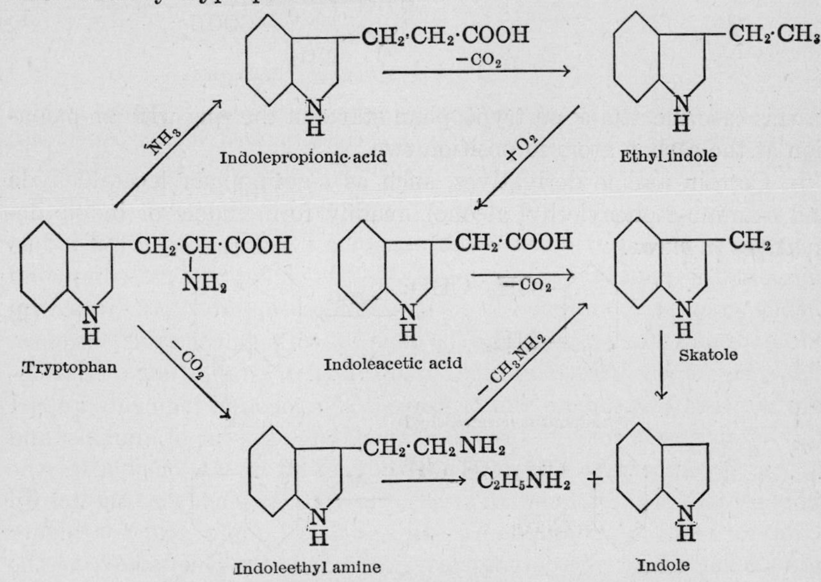

FIG. 4. A Scheme for the Breakdown of Tryptophan.

Since these early days numerous attempts have been made to elucidate the intermediary mechanism of indole formation by testing compounds which seemed to be likely intermediates [see Woods (1935), Happold and Hoyle (1935), Baker and Happold (1940)]. Among the compounds which have been tested but can be excluded as intermediates because they are attacked very slowly or not at all are 3-indolepropionic acid, 3-indoleethylamine, 3-indolelactic acid, 3-indolepyruvic acid, 3-indoleacrylic acid, 3-indoleglycine, 3-indolealdehyde, and 3-indolecarboxylic acid. These negative results led Krebs, Hafez, and Eggleston (1942) to conclude that the primary breakdown of tryptophan does not start in the side chain; they examined the hypothesis that the conversion of tryptophan into indole begins with the oxidation of the indole ring. In forming such a hypothesis they were guided by the following facts:

a. In certain organisms (rabbit, *Bacillus subtilis*) tryptophan is converted to kynurenine according to the following reaction [Kotake and his associates (1933)]:

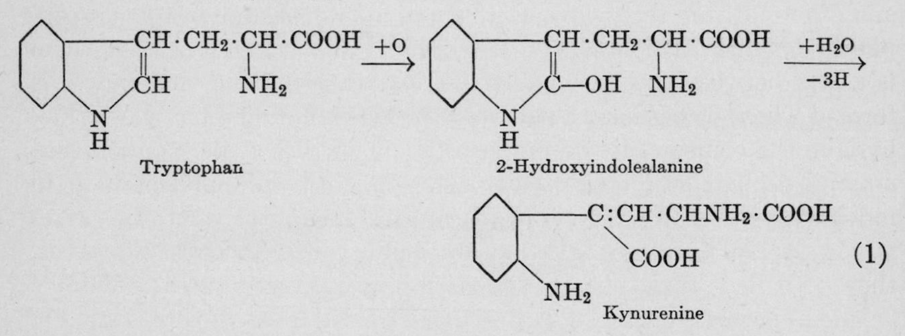

Tryptophan
2-Hydroxyindolealanine
Kynurenine

In this case the attack on tryptophan starts in the ring with an oxidation at the carbon atom in position two.

b. Certain aniline derivatives, such as *o*-aminophenylacetaldehyde and *o*-amino-β-phenylethyl alcohol, readily form indole or indole derivatives *in vitro:*

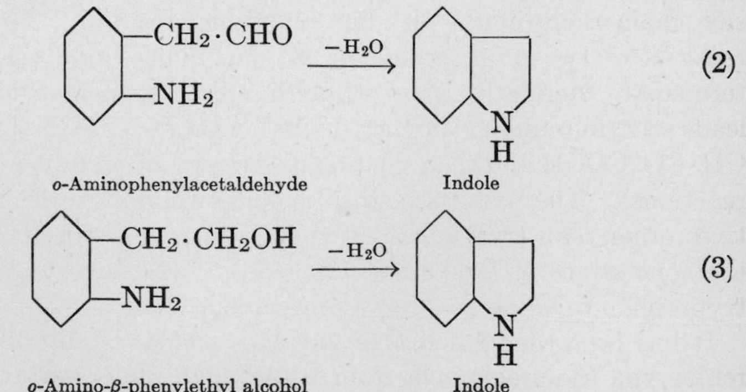

o-Aminophenylacetaldehyde
Indole
o-Amino-β-phenylethyl alcohol
Indole

From these data Krebs and his associates (1942) believe that the conversion of tryptophan into indole may start with an oxidation of the ring like that in equation (1), leading to an *o*-aniline derivative similar to or identical with kynurenine, and that the side chain of this compound is consequently broken down to *o*-aminophenylacetaldehyde, which in turn yields indole according to equation (2). If this hypothesis is correct, then *Escherichia coli* and other indole-forming bacteria should yield indole from kynurenine and similar *o*-aniline derivatives. Krebs and his associates tested several compounds of this type and found that one substance, *o*-amino-β-phenylethyl alcohol, reacted in the expected manner. They believe that the formation of indole from this compound is not necessarily connected with its formation from tryptophan because *E. coli* oxidizes ethyl alcohol and several of its homologs to the corresponding aldehydes. Furthermore, since the aldehyde arising from *o*-amino-β-phenylethyl alcohol is known to yield indole spontaneously, this alcohol might be expected to form indole on oxidation; the indole formation would in this case be "accidental" and different from the true mechanism of indole formation from tryptophan. On the other hand, these workers prefer to assume that there is a link between the two indole-yielding reactions and that indole is formed when, or because, a substrate yields *o*-amino-β-phenylacetaldehyde in the course of its decomposition. They are of the opinion that *o*-amino-β-phenylethyl alcohol is not necessarily an intermediate in indole formation from tryptophan; in fact, its rather slow rate of reaction at low concentrations argues against this theory. However, they do believe that the corresponding aldehyde is an intermediate.

The hypothesis of Krebs, Hafez, and Eggleston has the advantage of explaining the various types of tryptophan breakdown (formation of kynurenine, or kynurenic acid and anthranilic acid, and of indole) as modifications of one major scheme. In every case the primary step is the formation of an intermediate derivative (oxindole- or hydroxyindolealanine) followed by ring opening; the further breakdown of the side chain then differs with the individual reaction. For example, a removal of two or three hydrogen, depending upon whether the intermediate derivative is oxindolealanine or hydroxyindolealanine, leads to kynurenine; a further oxidation produces $H_2N \cdot C_6H_4 \cdot C(OH):CH \cdot CO \cdot COOH$ and then, by ring closure, kynurenic acid (see Kotake's reactions). The hypothesis also explains the failure of indole derivatives other than tryptophan to yield indole and is in accordance with the conclusions of Baker and Happold (1940) that the breakdown of tryptophan to indole requires an intact side chain.

It has been mentioned that *Bacillus subtilis* is able to form kynurenine and kynurenic acid from tryptophan under certain conditions.

This type of tryptophan breakdown has been studied rather extensively by Kotake and his associates (1933), who believe that the reactions involved may be written as follows:

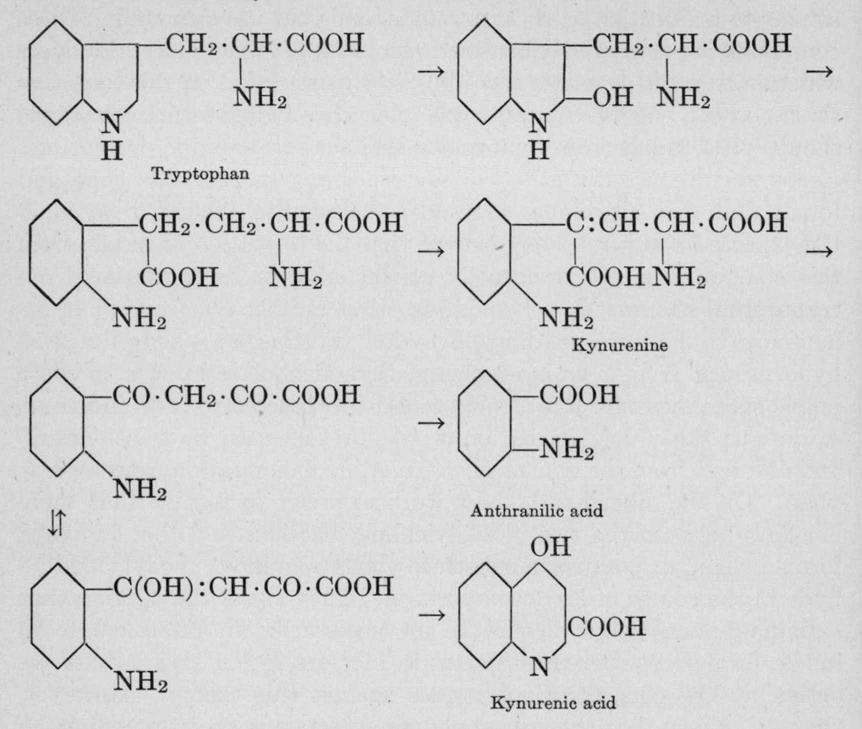

These reactions are substantiated by the fact that, when Kotake and his associates substituted kynurenine for tryptophan in the basal medium, kynurenic acid and anthranilic acid could be isolated as end products.

PEPTIDES

As early as 1905 to 1910 several investigators reported that bacteria, yeasts, and molds are capable of utilizing peptides as a source of nitrogen [see Buchanan and Fulmer (1930)]. However, since much of this early work was done with more or less indefinite mixtures of peptides, it is of only historical interest at the present time.

More recently several synthetic peptides have been prepared by Gorbach (1930), Bergmann and his associates (1932–1937), Berger, Johnson, and Peterson (1938), Imaizumi (1938), Elberg and Meyer (1939), Maschmann (1937–1939) and others [see Johnson and Berger (1942)] for metabolic studies. In most of the experiments in which microorganisms have been employed for the metabolic studies either "resting" cells or various types of cell-free enzyme preparations have been used, and the rate of peptide hydrolysis, specificity of enzyme preparation, and kind of activator have been determined. These studies were briefly discussed under the heading of bacterial peptidases in Chapter 6 and have been reviewed in some detail by Johnson and Berger (1942); these sources should be consulted for further details concerning the action of microorganisms on peptides.

PEPTONES, PROTEOSES, METAPROTEINS, AND PROTEINS

When proteins are hydrolyzed by acids, alkalies, or enzymes, they gradually undergo degradation into the following substances of decreasing molecular size:

Proteins → Metaproteins → Proteoses →

Peptones → Peptides → Amino acids

The intermediate products which are formed between proteins and amino acids should be considered classes of substances rather than individual compounds, for there exist no sharp lines of demarcation between the various classes; one class blends by imperceptible degrees into the next.

Peptones. Peptone-like bodies have been found free in certain plant and animal tissues, but the peptones which are now used for bacteriological purposes are all prepared from proteins by commercial methods. The methods of preparing peptones fall into the three following groups: (1) a hydrolysis of proteins by enzymes; (2) a hydrolysis of proteins by acids and alkalies; and (3) a combination of these two methods. In general, the peptones exhibit none of the colloidal properties of the true proteins, and they are readily diffusible through semipermeable membranes. As McAlpine and Brigham (1928) have pointed out, however, certain commercial brands of peptone, such as Witte peptone, actually contain considerable nitrogen in the form of protein bodies. Chemically, peptones are distinguishable from proteoses, metaproteins, and proteins by the fact that they are not precipitated when their solutions are saturated with ammonium sulfate, nor are they precipitated by such reagents as trichloracetic acid or picric acid; they are, however, precipitated to a certain extent by tannic acid and by phosphotungstic acid [Kemmerer and Heil (1941)]. In spite of the differences in precipitation between the peptones and proteoses these two kinds of substances are not easily separated from each other, and all commercial peptones contain a varying percentage of proteoses.

The data in Tables 5 and 6 show the results of typical quantitative chemical analyses of certain commercial and laboratory-prepared animal and vegetable peptones and proteoses which are used for bacteriological work. An examination of these tables indicates the following facts: (1) the commercial and laboratory-prepared peptones are fairly uniform in so far as their total nitrogen is concerned, and the vegetable peptones as a group give the lowest values; (2) both commercial and laboratory-prepared peptones vary widely in their con-

TABLE 5

TYPICAL ANALYSES OF DIFCO BACTO PEPTONES AND PROTEOSES

(From *Difco Manual of Dehydrated Culture Media and Reagents*, 7th Ed., 1943, p. 176)

	Bacto-Peptone	Bacto-Tryptone	Bacto-Tryptose	Neopeptone, Difco	Proteose-Peptone, Difco	Bacto-Protone
Total nitrogen	16.16	13.14	13.76	14.33	14.37	15.41
Primary proteose N	0.06	0.20	0.40	0.46	0.60	5.36
Secondary proteose N	0.68	1.63	2.83	3.03	4.03	7.60
Peptone N	15.38	11.29	10.52	10.72	9.74	2.40
Ammonia N	0.04	0.02	0.01	0.12	0.00	0.05
Free amino N (Van Slyke)	3.20	4.73	3.70	2.82	2.66	1.86
Amide N	0.49	1.11	1.03	1.23	0.94	....
Monoamino N	9.42	7.31	7.46	7.56	7.61	....
Diamino N	4.07	3.45	3.98	4.43	4.51	....
Tryptophan	0.29	0.77	0.64	0.73	0.51	1.03
Tyrosine	0.98	4.39	3.45	4.72	2.51	2.99
Cystine (Sullivan)	0.22	0.19	0.38	0.39	0.56	0.27
Organic sulfur	0.33	0.53	0.57	0.63	0.60	0.45
Inorganic sulfur	0.29	0.04	0.04	0.09	0.04	0.16
Phosphorus	0.22	0.97	0.72	0.19	0.47	0.27
Chlorine	0.27	0.29	2.12	0.84	3.95	0.38
Sodium	1.08	2.69	2.77	0.45	2.84	0.30
Potassium	0.22	0.30	0.50	0.85	0.70	0.06
Calcium	0.058	0.096	0.117	0.198	0.137	0.263
Magnesium	0.056	0.045	0.082	0.051	0.118	0.057
Manganese	Nil	Nil	0.0001	Nil	0.0002	Nil
Iron	0.0033	0.0104	0.0080	0.0041	0.0056	0.0023
Ash	3.53	7.28	8.45	3.90	9.61	2.50
Ether-soluble extract	0.37	0.30	0.31	0.30	0.32	0.31
Reaction (*p*H of 1% solution in distilled H_2O after autoclaving 20 min. at 121°C.	7.0	7.2	7.3	6.8	6.8	6.7

TABLE 6

PERCENTAGE CHEMICAL ANALYSIS OF COMMERCIAL AND LABORATORY-PREPARED PEPTONES

[From Hook and Fabian (1943)]

Name of Peptone	Total Nitrogen	Proteose Nitrogen		Peptone Nitrogen	Free NH_3 Nitrogen	Free NH_2 Nitrogen	Amino Nitrogen		Ash	pH*
		Primary	*Secondary*				*Van Slyke*	*Sorenson*		
Commercial Brands †										
Peptonum siccum, Armour	14.27	0.64	3.73	6.05	0.33	1.69	3.94	3.84	2.07	6.31
Peptone, special,‡ Armour	13.89	0.74	3.58	3.75	0.12	0.57	1.08	1.05	2.23	5.82
Peptone, Baker	15.43	0.03	3.68	13.92	0.09	0.25	1.39	1.36	1.07	5.21
Peptone, Cenco	15.38	0.41	5.04	11.91	0.09	0.48	0.85	0.81	1.26	5.53
Peptone, Chaissiang (French product)	13.15	0.00	0.50	5.02	0.07	1.21	3.25	3.24	1.58	4.91
Peptone, Eimer & Amend	16.14	0.01	1.25	13.86	0.06	0.27	1.13	1.05	0.70	5.15
Peptone (albumin) Eimer & Amend	11.21	0.36	1.16	6.58	0.08	0.45	1.41	1.36	3.98	5.98
Peptone, Fairchild	14.44	0.16	0.34	4.80	0.23	1.92	5.21	5.09	1.62	5.51
Peptone, Merck	15.83	0.00	0.37	12.53	0.06	0.36	1.83	1.74	1.18	4.89
Peptone, Pfanstiehl	13.56	0.08	1.40	6.69	0.17	1.31	3.94	2.89	3.21	5.17
Peptone N.P., Stearn	14.42	0.02	0.61	7.81	0.09	1.12	2.53	2.48	1.86	5.91
Peptone, Witte (1912)	14.48	1.71	6.79	10.55	0.02	0.32	1.85	1.79	1.57	7.60
Peptone, Witte (1940) (German products)	13.45	1.07	5.52	10.59	0.00	0.52	2.54	2.48	1.31	7.00
Peptone "CB," Wilson	11.86	0.11	0.98	4.46	0.13	1.58	3.71	3.67	4.69	6.93
Peptone "C," Wilson	11.48	0.19	2.13	2.65	0.13	1.58	3.90	3.81	6.36	7.08
Animal (Laboratory-Prepared)										
Peptone, beef muscle	14.19	0.22	6.23	10.54	0.21	0.47	1.63	1.57	1.19	6.46
Peptone, beef spleen §	14.64–14.84	0.57–1.22	2.31–2.94	9.92–10.94	0.02–0.24	0.67–0.71	2.11–2.39	2.07–2.29	1.75–2.16	6.72
Peptone, beef liver §	13.44–16.44	0.75–1.14	1.56–4.51	2.85– 9.23	0.13–0.19	0.57–1.17	1.61–6.17	1.52–5.97	3.11–8.04	....
Peptone, beef heart §	14.20–15.08	0.46–1.40	3.90–4.68	10.34–10.63	0.05–0.14	0.45–0.50	1.82–2.08	1.80–2.04	1.99–2.86	....
Peptone, beef brain §	11.99–15.00	0.08–0.33	0.69–1.11	3.12– 6.44	0.02–0.47	1.00–1.54	2.94–4.28	2.92–4.26	2.88–6.75	....
Peptone, pork	12.58	0.90	2.75	8.64	0.14	0.82	1.64	1.57	4.48	7.09
Vegetable (Laboratory-Prepared)										
Peptone, corn gluten hydrolysate ‖	7.66–12.24	0.09–0.13	0.06–0.14	0.08–0.27	0.0	2.87–3.75	5.54–7.16	5.28–7.10	1.32–2.79	....
Peptone, unhydrolyzed corn gluten	11.45	0.41	1.98	2.52	0.37	1.76	2.36	2.30	3.94	....
Tryptone, unhydrolyzed corn gluten	11.37	0.05	0.07	0.41	0.51	0.0	5.24	5.19	3.04	6.10

* pH values of 1 per cent solutions.
† The various Bacto-Difco products were also analyzed; but, since the results were similar to those listed in Table 5, they have been omitted here.
‡ Not a bacteriological peptone. § Range of two samples. ‖ Range of four samples.

tent of the various nitrogen fractions; (3) the vegetable peptones are lower in peptone nitrogen than the others, except for Bacto-protone; (4) the content of free ammonia nitrogen is low in all peptones; (5) the vegetable peptones are higher in free amino acid and amino nitrogen than are the commercial and laboratory-prepared animal peptones; (6) the sum of the nitrogen fractions does not equal the figure for total nitrogen, indicating that more than one nitrogen fraction was determined by the same analysis, or that certain forms of nitrogen were undeterminable by the technique; and (7) the *p*H values of the various peptones vary widely. Additional chemical and bacteriological data on peptones and proteoses will be found in the papers by McAlpine and Brigham (1928), Topshteĭn (1940), Krishnan and Narayanan (1941), Leifson (1941), and Hook and Fabian (1941, 1943). The publication by Hook and Fabian (1943), which presents a great deal of information on this subject, is especially valuable for reference.

The first references to the use of peptones for the cultivation of microorganisms appear to be those made by Naegeli from 1879 to 1882; he compared the nutritional value of peptones with that of ammonium tartrate and found that peptones served very well as a source of nitrogen for microorganisms. Soon afterward animal peptones became one of the most important constituents of culture media because of their content of amino acids and other nitrogenous compounds which are readily metabolized by microorganisms. More recently vegetable peptones have been recommended as a cheap source of nitrogen for growing certain bacteria [Hook and Fabian (1943)].

The dissimilation of peptones by microorganisms has been studied rather extensively in the past; Buchanan and Fulmer (1930) should be consulted for a review of the early literature on this subject. A few microbial metabolic end products which have been reported to arise from peptones are the following:

Metabolic End Product	*Reference*
Creatine and creatinine	Antonoff (1906), Fitzgerald and Schmidt (1912), Sears (1916, 1917), Fish and Beckwith (1939)
Urea	Iwanoff and Smirnowa (1927)
Acids: Amino acids	Sears (1916), Kendall (1922, 1923), Hucker (1924)
Acids: Hydrocyanic acid	Emerson, Cady, and Bailey (1913), Clawson and Young (1913)
Mercaptans, indole, etc.	Almy and James (1926)
Gases: NH_3, CO_2, H_2, etc.	Treece (1928)
Gases: H_2S	Almy and James (1926), Treece (1928), Tarr (1933, 1934), Zobell and Feltham (1934), Vaughn and Levine (1936), Tittsler and Sandholzer (1937), Hunter and Crecelius (1938), Utermohlen and Georgi (1940), Stekol and Ransmeier (1942), Ransmeier and Stekol (1942)

Since peptones are not distinct chemical entities, it is somewhat difficult to state from which fraction of them the various metabolic products arise. Also it is probable that, before the constituents of commercial peptones are synthesized into protoplasm by microbial cells, they must first undergo degradation into simpler nitrogenous substances, such as amino acids or ammonia, which under these conditions may be ephemeral. This supposition may account for the failure to detect large amounts of such compounds as end products of peptone metabolism.

According to Ludwig (1938), peptone serves as a source of nitrogen for *Chlorella* and some other algae; however, in certain green algae peptone is nonassimilable.

Proteoses. The proteoses differ from proteins and other protein degradation products in that the precipitate which appears when their solutions are treated with nitric acid usually dissolves when the mixture is heated and reappears when it is cooled. Proteoses are precipitated almost completely when their solutions are saturated with ammonium sulfate, but they are not coagulated by heat and they diffuse very slowly through semipermeable membranes. The chemical analysis of two commercial products (proteose-peptone Difco and Bacto-protone) which are high in proteose nitrogen is given in Table 5. It will also be seen from the data in this table and Table 6 that the commercial brands of peptone contain variable amounts of proteose nitrogen.

The metabolism of pure proteoses by microorganisms has not been investigated, although several workers [see, for example, Hucker (1924) have used crude proteose fractions in their studies and have found that they are not readily utilized by bacteria, especially in the absence of a fermentable carbohydrate.

Proteins.[6] Proteins are complex nitrogenous substances which, in general, contain carbon (50 to 55 per cent), hydrogen (7 per cent), nitrogen (15 to 19 percent), oxygen (25 to 30 per cent), sulfur (0.5 to 2.5 per cent), frequently phosphorus (0.4 per cent), and sometimes a halogen. As a class, proteins are characterized by a number of color reactions, by a series of precipitation tests, and by certain other physico-chemical properties characteristic of amphoteric colloids; for example, techniques and apparatus which measure the viscosity-concentration curves of protein solutions and show their appearance under the ultramicroscope and electron microscope, their behavior in the ultracentrifuge, their movement in an electric field, and their X-ray pattern are being used more and more extensively by various workers to

[6] The word protein is derived from the Greek and means preeminence. The term was first applied to the complex nitrogenous substances found in plant and animal tissues by Mulder in 1838–1839.

characterize proteins. In deciding whether a particular substance is a pure protein, the results of all these tests must be considered together. The color reactions are specific, not for proteins as such, but rather for certain chemical groups occurring in them; and, although the precipitation tests are typically those of amphoteric colloids, the various proteins nevertheless show marked differences in physical properties which can be detected only by some of the newer techniques.

Proteins are essential constituents of all living matter. They form with water, lipides, carbohydrates, and salts the colloidal complex known as protoplasm, and they seem to confer many physico-chemical properties, as well as biological specificity, to various types of cells. In addition to being an essential constituent of all living cells, proteins are present in eggs, in seeds, and in secretions such as milk and honey, which are intended as food for the developing young. Although plants, including many bacteria, are capable of synthesizing proteins from simple organic or inorganic compounds, this ability is lacking in higher animals, who are thus dependent upon proteins or their component parts for the continuance of life.

Under normal conditions proteins themselves are not oxidized to any great extent to release energy for cellular activities; the fuel consumed for this purpose is supplied primarily by carbohydrates and fats. During periods of starvation or in the absence of utilizable carbohydrate, however, many cells can and do utilize their own or other proteins. Also after the death of cells all the cellular proteins are eventually broken down into simpler nitrogenous substances by the activities of proteolytic enzymes. These simpler nitrogenous compounds may then be synthesized into new protoplasmic material by microorganisms and other types of cells.

Microorganisms play a very important role in the decomposition and alteration of proteins in nature, and several experimental studies have been conducted to determine the action of pure cultures of various organisms on several purified proteins. Proteins may undergo one or more types of changes as the result of microbial activities. Some protein solutions are coagulated, whereas others are dissimilated through the activities of hydrolytic and oxidative enzymes and then resynthesized into new compounds. Since the production of protein-coagulating enzymes by microorganisms was discussed in Chapter 6, only a few of the results of the dissimilation of proteins will be reviewed here.

The dissimilation of proteins in nature or under experimental conditions may result from the activities of aerobic, facultative, or anaerobic microorganisms. When the breakdown of proteins occurs in an aerobic environment, the process is usually spoken of as *decay*, which may be defined simply as a process in which the proteins are oxidized to stable compounds devoid of foul odors. On the other hand, when the decomposition takes place under anaerobic conditions, the process is termed *putrefaction*, which may be defined as a reaction in which the proteins are incompletely oxidized to unstable or foul-smelling compounds (for example, mercaptans, amines, fatty acids, indole, and hydrogen sulfide).

Before 1911 several workers [see Buchanan and Fulmer, Vol. III (1930), Waksman (1932)] reported that anaerobic bacteria degrade proteins and cause putrefaction. Bainbridge (1911), however, was unable to find any chemical evidence to show that several aerobic or facultative bacteria are able to decompose native egg albumin or serum protein. He employed a basal inorganic salt medium to which were added: (a) the proteins separately; (b) the proteins plus glucose; and (c) the proteins with simpler nitrogenous substances. In the medium containing only the native proteins as a source of nitrogen and carbon there was neither a change in the proteins nor an increase in the number of bacteria. When glucose was added as a source of energy, growth usually occurred, but the proteins were not degraded to any measurable extent. In the medium which contained sufficient nonprotein nitrogenous food to insure vigorous bacterial growth, only *Proteus vulgaris* was able to decompose the proteins.

In a series of papers by Rettger and his students [see Sperry and Rettger (1915), Rettger, Berman, and Sturges (1916), Berman and Rettger (1916, 1918)] the observations of Bainbridge were confirmed and extended. They employed aerobic, facultative, and anaerobic species of bacteria and the proteins edestin and egg albumin in both synthetic and nonsynthetic media. None of the fifteen or so species used was capable of utilizing the purified native proteins as a sole source of carbon and nitrogen. However, the addition of a trace of peptone or some other nitrogenous food material, which readily furnished the necessary nitrogen for bacterial growth and enzyme synthesis, permitted most of the organisms to digest the proteins. Similar results have been reported by other workers [see, for example, Hucker (1928), Frazier and Rupp (1931), Ludwig (1938)].

On the other hand, careful chemical studies by Robinson and Tartar (1917), Waksman (1920, 1932), Waksman and Lomanitz (1925), and Waksman and Starkey (1932) have shown that pure cultures of certain species of bacteria, molds, and actinomyces decompose purified animal and plant proteins. For example, the data cited in Table 7 show the results of the decomposition of four proteins by an active protein-decomposing mold, actinomyces, and bacterium. The basal medium employed consisted of inorganic salts, to which were added the various proteins (1.0 per cent) or the proteins plus glucose (0.8 per cent); incubation of cultures was carried out at 27° to 28° C. under aerobic conditions for the time given in the table. From the data in Table 7 it will be seen that with all three organisms there was a reduction of the insoluble protein and an increase of nitrogen in solution, as well as ammonia and amino nitrogen formation. Under the conditions of this experiment *Bacillus cereus* was more active than either the mold or

TABLE 7

DECOMPOSITION OF VEGETABLE AND ANIMAL PROTEINS BY MICROORGANISMS

[From Waksman and Starkey (1932)]

Protein	Organism	Age of Culture, days	Dry Weight of Residue,* mgm.	Nitrogen Content of Residue, mgm.	Nitrogen Content of Solution			Glucose (0.8%) Present in Medium	Glucose Left in Medium, mgm.
					Total Nitrogen, mgm.	NH_2 Nitrogen, mgm.	NH_3 Nitrogen, mgm.		
Edestin	Control		978	164.2	2.0	0	Trace	−	0
	Control		984	166.4	1.4	0	Trace	+	795
	Trichoderma koningi	9	604	85.1	79.6	28.3	32.6	−	0
	T. koningi	9	968	120.4	46.8	14.0	25.2	+	Trace
	Actinomyces viridochromogenus	15	862	140.8	25.3	4.5	11.7	−	0
	Act. viridochromogenus	15	823	121.8	41.4	4.8	27.8	+	0
	Bacillus cereus	9	408	65.0	100.3	22.8	40.1	−	0
	B. cereus	9	485	81.0	86.8	30.6	21.8	+	195
Gliadin	Control		954	135.0	2.1	0	0	−	0
	Control		962	135.6	1.7	0	0	+	795
	T. koningi	9	271	28.0	105.5	36.8	32.8	−	0
	T. koningi	9	927	90.7	44.8	17.4	10.0	+	75
	Act. viridochromogenus	15	792	109.8	25.1	3.5	15.2	−	0
	B. cereus	9	51	7.3	124.1	36.2	42.6	−	0
	B. cereus	9	559	71.9	62.4	14.0	6.7	+	525
Zein	Control		966	144.8	0.6	0	0	−	0
	Control		976	145.9	0.4	0	0	+	795
	T. koningi	13	718	97.3	45.5	14.0	26.8	−	0
	T. koningi	13	698	67.5	72.7	20.8	36.3	+	0
	B. cereus	13	128	17.9	114.8	27.8	46.5	−	0
	B. cereus	13	853	116.8	17.5	4.2	6.5	+	490
Casein †	Control				140.2	7.5	1.2	−	0
	T. koningi	10	232	17.2	118.0	12.6	44.7	−	0
	Act. viridochromogenus	15	95	10.2	128.6	13.3	19.2	−	0
	B. cereus	9	105	12.3	113.2	38.9	40.9	−	0

* Residue consists of undecomposed protein and cellular material which is retained by fine filter paper.
† Casein dissolved in 0.1 *N* NaOH; therefore the residue consists almost entirely of cellular material.

actinomyces, and the different proteins were not decomposed to the same extent by any one organism. When glucose was incorporated in the medium as a source of energy, less of the protein was decomposed, but a greater cellular synthesis was also taking place, as will be seen by comparing the figures for the nitrogen content of the residue with those for the nitrogen content of the solution.

An interesting point in connection with the utilization of proteins by various bacteria is the effect that glucose or other carbohydrates have on the decomposition process. In 1915 Kendall and Walker observed that, when a small amount (up to 0.3 per cent) of glucose was added to a gelatin medium, the secretion by *Proteus vulgaris* of the enzyme which liquefies gelatin was inhibited until the carbohydrate was completely utilized; also, when the concentration of glucose was above 0.3 per cent, the formation of the enzyme was permanently prevented. Control experiments showed that glucose did not inhibit the enzyme after it was formed, and interference due to high acidity was ruled out because the enzyme was eventually formed after small amounts (up to 0.3 per cent) of glucose were completely fermented. These workers concluded that *P. vulgaris* preferred a fermentable carbohydrate to protein for its energy requirements and that it would not attack the protein until the carbohydrate in the medium had been completely utilized; in other words, they believed that glucose protected, or exhibited a so-called protein-sparing action on, the protein constituents of the medium until it was completely utilized. These conclusions were criticized by Berman and Rettger (1918) and others. Berman and Rettger showed, for example, that organisms such as *Bacillus subtilis*, which ferment glucose very slowly, and *Aerobacter cloacae*, which produce end products that are not too acid, failed to exhibit a protein-sparing action, since protein decomposition occurred even before all the sugar was fermented. On the other hand, when organisms were employed such as *P. vulgaris* or *E. coli*, which produce large quantities of acidic end products during a short incubation period, a definite protein-sparing action was observed, providing the medium was not strongly buffered. If, however, an excess of phosphate buffer was added during the preparation of the sugar-protein medium, the limiting hydrogen-ion concentration was never reached during the early growth phase of the bacterial cultures, and protein decomposition occurred as rapidly in the presence of a fermentable carbohydrate as in its absence. Thus it may be concluded that a fermentable carbohydrate exhibits protein-sparing action only when it is rapidly fermented to strongly acidic end products in an unbuffered medium; then it is the acidic environment that inhibits bacterial growth and multiplication and consequently the elaboration of proteolytic enzymes.

REFERENCES

Abderhalden, E., G. Fromme, and P. Hirsch. 1913. *Z. physiol. Chem.*, **85**:131–135.
Ackermann, D., and P. Mey. 1906. *Centr. Bakt., I Abt. Orig.*, **42**:629–632.
Ackermann, D. 1908. *Z. physiol. Chem.*, **56**:305–315.
Ackermann, D. 1910. *Z. physiol. Chem.*, **69**:273–281.
Ackermann, D. 1913–1914. *Z. Biol.*, **62**:208–216; **63**:78–82.
Adler, E., V. Hellström, G. Günther, and H. v. Euler. 1938. *Z. Physiol. Chem.*, **255**:14–26.
Akobe, K. 1936. *Z. physiol. Chem.*, **244**:14–18.
Allinson, M. J. C. 1940. *Proc. Soc. Exptl. Biol. Med.*, **43**:736.
Almy, L. H., and L. H. James. 1926. *J. Bact.*, **12**:319–331.
Antonoff, N. 1906. *Centr. Bakt., I Abt. Orig.*, **43**:209–212.
Arai, M. 1921. *Biochem. Z.*, **122**:251–257.
Aubel, E., and F. Egami. 1936. *Bull. soc. chim. biol.*, **18**:1542–1550.
Aubel, E. 1938. *Compt. rend. soc. biol.*, **128**:45–46; *Compt. Rend.*, **207**:348–349.
Bainbridge, F. A. 1911. *J. Hyg.*, **11**:341–355.
Baker, J. W., and F. C. Happold. 1940. *Biochem. J.*, **34**:657–663.
Barger, G., and G. S. Walpole. 1909. *J. Physiol.*, **38**:343–352.
Barker, H. A. 1937. *Enzymologia*, **2**:175–182.
Barker, H. A., and J. V. Beck. 1941, 1942. *J. Biol. Chem.*, **141**:3–27; *J. Bact.*, **43**:291–304.
Benton, A. G. 1935. *J. Bact.*, **29**:449–465.
Berger, J., M. J. Johnson, and W. H. Peterson. 1938. *J. Biol. Chem.*, **124**:395–408; *J. Bact.*, **36**:521–545.
Bergmann, M., L. Zervas, H. Schleich, and F. Leinert. 1932. *Z. physiol. Chem.*, **212**:72–84.
Bergmann, M., and J. S. Fruton. 1937. *J. Biol. Chem.*, **117**:189–202.
Berman, N., and L. F. Rettger. 1916. *J. Bact.*, **1**:537–539.
Berman, N., and L. F. Rettger. 1918. *J. Bact.*, **3**:367–388, 389–402.
Bernheim, F., M. L. C. Bernheim, and M. D. Webster. 1935. *J. Biol. Chem.*, **110**:165–172.
Berthelot, A., and D. M. Bertrand. 1911. *Compt. rend.*, **154**:8126–1828.
Berthelot, A. 1917. *Compt. rend.*, **164**:196–199.
Bierema, S. 1909. *Centr. Bakt., II Abt.*, **23**:672–726.
Binkley, F. 1943. *J. Biol. Chem.*, **150**:261–262.
Blanchétière, A. 1916. *Compt. Rend.*, **163**:206–209.
Bodansky, M., V. B. Duff, and M. G. McKinney. 1941. *J. Biol. Chem.*, **140**: 365–371.
Bömeke, H. 1939. *Arch. Mikrobiol.*, **10**:385–445.
Bortels, H. 1940. *Arch. Mikrobiol.*, **11**:155–186.
Brasch, W. 1909. *Biochem. Z.*, **18**:380–390; **22**:403–408.
Braunstein, A. E., and M. G. Kritzmann. 1937. *Enzymologia*, **2**:129–146.
Braunstein, A. E. 1939. *Enzymologia*, **7**:25–52.
Buchanan, R. E., and E. I. Fulmer. 1930. *Physiology and Biochemistry of Bacteria*, vol. III. Williams & Wilkins Co., Baltimore.
Bucherer, H. 1935. *Centr. Bakt., II Abt.*, **93**:12–24.
Burk, D. 1930. *J. Phys. Chem.*, **34**:1174–1194, 1195–1209.
Burk, D., and H. Lineweaver. 1930. *J. Bact.*, **19**:389–414.
Burk, D. 1934. *Ergeb. Enzymforsch.*, **3**:23–56.

Burk, D., H. Lineweaver, and C. K. Horner. 1934. *J. Bact.*, **27**:325–340.
Burk, D., and C. K. Horner. 1939. *Wallerstein Labs. Commun. No.* 6, pp. 5–23.
Burk, D., and R. H. Burris. 1941. *Ann. Rev. Biochem.*, **10**:587–618.
Burris, R. H., and C. E. Miller. 1941. *Science*, **93**:114–115.
Burris, R. H., and P. W. Wilson. 1942. *J. Bact.*, **43**:7.
Burrows, W. 1939. *J. Infectious Diseases*, **65**:134–141.
Campbell, L. K. 1925. *Am. Rev. Tuberc.*, **11**:458–470.
Cardon, B. P. 1942. *Proc. Soc. Exptl. Biol. Med.*, **51**:267–268.
Carpenter, P. L. 1939. *J. Bact.*, **37**:11–20.
Chargaff, E., and D. B. Sprinson. 1943. *J. Biol. Chem.*, **148**:249–250.
Chatterjee, H. N. 1939. *Calcutta Med. J.*, **36**:179–180.
Chrzaszcz, T., and M. Zakomorny. 1934. *Biochem. Z.*, **275**:97–105.
Clawson, B. J., and C. C. Young. 1913. *J. Biol. Chem.*, **15**:419–422.
Clifton, C. E. 1940. *J. Bact.*, **39**:485–497.
Conn, H. J. 1936. *J. Bact.*, **31**:225–233.
Cook, R. P., and B. Woolf. 1928. *Biochem. J.*, **22**:474–481.
Cowie, G. A. 1920. *J. Agr. Sci.*, **10**:163–176.
Darby, W. J., and H. B. Lewis. 1942. *J. Biol. Chem.*, **146**:225–235.
den Dooren de Jong, L. E. 1926. "Bijdrage tot de Kennis van het Mineralisatie-process." Dissertation, Nijgh and van Ditmar, Rotterdam.
den Dooren de Jong, L. E. 1927. *Centr. Bakt., II Abt.*, **71**:193–232.
Desnuelle, P. 1939. *Enzymologia*, **6**:242–245, 387–391.
Desnuelle, P., and C. Fromageot. 1939. *Enzymologia*, **6**:80–87.
Desnuelle, P., E. Wookey, and C. Fromageot. 1940. *Enzymologia*, **8**:225–240.
Difco Laboratories, Inc. (Detroit). 1943. *Manual of Dehydrated Culture Media and Reagents*, 7th Ed. Rev.
Dubos, R. J., and B. F. Miller. 1937. *J. Biol. Chem.*, **121**:429–445.
Eggerth, A. H. 1939. *J. Bact.*, **37**:205–222.
Ehrlich, F. 1905. *Z. Ver. deut. Zucker-Ind.*, **55**:539. (Cited by Ehrlich, 1906.)
Ehrlich, F. 1906. *Biochem. Z.*, **1**:8–31.
Ehrlich, F. 1907. *Ber. deut. chem. Ges.*, **40**:1027–1047, 2538–2562.
Ehrlich, F. 1908. *Biochem. Z.*, **8**:438–466.
Ehrlich, F. 1911, 1912. *Ber. deut. chem. Ges.*, **44**:139–146; **45**:883–889.
Ehrlich, F., and K. A. Jacobsen. 1911. *Ber. deut. chem. Ges.*, **44**:888–897.
Ehrlich, F. 1914. *Biochem. Z.*, **63**:388–401.
Elberg, S. S., and K. F. Meyer. 1939. *J. Bact.*, **37**:541–565.
Ellinger, A. 1899, 1900. *Ber. deut. chem. Ges.*, **31**:3183–3186; **32**:3542–3546.
Ellinger, A. 1900. *Z. physiol. Chem.*, **29**:334–348.
Emerson, H. W., H. P. Cady, and E. H. S. Bailey. 1913. *J. Biol. Chem.*, **15**:415–417.
Emmerling, O. 1897. *Ber. deut. chem. Ges.*, **30**:1863–1868.
Emmerling, O., and O. Reiser. 1902. *Ber. deut. chem. Ges.*, **35**:700–702.
Epps, H. M. R. 1944. *Biochem. J.*, **38**:242–249.
Evans, W. C., W. C. R. Handley, and F. C. Happold. 1942. *Biochem. J.*, **36**:311–318.
Fearon, W. R. 1926. *Physiol. Rev.*, **6**:399–439.
Fearon, W. R. 1936. *Biochem. J.*, **30**:1652–1660.
Fearon, W. R. 1940. *An Introduction to Biochemistry.* C. V. Mosby Co., St. Louis.
Fildes, P. 1940, 1941. *Brit. J. Exptl. Path.*, **21**:315–319; **22**:293–298.

Fish, C. H., and T. D. Beckwith. 1939. *J. Bact.*, **37**:111–120.
Fitzgerald, J. G., and C. L. A. Schmidt. 1912. *Proc. Soc. Exptl. Biol. Med.*, **10**: 55–57.
Fox, S. W. 1943. *Chem. Rev.*, **32**:47–71.
Frazier, W. C., and P. Rupp. 1931. *J. Bact.*, **21**:263–271.
Fromageot, C., and P. Desnuelle. 1938. *Enzymologia*, **5**:57–59.
Fulmer, E. I., and L. M. Christensen. 1925. *J. Phys. Chem.*, **29**:1415–1418.
Gale, E. F. 1938. *Biochem. J.*, **32**:1583–1599.
Gale, E. F., and M. Stephenson. 1938, 1939. *Biochem. J.*, **32**:392–404; **33**:1245–1256.
Gale, E. F. 1940. *Bact. Rev.*, **4**:135–176.
Gale, E. F. 1940, 1941, 1942. *Biochem. J.*, **34**:392–413, 846–852, 853–857; **35**. 66–79; **36**:64–75.
Gale, E. F., and H. M. R. Epps. 1944. *Biochem. J.*, **38**:232–242, 250–256.
Geiger, E. 1944. *Proc. Soc. Exptl. Biol. Med.*, **55**:11–13.
Georgi, C. E. 1935. *J. Agr. Research*, **51**:597–612.
Gibson, T. 1934, 1935. *J. Bact.*, **28**:295–311, 313–322; **29**:491–502.
Gibson, T. 1935. *Arch. Mikrobiol.*, **6**:73–78; *Centr. Bakt., II Abt.*, **92**:364–380.
Gorbach, G. 1930. *Arch. Mikrobiol.*, **1**:537–576.
Gray, P. H. H. 1928. *Proc. Roy. Soc. London, B*, **102**:263–280.
Habild, G. 1939. *Z. Biol.*, **99**:421–430.
Hanke, M. T., and K. K. Koessler. 1924. *J. Biol. Chem.*, **59**:835–853, 855–866, 867–877.
Happold, F. C., and L. Hoyle. 1935. *Biochem. J.*, **29**:1918–1926.
Happold, F. C., and L. Hoyle. 1936. *Brit. J. Exptl. Path.*, **17**:136–143.
Happold, F. C., and A. Key. 1937. *Biochem. J.*, **31**:1323–1329.
Hills, G. M. 1940. *Biochem. J.*, **34**:1057–1069.
Hirai, K. 1919. *Acta Schol. Med. Univ. Imp. Kioto*, **3**:49–53.
Hirai, K. 1921. *Biochem. Z.*, **114**:71–80.
Hirai, K. 1939. *J. Biochem., Japan*, **29**:435–438.
Hock, C. W. 1940. *Biol. Bull.*, **79**:199–206.
Hock, C. W. 1941. *J. Marine Research*, **4**:99–106.
Hoogerheide, J. C., and W. Kocholaty. 1938. *Biochem. J.*, **32**:949–957.
Hook, A. E., and F. W. Fabian. 1941, 1943. *J. Bact.*, **41**:30–31; *Mich. Agr. Expt. Sta. Tech. Bull.* 185, pp. 1–34.
Hopkins, F. G., and S. W. Cole. 1903. *J. Physiol.*, **29**:451–466.
Horn, F. 1933. *Z. physiol. Chem.*, **216**:244–247.
Horner, C. K., D. Burk, F. E. Allison, and M. S. Sherman. 1942. *J. Agr. Research*, **65**:173–193.
Hucker, G. J. 1924, 1928. *N. Y. (Geneva) Agr. Expt. Sta. Tech. Bull.* 101, pp. 1–47; 141, pp. 1–13.
Hunter, C. A., and H. G. Crecelius. 1938. *J. Bact.*, **35**:185–196.
Imaizumi, M. 1938. *J. Biochem. (Japan)*, **27**:45–64, 65–79, 199–211, 213–225, 227–230.
Iwanoff, N. N. 1913. *Biochem. Z.*, **58**:217–224.
Iwanoff, N. N., and M. I. Smirnowa. 1927. *Biochem. Z.*, **181**:8–16.
Iwanoff, N. N., and A. N. Awetissowa. 1931. *Biochem. Z.*, **231**:67–78.
Iwanoff, N. N., and E. S. Zwetkoff. 1936. *Ann. Rev. Biochem.*, **5**:585–612.
Janke, A. 1930. *Arch. Mikrobiol.*, **1**:304–332.
Janke, A., and W. Tayenthal. 1937. *Biochem. Z.*, **289**:76–86.

Johnson, M. J., and J. Berger. 1942. *Advances in Enzymol.*, **2**:69–92.
Kemmerer, K. S., and G. P. Heil. 1941. *J. Lab. Clin. Med.*, **27**:260–263.
Kendall, A. I., and A. W. Walker. 1915. *J. Infectious Diseases*, **17**:442–453.
Kendall, A. I. 1922. *J. Infectious Diseases*, **30**:211–224.
Kendall, A. I. 1923. *Physiol. Rev.*, **3**:438–455.
Kendall, A. I., and E. Gebauer. 1930. *J. Infectious Diseases*, **47**:261–266.
Kiyokawa, M. 1933. *Z. physiol. Chem.*, **214**:38–41.
Klein, J. R. 1940. *J. Biol. Chem.*, **134**:43–57.
Kluyver, A. J., and H. J. L. Donker. 1926. *Chem. Zelle Gewebe.*, **13**:134–190.
Koessler, K. K., and M. T. Hanke. 1919. *J. Biol. Chem.*, **39**:539–584.
Koessler, K. K., M. T. Hanke, and M. S. Sheppard. 1928. *J. Infectious Diseases*, **43**:363–377.
Kondo, M. 1923. *Biochem. Z.*, **136**:198.
Koser, S. A. 1918. *J. Infectious Diseases*, **23**:377–379.
Kotake, Y., and associates. 1931, 1933. *Z. physiol. Chem.*, **195**:139–214; **214**:1–32.
Krebs, H. A., and L. V. Eggleston. 1940. *Enzymologia*, **7**:310–320.
Krebs, H. A. 1942. *Biochem. J.*, **36**:758–767, VIII, IX.
Krebs, H. A., M. M. Hafez, and L. V. Eggleston. 1942. *Biochem. J.*, **36**:306–310.
Krishnan, K. V., and E. K. Narayanan. 1941. *Indian J. Med. Res.*, **29**:541–545.
Leifson, E. 1941. *J. Bact.*, **41**:31.
Leuthardt, F. 1938. *Z. physiol. Chem.*, **252**:238–260.
Lichstein, H. C., and P. P. Cohen. 1945. *J. Biol. Chem.*, **157**:85–91.
Lieb, F., and B. Vallender. 1939. *Centr. Bakt., I Abt. Orig.*, **144**:528–530.
Lind, C. J., and P. W. Wilson. 1942. *Arch. Biochem.*, **1**:59–72.
Lindsey, G. A., and C. M. Rhines. 1932. *J. Bact.*, **24**:489–492.
Lineweaver, H. 1932. *J. Biol. Chem.*, **99**:575–593.
Linneweh, F. 1930. *Z. Biol.*, **90**:109–112.
Löhnis, F., and A. Sabaschnikoff. 1908. *Centr. Bakt., II Abt.*, **20**:322–332.
Ludwig, C. A. 1938. *Am. J. Botany*, **25**:448–458.
Lutwak-Mann, C. 1936. *Biochem. J.*, **30**:1405–1412.
Lutwak-Mann, C. 1941. *Biochem. J.*, **35**:610–626.
McAlpine, J. G., and G. D. Brigham. 1928. *J. Bact.*, **16**:251–256.
McCrudden, F. H. 1910. *J. Biol. Chem.*, **8**:109–114.
Majima, S. 1936. *Z. physiol. Chem.*, **243**:247–253.
Mannozzi-Torini, M., and R. Vendramini. 1941. *Boll. ist. sieroterap. milan.*, **20**:4–12, 13–18 (*Chem. Abstr.*, **35**:7444).
Maschmann, E. 1937–1939. *Biochem. Z.*, **294**:1–33; **295**:1–10, 351–368, 391–399, 400–401; **297**:284–296; **302**:332–368.
Meyer, K. 1913. *Biochem. Z.*, **57**:297–299.
Meyerhof, O., and D. Burk. 1928. *Z. physik. Chem., Abt. A*, **139**:117–142.
Meyers, F. P., and J. R. Porter. 1944. *J. Bact.*, **47**:435.
Miller, B. F., M. J. C. Allinson, and Z. Baker. 1939. *J. Biol. Chem.*, **130**:383–391.
Mischoustin, E. N. 1932. *Centr. Bakt., II Abt.*, **87**:150–166.
Mitchell, N. B., and M. Levine. 1938. *J. Bact.*, **36**:587–598.
Miyaji, K. 1925. *J. Chem. Soc. Japan*, **45**:391–450 (1926. *Chem. Abstr.*, **20**:2870).
Müller, A. 1857. *J. prakt. Chem.*, **70**:65–69.

Nawiasky, P. 1908. *Arch. Hyg.*, **66**:209–243.
Nencki, M. 1880. *Z. physiol. Chem.*, **4**:371–372.
Neuberg, C., and L. Karczag. 1909. *Biochem. Z.*, **18**:435–439.
Neuberg, C. 1911. *Biochem. Z.*, **37**:501–506.
Neuberg, C., and F. F. Nord. 1914. *Biochem. Z.*, **62**:482–488.
Neuberg, C., and W. H. Peterson. 1914. *Biochem. Z.*, **67**:32–45.
Neuberg, C., and M. Ringer. 1918. *Biochem. Z.*, **91**:131–136.
Niven, C. F., Jr., K. L. Smiley, and J. M. Sherman. 1942. *J. Bact.*, **43**:651–660.
Nord, F. F. 1919. *Biochem. Z.*, **95**:281–285.
Otani, Z., and K. Ichihara. 1925. *Folia Pharmacol. Japon.*, **1**:397–405.
Perotti, R. 1908. *Centr. Bakt., II Abt.*, **21**:200–231.
Pickett, M. J. 1943. *J. Biol. Chem.*, **151**:203–209.
Pringsheim, H. 1908. *Biochem. Z.*, **8**:128–131.
Quastel, J. H., and B. Woolf. 1926. *Biochem. J.*, **20**:545–555.
Raistrick, H. 1917, 1919. *Biochem. J.*, **11**:71–77; **13**:446–458.
Raistrick, H., and A. B. Clark. 1921. *Biochem. J.*, **15**:76–82.
Randall, W. A., and R. J. Reedy. 1939. *J. Lab. Clin. Med.*, **25**:315–316.
Ransmeier, J. C., and J. A. Stekol. 1942. *Proc. Soc. Exptl. Biol. Med.*, **51**:85–88, 92–94.
Rettger, L. F., N. Berman, and W. S. Sturges. 1916. *J. Bact.*, **1**:15–33.
Reuter, C. 1912. *Z. physiol. Chem.*, **78**:167–245.
Rhein, M. 1918, 1922. *Biochem. Z.*, **87**:123–128; *Compt. rend. soc. biol.*, **87**:575–577.
Robinson, R. H., and H. V. Tartar. 1917. *J. Biol. Chem.*, **30**:135–144.
Rose, W. C., W. J. Haines, J. E. Johnson, and D. T. Warner. 1943. *J. Biol. Chem.*, **148**:457–458.
Ruben, S., W. Z. Hassid, and M. D. Kamen. 1940. *Science*, **91**:578–579.
Rubentschik, L. 1925. *Centr. Bakt., II Abt.*, **64**:166–174; **65**:1–15.
Rubentschik, L. 1926. *Centr. Bakt., II Abt.*, **66**:161–180; **67**:167–194; **68**:161–179.
Rustigian, R., and C. A. Stuart. 1941. *Proc. Soc. Exptl. Biol. Med.*, **47**:108–112.
Sakaguchi, K., and Y. Shizume. 1937. *J. Agr. Chem. Soc. Japan*, **13**:309–312.
Salkowski, E., and H. Salkowski. 1879. *Ber. deut. chem. Ges.*, **12**:107–108, 648–655, 1438–1441.
Sasaki, T., and I. Otsuka. 1912, 1921. *Biochem. Z.*, **39**:208–215; **121**:167–170.
Sasaki, T. 1914. *Biochem. Z.*, **59**:429–435.
Sasaki, T. 1923. *J. Biochem. (Japan)*, **2**:251–254.
Schmidt, E. G., W. H. Peterson, and E. B. Fred. 1924. *J. Biol. Chem.*, **61**:163–175.
Schoenheimer, R. 1942. *The Dynamic State of Body Constituents.* Harvard University Press, Cambridge, Mass.
Schulte, T. L., and G. J. Thompson. 1941. *J. Urol.*, **45**:733–743.
Sears, H. J. 1916. *J. Infectious Diseases*, **19**:105–137.
Sears, H. J. 1917. *J. Bact.*, **2**:187–189.
Snell, E. E. 1943. *Arch. Biochem.*, **2**:389–394.
Sperry, J. A., and L. F. Rettger. 1915. *J. Biol. Chem.*, **20**:445–459.
Starkey, R. L. 1939. *Trans. 3rd Comm. Intern. Soc. Soil Sci.*, *A*:142–150.
Steinberg, R. A. 1938. *J. Agr. Research*, **57**:461–476.
Stekol, J. A., and J. C. Ransmeier. 1942. *Proc. Soc. Exptl. Biol. Med.*, **51**:88–91.
Stephenson, M., and E. F. Gale. 1937. *Biochem. J.*, **31**:1316–1322.
Stephenson, M. 1939. *Bacterial Metabolism.* Longmans, Green and Co., New York.

Stickland, L. H. 1934, 1935. *Biochem. J.*, **28**:1746–1759; **29**:889–898.
Stuart, L. S. 1936. *J. Am. Leather Chem. Assoc.*, **31**:119–120.
Sullivan, W. K. 1858. *Jahresber. Chemie*, **1858**:230–231.
Tanner, F. W. 1918. *J. Am. Chem. Soc.*, **40**:663–669.
Tarr, H. L. A. 1933, 1934. *Biochem. J.*, **27**:759–763, 1869–1874; **28**:192–198.
Tarr, H. L. A. 1941. *J. Fisheries Research Board Can.*, **5**:265–275.
Tatum, E. L., and D. M. Bonner. 1943. *J. Biol. Chem.*, **151**:349.
Thorne, R. S. W. 1937. *J. Inst. Brewing*, **43**:288–293.
Tittsler, R. P., and L. A. Sandholzer. 1937. *Am. J. Pub. Health*, **27**:1240–1242.
Topshteĭn, R. E. 1940. *Microbiology (U.S.S.R.)*, **9**:197–205.
Traetta Mosca, F. 1910. *Gazz. chim. ital.*, **40**:85–102.
Treece, E. L. 1928. *J. Infectious Diseases*, **42**:495–500.
Uemura, T. 1937. *J. Agr. Chem. Soc. Japan*, **13**:1146–1158.
Utermohlen, W. P., Jr., and C. E. Georgi. 1940. *J. Bact.*, **40**:449–459.
Utzino, S., M. Imaizumi, and M. Nakayama. 1938. *J. Biochem. (Japan)*, **27**: 257–264.
Vaughan, S. L. 1939. *J. Lab. Clin. Med.*, **24**:696–700.
Vaughn, R. H., and M. Levine. 1936. *J. Bact.*, **32**:65–73.
Vickery, H. B. 1941. *Annals N. Y. Acad. Sci.*, **41**:87–120.
Virtanen, A. I., and J. Tarnanen. 1932. *Biochem. Z.*, **250**:193–211.
Virtanen, A. I., and T. Laine. 1937. *Enzymologia*, **3**:266–270.
Virtanen, A. I., and J. Erkama. 1938. *Nature*, **142**:954.
Virtanen, A. I., and T. Laine. 1939. *Biochem. J.*, **33**:412–427.
Virtanen, A. I., T. Laine, and P. Rintala. 1940. *Enzymologia*, **9**:53–58.
Waksman, S. A. 1920. *J. Bact.*, **5**:1–30.
Waksman, S. A., and S. Lomanitz. 1925. *J. Agr. Research*, **30**:263–281.
Waksman, S. A. 1932. *Principles of Soil Microbiology*, 2nd Ed. Williams & Wilkins Co., Baltimore.
Waksman, S. A., and R. L. Starkey. 1932. *J. Bact.*, **23**:405–428.
Webster, M. D., and F. Bernheim. 1936. *J. Biol. Chem.*, **114**:265–271.
White, E. C., and J. H. Hill. 1941. *J. Urol.*, **45**:744–749, 749–759.
Wilson, J. B., and P. W. Wilson. 1941. *J. Bact.*, **42**:141–142.
Wilson, P. W., W. W. Umbreit, and S. B. Lee. 1938. *Biochem. J.*, **32**:2084–2095.
Wilson, P. W. 1940. *The Biochemistry of Symbiotic Nitrogen Fixation.* University of Wisconsin Press, Madison, Wisconsin.
Wirth, J. C., and F. F. Nord. 1943. *Arch. Biochem.*, **2**:463–468.
Wohlfeil, T., and P. Weiland. 1937. *Centr. Bakt., I Abt. Orig.*, **138**:388–400.
Wohlgemuth, J. 1905. *Z. physiol. Chem.*, **43**:469–475.
Woods, D. D. 1935. *Biochem. J.*, **29**:640–648, 649–655.
Woods, D. D. 1936, 1938. *Biochem. J.*, **30**:1934–1946; **32**:2000–2012.
Woods, D. D., and C. E. Clifton. 1937, 1938. *Biochem. J.*, **31**:1774–1788; **32**: 345–356.
Woods, D. D., and A. R. Trim. 1942. *Biochem. J.*, **36**:501–512.
Woolf, B. 1929. *Biochem. J.*, **23**:472–482.
Wyss, O., C. J. Lind, J. B. Wilson, and P. W. Wilson. 1941. *Biochem. J.*, **35**: 845–854.
Wyss, O., and P. W. Wilson. 1941. *Proc. Natl. Acad. Sci. U. S.*, **27**:162–168.
Yamagata, S. 1938. *Acta Phytochim. (Japan)*, **10**:283–295.
Zobell, C. E. 1932. *J. Bact.*, **24**:273–281.
Zobell, C. E., and C. B. Feltham. 1934. *J. Bact.*, **28**:169–176.
Zobell, C. E., and S. C. Rittenberg. 1938. *J. Bact.*, **35**:275–287.

10

MICROBIAL FERMENTATIONS

This chapter will be restricted to a brief discussion of certain microbial fermentations which are concerned with the production of *definite chemical compounds*. Some of the various reactions which may be considered in a broad sense as fermentations take place during the manufacture of alcoholic beverages; the preparation of certain foods, such as sauerkraut, pickles, cheeses, fermented milks, silage, and leavening agents; the making of legume cultures; the manufacture of some pharmaceutical materials, such as penicillin and streptomycin; the processing of hides and skins; the retting of flax and hemp and other processes in textile microbiology; and the curing of tobacco, tea, and other products. These fermentations, however, will not be discussed here, because some of them are not too well understood microbiologically, and others should be treated in courses in food, soil, dairy, pharmaceutical, and textile microbiology.

The word fermentation has undergone numerous changes in meaning during the past hundred years. According to derivation, it means merely a gentle bubbling or boiling condition, and it was in this sense that the term was first applied to the reactions occurring during the production of wine and other alcoholic beverages. After Gay-Lussac's studies of these processes the meaning was changed to signify the breakdown of sugar into alcohol and carbon dioxide, and after Pasteur's researches the word became more closely associated with microorganisms or their enzymes causing this breakdown.

A fermentation, in the broad sense in which the term is now used, may be defined as a metabolic process in which chemical changes are brought about in the organic substrate through the activities of enzymes secreted by microorganisms or other cells. The chemical changes produced by such activities depend upon the type of organism involved, the kind of substrate, and other factors, such as *p*H and oxygen supply. In respect to the oxygen supply two types of fermentation are recognized: *aerobic fermentation* (oxybiontic or aerobic processes; respiration), in which the dissimilation of the substrate is accompanied by absorption of oxygen, which acts as a hydrogen acceptor (for example, acetic acid fermentation and citric acid fermentation); and *anaerobic* *fermentation,* in which atmospheric oxygen does not take part, but other substances, such as aldehydes or pyruvic acid, serve as acceptors of hydrogen. Yeasts, certain bacteria, and some molds are capable of producing fermentations of this second type (for example, alcoholic fermentation, acetone-butyl alcohol fermentation, and lactic acid fermentation).

Certain of the fermentation processes are well established on an industrial basis, and some others offer interesting possibilities. This point is indicated by the fact that the bibliography compiled by Fulmer and Werkman (1930) lists 112 different chemical compounds which arise from the action of various microorganisms on nonnitrogenous organic compounds and by the fact that since 1930 a large number of new products have been discovered and studied by various workers, among whom Raistrick and his associates in England are outstanding.

In view of the variety of compounds which it is possible to produce by fermentation processes it might be assumed that a large number of organic chemicals would be manufactured by fermentation methods.

TABLE 1

THE RECENT DOMESTIC PRODUCTION OF CHEMICALS DERIVED ENTIRELY OR PARTIALLY FROM FERMENTATION INDUSTRIES

[From Wells and Ward (1939)]

Chemical	Number of Establishments	Production	Sales, pounds	Value, dollars
Acetone	6 *	201,506,334 lb. †	121,172,975 †	5,571,188 †
Butyl alcohols, total	6	164,568,813 lb. †	61,313,850 †	4,621,665 †
Calcium lactate	2			
Calcium gluconate	1	500,000 lb. ‡		
Citric acid	3 or 4	10,493,068 lb.		2,768,377
Ethyl alcohol				
Synthetic	1	70,000,000 § proof gal.		
Total	38	515,000,000 § proof gal.		
Lactic acid				
Edible	5		1,492,301 †	309,324
Medicinal	2			
Technical	5	1,869,365 lb. †	1,671,237 †	212,276
Sorbose		100,000 lb. ‡		

* Probably 2 or 3 synthetic plants.

† Wells and Ward's figures corrected to 1940 values [*U. S. Tariff Comm. Rept.* 148 (1940)].

‡ Private unofficial estimate.

§ Figures listed by Liebmann for 1943 in *Wallerstein Labs. Commun.* (1942), **5**:136.

However, this assumption is not justified, and an appraisal of the situation indicates that an expanded biochemical industry in this country is unlikely for some time. Deterrents may either be inherent in certain biological processes in the form of excessive operational cost, unavailability of suitable raw materials, low yields, or sluggish fermentations or may appear as competitive synthetic chemical processes. On the other hand, the economic success of several fermentative reactions which are concerned with the production of definite chemical compounds is well recognized (see Table 1), and more possibilities appear as time passes. Such success is due to several causes. Among them are the ability of the selected organism to give a high and consistent yield of the desired product in a reasonable time from a cheap, available raw substrate, the easy recovery of the product in a pure form, and, often the decisive factor, the production of a unique product which is in demand but which it is difficult to obtain by other methods.

Three groups of organisms are of service in the fermentation industries. Yeasts are utilized in the production of ethyl alcohol, alcoholic beverages, leavening agents, and yeast concentrates and may be employed to produce glycerol; bacteria are of use in the preparation of butyl alcohol, acetone and other solvents, lactic and other acids, 2:3-butylene glycol, sorbose, and other products; and molds are employed in the manufacture of citric acid, gluconic acid, gallic acid, kojic acid, and miscellaneous products.

A. YEAST FERMENTATIONS

Various yeasts are used extensively in the fermentation industry for the production of industrial ethyl alcohol and, to a very small extent, glycerol; the manufacture of malt beverages (brewing), wines, and distilled spirits; and the production of miscellaneous products, such as leavening agents and vitamin concentrates. The fermentations concerned in the production of pure chemicals will be discussed briefly; for additional reading the references and the books *Industrial Microbiology* by Prescott and Dunn (1940) and *Enzyme Technology* by Tauber (1943) should be consulted.

INDUSTRIAL ALCOHOL PRODUCTION (ALCOHOLIC FERMENTATION)

The term industrial alcohol implies the industrial use of ethyl alcohol. Ethyl alcohol or ethanol ($CH_3 \cdot CH_2OH$) is probably one of the world's oldest and best-known chemical compounds. The word alcohol itself is derived from two Arabic words, *al* and *kohl*, which were first used to denote a finely ground powder employed by Oriental women to darken their eyebrows. It is believed that the word alcohol came into being because of the resemblance between the methods used to obtain these fine powders and those used for the distilling of "spirits." About A.D. 1500 the word was adopted for a volatile liquid, and gradually the name became restricted to the product that is known today as ethyl alcohol.

So extensive is the use of ethyl alcohol in industry and in the arts and sciences that, with the exception of water, it may be regarded as the most important accessory chemical employed today. The diversified products in which it is used comprise an almost endless list, ranging from high explosives to synthetic rubber and blends of alcohol and gasoline for motor fuels, from perfumes to cleaning fluids, from food flavorings to shellac, from baby rattles to embalming fluid, from medicines to tobacco (see the discussion on the uses of alcohol, p. 927, in this chapter). Probably everyone depends in one way or another on the ability of yeast to convert sugars to alcohol and other end products.

The quantity of pure alcohol produced in the United States has steadily increased during the past 20 years. In 1920 the industrial alcohol plants in operation produced 18,933,551 proof gal.;[1] in 1930, 191,859,342 proof gal.; in 1937, 223,181,228 proof gal.; and in 1941, 298,845,417 proof gal. For 1943 Liebmann (1942) estimated the total production figures as follows:

Source	*Quantity, million proof gallons*
Industrial alcohol plants (from molasses and grains)	225
Whisky distilleries	
High-proof alcohol	120
High wines for redistilling	100
Synthetic alcohol (from ethylene gas)	70
Total	515

It has been estimated that 609,000,000 gal. of industrial alcohol was manufactured in 1944.

The states in this country producing the largest amounts of alcohol in 1941 were Pennsylvania, Louisiana, New Jersey, West Virginia,

[1] Proof is an old English term for strength or quality of spirit. In the United States, for example, 100 proof spirit contains 50 per cent by volume of alcohol. In other countries alcoholic strengths are frequently measured by other systems. Proof gallons divided by 1.9 equals United States wine gallons of 95 per cent concentration; units are based upon spirits at 60°F. (15.5°C.), at which temperature ethyl alcohol has a specific gravity of 0.7939.

Maryland, and Indiana, in the order named; their production accounted for 90.4 per cent of the total given in Table 2.

Raw Materials Used for Alcohol Production.[2] The most important raw materials used for producing ethyl alcohol may be allocated to the following four groups:

TABLE 2

ETHYL ALCOHOL PRODUCTION, BY KINDS OF MATERIALS USED, IN THE UNITED STATES AND TERRITORIES FOR THE FISCAL YEAR 1941 *

Kind of Material	Quantity Used	Alcohol Produced	
		proof gallons	per cent of total
Molasses †	220,898,526 gal.	210,426,805	70.41
Ethyl sulfate	53,399,664 gal.	69,902,800	23.39
Grain †	199,119,727 lb.	17,532,441	5.87
Pineapple juice	1,831,381 gal.	227,326	0.08
Cellulose pulp, chemical and crude alcohol mixtures			
Crude alcohol mixture	2,365,256 gal.		
Cellulose pulp and chemical mixtures	15,365,950 lb.	575,730	0.19
Other mixtures			
Molasses	921,866 gal.		
Corn sugar by-product	2,245,793 lb.		
Malt	1,265,953 lb.		
Corn	1,110,284 lb.	180,315 ‡	0.06
Potatoes	686,585 lb.		
Barley	8,758 lb.		
Bran	5,894 lb.		
Total		298,845,417	100.00

* United States Treasury Department, Bureau of Internal Revenue, Alcohol Tax Unit, Statistics on Alcohol for Fiscal Year Ending June 30, 1941. Released February 5, 1942.

† Additional amounts used in combination with other materials.

‡ Includes 1,045 proof gal. produced at experimental plants from materials not shown.

1. Saccharine materials, such as blackstrap molasses, sugar beet, sugar cane, fruit juices, and cheese whey.

2. Starchy materials, such as potatoes, Jerusalem artichokes, cassava, and cereals (corn, rye, wheat, barley, rice, etc.).

[2] For additional information on this subject Jacobs and Newton (1938), Beresford and Christensen (1941), and Willkie and Kolachov (1942) should be consulted

3. Cellulose-containing materials, such as wood pulp, and waste sulfite liquor.

4. Ethylene and acetylene gases and other substances—synthetic processes.

In normal times about 70 to 75 per cent of the industrial alcohol produced in this country is derived from the fermentation of molasses; a variety of products make up the source of the remaining percentage (Table 2). The production of industrial alcohol from molasses practically ceased in this country in 1942 because of the difficulty of obtaining molasses; however, many plants readily converted to the use of grain products, particularly corn and granular wheat flour [see Singleton (1943), Unger (1943), Keyes (1943), and Handren (1943)]. Thus in 1943 about 62 per cent of the industrial alcohol produced in this country was made from grains and 23 per cent from molasses; 14 per cent was prepared synthetically.

In other countries different types of raw products are utilized for the production of alcohol by fermentation methods. For example, in Germany potatoes have been used for many years as the chief raw material; in France and Italy sugar beets and fruit juices are employed; and in Sweden and Norway wood and waste sulfite liquor from wood pulp mills are the chief raw products utilized. Alcohol has been produced in Sweden from sulfite liquor for over 35 years; the planned output for 1941 was 18,500,000 gal. [Hanson (1942)].

Whereas the manufacturer is mainly concerned with the yield of alcohol per ton of raw material used, the farmer is interested in the yield per acre. The following figures show the probable average alcohol yield per ton and per acre of some raw products:

Average Yield of 99.5 Per Cent Alcohol, gallons

	Ton	*Acre*		*Ton*	*Acre*
Wheat	85.0	33.0	Potatoes, sweet	34.2	141.0
Corn	84.0	88.8	Potatoes, white	22.9	178.0
Raisins	81.4	102.0	Sugar beets	22.1	287.0
Rye	78.8	23.8	Jerusalem artichokes	20.0	180.0
Molasses (blackstrap)	70.4	45.0	Sugar cane (Louisiana)	15.2	268.0
Sorghum cane	70.4	26.4	Grapes	15.1	90.4
Oats	63.6	36.3	Carrots	9.8	121.0

These figures were calculated by Jacobs and Newton (1938) and are cited merely to show the relative importance or value of certain crops for alcohol production. Wood pulp and other cellulose-containing substances offer great possibilities as raw materials for the production of industrial alcohol and other organic solvents. Scholler (1936), Bergius (1937), Giordani (1939), Wiley, Johnson, McCoy, and Peterson (1941), Rosten (1941), Hanson (1942), and Wise (1943), for example, have described methods for the production of alcohol and many other by-products from wood and waste sulfite liquor.

It is also very important to have an adequate supply of water available for the manufacture of industrial alcohol. Some idea of the quantity needed can be realized from the following table of water and steam requirements of a modern grain distillery producing high-proof alcohol [Boruff, Smith, and Walker (1943)]:

	Water per Bushel of Grain Processed, gallons	*Steam per Bushel of Grain Processed,* pounds
Processing		
Cooking (batch-pressure) and sterilizing	36	36
Mash coolers	78	...
Fermenter cooling coils	70	...
Stills, high-proof alcohol	94	100
Stillage recovery (screenings and solubles)		
Evaporators, stillage	430	87
Dryers	...	55
Carbon dioxide recovery, powerhouse, administration, etc.	57	...
Total	765	278

Special treatment of the water is often necessary; this requirement depends on its composition and usage.

Outline of the Industrial Fermentation Process. The production of ethyl alcohol by fermentation methods will be discussed under the following five headings: (1) preliminary treatment of raw materials; (2) preparation of starter (yeast culture development); (3) fermentation of the mash; (4) distilling and refining the alcohol; and (5) by-products (slop waste and fusel oil). Although efficient production of alcohol depends upon all of the first four operations, the general statement can be made that, after the preliminary adjustments in the various raw materials, the method of fermentation and the technique for the recovery of the alcohol from different substrates are quite similar.

1. Preliminary Treatment of Raw Materials. The procedure followed in the production of ethyl alcohol by fermentation methods depends partly upon the kind of raw material used. A few examples may be cited to illustrate this point. Figures 1 and 2 show also the preliminary steps necessary for the treatment of potatoes, corn, and molasses before they can be fermented by yeast.

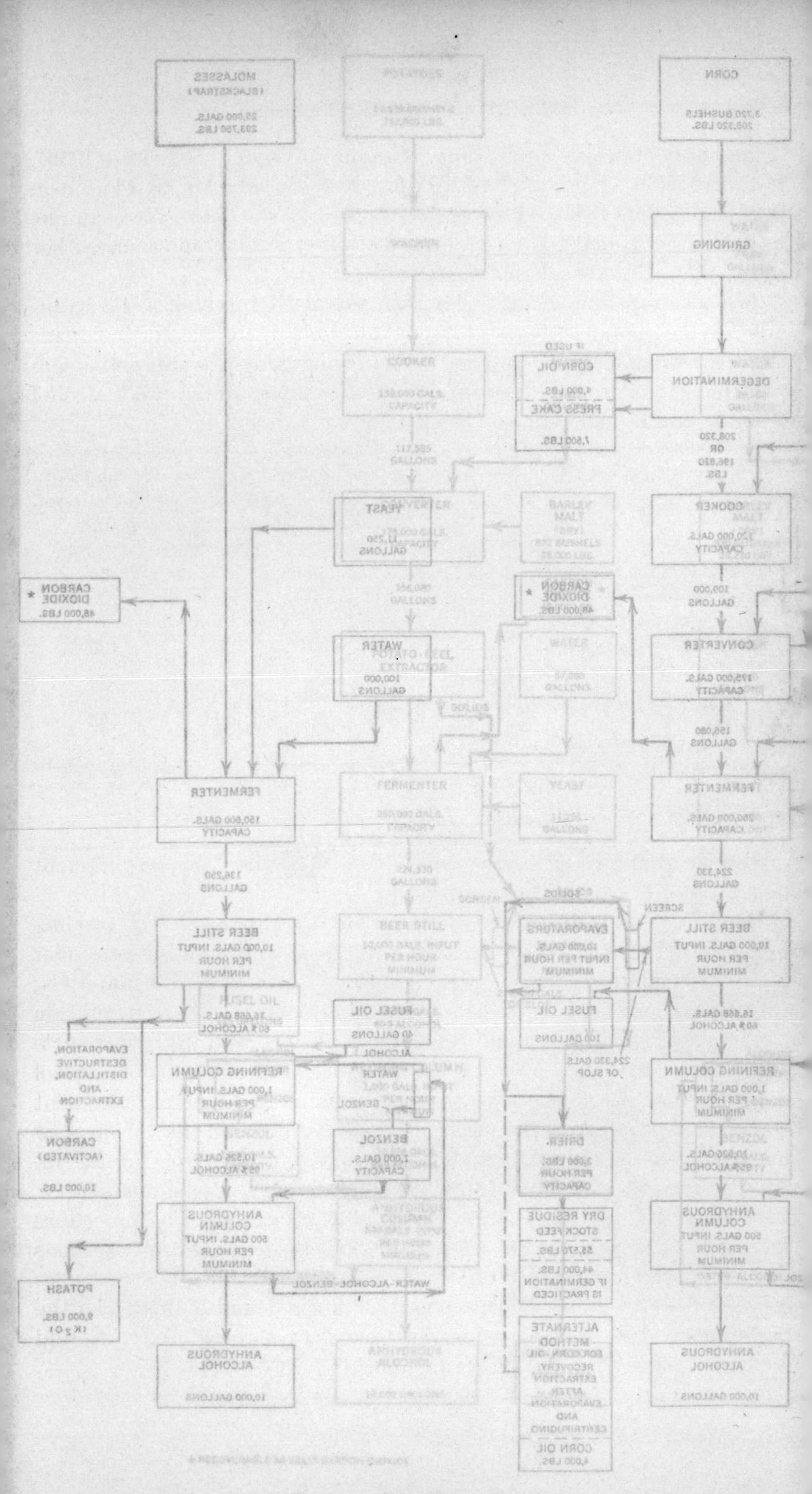

From Potatoes, Corn, and Molasses. (From Jacobs and Newton, 1938.)

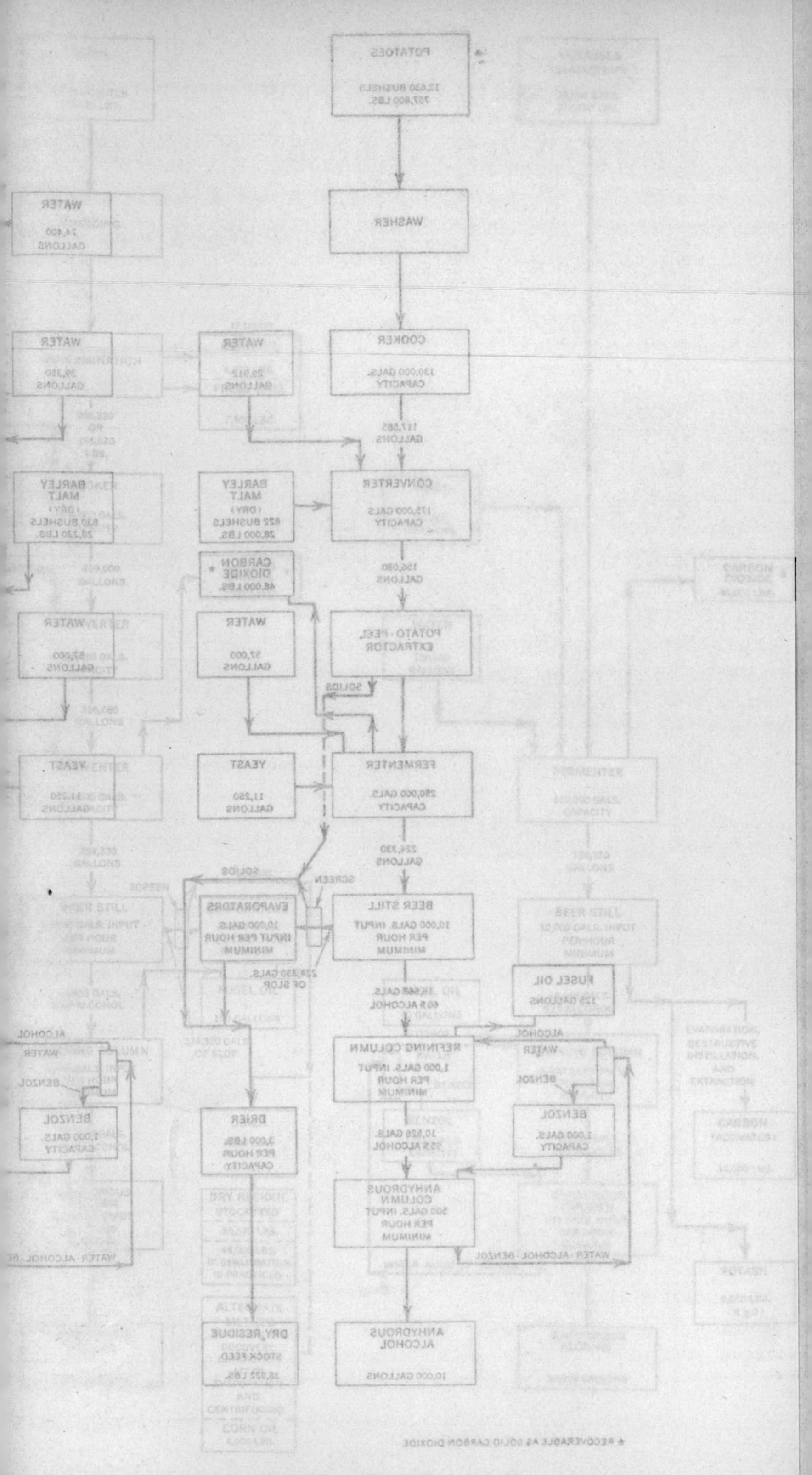

Fig. 1. Flow Sheet Showing the Production of Alcohol [illegible] Newton, 1938.)

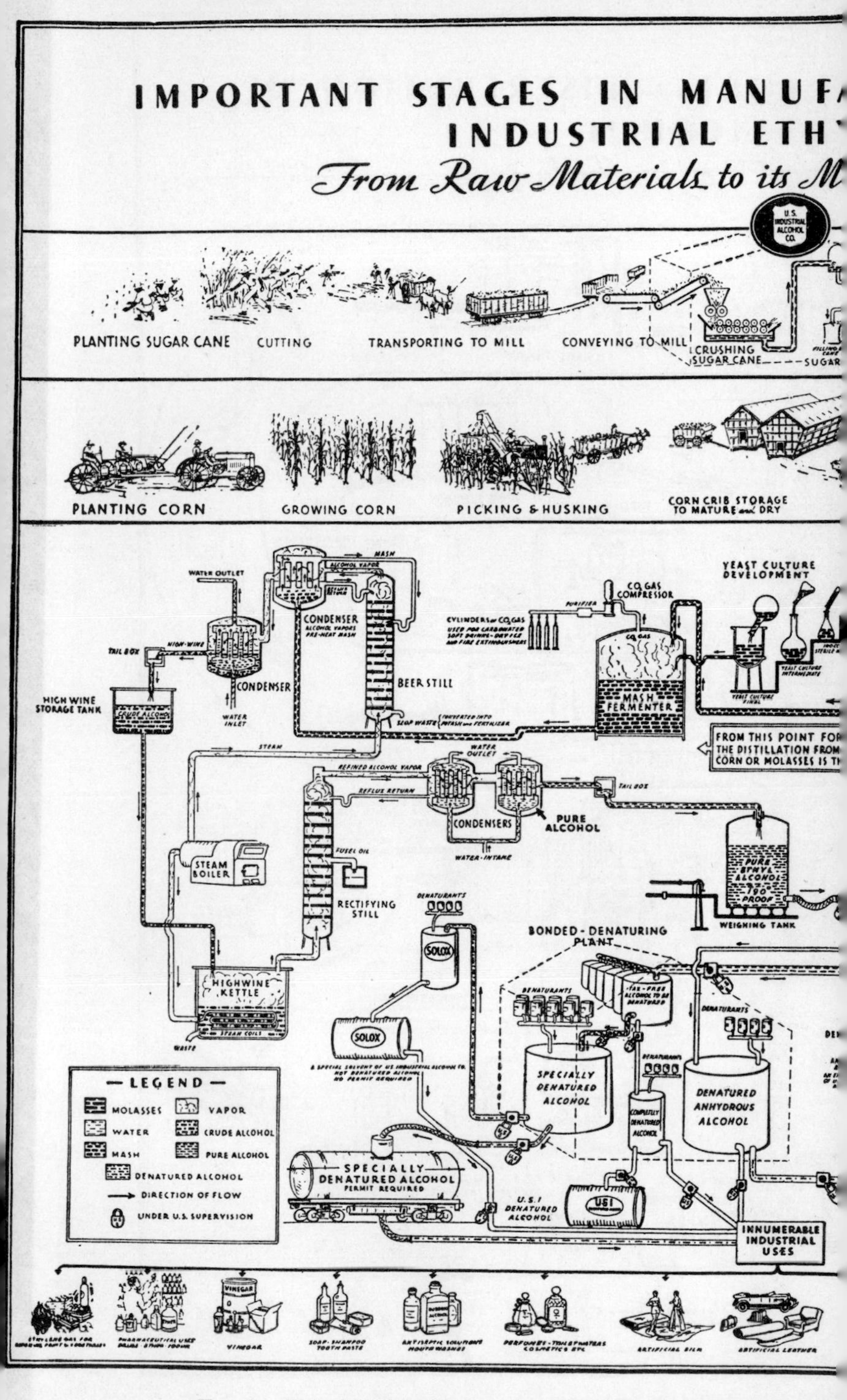

FIG. 2. Pictorial Flow Sheet of Industrial Alcohol Manufacture.

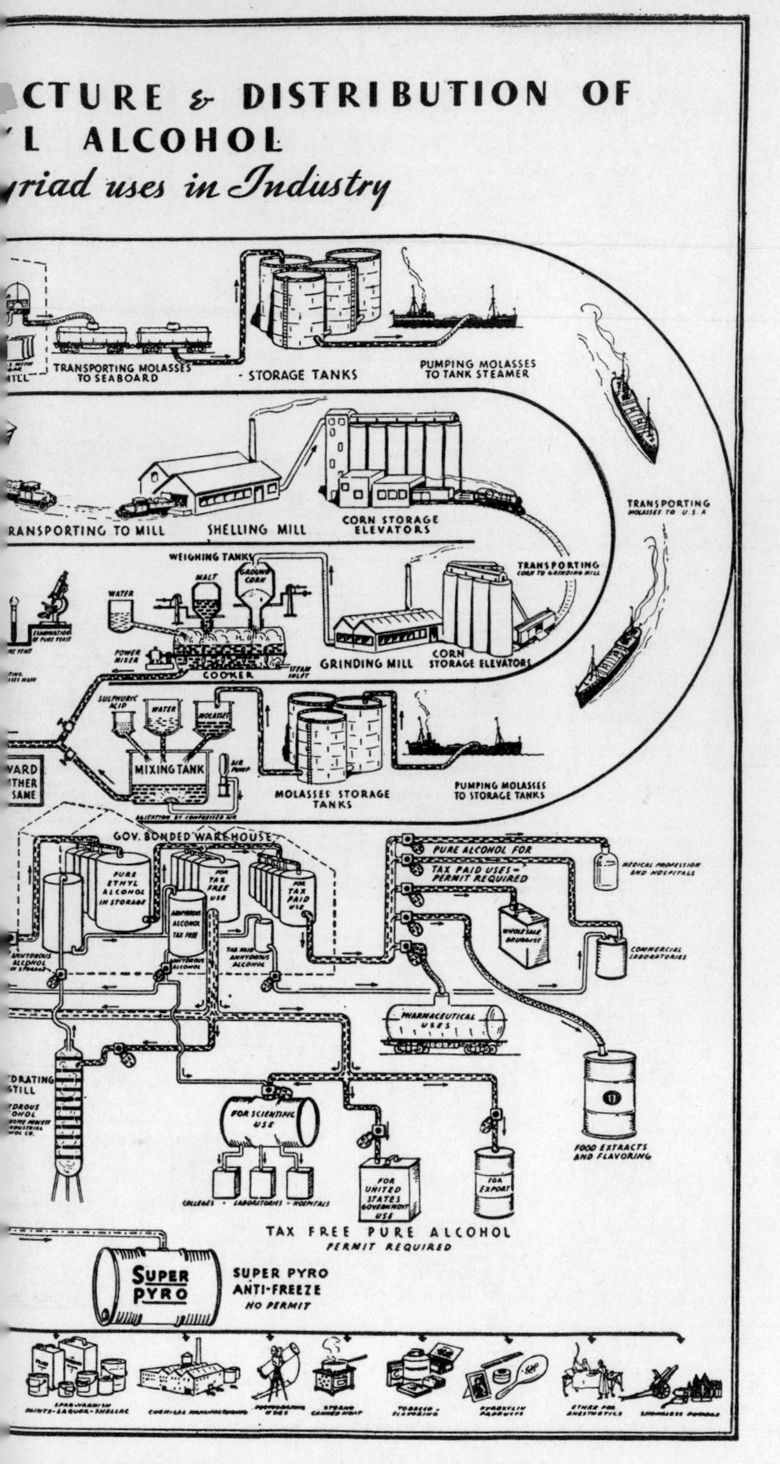

(Courtesy, United States Industrial Chemicals, Inc.)

Saccharine materials usually require little or no special treatment, other than *p*H adjustment and dilution, before fermentation. For example, blackstrap molasses, containing 50 to 55 per cent total sugar (mainly sucrose), and high-test molasses, containing up to 78 per cent total sugar, are adjusted to *p*H 4.5 to 5.0 and diluted until they contain 12 to 15 per cent sugar. Frequently ammonium phosphate or sulfate is added in amounts of 0.075 to 0.1 per cent to correct phosphorus or nitrogen deficiencies for the yeast. Most fruit juices require only *p*H adjustment, dilution, and sulfur dioxide treatment (to prevent abnormal fermentation due to bacteria) before fermentation. Sweet rennet cheese whey, containing lactose, is heated to boiling, run through a filter press, adjusted to *p*H 4.5 with sulfuric acid, cooled, and fortified with ammonium sulfate (0.013 per cent), and then is ready for fermentation [Browne (1941)].

Starchy materials have to be disintegrated by grinding or cooking, or by both processes, and then saccharified (hydrolyzed) before they can be fermented to alcohol by yeast. When grain such as corn is used, the oil-bearing germ is usually removed before cooking. The cooking of starchy materials is generally carried out in large retorts or other vessels, which are heated by steam under pressure at 80°C. (176°F.) to 182.2°C. (328°F.) for periods varying from a few minutes to 3 hours, depending upon what type of raw material is used and whether the batch cycle process or the rapid, continuous process is employed [see Gallagher, Bilford, Stark, and Kolachov (1942), DeBecze and Rosenblatt (1943)]. After cooking, the softened and disintegrated material is blown through a tube to a large vat, cooled to the mashing temperature of 50° to 63°C. (122° to 155.4°F.), and then saccharified by one of several methods. Saccharification, or hydrolysis of the starch, is necessary because yeasts do not secrete diastase (amylase). Acid hydrolysis of the starch has been practiced in the past but industrially is not so widely used today as is enzymatic hydrolysis. The enzymes used for saccharification may come from: (a) barley malt, (b) wheat which has been specially treated, or (c) various microorganisms.

The use of malt or germinated barley for the hydrolysis of starchy materials involves adding a certain amount of ground malt to the cooled, pastefied grain and then allowing its enzymes to act until the desired changes have taken place. In the past it has been customary to convert the starch of the main mash to fermentable sugars, which are then pumped to the fermenters. New methods described by Gallagher, Bilford, Stark, and Kolachov (1942), however, make use of a so-called rapid, continuous process for the production of alcohol from cornstarch mashes and malt. The malt is metered out through a pump and mixed with the mash, which is being pumped through a long pipe (approximately 105 ft.); the malt is in contact with the mash for 40 to 60 seconds at 62.8°C. prior to cooling and fermentation. The alcohol yields on such quickly converted mashes are about 2 per cent higher than on those obtained with the older standard practice of 30 to 60 minutes' conversion at 62.8°C. (145°F.).

When wheat meal or flour is used as the source of raw material, it may be saccharified by its own enzymes. The technique is known as the Balls-Tucker process [see Taylor (1943)]. It consists of the use of a 0.5 per cent sodium sulfite solution to extract the diastase from the ground wheat before it is cooked and the addition of this sulfite-diastase mixture to the grain after cooking to convert the starch to fermentable sugars. Such a technique cuts the cost of alcohol production, since barley malt or mold diastase is not required.

Mold enzyme preparations are now widely used to hydrolyze the starch in corn and wheat for industrial alcohol production. The process has been developed to a high degree of efficiency by several workers, especially Schoene, Fulmer, and Underkofler (1940), Underkofler (1942), Hao, Fulmer, and Underkofler (1943), and Roberts, Laufer, Stewart, and Saletan (1944). Briefly the method consists of growing certain molds, especially strains of *Aspergillus oryzae*, on a sterilized, acidified mixture of water and wheat bran in small rotary drums or in aluminum pots equipped for aeration. The temperature is maintained at 35° to 45°C. by controlled rotation and aeration, or by aeration alone if the aluminum pots are used. After about 20 to 40 hours' incubation in such an environment, the moldy bran is dried in air at room temperature and ground in a mill to a coarse powder. This powder is then used for the saccharification of cooked grain mashes in a manner similar to that employed for malt. On the average about 10 to 12 per cent higher yields of ethyl alcohol are obtained with moldy bran than with good dried barley malt. In fact, under optimum conditions and with *Aspergillus oryzae* bran alcohol yields up to 95 per cent of theory have been obtained.

Jerusalem artichokes have been used on a small scale to produce ethyl alcohol [see Underkofler, McPherson, and Fulmer (1937)]. Prefermentation treatments involve extraction of the fresh or dried tuber chips with water in a diffusion battery at 80°C., concentration of the extract under reduced pressure to a sirup containing over 70 per cent total solids, conversion of polysaccharides into simpler sugars by mild acid (*p*H 1.5 to 1.75) hydrolysis at 80°C. for 1 or 2 hours, adjustment of the *p*H to 5.5, and dilution of the mash so that it contains carbohydrate equivalent to 16 per cent reducing sugar. The dilute mash is then sterilized, cooled to 30°C., and inoculated; no additional nutrients need be added.

The starch powders from other plants, such as cassava, have also been used as substrates for alcoholic fermentation, but they are not as widely employed as the starchy materials mentioned [see Banzon (1941)].

Cellulose-containing materials and waste sulfite liquors offer interesting possibilities as raw materials for the production of ethyl alcohol and various other substances by fermentation methods [see reviews by Hanson (1942) and Wise (1943)]. Before fermentation wood and other cellulose-containing materials must be disintegrated by special shredders and hydrolyzed to fermentable sugars by mineral acids (H_2SO_4 or HCl), either at room temperature or at higher temperatures by steam under pressure. The sugars are then recovered as a sirup from the furfural, lignin, and acids by diffusion, evaporation, neutralization, and filtration or by other special treatments. According to Bergius (1937), approximately 80 per cent of the sugar obtained by the hydrolysis of wood is fermented to alcohol, a long ton of dry wood yielding 85 to 90 gal. of 95 per cent alcohol. The other 20 per cent of the sugar may be recovered and used for animal food or for other purposes.

Sulfite liquor, a by-product in the manufacture of pulp from wood, contains about 1.5 to 5.0 per cent carbohydrate in the form of glucose (50 per cent), mannose (15 per cent), galactose (8 per cent), and nonfermentable pentosans (27 per cent) consisting of xylose and arabinose. Because the *p*H of sulfite liquor is below the most favorable range for yeast activity and because sulfur dioxide in the liquor is highly poisonous to yeast, special treatment is necessary before fermentation. The free SO_2 is removed by heating (90°C.) and aeration (about 2 hours) at a *p*H above 5.5. Lime, or preferably calcium carbonate, may be used for neutralization. After neutralization, which requires 4 to 5 hours, the liquor is allowed to stand for about the same length of time to permit certain solids to settle; then it is cooled to a fermentation temperature of 27°C. (80.6°F.). Usually it is necessary to supply additional nutrients for the growth of the yeast; these may consist of ammonium salts (phosphate or sulfate), hydrolyzed skim milk, or a yeast extract prepared by autodigestion of yeast at an elevated temperature. According to Hanson (1942), the main advantages of employing sulfite liquor as a raw material for alcohol production are: (1) use of a strictly waste material and (2) decrease in stream pollution. On the other hand, some of the drawbacks include: (1) difficulties in the operation of the sulfite mill so as to produce sulfite liquor with a consistently high sugar content, (2) adverse effect on the pulp if a high alcohol yield is wanted, (3) necessity for special treatment of liquor before fermentation, (4) large volume of liquor to be handled, and (5) small yield of alcohol.

2. PREPARATION OF STARTER (YEAST CULTURE DEVELOPMENT). The strain or race of yeast employed in alcohol production must possess uniform and stable characteristics and must be able to tolerate high concentrations of alcohol. In respect to this second point the study by W. D. Gray (1941) of the alcohol tolerance of yeasts is of interest. On the basis of their alcohol tolerances all the yeasts investigated by Gray may be divided into six groups:

a. Yeasts of extremely low alcohol tolerance.

Strains utilizing not over 77.2 per cent of the available glucose in 24 hours at 30°C. in 10 per cent yeast water–1.5 per cent glucose medium of *p*H 4.30 to 4.38, containing 4.76 to 4.82 per cent or less alcohol by weight:

"Yeast 32" (a contaminant from an open fermenter originally set with the "D.C.L. strain").
Willia anomala (a yeast used for ripening Japanese rice beer).
"Black yeast" (occurring as a contaminant of commercial yeast).

b. Yeasts of low alcohol tolerance.

Strains utilizing not over 95.8 per cent of the glucose in the foregoing medium containing 6.66 to 6.75 per cent alcohol:

Saccharomyces cerevisiae ("S.C. strain").
"A strain" (producing a raspberry-like odor in mash after 24 hours).
Zygosaccharomyces soja (a yeast used in the preparation of Japanese rice beer).
Torula lactosa.

c. Yeasts of moderate alcohol tolerance.

Strains utilizing not over 97.4 per cent of the glucose in the foregoing medium containing 6.66 to 7.72 per cent alcohol:

Saccharomyces cerevisiae ("D.C.L. strain").
Schizosaccharomyces mellacei (a yeast used in the preparation of Jamaica rum from molasses).
Torula cremoris.

d. Yeasts of average alcohol tolerance (all yeasts of this group may be considered as being quite efficient and suitable for industrial use).

Strains utilizing not over 97.9 per cent of the glucose in the foregoing medium containing 8.56 to 9.52 per cent alcohol:

Saccharomyces ellipsoideus ("Yeast 21"—Tokay wine yeast).
Saccharomyces cerevisiae ("Rasse XII strain," "Yeast 23"—Burgundy wine yeast).
Saccharomyces cerevisiae ("L.3 strain," *Schizosaccharomyces verdermani?*).
"Yeast 30" (a contaminant in vitamin B_1–free wort).
Schizosaccharomyces pombé (a yeast used in the preparation of South African negro millet beer).

e. Yeasts of high alcohol tolerance.

Strains utilizing not over 97.7 per cent of the glucose in the foregoing medium containing 10.47 to 10.61 per cent alcohol:

Saccharomyces cerevisiae ("Rasse M strain").
Saccharomyces cerevisiae ("R strain"—a European strain good for rye fermentations).

f. Yeasts of extremely high alcohol tolerance.

Strains utilizing 96.8 per cent of the available glucose in the foregoing medium containing 11.58 per cent alcohol, and approximately 95 per cent of the glucose when the medium contained 13 per cent alcohol:

Saccharomyces cerevisiae ("Brown-Forman strain").

Although strains or races of *Saccharomyces cerevisiae* are generally used for the production of alcohol by fermentation methods, other species of yeasts may be employed under certain conditions. For example, *Torula cremoris* and *Torula lactosa* have been used by Browne (1941) for the production of ethyl alcohol from cheese whey, and *Schizosaccharomyces pombé* appears to be the best yeast for the fermentation of Jerusalem artichoke mashes. For information on the classification and identification of the yeasts the review by Henrici (1941) should be consulted.

The preparation of the starter for inoculation ("pitching") of the main mash has to be carried out in several steps under aseptic conditions. First, a young, pure culture of the desired strain of yeast is grown in a tube of yeast extract-glucose broth or wort broth for 24 to 48 hours at 24° to 30°C. This culture is then used to inoculate a larger tube or flask of sterile mash. After incubation this culture is used to seed a still larger flask of sterile mash. Such a "build-up" procedure is continued two or three times more until finally a "starter" of several thousand gallons is obtained; this starter is then used to inoculate the main mash in large fermentation vats. Aeration is of benefit in preparing a good starter containing a great number of yeast cells, since it breaks up clumps of cells and removes toxic metabolic gases. Usually specially designed apparatus, such as the Magné automatic yeast propagator, was used in the past to prepare the final starter. Because of the large-capacity equipment and long over-all processing time required by present methods for the preparation of distillers' yeast, however, Unger, Stark, Scalf, and Kolachov (1942) developed a rapid, continuous aerobic process for the manufacture of yeast. Their original report should be consulted for details, but basically their method consists of growing the yeast in a specially designed apparatus on a sterile barley-malt-wort-ammonium sulfate medium of *p*H 4.0 to 4.2 at 28° to 30°C. and aerating with sterile air. After about 4 hours of active growth the yeast wort is removed continuously at the bottom of the apparatus and pumped to a centrifuge, where the yeast cell concentration is increased from about 500,000,000 to 2,000,000,000 per milliliter. The supernatant fluid, containing about 1.75 per cent alcohol, is returned to the distillery, and the yeast is transferred to refrigerated storage and kept there until needed. This method produces a pure-culture yeast of strong fermenting activity at an original concentration of 500,000,000 cells per milliliter of medium, in comparison with the usual 150,000,000 per milliliter obtained by the sour-mash anaerobic process.

3. Fermentation of the Mash. After the preliminary adjustments, such as securing a *p*H of 4.5 to 5.0 and diluting to 12 to 15 per cent sugar, are made in the various raw materials, they are pumped to the fermenters, where the temperature is regulated to 70° to 80°F. (21.1° to 26.6°C.), and inoculated ("pitched") with the starter. Ordinarily the main mash is inoculated with a starter that represents from 5 to 25 per cent of its volume. The yeast in the starter soon uses up the oxygen in the main mash, and active anaerobic alcoholic fermentation sets in. During the anaerobic fermentation the temperature is maintained at 70° to 80°F. (21.1° to 26.6°C.) by cooling coils or sprays on the outside of the fermenters. If this is not done, the temperature of the mash may rise to a point where the growth of the yeast is retarded, bacterial development may take place, or some of the alcohol may be lost by evaporation. During the fermentation carbon dioxide is evolved; this gas maintains anaerobic conditions and may also be recovered and used for a variety of purposes. Although the rate of fermentation depends on the temperature, sugar concentration, and other factors, the process is usually complete in about 48 to 96 hours.

Newer methods are now widely used for the fermentation of certain mashes. For example, a continuous process for the alcoholic fermentation of molasses has been developed by Bilford, Scalf, Stark, and Kolachov (1942). It is based on the use of a single-vessel, continuous fermentation system and a storage tank. Molasses mashes, aerated with CO_2 at 32.2°C. (90°F.) and containing 12 to 13 per cent sugar, are fermented 92 to 94 per cent in 4- to 10-hour cycles; yeast inoculation (prepared by the continuous process) is necessary only at the beginning of the run. Such a process is more efficient in time, equipment, and production [see DeBecze and Rosenblatt (1943)].

4. DISTILLING AND REFINING THE ALCOHOL. After fermentation is complete, the fermented mash (beer) is transferred to condensers and beer stills and finally to rectifying stills and condensers, where the ethyl alcohol and fusel oil are separated from the other constituents of the mash ("slop waste"). During distillation in the first condensers and beer stills, fractions containing approximately 60 to 90 per cent alcohol, and spoken of as "high wines," are separated from the slop waste. These high wines are then separated from fusel oil and concentrated to 95 per cent alcohol by passage through rectifying stills and condensers. The 95 per cent (190 proof) ethyl alcohol may be further purified, dehydrated, or denatured as prescribed by the Bureau of Internal Revenue [see Figs. 1 and 2; also United States Department of the Treasury, Bureau of Industrial Alcohol, *Regulation* 3 (1931), United States Department of the Treasury, Bureau of Internal Revenue, *Appendix to Regulation* 3 (1939), and Wentworth, Othmer, and Pohler (1943)].

5. BY-PRODUCTS (SLOP WASTE AND FUSEL OIL). The residue material from the beer stills, called slop waste, constitutes an important by-product of the industrial alcohol industry. The solids may be concentrated, dried, and sold as stock feed or fertilizer, or they may be used as raw material to produce a variety of other products. These by-products contain vitamins (at least nine members of the B group and carotene), nitrogenous substances, fats, and minerals and are of high nutritive value as food for animals [Bauernfeind, Garey, Baumgarten, Stone, and Boruff (1944)]. Such compounds as the suga *d*-allulose and a substance with the formula $C_{30}H_{54}O_{18}N_5P$ have also been isolated from distillery slops by Zerban and Sattler (1942).

The fusel oil is separated from the alcohol during the refining of the high wines; it constitutes about 0.1 to 0.7 per cent of the crude distilled spirit. The composition and quantity of fusel oil vary, however, with the raw material used (see Fig. 1). According to data cited by

Jacobs and Newton (1938) and Joslyn and Amerine (1941), fusel oil from the fermentation of various substrates shows considerable variation in its composition (see Table 3). This variation is probably due to several factors, such as the composition of the raw material, the type of yeast employed, the variable fermentation conditions, and the method of distillation. Usually in industry the fusel oil is not refined or separated into its component parts, but instead is used in its crude form as a lacquer solvent. Methods are available, however, for the purification of either grain or molasses fusel oil [see, for example, Swallen and Tindall (1942)].

The Mechanism of Ethyl Alcohol Fermentation.[3] A great deal has been written about the mechanism of alcoholic fermentation since Gay-Lussac formulated his classical equation during the early part of

TABLE 3

PERCENTAGE COMPOSITION OF FUSEL OIL FROM VARIOUS SOURCES

[Data cited by Jacobs and Newton (1938) and Joslyn and Amerine (1941)]

Source	Alcohol, per cent					Residue
	n-Propyl	*n*-Butyl	Isobutyl	*n*-Amyl	Isoamyl	
Potato spirit (3 samples)	3.9–6.9	....	16.5–24.4	68.8–79.5	....	0.04–0.14 *
Fermented molasses	13.0	....	42.0	36.0	....	9.0
Brandy (3 samples)	11.7–12.1	0.0–63.8	0.0–4.5	24.5–85.0	....	†
Whiskey (2 samples)	1.7–20.4	....	12.2–23.9	14.6–23.4	36.3–59.7	3.0–4.8
Fermented sugar-yeast extract	3.7	0.0	2.7	93.6	....	0.0

* Hexyl alcohol demonstrated in one sample, and acids, esters, and furfural in another.

† Hexyl and heptyl alcohols demonstrated in one sample.

[3] For additional reading the books by Harden (1932) and Stephenson (1939) and the more recent reviews by Joslyn (1940), Nord (1940), Werkman and Wood (1942), Cori (1942), Neuberg (1942), and Meyerhof (1942, 1943) should be consulted.

the last century. Gay-Lussac believed that the following reaction accounted for the chemical changes occurring during alcoholic fermentation of sugar by yeast:

$$C_6H_{12}O_6 \rightarrow 2C_2H_5OH + 2CO_2$$

Although this equation still indicates the over-all reaction for the production of alcohol from sugar by yeast, we now know that the fermentation process is not as simple as the reaction suggests, because, actually, the end products arise from a chain of reactions involving several ephemeral intermediate compounds, and the main products (ethyl alcohol and carbon dioxide) of the fermentation account for only about 95 per cent of the sugar transformed.

The quantity of products encountered in alcoholic fermentation, calculated on the basis of percentage of sugar fermented, and demonstrated by several workers, is indicated in Table 4. From these data

TABLE 4

PRODUCTS * OF THE ALCOHOLIC FERMENTATION OF SUGAR BY YEAST

[From Joslyn (1940)]

Product	Theory	Industrial Fermentations	Pasteur Data	Experimental Investigations with		
				Champagne Yeast	Rkatsiteh Yeast	Steinberg Yeast
Alcohol	51.1 *	48.4	48.6	47.8	48.1	48.0
Carbon dioxide	48.9	46.5	47.0	47.0	47.6	47.6
Acetaldehyde		0.0–0.08		0.01	0.04	0.02
Acetic acid		0.05–0.25		0.61	0.50	0.65
2,3-Butylene glycol				0.06	0.09	0.10
Glycerol		2.5–3.6	3.1	2.99	2.61	2.75
Lactic acid		0.0–0.2		0.40	0.28	0.40
Succinic acid		0.5–0.7	0.6	0.020–0.045		0.015–0.053
Fusel oil		0.35–0.5				
Furfural		Trace				
Total	100.0	98.3–100.23	99.3	98.89–98.915	99.22	99.535–99.573

* Percentage of sugar transformed.

it will be seen that alcohol and carbon dioxide are the main products of the fermentation, and a variety of other so-called by-products, which are largely responsible for the flavors and aroma acquired during fermentation, accounts for the remaining percentage of the sugar transformed. In addition to these substances yeast cells and other nitrogenous materials accumulate during fermentation.

In formulating a scheme to depict the reactions which occur during alcoholic fermentation, all the substances listed in Table 4 should be taken into consideration, as well as any transitory intermediate compounds which can be isolated or demonstrated by fixation methods, selective poisons, or dialysis or detected by other techniques in which yeast juice preparations are employed to study isolated reactions. It should be mentioned also that a great deal of our present information concerning the mechanism of alcoholic fermentation has been gained by correlated studies on the related mechanism of lactic acid formation by muscle extracts.

The so-called Neuberg scheme for alcoholic fermentation was accepted as quite plausible and experimentally sound until the work, starting about 1933, of Embden, Parnas, Warburg and Christian, Meyerhof, Cori, and others. In the Neuberg scheme a molecule of hexose sugar, after suitable activation, is converted into two molecules of triose, yielding methylglyoxal. Two molecules of methylglyoxal, undergoing intermolecular oxidation-reduction, are transformed into glycerol and pyruvic acid; the pyruvic acid is then decomposed by the enzyme carboxylase into acetaldehyde and carbon dioxide. The aldehyde so formed reacts with another molecule of methylglyoxal to yield ethyl alcohol and pyruvic acid, which is again decarboxylated. In this scheme glycerol should be formed only in the initial stages of fermentation, and, once the stationary stage (in which acetaldehyde enters into intermolecular oxidation-reduction with methylglyoxal) is reached, further formation of glycerol should cease; it could occur thereafter only when the dismutation involves reduction of methylglyoxal.

The advantage of the Neuberg scheme of fermentation over the older postulated theories is its flexibility. On the assumption that pyruvic acid is converted into acetaldehyde and carbon dioxide as rapidly as it is formed, we have in the medium two hydrogen donators (acetaldehyde and methylglyoxal) and two hydrogen acceptors (acetaldehyde and methylglyoxal). When acetaldehyde serves as a hydrogen acceptor and methylglyoxal as a hydrogen donator, ethyl alcohol and pyruvic acid are formed. According to this view, the ordinary Gay-

Lussac equation ($C_6H_{12}O_6 \rightarrow 2C_2H_5OH + 2CO_2$) is fulfilled according to Scheme I.

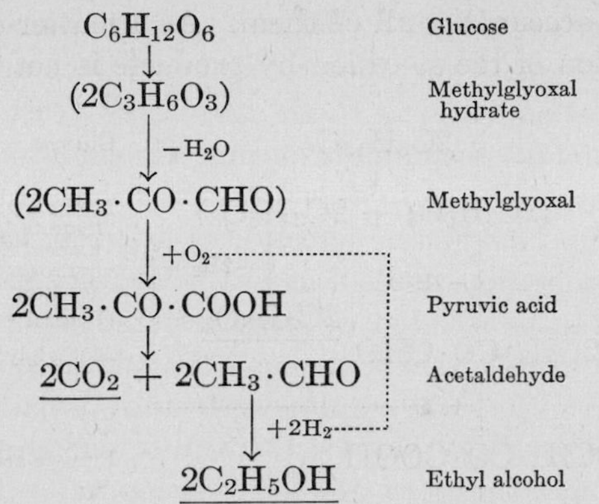

SCHEME I. Neuberg's Normal Fermentation.

On the other hand, when the acetaldehyde is prevented from acting as the sole hydrogen acceptor, as Neuberg found to be the situation in the presence of added alkali, the normal course of the fermentation is modified. A second hydrogen acceptor (an unstable compound which Neuberg did not identify but which has the formula $C_3H_6O_3$) then becomes active and competes with acetaldehyde for the hydrogen liberated when methylglyoxal is oxidized; by accepting the hydrogen, this second compound is reduced to glycerol (see Scheme II). Under such conditions the acetaldehyde is not completely reduced to alcohol, as in Scheme I, but instead undergoes a Cannizzaro reaction in which half the molecules are oxidized to acetic acid and the other half are reduced to ethyl alcohol (Scheme II). Neuberg and his associates were also able to prove the presence of acetaldehyde in fermentation mixtures by the addition of sulfite. Under such conditions the sulfite unites with part of the acetaldehyde before it has been oxidized or reduced and renders it inactive; the aldehyde so fixed was recovered and identified by Neuberg and his associates. When acetaldehyde is fixed by such a technique, it can no longer serve as a hydrogen acceptor, as in Scheme I; but, as in Scheme II, it is replaced by an unstable triose compound, $C_3H_6O_3$, which is easily reduced to glycerol. Therefore, for every molecule of acetaldehyde fixed by sulfite, a corresponding molecule of glycerol is to be expected, and it occurs. Scheme III illustrates the course of events under the circumstances which have just been outlined.

Although these schemes account in a qualitative way for certain of the by-products found in normal alcoholic fermentation, they do not quantitatively account for all of them. As a matter of fact, however, the accumulation of the so-called by-products is not regular and pro-

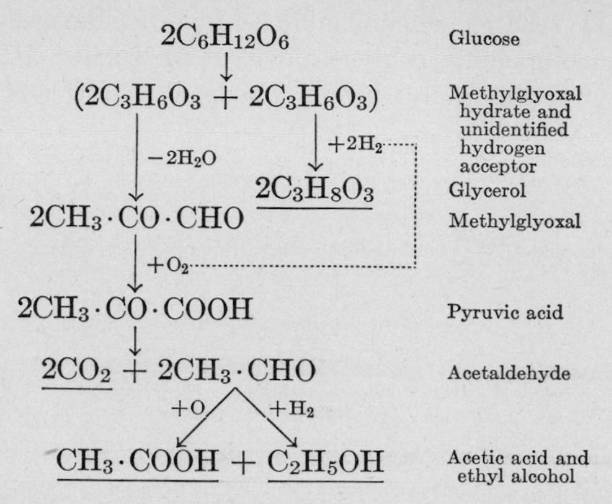

SCHEME II. Neuberg's Fermentation in the Presence of Alkali.

portional to the quantity of sugar dissimilated, but varies depending on the stage of fermentation, the substrate, and the experimental conditions.

The essential differences between the Neuberg scheme and Scheme IV, which is believed at present to account best for the equilibria in

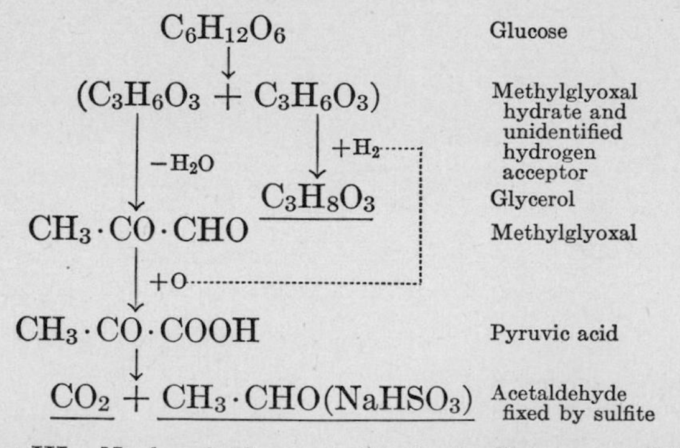

SCHEME III. Neuberg's Fermentation in the Presence of Sulfite.

alcoholic fermentation, lie in the nature of the triose intermediates and in the more intimate intervention of phosphate than was previously believed to exist. Neuberg regarded methylglyoxal as an intermediate product of fermentation; but, since this substance is not fermented to any extent, many people regard it as an inactive stabilization product of a more active isomeric compound. The intermediate trioses which are now believed to occur in alcoholic fermentation are shown in Scheme IV, the so-called Embden-Meyerhof-Parnas scheme, and include such compounds as glyceraldehyde phosphate ($H_2O_3P \cdot OCH_2 \cdot CHOH \cdot CHO$), dihydroxyacetone phosphate ($CH_2OH \cdot CO \cdot CH_2O \cdot$

Polysaccharide (starch or glycogen) ⇅ * $\pm K_2HPO_4$ Glucose-1-phosphate (Cori ester)

Glucose-1-phosphate (Cori ester) ⇄ * Glucose-6-phosphate

Glucose ↓ * +ATP → Glucose-6-phosphate (Robison ester) + ADP (1)

Glucose-6-phosphate ⇅ Fructose-6-phosphate (Neuberg ester) (2)

Fructose-6-phosphate ⇅ * +ATP → Fructose-1:6-diphosphate + ADP (Harden-Young ester) (3)

Fructose-1:6-diphosphate ⇅ Dihydroxyacetone phosphate ⇄ 3-Glyceraldehyde phosphate (4)

Dihydroxyacetone phosphate $+H_2$-DPN → α-Glycerophosphate; α-Glycerophosphate +DPN → Dihydroxyacetone phosphate

α-Glycerophosphate ↓ $+H_2O$ → Glycerol + H_3PO_4

3-Glyceraldehyde phosphate ⇅ ? $\pm K_2HPO_4$ → 1:3-Diphosphoglyceraldehyde (5)

1:3-Diphosphoglyceraldehyde ⇅ +DPN → 1:3-Diphosphoglyceric acid + H_2DPN (6)

1:3-Diphosphoglyceric acid ⇅ * +ADP → 3-Phosphoglyceric acid + ATP (7)

3-Phosphoglyceric acid ⇅ * → 2-Phosphoglyceric acid (8)

2-Phosphoglyceric acid ⇅ $\pm H_2O$ → (Enol) Phosphopyruvic acid (9)

(Enol) Phosphopyruvic acid ↓ * +ADP → Pyruvic acid + ATP (10)

Lactic acid ⇄ Pyruvic acid ($+H_2$-DPN toward lactic acid; +DPN toward pyruvic acid)

Pyruvic acid ↓ +DPT → Acetaldehyde + CO_2 (11)

Acetaldehyde ⇅ $+H_2$DPN → Ethyl alcohol + DPN (12)

* Mg^{++} or Mn^{++} ions required.

Abbreviations for the dialyzable components:

ATP = adenosine triphosphate.
ADP = adenosine diphosphate.
K_2HPO_4 = inorganic phosphate.
? = reaction not proved definitely.
DPN = diphosphopyridine nucleotide.
H_2-DPN = reduced diphosphopyridine nucleotide.
DPT = diphosphothiamin.

SCHEME IV. Alcoholic Fermentation by the Embden-Meyerhof-Parnas Scheme and the Cori Scheme for the Fermentation and Synthesis of Polysaccharides [From Meyerhof (1942–1943) and Cori (1942)].

PO_3H_2), 3-phosphoglyceric acid ($H_2O_3P \cdot OCH_2 \cdot CHOH \cdot COOH$), and phosphopyruvic acid ($CH_2{:}COPO_3H_2 \cdot COOH$). The fact that all the reactions postulated by the Embden-Meyerhof-Parnas scheme take place at high velocities with enzyme preparations from yeast juice adds validity to this scheme and has resulted in general acceptance of the view that the reactions probably represent the course of events in the intact yeast cell. The Embden-Meyerhof-Parnas scheme consists of a series of phosphorylation, hydrolytic, and oxidation-reduction reactions, many of which are in equilibrium.

The outline of Scheme IV shows that at least twelve separate enzymes are involved in alcoholic fermentation, as well as five dialyzable components, without which some of the enzymes are unable to act. Several of the enzymes have been obtained as crystalline proteins from yeast juice, whereas others have been isolated in a highly purified state. Among the dialyzable components magnesium ions may be mentioned here; the others will be discussed as the separate reactions are taken up. Magnesium ions are needed, as the asterisks indicate in the scheme, whenever there is a transfer of a phosphate group within the molecule itself or from one molecule to another; Mg^{++} ions can be replaced in all these cases by Mn^{++} ions.

Alcoholic fermentation begins with the phosphorylation of glucose by the coenzyme system discovered in 1930 to 1935 by Lohmann and known as adenosine triphosphate (ATP)—adenosine diphosphate (ADP)—adenylic acid (AMP). This system was discussed in greater detail in Chapter 6. In brief, however, ATP is a compound made up of the purine base adenine, the five-carbon sugar ribose, and three phosphoric acid groups in pyrophosphate linkage; the reactive part of the molecule may be represented as follows:

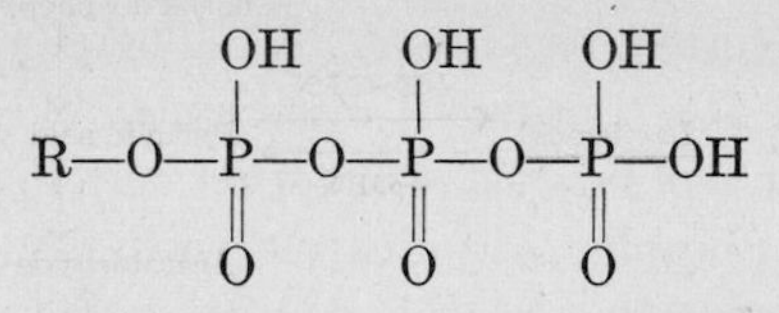

Two of the phosphate groups can be transferred successively to other compounds, but for simplicity the transfer of only one phosphate group is shown in the scheme. The enzyme responsible for the phosphate transfer to glucose is known as *hexokinase;* it is present in yeast in high concentration, is relatively stable, and can be obtained in partially purified form. Hexokinase is also present in animal tissues, but it is not so stable or as soluble in water as yeast hexokinase.

In reaction 1, glucose with the aid of hexokinase accepts a phosphate group from ATP and is thereby converted to glucose-6-phosphate, or the so-called Robison ester, while ATP, losing one phosphate group, is changed to adenosine diphosphate (ADP). Fructose and mannose, two other sugars which are fermented by yeast, are also phosphorylated in a similar manner on carbon atom six by ATP, as is shown in reaction 2, where glucose-6-phosphate and fructose-6-phosphate, as well as mannose-6-phosphate, are interconvertible through enzymatic action. These three sugars therefore follow the same course of fermentation once they have been phosphorylated. Another reaction in which ATP serves as a phosphate donor is 3, in which fructose-6-phosphate is transformed to fructose-1:6-diphosphate, or the Harden-Young ester. These first three reactions show how the sugar esters which were discovered a number of years ago by Harden and Young, Robison, and Neuberg are formed during alcoholic fermentation.

When the phosphorylation reaction was first discovered in alcoholic fermentation by Harden and Young, it was thought of as a process whereby the glucose was prepared for dissimilation; that is, the introduction of two phosphate groups into the glucose molecule to form hexose diphosphate was believed to develop lines of cleavage of the molecule into two triose phosphates. It is now clear, however, that in addition phosphorylation is a very important reaction in several stages of cellular metabolism by all types of cells (yeasts, bacteria, and plant and muscle tissues), since it results in the accumulation at the PO_4-linkage of large quantities of energy which can be utilized by the cell [see reviews by Lipmann (1941) and Werkman and Wood (1942)].

Since ATP, the phosphate donor in reactions 1 and 3, is generally present in only small amounts in yeast cells and other tissues, it is obvious that, if it is used up in these reactions, there must be a mechanism present for its regeneration; otherwise fermentation would soon stop. We see in reactions 7 and 10 that this is actually the situation, since ADP is converted back to ATP. Therefore during alcoholic fermentation there is a continuous interchange of phosphate between ATP and ADP. It is of interest to mention here that in animal tissues ATP may donate phosphate to creatine with the aid of the enzyme phosphorylase, thus forming AMP and creatine phosphate, which serves as a reservoir of phosphate:

$$\underset{\text{(ATP)}}{\text{Adenosine triphosphate}} + 2\ \text{Creatine} \rightleftarrows \underset{\text{(Adenylic acid or AMP)}}{\text{Adenosine monophosphate}} + 2\ \text{Creatine phosphate}$$

At present there is little or no evidence to indicate that yeasts and bacteria use this method to store phosphate. It has been shown by Parnas and his associates, however, that yeast can rapidly phosphorylate adenosine (adenine + ribose) to form adenosine-5′-monophosphate (adenylic acid), but that animal tissues cannot. Thus the cells of microorganisms may not have to store phosphate in the form of creatine phosphate, if they can synthesize their own organic phosphate coenzymes.

After the phosphorylation of glucose (or mannose or fructose) an interesting cleavage takes place (reaction 4). By hydrolysis and rearrangement the hexose diphosphate molecule is split, forming a molecule of glyceraldehyde phosphate and one of dihydroxyacetone phosphate, as is indicated in the following equation:

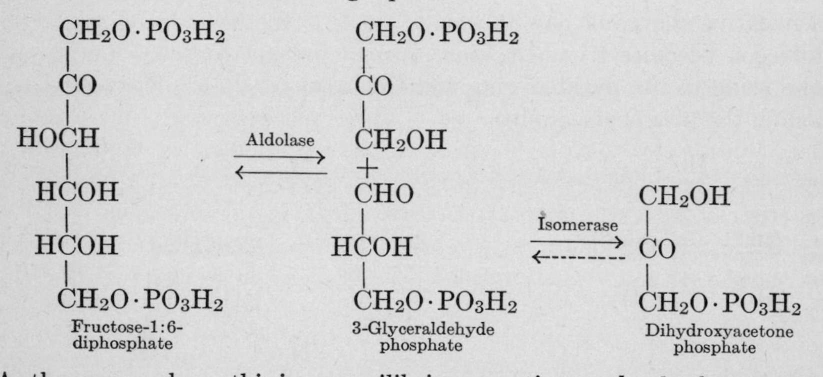

As the arrows show, this is an equilibrium reaction, and only the concentration of the participants causes it to progress toward fermentation. The two enzymes involved in the splitting of hexose diphosphate into triose phosphate and the interconversion of the two isomeric trioses are *aldolase* and *isomerase*, respectively. In addition to being present in yeast and muscle tissues, these two enzymes have been demonstrated in bacteria by Utter and Werkman (1941).

Up to this point we may say that the glucose molecule has been rearranged to an active form which can undergo oxidation-reduction. One of the essential features of fermentation is an oxidation-reduction reaction, and these triose phosphates are the starting points for the oxidation-reduction reactions which follow. Reactions 5 and 6 are the oxidative portion, mediated by diphosphopyridine nucleotide, and consist of the change of the aldehyde group of 3-glyceraldehyde phosphate to carboxyl group, thus forming glyceric acid phosphate. On the other hand, the reductive portion is shown in reaction 12, where acetaldehyde[4] accepts two hydrogen atoms from reduced diphos-

[4] In muscle glycolysis pyruvic acid serves as a hydrogen acceptor and in so doing is converted to lactic acid, or acetaldehyde may react immediately with a second molecule of pyruvic acid to form an intermediate compound which is decarboxylated to acetylmethylcarbinol [Green, Westerfeld, Vennesland, and Knox (1941, 1942)]:

$$CH_3 \cdot CO \cdot COOH + CH_3 \cdot CHO \rightarrow \begin{matrix}\text{Intermediate}\\ \text{compound}\end{matrix} \rightarrow CH_3 \cdot CO \cdot CHOH \cdot CH_3 + CO_2$$

phopyridine nucleotide (H_2-DPN) and is thereby converted to ethyl alcohol.

The mediator of reaction 6, as we have just stated, is the cozymase of Harden and Young, the chemical nature of which has been elucidated by von Euler, Warburg, and others (see Chapter 6). Cozymase or, more correctly, diphosphopyridine nucleotide (abbreviated DPN) can exist in an oxidized and in a reduced form, owing to a change in valency of the pyridine nitrogen. In the oxidized state the nitrogen has a valence of five and displays a positive charge which is neutralized by a negative charge of one phosphate group. In the reduced state the nitrogen becomes trivalent, since two hydrogen atoms are taken up, one going to the pyridine ring and the other forming a free hydrogen ion on the phosphate group:

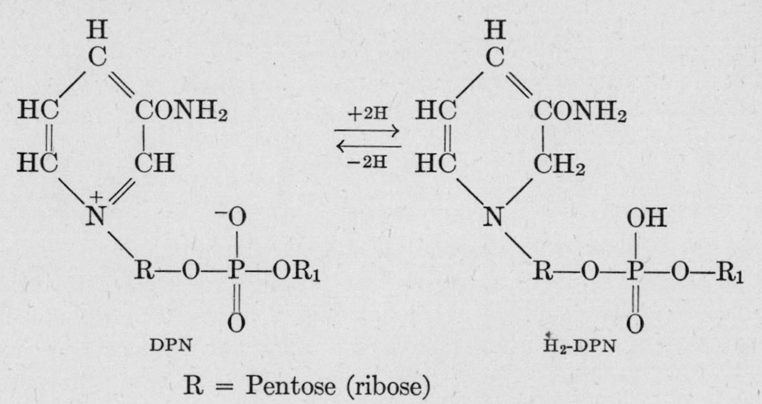

R = Pentose (ribose)

R_1 = Adenosine-5′-phosphoric acid

In reaction 6 glyceraldehyde is oxidized to an acid, whereas diphosphopyridine nucleotide (DPN) is reduced to H_2-DPN. The reduced pyridine nucleotide is reoxidized in reaction 12 and thus can again enter into reaction 6. Therefore in addition to the turnover ATP $\rightleftarrows$ ADP, which has been mentioned, there also occurs a continuous shuttle between DPN $\rightleftarrows$ H_2-DPN during fermentation.

Let us now examine reactions 5 and 6 more closely to see how the oxidation of the aldehyde group is accomplished. A classical way to show the oxidation of an aldehyde group to a carboxyl group is first to add the elements of water to form an aldehyde-hydrate intermediate, followed by the removal of two hydrogens:

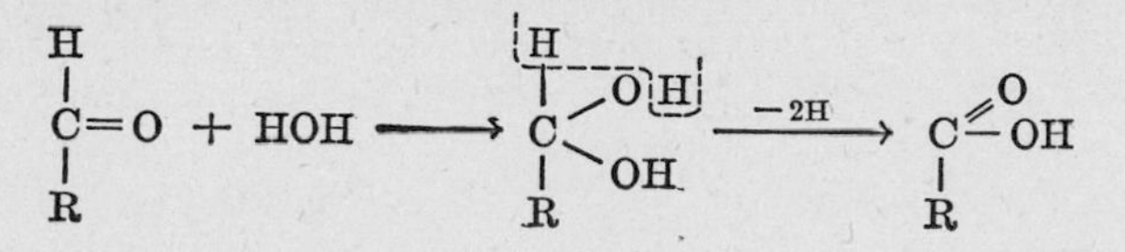

Since such a reaction is usually irreversible, this example does not fit in alcoholic fermentation. It has been observed by several workers, however, that the rate of the enzymatic reactions 5 and 6 is actually dependent upon the concentration of inorganic phosphate in the medium, and that in dialyzed yeast juice these reactions do not occur at all without the addition of inorganic phosphate. Therefore it is at this point in the fermentation that inorganic phosphate enters the system, and what apparently happens is that phosphate replaces water in the oxidation of the aldehyde group:

$$\underset{\underset{R}{|}}{\overset{\overset{H}{|}}{C}}{=}O + \begin{matrix}HO & & OH\\ & \diagdown P{=}O & \\ HO & & \end{matrix} \longrightarrow \underset{\underset{R}{|}}{\overset{\overset{H}{|}}{C}}{-}O{-}\underset{\underset{OH}{|}}{\overset{\overset{OH}{|}}{P}}{=}O \xrightarrow{-2H} \underset{\underset{R}{|}}{\overset{O}{\overset{\|}{C}}}{-}O{-}\underset{\underset{OH}{|}}{\overset{\overset{OH}{|}}{P}}{=}O$$

If R in this case represents the rest of the 3-glyceraldehyde phosphate molecule, then the addition of phosphoric acid to the aldehyde portion of the molecule gives the intermediate 1,3-diphosphoglyceraldehyde, which in turn may be dehydrogenated by DPN to give 1,3-diphosphoglyceric acid (reaction 6). This compound has actually been isolated by Warburg and Christian, a fact which adds additional support to the foregoing scheme. It should be mentioned, however, that Meyerhof (1943) has been unable to demonstrate the independent existence of a diphosphoglyceraldehyde; thus the assumption made by Warburg and Christian must await further study before it can be accepted as final.

In reaction 7 we see that the carboxyl phosphate of 1,3-diphosphoglyceraldehyde is removed with the formation of 1,3-diphosphoglyceric acid and that ADP accepts this phosphate. Therefore the over-all reaction (consisting of 5, 6, and 7) may be written:

$$\underset{\underset{R}{|}}{\overset{\overset{H}{|}}{C}}{=}O + H_3PO_4 + DPN + ADP \rightleftarrows \underset{R\ \ \ OH}{\overset{O}{\overset{/\!/}{C}}} + H_2\text{-}DPN + ATP$$

This fermentation reaction accomplishes two things: (1) It provides for the entrance of inorganic phosphate into the system and thus provides a way for the regeneration of ATP; and (2) it starts the hydrogen transfer by way of the pyridine nucleotide (DPN). Another interesting point about this reaction is that it is reversible, and therefore it makes possible synthetic reactions for the building up of reserve sugars from small molecules.

According to the original view of Embden and Meyerhof, during the initial stages of fermentation (the so-called induction period), before acetaldehyde or pyruvic acid is formed, two molecules of triose phosphate undergo a self-oxidation and reduction (that is, a dismutation or Cannizzaro reaction) leading to the production of one molecule of α-glycerophosphate and one molecule of 3-phosphoglyceric acid:

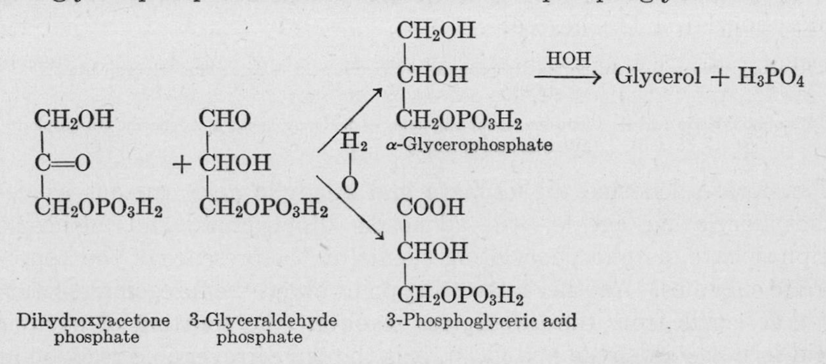

This reaction may take place under certain conditions in alcoholic fermentation, but it is considered less important now than when it was first proposed, because, as we have shown, another phosphate intermediate may be formed between 3-glyceraldehyde phosphate and 3-phosphoglyceric acid.

The characteristic intermediate of the Embden-Meyerhof-Parnas scheme is 3-phosphoglyceric acid, since it is the mother substance of ethyl alcohol. As is shown in reaction 8, the enzyme *phosphomutase* causes a shift of the phosphate group from the third to the second carbon atom, forming 2-phosphoglyceric acid:

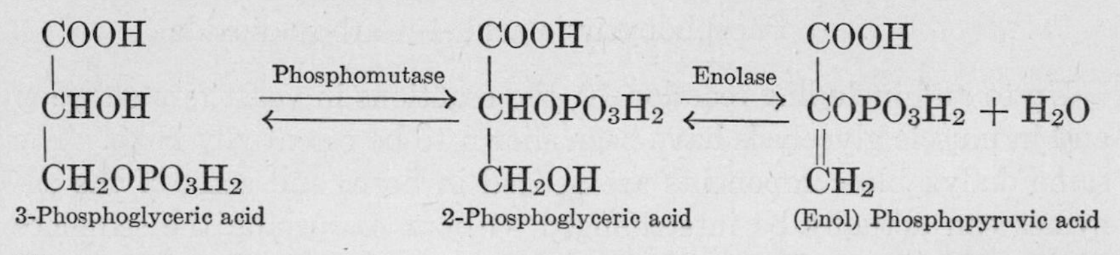

Then 2-phosphoglyceric acid undergoes a change catalyzed by the enzyme *enolase*, with the formation of phosphopyruvic acid and water (reaction 9). The enolase of yeast and animal tissues is a magnesium protein complex. Warburg and Christian (1941) crystallized it as the mercury salt and then removed the mercury by dialysis against HCN. The free protein was found to be inactive, but it became active when magnesium, manganese, or zinc was added. This enzyme is highly sensitive to fluoride when phosphates are also present, forming an inactive magnesium fluoride-phosphate complex with the protein. Thus one of the most specific inhibitions of fermentation can now be explained by this reaction.

In reaction 10 we see that phosphopyruvic acid donates its phosphate group to adenosine diphosphate (or adenosine monophosphate), which becomes adenosine triphosphate, the compound which originally phosphorylated the hexose:

Phosphopyruvic acid + Adenosine diphosphate (ADP) → Pyruvic acid + Adenosine triphosphate (ATP)

2-Phosphopyruvic acid + Adenosine monophosphate (Adenylic acid or AMP) → 2-Pyruvic acid + Adenosine triphosphate (ATP)

Therefore, adenosine diphosphate and adenylic acid can act as dephosphorylating agents, and adenosine diphosphate and adenosine triphosphate, as phosphorylating agents, in the presence of the appropriate enzymes. Another interesting point about the foregoing reaction is that, aside from the *carboxylase* reaction (the splitting of pyruvic acid into acetaldehyde and CO_2), it is the only irreversible reaction of fermentation. This point is important, because phosphopyruvic acid can be synthesized from lactic acid and transformed into glycogen by a reversal of the corresponding glycolytic breakdown. This synthesis, however, does not proceed directly from pyruvic acid to phosphopyruvic acid but probably takes the following path [Meyerhof (1943)]:

Pyruvic acid + Carbon dioxide

→ Oxalacetic acid + Phosphoric acid

→ Phosphooxalacetic acid

→ Phosphopyruvic acid + Carbon dioxide

Up to and including reaction 10, the reactions in yeast fermentation and in muscle glycolysis have been shown to be essentially alike. The same dialyzable components are needed in both, and some of the enzymes can actually be interchanged without disturbing the sequence of these reactions. From this point, however, the two interesting processes differ. Yeast contains the specific enzyme *carboxylase* which, with the aid of diphosphothiamin (DPT), decarboxylates pyruvic acid to acetaldehyde and carbon dioxide:

$$\text{Pyruvic acid} + \text{DPT} \xrightarrow{\text{Carboxylase}} \text{Acetaldehyde} + CO_2$$

This reaction is the source of the carbon dioxide formed during fermentation and provides the acetaldehyde, which then undergoes reduction at the expense of reduced pyridine nucleotide (H_2-DPN) to ethyl alcohol (reaction 12). Animal tissues do not have the specific enzyme carboxylase, and they are therefore unable to form acetaldehyde by this means. In such cases diphosphothiamin (cocarboxylase) is linked to another enzyme which initiates the oxidation of pyruvic acid to lactic acid, or it functions in a reaction where acetaldehyde and pyruvic acid rapidly condense to form acetylmethylcarbinol [Green, Westerfeld, Vennesland, and Knox (1942)]:

$$CH_3 \cdot CO \cdot COOH + CH_3 \cdot CHO \rightarrow CH_3 \cdot CO \cdot CHOH \cdot CH_3 + CO_2$$

Although the role played by diphosphothiamin in lactic acid formation is not clear, pyruvic acid in some way accepts hydrogen from reduced pyridine nucleotide (H_2-DPN) and is thereby reduced to lactic acid. In the lactic acid bacteria the reaction is similar to that in muscle tissues, in that pyruvic acid is the hydrogen acceptor [see Werkman and Wood (1942)]. If acetaldehyde is removed from the system by "fixation" with a binder such as sulfite, alcohol is not formed as shown in reaction 12. Then another molecule of glyceraldehyde phosphate may accept hydrogen from H_2-DPN to form α-glycerophosphate:

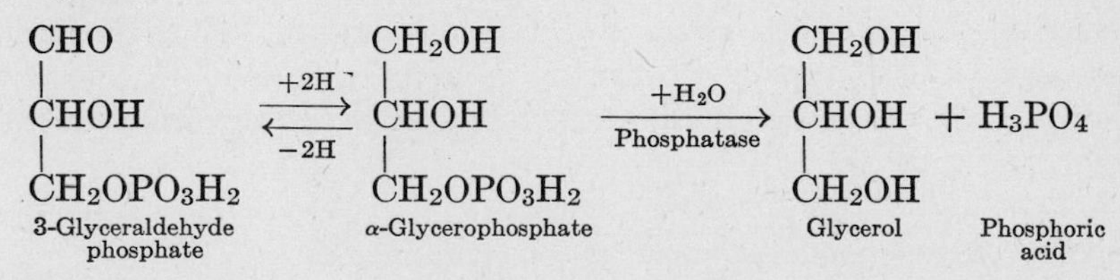

The α-glycerophosphate may then be hydrolyzed by the enzyme *phosphatase* to glycerol and phosphoric acid, a reaction which demonstrates how glycerol is formed during alcoholic fermentation. The various biochemical methods for producing glycerol actually make use of this fixation process.

The purpose of the twelve enzymatic reactions in Scheme IV is to provide energy for the yeast cells, especially in an environment of oxygen want. In the conversion of glucose to alcohol there is a decrease in the energy content of the system, and a large part of the difference in energy content is utilized by the fermenting yeast cells for growth and for other synthetic processes. That anaerobic reactions of this nature are comparatively inefficient for providing energy is known by the fact that six times as much energy can be obtained by the cell from the complete combustion of glucose to water and carbon dioxide as from its fermentation to alcohol. Let us digress therefore for a moment and inquire what happens to the fermentation process if an excess of oxygen is made available. When glucose is the substrate undergoing aerobic dissimilation by intact yeast, the initial phosphorylation reactions and the first oxidation (glyceraldehyde phosphate to glyceric acid phosphate)–reduction (DPN to H_2DPN) reaction are the same as in fermentation. At this point, however, the similarity ceases. The reduced pyridine nucleotide reacts with an enzyme which belongs to the class of flavoproteins or yellow enzymes, instead of reacting with acetaldehyde as it does in alcoholic fermentation. This yellow enzyme shuttles between an oxidized and a reduced form and thereby transports hydrogen by way of the cytochrome–cytochrome oxidase system to molecular oxygen. Such a transfer reoxidizes the reduced pyridine nucleotide so it can again enter into reaction 6. If the fermentation has been in progress before the oxygen is added, some pyruvic acid and acetaldehyde will be formed; but, since they cannot compete with oxygen as a hydrogen acceptor, they are disposed of by oxidation through the intervention of catalysts, which in turn finally react with oxygen through the cytochrome–cytochrome oxidase system.

Although the foregoing reactions account for the main products in alcoholic fermentation by yeasts, they do not account for them all. Other substances, such as formic, acetic, and succinic acids, 2:3-butylene glycol, fusel oil, and other compounds, have been shown to occur as by-products (see Table 4). Reactions have been suggested to account for these products, but in some cases they have not been proved experimentally. For example, acetic acid may arise from the dismutation of acetaldehyde as suggested by Neuberg, or it may be formed from pyruvic acid by the following reaction, which would also account for formic acid:

$$CH_3 \cdot CO \cdot COOH + H_2O \rightarrow CH_3 \cdot COOH + HCOOH$$

Succinic acid has been thought to arise from glutamic acid during fermentation through the following series of changes [see Harden (1932)]:

$$HOOC \cdot CH_2 \cdot CH_2 \cdot CH(NH_2) \cdot COOH \quad \text{Glutamic acid}$$
$$\downarrow$$
$$NH_3 + HOOC \cdot CH_2 \cdot CH_2 \cdot CO \cdot COOH \quad \alpha\text{-Ketoglutaric}$$
$$\downarrow$$
$$CO_2 + HOOC \cdot CH_2 \cdot CH_2 \cdot CHO \quad \text{Succinic semialdehyde}$$
$$\downarrow$$
$$HOOC \cdot CH_2 \cdot CH_2 \cdot COOH \quad \text{Succinic acid}$$

However, more recent studies by Wood and Werkman at Ames show that succinic acid may also arise from pyruvic acid by the so-called carbon dioxide fixation reaction:

$$CO_2 + \underset{\text{Pyruvic acid}}{HCH_2 \cdot CO \cdot COOH} \rightleftarrows \underset{\text{Oxaloacetic acid}}{COOH \cdot CH_2 \cdot CO \cdot COOH}$$

$$\underset{\text{Oxaloacetic acid}}{HOOC \cdot CH_2 \cdot CO \cdot COOH} + 4H \rightarrow \underset{\text{Succinic acid}}{HOOC \cdot CH_2 \cdot CH_2 \cdot COOH} + H_2O$$

It has been suggested by Kluyver (1931) and by others that 2,3-butylene glycol may arise in fermentations by the condensation of two molecules of acetaldehyde to form acetylmethylcarbinol, which is then reduced to 2,3-butylene glycol:

$$\underset{\text{Acetaldehyde}}{CH_3 \cdot CHO + OHC \cdot CH_3} \rightarrow \underset{\text{Acetylmethylcarbinol}}{CH_3 \cdot CO \cdot CHOH \cdot CH_3} \xrightarrow{+2H}$$

$$\underset{\text{2:3-Butylene glycol}}{CH_3 \cdot CHOH \cdot CHOH \cdot CH_3}$$

It is also probable that acetylmethylcarbinol, the precursor of 2:3-butylene glycol, arises from a condensation of pyruvic acid and acetaldehyde, as suggested by Green, Westerfeld, Vennesland, and Knox (1941, 1942). The reaction may be written as follows:

$$CH_3 \cdot CO \cdot COOH + OCH \cdot CH_3 \rightarrow CH_3 \cdot CO \cdot CHOH \cdot CH_3 + CO_2$$

The composition of the fusel oil formed in alcoholic fermentation has already been mentioned (see Table 3). Although little experimental evidence is available concerning the source of the compounds which make up fusel oil, it is believed that certain of them arise from nitrogen metabolism on the part of the yeast. For example, amyl alcohol and isoamyl alcohol may be derived from the hydrolytic decarboxylation and deamination of the amino acids isoleucine and leucine, respectively:

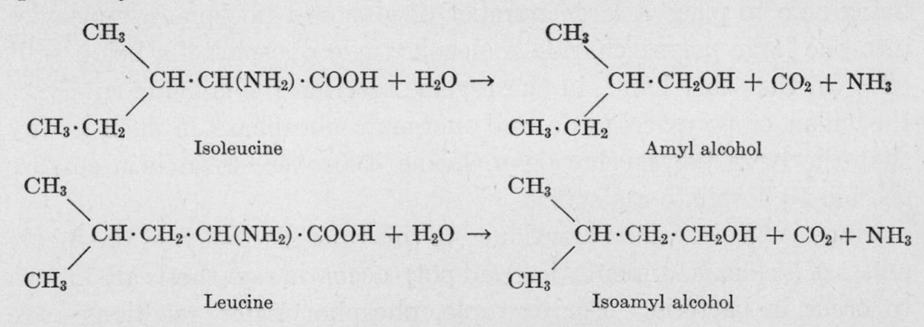

Before we leave this subject, brief mention should be made of the mechanism involved in the conversion of glucose to polysaccharide, because it may be used to illustrate reversible enzymatic reactions.

When yeast cells are abundantly supplied with glucose and at the same time aerated, they are able to store glucose in the form of a reserve polysaccharide which closely resembles glycogen. The synthetic reactions involved in this process are listed in Scheme IV and may be written as follows:

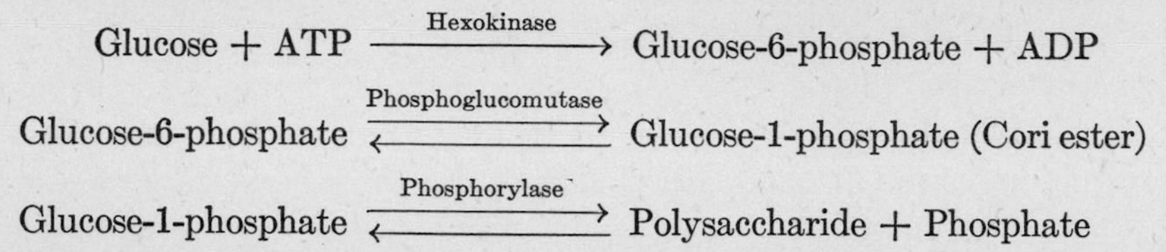

The first reaction which is catalyzed by the enzyme hexokinase has been discussed, and it may be seen that this reaction initiates any further transformation of the glucose molecule, whether it be alcoholic fermentation, oxidation, or polymerization to a polysaccharide. In order for glucose-6-phosphate to be converted to glycogen it must first undergo a molecular rearrangement in which the phosphate group migrates from the six to the one position of the glucose molecule. This reversible reaction is catalyzed by the enzyme *phosphoglucomutase*, which occurs in yeasts and many plant and animal tissues. The enzyme *phosphorylase*, which catalyzes the last reaction, has been studied in some detail by Cori and his associates in this country, Hanes (1940) in England, and others. It has been found in yeasts, potatoes, and other polysaccharide-containing plant tissues, and it has been isolated in a highly purified crystalline form from rabbit muscle by Green, Cori, and Cori (1942, 1943); it is a protein with a molecular weight between 340,000 and 400,000 and contains adenylic acid as a prosthetic group. Phosphorylase exhibits the interesting property of being able to place a large number of glucose-1-phosphate molecules into one large polysaccharide molecule while phosphate is being split off. On the other hand, in the reverse reaction the enzyme catalyzes the union of polysaccharide and inorganic phosphate in such a way that the large polysaccharide molecule is broken down into smaller glucose-1-phosphate molecules.

Many of the reactions mentioned in this brief discussion of the mechanism of alcoholic fermentation and polysaccharide synthesis are known to occur in bacteria. For example, phosphorylation reactions have been demonstrated on several occasions, and phosphoglyceric acid has actually been isolated during the dissimilation of glucose by bacteria. Furthermore, the aldolase and isomerase equilibria have been shown to exist in bacteria [see the review by Werkman and Wood

(1942)]. Although most bacteria do not form ethyl alcohol as the principal end product during sugar dissimilation, it can be assumed that they are endowed with additional enzyme systems which provide for alternate pathways of dissimilation of some of the intermediate compounds.

Important Uses of Industrial Alcohol. So widespread is the use of ethyl alcohol that, next to water, it is regarded as the most important chemical employed today. Figure 3 shows some of the more important uses of industrial alcohol. Ethyl alcohol also has several wartime uses which augment its importance. For example, it is used as a partial solvent in the manufacture of smokeless powder and as a basic raw material in the synthesis of butadiene, a component of the synthetic rubber, Buna S. It is employed as a raw material in the manufacture of ethylene, which in turn is important in the synthesis of mustard gas and in the production of styrene, another component of Buna S [Keyes (1943)].

GLYCEROL FERMENTATION

Glycerol (from the Greek *glykeros*, sweet) is an odorless, colorless, sirupy liquid with a sweet taste. Chemically it is a trihydric alcohol having the formula $CH_2OH \cdot CHOH \cdot CH_2OH$. It was first prepared from fats and oils by Scheele about 1779.

Although most commercial glycerol is prepared from fats and oils during the making of soaps, or from synthetic processes, it can be manufactured by fermentation methods. As early as 1858 Pasteur found that glycerol was formed during alcoholic fermentation by yeast to the extent of about 3.5 per cent, on the basis of the weight of sugar fermented. However, it was not until World War I that industrial methods were worked out for its production by Connstein and Lüdecke and Zerner in Germany, Cocking and Lilly in England, and Eoff, Linder, and Beyer in the United States. Although these workers were the originators of the fermentation processes for the manufacturer of glycerol, the merit for having recognized such possibilities must be ascribed to Neuberg and Reinfurth (1918). While these workers were conducting experiments on aldehyde fixation with sodium sulfite in an effort to elucidate the mechanism of alcoholic fermentation, they discovered that such a fixation increased greatly the amount of glycerol formed; for example, under normal conditions only about 3.5 per cent glycerol is formed, but they observed that five to ten times this quantity was produced when sulfite was added to the fermentation mixture

The following reaction was given to account for the chemistry of the process:

$$\underset{\text{Glucose}}{C_6H_{12}O_6} + \underset{\text{Sodium sulfite}}{Na_2SO_3} + H_2O \rightarrow$$

$$NaHCO_3 + \underset{\text{"Fixed" acetaldehyde which cannot undergo normal reduction to alcohol}}{CH_3 \cdot CHO \cdot NaHSO_3} + \underset{\text{Glycerol}}{C_3H_8O_3}$$

Other details of the course of events occurring in the so-called Neuberg scheme will be found in the discussion of the mechanism of alcoholic fermentation.

Outline of the Industrial Fermentation Processes. Three well-known fermentation processes for the production of glycerol were worked out during or soon after World War I, and modifications of them are still being patented [see Haehn (1938), Walmesley (1939), I. G. Farbenindustrie (1942)]. The extent to which these processes are being used today is not known definitely, but it is certainly much less than a decade or two ago, because of the comparatively plentiful supply of fat products and the increased use of synthetic methods for the manufacture of glycerol. Duchenne (1942), however, has calculated that a cane sugar factory producing 8,000 tons of molasses a year can manufacture 6 tons of glycerol per day by fermentation methods. This fact suggests that certain by-products may be used for glycerol fermentation.

The fermentation methods so far described for the production of glycerol are very similar in that the basal medium contains a fermentable sugar and usually nutrient salts, yeasts are used to produce the fermentation, and fixative agents are added at various intervals during the fermentation to bind the aldehyde or other products and increase the yield of glycerol. For complete details of these processes and their modifications the original articles cited on pp. 928 to 930, the monograph by Lawrie (1928), and the articles by Duchenne (1942) and Lees (1944) should be consulted.

THE CONNSTEIN-LÜDECKE (GERMAN SULFITE) PROCESS. Early in World War I the Germans realized that there would be a serious shortage of glycerol for explosives and, utilizing the facts presented by Neuberg and his associates, worked out the technical production of glycerol by fermentation; the details of the process were kept secret until after the war, when Connstein and Lüdecke (1919) and Zerner (1920) published their results (see Table 5). The basis of the process is that acetaldehyde is fixed by sodium sulfite (see Scheme III, p. 914):

$$CH_3 \cdot CHO + Na_2SO_3 + CO_2 + H_2O \rightarrow CH_3 \cdot CHO \cdot HSO_3Na + NaHCO_3$$

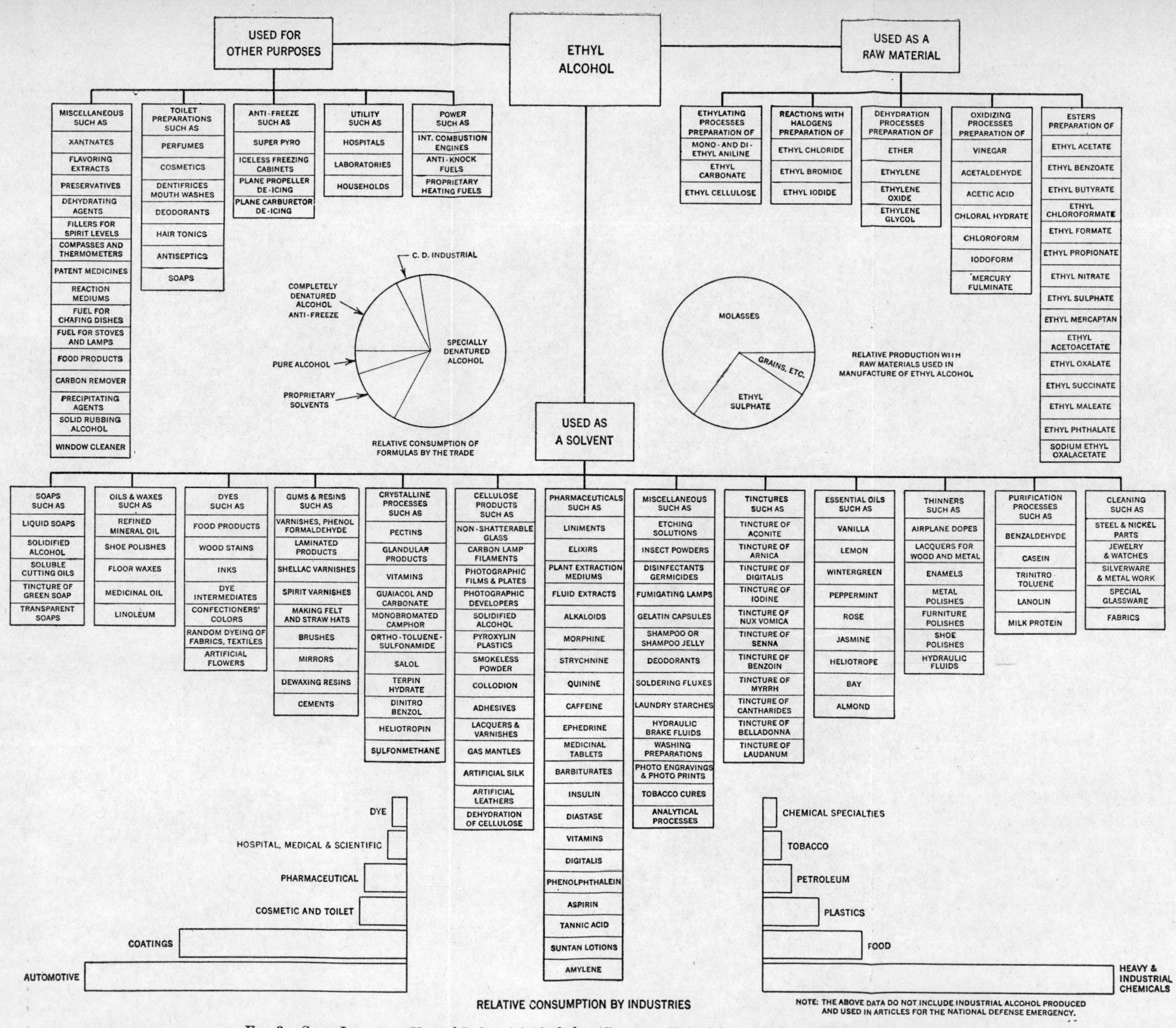

FIG. 3. Some Important Uses of Industrial Alcohol. (Courtesy, United States Industrial Chemicals, Inc.)

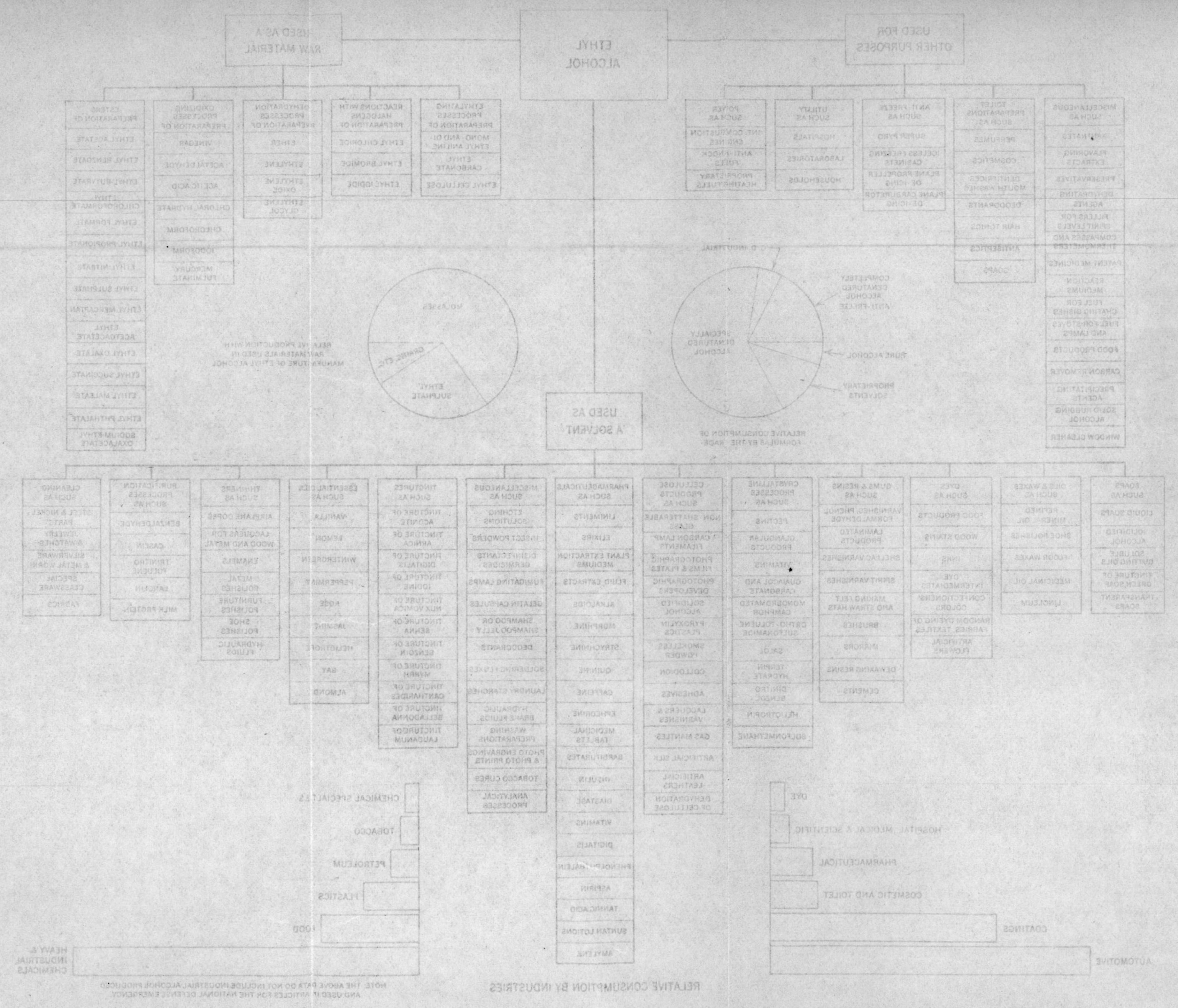

FIG. 8. Some Important Uses of Industrial Alcohol. (Courtesy, United States Industrial Chemicals, Inc.)

Therefore, the reduction of acetaldehyde to alcohol is partially or completely prevented, and glycerol accumulates in a greater quantity than it does in normal alcoholic fermentation.

In order to recover and purify the glycerol, the raw fermented slop was distilled to remove the acetaldehyde and alcohol. The sulfite in the residue was precipitated as calcium sulfite by the addition of calcium chloride and was filtered out. The excess calcium remaining in the filtrate was removed as calcium carbonate by the addition of sodium carbonate. Technically pure glycerol was then obtained after evaporation by distillation under reduced pressure. During World War I the plants in operation in Germany produced about 1,000 tons of glycerol per month by this process.

THE COCKING-LILLY (SULFITE-BISULFITE) PROCESS. This process was developed in England by Cocking and Lilly and patented in 1921 [see Lawrie (1928)]; it is a modification of the sulfite method of Connstein and Lüdecke in that neutral mixtures of sodium sulfite and sodium bisulfite are added to the fermenting mash to produce the following reaction:

$$Na_2SO_3 + NaHSO_3 + CO_2 + H_2O \rightarrow 2NaHSO_3 + NaHCO_3$$

This reaction results in the production of twice the amount of bisulfite that occurs when sulfite is added alone. Therefore, more of the acetaldehyde is fixed at an earlier stage in the fermentation, and larger amounts of glycerol are formed (see Table 5). A modification of this process has recently been proposed by Duchenne (1942) (see Table 5).

THE EOFF-LINDER-BEYER (AMERICAN SODIUM CARBONATE) PROCESS. This process was developed during World War I by Eoff, Linder, and Beyer (1919), but it was never used to manufacture glycerol for war purposes. Eoff and his associates, however, carried out a few small-plant-scale fermentations at the glycerol refinery of William F. Jobbins, Inc., Aurora, Illinois, and on a 15,000-gal. scale were able to get glycerol yields of 18 to 25 per cent. The process was based on Neuberg's results (see Scheme II on p. 914) in using an alkaline medium for the alcoholic fermentation of sugars. Sodium carbonate in the form of soda ash was used to neutralize the acetic acid and other acids formed, although potassium carbonate, sodium and potassium hydroxides, sodium perborate, and other alkaline-producing substances gave favorable results.

The Mechanism of Glycerol Fermentation. The first explanation of the mechanism of the formation of glycerol in the alcoholic fermentation of sugars by yeast was presented by Neuberg and Reinfurth (1918). As we have already mentioned, they showed that acetaldehyde was drawn into a complex combination with sulfite or other

TABLE 5

COMPARATIVE DATA ON THE BETTER-KNOWN METHODS FOR PRODUCING GLYCEROL BY FERMENTATION PROCESSES

Method	Substrate			Strain or Type of Yeast	Incubation Temperature	Aldehyde or Acid Fixative	Percentage * of Sugar Fermented as				
	Sugar	Salt, etc.	Reaction				Glycerol	Alcohol	Acetic Acid	Aldehyde	CO_2
Connstein and Lüdecke (1919)	Sucrose (beet sugar) or others (10%)	Na_2HPO_4, $MgSO_4$, etc.	Alkaline	Any strain of fresh yeast	30°C. for 48–60 hours	Na_2SO_3	16–25	29–40	...	2.5	29
Cocking and Lilly (1921)	Molasses, cane sugar, etc.		Alkaline	Pressed yeast	36°C. for 5–9 days	Na_2SO_3 + $NaHSO_3$	24–49	26–50	...	12–23	..
Duchenne (1942)	Molasses		Alkaline	*Saccharomyces ellipsoideus*	35°C. for 5 days	$CaSO_3$ + $Ca(HSO_3)_2$	10.1–15.3	9.80–13.4	...	...	..
Eoff, Linder and Beyer (1919)	Blackstrap molasses (17.5–20.0%)	NH_4Cl, malt sprouts	Alkaline	*Saccharomyces cerevisiae*, *S. ellipsoideus*	30°–32°C. for 5–7 days	Na_2CO_3 or other alkalies	18–25	36	7.0	...	36

* Figures are only approximate, since in certain cases they were not all obtained in the same experiment.

fixatives and therefore was not so easily reduced to alcohol as was free aldehyde formed transitorily during normal fermentation. The hydrogen remaining free then attached itself to another acceptor which underwent reduction to glycerol; this second acceptor was not identified by Neuberg and his associates. More recently our information on the intermediate products occurring during alcoholic fermentation has expanded, and, according to Negelein and Brömel (1939), glycerol is formed when the natural oxidation reaction:

$$\underset{\text{(Reduced coenzyme I)}}{\text{Dihydropyridine nucleotide phosphate}} + \text{Acetaldehyde} \rightarrow \underset{\text{(Oxidized coenzyme I)}}{\text{Pyridine nucleotide phosphate}} + \text{Alcohol}$$

is interrupted by the binding of aldehyde and the following reaction takes place:

$$\underset{\text{(Reduced coenzyme I)}}{\text{Dihydropyridine nucleotide phosphate}} + \text{Triosephosphate} \rightarrow \underset{\text{(Oxidized coenzyme I)}}{\text{Pyridine nucleotide phosphate}} + \text{Glycerol (phosphate)}$$

Important Uses of Glycerol. The uses of glycerol are extremely varied; in fact, Lawrie (1928) lists over ninety products of which glycerol is a constituent, and new uses are continually being found. For example, it is employed in the manufacture of explosives, as a sweetening agent, as an antifreezing agent, and as a constituent of perfumes, ink, adhesives, modeling clays, shoe polishes, lotions, and linoleum.

OTHER YEAST FERMENTATION PRODUCTS

Certain yeasts can be employed to prepare *l*-acetylphenylcarbinol, which in turn may be used to synthesize the alkaloid drug *l*-ephedrine [see Tauber (1943)]:

$$\underset{l\text{-Acetylphenyl carbinol}}{C_6H_5 \cdot CHOH \cdot CO \cdot CH_3} + \underset{\text{Methylamine}}{CH_3 \cdot NH_2} \rightarrow$$

$$C_6H_5 \cdot CHOH \cdot \underset{\underset{CH_3}{|}}{C}{:}N \cdot CH_3 \xrightarrow[\text{Catalyst}]{+H_2} \underset{l\text{-Ephedrine}}{C_6H_5 \cdot CHOH \cdot \underset{\underset{CH_3}{|}}{CH} \cdot NH \cdot CH_3}$$

This process has been patented by Hildebrand and Klavehn (1934), who reported that 25 to 45 g. of *l*-ephedrine hydrochloride can be obtained by special catalytic treatment of 120 g. of Neuberg's oil fermentation product (containing about 27.4 per cent *l*-acetylphenylcarbinol) and 10 g. of methylamine. The product obtained by this means is identical in every respect with the natural *l*-ephedrine extracted from the Chinese plant, *ma huang*.

TABLE 6

APPROXIMATE PRODUCTION OF ALCOHOLIC BEVERAGES (BEERS, WINES, AND DISTILLED SPIRITS) IN GALLONS IN THE UNITED STATES FOR THE FISCAL YEARS 1939 AND 1941 TO 1944

(Data from United States Treasury Department, Bureau of Internal Revenue, Alcohol Tax Unit, Washington, D. C.; United States Brewers' Association, New York; Wine Institute, San Francisco; Distilled Spirits Institute, Washington, D. C.)

Alcoholic Beverage	1939	1941	1942	1943	1944
Malt-beverages (beers), gallons *	1,669,987,143	1,711,629,350	2,158,732,085	2,326,295,924	2,531,195,539
Wines, gallons †					
Still wines ‡	231,959,287	286,371,423	313,706,263	195,188,152	264,852,755
Sparkling wines §	417,735	1,138,164	1,536,344	1,272,487	1,886,972
Distilled spirits, as tax gallons ‖					
Whisky	93,033,917	121,851,983	120,257,424	19,529,698	....
Rum	2,442,689	2,614,946	3,106,125	2,314,227	2,212,456
Gin	6,279,119	5,177,357	5,344,956	1,449,146	....
Brandy	27,446,296	25,363,877	29,273,293	16,623,903	21,590,999
Other spirits (cordials, liqueurs, etc.)	16,154,155	20,200,583	....	....	....

* Data usually reported as 31-gal. barrels.
† Standard wine gallon of 231 cu. in.
‡ Amount of material removed from fermenters, including that to be used for distilling purposes.
§ Data usually reported as half-pint units.
‖ The tax on distilled spirits is collected on the basis of proof gallons for spirits of 100 proof or over and on the basis of wine gallons for spirits of less than 100 proof. The proof of spirits is twice the percentage of the content (by volume) of ethyl alcohol; spirits containing 50% of ethyl alcohol by volume under standard conditions are thus 100 proof. A standard proof gallon is a wine gallon of 100 proof spirits.

Yeast enzymes may be employed in the preparation of fructose-1:6-diphosphate, 3-phosphoglycerate, and other intermediate compounds which occur during alcoholic fermentation [see Tauber (1943)].

We have already mentioned that yeasts play a most important role in numerous other industries. For example, they are used in the manufacture of malt beverages (beers), wines, distilled liquors, and other alcoholic beverages. Some idea of the size of these industries will be realized by observing the production figures compiled in Table 6.

Frey (1930) and Frey, Kirby, and Schultz (1936) state that approximately 230,000,000 lb. of yeast are produced annually in the United States. Most of this quantity is used in bread-making and as a source of vitamins; however, some of it is employed to prepare glutathione, nucleic acid and its decomposition products, soluble proteins or extracts for food purposes, enzymes, and several other substances. Certain species of yeast are also employed in Germany and other countries as a source of fats.

Since many of the products mentioned cannot be regarded as pure chemicals, their manufacture will not be discussed here. For additional reading on this subject the books by Prescott and Dunn (1940) and Tauber (1943) should be consulted.

B. BACTERIAL FERMENTATIONS

Several organic compounds are now produced industrially by bacterial means, and in the future greater use may be made of such methods to manufacture a variety of substances. At present not all the bacterial fermentations described below are carried on at an industrial scale; in fact, certain ones are of only academic interest. For some of these, however, experimental or pilot-plant methods are available should it be necessary to use them under conditions of unusual demand.

It is usually convenient to allocate the bacterial fermentations to the following two groups, based upon their relationship to atmospheric oxygen:

I. *Anoxidative* (*anoxybiontic*) *bacterial fermentations*, which are essentially anaerobic or microaerophilic in character. Included in this group are: lactic acid fermentation, propionic acid fermentation, colon-typhoid-dysentery fermentations, 2:3-butylene glycol fermentation, butyric acid fermentation, butanol-acetone fermentation, butanol-isopropyl alcohol fermentation, ethyl alcohol-acetone fermentation, and miscellaneous anaerobic fermentations.

II. *Oxidative* (*oxybiontic*) *bacterial fermentations*, which are primarily aerobic in nature. These include: acetic acid fermentation, *l*-sorbose fermentation, dihydroxyacetone fermentation, gluconic acid fermentations, *d*-tartaric acid fermentation, and miscellaneous aerobic dissimilations.

These bacterial fermentations will now be discussed briefly in the foregoing order.

I. Anoxidative (Anoxybiontic) Bacterial Fermentations

LACTIC ACID FERMENTATION

Lactic acid, or α-hydroxypropionic acid ($CH_3 \cdot CHOH \cdot COOH$), was first discovered by Scheele in 1870 and is one of the oldest-known organic acids. Although it was first isolated from sour milk, it has since been found to be very widely distributed in nature. Since lactic acid contains an asymmetric carbon atom, it exists in two optically isomeric forms. The form of the acid commonly known as sarcolactic occurs in blood and has a (+) rotation but the *l*-configuration. It is therefore correctly designated as *l*-(+)-lactic acid, and its mirror image as *d*-(−)-lactic acid, but commercial technology makes no distinction. In fact, the lactic acid of commerce is usually the racemic mixture. Both of these isomers occur freely in nature.

Lactic acid can be produced by purely chemical means or by fermentation methods [Peckham (1944)]. Chemically it may be prepared in a maximum of 50 per cent yield by the alkaline (KOH) degradation of hexose sugars under normal atmospheric conditions or in somewhat greater yields by superimposed temperature (200° to 250°C.) and pressure (20 atm.), or it may be synthesized from the interaction of acetaldehyde and carbon monoxide in the presence of a catalyst at 130° to 200°C. under pressure (900 atm.). Since none of these ways is as yet adaptable to industrial practice, direct fermentation methods provide the sole commercial source of the acid, at least in this country.

As early as 1881 C. E. Avery of Littleton, Massachusetts, produced lactic acid on a small technical scale by fermentation methods, but the process was uncertain for a number of years. However, in 1895 Wehmer employed pure cultures of *Lactobacillus delbrückii* in industrial operations at high incubation temperatures (about 50°C.) and obtained yields up to 90 per cent of theory. Since that time the industry has grown in size and importance.

Before World War II the total world production of all grades of lactic acid was approximately 6,000 tons per year [Bernhauer (1939)]. Of this total the United States produced about 2,500 tons. During 1942 and 1943 production in this country practically doubled [Peckham (1944)].

Lactic acid is now customarily marketed in four grades and in several concentrations in each grade. These include:

1. *Crude or technical grade lactic acid*, usually sold in aqueous solutions of 22, 44, or 80 per cent concentrations, is used for deliming and plumping hides, for dyeing textile goods, and as flux for soft solders.

2. *Edible grade lactic acid*, customarily sold at 50 or 80 per cent concentrations, is used for a number of food purposes, for example, in confections, extracts, fruit juices and essences, and brines for packing green olives, pickles, and other products. It is used to acidify worts in the manufacture of beer, to remove the carbonate hardness of liquor, and to inhibit the development of butyric acid bacteria in the manufacture of yeast.

3. *Plastic grade lactic acid*, also sold in 50 and 80 per cent concentrations, is now widely used in the preparation of various plastics.

4. *U.S.P. grade lactic acid*, the best available quality, is marketed as 75 and 85 per cent concentrations. It is used mainly in the pharmaceutical industry as a modifier for cow's milk for infant feeding and for many less familiar medical purposes.

Many uses have also been found for certain salts and derivatives of lactic acid. For example, calcium lactate is used in some baking powders; sodium lactate is employed to aid in the retention of moisture by tobacco and other substances; and iron and copper lactates are

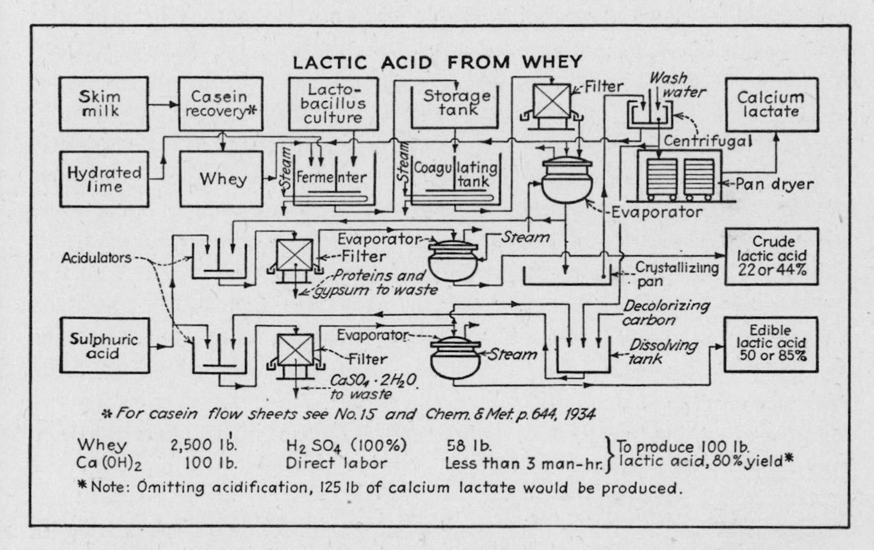

FIG. 4. Flow Sheet of Lactic Acid from Whey by Fermentation. (Courtesy, *Chemical and Metallurgical Engineering*, McGraw-Hill Publishing Company.)

used for various purposes. The methyl, ethyl, and butyl esters are in commercial use in the manufacture of inks, plastics, and lacquers. New uses are continually being found for lactic acid and its derivatives. The natural preservation of sauerkraut, pickles, silage, and certain cheese and milk products is due mainly to their lactic acid content.

Outline of the Industrial Fermentation Process.[5] The industrial production of lactic acid will be discussed under the following headings: (1) raw materials and their treatment; (2) choice of organisms and preparation of the starter; (3) fermentation of the mash; and (4) yield, recovery, purification, and separation into grades. Each of these steps has a marked influence on the yield and properties of the final product. Figure 4 is a flow sheet showing the steps in the manu-

[5] For more complete details of the industrial production of lactic acid and its derivatives Garrett (1930), Whittier and Rogers (1931), Olive (1936), Burton (1937), Smith and Claborn (1939), Prescott and Dunn (1940), and Peckham (1944) should be consulted.

facture of lactic acid from whey. In general, the same procedure is used with other raw materials [see Peckham (1944)].

1. Raw Materials and Their Treatment. Any one of a variety of carbohydrate-containing materials can be used for lactic acid fermentation. The choice of material depends upon its availability, its fermentability with or without preliminary treatment, and its cost. In this country starch hydrolyzates, molasses, and whey are commonly used in the commercial manufacture of lactic acid; in Germany potato starch is usually employed; and in Italy whey, molasses, and sugar-beet juice are used. Wood sugar (xylose), Jerusalem artichoke tubers, and other carbohydrate substances have been employed experimentally but are not widely used today.

Substances which contain glucose, sucrose, or lactose in their natural form require little or no preliminary treatment before fermentation, but polysaccharides, such as corn and potato starch or Jerusalem artichokes, must first be hydrolyzed to maltose or glucose, or to levulose, respectively, by the action of amylases (malt or fungal) or acids before they can be fermented.

Crude or technical grade lactic acid is generally manufactured from unrefined substrates, and some of the better grades are likewise made from crude materials and then purified. An alternative method for the better grades is to use refined sugar as a substrate, so that the lactic acid requires less purification.

Many of the substrates we have mentioned are low in nitrogenous substances, growth factors, and inorganic ions which are required for the development of the various lactic acid bacteria. This is especially true of starch hydrolyzates and molasses. The addition of inorganic phosphate, sulfate, and other inorganic ions, together with such accessory nutrients as are found in malt sprouts, steep water, or thin grain residues, usually corrects these deficiencies [Stiles and Pruess (1938)]. Some of the known growth factors that are required by the lactic acid bacteria are mentioned in Chapter 7.

2. Choice of Organism[6] and Preparation of the Starter. Several species of lactic acid bacteria can be used for the production of lactic acid commercially, and certain molds are also adaptable. The selection of the organism depends primarily upon the type of car-

[6] *Bergey's Manual* (1939) should be consulted for information on the classification of the lactic acid bacteria into those (homofermentative) which produce primarily lactic acid from carbohydrates and those (heterofermentative) which form lactic acid and considerable amounts of by-products (CO_2, alcohol, acetic acid; mannitol from levulose). It is also of interest that certain organisms which normally produce only traces of lactic acid can be made to form quite large amounts under special conditions [see Bernhauer (1939)].

bohydrate being fermented and the temperature to be used. *Lactobacillus delbrückii*, *Lactobacillus bulgaricus*, *Bacillus dextrolacticus*, or *Streptococcus lactis* can be employed where *d*- or *i*-lactic acid is to be produced. On the other hand, strains of *Leuconostoc mesenteroides* and *Lactobacillus caucasicus* can be used to make *l*-lactic acid. *Lactobacillus bulgaricus* is favored where milk or whey is the substrate, whereas *L. delbrückii*, which does not ferment lactose, is preferred when the substrate contains dextrose or maltose. *Bacillus dextrolacticus* produces large yields of *d*-lactic acid from levulose [Andersen and Greaves (1942)]. *Lactobacillus bulgaricus*, *L. delbrückii*, and *B. dextrolacticus* have an added advantage over most of the others mentioned in that they grow at high temperatures (45° to 50°C.).

Other lactic acid bacteria (heterofermentative), such as *Lactobacillus brevis* (*Lactobacillus pentoaceticus*, *Lactobacillus lycopersici*) and *Lactobacillus buchneri* (*Lactobacillus mannitopoeus*), usually produce *i*-lactic acid along with considerable amounts of by-products (CO_2, ethyl alcohol, acetic acid; and mannitol from levulose). These organisms are of little value in this country as far as lactic acid production is concerned, but they have been used somewhat in Italy to produce mannitol from levulose [Bernhauer (1939)].

The preparation of the starter is begun in the laboratory by inoculating a flask containing about 1 liter of sterile mash (whey or glucose-malt-extract-salt medium) with 10 ml. of a young, actively growing culture of the desired species, usually strains of *L. delbrückii* or *L. bulgaricus*. After incubation for 24 hours at 42° to 45°C. (108° to 113°F.) the contents of the flask are added to a larger batch of starter mash and again incubated under similar conditions. This step-up procedure is continued until a starter is obtained which has about one-tenth the volume of the main mash to be fermented. Large glass-lined steel tanks of about 500-gal. capacity, which can be easily sterilized, are sometimes used to prepare the final starter.

3. Fermentation of the Mash. Various types of vats (fermenters) may be used for lactic acid fermentation. Usually they are wood tanks about 5,000 to 6,000 gal. in capacity and equipped with mechanical stirrers and heating coils to keep the neutralizing agent well mixed and to control the temperature.

After the raw material to be used has received its preliminary treatment, including hydrolysis and removal of casein, it is placed in the fermenter and diluted with water so that the sugar concentration is between 5 and 20 per cent. The amount of water added depends upon the nature of the raw material, the strain of organism to be employed, and other conditions. The special nutrients and calcium carbonate are then added, the pH is adjusted to a slightly acid reaction, and the mash is pasteurized. After pasteurization the temperature is reduced to the optimum for fermentation, and the mash is inoculated with the starter. In fermentations in which *Lactobacillus delbrückii*, *Lactobacillus bulgaricus*, and *Bacillus dextrolacticus* are used a temperature between 45° and 50°C. (113° and 122°F.) is usually maintained. Other lactic acid bacteria, such as *Streptococcus lactis*, require a temperature of about 30°C. A high fermentation temperature eliminates most contamination problems and permits the use of a mash which has been pasteurized, in contrast to the sterile growing medium required for mesophilic bacteria.

Oxygen is not required for lactic acid fermentation, since this process is microaerophilic or anaerobic in character.

The lactic acid formed by the bacteria reacts with the free calcium carbonate present, producing calcium lactate and carbon dioxide gas. This reaction prevents the pH of the mash from becoming so low as to inhibit the activities of the bacteria. Sometimes the calcium carbonate or hydroxide is added to the mash at intervals of about every 6 hours during fermentation, so that the acidity does not rise above approximately 0.6 per cent.

After fermentation is complete (2 to 6 days), the acid may be neutralized to about 0.1 per cent and the mash heated in a tank at 82° to 96°C. (180° to 205°F.) to coagulate the proteins present and to destroy the bacteria.

4. Yield, Recovery, Purification, and Separation into Grades. The theoretical yield of lactic acid with homofermentative lactic acid bacteria is 100 per cent of the weight of the sugar fermented, according to the over-all equation:

$$\underset{180}{C_6H_{12}O_6} \rightarrow \underset{2 \times 90}{2CH_3 \cdot CHOH \cdot COOH}$$

Such a yield has been obtained experimentally on several occasions, but in commercial practice it is never obtained. It is believed that part of the sugar is utilized by the organisms in their metabolism; therefore yields of 90 to 96 per cent are considered normal. Further losses also occur during subsequent processing, so in typical plant operations yields in the order of 85 per cent are most common.

The technology of the recovery of pure calcium lactate or lactic acid from the crude calcium lactate solution resulting from fermentation varies considerably. As the flow sheet (Fig. 4) shows, the calcium lactate can be purified by evaporation and crystallization, followed by washing, centrifuging, and drying. The details for this process are discussed at some length by Olive (1936), Walsh, Needle, and Daley (1939), Prescott and Dunn (1940), and Peckham (1944). The recovery of crude grade lactic acid is accomplished by decomposing the crude calcium lactate resulting from the fermentation by means of acidulation with sulfuric acid, followed by filtration and evaporation. Edible grade lactic acid may be recovered in much the same way, except that the purified calcium lactate is used instead of the crude material (see Fig. 4). An alternate procedure for the recovery of edible lactic acid has been discussed by Peckham (1944). It involves the extraction of crude lactic acid with a suitable solvent (isopropyl ether), followed by a second extraction of the lactic acid from the isopropyl ether by passing the solution through pure water. U.S.P. lactic acid can be produced by steam distillation under relatively high vacuum, by the solvent extraction procedure outlined, or by preparation of the ester, methyl lactate, which is fractionally distilled and hydrolyzed and the methanol removed by distillation [see Smith and Claborn (1939), Peckham (1944)].

The Mechanisms of the Lactic Acid Fermentations. It has been stated that the lactic acid bacteria can be conveniently allocated to two groups, that is, the homofermentative and the heterofermentative types. Since the chemistry of the fermentations which these two types catalyze is somewhat different, each will be discussed separately.

THE HOMOFERMENTATIVE BACTERIA. The bacteria, such as *Lactobacillus delbrückii*, *Lactobacillus bulgaricus*, and *Bacillus dextrolacticus*, which belong to this group produce only lactic acid from glucose and other sugars, according to the over-all equation:

$$C_6H_{12}O_6 \rightarrow 2CH_3 \cdot CHOH \cdot COOH$$

The process, however, is not so simple as this general equation seems to indicate, because several ephemeral intermediate compounds are known to occur during the course of the fermentation.

The initial stages of lactic acid fermentation seem to be similar to those of ethyl alcohol fermentation, in that the sugar being fermented is first phosphorylated and then dissimilated to form a triose compound [see pp. 910 to 927 on alcoholic fermentation and Bernhauer (1939)]. Although the reactions which occur between this triose and lactic acid have not been fully proved, two possible mechanisms have been suggested. One involves the formation, as the final intermediate, of methylglyoxal, which is in turn converted to lactic acid by glyoxalase and its coenzyme, glutathione (see Chapter 7):

$$\underset{\text{Methylglyoxal}}{CH_3 \cdot CO \cdot CHO} + H_2O \xrightarrow{\text{Glyoxalase}} \underset{\text{Lactic acid}}{CH_3 \cdot CHOH \cdot COOH}$$

The second mechanism involves the dissimilation of the sugar to pyruvic acid in a manner similar to that occurring in alcoholic fermentation. The pyruvic acid is then reduced to lactic acid:

$$\underset{\text{Pyruvic acid}}{CH_3 \cdot CO \cdot COOH} + 2H \rightarrow \underset{\text{Lactic acid}}{CH_3 \cdot CHOH \cdot COOH}$$

Bernhauer (1939) cites experimental data which suggest that either or both of these mechanisms may be operative during lactic acid fermentation.

THE HETEROFERMENTATIVE BACTERIA. The bacteria, such as *Lactobacillus brevis*, *Lactobacillus buchneri*, and *Leuconostoc dextranicum*, of this group form lactic acid, together with appreciable quantities of ethyl alcohol, acetic acid, carbon dioxide, and glycerol from glucose; mannitol is also formed from levulose. Therefore any scheme which is set up to explain the dissimilation of sugar must include all these end products. Several workers have studied the mechanism of the formation of the final products by the heterofermentative lactic acid bacteria [see Bernhauer (1939), Prescott and Dunn (1940)]. The studies by

TABLE 7

DISSIMILATION OF GLUCOSE AND LEVULOSE BY HETEROFERMENTATIVE LACTIC ACID BACTERIA

[From Nelson and Werkman (1940)]

	Leuconostoc dextranicum		*Lactobacillus brevis*	
	Glucose, millimols	Levulose, millimols	Glucose, millimols	Levulose, millimols
Hexose fermented	100	100	100	100
Products formed				
Ethyl alcohol	81.2	51.2	74.1	0.8
Acetic acid	10.8	34.9	15.3	40.3
Carbon dioxide	86.5	77.5	81.0	44.7
Lactic acid	83.5	53.4	83.1	33.1
Glycerol	24.0	2.1	32.6	3.8
Mannitol	......	29.8	......	62.3
	per cent	per cent	per cent	per cent
Carbon recovery	98.9	99.1	101.1	101.9

Nelson and Werkman (1935, 1936, 1940) may be cited as one example, since they best explain the most recent viewpoints on this subject.

The data in Table 7 show the kinds and quantities of products formed from glucose and levulose by *Leuconostoc dextranicum* and *Lactobacillus brevis* (*L. lycopersici*). The experiments were carried out under anaerobic conditions at 30°C. for 21 days; a medium containing hexose, yeast extract, peptone, and phosphate salts was used. The data in the table show a marked difference between the products of the two hexoses. For example, a large amount of mannitol was formed from levulose but not from glucose, and *Leuconostoc dextranicum* produced less mannitol and more alcohol from levulose than did *Lactobacillus brevis*.

When Nelson and Werkman applied their experimental data in Table 7 to the following scheme, they found that their data were in good agreement with calculated values. Therefore the scheme outlined in Fig. 5 seems to represent most of the chemical events which

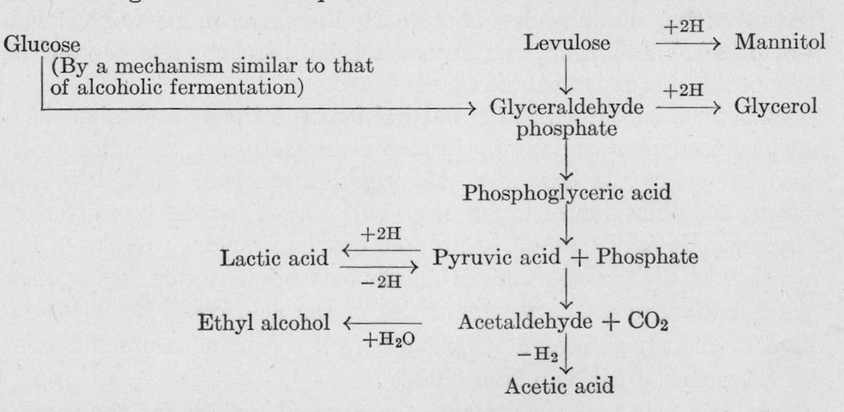

FIG. 5. Scheme for the Dissimilation of Hexoses by Heterofermentative Lactic Acid Bacteria [From Nelson and Werkman (1940)].

occur in heterofermentative lactic acid fermentation. An alternate course for the formation of lactic acid, acetic acid, and carbon dioxide may arise from the dismutation of pyruvic acid:

$$2CH_3\cdot CO\cdot COOH \xrightarrow{+H_2O} CH_3\cdot COOH + CO_2 + CH_3\cdot CHOH\cdot COOH$$

where one molecule of pyruvic acid is oxidized to acetic acid and CO_2, and another is reduced to lactic acid.

PROPIONIC ACID FERMENTATION

Propionic acid ($CH_3\cdot CH_2\cdot COOH$) was probably first discovered by Nöllner in 1841, when he isolated a substance from tartrate fermentation which he termed Pseudo-Essigsäure. Three years later

Gottlieb discovered a similar acid, which he called metacetonic acid, and in 1846 and 1847 Nicklès called Nöllner's acid acide-butyro-acétique, to indicate its place between acetic and butyric acids. Finally in 1847 Dumas and his students showed that these three acids were the same and proposed the name propionic acid. During the next forty years research by Strecker, Fitz, Pasteur, and others added to our knowledge of propionic acid fermentation, but all these early studies were carried out with cultures of doubtful purity.

In 1898 Orla-Jensen began his studies of the formation of the characteristic eyes in Swiss cheese, but it was not until 1906 that he and von Freudenreich were able to isolate the causative organism and to show that propionic acid and carbon dioxide were the prominent products formed during the ripening of Emmenthaler cheese. After these early reports on the production of propionic acid numerous studies were undertaken in this country and abroad to determine the importance of the propionic acid bacteria in Swiss cheese and other natural fermentations. For a review of the early literature on this subject van Niel (1928), Foote, Fred, and Peterson (1930), and the references cited later in this discussion should be consulted.

Aside from its occurrence in natural fermentations propionic acid is not produced commercially by fermentation methods. Chemical processes involving the oxidation of propyl alcohol or methyl propyl ketone, the reduction of lactic or propiolic acids, or the hydrolysis of ethyl cyanide may be used to prepare propionic acid. In spite of the fact that at the present time propionic acid fermentation is primarily of academic interest, large quantities of the acid could be manufactured by industrial fermentation methods if a demand arose [Whittier and Sherman (1923), van Niel (1928)].

Propionic acid and its derivatives are used mainly for the manufacture of perfume esters, for artificial fruit flavors, and as solvents for pyroxylin and related substances.

The Fermentation Process. The propionic acid bacteria are widely distributed in nature. They are most easily isolated from certain types of Swiss cheese, but they also occur in other dairy products and in silage, soil, and other places. *Bergey's Manual* (1939) recognizes eleven species in the genus *Propionibacterium*, based mainly on the careful cultural, physiological, and serological studies by van Niel (1928), Werkman and Brown (1933), and Hitchner (1934). These references should be consulted for details on the differentiation of the eleven species. The better-known of these eleven species of *Propionibacterium* are *P. freudenreichii*, *P. jensenii*, *P. shermanii*, *P. pentosaceum*, *P. arabinosum*, *P. peterssonii*, and *P. technicum*.

A number of substances can serve as a substrate for propionic acid fermentation. Lactose, maltose, glucose, levulose, glycerol, and lactate in 1 to 3 per cent concentrations are commonly used in experimental studies, but other organic acids, alcohols, sugars, and their degradation products can also be employed. *Propionibacterium technicum* also has the ability to ferment starch, dextrin, and glycogen. Ammonium sulfate, peptones, whey, yeast extract, malt sprouts, and corn meal in 0.5 to 1 per cent concentrations serve as a source of nitrogen for the propionic acid bacteria. When ammonium sulfate is used in the medium, growth is usually accelerated by adding amino acids and certain growth factors (see Chapter 7). In addition to these substances inorganic salts, such as Speakman's mixture, are essential for growth and acid production.

The optimum *p*H for the normal fermentation of sugars is usually between 6.8 and 7.2; Wood, Erb, and Werkman (1937), however, found that the dissimilation of pyruvic acid by cell suspensions of propionic acid bacteria occurs most rapidly at *p*H 5.5. The most favorable temperature is about 30°C., although the organisms will

TABLE 8

Conditions of the Experiments Shown in Table 9

[From Wood and Werkman (1936)]

Species and Fermentation Number		Age of Inoculum, days	Medium			Incubation Temperature, °C.	Period of Incubation, days
			Glucose, per cent	$CaCO_3$, per cent	Bacto-Yeast Extract, per cent		
Propionibacterium arabinosum	1	5	3.0	1.4	0.5	37	18
	2	5	2.1	1.0	0.35	30	18
Propionibacterium pentosaceum	3	5	3.0	1.4	0.5	37	15
	4	5	3.0	1.4	0.5	30	15
Propionibacterium shermanii	5	2	3.0	1.5	0.4	30	40
	6	2	3.0	1.5	0.4	30	40
Propionibacterium peterssonii	7	5	2.4	2.5	0.5	30	12
	8	5	2.4	2.0	0.7	30	12

grow at 37°C. The fermentation is usually complete in 7 to 12 days, depending upon the species, the medium, and other factors. By a special semicontinuous fermentation process van Niel (1928) has demonstrated, however, that the fermentation can be reduced to as short as 48 hours.

The principal end products of propionic acid fermentation are propionic acid, acetic acid, and carbon dioxide. Usually succinic acid is also produced, and traces of lactic acid, acetylmethylcarbinol, and other substances are sometimes encountered. The fermentation balance sheet from one of Wood and Werkman's studies is given in Table 9. Other fermentation data will be found in the references cited by Wood and Werkman (1936, 1940) and Bernhauer (1939) and in the monograph by van Niel (1928).

The results presented in Table 9 are not entirely in agreement with others reported in the literature. For example, the ratios of propionic to acetic acid vary from 2.13 to 14.72, and those of CO_2 to acetic acid from 0.92 to 6.29; the succinic acid fluctuates from 7.9 to 23.8 m. Mol. (millimols) per 100 m. Mol. of fermented glucose. Virtanen and van Niel found the ratio of CO_2 to acetic acid to be substantially 1.0, and the ratio of propionic to acetic acid usually has been found to be approximately 2.0, although van Niel reported ratios as high as about 5.0. At present it is impossible to explain why Wood and Werkman's results differ so markedly from those of other investigators. However, they

TABLE 9

Dissimilation of Glucose by the Propionic Acid Bacteria Listed in Table 8

[From Wood and Werkman (1936)]

Fermentation Number	Glucose Fermented per Liter, m. Mol.	Quantities Formed per 100 m. Mol. of Glucose Fermented, m. Mol.					Ratio of CO_2 to Acetic Acid	Ratio of Propionic to Acetic Acid	Carbon Recovered, per cent
		Propionic Acid	Acetic Acid	CO_2	Succinic Acid	Nonreducing Material			
1	145.3	139.1	17.8	63.6	13.2	2.8	3.59	7.82	97.6
2	109.5	148.8	10.1	63.6	7.9	3.7	6.29	14.72	97.4
3	155.9	127.8	16.6	52.3	21.1	2.8	3.15	7.70	95.0
4	156.9	116.3	22.7	42.6	23.8	3.7	1.88	5.13	92.5
5 *	164.1	104.0	44.6	47.4	12.6	4.3	1.06	2.33	88.0
6 *	163.9	106.1	45.9	47.0	15.0	4.1	1.02	2.33	91.2
7	133.0	114.8	54.0	51.5	11.8	8.9	0.95	2.13	100.6
8	133.0	117.8	55.4	51.2	8.1	... †	0.92	2.13	91.3 †

* Small amount of lactic acid produced per 100 m. Mol. of glucose fermented.
† Nonreducing material not analyzed.

show that a number of factors influence propionic acid fermentation and that conclusions should not be drawn from a single set of data.

The Mechanism of Propionic Acid Fermentation. Several workers have studied the mechanism of propionic acid fermentation since 1878, when Fitz first observed that propionic acid, acetic acid, and carbon dioxide can be formed from lactic acid by the action of microbes. The consensus now is that the introductory phases of the fermentation of sugars by the propionic acid bacteria are similar to those in alcoholic fermentation, in that phosphorylation reactions and many of the same intermediates occur. In fact, hexose phosphate, methylglyoxal, phosphoglyceric acid, pyruvic acid, lactic acid, and propionaldehyde have all been demonstrated by various workers [see Wood and Werkman (1936), Werkman, Stone, and Wood (1937), Bernhauer (1939)]. Thus any mechanism proposed for this fermentation must take into consideration not only the final products but also these known intermediates. The formulation of a rigid pathway for the production of the end products is not possible, however, because the biological breakdown of sugars and related substances by bacteria probably takes place by more than one mechanism.

One scheme for the production of the main products (propionic acid, acetic acid, CO_2) from glucose in propionic acid fermentation involves the following reactions [see Kluyver (1931), Bernhauer (1939)]:

$$C_6H_{12}O_6 \rightarrow \underset{\text{Methylglyoxal hydrate}}{2CH_3 \cdot CO \cdot CH(OH)_2} \rightarrow \underset{\text{Lactic acid}}{2CH_3 \cdot CHOH \cdot COOH}$$

$$CH_3 \cdot CHOH \cdot COOH \rightarrow \underset{\text{Pyruvic acid}}{CH_3 \cdot CO \cdot COOH} + 2H$$

$$\downarrow$$

$$CH_3 \cdot C(OH)_2 \cdot COOH \rightarrow \underset{\text{Acetic acid}}{CH_3 \cdot COOH} + CO_2 + 2H$$

$$CH_3 \cdot CHOH \cdot COOH + 2H \rightarrow \underset{\text{Propionic acid}}{CH_3 \cdot CH_2 \cdot COOH} + H_2O$$

A second possibility for the events occurring in this fermentation includes methylglyoxal and propionaldehyde as intermediates:

$$\underset{\text{Methylglyoxal hydrate}}{CH_3 \cdot CO \cdot CH(OH)_2} + H_2O \rightarrow CH_3 \cdot COOH + CO_2 + 4H$$

$$\underset{\text{Methylglyoxal}}{CH_3 \cdot CO \cdot CHO} + 2H \rightarrow$$

$$[CH_3 \cdot CHOH \cdot CHO] \rightarrow \underset{\text{Propionaldehyde}}{CH_3 \cdot CH_2 \cdot CHO} + H_2O$$

$$\downarrow {\scriptstyle +H_2O,\ -2H} \qquad\qquad \downarrow {\scriptstyle +H_2O,\ -2H}$$

$$\underset{\text{Lactic acid}}{CH_3 \cdot CHOH \cdot COOH} \qquad \underset{\text{Propionic acid}}{CH_3 \cdot CH_2 \cdot COOH}$$

This type of fermentation was postulated by Wood and Werkman (1934), using *Propionibacterium arabinosum* and glycerol as a substrate; propionaldehyde was isolated as an intermediate.

A third possible mechanism involves the breakdown of the sugar through phosphoglyceric acid to pyruvic acid in a manner similar to that in alcoholic fermentation. The pyruvic acid then undergoes a dismutation, according to the following equation (see Chapter 6):

$$2CH_3 \cdot CO \cdot COOH + H_2O \rightarrow CH_3 \cdot COOH + CO_2 + CH_3 \cdot CHOH \cdot COOH$$

where one molecule of pyruvic acid is oxidized to acetic acid and CO_2, and another is reduced to lactic acid. The lactic acid so formed may then be reduced to propionic acid:

$$CH_3 \cdot CHOH \cdot COOH + 2H \rightarrow CH_3 \cdot CH_2 \cdot COOH + H_2O$$

Before about 1935 it was believed that the succinic acid formed by the propionic acid bacteria arose either from the hexose molecule being split into C_4 and C_2 compounds, from acetic acid, or from the nitrogenous constituents of the medium. In that year Wood and Werkman began their studies on the source of succinic acid, which is formed from glycerol by the propionic acid bacteria. Later studies led them to assume that the succinic acid is actually synthesized from pyruvic acid and CO_2. This assumption has since been shown to be correct as the result of studies using isotopic carbon in CO_2 and demonstrating its presence in succinic acid [see Carson, Foster, Ruben, and Barker (1941), Werkman and Wood (1942)]. The synthesis of succinic acid from pyruvic acid by CO_2 fixation has been explained in one way by the following reactions [see Krebs and Eggleston (1941), Werkman and Wood (1942)]:

$$\underset{\text{Pyruvic acid}}{CH_3 \cdot CO \cdot COOH} + CO_2 \rightarrow \underset{\text{Oxaloacetic acid}}{HOOC \cdot CH_2 \cdot CO \cdot COOH} \xrightarrow{+2H}$$

$$\underset{l\text{-Malic acid}}{HOOC \cdot CH_2 \cdot CHOH \cdot COOH} \xrightarrow{-H_2O}$$

$$\underset{\text{Fumaric acid}}{HOOC \cdot CH{:}CH \cdot COOH} \xrightarrow{+2H} \underset{\text{Succinic acid}}{HOOC \cdot CH_2 \cdot CH_2 \cdot COOH}$$

It has also been suggested that under certain conditions succinic acid can be converted to propionic acid by a decarboxylation reaction [Wood and Werkman (1936)].

COLON-TYPHOID-DYSENTERY FERMENTATIONS

Several end products are formed as the result of the dissimilation of sugars and related substances by the colon-typhoid-dysentery bacteria, but none of the products predominates sufficiently to characterize the fermentations on such a basis. In general, however, these fermentations can be classified on the group or generic basis as follows: (1) *Escherichia-Salmonella* type; (2) *coli-aerogenes*-intermediate type; (3) *Eberthella-Shigella* type; (4) *Aerobacter* type. None of these fermentations is of industrial importance, with the exception of the fourth type, which may be used for the production of 2:3-butylene glycol, but they were among the first fermentations to be studied and are of considerable academic interest. They will be discussed briefly in order.

1. The *Escherichia-Salmonella* Type of Fermentation. When *Escherichia coli* and related species are cultivated in a glucose-inorganic salt medium or other similar media, the sugar is dissimilated to lactic acid, acetic acid, formic acid, ethyl alcohol, and the gases CO_2 and H_2; usually succinic acid also appears as an end product. As we have mentioned, this type of sugar dissimilation is not restricted to the *Escherichia* species but is characteristic of most of the paratyphoid bacilli also.

The proportionate amount of the various end products formed by these bacteria depends upon the strain used, as well as the conditions of the experiment. An example to illustrate the importance of experimental conditions may be cited from the work of Tikka (1935), in which a strain of *E. coli* was allowed to dissimilate glucose at different

TABLE 10

FERMENTATION OF GLUCOSE AT DIFFERENT *p*H LEVELS BY *Escherichia coli*

[From Tikka (1935)]

Experiment Number	*p*H	Lactic Acid,		Acetic Acid,		Formic Acid,		Ethyl Alcohol,		H_2, cu. cm.
		mg.	%	mg.	%	mg.	%	mg.	%	
1	7.1	815	20.4	724	18.1	994	16.2	645	21.0	45
2	7.1	860	21.5	812	20.3	736	12.0	676	22.0	46
3	6.4	926	46.3	90	4.5	85	2.8	325	21.1	181
4	6.4	816	40.8	120	6.0	113	3.7	296	19.3	146
5	7.4	82	4.1	588	29.4	622	20.2	340	22.1	29
6	7.6	54	2.7	683	34.1	822	26.8	325	21.1	37

*p*H levels. The results of this study are given in Table 10, where it will be seen that the amount of alcohol produced remains quite constant at different *p*H levels, but that lactic acid accumulates if the reaction is acid (*p*H 6.4), whereas acetic and formic acids predominate if the reaction is alkaline (*p*H 7.4 to 7.6).

Several theories have been postulated for the mechanism of dissimilation of sugars by *E. coli* since Harden and Grey performed their fundamental work in this field during the early part of this century [see Scheffer (1928), Kluyver (1931, 1935), Tikka (1935), Stephenson (1939), Bernhauer (1939)]. The present opinion is that the early stages of this fermentation are very similar to those occurring in alcoholic fermentation by yeast, in that the sugar is first phosphorylated and then split to the usual triose compounds. The scheme proposed by Tikka (1935) is given to illustrate the way in which most of the end products may be formed.

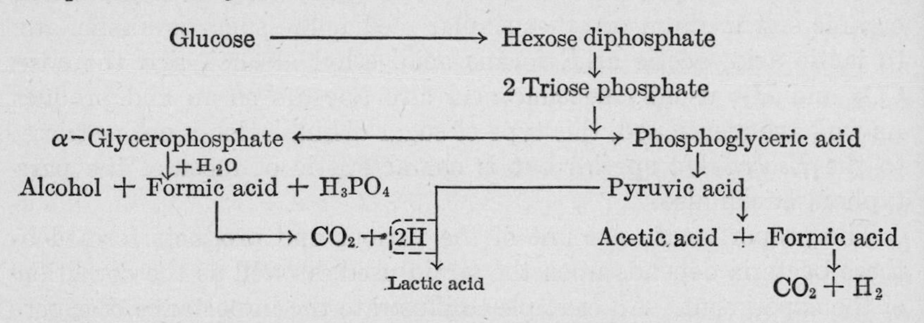

Although Tikka's scheme is supported by considerable experimental data, it is quite probable that alternate pathways are also followed under certain conditions. For example, methylglyoxal has been postulated by several workers as the precursor of lactic acid.

The succinic acid produced from sugars by *E. coli* and related species may be formed in several ways. Kluyver (1931, 1935) suggested that the nonphosphorylated hexose molecule may be split into C_4 and C_2 compounds, which then undergo internal oxidation-reduction to yield succinic acid and acetaldehyde, respectively:

$$\text{Glucose} \rightarrow \underset{\text{Dialdehyde of tartaric acid}}{OHC \cdot CHOH \cdot CHOH \cdot CHO} + \underset{\text{Ethylene glycol}}{CH_2OH \cdot CH_2OH}$$

$$\downarrow \qquad\qquad\qquad\qquad \downarrow$$

$$HOOC \cdot CH_2 \cdot CH_2 \cdot COOH \qquad CH_3 \cdot CHO + H_2O$$

$$\downarrow$$

$$CH_3 \cdot COOH + CH_3 \cdot CH_2OH$$

Endo (1938), on the other hand, has postulated that succinic acid may arise from pyruvic acid and acetic acid through α-ketoglutaric acid as an intermediate:

$$CH_3 \cdot CO \cdot COOH + CH_3 \cdot COOH + O_2 \rightarrow$$
$$HOOC \cdot CO \cdot CH_2 \cdot CH_2 \cdot COOH \ (+ H_2O) \rightarrow$$
$$HOOC \cdot CH_2 \cdot CH_2 \cdot COOH + CO_2$$

Another possibility is that succinic acid arises from pyruvic acid by the CO_2-fixation reaction of Wood and Werkman (see Chapters 6 and 7).

2. The *Coli-Aerogenes*-Intermediate Type of Fermentation. Certain coliform bacteria do not conform to the usual tests for differentiating *Escherichia coli* from *Aerobacter aerogenes*. These organisms have been termed intermediates or placed in the genus *Citrobacter*, originally proposed by Werkman and Gillen in 1932. One of the most characteristic points about the organisms of this group is that they form trimethylene glycol ($HOCH_2 \cdot CH_2 \cdot CH_2OH$) from glycerol, in addition to the usual coli-type end products. Yields of trimethylene glycol varying from 30 to 60 per cent of the glycerol fermented have been obtained [Mickelson and Werkman (1940)]. Little is known about the mechanism involved in the reduction of glycerol to trimethylene glycol, but Mickelson and Werkman believe that acrolein may be an intermediate.

3. The *Eberthella-Shigella* Type of Fermentation. The products of the dissimilation of sugars by *Eberthella typhosa, Shigella dysenteriae*, and related species are very similar to those formed by *Escherichia coli*, with two exceptions [see Scheffer (1928)]. In general, the organisms of this group lack the ability to decompose formic acid to CO_2 and H_2, and therefore do not produce gas in carbohydrate media. Reynolds, McCleskey, and Werkman (1934) have shown, however, that *Shigella paradysenteriae* var. *sonnei* slowly decomposes formic acid under aerobic conditions, presumably to CO_2 and H_2O:

$$2HCOOH + O_2 \rightarrow 2CO_2 + H_2O$$

4. The *Aerobacter* Type of Fermentation. The *Aerobacter* species dissimilate sugars in a somewhat different manner from the organisms we have mentioned. The products of this type of fermentation are lactic acid, acetic acid, formic acid, ethyl alcohol, acetylmethylcarbinol, 2:3-butylene glycol, CO_2, and H_2. Ordinarily succinic acid does not occur in this type of fermentation, and even the other acid products are formed in considerably smaller quantities than in the *Escherichia-Salmonella* type of dissimilation.

The fundamental work on the *Aerobacter* type of fermentation dates back to 1906–1912, when Harden and his students discovered that 2:3-butylene glycol was a product of sugar breakdown by *Aerobacter aerogenes*. Since that time numerous studies have been published on the dissimilation of sugars, organic acids, and related substances by various *Aerobacter* species [see Scheffer (1928), Stone and Werkman (1936), Reynolds, Jacobsson, and Werkman (1937), Reynolds and Werkman (1937)]. The study by Reynolds and Werkman (1937) may be cited as one example in which all the end products have been determined throughout the course of the fermentation of glucose by *Aerobacter indologenes* (see Table 11). The results in Table 11 reveal

TABLE 11

DISSIMILATION OF GLUCOSE AT VARIOUS TIMES BY *Aerobacter indologenes*, GLUCOSE FERMENTED AND PRODUCTS IN MILLIMOLS PER LITER

[From Reynolds and Werkman (1937)]

Time, hours	Glucose Fermented	Hydrogen	Carbon Dioxide	Formic Acid	Ethyl Alcohol	Acetic Acid	Lactic Acid	Acetylmethylcarbinol	2:3-Butylene Glycol	Carbon Recovered, per cent
24	14.3	0.0	7.12	21.0	16.7	6.0	0.55	0.226	6.0	116.3
31	36.1	2.26	34.35	24.0	22.7	8.6	1.47	0.78	16.7	90.5
35	41.0	3.44	46.50	30.0	30.6	6.8	3.29	0.452	22.3	102.5
47	61.1	7.07	85.6	33.2	43.0	5.0	3.90	1.22	35.4	102.0
64	82.5	17.32	110.5	31.7	55.2	2.9	4.13	0.452	49.8	95.3
81	100.3	23.95	144.3	34.6	68.3	1.7	4.02	0.11	66.0	99.0
110	123.8	34.2	189.0	34.6	82.5	1.1	3.68	0.89	79.4	97.0
209	127.3	45.0	218.3	21.6	88.3	0.6	3.68	0.0	84.2	100.3

that three products—formic acid, acetic acid, and acetylmethylcarbinol—undergo such decreases after previous accumulation that they can be assigned significant roles as intermediates.

Several schemes have been suggested to account for the breakdown of sugars by the *Aerobacter* species. Two of the better known may be cited. After quantitative carbon balance experiments Scheffer (1928) and Kluyver (1931, 1935) proposed the following reactions for the events occurring in the fermentation of glucose by *Aerobacter aerogenes* and *Aerobacter cloacae:*

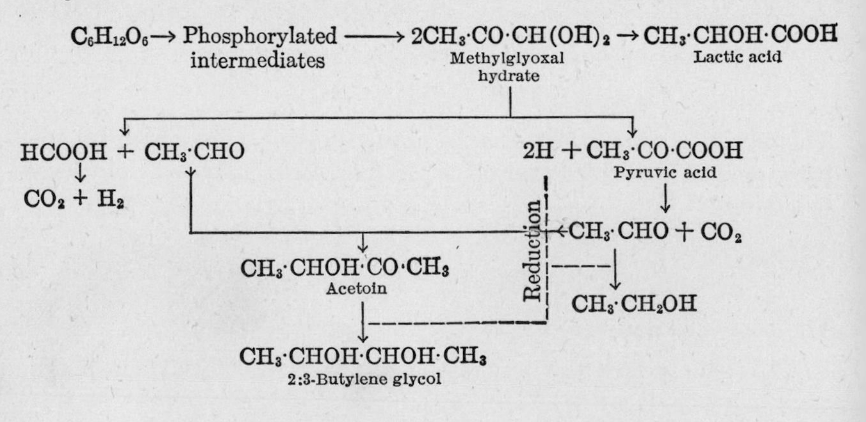

In this scheme it will be seen that methylglyoxal hydrate is postulated as the key intermediate product. It is partially converted into lactic acid by the enzyme glyoxalase, partially broken down to give pyruvic acid and active hydrogen, and partially dissimilated to give formic acid and acetaldehyde. The formic acid is then enzymatically decomposed by formic dehydrogenase and hydrogenase to give CO_2 and H_2, as occurs with *Escherichia coli*. The pyruvic acid is decarboxylated by carboxylase or a similar enzyme to acetaldehyde and CO_2. The molecule of acetaldehyde arising from this source is then condensed with the one formed directly from methylglyoxal hydrate to yield acetylmethylcarbinol (acetoin). The active hydrogen liberated when methylglyoxal hydrate is converted to pyruvic acid is then partially utilized to reduce some of the acetaldehyde to ethyl alcohol and partially to reduce some of the acetoin to 2:3-butylene glycol.

Reynolds and Werkman (1937) have postulated a somewhat different scheme, using their experimental data cited in Table 11. They believe that the glucose molecule is dissimilated to pyruvic acid by a series of reactions very similar to those occurring in alcoholic fermentation by yeast and that pyruvic acid, rather than methylglyoxal hydrate, is the key intermediate substance. In their scheme part of the pyruvic acid is dismutated to acetic and formic acids. The formic acid then undergoes further breakdown to CO_2 and H_2, and the acetic acid is slowly reduced to acetaldehyde, as is shown by its disappearance in Table 11. Lactic acid also arises from pyruvic acid by an enzymatic reduction reaction, and some of the pyruvic acid is decarboxylated to yield acetaldehyde. The following equations may be written to illustrate the formation of these substances from pyruvic acid:

$$CH_3\cdot CO\cdot COOH + HOH \rightarrow CH_3\cdot COOH + HCOOH$$

$$CH_3\cdot COOH \xrightarrow{+2H} CH_3\cdot CHO + H_2O \qquad HCOOH \rightarrow CO_2 + H_2$$

$$CH_3\cdot CO\cdot COOH + 2H \rightarrow CH_3\cdot CHOH\cdot COOH$$

$$CH_3\cdot CO\cdot COOH \rightarrow CH_3\cdot CHO + CO_2$$

The acetaldehyde formed directly and indirectly (through acetic acid) from pyruvic acid can then be reduced to ethyl alcohol or condensed to acetoin:

$$CH_3\cdot CHO + 2H \rightarrow CH_3\cdot CH_2OH$$

$$2CH_3\cdot CHO \rightarrow CH_3\cdot CHOH\cdot CO\cdot CH_3$$

The condensation of acetaldehyde and pyruvic acid,

$$CH_3\cdot CHO + HOOC\cdot CO\cdot CH_3 \rightarrow CH_3\cdot CHOH\cdot CO\cdot CH_3 + CO_2,$$

may be an alternate pathway used by these organisms to form acetoin. The formation of 2:3-butylene glycol by *Aerobacter* species can be accounted for by the reduction of acetoin:

$$CH_3 \cdot CHOH \cdot CO \cdot CH_3 + 2H \rightarrow CH_3 \cdot CHOH \cdot CHOH \cdot CH_3$$

The fact that the acetoin values in Table 11 decrease as the 2:3-butylene glycol values increase lends support to this reaction.

2:3-BUTYLENE GLYCOL FERMENTATION

Harden and his associates discovered 2:3-butylene glycol (or 2:3-butanediol) as one of the products of sugar dissimilation by certain *Aerobacter* species in 1906, but it has been only within the past few years that chemists have become interested in this substance. This interest has been stimulated primarily by the fact that 2:3-butylene glycol ($CH_3 \cdot CHOH \cdot CHOH \cdot CH_3$) can serve as a precursor of butadiene ($CH_2 : CH \cdot CH : CH_2$), which is in great demand for the manufacture of synthetic rubber. Butylene glycol, however, has other uses too, and in the future it may become one of our more important organic compounds. For example, it can be employed to impregnate wood and textiles to make them resistant against alkalies, to synthesize phthalic anhydride resins, to manufacture certain antifreeze preparations, and to act as a solvent for several dyes.

The organisms responsible for this type of fermentation include certain *Aerobacter* species, *Bacillus polymyxa*, *Proteus hydrophilus* (*Aeromonas hydrophila*), *Bacterium asiaticus-mobilis* and other related species [see Birkinshaw, Charles, and Clutterbuck (1931), Fulmer, Christensen, and Kendall (1933), Stahly and Werkman (1942), Stanier *et al.* (1944), Ward, Pettijohn, Lockwood, and Coghill (1944), Christensen (1944), Perlman (1944)]. The mesodextro-2:3-butylene glycol mixture is produced in *Aerobacter aerogenes* fermentations, whereas *Proteus hydrophilus* forms a mixture of the *l*- and meso-forms with a preponderance of the meso-form. *Bacillus polymyxa*, on the other hand, produces levoglycol.

Fulmer, Christensen, and Kendall (1933) were the first to show that large quantities of 2:3-butylene glycol can be produced experimentally through fermentation of sugar (sucrose) by *Aerobacter pectinovorum* and other related species. They used a synthetic medium containing ammonium chloride (0.25 per cent), potassium phosphate (0.15 per cent), calcium chloride (0.15 per cent), magnesium sulfate (0.2 per cent), and sucrose in varying amounts (2 to 12 per cent, optimum about 6 per cent). The optimum reaction for the fermentation was *p*H 6.0, and the incubation temperature was 37.5°C. for 18 days.

The glycol was determined by vacuum distillation and weighing or by refractive index measurements. The best yield of glycol per 100 g. of sucrose fermented was 46.9 per cent, when an 8.0 per cent sucrose medium was used. Higher and lower concentrations of sugar gave lower yields.

More recently several industrial research laboratories (Schenley and others) have produced 2:3-butylene glycol on a pilot-plant scale for butadiene manufacture, and larger operations may now be under way. According to an article in *Chemical Industries* [(1943) **53:**198], the pilot-plant process for butadiene manufacture involves the fermention of corn or wheat mashes [7] to 2:3-butylene glycol, followed by acetylation and pyrolysis to yield butadiene. Grain is fed in meal form, into mash tubs, where it is mixed with water and then pumped to steam cookers. After sterilization the mash is placed in fermenters, and a specially prepared bacterial culture is added to convert the sugar to butylene glycol. After fermentation the resulting "distiller's beer" is permitted to settle, and then the clear supernatant is filtered off and pumped to an evaporator for concentration. Butylene glycol is recovered from this concentrate by countercurrent extraction with butanol, and the two components are separated by distillation [also see Blom, Reed, Efron, and Mustakas (1945)]. To obtain butadiene the glycol is esterified with acetic acid to form butane diacetate, which is then cracked to butadiene by heating to 1,100°F. (593°C.) in a molten lead bath. The butadiene passes off as a gas and is liquefied by compression and cooling.

The mechanism of 2:3-butylene glycol fermentation is the same as that for *Aerobacter* species (see pp. 949 to 952). Further data on this specific subject will be found in the papers by Stahly and Werkman (1942) and Stanier and his associates (1944).

BUTYRIC ACID FERMENTATION

The production of butyric acid from carbohydrates by bacterial action was first noted by Pasteur in 1861. After this discovery several reports appeared from about 1882 to 1910 by Fitz, Baier, Winogradsky, Buchner, and Meisenheimer, Bredemann, and others in which they showed that numerous anaerobic bacilli are capable of producing varying amounts of butyric acid from sugars and related substances. According to Kluyver (1931), the simplest butyric acid formation is effected by certain "true" butyric acid bacteria, such as *Clostridium sac-*

[7] Perlman (1944) has also shown that wood hydrolyzates can be utilized by *Aerobacter aerogenes* for 2:3-butylene glycol production. Wood sugar solutions up to about 17 per cent are completely fermented, yielding about 35 per cent glycol.

charobutyricum.[8] In this reaction only four main fermentation products (butyric acid, acetic acid, CO_2, and H_2) are encountered, along with a trace of formic acid. On the other hand, certain closely related species produce only small amounts of butyric acid, together with some eight or ten other compounds.

The true butyric acid fermentation is of little importance from an industrial standpoint, but it is of considerable academic interest, because it serves as a starting point for a better understanding of the

TABLE 12

FERMENTATION BALANCE OF GLUCOSE,* USING *Clostridium saccharobutylicum*

[From Kluyver (1931)]

Products	Amount, grams	Glucose Fermented, per cent	Number of Molecules per 50 Molecules of Glucose Fermented		
			CO_2	H_2	Acetaldehyde
Glucose added	39.45				
Glucose unfermented	3.10				
Glucose fermented	36.35				
Carbon dioxide	17.4	47.8	97.8		
Hydrogen	0.94	2.59	....	116.6	
Formic acid	Trace				
Acetic acid	5.17	14.2	....	−21.3	21.3
Butyric acid	13.4	36.9	....	......	75.5
Total		103.49	97.8	95.3	96.8

* Medium containing yeast extract, glucose, and $CaCO_3$ incubated at 30°C.

mechanisms of the more complicated butanol-acetone and butanol-isopropyl alcohol fermentations. Kluyver (1931, 1935) and his associates studied this problem in some detail and expressed the opinion that the early stages of the fermentation are similar to those which occur in alcoholic fermentation by yeast; that is, the sugar is first phosphorylated and then split into triose intermediate compounds,

[8] According to *Bergey's Manual* (1939), this species is probably synonymous with *Clostridium butyricum.*

such as methylglyoxal hydrate. They formulated the following reactions for the true butyric acid fermentation of glucose:

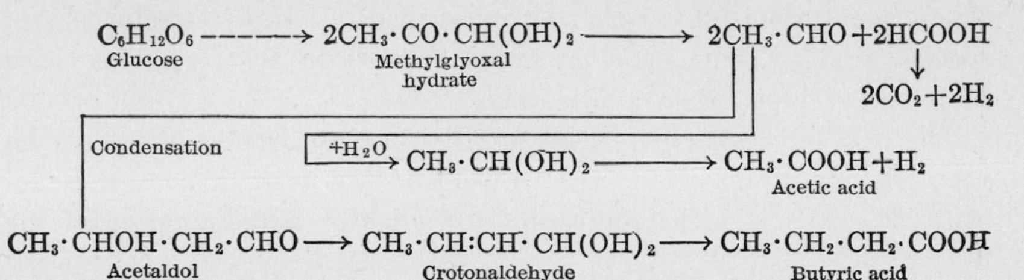

This scheme is essentially of a hypothetical nature, because, as Bernhauer (1939) brought out, the acetaldehyde could also arise through pyruvic acid, and the aldol condensation could occur by an alternate reaction. Simon (1943) has also shown that the internal reactions occurring in butyric acid fermentation may be quite complicated. The Kluyver scheme has some merit, however, since experimental tests show that the quantities of the various fermentation products formed correspond very well with the assumed mode of their origin (see Table 12). Thus the weight of the carbon dioxide formed is equivalent to approximately one-half the weight of the glucose fermented. The number of molecules of acetaldehyde required for the formation of acetic acid and butyric acid is essentially equivalent to the number of molecules of carbon dioxide produced. Also the total number of molecules of hydrogen gas evolved is greater than the number of molecules of acetic acid produced by approximately the amount of carbon dioxide formed.

BUTANOL-ACETONE FERMENTATION

Credit for the discovery of butanol or butyl alcohol ($CH_3 \cdot CH_2 \cdot CH_2 \cdot CH_2OH$) as a product of sugar fermentation by bacteria probably belongs to Pasteur, who in 1861 showed that this alcohol is formed by certain of the butyric acid-producing bacteria. After Pasteur's study numerous other reports appeared from about 1875 to 1910 by Fitz, Gruber, Grimbert, Beijerinck, Emmerling, Buchner, Meisenheimer, and others in which bacteria capable of producing butanol were described and studied. Although acetone ($CH_3 \cdot CO \cdot CH_3$) has been known chemically for over one hundred years, it was not until 1905 that Schardinger demonstrated it to be a fermentation product of *Bacillus macerans*. Since that time other bacteria have been isolated which produce greater amounts of acetone than Schardinger's bacillus.

After a few early studies, such as the ones mentioned above, the history of butanol-acetone fermentation becomes quite interesting. About

1910 rumors reached England from Germany to the effect that Fritz Haber had succeeded in making rubber from the fermentation products of potatoes. At that time the English firm of Strange and Graham, Ltd., hired Perkin, Weizmann, and Fernbach to do research on synthetic rubber and the raw materials from which it might be made. The raw products given special attention were isoamyl alcohol, acetone, and butanol, from which isoprene, dimethylbutadiene, and butadiene, respectively, could be synthesized. Isoamyl alcohol and acetone were available in only small amounts, and butanol had never been made commercially at that time. These research workers decided that butadiene was the best material for rubber synthesis, and they therefore turned to developing fermentation processes for the production of butanol, from which butadiene could be synthesized.

In 1911 Fernbach isolated an organism which he designated as the FB bacillus. This organism would not attack corn mashes, but it did ferment potatoes, yielding butanol as well as acetone. This discovery was granted an English patent, but for several reasons was abandoned about 1916. Although Weizmann severed his connections with the Strange and Graham research group in 1912, he continued to work on this fermentation problem, and after about two years he isolated an organism which he called the BY bacillus. This organism possessed outstanding fermentation characteristics and attacked corn and other grains without the addition of any other nutrient.

Soon after the start of World War I large quantities of acetone were seriously needed in the manufacture of cordite, the British high explosive, and of "dopes" for airplane wings. Up to that time acetone had been made from calcium acetate, which was produced chiefly in Austria and the United States. Acetone from Austria was of course not available to England, and production in this country was almost negligible in comparison to the large and sudden demand. Strange and Graham therefore contracted to supply acetone to the British government. At first they used Fernbach's organism, but production was uncertain and unsatisfactory because of the ineffectiveness of this bacillus. Thus in 1916 the BY bacillus of Weizmann was substituted, and marked progress was made in production. One or two other plants were put in operation about this time, and at least one of them produced as much as 2,340 lb. of acetone per week. However, at that time a bushel of corn (56 lb.) produced only 10 or 11 lb. of solvents, consisting of approximately 60 parts of butanol, 30 parts of acetone, and 10 parts of ethanol. Thus 56 lb. of grain had to be imported to obtain 3 lb. of acetone. With shipping space at a premium a shortage of grain soon developed in England, and it became evident that the process had to be carried out closer to the source of the raw material. A plant was therefore established in Canada; it produced some 3,000 tons of acetone in 2 years. About the time the United States entered the war two distilleries in Terre Haute, Indiana, were converted to acetone production by the Weizmann process, but operations had only nicely started when the armistice was signed and the plants had to be shut down for lack of a market. However, through extensive researches on the part of the chemist, engineer, and bacteriologist the industry was soon revived to meet the tremendous demands of the nitrocellulose lacquer industry for butanol and butyl acetate as solvents.

At the present time no other bacterial fermentation process plays such an important role in the production of various solvents and other chemicals as does the butanol-acetone fermentation. However, it should be mentioned that butanol and acetone can now be made either synthetically or by means of fermentation. For example, in 1941 about 155,000,000 lb. of butanol was produced in this country, 70 per cent being by fermentation and 30 per cent by synthetic methods. The demand for acetone has likewise grown so enormously that today more is being produced synthetically than by fermentation [Wynkoop (1943)].

For additional reading on the interesting history of butanol-acetone fermentation Gabriel (1928), Gabriel and Crawford (1930), Kelly (1936), Prescott and Dunn (1940), and Wynkoop (1943) should be consulted.

Outline of the Industrial Fermentation Process. The production of *n*-butanol and acetone by the so-called Weizmann process has already been described in some detail by Killeffer (1927) and Prescott and Dunn (1940), and new modifications are continually being patented.[9] Therefore in the following discussion the process will be summarized in general terms under six headings, to explain the steps shown in *Chemical and Metallurgical Engineering*'s flow sheet (Fig. 6). For more technical information the patent literature should be consulted.

1. Raw Materials Used and Preparation of the Mash. A great variety of raw materials may be used as the substrate in butanol-acetone fermentation. Low-grade corn and molasses are the main basic raw materials employed industrially in this country, but other substances, such as rice, peanut and oat hulls, corn cobs, Jerusalem artichokes, horse chestnuts, Irish moss, heated whey, waste-sulfite liquor, and var-

[9] For example, see U. S. Patents by J. C. Woodruff, H. R. Stiles, and D. A. Legg (1937), A. Frey and H. Glück (1939), A. Frey, H. Glück, and H. Oehme (1939), F. M. Hildebrandt and N. M. Erb (1939), N. R. Tarvin (1941), C. F. Arzberger (1943).

ious starches (rice, potato, cassava, tapioca) and sugars, have been used experimentally [Gill (1919), Robinson (1922), Fred, Peterson, and Anderson (1923), Waksman and Kirsh (1933), Underkofler and Hunter (1938), Wiley, Johnson, McCoy, and Peterson (1941), Wendland, Fulmer, and Underkofler (1941), Guymon, Underkofler, and Fulmer (1941), Banzon (1941)].

When whole grain such as corn is used as the raw material, it is first degermed to remove the oil; then on its way to the roller mill it is passed over a magnetic separator to remove any scrap metal. From the mill

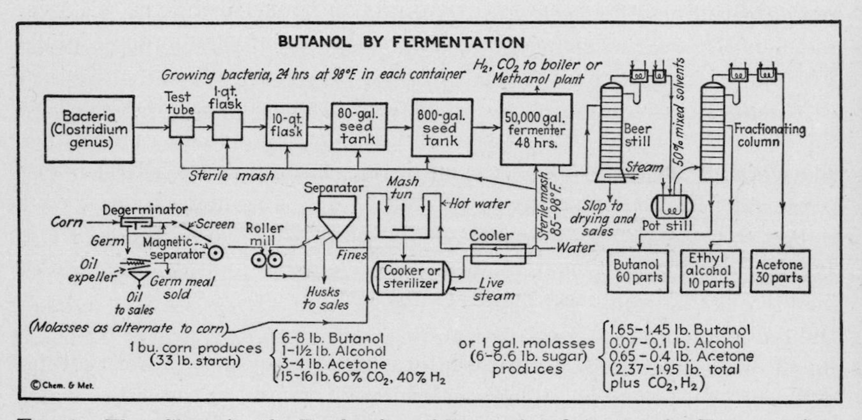

FIG. 6. Flow Sheet for the Production of Butanol and Acetone by Fermentation. (Courtesy, *Chemical and Metallurgical Engineering*, McGraw-Hill Publishing Company.)

the coarse meal goes to a separator, where the husks are removed from the fine meal. The fine meal (about 6,100 lb.) is then conveyed to a large mash tun of approximately 10,000-gal. capacity, where it is mixed with warm water (71°C.) to give a concentration of 6 to 8 per cent. From the mash tun the charge is dropped into a cooker, which is essentially an autoclave provided with a motor-driven rake agitator. In the cooker the charge is cooked for 2 hours under a pressure of about 30 lb. of steam. This process sterilizes the mash and produces some hydrolysis or dissolution of the starch. The mash is then blown to the fermenter by its own pressure. In passing to the fermenter, the sterile starch mass is cooled in a water-cooled heat exchanger to about 85° to 98°F. (30° to 37°C.). The heat given up by the mash is absorbed by fresh water on its way to the mash tun (see Fig. 6). As the starchy solution enters the fermenter, it is of approximately the consistency of ordinary flour paste. It is essential to note that no malt or other saccharifying agent is used and that the mash is primarily starch and not sugar.

Considerable research has been done on the substances present in corn mashes which are essential for normal yields of solvents. For example, Weinstein and Rettger (1932, 1933) reported that a prolamine-containing substance was necessary for the production of normal amounts of acetone and butanol by fermentation. On the other hand, Tatum, Peterson, and Fred (1935), Weizmann and Rosenfeld (1937), and others believe that complex nitrogenous substances, such as peptones and prolamines, are not essential, providing asparagine and certain growth factors are present. A great deal of progress has been made in the past few years in determining the growth-factor requirements of *Clostridium acetobutylicum* and other butanol-forming bacteria. For a brief discussion on this subject see Chapter 7.

When a sugar-containing raw material, such as molasses, is employed for butanol fermentation, it usually requires some special treatment. For example, concentrated blackstrap molasses is usually acidified and sterilized before it is diluted with sterile water containing aqua ammonia and a chalk slurry to adjust the reaction. Hildebrandt and Erb (1939) believe that this procedure has certain advantages, since artificially acidified molasses makes sterilization more certain and reduces the tendency of the sugar to decompose during sterilization at 15 to 20 lb. of pressure for 30 to 60 minutes. Molasses mashes are usually deficient in nitrogenous substances and certain salts. To correct these deficiencies nitrogenous substances and salts, such as autolyzed yeast, ammonium salts, phosphates, potassium, and nitrate, are added either before the molasses is sterilized or afterward in the form of sterile mixtures. Examples of the limits set for certain important factors in preparing a final molasses mash are: temperature 90° to 95°F. (32.2° to 35°C.), sugar 4 to 6 per cent, Brix 8° to 10°, *p*H 5.5 to 6.5, and volume of starter 1.0 to 4.0 per cent [Hildebrandt and Erb (1939)].

2. Choice of Organism and Preparation of the Starter. Several anaerobic bacteria are capable of forming butanol and acetone as end products of metabolism, but only a few known species are capable of producing these solvents in sufficient amounts to make their use in industry practical. Before about 1926 considerable confusion existed in the literature in respect to the terminology of the butanol-acetone-forming bacteria. McCoy, Fred, Peterson, and Hastings (1926, 1930), however, carried out extensive studies of the cultural and physiological characteristics of the butanol-acetone organisms and the butyric acid-forming bacteria. They cleared up much of the confusion when they adequately separated these two groups of bacteria and when they suggested the name *Clostridium acetobutylicum* for the acetone-butanol organism previously isolated by Weizmann. This name has now been generally adopted; and, according to *Bergey's Manual* (1939), other

names, such as *Bacillus granulobacter* and *Clostridium acetonegenum*, are synonyms which should be discarded.

The early commercial production of butanol and acetone by fermentation was effected by fermenting starch (corn) mashes by means of bacteria of the *Cl. acetobutylicum* type. This process, however, was limited somewhat by the type of carbohydrate used and in the ratio of products obtainable. Subsequently a new group of butanol-producing bacteria has been discovered which are capable of fermenting soluble carbohydrate (for example, molasses) mashes, forming different ratios of neutral products. Various species and strains of this group produce ratios of butanol ranging from 55 to 74 per cent, acetone in proportions from 5 to over 40 per cent, and amounts of ethanol as low as 2 per cent, by weight of the total solvents. The organisms of this group, which have been described primarily in the patent literature, include such species as *Clostridium saccharo-acetobutylicum*, *Clostridium inverto-acetobutylicum*, *Clostridium saccharo-butyl-acetonicum-liquefaciens*, and *Clostridium celerifactor* [see, for example, Hildebrandt and Erb (1939), Tarvin (1941)]. Specific strains of these species are sometimes further designated by Greek letters, alpha (α), beta (β), etc., for example, *Cl. saccharo-acetobutylicum-*β.

From this discussion it will be seen that the choice of an organism for butanol-acetone fermentation depends upon the nature of the raw material being used, the ratio of the end products desired, and other factors.

The preparation of the starter or seed for large-scale fermentations starts in the laboratory, where a vigorous bacterial strain is constantly maintained. It is interesting to note that several investigators have observed that continued subculture of the stock culture in common laboratory media results in the organism becoming sluggish, a condition which reduces the yield of solvents. However, it has been found that, by maintaining the spores of the organism in sterile soil, alkaline-buffered mashes, or other substances and by subjecting these spores to heat shock or pasteurization (100°C. for 1 to 2 minutes) just before their use, the solvent-producing ability of the culture can be maintained at a high level. After these steps the culture is first grown in a test tube containing sterile mash for 24 hours at 37°C. (98°F.) and then transferred to a larger amount of the same sterile mash. This build-up process is continued under carefully controlled conditions until a starter equal to about 1 to 4 per cent of the main mash is obtained (see Fig. 6). The main mash is then inoculated with the final starter by direct mixing or by so adding the starter that it does not mix at once with the main mash but lies on the upper surface in an almost undisturbed layer. Layering the starter in this way on molasses mashes permits the communal action of the bacteria to come into play.

3. FERMENTATION OF THE MASH. Butanol-acetone fermentation is carried out in a closed fermenter, and it is essential to steam-sterilize the fermenter, pipes, and other equipment with which the mash or starter comes into contact if a satisfactory yield of solvents is to be obtained. Unless sterile conditions prevail, the lactic acid bacteria and other organisms cause considerable trouble in this fermentation [Fred,

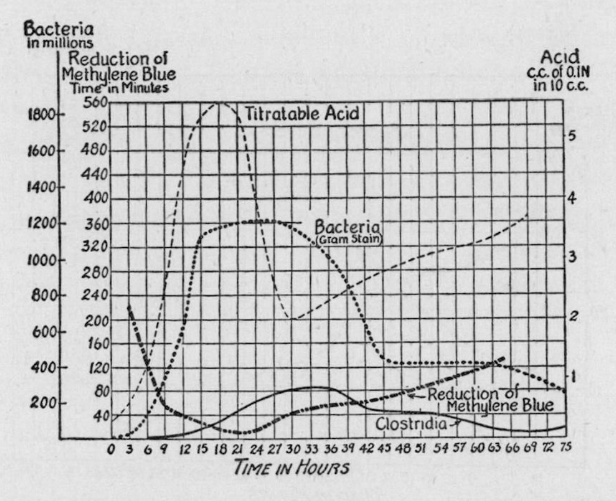

FIG. 7. Number of Bacteria, Time of Reduction of Methylene Blue, and Acid Production during Butanol-Acetone Fermentation by *Clostridium acetobutylicum*. (From Peterson and Fred, 1932.)

Peterson, and Mulvania (1936)]. Various techniques are employed to detect contamination in the fermenting mash; perhaps the most sensitive way is to compare observations on gas evolution and titratable acidity with those of known normal fermentations. For example, gas evolution in starch mashes should increase uniformly after about 12 to 18 hours, and the titratable acidity should rise to a peak in 15 to 20 hours and then drop rapidly during the next 10 hours (see Figs. 7 to 11). In contaminated mashes the evolution of gas during the early stages of fermentation may be slow or may stop entirely, and the acidity may continue to rise after the normal maximum has been reached. The solvents, on the other hand, increase very slowly during the first 24 hours in normal fermentation of starch mashes, but then they increase at a more rapid rate as the titratable acidity decreases (see Fig. 9). The decrease in starch, the increase in soluble nitrogen, and other data on the butanol-acetone fermentation of corn mash are given in Figs. 7 to 11, taken from the paper by Peterson and Fred

(1932). Other similar data on the fermentation of glucose, mannitol, calcium gluconate, and arabinose by *Clostridium acetobutylicum* will be found in the paper by Johnson, Peterson, and Fred (1931).

The optimum temperature for acetone-butanol fermentation varies somewhat, depending upon the type of mash and the species employed. Starch mashes being fermented by *Cl. acetobutylicum* are usually controlled at about 37°C., whereas soluble carbohydrate mashes being fermented by other related species are held preferably at 30° to 35°C.

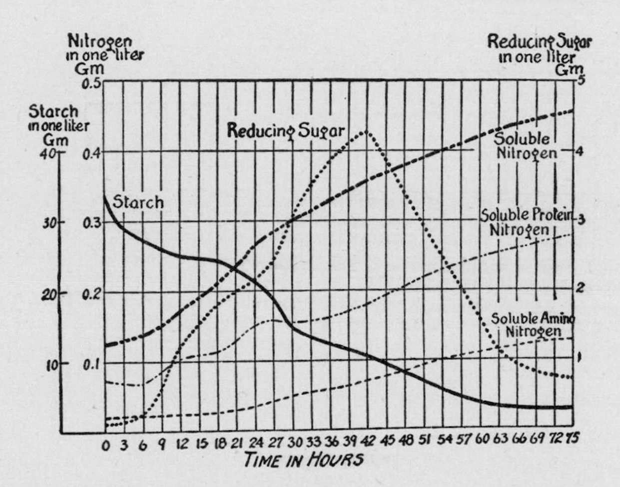

FIG. 8. Changes in Carbohydrates and Forms of Nitrogen during Butanol-Acetone Fermentation by *Clostridium acetobutylicum.* (From Peterson and Fred, 1932.)

The lower fermentation temperatures have an advantage in that less solvent is lost by evaporation. A pH range between 5.5 and 6.5 is usually satisfactory for all kinds of substrates. This range may be maintained by the introduction of certain materials into the mash before fermentation. For example, the addition of calcium carbonate or other insoluble nontoxic bases in an amount sufficient to neutralize any free acidity, plus an amount in excess of this one to the extent of about 5 to 7 per cent of the weight of the calculated sugar, will maintain the reaction within the operative range.

Active fermentation starts about 2 to 3 hours after the mash has been inoculated and is usually complete in 40 to 48 hours. The fermented mash contains between 2 and 4 per cent of solvents at the end of the fermentation.

4. YIELD AND RECOVERY OF END PRODUCTS. The most important products formed in butanol-acetone fermentation are butanol, acetone, ethyl alcohol, and the gases CO_2 and H_2. The approximate yield of

these substances under various conditions is shown in Fig. 6, p. 958, and Table 13. It will be seen from this table that other substances, such as various acids and acetoin, are also frequently encountered as end products in this fermentation.

In addition to the substances mentioned, a yellow oil and the vitamin riboflavin can also be recovered from this fermentation when grain mashes are used. According to Marvel and Broderick (1925), the yellow oil constitutes 0.5 to 1.0 per cent of the total yield of solvents

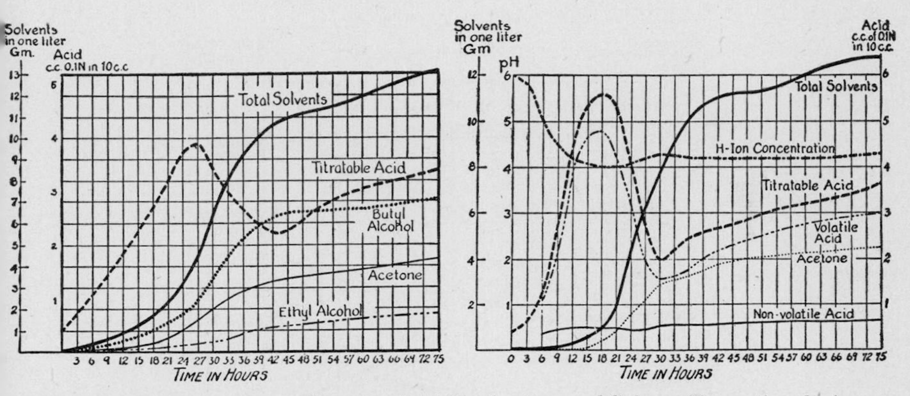

Fig. 9. Two Experiments Showing Acid Production and Solvent Formation during Butanol-Acetone Fermentation by *Clostridium acetobutylicum*. (From Peterson and Fred, 1932.)

and consists of a high-boiling-point mixture of *n*-butyl, amyl, isoamyl, and *n*-hexyl alcohols and the *n*-butyric, caprylic, and capric esters of these alcohols. Yields of riboflavin of over 500 μg. per gram of dried fermentation filtrate have been reported by Arzberger (1943). The synthesis of this vitamin by *Clostridium acetobutylicum* is inhibited by as little as 3.2 mg. per liter of mash of certain metals, particularly iron, cobalt, nickel, copper, lead, and zinc.

The three primary end products (butanol, acetone, ethanol) are recovered by the usual continuous-type beer still and a fractionation column (see Fig. 6). The beer still concentrates the solvents by about 50 per cent, and then the column still separates this concentrate into the three components.

5. By-products Produced. When a grain mash is used for butanol-acetone fermentation, by-products occur at four points in the process (see Fig. 6). First, the germ oil and meal are present when the grain is being prepared for the roller mill; second, the husks are separated from the corn meal after the milling process; third, a mixture of CO_2 and H_2 is produced during fermentation; and, fourth, the spent grain is

TABLE 13

PRODUCTS OF BUTANOL-ACETONE FERMENTATION BY VARIOUS ANAEROBIC BACILLI

[From Davies and Stephenson (1941) and others]

Organism and Type of Medium	Product as Percentage of Substrate (as Sugar) Fermented										Reference
	Acetone	Butanol	Ethanol	Acetic Acid	Butyric Acid	Acetoin	CO_2	H_2	Formic Acid	Lactic Acid	
Clostridium acetobutylicum											
Peptone + salt +											
glucose (1%)	4.1	8.8	1.1	.....	.....	...	....	....	...	...	Johnson, Peterson, and Fred (1931)
glucose (2%)	8.3	20.5	2.5	.....	.....	...	....	....	...	...	
glucose (4%)	9.5	19.6	3.9	.....	.....	...	....	....	...	...	
Yeast water + glucose (2.5%)	2.8	17	1.6	....	......	...	....	....	...	...	Langlykke, Peterson and McCoy (1935)
Yeast water + glucose (2%)	3.4	20.2	....	10.3	10.5	...	51.7	1.75	Nil	Trace	Donker (1926)
Maize meal (4%)	8.8	22.6	....	3.4	2	2.4	55.1	1.75	Nil	"	
Yeast water + glucose (2%)	7.2	23	2.4	4.7	2.1	3.1	54.0	1.5	Trace	...	van der Lek (1930)
Maize meal (2–8%) (industrial scale)	12.1	22.7	1.9	.....	.....	...	....	....	...	...	Speakman (1920)
Maize meal (6.5%) (1,540 gal. mash)	9.7	23.1	....	0.93	0.69	...	56.9	1.44	...	...	Reilly *et al.* (1920)
Maize meal (7.4%)	14.2	26.4	3	0.71	1.55	...	....	....	0.08	...	Stiles *et al.* (1929)
Maize meal (4.3%)	8.5	23.4	0.45	2.2	1.44	4.1	....	....	...	Nil	Davies and Stephenson (1941)
Tryptic digest of liver + salts + asparagine +											
glucose (2%)	7.9	23.8	Nil	5.73	6.75	...	....	....	...	...	
glucose (2%) in 0.20 *M* acetate	14.2	21.2	0.2	.....	.....	...	....	....	...	...	
Clostridium saccharo-acetobutylicum											
Cane molasses + $(NH_4)_2SO_4$ + $CaCO_3$	25–32	68–73	1–3	.....	.....	...	....	....	...	...	Woodruff, Stiles, and Legg (1937)
Clostridium celerifactor											
Hydrolyzed molasses + aqua ammonia + $CaCO_3$	38	60	2.0	.....	.....	...	....	....	...	...	Hildebrandt and Erb (1939)

recovered from the beer still after the mash has been fermented. The fermentation gases and residue also occur when molasses is used as the substrate.

The various grain and molasses residues are now widely used as feed for livestock. According to Groschke and Bird (1941) and Braude and Foot (1942), such residues have high nutritional value. The gases are purified by "scrubbing" with water and then are used to produce

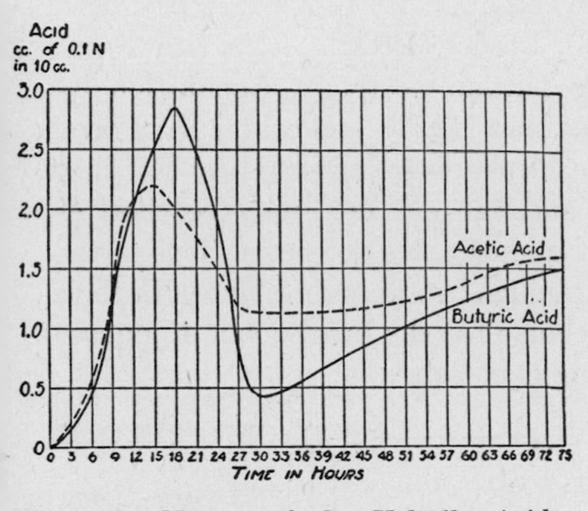

FIG. 10. Nature of the Volatile Acids Formed during Butanol-Acetone Fermentation of *Clostridium acetobutylicum*. (From Peterson and Fred, 1932.)

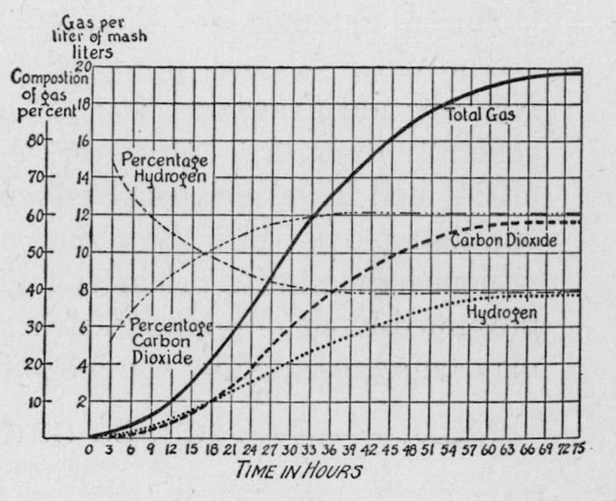

FIG. 11. Gas Production during Butanol-Acetone Fermentation by *Clostridium acetobutylicum*. (From Peterson and Fred, 1932.)

synthetic methanol or ammonia by catalytic process. Part of the CO_2 may also be used to manufacture dry ice.

6. USES OF THE MAIN FERMENTATION PRODUCTS. Acetone was the important product of this fermentation during World War I, but now butanol is of greater importance. A few of the uses of these products, as well as methanol, which is a synthetic by-product, are presented in Fig. 12. New uses are continually being found for these substances [see Wynkoop (1943)].

The Mechanism of Butanol-Acetone Fermentation. Several mechanisms or schemes have been proposed to account for the end products arising in normal butanol-acetone fermentation. However, to be acceptable, a scheme must satisfy conditions in respect to the rate of formation, as well as the relative proportions, of each of the eight or nine products formed in the dissimilation of carbohydrates (see Table 13). For example, the data in Fig. 10 show that during butanol-acetone fermentation butyric acid disappears more rapidly and more completely than does acetic acid. According to several investigators, this fact accounts for the production of a greater proportion of butanol than of acetone. As Figs. 9 and 10 show, the decrease in butyric acid is coincidental with the increase in butanol. Also it has been shown that the addition of butyric acid to a fermenting mash increases the yield of butanol. These facts suggest that butanol arises in this fermentation through butyric acid. On the other hand, a decrease in acetic acid is accompanied by an increase in acetone (see Figs. 9 and 10), and the addition of acetic acid, acetoacetic acid, or pyruvic acid to the mash increases the quantity of acetone produced [Johnson, Peterson, and Fred (1933), Davies (1942)].

The older schemes proposed for butanol-acetone fermentation by Neuberg and Arinstein (1921), Speakman (1923), and others have been generally discarded. However, the mechanism suggested by Kluyver (1931) and his associates, Donker and van der Lek, may be cited as one example in which the results of quantitative determinations of the various fermentation products are in much better accordance with their presumed mode of origin. Their scheme for the breakdown of glucose may be represented by the following equations:

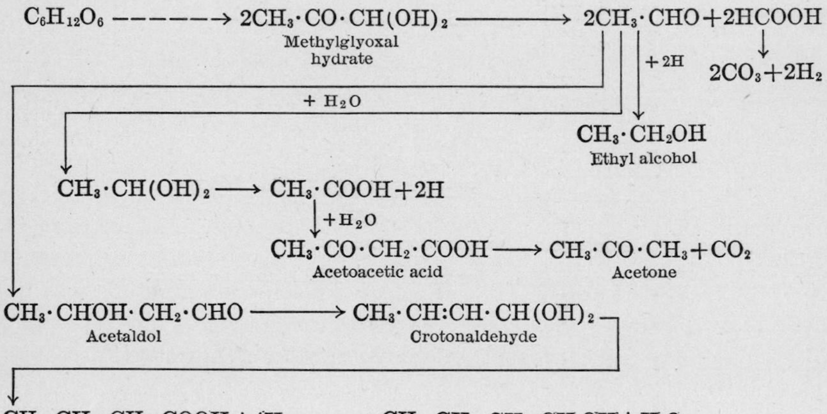

Even though this scheme accords with some of the facts for butanol-acetone fermentation, it is still incomplete in view of certain recent findings. For instance, it does not account for the formation of the small amount of acetoin which is usually encountered in this fermentation. Also it seems unlikely that methylglyoxal and acetaldol are normal intermediates, since they are known to be quite toxic even in small amounts. Furthermore, acetic acid may arise through the acetyl phosphate reaction of Lipmann rather than by way of acetaldehyde hydrate. In view of these facts the study by Simon (1943) is very interesting. Simon believes that the assumption of enzyme systems

C. S. C. PRODUCTS AND THEIR USES

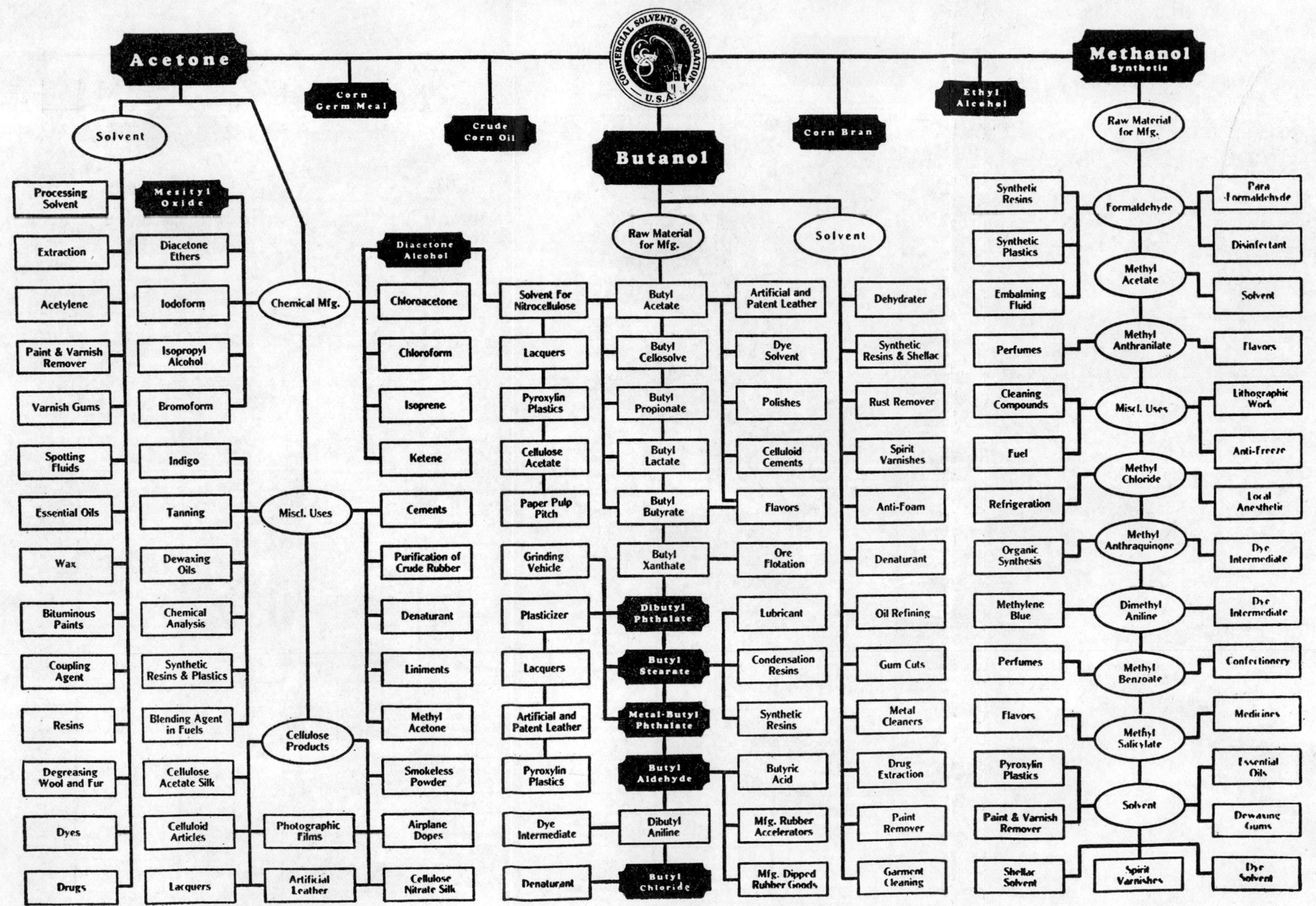

FIG. 12. A Few Uses of the Products of Butanol-Acetone Fermentation. (Compiled by Commercial Solvents Corporation.)

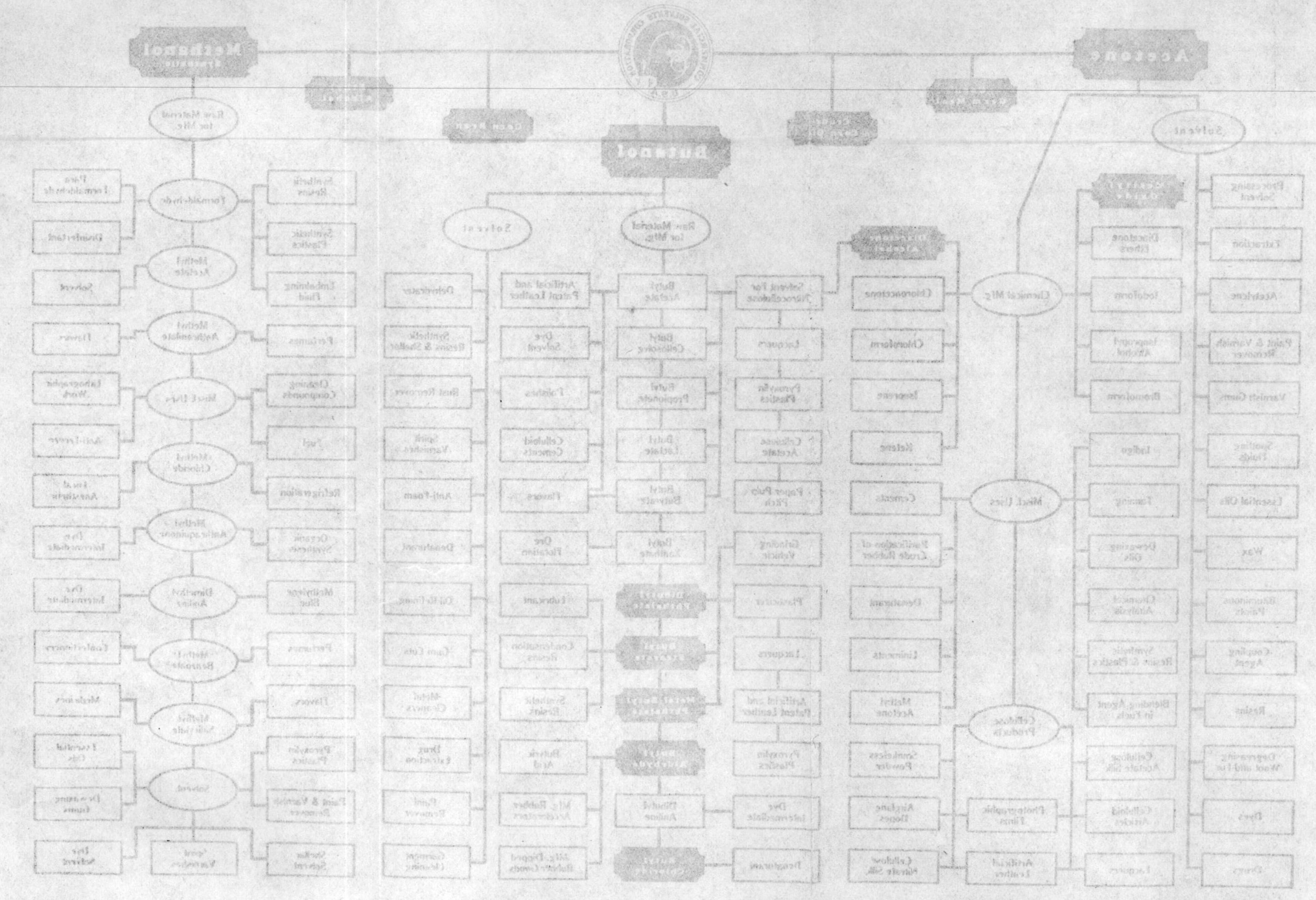

Fig. 12. A Few Uses of the Products of Butanol-Acetone Fermentation. (Compiled by Commercial Solvents Corporation.)

similar to those known to exist in yeast and lactic acid bacteria, which break sugar down into C_3 compounds, has to be discarded in favor of a different mechanism for *Clostridium acetobutylicum.* This conclusion was reached after it was observed that the C_1 atom of five- or six-carbon compounds did not play a part in the formation of C_4 products, such as butyric acid or butanol. For example, if the aldehyde group of glucose was changed to a carboxyl group (gluconic acid) or to a CH_2OH group (mannitol, sorbitol) or to glucose-1-phosphate (Cori ester), butyric acid was formed in all cases. However, if the CH_2OH group at carbon six on glucose was replaced by a carboxyl (galacturonic acid), only acetic acid was formed. Likewise, when glucose-6-phosphate was used, only traces of butyric acid were formed, and glucose-1:6-phosphate yielded only acetic acid. Phosphoglyceric acid and glycerophosphate were not attacked at all, and pyruvic acid yielded only acetic acid. It seems quite likely, however, that acetoacetic acid is the precursor of acetone and that butanol arises in some manner from butyric acid. In fact, Davies (1942, 1943) has actually isolated from *Cl. acetobutylicum* the enzyme system which is responsible for the decarboxylation of acetoacetic acid to acetone, but more enzyme studies are needed in this field before we can say definitely by which route the end products arise in butanol-acetone fermentation.

BUTANOL-ISOPROPYL ALCOHOL FERMENTATION

This fermentation, in which butanol and isopropyl alcohol are the most important end products, has much in common with true butyric fermentation and butanol-acetone fermentation. In fact, the bacteria responsible for all three are so closely related in many respects that it is sometimes quite difficult to separate them taxonomically. Usually, however, qualitative and quantitative analyses of the end products of sugar dissimilation are somewhat different for the various species or strains responsible for the three fermentations, and, as a result, they are generally regarded as separate fermentations.

The occurrence of butyric acid and butanol as fermentation products of anaerobic bacilli was discovered by Pasteur and Fitz during the second half of the last century. Isopropyl alcohol, on the other hand, was not isolated from fermentation mixtures until about 1906, when Pringsheim showed that it was formed by certain bacteria. Since that time several organisms, including some strains of the true butyric acid and butanol-acetone bacteria, have been found to produce isopropyl alcohol in varying quantities. The bacteria which form the greatest amounts of this alcohol, however, are usually strains of *Clostridium butylicum* and *Bacillus technicus.*

Butanol and isopropyl alcohol are both good solvents, and they are widely used in certain industries. The production of isopropyl alcohol by fermentation, however, is not of great importance industrially, because the present demand is being met by various petroleum-cracking processes. On the other hand, this fermentation is of some academic interest, and it could probably be placed on an industrial basis if the demand became unusually great. A few general remarks concerning this fermentation will be made; for more details the theses and papers by Donker (1926), Morikawa (1927), Morikawa and Prescott (1927), van der Lek (1930), Dunn (1934), Osburn (1935), Osburn and Werkman (1935), Osburn, Brown, and Werkman (1937, 1938), Langlykke, Peterson, and McCoy (1935), Langlykke, Peterson, and Fred (1937), Sjolander, Langlykke, and Peterson (1938), and Brown, Stahly, and Werkman (1938) should be consulted.

As we have mentioned, certain strains of *Cl. butylicum* produce quite large amounts of butanol and isopropyl alcohol from sugars. As a result this species has been widely studied. In general, the optimum growth conditions for this organism are the same as those needed for the cultivation of the butanol-acetone bacteria. Glucose, wood sugars, and other carbohydrates can be used as a substrate; yeast extract, malt sprouts, peptones, corn-steep water, corn gluten, and liver extracts have been employed as a source of nitrogen and growth factors. The best temperature for growth is 37°C., and the optimum reaction is between pH 6.5 and 7.2. The fermentation is complete in 3 to 7 days. The quantities of end products formed from sugars by *Cl.*

TABLE 14

FERMENTATION OF GLUCOSE * BY *Clostridium butylicum*

[From Osburn, Brown, and Werkman (1937)]

Experiment Number	Millimols of Products per 100 m. Mol. of Glucose Fermented							Carbon Recovered, per cent
	Alcohols			Acids		Carbon Dioxide	Hydrogen	
	Butyl	*Isopropyl*	*Ethyl*	*Butyric*	*Acetic*			
1	57.6	15.1	2.9	15.1	9.1	166.5	75.8	87.0
2	66.6	15.1	0.0	6.1	21.2	197.0	72.7	95.0
3	58.6	12.1	0.0	17.2	17.2	203.5	77.6	96.3
4	65.5	13.8	2.3	13.8	10.3	189.5	86.2	95.6
5	54.1	18.0	0.0	15.5	12.9	222.0	107.0	96.2

* Medium: glucose 2%, peptone 0.7%, yeast extract 0.2%, and K_2HPO_4 0.1% in the presence of nitrogen.

butylicum vary considerably, depending upon the strain of organism, the sugar, and other factors. For example, Sjolander, Langlykke, and Peterson (1938) observed that more isopropyl alcohol was formed from crude hemlock and beechwood sugars than from glucose, but this situation was later found to be due to the acetic acid contained in the wood hydrolyzates. The addition of asparagine to certain mashes causes greater yields of butanol to be formed in place of butyric acid by *Cl. butylicum* [Brown, Stahly, and Werkman (1938)]. In spite of these slight modifications the final products usually include butyl and isopropyl alcohols, butyric and acetic acids, carbon dioxide and hydrogen gases, and sometimes traces of acetone and formic acid. Results of a few typical laboratory experiments are given in Table 14 to illustrate the quantities of products formed from glucose.

An interesting change occurs in the fermentation of sugars by *Cl. butylicum* when relatively large concentrations of sodium bicarbonate are present (see Table 15). Alcohol production is almost completely suppressed, and the salts of formic, acetic, butyric, lactic, and propionic acids and methylglyoxal accumulate in the medium.

The fermentation brought about by *Bacillus technicus* is quite similar to that described for *Cl. butylicum*. Fermented sugars (or koji rice) yield chiefly butyl and isopropyl alcohols, with variable ratios of hydrogen and carbon dioxide gas. Small amounts of butyric and acetic acids and traces of acetone also occur, but no ethyl alcohol is formed.

TABLE 15

FERMENTATION OF GLUCOSE * BY *Clostridium butylicum* IN THE PRESENCE OF SODIUM BICARBONATE †

[From Osburn, Brown, and Werkman (1937)]

Experiment Number	Millimols of Products per 100 m. Mol. of Glucose Fermented									Carbon Recovered, per cent
	Alcohols		Acids					Carbon Dioxide	Hydrogen	
	Butyl	*Isopropyl*	*Butyric*	*Acetic*	*Pyruvic*	*Lactic*	*Formic*			
1	3.0	0.0	54.0	24.0	3.0	43.5	0.0	135.0	135.9	91.7
2	3.0	3.0	51.0	33.0	12.0	37.8	0.0	138.0	150.0	96.5
3	5.4	1.8	33.7	27.0	11.2	56.2	27.0	91.5	87.4	89.4
4	6.7	1.9	30.6	35.4	7.6	60.2	47.8	74.6	57.9	92.0

* Medium: glucose 2%, peptone 0.7%, yeast extract 0.2%, and K_2HPO_4 0.1% in the presence of nitrogen.

† Sodium bicarbonate (8% solution) added about 14 hours after the start of fermentation; amount added equal to weight of glucose being fermented.

Under optimum conditions (pH 5 to 7, temperature 30° to 37°C., sugar 10 to 13 per cent, etc.) this facultative bacillus yields about 30 per cent of alcohols, with a 2 : 1 or 3 : 1 ratio of butyl to isopropyl.

It is fairly well agreed among investigators that the intermediate reactions in this fermentation are similar to those occurring in butanol-acetone fermentation, except that the acetone is reduced to isopropyl alcohol,

$$CH_3 \cdot CO \cdot CH_3 + 2H \rightarrow CH_3 \cdot CHOH \cdot CH_3$$

instead of accumulating in the solution. Some insight into the intermediate processes has been gained by determining the effect of adding various substances to glucose mashes undergoing fermentation [see Langlykke, Peterson, and Fred (1937), Osburn, Brown, and Werkman (1938)]. For example, added butyric acid is reduced to butanol; added acetic acid or acetone increases the yield of isopropyl alcohol. Acetaldehyde is converted to small amounts of ethanol and traces of acetylmethylcarbinol and 2:3-butylene glycol. The addition of pyruvic acid increases the yields of butyl and isopropyl alcohol, which are normally formed from glucose. All these facts therefore add support to a scheme in which butanol arises from butyric acid, isopropyl alcohol is formed from acetic acid by way of acetoacetic acid and acetone, and traces of ethyl alcohol are produced from pyruvic acid by decarboxylation and reduction.

ETHYL ALCOHOL-ACETONE FERMENTATION

Ethyl alcohol-acetone fermentation is now primarily of historic and academic interest, although during World War I it was thought for a while that this process might constitute an inexpensive method for the production of acetone from cheap carbohydrates. In fact, the process was granted a patent at that time [Northrop (1919)].

Acetone was first shown to be a fermentation product of *Bacillus macerans* by Schardinger about 1905 and of *Bacillus violarius-acetonicus* by Bréaudat in 1906. Acetone, ethyl alcohol, acetic and formic acids, and gases were produced during the fermentation of potato starch by *B. macerans*. Since Schardinger's discovery several other species of bacteria have been isolated and described as possessing similar fermentative properties. From the results of a study by Porter, McCleskey, and Levine (1937), however, it would appear that only two valid species belong to this group:[10] *Bacillus polymyxa* and *Bacillus macerans* (*Bacillus acetoethylicus*).

[10] Donker (1926) placed the organisms of this group in a new genus, which he called *Aerobacillus*. Because of the relative unimportance of these organisms the genus has not been recognized by *Bergey's Manual* (1939).

The *B. macerans* type of fermentation differs in several respects from the anaerobic fermentations just described. For example, the causative organism is not a strict anaerobe, but rather is facultative, since it can be cultivated under aerobic conditions. A great variety of substances, including pentoses, hexoses, pectin, starch, glycogen, polyhydric alcohols, and hydrolyzed corn cobs, oat, and peanut hulls, will serve as a substrate. The optimum fermentation temperature is about 40°C. The best yield of solvents occurs when the initial *p*H is between 7.6 and 8.4; at higher *p*H levels the formation of organic acids is favored, and later in the fermentation, when the reaction becomes acid (*p*H 5.8 to 6.0), the yield of acetone and ethanol increases. Growth, however, occurs between *p*H 4.6 and 9.8. The time required for the fermentation to reach completion is usually 5 to 7 days. The yield of end products varies considerably, depending upon the strain of organism used, the carbohydrate, and other factors. *Bacillus macerans* usually produces between 3 to 10 per cent acetone, 7 to 40 per cent ethanol, and 1 to 4 per cent volatile (acetic) and nonvolatile (lactic) acids; considerable gas also arises, as well as traces of other products (see Table 16).

TABLE 16

FERMENTATION OF GLUCOSE * BY *Bacillus macerans* AND *Bacillus polymyxa*

[From Donker (1926)]

	Percentage of Glucose Fermented by	
Product	*Bacillus macerans*	*Bacillus polymyxa*
Carbon dioxide	52.6	46.9
Hydrogen	1.52	0.83
Formic acid	2.6	.....
Lactic acid	Trace	Trace
Acetic acid	5.2	4.9
Butyric acid	.....	.....
Butyl alcohol	.....	0.8
Ethyl alcohol	31.2	22.5
Acetone	9.1	0.3
Acetylmethylcarbinol	Trace	Trace
2:3-Butylene glycol	0.6	19.1

* Medium: yeast water, glucose 2%, and chalk 1%. Incubation: about 8 days at 30° to 37°C.

Bacillus polymyxa produces a somewhat different type of fermentation from *B. macerans* (see Table 16). In fact, its fermentation closely resembles that of *Aerobacter aerogenes*, in which much slime, a considerable quantity of 2:3-butylene glycol, and traces of acetylmethylcarbinol and other products are formed (see pp. 952 to 953 on 2:3-butylene glycol fermentation).

Several theories have been suggested in the past for the mechanism of the ethyl alcohol-acetone fermentation. The better known have been proposed by Speakman (1925), Bakonyi (1926), and Donker (1926). However, in view of the more recent findings on the internal mechanism of sugar breakdown by cells, it is felt that the schemes put forth by these workers need to be studied further before any of them can be accepted. The original reports by these investigators should be consulted for details.

For further reading on ethyl alcohol-acetone fermentation the thesis by Donker (1926) and the papers by Northrop, Ashe, and Senior (1919), Northrop, Ashe, and Morgan (1919), Arzberger, Peterson, and Fred (1920), Peterson, Fred, and Verhulst (1921), Fred, Peterson, and Anderson (1923), Speakman (1925), Bakonyi (1926), Porter, McCleskey, and Levine (1937), Zaïtsev (1939), Stahly and Werkman (1942), Stanier *et al.* (1944), and Ward, Pettijohn, Lockwood, and Coghill (1944) should be consulted.

MISCELLANEOUS ANAEROBIC FERMENTATIONS

Numerous other organic substances can be formed as the result of activities of the anaerobic bacteria. All the processes leading to the formation of these compounds are of some academic interest, but none is of importance commercially at the present time with the exception of riboflavin production. A few examples may be mentioned.

Alcoholic Fermentation. Although a great many bacteria produce small amounts or traces of ethyl alcohol from sugars, only two or three species are known which can produce relatively large amounts of this alcohol. An organism tentatively called *Clostridium ethylicum* has been studied by Weizmann (1938). It is capable of fermenting glucose or sucrose, yielding about 26 per cent alcohol, CO_2, and H_2, with traces of volatile acids and amines. Even more active in this respect, however, is *Pseudomonas lindneri* (*Termobacterium mobile*), which was first isolated by Lindner in 1930 from pulqué, the Mexican national beverage made from the juice of cacti (*Agave* species). The principal products of the fermentation of glucose by this organism in an inorganic medium are ethyl alcohol (41 to 45 per cent), CO_2 (45 per cent), lactic acid (6 to 7 per cent), and traces of other acids, glycerol, acetylmethylcarbinol, and higher esters and alcohols [Kluyver (1931), Schreder, Brunner, and Hampe (1934)]. Although it has been reported that *Sarcina ventriculi* is capable of growing aerobically, it is of interest to mention here that this organism is also able to produce an almost truly anaerobic alcoholic fermentation of glucose. The end products consist of about 43 to 44 per cent ethyl alcohol, 47 per cent CO_2, and small percentages of other substances, such as acetic and formic acids, acetylmethylcarbinol, and gaseous hydrogen [Smit (1930)].

Propylene Glycol Fermentation. Castellani (1931) and Kluyver and Schnellen (1937) have studied an organism known as *Bacterium rhamnosifermentans*, which forms large amounts of propylene glycol ($CH_3 \cdot CHOH \cdot CH_2OH$) from the methyl pentose, rhamnose ($CH_3 \cdot CHOH \cdot CHOH \cdot CHOH \cdot CHOH \cdot CHO$). This bacterium is thought to be closely related to certain *Escherichia* species, although it exhibits considerable selective action in respect to the carbohydrates fermented and the nitrogen compounds utilized. For example, rhamnose is fermented more readily than other sugars, and peptone serves as a better source of nitrogen than do other substances, such as yeast water. The fermentation of rhamnose yields about 50 per cent propylene glycol, 22.5 per cent succinic acid, 24.4 per cent acetic acid, 5.0 per cent CO_2, and traces of formic acid, ethyl alcohol, and gaseous hydrogen.

Riboflavin Production. With slight modifications of the usual butanol fermentation process quite large yields of riboflavin can be recovered from the fermented mash. The synthesis of this vitamin by *Clostridium acetobutylicum* and related species was first disclosed by Miner in 1940, but yields of only about 25 to 60 μg. of riboflavin per gram were obtained. Later Arzberger (1943) was granted a patent for a process which has been greatly improved by excluding certain toxic metals. Yields as high as 3,000 μg. of riboflavin per gram of dried filtrate are now obtainable.

Other Fermentations. Besides the substances we have mentioned, other organic acids, alcohols, and methane can be produced from carbohydrates and related substances by bacterial action under anaerobic conditions. For example, the anaerobic dismutation of higher aldehydes by bacteria of the genus *Acetobacter* has been investigated by Neuberg and Windisch and Molinari [see Butlin (1936)]. They found that such species as *Acetobacter xylinum* and *Acetobacter ascendens* convert propionaldehyde to propionic acid and propyl alcohol, thus:

$$2CH_3 \cdot CH_2 \cdot CHO + H_2O \rightarrow CH_3 \cdot CH_2 \cdot COOH + CH_3 \cdot CH_2 \cdot CH_2OH$$

where one molecule of the aldehyde is oxidized to the acid, while another is simultaneously reduced to the alcohol. Other aldehydes, such as *n*-butyraldehyde, isovaleraldehyde, benzaldehyde, cinnamaldehyde ($C_6H_5CH{:}CH \cdot CHO$), and anisealdehyde ($CH_3O \cdot C_6H_4 \cdot CHO$), were similarly dismutated to their respective acids and alcohols. Likewise furfural was changed to furfuryl alcohol and pyromucic acid, thus:

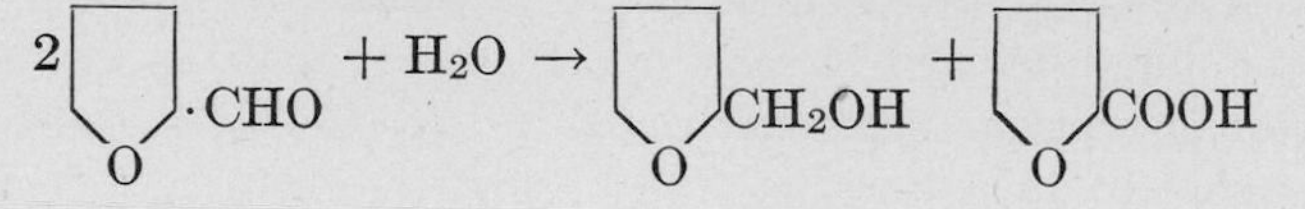

and citronellal (a mixture of stereoisomeric ten-carbon aldehydes) was dismutated to citronellol and citronellic acid. In general, the chemistry of the above processes is less well known than is that of some of the fermentations listed on the preceding pages.

The fermentative utilization of various cellulose-containing materials offers numerous interesting possibilities in the field of fermentations, and such substances have already been extensively studied by several investigators [see Fulmer (1936), Norman (1937), Bernhauer (1939), Thaysen (1939), Buswell and Hatfield (1939), Waksman (1940), Norman and Fuller (1942)].

II. Oxidative (Oxybiontic) Bacterial Fermentations

ACETIC ACID FERMENTATION (ACETIFICATION [11])

The acetification process is one of the longest known and used of our so-called fermentations. In fact, like the alcoholic and lactic acid fermentations, its history dates back to antiquity, when the ancients knew dilute acetic acid as vinegar,[12] which was obtained by allowing wine to undergo a natural souring. Some time between the fourteenth and seventeenth centuries vinegar brewing was established as a separate industry. Prior to that time it was made exclusively in the household; later it was just a by-product of the wine producer and the brewer.

Certain of the practical conditions necessary for vinegar manufacture from alcoholic solutions were known empirically for many years before it was recognized that the oxidation of alcohol to acetic acid was a result of the action of living organisms. For example, the production of beer and wine vinegar in a so-called generator, where sufficient oxygen could be supplied to hasten the process, dates back to about 1670. Before that time it was made by a much slower method. Later

[11] Acetification is probably a more appropriate term than acetic acid fermentation or vinegar fermentation for this process, since the transformation of ethyl alcohol to acetic acid is an oxidative process and not fermentative in the strictest Pasteurian sense.

[12] The word vinegar means literally sour or sharp wine, according to its derivation from the French *vinaigre* (*vin*, wine, + *aigre*, sour or sharp).

(1732) vinegar was made by the Dutchman, Boerhaave, by an even faster method, and finally the German, or quick-vinegar, process was introduced by Schützenbach in 1815 to 1826. In 1786 and 1793 Rozier and Lavoisier had already demonstrated that air was a necessary factor for vinegar production and had recognized it as an oxidative process. In 1814 Berzelius established the constitution of acetic acid, and Davy and Döbereiner synthesized it from wine in 1820 to 1821, using platinum black as a catalyst. A year after acetic acid was synthesized, Persoon made a botanical study of the membrane ("vinegar skin" or "mother of vinegar") growing on the surface of vinegar liquids and gave the name *Mycoderma* to such films, and in 1837 Kützing showed that these membranes contained minute organisms which he believed were associated with the acetification of alcohol. Berzelius and Liebig, who dominated chemistry at that time, however, sneered at these facts, since they believed the formation of the membrane was incidental rather than causal. Finally Pasteur's classical experiments in 1868 proved the living nature of mother of vinegar and confirmed the view put forward by Kützing that the minute organisms which form a scum on beer and wine were really responsible for acetification. During the next forty years after Pasteur's discoveries several species of vinegar bacteria were described and studied by Hansen, Lafar, Henneberg, Beijerinck, Brown, Hoyer, and others, and in 1903 the alcohol-oxidase enzyme system of vinegar bacteria was discovered by Buchner and Meisenheimer. For additional reading on the interesting history of acetic or vinegar fermentation the excellent review by Vaughn (1942) should be consulted.

According to Bernhauer (1939), the world production of acetic acid is about 270,000 tons, of which 40 per cent is made by fermentation, 30 per cent by the distillation of wood, and 30 per cent by synthesis. In the United States over 75,000 tons of acetic acid and its derivatives was manufactured in 1938, and about twice this amount was made in 1941. Probably the greatest use of acetic acid is in ordinary vinegar, where it is used as a condiment directly on the table or as an ingredient in the manufacture of mayonnaise, French dressing, relishes, and other food articles. In addition to ordinary cider, wine, and malt vinegars there are various special kinds, such as distilled or spirit vinegar, tarragon, and other herb vinegars. In this country the minimum amount of acetic acid allowed for such vinegars is 4 g. per 100 ml. at 20°C.; the vinegars also contain extractives and other substances which characterize the product. So-called vinegar essence, or double vinegar, is made from distilled spirits and may contain as much as 14 per cent acetic acid. Acetic acid has many other uses, and a great deal of the supply for these purposes is produced synthetically or by the distillation of wood. For example, it is used to produce esters which are employed in the paint and perfume industries and to make acetic anhydride, acetone, and acetyl cellulose.

Outline of the Acetic Acid Fermentation Process. There are two well-known fermentation methods for the production of acetic acid of vinegar: the *slow* process and the *quick* process. In the slow process the mash to be acetified is kept completely immobile, whereas in the quick method it is kept in movement, at least part of the time. The more important and more generally used method is the quick-vinegar process; but, although the slow process is now used to only a small extent, it produces a product of the finest quality, which is especially rich in aromatic matter. Whichever method is employed, it must be realized that vinegar making is of necessity a two-phase process; the raw material must undergo alcoholic fermentation before acetification can proceed.

Vinegar making is closely related to the food industries, and the production and uses of vinegar are usually discussed in some detail in food bacteriology courses. However, since it is essentially an aqueous solution of acetic acid, and since concentrated acetic acid or acetate esters can be obtained from it, the process will be outlined briefly. For more details on the manufacture of vinegar Fetzer (1930), Hansen (1935), Cruess (1938), Prescott and Dunn (1940), Hildebrandt (1941), Vaughn (1942), Tanner (1944), and the references cited by these workers should be consulted.

Raw Materials and Their Preparation. Vinegar can be produced from almost any substance which is capable of yielding alcohol by yeast fermentation. Apples, grapes or other fruit, malted barley, sugar from corn and other grains, potatoes, molasses, and honey have been used for vinegar manufacture. The preparation of these materials for vinegar stock depends upon their nature. The juice of fruit must be expressed; the polysaccharide of starchy materials must be hydrolyzed to a sugary solution for fermentation. Fruit juices are widely used in France and other European countries as a raw product, whereas malted grains are largely employed in England, and grape and apple juices, corn sugar, and distilled spirits are used in the United States.

In most fruits the yeast naturally present in the expressed juices is sufficient to bring about satisfactory alcoholic fermentation. To insure normal fermentation, however, the juice is frequently inoculated with a yeast starter which, in turn, may be developed from special strains of yeast (*Saccharomyces ellipsoideus*). Grain mashes, after hydrolysis with malt or by other means, are inoculated with a particularly pure strain of brewer's yeast or with other similar strains.

It is usually desirable to control the alcoholic fermentation to inhibit the lactic and acetic acid bacteria and to obtain maximum yields. In general, such control involves the adjustment of the sugar concentration in the mash to about 9 to 10 per cent, maintenance of an optimum fermentation temperature (24° to 27°C.), treatment of the mash with sulfur dioxide to prevent infection, and a storage period of 2 to 3 weeks after the fermentation is complete to allow the yeast and other solids to settle. The clear liquid is then drawn off, and the optimum alcohol concentration is adjusted to assure proper acetification. Alcohol concentrations between 5 and 13 per cent by volume are successfully acetified; higher concentrations are distinctly toxic to the acetic acid bacteria, and lower concentrations usually result in overoxidation and loss of aroma and flavor.

ACETIFICATION. The acetification of alcoholic solutions to make dilute acetic acid or vinegar is accomplished either by the slow method in barrels or by the quick method in generators.

The best known of the slow methods is the *Orleans process*, in which acetification is carried out in a horizontal, half-filled barrel, 50 to 54 gal. in capacity. The barrel has holes at the top for the admission of air and is equipped with a thermometer, a funnel tube for pouring in fresh stock below the liquid surface, and a spigot or swan-neck at the bottom to draw off the finished vinegar. The process is started by filling one-fourth to one-third of the barrel with a good unpasteurized stock and then inoculating it with 3 to 4 gal. of a starter containing active acetic acid bacteria. Although many workers have recommended the use of pure cultures of acetic acid bacteria for the production of vinegar, such practice has not been generally accepted for several reasons. For example, the construction of various equipment does not permit easy sterilization, and the pasteurization of vinegar stock is uneconomical. The most common species which can be isolated from active vinegar starters consist of *Acetobacter aceti*, *Acetobacter xylinum*, *Acetobacter rancens*, and *Acetobacter melanogenum* [see the classification of species by Vaughn (1942)].

After a few days at 20°C. a film forms on the surface of the liquid in the barrel, and the active acetification process increases the temperature 2° to 3°C. At weekly intervals for a month fresh stock is added through the funnel tube until the barrel is about one-half full. After 5 weeks 3 or 4 gal. of vinegar is removed, and the same volume of stock is replaced. By repeating this operation at weekly intervals the process becomes continuous.

Several modifications of the slow method have been introduced. For example, Pasteur recommended a light grating of wood or float on the surface of the liquid to support the bacterial film and keep it intact during active acetification. He also suggested that shallow vats might work very well for acetic acid fermentation.

The quick, generator method is now generally used in industry because, as its name implies, it is faster than the slow process. Several modifications of this method have also been devised; the more important are known as the *Boerhaave process*, the *Michaelis process*, the *English round-pump process*, and the *Frings process* [see Hansen (1935), Bernhauer (1939), Vaughn (1942)]. A laboratory-sized, experimental quick-vinegar generator has also been designed by Hildebrandt (1941) for control work and for use in testing various factors affecting the acetification process.

Almost all the standard quick methods involve the use of an upright acidifier (usually of wood) divided into three compartments and so designed as to afford a maximum of surface exposure and an optimum amount of air. The lower part of the generator is equipped with a false perforated bottom and a closed vinegar-collection compartment with a spigot below. The central acetification compartment just above the false bottom is quite large and is usually packed with a percolating medium, such as beechwood shavings, upon which the bacteria colonize. Other loose-packing material, however, such as excelsior, rattan, corn cobs, coke, and lump pumice, which offer large surface areas but do not impart off-flavors and odors to the vinegar, can be used in the acetification compartment. Near the top of the generator and above the percolating medium is a perforated top or distributing head, over which is arranged a rotating sprinkler or an automatic tilting device for distribution of the vinegar and alcohol-containing substrate over the percolating medium. Such generators are equipped with thermometers and air vents and usually contain an automatic centrifugal pump to force the mix intermittently from the bottom compartment to the sprinkling device at the top. The mix may be recirculated through the same generator until the desired acetification occurs, or it may be passed through two or more generators connected in series. Since the oxidation of alcohol to acetic acid liberates considerable heat, the temperature of the generators must be carefully controlled; some types of generators, for example, Frings, are equipped with a special cooling device. In the United States temperatures of 26° to 32°C. (79° to 89°F.) are recommended, but somewhat higher values are used in other countries. According to Fetzer (1930), some large vinegar producers have as many as 7,000 generators producing, which yield approximately 20,000,000 gal. of 10 per cent vinegar per year. The newer type Frings generator, however, is larger and more efficient than these older generators, and fewer would be required to produce the same amount of vinegar.

YIELD, AGING, AND PREPARATION FOR MARKET. The acetification process is allowed to proceed until the vinegar reaches its proper strength. According to Cruess, approximately 1.26 g. of acetic acid is obtained from 1 g. of ethyl alcohol under favorable conditions. Calculated on the basis of sugar, this yield corresponds to about 50 to 55 parts of acetic acid per 100 parts of sugar. The amount of acetic acid present at any given time during the acetification process may be calculated by steam-distilling a sample of the vinegar stock and titrating the acid in the distillate (1 ml. 0.10 N alkali = 6 mg. acetic acid = 4.6 mg. ethanol).

After the vinegar has reached its maximum strength, it is placed in barrels or storage tanks for 6 to 18 months' aging. The storage containers must be completely filled and tightly sealed to exclude oxygen; otherwise certain species of *Acetobacter*, such as *Acetobacter aceti* and *Acetobacter xylinum*, will gradually oxidize the acetic acid to carbon dioxide and water. In the slow-vinegar process considerable aging occurs during the course of manufacture; spirit vinegar, which is essentially a dilute acetic acid solution, is not improved by aging.

After the aging period vinegar is usually clarified by filtration, pasteurized at 60° to 68°C. (140° to 155°F.) for 30 minutes, and then placed in well-filled, noncorrosive containers for market.

Mechanism of the Acetification Process. It is generally believed that the oxidation of alcohol to acetic acid by *Acetobacter* species is a two-step process, in which acetaldehyde or its hydrate serves as an intermediate [see Bertho (1932), Janke and Kropacsy (1935), Butlin (1936)]. Thus alcohol is first dehydrogenated to acetaldehyde; then the acetaldehyde becomes hydrated and is changed into acetic acid by further dehydrogenation.

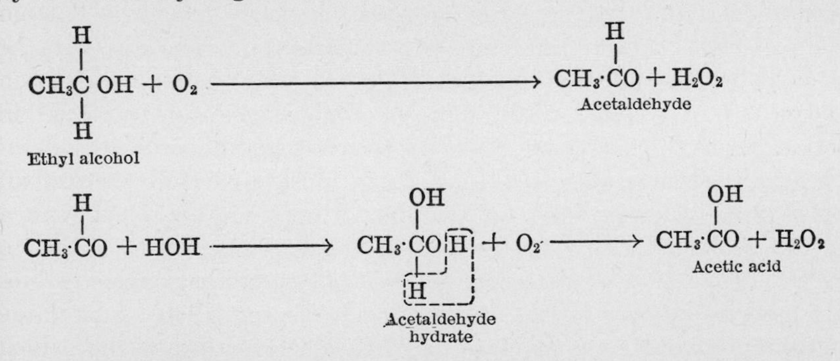

Hoyer first showed in 1899 that acetaldehyde is an intermediate in the acetification process. Since that time it has been observed by numerous workers that in an incorrect vinegar-making process, considerable acetaldehyde appears in the generator. Neuberg and his associates have also demonstrated acetaldehyde in this fermentation through calcium sulfite fixation.

In a natural environment oxygen plays the role of a hydrogen acceptor in the foregoing reactions. Under experimental conditions, however, other substances, such as quinone and methylene blue, will serve as hydrogen acceptors. Under anaerobic conditions, especially at high *p*H values (7.6 to 8.4), and to some extent in an aerobic environment, acetaldehyde may act as the hydrogen acceptor for acetaldehyde hydrate. The result is a dismutative change (Cannizzaro reaction) in which one molecule of acetaldehyde is reduced to ethyl alcohol and one of hydrated acetaldehyde is oxidized (dehydrogenated) to acetic acid; thus:

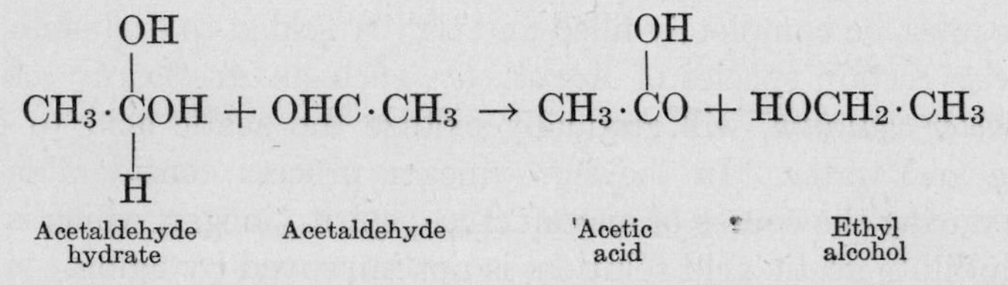

Although the foregoing equations represent the over-all acetification process, they are only an approximate explanation of the reactions involved. As indicated above, the amounts of alcohol, acetaldehyde, and acetic acid present at any given stage of the process depend upon several factors, such as oxygen supply, reaction (*p*H), temperature, and species of acetic acid bacteria. It is also quite possible, in view of recent findings by Lipmann and others, that some phosphorylated compound occurs as an intermediate. Finally it should be mentioned that under certain conditions some acetic acid bacteria oxidize acetic acid to other products.

l-SORBOSE FERMENTATION

In 1896 Bertrand isolated an organism which he called the sorbose bacterium (*Acetobacter xylinum*) because of its ability to oxidize sorbitol to the corresponding β-keto carbohydrate, sorbose.

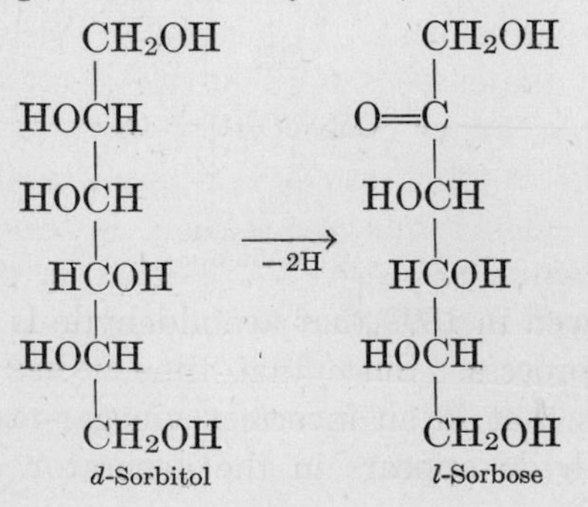

Since that time other *Acetobacter* species besides *Acetobacter xylinum* have been shown to possess this same property; in fact, *Acetobacter suboxydans*, *Acetobacter xylinoides*, and *Acetobacter melanogenum* appear to give the best yields of any species in this genus [see Butlin (1936), Fulmer, Dunning, Guymon and Underkofler (1936), Kresling (1940)].

l-Sorbose is a compound of practical interest today because of its use in the synthesis of ascorbic acid (vitamin C). Reichstein and Grüssner (1934) first demonstrated the importance of the *Acetobacter* species in this synthesis when they prepared ascorbic acid from glucose by the following reactions:

$$\text{Glucose} \xrightarrow{\text{H+Pt}} d\text{-Sorbitol} \xrightarrow{A.\ xylinum} l\text{-Sorbose} \xrightarrow{\text{Acetone}}$$

$$\text{Diacetone sorbose} \xrightarrow{\text{KMnO}_4} \text{Diacetone Sorbonic acid} \xrightarrow{\text{HCl}}$$

$$l\text{-Sorbonic acid} \xrightarrow{\text{HCl}} l\text{-Ascorbic acid.}$$

In the United States and Russia other species, such as *A. suboxydans* and *A. melanogenum*, are now used in place of *A. xylinum* for the conversion of *d*-sorbitol to *l*-sorbose in this scheme.

Sorbose can be made from sorbitol by two fermentation methods: (1) by surface growth of the bacteria in flasks or vats, and (2) by submerged growths in aerated rotary-drum fermenters [Fulmer, Dunning, Guymon, and Underkofler (1936), Wells, Stubbs, Lockwood, and Roe (1937), Wells, Lockwood, Stubbs, Porges, and Gastrock (1939)]. In either of these methods a medium containing sorbitol in concentrations between 10 and 35 per cent, yeast extract (0.5 per cent) or corn-steep liquor (0.3 per cent), and sometimes salts ($CaCO_3$, Na_2SO_4) at *p*H 4.2 to 6.4 may be used. Incubation at 28° to 30°C. under highly aerobic conditions is optimum for the fermentation.

Yields of about 80 per cent sorbose have been obtained from 15.4 per cent sorbitol in 9 to 12 days with the surface-growth method; higher concentrations of sorbitol are converted more slowly. With aerated rotary-drum fermenters, however, even better yields are obtainable, and in a shorter time. For example, Wells and his associates (1939) found that under controlled laboratory conditions *d*-sorbitol concentrations up to 30 per cent were rapidly and efficiently oxidized to *l*-sorbose. In 10, 20, and 30 per cent sorbitol solutions practically quantitative conversion occurred during fermentation periods of 13.5, 24, and 45 hours, respectively. Results of pilot-plant-scale experiments were essentially the same as those obtained in the laboratory, although some sorbose was lost during the recovery and purification process. For instance, in one experiment in which a 30 per cent sorbitol solution and an incubation temperature of 30°C. for 34 hours were used the following data were obtained:

Total sorbitol available (dry basis)	163.4 kg.
Total sorbose produced	151.0 kg.
Total sorbose recovered	114.3 kg.
Weight yield, based on sorbose produced	92.4%
Weight yield, based on sorbitol recovered	69.8%

For more interesting details of this fermentation process, the references cited on the preceding pages should be consulted.

DIHYDROXYACETONE FERMENTATION

Dihydroxyacetone is a white, crystalline substance with a characteristic odor and a sweet, cooling taste. It may be used as a sweetener for diabetic foods and for other purposes. The compound can be prepared by chemical means, such as the action of sodium hypobromite on glycerol, but the yield is not good [Butlin (1938)]. It can be obtained biologically, however, through dehydrogenation of glycerol by certain species of *Acetobacter*. This oxidation reaction may be written as:

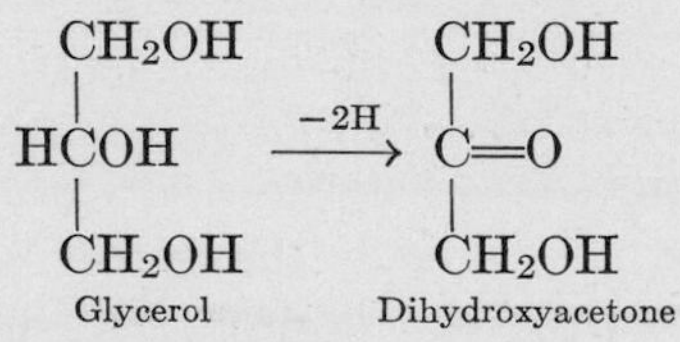

Glycerol Dihydroxyacetone

In this reaction the two activated hydrogen atoms are accepted by oxygen.

Bertrand, working with his sorbose bacterium (*Acetobacter xylinum*) in 1898, first produced dihydroxyacetone by means of microorganisms. This discovery has since been confirmed by Visser't Hooft (1925), Virtanen and Nordlund (1933), Underkofler and Fulmer (1937), Butlin (1938), and others, who have further improved the process and have shown that other species of *Acetobacter*, such as *Acetobacter suboxydans*, likewise possess this ability to convert glycerol to dihydroxyacetone. It should also be mentioned that some *Acetobacter* species carry the oxidation of glycerol beyond the dihydroxyacetone stage.

The medium used for this fermentation usually contains glycerol (5 to 25 per cent) yeast extract (0.5 per cent), and KH_2PO_4(0.1 to 0.3 per cent) and is adjusted to a *p*H of 6.5 to 7.0. The lower concentrations of glycerol are oxidized most rapidly; concentrations of phosphate above 0.3 per cent decrease the yield. Incubation at 28° to 30°C. is optimum, and strong aeration greatly increases the yield of dihydroxyacetone. A 25 per cent glycerol solution under optimum conditions is almost quantitatively transformed by *A. suboxydans* in 12 days, and a 15 per cent solution gives a 95 per cent yield of dihydroxyacetone in 3 to 4 days. The dihydroxyacetone may be recovered and purified by several methods without much loss of material.

GLUCONIC ACID FERMENTATIONS

Gluconic acid [$CH_2OH \cdot (CHOH)_4 \cdot COOH$] may be prepared by various chemical means and by biological methods in which microorganisms are used. The production of *d*-gluconic acid, *d*-5-ketogluconic acid, *d*-2-ketogluconic acid, and *d*-aldehyde-gluconic acid from glucose by microbial means has been studied rather extensively by several workers during the past few years. A general outline of the bacterial processes will be given below; the literature should be consulted for more details [see Hermann (1929), Takahashi and Asai (1930, 1933), Hermann and Neuschul (1935), Pervozvanskiĭ and Ivashkevich (1939), Stubbs, Lockwood, Roe, Tabenkin, and Ward (1940), Lockwood, Tabenkin, and Ward (1941), Porges, Clark, and Gastrock (1942), Lockwood (1942), Stubbs, Lockwood, Roe, and Ward (1943)].

The various gluconic acids and their salts are widely used today for several purposes. For example, they may be employed in the manufacture of certain medicinal and pharmaceutical preparations, in the tanning industry, as an ingredient in certain metal polishes, and for the preparation of tartaric acid and other substances. Furthermore these acids are of interest because they offer a means of extending the industrial utilization of certain agricultural products.

Gluconic acid was first found to be a metabolic product of acetic acid bacteria by Boutroux in 1878–1880. Since that time numerous other microorganisms have been shown to produce the same acid. It has been only since about 1940, however, that the production of the ketogluconic acids by bacterial means has been fully realized. Stubbs, Lockwood, Roe, Tabenkin, and Ward (1940) found that the rates of formation and yields of the ketogluconic acids produced by bacteria could be greatly increased through the use of rotary-drum fermenters, aeration, and other special techniques.

The 5-ketogluconic acid fermentation is brought about by various *Acetobacter* species, with *Acetobacter suboxydans* giving the best yields. A suitable medium contains glucose (10 per cent) as a substrate and corn-steep liquor (0.5 per cent) or other substances as a nutrient. A sterile slurry of $CaCO_3$ is used as a neutralizer during the fermentation. Aeration is essential for a rapid and maximum yield of ketogluconic acid; a gauge pressure of about 30 lb. per square inch and a sterile air flow of at least 400 cu. cm. per liter of culture medium per minute are optimum. Fermentation periods vary from 25 to 50 hours at 25° to 30°C., but yields as high as 90 per cent may be obtained in 33 hours. Fermentation occurs in two successive steps: (1) the oxidation of glucose to gluconic acid, and (2) the further oxidation of gluconic acid to 5-ketogluconic acid. The second step does not begin until the first is substantially complete. The bacterial population increases in the first stage but not in the second.

Although it has been reported that certain *Acetobacter* species also produce 2-ketogluconic acid, much better results are obtained with various *Pseudomonas* species [Stubbs *et al.* (1940), Lockwood, Tabenkin, and Ward (1941)]. A medium containing glucose (10 per cent), corn-steep liquor (0.5 per cent), salts (KH_2PO_4, 0.06 per cent; $MgSO_4 \cdot 7H_2O$, 0.025 per cent), and urea (0.2 per cent) has been found suitable for 2-ketogluconic acid production. The medium is incubated at 25° to 30°C. for 2 to 4 days in a rotary-drum fermenter, strongly aerated, and rotated at thirteen revolutions per minute. With a strain of *Pseudomonas fluorescens* approximately 82 per cent yields of 2-ketogluconic acid are obtainable in 25 hours. In this fermentation 2-ketogluconic acid formation occurs simultaneously with glucose utilization, and bacterial growth takes place during the entire period. These events are in direct contrast with those occurring in 5-ketogluconic acid fermentation.

Little is known about the formation of aldehyde-gluconic acid by bacteria, since the isolation and pure preparation of this acid are difficult [Bernhauer (1939)].

The mechanisms involved in the production of the gluconic acids from glucose by microorganisms have not been studied very extensively. It is assumed, however, that the processes are simple dehydrogenation reactions in which gluconic acid is the first oxidation product formed from glucose. The transformation of gluconic acid to the keto- and aldehyde-gluconic acids may be represented by the following reactions, depending upon whether secondary or primary carbinol groups are attacked [Bernhauer (1939)]:

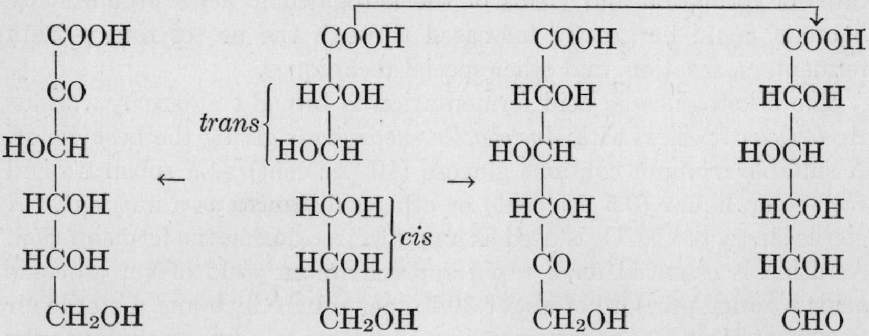

COOH			COOH		COOH	COOH
CO		*trans* {	HCOH		HCOH	HCOH
HOCH			HOCH		HOCH	HOCH
HCOH	←		HCOH	→	HCOH	HCOH
HCOH			HCOH } *cis*		CO	HCOH
CH_2OH			CH_2OH		CH_2OH	CHO
d-2-Ketogluconic acid (*d*-Glucosonic acid)			*d*-Gluconic acid		*d*-5-Ketogluconic acid (*l*-Sorburonic acid)	*d*-Aldehyde-gluconic acid (*l*-Guluronic acid)

(An arrow leads from *d*-gluconic acid to *d*-aldehyde-gluconic acid.)

Further discussion of the production of gluconic acid by microorganisms will be found on pp. 999 to 1005 on mold fermentations.

d-TARTARIC ACID FERMENTATION

Tartaric acid has been obtained for many years as a by-product of the wine industry and by various chemical methods. With some of these methods, however, mixtures of *dextro-*, *meso-*, and *dl*-tartaric acids with oxalic and other acids are obtained. Furthermore, it is quite difficult and commercially impractical to separate these compounds. More recently Pasternack and Brown (1940), Lockwood (1942), and Kamlet (1943) have described methods, which partly or completely involve the use of microorganisms, for the preparation of *d*-tartaric acid,

```
        HO H
        |  |
HOOC·C·C·COOH,
        |  |
        H  OH
```

substantially free of isomers and other substances. The method used by Pasternack and Brown and by Lockwood begins with 5-ketogluconic acid, which is obtained by chemical or biological processes This acid or its salt is then oxidized to tartaric acid by oxygen and metallic catalysts. Kamlet's method, on the other hand, produces tartaric acid directly by the oxidative dissimilation of glucose by *Acetobacter suboxydans*.

For details of the fermentation method the patent by Kamlet (1943) should be consulted. Briefly, however, it consists of cultivating a young culture of the organism in a medium containing glucose (10 per cent), corn-steep liquor or autolyzed yeast, and small amounts (for example, 0.1 to 0.5 per cent of the weight of glucose) of a vanadium compound, such as V_2O_5, as a catalyst. Strong aeration is essential, and the optimum temperature for the fermentation is 28° to 30°C. By the periodic addition of a sterile slurry of sodium carbonate the reaction of the medium is kept at *p*H 5.5 to 6.0. The conversion of glucose to *d*-tartaric acid is complete in 8 to 24 hours, after which the acid is recovered by filtration and other treatments and finally precipitated as the potassium acid tartrate.

Tartaric acid has several pharmaceutical uses, such as the preparation of effervescent powders. It is also used in industry for making baking powders, dyeing and printing fabrics, photography, and tanning.

MISCELLANEOUS AEROBIC BACTERIAL DISSIMILATIONS

Various aerobic bacteria produce a great variety of other substances through their oxidative activities on carbohydrates, polyhydroxy alcohols, and related compounds. Certain of these oxidations are unique in character, but with few exceptions they are of only scientific interest. A few examples are cited in Table 17, and others will be found in the literature and in Chapter 8.

From 1898 to 1904 Bertrand found that certain acetic acid bacteria would convert *l*-arabinose to *l*-arabonic acid, *l*-xylose to *l*-xylonic acid, galactose to galactonic acid, and mannose to mannonic acid. Since that time other workers have observed the same phenomenon with other bacteria.

Bertrand also observed that his sorbose bacterium (*Acetobacter xylinum*) would oxidize certain polyhydroxy alcohols (erythritol, *l*-arabitol, *d*-sorbitol, mannitol, perseitol, and volemitol) into their corresponding β-ketone sugars, but other alcohols (xylitol, dulcitol, and iditol) were not dehydrogenated. On the basis of these results a general regularity for the oxidation of secondary carbinol groups by the acetic acid bacteria was deduced; this is now known as *Bertrand's rule*. Thus a configuration which is favorable for dehydrogenation is one in which the carbinol group to be oxidized is in proximity to a second OH-group or in the *cis*-position; on the other hand, carbinol groups in which this arrangement is different are not attacked:

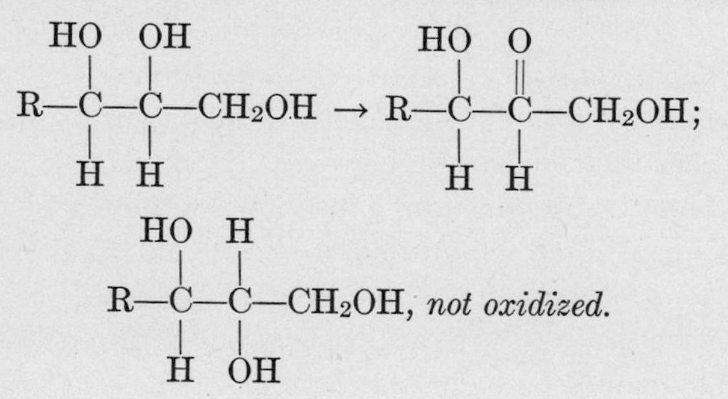

All the alcohols which have been mentioned fit this general rule, but there are also a few exceptions [Butlin (1936)]. Certain other *Acetobacter* species are capable of producing similar oxidative reactions. For instance, Tilden (1939) found that *Acetobacter suboxydans* converts perseitol quantitatively to perseulose, and Pitcher (1941) observed that about 78 per cent of the ketose substance formed from *i*-inositol by the same organism consists of a diketo-*i*-inositol.

The formation of aldoses from alcohols has been seldom observed, according to Bernhauer (1939). He notes, however, that certain organisms are capable of oxidizing mannitol to mannose and dulcitol to galactose.

TABLE 17

MISCELLANEOUS SUBSTRATES OXIDIZED BY CERTAIN AEROBIC BACTERIA AND THE PRODUCTS FORMED

[From Takahashi and Asai (1933, 1936), Butlin (1936), Tilden (1939), Pitcher (1941), and Others]

Substrate	Product
CH_2OH CH_2OH Ethylene glycol	$COOH$ CH_2OH Glycolic acid
CH_3 $HCOH$ CH_2OH Propylene glycol	CH_3 $C{=}O$ CH_2OH Acetol
CH_3 $HCOH$ $HCOH$ CH_3 2:3-Butylene glycol	CH_3 $C{=}O$ $HCOH$ CH_3 Acetylmethylcarbinol
CH_3 $C{=}O$ $HCOH$ CH_3 Acetylmethylcarbinol	CH_3 $C{=}O$ $C{=}O$ CH_3 Diacetyl
CH_2OH $HOCH$ $HOCH$ CH_2OH Erythritol	CH_2OH $O{=}C$ $HOCH$ CH_2OH Erythrulose
CH_2OH $HCOH$ $HCOH$ $HOCH$ CH_2OH Arabitol	CH_2OH $C{=}O$ $HCOH$ $HOCH$ CH_2OH "Arabinulose"
CH_2OH $HOCH$ $HOCH$ $HOCH$ CH_2OH *i*-Adonitol	CH_2OH $O{=}C$ $HOCH$ $HOCH$ CH_2OH "Adoninulose"
CHO $HCOH$ $HOCH$ $HCOH$ CH_2OH Xylose	$COOH$ $HCOH$ $HOCH$ $HCOH$ CH_2OH Xylonic acid
CHO $HCOH$ $HOCH$ $HOCH$ CH_2OH Arabinose	$COOH$ $HCOH$ $HOCH$ $HOCH$ CH_2OH Arabonic acid
CH_2OH $HOCH$ $HOCH$ $HCOH$ $HCOH$ CH_2OH *d*-Mannitol	CH_2OH $O{=}C$ $HOCH$ $HCOH$ $HCOH$ CH_2OH *d*-Levulose
	$HC\text{–}CO\text{–}COH$ $HOH_2CC\text{—}O\text{—}CH$ Kojic acid

TABLE 17 (*Continued*)

MISCELLANEOUS SUBSTRATES OXIDIZED BY CERTAIN AEROBIC BACTERIA AND THE PRODUCTS FORMED

[From Takahashi and Asai (1933, 1936), Butlin (1936), Tilden (1939), Pitcher (1941), and Others]

Substrate	Product	Substrate	Product
CHOH HCOH HCOH HCOH HCOH CHOH Inositol	"Diketoinositol"	CH_2OH HCOH HCOH HCOH HOCH HCOH CH_2OH Perseitol	CH_2OH CO HCOH HCOH HOCH HCOH CH_2OH Perseulose
CHO HCOH HOCH HOCH HCOH CH_2OH *d*-Galactose	COOH HCOH HOCH HOCH HCOH CH_2OH Galactonic acid HOC–CO–CH HC—O—C·COOH Komenic acid	CH_2OH HOCH HOCH HOCH HOCH HCOH CH_2OH Volemitol	Ketoheptose (*not identified*)

Takahashi and Asai (1933, 1936) have isolated certain species of *Acetobacter* from fruits which form kojic acid from mannitol and levulose and komenic acid from galactose.

Other bacteria, such as streptococci, oxidize 2·3-butylene glycol to acetylmethylcarbinol, which in turn may be oxidized to diacetyl. Acetylmethylcarbinol and diacetyl are of special economic interest because they are chiefly responsible for the aroma of good butter [see Michaelian and Hammer (1935, 1936), Hammer, Stahly, Werkman, and Michaelian (1935)].

Alcaligenes fecalis oxidizes several steroid compounds, such as cholic acid (3:7:12-trihydroxycholanic acid), desoxycholic acid (3:12-dihydroxycholanic acid), hyodesoxycholic acid (3:6-dihydroxycholanic acid), lithocholic acid (3-hydroxycholanic acid), and dehydroisoandrosterone, to their keto derivatives but has no action on estradiol (3:17-dihydroxy-13-methyl, on ring structure in cholic acid formula) and estriol [see Hughes and Schmidt (1942), Schmidt, Hughes, Green, and Cooper (1942), Hoehn, Schmidt, and Hughes (1944)]. Cholic acid has the following formula:

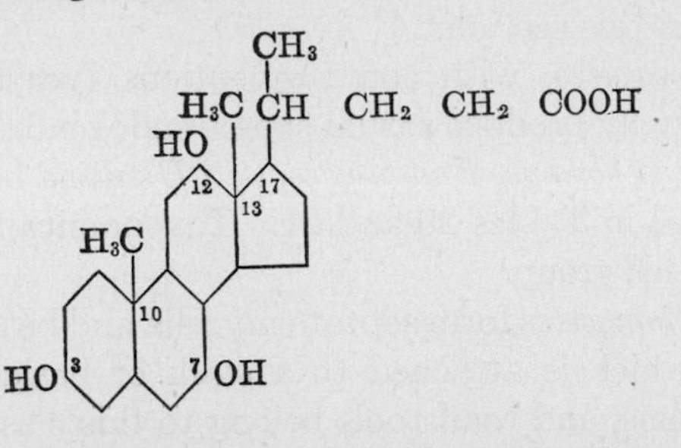

The end product of the action of *Alcaligenes fecalis* on cholic acid has been identified as 3:7:12-triketocholanic acid. It has been isolated in pure form and in 83 per cent of the theoretical yield from media containing up to about 1 per cent concentrations of cholic acid which has been incubated at 37°C. for 7 days. Concentrations of cholic acid above 1.8 per cent are not oxidized. A well-aerated medium favors the reaction. Analysis of the process at various intervals indicates that the 7-keto acid is the first oxidation product of cholic acid, the 7:12-diketo acid the second, and the 7 12 3-triketo acid the last. This fact indicates that the hydroxyls of cholic acid undergo oxidation by *A. fecalis* in the same order as when they are treated with chromic acid.

Mamoli and his associates [see Mamoli and Schramm (1938), Mamoli (1938), Mamoli, Koch, and Teschen (1939)], and Arnaudi (1939) have also reported that some *Corynebacterium* species, yeast, and other organisms oxidize certain sex hormones, such as dehydroisoandrosterone to androstenedione, but the cholic acid compounds used by Hughes, Schmidt, and their associates were not employed in these studies.

C. MOLD FERMENTATIONS

The group of microorganisms known commonly as molds differ in many respects from yeasts and bacteria. For example, morphologically they are multicellular rather than unicellular organisms; physiologically they are essentially aerobic in nature; and they seem to have greater and more diverse synthetic powers than the true yeasts and bacteria.

The organisms, or fungi, which are frequently classified with the molds may be divided into three or four main classes.[13] They are:

[13] For more details on the classification of these organisms Bessey's (1935) oı another book on mycology should be consulted.

1. The *Phycomycetes*, which usually possess nonseptate mycelia. Several families and many genera belong to this class. Three genera, *Mucor*, *Rhizopus*, and *Circinella*, may be cited as examples which will be mentioned in this section.

2. The *Ascomycetes*, with some exceptions (yeasts), have septate mycelia and usually produce sexual spores endogenously in sacs or asci. The genera *Byssochlamys*, *Endomyces*, and *Ustulina* belong to this class and will be cited in Tables 20 and 21. Taxonomically the true yeasts also belong to this group.

3. The *Basidiomycetes* form septate mycelia and bear sexual spores on a sterigmata, which is attached to a stalk or basidium. The rusts, smuts, mushrooms, and toadstools belong to this class. None of these forms will be discussed here, except that one species of the genus *Boletus* will be cited in Table 21.

4. The *Fungi imperfecti* usually possess septate mycelia, and their characteristic method of multiplication is by means of free-borne conidia (spores). Some species, however, form oidia and chlamydospores. The genera in this class which will be mentioned in the discussion or listed in Tables 18 to 21 include: *Aspergillus*, *Penicillium*, *Fusarium*, *Oöspora* (*Oidium*), *Monilia*, *Botrytis*, *Alternaria*, *Cladosporium*, *Helminthosporium*, *Clasterosporium*, *Caldariomyces* (*Fumago*), and *Verticellium*.

Molds bring about many beneficial changes in nature, but some of their activities are harmful, causing diseases in plants and animals. A discussion of the role played by these organisms in the soil, in the deterioration and destruction of timber, textiles, and foods, in the preparation of food products, and in disease processes is beyond the scope of this book. In accordance with the general policy of considering in this chapter the formation and isolation of known chemical substances, however, a few mold fermentations will be discussed, and several known mold-metabolic products of scientific interest will be listed in tables to illustrate the diverse synthesizing powers of the molds.

CITRIC ACID FERMENTATION

Although citric acid, $HOOC \cdot CH_2 \cdot C(OH)(COOH) \cdot CH_2 \cdot COOH$, was first isolated in a crystalline state from lemon juice by Scheele in 1784, it was some 50 years later (1838) that Liebig showed it to be a tribasic acid, and not until 1893 did Wehmer find that it was a product of mold metabolism.

Citric acid and its derivatives have many important uses today; in fact, more than 26,000,000 lb. is produced in this country each year to take care of the demands. According to Wells and Herrick (1938), about 65 per cent of the citric acid used in the United States is employed in pharmaceutical products, such as citrates and effervescent salts, 15 per cent in foods (flavoring extracts, soft drinks, etc.,) 9 per cent in candies, and smaller amounts as an ingredient in ink, silvering agents, and engraving solutions, and in dyeing and printing calico. More recent research indicates that citric acid can be used in the manufacture of certain types of resins, dyes, and other products.

Many plant tissues, especially those of the citrus variety, contain citric acid. In citrus fruits, sloes, and cranberries it is present in quite large amounts, along with traces of malic acid; but in fruits such as the cherry, strawberry, and raspberry these two acids occur in about equal proportion. The chief commercial sources for natural citric acid are cull lemons, limes, and pineapples [Wells and Herrick (1938), Schofield (1943)]. Before 1922 Italy and Sicily produced about 90 per cent of the world supply of calcium citrate, the raw material used in the manufacture of natural citric acid. Other countries, including the United States, were almost entirely dependent on the Italian producers for their supply of these materials at that time. In fact, in 1922 we imported about 16,000,000 lb. of calcium citrate and more than 1,000,000 lb. of citric acid. Since 1927, however, very little calcium citrate and citric acid have been imported into this country because our domestic production has risen to a point where our demands can be supplied. This change is attributed in part to the following four factors [Wells and Herrick (1938)]: (1) the Tariff Act of 1922, which increased the duty on calcium citrate from 1 to 7 cents per pound and on citric acid from 5 to 17 cents per pound; (2) the large increase in acreage of lemon trees in California; (3) our increased imports of concentrated lemon juice; and (4) the large-scale manufacture of fermentation citric acid which began about 1923. Italy, Sicily, California, Hawaii, and the West Indies are the only places in the world where natural citric acid is produced today. Only about one-third of our domestic production is natural citric acid.

The production of citric acid from sugars by mold fermentation was first discovered and patented by Wehmer about 1893. Since that time the process has been studied by numerous workers, who have been particularly interested in the various types of fungi which form citric acid, the factors which influence the fermentation, and the unique mechanism by which sugar is converted into citric acid with its branched chain. More than two-thirds of our domestic production of citric acid, or about 17,000,000 lb., is now supplied by the fermentation industry. The acid is also made by this method in Belgium, Czechoslovakia, Germany, Great Britain, Japan, Russia, and other countries. Production figures for these countries, however, are unavailable.

It is not the purpose of this discussion to survey all the work which has been done on the mycological production of citric acid, but rather to outline briefly the fermentation process in so far as it is known. More complete details will be found in the literature [see Bernhauer (1939), Bernhauer and Iglauer (1936), Bernhauer, Iglauer, and Knobloch (1941), Cahn (1935), Challenger (1929), Chatterjee (1942), Chrzaszcz and Leonhard (1936), Currie (1917), Doelger and Prescott (1934), Prescott and Dunn (1940), Smith (1942), Smyth and Obold (1930), von Loesecke (1945), Wells and Ward (1939)].

Outline of the Industrial Fermentation Process. The production of citric acid on a commercial scale by fermentation methods has been developed largely within the past 20 years, even though it has been known for more than 50 years that certain molds form large amounts of this acid from sugars. Numerous factors are involved in the efficient large-scale operation of this process. These factors include the choice of the proper mold strain, the use of a suitable medium, and the control of such details as the ratio of the surface area to the volume of the substrate, the *p*H, the oxygen supply, and the temperature. Lack of knowledge concerning these factors was partly responsible for the slow development of this fermentation on a commercial basis.

Wehmer first used a particular group of *Penicillium*-like fungi for citric acid production. He appropriately named these fungi *Citromyces*, the species *Citromyces glaber* and *Citromyces pfefferianus* being the ones with which he obtained the best results. Since Wehmer's early publications Thom and his associates and others have shown that a large number of fungi in several genera have the ability to form citric acid in variable amounts. Certain strains of *Aspergillus niger* are now most commonly employed in citric acid fermentation, because they give uniformly high yields with minimum amounts of undesirable products. Heavy suspensions of spores are generally used to inoculate the substrate. The spores can be preserved by desiccation [Bernhauer, Iglauer, and Knobloch (1941)].

Substrates, usually sugars, containing 2 to 7 or 12 carbon atoms yield citric acid. The highest yields have usually been obtained from 12 to 20 per cent solutions of sucrose, but in some instances fructose, glucose, molasses, and other substances appear to serve about as well as a carbon source. Nitrogen may be supplied in the form of either ammonium salts or nitrates. Usually NH_4NO_3 in concentrations of 0.16 to 0.32 per cent has been shown to give high yields of acid. Several workers have also found that NH_4Cl, $NaNO_3$, and KNO_3 serve as good sources of nitrogen for certain citric acid-producing molds.

It is impossible to make a general statement about the inorganic salts which give the best results in citric acid fermentation. It appears that the mineral requirements vary with the strain of organism being used and with other factors. The known essential elements, aside from carbon, oxygen, and nitrogen, are potassium, phosphorus, magnesium, and sulfur. These are conveniently supplied by KH_2PO_4 in amounts varying from 0.03 to 0.1 per cent and by $MgSO_4 \cdot 7H_2O$ in concentrations from 0.01 to 0.05 per cent. Several investigators claim that trace amounts of zinc, iron, manganese, and other elements are also essential for the best growth of molds, and in some cases it seems fairly well established that certain of these elements influence acid formation Probably most of these trace elements are present in sufficient amounts in the other ingredients used in the media.

The initial adjustment of the reaction of the medium is of primary importance in this fermentation; in general, the best citric acid-producing mold strains possess the greatest tolerance to low *p*H values. In the laboratory successful fermentations have been conducted without resorting to heat sterilization of the medium, providing that the initial *p*H is adjusted to 1.6 to 3.0 with normal hydrochloric acid. Sulfuric, nitric, acetic, and formic acids have been found to be inferior to hydrochloric for adjusting the reaction. Currie, Doelger, and Prescott and others have shown that a low *p*H favors the formation of citric acid, suppresses the production of oxalic acid, and minimizes the danger of contamination. It is known that contamination difficulties were at least partly responsible for the failure of the early attempts made in Europe to establish this fermentation process on a commercial scale. These difficulties were due more or less directly to the older practice of neutralizing the citric acid as it was formed with calcium carbonate. Present practice does not call for neutralization of the acid during the fermentation. In this respect this process differs from some of the other mold fermentations, such as gluconic acid fermentation.

The relation between the surface area of the fungus growth and the volume of the substrate is an important factor which partially controls acid formation. Since the conversion of sugar into citric acid occurs within the cells of the mold growing on the surface of the substrate, diffusion processes play an important role in the transfer of sugar into, and of products away from, the mycelium. The ratio of surface area (square centimeters) to volume (milliliters) should be so adjusted as to allow maximum citric acid production in the shortest period of time. A ratio between 1.0 and 2.0 usually gives optimum results when a surface growth in shallow pans is used. Cahn (1935) has also obtained good results by absorbing sugar solutions on beet pulp or cane pulp, which furnishes a large surface for fungus growth. Shallow pans made of highest-purity aluminum are apparently used industrially for citric acid fermentation. In pilot-plant studies May and his associates employed pans measuring 43 × 43 × 2 in. with a capacity of 48 liters of substrate. On the basis of a 7-day process and a 50 per cent-weight yield of citric acid from 20 per cent sucrose solutions, it has been calculated that between 30,000 and 40,000 pans of this size would be required to manufacture the estimated 17,000,000 lb. of citric acid produced annually by fermentation in the United States.

Citric acid fermentation is usually carried out at a temperature between 25° and 35°C., although temperatures as low as 20° and as high as 40°C. have been used with fair results. Little information is available concerning the effect of other factors, such as aeration and agitation, on this process. We assume that only small amounts of air are required to supply the necessary oxygen for the metabolic activities of the mold, since several workers have observed that large amounts of air have an adverse effect on the yield of citric acid. It has also been reported that agitation of the medium by gentle or moderate shaking retards the rate of acid production. Szücs (1944), however, has been granted a patent for a citric acid fermentation process which involves both gentle aeration and agitation.

In the manufacture of citric acid by the shallow-pan method fermentation is complete in about 7 to 10 days. If the substrate is absorbed on a porous material (beet or cane pulp), however, the time can be reduced to 2 or 3 days.

The usual yield of citric acid is about 50 to 60 per cent of the weight of the sugar employed and 90 to 95 per cent of the sugar consumed. Greater yields have been reported under special conditions. The course of the fermentation can be followed by making sugar determinations and acid titrations at various intervals after the substrate has been inoculated. One milliliter of $0.1N$ alkali in the titration corresponds to 6.4 mg. of anhydrous citric acid.

Recovery of Citric Acid. After fermentation is complete, the solution is drained off and the mycelium mat is pressed to remove any acid present in the tissue. The citric acid may then be recovered by one of two methods: the first involves direct crystallization of the acid after yeast fermentation of the residual carbohydrate in the solution, and the second involves separation of the acid from the solution as the calcium salt, which is then reconverted to the acid by treatment with an equivalent amount of sulfuric acid.

The Mechanism of Citric Acid Fermentation. Much of the literature [14] dealing with citric acid fermentation has been concerned with efforts to explain the conversion of carbon-containing compounds to citric acid. Most of the hypotheses which have been proposed to explain this process are unsatisfactory, but, in general, they have centered around two points. The first involves a series of reactions in which the glucose chain is not broken into simpler units but merely becomes transformed in some way to citric acid with its branched chain. The second involves the breakdown of the sugar molecule into simpler compounds, such as acetaldehyde or acetic acid, which are then used to synthesize citric acid.

Franzen and Schmitt, Challenger and his associates, and others have presented evidence which supports the first point. They suggested that the production of citric acid from glucose by plants, and presumably also by molds, passes through gluconic and saccharic acids. The saccharic acid then loses two molecules of water to give the dienol of diketoadipic acid:

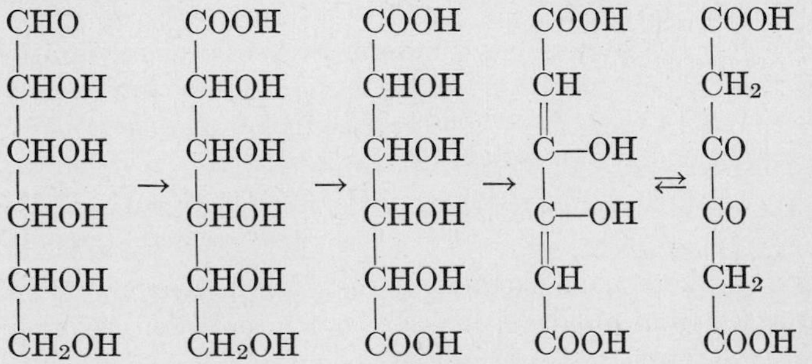

$$\begin{array}{lclclclcl}
\mathrm{CHO} & & \mathrm{COOH} & & \mathrm{COOH} & & \mathrm{COOH} & & \mathrm{COOH} \\
| & & | & & | & & | & & | \\
\mathrm{CHOH} & & \mathrm{CHOH} & & \mathrm{CHOH} & & \mathrm{CH} & & \mathrm{CH_2} \\
| & & | & & | & & \| & & | \\
\mathrm{CHOH} & & \mathrm{CHOH} & & \mathrm{CHOH} & & \mathrm{C{-}OH} & & \mathrm{CO} \\
| & \rightarrow & | & \rightarrow & | & \rightarrow & | & \rightleftarrows & | \\
\mathrm{CHOH} & & \mathrm{CHOH} & & \mathrm{CHOH} & & \mathrm{C{-}OH} & & \mathrm{CO} \\
| & & | & & | & & \| & & | \\
\mathrm{CHOH} & & \mathrm{CHOH} & & \mathrm{CHOH} & & \mathrm{CH} & & \mathrm{CH_2} \\
| & & | & & | & & | & & | \\
\mathrm{CH_2OH} & & \mathrm{CH_2OH} & & \mathrm{COOH} & & \mathrm{COOH} & & \mathrm{COOH} \\
\text{Glucose} & & \text{Gluconic acid} & & \text{Saccharic acid} & & & & \beta\text{-}\gamma\text{-Diketoadipic acid}
\end{array}$$

These initial reactions are supported by the fact that the production of gluconic acid by *Aspergillus niger* and other molds has been repeatedly demonstrated, and the formation of citric acid from gluconic acid has been observed. Furthermore, saccharic acid has been isolated from cultures of *Aspergillus niger* on glucose; citric acid has also been obtained by cultivating the same mold on potassium hydrogen saccharate; and calcium saccharate and calcium citrate have been obtained when the mold is grown on calcium gluconate. On the other hand, all attempts to detect diketoadipic acid in cultures of molds on glucose or potassium hydrogen saccharate have failed thus far; and, when the diketo acid is added to media, it is not fermented to citric acid. Until

[14] For more discussion than can be presented here and for references to the literature on this subject Challenger (1929), Wells, Moyer, and May (1936), Bernhauer (1939), Prescott and Dunn (1940), and von Loesecke (1945) should be consulted.

some measure of success has been obtained in these attempts, this view cannot be regarded as entirely established. Further evidence in favor of the hypothesis has been furnished, however, by the formation of citric acid when *Aspergillus niger* is grown upon solutions of salts of adipic and muconic acids. Presumably the production of citric acid from adipic acid proceeds by way of a double β-γ-diketoadipic acid:

$$\underset{\text{Adipic acid}}{HOOC\cdot CH_2\cdot CH_2\cdot CH_2\cdot CH_2\cdot COOH} \rightarrow \underset{\beta\text{-}\gamma\text{-Diketoadipic acid}}{HOOC\cdot CH_2\cdot CO\cdot CO\cdot CH_2\cdot COOH}$$

The corresponding β-γ-dihydroxyadipic acid is probably the first product of oxidation, and the production of citric acid from muconic acid is apparently dependent on this acid as an intermediate.

$$\underset{\text{Muconic acid}}{HOOC\cdot CH{:}CH\cdot CH{:}CH\cdot COOH} \rightarrow \underset{\beta\text{-}\gamma\text{-Dihydroxyadipic acid}}{HOOC\cdot CH_2\cdot CHOH\cdot CHOH\cdot CH_2\cdot COOH}$$

It is assumed that citric acid arises from β-γ-diketoadipic acid by a benzilic acid transformation, a process which is known to occur *in vitro* in the presence of alkali:

$$\underset{\beta\text{-}\gamma\text{-Diketoadipic acid}}{HOOC\cdot CH_2\cdot CO\cdot CO\cdot CH_2\cdot COOH} + HOH \rightarrow \underset{\text{Citric acid}}{HOOC\cdot CH_2\cdot C(OH)(COOH)\cdot CH_2\cdot COOH}$$

Several workers have suggested that the gluconic and saccharic acids isolated from mold cultures are not intermediate compounds in the formation of citric acid but are produced by side reactions. The studies of these investigators appear to support the second point mentioned, that is, the breakdown of sugar into simpler compounds for the synthesis of citric acid. These workers assume that glucose breaks down to compounds containing three carbon atoms, as in alcoholic fermentation by yeast, which then unite in some way to form citric acid. The three more important synthetic reactions involving acetaldehyde or acetic acid are believed to be as follows:

1. The condensation of three molecules of acetaldehyde followed by an oxidation to citric acid:

$$\begin{array}{l} H\text{—}CH_2\cdot CHO \\ \quad + \\ O{=}CH\cdot CH_3 \\ \quad + \\ H\text{—}CH_2\cdot CHO \end{array} \rightarrow \begin{array}{c} CH_2\cdot CHO \\ | \\ HC\cdot CH_3 \\ | \\ CH_2\cdot CHO \end{array} \rightarrow \begin{array}{c} CH_2\cdot COOH \\ | \\ HOC\cdot COOH \\ | \\ CH_2\cdot COOH \end{array}$$

Acetaldehyde — Citric acid

2. The union of acetic and succinic acids to form tricarballylic acid, which is oxidized to aconitic acid. Citric acid is then formed by the hydration of aconitic acid:

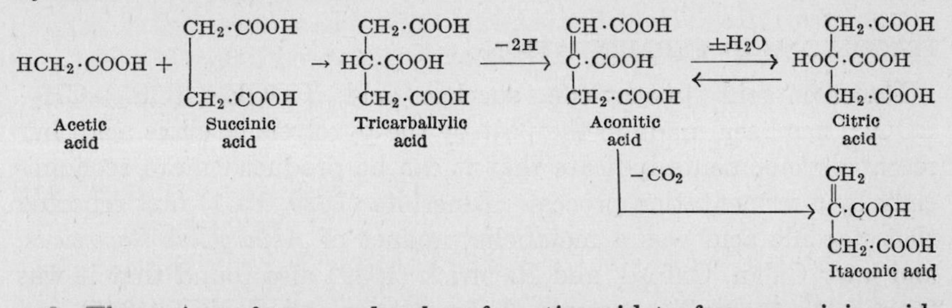

3. The union of two molecules of acetic acid to form succinic acid, which is then oxidized to fumaric acid. Fumaric acid is then hydrated to yield malic acid, which in turn combines with another molecule of acetic acid to form citric acid:

$$\underset{\text{Acetic acid}}{2CH_3 \cdot COOH} \rightarrow \underset{\text{Succinic acid}}{HOOC \cdot CH_2CH_2 \cdot COOH} \rightarrow \underset{\text{Fumaric acid}}{HOOC \cdot CH{:}CH \cdot COOH}$$

$$\xrightarrow{+H_2O} \underset{\text{Malic acid}}{\begin{matrix} CHOH \cdot COOH \\ | \\ CH_2 \cdot COOH \end{matrix}}$$

$$\underset{\text{Citric acid}}{\begin{matrix} CH_2 \cdot COOH \\ | \\ HOC \cdot COOH \\ | \\ CH_2 \cdot COOH \end{matrix}} \leftarrow \underset{\text{Acetic acid}}{CH_3COOH} + \underset{\text{Malic acid}}{\begin{matrix} CHOH \cdot COOH \\ | \\ CH_2 \cdot COOH \end{matrix}}$$

For this third mechanism to be correct, according to Wells, Moyer, and May (1936), certain quantitative relationships should exist: (1) the citric acid : CO_2 weight ratio should not exceed 1.45 : 1.0, and (2) the weight yield of citric acid should not be more than 71.1 per cent. To test these points Wells and his associates carried out carbon balance experiments, with *Aspergillus niger* growing on solutions containing glucose as the sole source of carbon. Their results show that the theoretical ratio of citric acid : CO_2 is greatly exceeded; in fact, the values for 5- to 12-day experiments consistently ranged from about 3.5 to 4.0. The weight yields of citric acid obtained were also much greater than the maximum theoretical values, being 85 to 90 per cent for 5- to 12-day experiments. Approximately 98 per cent of the carbon was accounted for in their studies. On the basis of these results, therefore, it seems unlikely that an alcoholic type of fermentation with acetic acid as the key intermediate occurs before citric acid is formed.

In spite of all the work which has been done on this problem, the mechanism of the mycological production of citric acid is still obscure, and no one theory proposed accounts for all the facts which have been observed. Possibly more than one pathway is used by fungi in the formation of this acid. Perhaps a modified citric acid cycle, as discussed in Chapter 6, together with some of the data mentioned above, will serve to explain the process.

ITACONIC ACID FERMENTATION

Itaconic acid [methylene succinic acid, $COOH \cdot C(CH_2) \cdot CH_2 \cdot COOH$] has been made in the past by the pyrolysis of citric acid, but recent developments indicate that it can be produced more economically by a fermentation process. Kinoshita (1929, 1931) first reported that itaconic acid was a metabolic product of *Aspergillus itaconicus*, and later Calan, Oxford, and Raistrick (1939) also found that it was formed by *Aspergillus terreus*. Later Moyer and Coghill (1945) and Lockwood and Ward (1945) outlined laboratory-scale and semipilot-plant-scale methods for the production of itaconic acid by *Aspergillus terreus*.

The semipilot-plant fermentation process for the manufacture of itaconic acid is carried out in shallow aluminum pans, 22 × 36 × 2 in., in a specially designed cabinet. The cabinet is constructed so that it can be sterilized with flowing steam and later aerated with sterile air during the fermentation. Twelve liters of the following medium are placed in each pan in the cabinet:

Glucose	165	g.
$MgSO_4 \cdot 7H_2O$	4.4	g.
NH_4NO_3	2.5	g.
NaCl	0.4	g.
$ZnSO_4 \cdot 7H_2O$	0.0044	g.
Nitric acid (sp. gr. 1.42)	1.6	ml.
Corn-steep liquor (concentrated)	4	ml.
Distilled water to	1,000	ml.
*p*H	2.0	

This medium is inoculated with a suspension of spores; then the atmosphere in the cabinet is aerated at the rate of 5 liters of humidified sterile air per minute for 12 days. The temperature is controlled at 30° to 32°C.

The itaconic acid is recovered from the fermented medium by crystallization after the medium has been concentrated on a steam bath and cooled. The data in Table 18 illustrate typical results for this fermentation process. It will be seen that yields representing approximately 50 per cent of theory, and in excess of 25 per cent on a weight basis, are obtained.

Little is known concerning the mechanism of itaconic acid production by molds. Kinoshita (1929, 1931) believed that this acid arises from

TABLE 18

PRODUCTION OF ITACONIC ACID FROM GLUCOSE BY *Aspergillus terreus*

[From Lockwood and Ward (1945)]

	Pan 1	*Pan 2*
Initial glucose, grams	1,800	1,800
Glucose consumed, grams	1,583	1,539
Itaconic acid produced, grams	569	602
Yield of itaconic acid,* per cent	49.9	54.3
Itaconic acid recovered by crystallization, grams	453	490
Recovery efficiency, per cent	79.7	81.4
Recovery weight yield,† per cent	25.2	27.2
Mycelial weight, grams	222	144

* Based on glucose consumed, assuming that 1 mole of glucose yields 1 mole of itaconic acid.

† Ratio of grams of itaconic acid recovered to grams of glucose supplied.

citric acid with aconitic acid as an ephemeral intermediate, but this theory has not been proved.

Itaconic acid offers considerable promise as one of the raw materials for the manufacture of certain plastics and detergents. The quality of the product obtained by the fermentation process is such that further purification appears to be unnecessary before esterification in resin manufacture.

GLUCONIC ACID FERMENTATION

It has been known for a number of years that gluconic acid, $CH_2OH \cdot (CHOH)_4 \cdot COOH$, is a metabolic product of certain microorganisms. In fact, in 1878 Boutroux showed that glucose is converted to this acid by bacteria (*Acetobacter aceti*), and in 1922 Molliard observed that molds (*Aspergillus niger*) form gluconic acid, as well as citric and oxalic acids, from sugar. Later Bernhauer (1924) isolated a strain of *Aspergillus niger* which produced gluconic acid almost exclusively when calcium carbonate was added to glucose-containing media of low nitrogen content.

Since these early reports appeared, a number of molds of the genera *Aspergillus* and *Penicillium* have been found to produce gluconic acid, but some other fungi, like *Mucor*, *Fusarium*, and *Monilia* species, form only traces or none at all. The most active gluconic acid-forming species include certain strains of *Aspergillus niger*, *Aspergillus fumaricus*, *Penicillium purpurogenum-rubrisclerotium*, *Penicillium chrysogenum*, and *Penicillium trzebinski*. Some of these strains convert glucose almost quantitatively to gluconic acid under controlled conditions [see May, Herrick, Thom, and Church (1927), Herrick and May (1928), Moyer, Umberger, and Stubbs (1940), Knobloch and Mayer (1941)].

Gluconic acid can be made by chemical means, but for the most part the techniques are unsatisfactory for commercial operations. On the other hand, fermentation methods have been developed to a point where yields of gluconic acid up to 90 to 99 per cent of the glucose consumed can be obtained. According to Wells and Ward (1939), about 500,000 lb. of calcium gluconate is produced in this country each year.

Outline of the Industrial Fermentation Process (Pilot-Plant Scale). The older fermentation methods for producing gluconic acid consisted of growing one of the molds on a glucose-mineral salt medium of *p*H 3.0 to 6.4 in large flasks or in shallow aluminum pans arranged in cabinets especially designed to prevent contamination. In such containers under ideal conditions, for example, a medium surface area (square centimeters)–volume (milliliters) ratio of 0.4 to 0.5, glucose solutions of 15 to 20 per cent yielded only about 50 to 80 per cent gluconic acid after 8 to 14 days at 25° to 30°C. [see May, Herrick, Moyer, and Wells (1934), Moyer, May, and Herrick (1936), Bernhauer (1939)].

More recently several new techniques have been developed for gluconic acid fermentation which not only increase the yield by 20 to 40 per cent but also shorten the time from several days to one day or less. The first important improvement came when the rotary-drum apparatus was devised for the production of this acid and other substances by submerged mold growths under increased air pressure [see Herrick, Hellbach, and May (1935), Wells, Lynch, Herrick, and May (1937), Gastrock, Porges, Wells, and Moyer (1938)]. This apparatus consists essentially of a horizontally mounted, hollow, cylindrically shaped aluminum drum, which is closed at both ends. It is equipped on the interior with buckets and baffles welded to the shell. They are to keep the fermenting culture thoroughly aerated and mixed with the liquid substrate while the drum is being rotated. Means for charging and emptying the drum, for rotating it at different speeds, for permitting humidified sterile air under pressure to pass through, and for sterilizing it are also provided. Several sizes of drums, ranging in total capacity from about 5 gal. to 420 gal., have been made; specifications and construction data will be found in the references just cited.

Other new improvements in gluconic acid fermentation have been concerned with the optimum effect of agitation or speed of rotation of the drum fermenter, the air flow and air pressure through or within the drum, the choice of the proper mold, the development of the inoculum, the composition of the fermentation solution, and the repeated recovery and reuse of the submerged mold growths. These factors will be mentioned briefly below. For more details the original studies by Wells, Moyer, Stubbs, Roe, Herrick, and May (1937), Moyer, Wells,

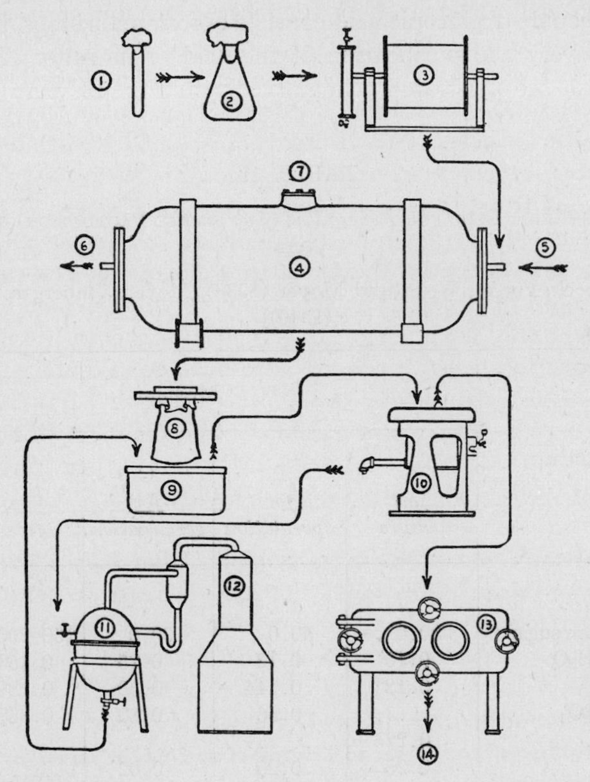

1. Tube culture
2. Sporulation flasks
3. Small rotating aluminum germination drum (17-liter volume)
4. Large rotating aluminum drum fermenter (540-liter volume)
5. Inlet for adding water for fermentation solution, inoculum from 3, and air during fermentation
6. Air outlet
7. Handhole for adding ingredients, removing mash, and cleaning
8. Bag filter or press
9. Aluminum tank for neutralization with calcium hydroxide milk
10. Centrifuge (stainless steel basket, aluminum-lined curb)
11. Vacuum evaporator for mother liquors
12. Condenser
13. Vacuum drier
14. To calcium gluconate storage

Fig. 13. Flow Sheet of Gluconic Acid Production by Mold Fermentation. (From Gastrock, Porges, Wells, and Moyer, 1938.)

Stubbs, Herrick, and May (1937), Gastrock, Porges, Wells, and Moyer (1938), and Porges, Clark, and associates (1940, 1941) should be consulted.

In general, the rotary-drum fermentation process for the production of large amounts of gluconic acid consists of four main steps, in addition to the recovery and purification of the acid or its salts. These four steps, which are illustrated schematically in Fig. 13, may be briefly described.

TABLE 19

SUMMARY OF MEDIA USED FOR *Aspergillus niger* IN THE PRODUCTION OF GLUCONIC ACID

[From Gastrock, Porges, Wells, and Moyer (1938), Moyer, Umberger, and Stubbs (1940)]

Ingredient	Medium				
	A *for culture*	B *for sporulation*	C *for germination*	D *for fermentation*	
Grams per liter					
Refined corn sugar *	30.0	50.0	100.0	150–200	200–300
$MgSO_4 \cdot 7H_2O$	0.10	0.12	0.25	0.156	0.156
KH_2PO_4	0.12	0.144	0.30	0.188	0.188
$(NH_4)_2HPO_4$	....	0.56	0.80	0.388	0.50
NH_4NO_3	0.225	......	....	....	....
Peptone	0.25	0.20	0.02	....	....
Potatoes	200.0	......	....	....	....
Agar	20.0	1.5	....	....	....
$CaCO_3$	4.0	......	37.5 †	26.0 †	26.0 †
Boron (p.p.m.) ‡	....	......	....	....	500–1,500
Milliliters per liter					
Beer	....	45.0	40.0	....	....
Corn-steep liquor	....	......	....	....	2.0–3.0
Kind of water	Distilled	Distilled	Tap	Tap	Tap

* Refined corn sugar, containing 91.5% of glucose and corresponding closely to glucose monohydrate, was usually used.

† Sterilized separately and added at once or at intervals to the medium in the rotary-drum fermenters.

‡ Boron (boric acid or borax) prevented precipitation of calcium gluconate and permitted greater sugar concentration.

First a suitable mold, usually a strain (U. S. Dept. Agr. No. 67 or 3) of *Aspergillus niger*, is cultured on slants of medium A (Table 19) for 7 days at 30°C. These slant cultures are then employed to inoculate twenty or more 1-liter Erlenmeyer flasks, each containing 150 ml. of semisolid agar medium B, which has been found to be optimum for spore development. After these flasks have been incubated for 7 days at 30°C., the resulting mycelium with its heavy crop of spores is aseptically transferred to a vessel containing about 17 liters of medium C and macerated with a mechanical agitator. This mass is then divided into two portions, a proportionate amount of a sterile $CaCO_3$ slurry is added, and each portion is transferred aseptically to small rotary-drum fermenters to permit spore germination and growth. The amount of macerated material added to the small drum fermenters should not occupy more than one-third of the total volume of the drum. Optimum germination and growth occur in 24 hours at 30°C. when the following optimum drum conditions are maintained:

Sterile air pressure	30 lbs. per square inch gauge (155 mm. Hg)
Air flow	375 cu. cm. per liter per minute
Speed of rotation	5.8 r.p.m.

After germination the starter solution is blown, by way of hose connections, directly from the small rotary fermenters to a large 420-gal. drum containing about 140 gal. of one of the substrates listed under medium D; the substrate in the last column is now considered optimum, since greater sugar concentrations can be employed. The optimum drum conditions for large-scale fermentations are essentially the same as those used for small rotary fermenters, except that the air flow is usually increased to 440 cu. cm. per liter per minute, the speed of the rotating drum is increased to 6.0 to 9.5 r.p.m., and an antifoam agent (octadecyl alcohol) is added at frequent intervals.

The most favorable reaction for the main fermentation is about *p*H 5.0. This reaction can be maintained by the addition of a sterile slurry of calcium carbonate in the amount of 2.6 g. of $CaCO_3$ per 100 ml. of medium. The optimum temperature for gluconic acid fermentation is about 30°C. However, because of the exothermic nature of this oxidative reaction, the temperature of the contents of the large drum will increase during fermentation to a value more than 10°C. in excess of the optimum unless it is controlled. A thermostatically regulated water spray applied to the exterior of the drum is generally used to keep the temperature at the proper value.

The quantity of gluconic acid formed varies somewhat from one run to the next, depending upon the factors mentioned. In a typical fermentation carried out by Gastrock and his associates in 1938 with germinated spores, a charge of 91 kg. (200 lb.) of refined corn sugar in a total volume of 530 liters (140 gal.) was fermented in less than 24 hours, with yields of gluconic acid in excess of 95 per cent of the sugar present and 97 per cent of the sugar consumed.

The main difficulties encountered in this process, especially when sugar solutions of 20 per cent or more are used, have been the inhibition of fermentation by the precipitation of calcium gluconate on the mold mycelium, and injury to the fermenting organism by exposure to free gluconic acid. These defects have now been overcome by the selection of new strains of molds and by the addition of boron compounds (boric acid or borax) with an excess of calcium carbonate during the fermentation. The boron salts form soluble complexes with calcium gluconate. In fact, the precipitation of calcium gluconate during the normal fermentation of 20, 25, 30, and 35 per cent glucose substrates can be prevented by the presence of 500, 1,000, 1,500, and 2,500 p.p.m., respectively, of boron [Moyer, Umberger, and Stubbs (1940)].

Porges, Clark, and their associates (1940, 1941) have further improved this method of gluconic acid production by placing it on a semicontinuous basis. This improvement is achieved by recovering and reusing the submerged growths of *Aspergillus niger* (strain No. 67) in nine to thirteen fermentations. Such a procedure eliminates the lag period which occurs in single-batch fermentation and thus saves time (8 to 12 hours), equipment, and effort.

Recovery of Calcium Gluconate. At the end of the fermentation the solution contained in the rotary fermenters is transferred through a pipe line to cotton bags, or a leaf-type pressure filter of aluminum, in order to remove the mycelial growth. The calcium gluconate is then recovered by adding a suspension of calcium hydroxide to the clear filtrate. Crystallization of the salt occurs in 24 to 48 hours at about 20°C. The gluconate crystals are separated from the mother liquor by centrifugation, washed twice with cold water, and dried in aluminum pans at a temperature below 80°C. The mother liquor and the washings are concentrated under vacuum, and a second crop of calcium gluconate is recovered. The steps in this process are presented schematically in the form of a flow sheet in Fig. 13 [Gastrock, Porges, Wells, and Moyer (1938)].

Mechanism of Gluconic Acid Fermentation. In gluconic acid fermentation glucose is oxidized to gluconic acid by a glucose oxidase:

$$\underset{\text{Glucose}}{HOH_2C\cdot(CHOH)_4\cdot CHO} + \tfrac{1}{2}O_2 \rightarrow \underset{\text{Gluconic acid}}{HOH_2C\cdot(CHOH)_4\cdot COOH}$$

By alcohol precipitation of the aqueous extract of the mycelium the enzyme can be quite easily isolated from the pressed juice of gluconic acid-forming molds. Certain strains of *Aspergillus niger* not only oxidize *d*-glucose to *d*-gluconic acid but likewise convert *d*-mannose to *d*-mannonic acid and *d*-galactose to *d*-galactonic acid. Maltose, sucrose, lactose, and some other carbohydrates also yield small amounts of gluconic and similar acids [Knobloch and Mayer (1941)].

FUMARIC ACID FERMENTATION

Fumaric acid, HOOC·CH:CH·COOH, has been known chemically for many years and was first reported to be a mold-metabolic product by Ehrlich in 1911. It is now known that the formation of large amounts of this acid by molds is mainly limited to species of *Rhizopus*, especially strains of female races of *Rhizopus nigricans*. However, species in other genera, such as *Mucor*, *Circinella*, *Cunninghamella*, *Penicillium*, and *Aspergillus*, also produce small amounts [Bernhauer and Thole (1936), Foster and Waksman (1939), Waksman (1943), Kane, Finlay, and Amann (1943)].

Early studies on the production of fumaric acid by *Rhizopus nigricans* reported yields which were either variable or insufficient for the utilization of the process for industrial purposes. More recent studies by Foster, Waksman, Kane, and their associates, however, show that yields of 40 to 50 per cent, on the basis of the sugar consumed, are possible with certain specific strains of this mold. These methods have been patented and are probably being used commercially.

A variety of carbohydrate substances may be employed as a substrate. Glucose, sucrose, molasses, and other sugar-containing substances appear to give the best yields, although starchy materials can also be used. The most favorable sources of nitrogen have been found to be ammonium sulfate and other salts of ammonia. It is highly important to have a proper carbohydrate–nitrogen ratio in the culture medium; otherwise the rate of production of fumaric acid will be delayed, and the yield will be reduced. Waksman found that the presence of 0.2 to 0.5 g. of nitrogen salt per liter of medium containing 50 to 150 g. of carbohydrate gave favorable results.

The other constitutents necessary for a good basal medium include nutrient mineral salts [$(NH_4)_2SO_4$, 0.2 per cent; $MgSO_4 \cdot 7H_2O$, 0.05 per cent; K_2HPO_4, 0.05 per cent] and a neutralizing agent, such as calcium carbonate or a soluble hydroxide. Since an alkaline environment has a depressive effect on the germination of *Rhizopus* spores, the neutralizing agent should be added to the medium after mycelial growth has started. It is preferable to adjust the *p*H periodically at frequent intervals to approximately 5.0 to 6.5.

The presence of certain catalytic or trace elements in the medium also markedly modifies the growth of the fungus and the production of fumaric acid. Specifically, zinc has a decidedly stimulating effect upon the mycelial growth of *Rhizopus* at the expense of the accumulation of fumaric acid, whereas iron has just the reverse effect. It is possible, though, to balance the culture medium in such a way with these elements as to produce, first, the optimum mycelial growth through the presence of zinc, $ZnSO_4 \cdot 7H_2O$, 0.0001 to 0.001 per cent; and, second, the maximum formation of fumaric acid by the presence of iron, $Fe_2(SO_4)_3$, 0.0001 to 0.002 per cent.

The sterile nutrient solution is fermented in tanks where it can be converted to fumaric acid or its salt by a stationary surface growth in 5 to 7 days at 28° to 35°C. or by a submerged growth in 24 to 48 hours, providing the medium is agitated and aerated. The original nutrient solution may also be drawn off, and a new batch of carbohydrate solution added to the mass of fungal mycelium in the container. The fermentation of this replaced sugar by the preformed mycelium begins quickly at a high rate, so that considerable economy of time results. After several sugar replacements, though, the fermenting capacity of the mycelium mass gradually diminishes.

The production of fumaric acid from glucose by mold fermentation may be represented by the following chemical equation:

$$\underset{\text{Glucose}}{C_6H_{12}O_6} + 3O_2 \rightarrow \underset{\text{Fumaric acid}}{C_4H_4O_4} + 2CO_2 + 4H_2O$$

Actually, however, the process is more complicated than this simple equation indicates, and not too much is known concerning the intermediate steps between glucose and fumaric acid. After surveying the literature on this subject and carrying out personal researches as well, Bernhauer (1939) concluded that the formation of this acid may take place in conjunction with an alcoholic type of fermentation. Thus he believed the following course of events may occur:

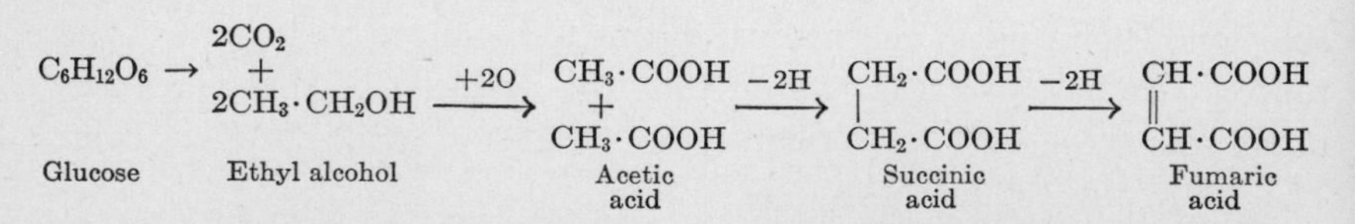

Although data are still lacking to prove such a scheme, it is known that alcohol, as well as acetic acid, can be converted to succinic acid and fumaric acid by *Rhizopus nigricans*.

GALLIC ACID FERMENTATION

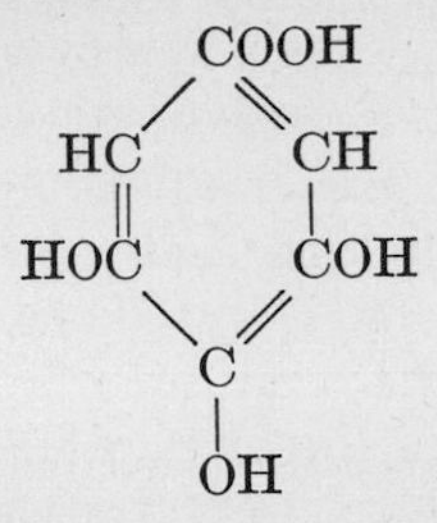

Gallic acid (3:4:5-trihydroxybenzoic acid) was first prepared from decomposed gall nuts by Scheele about 1786, but it was not until 1867 that Van Tieghem demonstrated that the formation of this acid was due to the action of molds on tannins. Besides being present in gall nuts gallic acid also occurs in sumac, tea, and many other plants, usually in the form of tannin glucosides. The acid is prepared chemically by boiling tannin extracts with dilute sulfuric acid or by fermenting such extracts with molds; it has also been obtained synthetically by various reactions.

The early literature on the fermentation process for producing gallic acid has been fully reviewed by Knudson (1913), and more recent studies on the process have been carried out by Kuo (1939), Hsieh (1939), Wei (1939), and Fang (1940).

The older fermentation methods for preparing gallic acid consisted simply of allowing tannin-containing substances to undergo decomposition in a moistened heap for about a month, after which the gallic acid was leached out. Newer methods, which are based on experiments carried out by Calmette in 1902, employ clear tannin extracts which are sterilized and then inoculated with a pure culture of *Aspergillus niger* or *Aspergillus gallomyces*. The mold inoculum is frequently prepared in a dry state after cultivation on a cooked rice-wheat bran medium. Tannin solutions of 10° to 20° Baumé are commonly employed, and fermentation is complete in 10 to 20 days at 20° to 30°C. Knudson obtained the best yields with a limited air supply, but sometimes the solution is agitated by mechanical means to facilitate hydrolysis of the tannin. It has also been stated that the addition of yeast or other organisms accelerates the fermentation. Yields of gallic acid vary from 10 to 20 g. per 100 ml. of tannin solution.

Gallic acid has a few pharmaceutical and medicinal uses, and it is employed in engraving, tanning, and the manufacture of pyrogallol, certain inks, and dyes.

KOJIC ACID FERMENTATION

The production of kojic acid by molds was first observed by Saito in 1907, but the constitution of the acid was not established until 1924, when Yabuta found it to be 2-hydroxymethyl-5-hydroxy-γ-pyrone,

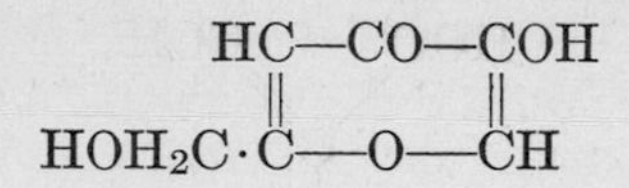

Since 1924 numerous papers have appeared on the various aspects of kojic acid fermentation [see Barham and Smits (1934, 1936), Wells and Ward (1939), Prescott and Dunn (1940)]. The process is technically unimportant at present, however, because few uses have been found for kojic acid and its numerous derivatives. Only a few experimental dyes and resins have been prepared from the acid. It is also known to be bacteriostatic in certain concentrations and to inhibit the growth of Gram-negative organisms more strongly than Gram-positive ones. It is toxic for laboratory animals.

Several molds of the genus *Aspergillus* (*Aspergillus oryzae*, *Aspergillus flavus*, *Aspergillus tamarii*, *Aspergillus parasiticus*, *Aspergillus clavatus*, and *Aspergillus fumigatus*), one *Penicillium* species (*Penicillium daleae*), and a few bacteria (*Acetobacter* species) are known to form kojic acid from a variety of organic substances.

Any one of a number of carbon-containing substances can be employed in this fermentation. The best yields, in general, are obtained by using 5 to 30 per cent concentrations of sucrose, maltose, glucose, sorbitol, xylose, or dihydroxyacetone, but the same concentrations of simpler alcohols and organic acids give little or no kojic acid [Katagiri and Kitahara (1933), Barham and Smits (1934, 1936)]. Ammonium nitrate (0.04 to 0.1 per cent) serves as an excellent source of nitrogen, although ammonium sulfate and other nitrogenous substances can be utilized by the molds. The inorganic salts which have been employed by most workers include KH_2PO_4 (0.06 to 0.1 per cent), $MgSO_4 \cdot 7H_2O$ (0.5 per cent), and KCl (0.01 per cent). Iron and calcium salts may be inhibitory to this fermentation, but zinc salts have little influence. The fermentation occurs in media with a reaction between *p*H 2.0 and 5.0, although the optimum seems to be at 2.5 and 3.5. Incubation temperatures of 15° to 35°C. have been employed; the optimum is near 30°C. The fermentation usually required 7 to 30 days for completion, the period depending upon the species of mold, temperature of incubation, substrate (type of compound, *p*H, and salts), and other factors. Yields of kojic acid from below 5.0 per cent to above 50 per cent have been reported by various workers for different substrates. It is also of interest that, when certain substances unrelated to the substrate are added to the medium, the yield of kojic acid is increased. For example, May, Ward, and Herrick (1932) found that ethylene chlorhydrin (0.01 to 0.015 per cent) increases production 25 to 35 per cent over the control substrates in a 10-day fermentation period at 30°C. On the other hand, thiourea, thioglycollic acid, chloracetone, and a few other substances exert a marked inhibitory effect.

There is little agreement on the mechanism of kojic acid formation by the molds. As a result several theories have been proposed to explain the process [see Yabuta (1924), Birkinshaw, Charles, Lilly, and Raistrick (1931), Challenger, Klein, and Walker (1931), May, Moyer, Wells, and Herrick (1931), Kluyver and Perquin (1933), Gould (1938)].

Yabuta and others have suggested that the conversion of hexoses (glucose or fructose) to kojic acid is a simple process of direct oxidation combined with dehydration.

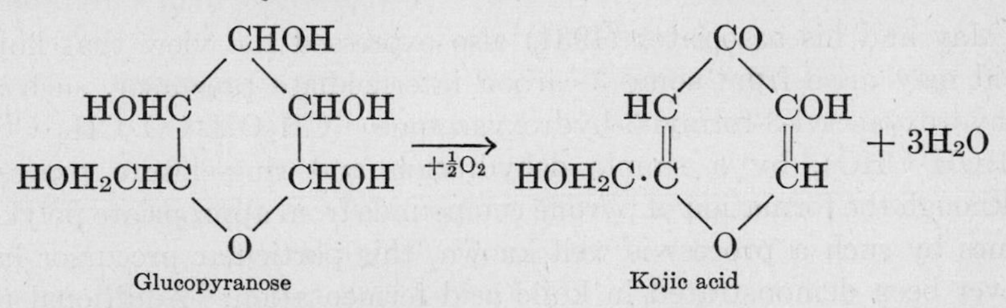

Glucopyranose Kojic acid

Even though quite large amounts of kojic acid are formed from glucose, other simpler compounds, such as xylose and dihydroxyacetone, also yield this acid. Therefore the foregoing reaction does not fully explain the events occurring with these simpler substances, unless they are first converted to a hexose.

Since traces of ethyl alcohol frequently occur in kojic acid fermentation, Birkinshaw, Charles, Lilly, and Raistrick (1931) expressed the opinion that kojic acid may arise through condensation of acetaldehyde, or some other intermediate, which normally occurs in a true alcoholic fermentation. This opinion, however, does not agree with the experiments of Katagiri and Kitahara (1933) and Gould (1938). These workers found that no kojic acid could be detected in media containing hexose monophosphate, hexose diphosphate, methylglyoxal, pyruvic acid, lactic acid, acetic acid, or other substances which sometimes occur in alcoholic fermentation. The addition of aldehyde-fixing agents (sulfite, dimedon) failed to prevent kojic acid formation from glucose, and fixation compounds could not be isolated from the medium during fermentation. Furthermore, by using certain enzyme poisons, Gould concluded that the production of kojic acid from glucose probably does not take place by means of the usual phosphoric esters. On the other hand, glycerol yields a small amount, and dihydroxyacetone quite a large quantity, of kojic acid. This fact suggests that some 3-carbon compound may be involved in the synthesis of the pyrone nucleus. In this connection the scheme proposed by Challenger, Klein, and Walker (1931) for the formation of kojic acid is of interest. They suggested that two molecules of dihydroxyacetone may be condensed by dehydration and oxidation to yield kojic acid:

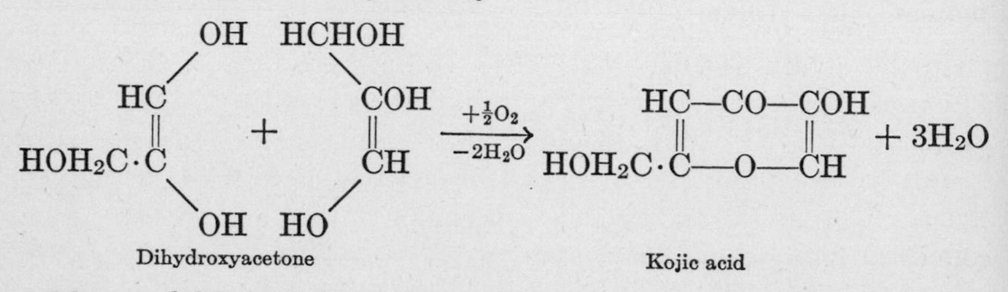

Dihydroxyacetone Kojic acid

May and his associates (1931) also expressed the view that kojic acid may arise from some 3-carbon intermediate precursor, such as 1-hydroxyacetyl-3-formyl-3-hydroxyacetone ($CH_2OH \cdot CO \cdot CH_2 \cdot CO \cdot CHOH \cdot CHO$), by a simple dehydration and ring-closure process. Although the formation of pyrone compounds from appropriate polyketones by such a process is well known, this particular precursor has never been demonstrated in kojic acid fermentation. Additional research must therefore be done before we can say definitely how kojic acid is formed from various substances.

OXALIC ACID FERMENTATION

Oxalic acid, $HOOC \cdot COOH$, was first isolated in 1769 and is one of the oldest known organic acids. It occurs as a salt in many plants and as a free acid in certain fungi. From 1886 to 1891 DeBary and Wehmer noted that oxalic acid was formed in quite large quantities from various carbohydrates by molds, such as *Aspergillus niger* and *Penicillium glaucum*, and suggested that it might be manufactured on a commercial scale by such fungi. The fermentation process has never been employed commercially, however, because oxalic acid can be obtained more cheaply by chemical methods.

Cane sugar solutions (10 to 15 per cent), containing the usual nutrient salts and a neutralizing agent, are fermented to oxalic acid salts by certain strains of *Aspergillus niger* in about 14 days at 30° to 35°C. [Bernhauer (1939)]. Also, when citric acid and fumaric acid fermentations are not carefully controlled (temperature below 30°C., acid reaction, etc.), oxalic acid is formed in quite large quantities.

The conversion of glucose to oxalic acid by molds may be represented by the following chemical equation [Bernhauer (1939)]:

$$\underset{\text{Glucose}}{C_6H_{12}O_6} + 4\tfrac{1}{2}O_2 \rightarrow \underset{\text{Oxalic acid}}{3C_2H_2O_4} + 3H_2O$$

It is believed by some investigators that glyoxalic acid is the key intermediate precursor of oxalic acid and that it arises from fumaric acid or acetic acid [Bernhauer (1939); see also Challenger, Subramaniam, and Walker (1927)]:

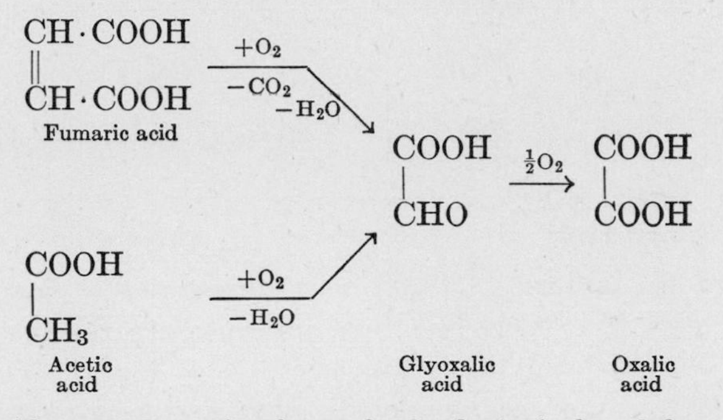

Oxalic acid may also arise from the hydrolytic breakdown of oxaloacetic acid [Raistrick and Clark (1919)]:

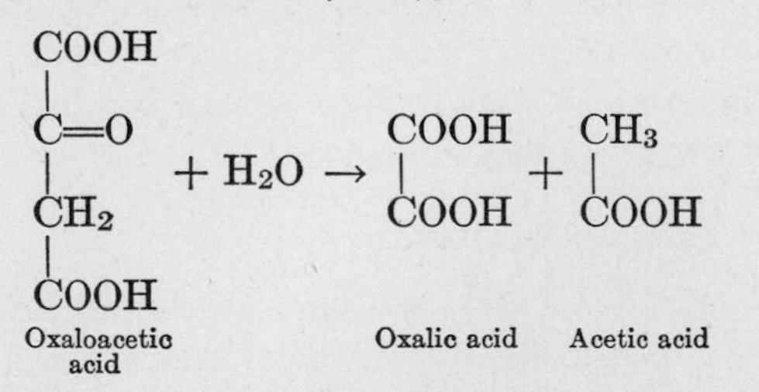

Oxalic acid is produced from citric acid, presumably through acetic and glyoxalic acids as intermediates. Very small amounts of oxalic acid are formed from lactic, pyruvic, and propionic acids, but none is produced from butyric or formic acids. These compounds thus appear to be excluded as intermediates.

MISCELLANEOUS ACIDS FORMED BY MOLDS

Under certain conditions when the various fungi or molds are cultivated on simple substrates (glucose-mineral salt media), they produce a great variety of organic acids besides those mentioned on 990 to 1011. Examples of several such acids are listed in Table 20. It will be seen by referring to this table that these interesting compounds range from the simpler acids to substances containing nonbenzenoid rings (de-

TABLE 20

MISCELLANEOUS ACIDS PRODUCED BY FUNGI

Acid	Formula	Produced by	Reference
Aconitic M.P. 191°C.	HOOC·CH₂C=CH·COOH | COOH	*Aspergillus niger*	Bernhauer and Böckl (1932)
Aspergillic M.P. 84°–96°C.	$C_{12}H_{20}N_2O_2$	*Aspergillus flavus*	White and Hill (1943)
Byssochlamic M.P. 163.5°C.	$C_{18}H_{20}O_6$	*Byssochlamys fulva*	Raistrick and Smith (1933)
Carlic (*l*-α[γ-hydroxybutyryl]-γ-carboxymethyltetronic acid) M.P. 176°C.	O——C——CH·CO·CH₂·CH₂·CH₂ (ring closed through —O— from CH to terminal CH₂) | | | OC CH CO \\ / \\ / C O | H₂	*Penicillium charlesii*	Clutterbuck, Raistrick, and Reuter (1935)
Carlosic (*l*-α-butyryl-γ-carboxymethyltetronic acid) M.P. 181°C.	HO·C==C·CO·CH₂·CH₂·CH₃ | | HOOC·H₂CCH CO \\ / O	*Penicillium charlesii*	Clutterbuck, Raistrick, and Reuter (1935)
Carolinic (α[β-carboxypropionyl]-γ-methyltetronic acid) M.P. 129°C.	HO·C==C·CO·CH₂·CH₂·COOH | | H₃C·CH CO \\ / O	*Penicillium charlesii*	Clutterbuck, Raistrick, and Reuter (1935)

3:5-Dihydroxyphthalic M.P. 188°–190°C.	COOH, —COOH, —OH, HO (benzene ring)	*Penicillium brevi-compactum*	Oxford and Raistrick (1932)
Dimethylpyruvic	H_3C, H, $C\cdot CO\cdot COOH$, H_3C	*Aspergillus niger*	Hida (1935) [cited by Birkinshaw (1937)]
Emodic (4:5:7-trihydroxyanthraquinone-2-carboxylic acid) M.P. 363°–365°C.	O, HO, COOH, OH O OH (anthraquinone ring)	*Penicillium cyclopium*	Anslow, Breen, and Raistrick (1940)
l-Ethylene oxide-α-β-dicarboxylic acid M.P. 179°–180°C.	$HOOC\cdot CH$, O, $HC\cdot COOH$	*Penicillium viniferum*, *Monilia formosa*	Sakaguchi, Inoue, and Tada (1939)
Formic	HCOOH	*Aspergillus oryzae*	Takodoro (1935)
Fulvic M.P. 246°C.	$C_{14}H_{12}O_8$	*Penicillium griseo-fulvum*, etc.	Oxford, Raistrick, and Simonart (1935)
Gentisic (2:5-dihydroxybenzoic acid) M.P. 197°–198°C.	COOH, OH, HO (benzene ring)	*Penicillium griseo-fulvum*, etc.	Raistrick and Simonart (1933)
Glaucanic (very similar to byssochlamic acid)	$C_{18}H_{20}O_6$	Certain strains of *Penicillium glaucum*	Birkinshaw (1937)

TABLE 20 (*Continued*)

MISCELLANEOUS ACIDS PRODUCED BY FUNGI

Acid	Formula	Produced by	Reference
Glaucic M.P. 237°–238°C.	$C_{17}H_{22}O_5$	*Aspergillus glaucus*	Sumiki (1933)
Glauconic	$C_{18}H_{20}O_7$	Strains of *Penicillium glaucum*	Birkinshaw (1937)
Glucuronic	CHO–(CHOH)$_4$–COOH	*Ustulina vulgaris*	Wünschendorff and Killian (1928)
Glycolic and glyoxylic	H_2COH–COOH CHO–COOH	*Aspergillus niger*	Bernhauer and Scheuer (1932) [cited by Birkinshaw (1937)]
Helvolic M.P. 204.5°–205.5°C.	$C_{32}H_{44}O_8$	*Aspergillus fumigatus*	Chain, Florey, Jennings, and Williams (1943)
2-Hydroxymethylfurane-5-carboxylic (Sumiki's acid)	HC═CH ring: HOOC·C═(HC)–(CH)═C·CH$_2$OH, C–O–C (furan ring)	*Aspergillus glaucus*, *Aspergillus clavatus*, *Aspergillus oryzae*, etc.	Sumiki (1929) [cited by Birkinshaw (1937)]

γ-Ketopentadecoic M.P. 92.6°C.	$H_3C \cdot (CH_2)_{10} \cdot CO \cdot (CH_2)_2 \cdot COOH$	*Penicillium spiculisporum*	Raistrick (1938)
Lactic	$CH_3 \cdot CHOH \cdot COOH$	*Mucor* and *Rhizopus* species	Raistrick (1938)
Luteic	Glucose and malonic acid formed on hydrolysis	*Penicillium luteum*	Birkinshaw and Raistrick (1933)
Malic	$HOOC \cdot CH_2 \cdot CHOH \cdot COOH$	*Aspergillus* and *Clasterosporium*, species	Birkinshaw (1937)
l-γ-Methyltetronic M.P. 115°C.	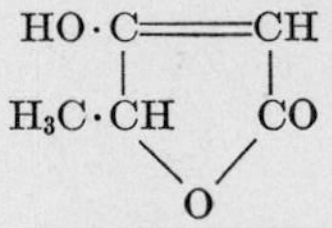 HO·C═CH H_3C·CH CO O	*Penicillium charlesii*	Clutterbuck, Raistrick, and Reuter (1935)
Methylsalicylic (6-hydroxy-2-methylbenzoic acid)	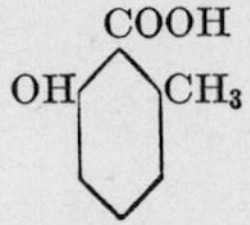 COOH OH (benzene ring) CH_3	*Penicillium griseo-fulvum*, *Penicillium flexuosum*	Oxford, Raistrick, and Simonart (1935)
Minioluteic (γ-lactone of α-β-dihydroxy-*n*-tetradecanoic acid) M.P. 171°C.	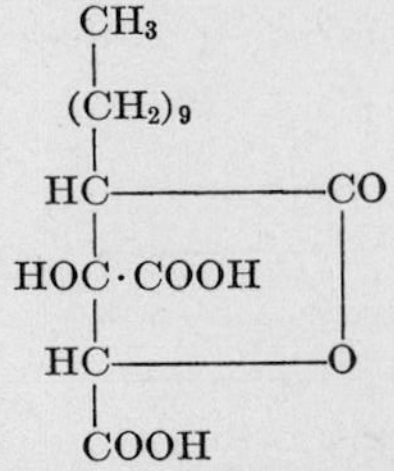 CH_3 $(CH_2)_9$ HC——CO HOC·COOH HC——O COOH	*Penicillium minio-luteum*	Birkinshaw and Raistrick (1934)

TABLE 20 (*Continued*)

MISCELLANEOUS ACIDS PRODUCED BY FUNGI

Acid	Formula	Produced by	Reference
Mycophenolic M.P. 141°C.	O ‖ OH C HOOC O H_3CO C··· } C_5H_{12} CH_3 C·········	*Penicillium brevi-compactum*	Clutterbuck and Raistrick (1933)
Penicillic (γ-keto-β-methoxy-δ-methylene-Δ^{α}-hexenoic acid or the corresponding γ-hydroxylactone) M.P. 83°–84°C.	H_3C OCH_3 C·CO·C=CH·COOH H_2C or H_3C $OHOCH_3$ C·C· C=CH·CO H_2C O	*Penicillium puberulum, Penicillium cyclopium*	Birkinshaw, Oxford, and Raistrick (1936)
Puberulic M.P. 296°C.	OH COOH HO CHO OH	*Penicillium puberulum, Penicillium aurantio-virens*	Birkinshaw and Raistrick (1932)

Pyruvic	$CH_3 \cdot CO \cdot COOH$	*Aspergillus niger*	Hida (1935) [cited by Birkinshaw (1937)]
Spiculisporic (γ-lactone of γ-hydroxy-β-δ-dicarboxy-pentadecoic acid)	CH_3 | $(CH_2)_9$ | $HC \cdot COOH$ | HC—┐ | | $HC \cdot COOH$ O | | CH_2 | | | CO—┘	*Penicillium spiculisporum*	Clutterbuck, Raistrick, and Rintoul (1931) Birkinshaw and Raistrick (1934)
Succinic	$CH_2 \cdot COOH$ | $CH_2 \cdot COOH$	*Mucor* species, *Aspergillus terreus*, *Penicillium aurantio-virens*	Birkinshaw (1937)
Stipitatic M.P. 302°–304°C.	$C_8H_6O_5$	*Penicillium stipitatum*	Birkinshaw, Chambers, and Raistrick (1942)
Terrestric (hydrate) (α-[l-γ-hydroxy-n-hexanoyl]-l-γ-methyltetronic acid) M.P. 89°C.	$HO \cdot C = C \cdot CO \cdot (CH_2)_2 \cdot CHOH \cdot C_2H_5$ | | $H_3C \cdot CH$ CO \ / O	*Penicillium terrestre*	Birkinshaw and Raistrick (1936)

TABLE 21

MISCELLANEOUS METABOLIC PRODUCTS OF FUNGI

[From Iwanoff and Zwetkoff (1936), Birkinshaw (1937), Lockwood and Moyer (1938), Raistrick (1938, 1940), and Others]

Product	Formula	Produced By
Aldehydes		
Acetaldehyde	$CH_3 \cdot CHO$	*Aspergillus, Mucor,* and *Penicillium* species
Anisaldehyde [1] (*p*-methoxybenzaldehyde)	$CH_3O \cdot C_6H_4 \cdot CHO$	*Trametes suaveolens*
Palitantin [2] (unsaturated dihydroxyaldehyde) M.P. 135°–163°C.	$C_{14}H_{22}O_4$	*Penicillium palitans*
Alcohols		
Ethyl [3]	C_2H_5OH	*Fusarium lini* and related species: certain *Aspergillus* and *Penicillium* species
Gentisyl [4] (2:5-dihydroxybenzyl alcohol) M.P. 100°C.	Benzene ring with OH (top), CH_2OH, OH (bottom)	*Penicillium patulum*
Glycerol	$CH_2OH \cdot CHOH \cdot CH_2OH$	Certain *Aspergillus, Helminthosporium,* and *Clasterosporium* species
i-Erythritol	$HOCH_2 \cdot (CHOH)_2 \cdot CH_2OH$	*Penicillium* species
Mannitol	$HOCH_2 \cdot (CHOH)_4 \cdot CH_2OH$	*Byssochlamys fulva, Aspergillus, Penicillium, Helminthosporium,* and *Clasterosporium* species
Esters		
Ethyl acetate	$CH_3 \cdot COOC_2H_5$	*Penicillium digitatum*
Methyl anisate [1]	$CH_3O \cdot C_6H_4 \cdot COO \cdot CH_3$	*Trametes suaveolens*
Nitrogenous substances		
Alkaloids	$C_{16}H_{16}O_2N_2$, $C_{19}H_{23}O_2N_3$, $C_{21}H_{27}O_3N_3$, etc.	Ergot
Choline	$(CH_3)_3NOH \cdot CH_2 \cdot CH_2OH$	*Boletus elegans*
Hydroxylamine	NH_2OH	*Aspergillus niger*
Nitrogenous acid [5]	$C_{22}H_{28}O_5N$	*Penicillium griseo-fulvum*
Nitrogenous acid [5]	$C_{40}H_{79}O_5N$	*Penicillium brefeldianum*
Phenylethylamine	$(C_6H_5) \cdot (C_2H_5)NH$	*Boletus luteus*
Urea	$H_2N \cdot CO \cdot NH_2$	*Aspergillus niger*
Proteins, amino acids, etc.		

[1] Birkinshaw, Bracken, and Findlay (1944).
[2] Birkinshaw and Raistrick (1936).
[3] Nord (1939), Gould and Tytell (1941), Tytell and Gould (1941).
[4] Birkinshaw, Bracken, and Raistrick (1944).
[5] Oxford, Raistrick, and Simonart (1935).

TABLE 21 (*Continued*)

MISCELLANEOUS METABOLIC PRODUCTS OF FUNGI

[From Iwanoff and Zwetkoff (1936), Birkinshaw (1937), Lockwood and Moyer (1938), Raistrick (1938, 1940), and Others]

Product	Formula	Produced By
Sulfur substances		
Thiourea	$H_2N \cdot CS \cdot NH_2$	*Verticillium albo-atrum*, *Botrytis cinerea*
Cyclic choline [6]	$(CH_3)_3N \cdot CH_2 \cdot CH_2O \cdot SO_2$ └──O──┘	*Aspergillus sydowi*
Chlorine substances		
Caldariomycin [7] (2:2-dichlorocyclopentane-1:3-diol) M.P. 121°C.	Cl_2 | C / \\ HCOH HCOH | | H_2C——CH_2	*Caldariomyces* (*Fumago*)
Erdin [8] M.P. 211°C.	$C_{15}H_7O_6(OCH_3)Cl_2$	*Aspergillus terreus*
Geodin [8] M.P. 235°C.	$C_{15}H_6O_5(OCH_3)_2Cl_2$	*Aspergillus terreus*
Griseofulvin [9] M.P. 218°–219°C.	OCH_3 =O H_3CO Cl O CH_3 $COOCH_3$	*Penicillium griseo-fulvum*
Arsenic and selenium substances [10]		
Dimethyl-*n*-propylarsine	$(CH_3)_2 \cdot As \cdot (C_3H_7)$	*Penicillium brevicaule*
Dimethyl selenide	$Se \cdot (CH_3)_2$	
Trimethylarsine	$As \cdot (CH_3)_3$	
Miscellaneous substances		
Mellein or ochracin M.P. 58°C.	O ‖ OH C O | $CH \cdot C_2H_5$	*Penicillium griseo-fulvum*, *Aspergillus melleus*, *Aspergillus ochraceus*

[6] Woolley and Peterson (1937).
[7] Clutterbuck, Mukhopadhyay, Oxford, and Raistrick (1940).
[8] Calam, Clutterbuck, Oxford, and Raistrick (1939).
[9] Oxford, Raistrick, and Simonart (1939).
[10] Thom and Raper (1932), Challenger and Rawlings (1936).

TABLE 21 (*Continued*)

MISCELLANEOUS METABOLIC PRODUCTS OF FUNGI

[From Iwanoff and Zwetkoff (1936), Birkinshaw (1937), Lockwood and Moyer (1938), Raistrick (1938, 1940), and Others]

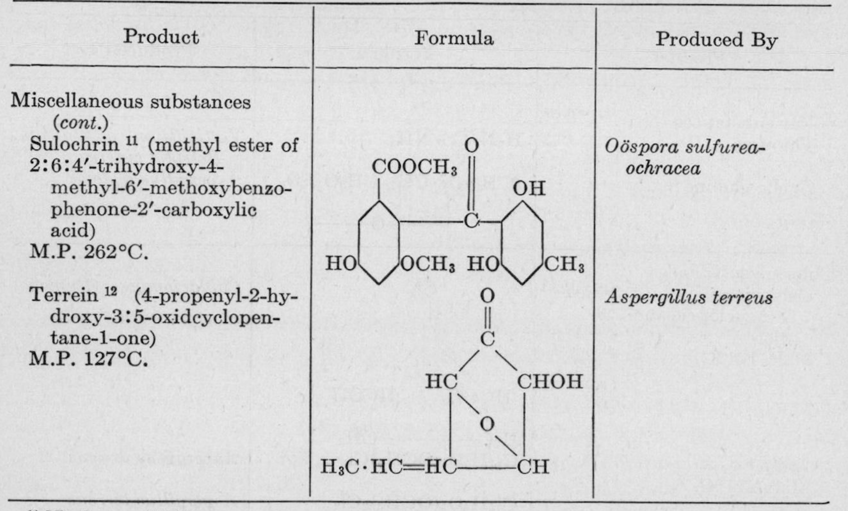

Product	Formula	Produced By
Miscellaneous substances (*cont.*)		
Sulochrin [11] (methyl ester of 2:6:4′-trihydroxy-4-methyl-6′-methoxybenzophenone-2′-carboxylic acid) M.P. 262°C.		*Oöspora sulfurea-ochracea*
Terrein [12] (4-propenyl-2-hydroxy-3:5-oxidcyclopentane-1-one) M.P. 127°C.		*Aspergillus terreus*

[11] Nisikawa (1940).
[12] Clutterbuck, Raistrick, and Reuter (1937).

rivatives of furane, tetronic acid, etc.) and benzenoid nuclei (derivatives of benzene, anthraquinone, etc.). Although several of these acids are synthesized in quite large quantities by certain fungi, little is known about the reasons for their elaboration.

For additional information on these miscellaneous acids the reports cited in Table 20, the collection of papers by Professor Raistrick and his associates (1931), and the extensive reviews by Iwanoff and Zwetkoff (1936), Clutterbuck (1936), Birkinshaw (1937), Lockwood and Moyer (1938), Raistrick (1938, 1940), and Tatum (1944) should be consulted.

MISCELLANEOUS METABOLIC PRODUCTS FORMED BY MOLDS

Quite a number of fungus-metabolic products other than acids are known chemically. These include various aldehydes, alcohols (for example, ethyl, glycerol, and mannitol), pigments, lipides and sterols, vitamins, chlorine- and arsenic-containing compounds, polysaccharides, and nitrogenous substances. Since certain of these substances, such as pigments, polysaccharides, and lipides, have been mentioned in Chapter 5, only a few additional compounds are listed here (see Table 21).

Most of the substances in Table 21 are of only academic interest, but they serve to show the diverse synthesizing powers of the molds.

REFERENCES

Andersen, A. A., and J. E. Greaves. 1942. *Ind. Eng. Chem.*, **34**:1522–1526.

Anslow, W. K., J. Breen, and H. Raistrick. 1940. *Biochem. J.*, **34**:159–168.

Arnaudi, C. 1939. *Boll. sez. ital., Soc. intern. microbiol.*, **11**:208–211 (1940. *Chem. Abstr.*, **34**:3301).

Arzberger, C. F., W. H. Peterson, and E. B. Fred. 1920. *J. Biol. Chem.*, **44**: 465–479.

Arzberger, C. F. 1943. U. S. Patent 2,326,425. Aug. 10.

Bakonyi, S. 1926. *Biochem. Z.*, **169**:125–128.

Banzon, J. 1941. *Iowa State College J. Sci.*, **16**:15–18.

Barham, H. N., and B. L. Smits. 1934. *Trans. Kansas Acad. Sci.*, **37**:91–113.

Barham, H. N., and B. L. Smits. 1936. *Ind. Eng. Chem.*, **28**:567–570.

Bauernfeind, J. C., J. C. Garey, W. Baumgarten, L. Stone, and C. S. Boruff. 1944. *Ind. Eng. Chem.*, **36**:76–78.

Beresford, H., and L. M. Christensen. 1941. *Univ. Idaho Agr. Expt. Sta. Bull.* 241. 28 pp.

Bergey, D. H., R. S. Breed, E. G. D. Murray, and A. P. Hitchens. 1939. *Bergey's Manual of Determinative Bacteriology*, 5th Ed. Williams and Wilkins Co., Baltimore.

Bergius, F. 1937. *Ind. Eng. Chem.*, **29**:247–253.

Bernhauer, K. 1924. *Biochem. Z.*, **153**:517–521.

Bernhauer, K., and N. Böckl. 1932. *Biochem. Z.*, **253**:16–24, 25–29.

Bernhauer, K., and Z. Scheuer. 1932. *Biochem. Z.*, **253**:11–15.

Bernhauer, K., and A. Iglauer. 1936. *Biochem. Z.*, **286**:45–59.

Bernhauer, K., and H. Thole. 1936. *Biochem. Z.*, **287**:167–171.

Bernhauer, K. 1939. *Gärungschemisches Praktikum*, 2nd Ed. Julius Springer, Berlin.

Bernhauer, K., A. Iglauer, and H. Knobloch. 1941. *Biochem. Z.*, **307**:293–297, 298–306.

Bertho, A. 1932. *Ergeb. Enzymforsch.*, **1**:231–269.

Bessey, E. A. 1935. *A Text-Book of Mycology*. P. Blakiston's Son and Co., Inc., Philadelphia.

Bilford, H. R., R. E. Scalf, W. H. Stark, and P. J. Kolachov. 1942. *Ind. Eng. Chem.*, **34**:1406–1410.

Birkinshaw, J. H., J. H. V. Charles, and P. W. Clutterbuck. 1931. *Biochem. J.*, **25**:1522–1539.

Birkinshaw, J. H., J. H. V. Charles, C. H. Lilly, and H. Raistrick. 1931. *Phil. Trans. Roy. Soc. London, B*, **220**:127–138.

Birkinshaw, J. H., and H. Raistrick. 1932, 1933, 1934, 1936. *Biochem. J.*, **26**: 441–453; **27**:370–375; **28**:828–836; **30**:801–808, 2194–2200.

Birkinshaw, J. H., A. E. Oxford, and H. Raistrick. 1936. *Biochem. J.*, **30**:394–411.

Birkinshaw, J. H. 1937. *Biol. Rev., Cambridge Phil. Soc.*, **12**:357–392.

Birkinshaw, J. H., A. R. Chambers, and H. Raistrick. 1942. *Biochem. J.*, **36**: 242–251.

Birkinshaw, J. H., A. Bracken, and W. P. K. Findlay. 1944. *Biochem. J.*, **38**: 131–132.

Birkinshaw, J. H., A. Bracken, and H. Raistrick. 1944. *Biochem. J.*, **37**:726–728.

Blom, R. H., D. L. Reed, A. Efron, and G. C. Mustakas. 1945. *Ind. Eng. Chem.*, **37**:865–870.

Boruff, C. S., B. Smith, and M. G. Walker. 1943. *Ind. Eng. Chem.*, **35**.1211–1213.
Braude, R., and A. S. Foot. 1942. *J. Agr. Sci.*, **32**:324–329.
Brown, R. W., G. L. Stahly, and C. H. Werkman. 1938. *Iowa State College J. Sci.*, **12**:245–251.
Browne, H. H. 1941. *Am. Chem. Soc., News Ed.*, **19**:1272, 1276.
Buchanan, R. E., and E. I. Fulmer. 1930. *Physiology and Biochemistry of Bacteria,* Vol. III. *Effects of Microorganisms upon Environment. Fermentative and Other Changes Produced.* Williams and Wilkins Co., Baltimore.
Burton, L. V. 1937. *Food Industries*, **9**:571–575, 617–618, 634–636.
Buswell, A. M., and W. D. Hatfield. 1939. *Illinois State Water Survey Bull.* 32. Urbana.
Butlin, K. R. 1936. "Survey of the Biochemical Activities of the Acetic Acid Bacteria." *Dept. Sci. Ind. Research, Chem. Research Special Rept.* 2. H. M. Stationery Office, London.
Butlin, K. R. 1938. *J. Soc. Chem. Ind.*, **57**:463–464.
Cahn, F. J. 1935. *Ind. Eng. Chem.*, **27**:201–204.
Calam, C. T., P. W. Clutterbuck, A. E. Oxford, and H. Raistrick. 1939. *Biochem. J.*, **33**:579–588.
Calam, C. T., A. E. Oxford, and H. Raistrick. 1939. *Biochem. J.*, **33**:1488–1495.
Carson, S. F., J. W. Foster, S. Ruben, and H. A. Barker. 1941. *Proc. Natl. Acad. Sci. U. S.*, **27**:229–235.
Castellani, A. 1931. *Ann. inst. Pasteur,* **47**:297–305.
Chain, E., H. W. Florey, M. A. Jennings, and T. I. Williams. 1943. *Brit. J. Exptl. Path.*, **24**:108–119.
Challenger, F., V. Subramanian, and T. K. Walker. 1927. *J. Chem. Soc.*, **1927**: 200–208.
Challenger, F. 1929. *Ind. Chemist,* **5**:181–184.
Challenger, F., L. Klein, and T. K. Walker. 1931. *J. Chem. Soc.*, **1931**:16–23.
Challenger, F., and A. A. Rawlings. 1936. *J. Chem. Soc.*, **1936**:264–267.
Chatterjee, N. P. 1942. *J. Indian Chem. Soc., Ind. and News Ed.*, **5**:201–205.
Christensen, L. M. 1944. U. S. Patent 2,344,025. Mar. 14.
Chrzaszcz, T., and K. Leonhard. 1936. *Biochem. J.*, **30**:1947–1952.
Clutterbuck, P. W., H. Raistrick, and M. L. Rintoul. 1931. *Phil. Trans. Roy. Soc. London, B,* **220**:301–330.
Clutterbuck, P. W., and H. Raistrick. 1933. *Biochem. J.*, **27**:654–667.
Clutterbuck, P. W., H. Raistrick, and F. Reuter. 1935. *Biochem. J.*, **29**:300–321, 871–883, 1300–1309.
Clutterbuck, P. W. 1936. *J. Soc. Chem. Ind.*, **55**:55T–61T.
Clutterbuck, P. W., H. Raistrick, and F. Reuter. 1937. *Biochem. J.*, **31**:987–1002.
Clutterbuck, P. W., S. L. Mukhopadhyay, A. E. Oxford, and H. Raistrick. 1940. *Biochem. J.*, **34**:664–677.
Connstein, W., and K. Lüdecke. 1919. *Ber. deut. chem. Ges.*, **52**:1385–1391.
Cori, C. F. 1942. *Proc. Am. Soc. Brewing Chemists, 5th Ann. Meeting,* May 25–27. 9 pp.
Cori, G. T., and C. F. Cori. 1943. *J. Biol. Chem.*, **151**:57–63.
Cruess, W. V. 1938. *Commercial Fruit and Vegetable Products*, 2nd Ed. McGraw-Hill Book Co., New York.
Currie, J. N. 1917. *J. Biol. Chem.*, **31**:15–37.
Davies, R., and M. Stephenson. 1941. *Biochem. J.*, **35**:1320–1331.

Davies, R. 1942, 1943. *Biochem. J.*, **36**:582–599; **37**:230–238.

DeBecze, G., and M. Rosenblatt. 1943. *Am. Brewer*, **76**(2):11–16, 30, 32, 34.

Doelger, W. P., and S. C. Prescott. 1934. *Ind. Eng. Chem.*, **26**:1142–1149.

Donker, H. J. L. 1926. "Bijdrage tot de Kennis der Boterzuurbutylalcohol en Acetongistingen." Dissertation, Technische Hoogeschool, Delft, Holland. W. D. Meinema, Publisher, Delft.

Duchenne, J. O. 1942. *Proc. 16th Ann. Congr. So. African Sugar Tech. Assoc.*, **1942**:45–47 (1942. *Chem. Abstr.*, **36**:7226).

Dunn, C. G. 1934. "A Biochemical Investigation of the Metabolic Activities of *Bacillus technicus*." Thesis, Massachusetts Institute of Technology, Cambridge. [Original not seen; quoted by Prescott and Dunn (1940)].

Emde, H. 1935. *Biochem. Z.*, **275**:373–374.

Endo, S. 1938. *Biochem. Z.*, **296**:56–70.

Eoff, J. R., W. V. Linder, and G. F. Beyer. 1919. *Ind. Eng. Chem.*, **11**:842–845.

Fang, S.-F. 1940. *Hwang-Hai*, **1**(5):5–8 (1940. *Chem. Abstr.*, **34**:6008).

Farbenindustrie, A.-G., I. G. 1942. German Patent 727,555. Oct. 1 (1943. *Chem. Abstr.*, **37**:6817).

Fetzer, W. R. 1930. *Food Industries*, **2**:489–491.

Foote, M., E. B. Fred, and W. H. Peterson. 1930. *Centr. Bakt., II Abt.*, **82**: 379–389.

Foster, J. W., and S. A. Waksman. 1939. *J. Am. Chem. Soc.*, **61**:127–135; *J. Bact.*, **37**:599–617.

Fred, E. B., W. H. Peterson, and J. A. Anderson. 1923. *Ind. Eng. Chem.*, **15**:126.

Fred, E. B., W. H. Peterson, and M. Mulvania. 1936. *J. Bact.*, **11**:323–343.

Frey, A., and H. Glück. 1939. U. S. Patent 2,146,892. Feb. 11.

Frey, A., H. Glück, and H. Oehme. 1939. U. S. Patent 2,166,047. July 11.

Frey, C. N. 1930. *Ind. Eng. Chem.*, **22**:1154–1162.

Frey, C. N., G. W. Kirby, and A. Schultz. 1936. *Ind. Eng. Chem.*, **28**:879–884.

Fulmer, E. I., and C. H. Werkman. 1930. *An Index to the Chemical Action of Microorganisms on the Non-Nitrogenous Organic Compounds.* Charles C. Thomas Co., Springfield, Ill.

Fulmer, E. I., L. M. Christensen, and A. R. Kendall. 1933. *Ind. Eng. Chem.*, **25**:798–800.

Fulmer, E. I. 1936. *Ind. Eng. Chem.*, **28**:778–782.

Fulmer, E. I., J. W. Dunning, J. F. Guymon, and L. A. Underkofler. 1936. *J. Am. Chem. Soc.*, **58**:1012–1013.

Gabriel, C. L. 1928. *Ind. Eng. Chem.*, **20**:1063–1067.

Gabriel, C. L., and F. M. Crawford. 1930. *Ind. Eng. Chem.*, **22**:1163–1165.

Gallagher, F. H., H. R. Bilford, W. H. Stark, and P. J. Kolachov. 1942. *Ind. Eng. Chem.*, **34**:1395–1397.

Garrett, J. F. 1930. *Ind. Eng. Chem.*, **22**:1153–1154.

Gastrock, E. A., N. Porges, P. A. Wells, and A. J. Moyer. 1938. *Ind. Eng. Chem.* **30**:782–789.

Gill, A. 1919. *J. Soc. Chem. Ind.*, **38**:273T–282T, 411T–412T.

Giordani, M. 1939. *Chimica e industria (Italy)*, **21**:265–272.

Gould, B. S. 1938. *Biochem. J.*, **32**:797–802.

Gould, B. S., and A. A. Tytell. 1941. *J. Gen. Physiol.*, **24**:655–667.

Gray, W. D. 1941. *J. Bact.*, **42**:561–574.

Green, A. A., G. T. Cori, and C. F. Cori. 1942. *J. Biol. Chem.*, **142**:447–448

Green, A. A., and G. T. Cori. 1943. *J. Biol. Chem.*, **151**:21–29.

Green, D. E., W. W. Westerfeld, B. Vennesland, and W. E. Knox. 1941, 1942 *J. Biol. Chem.*, **140**:683–684; **145**:69–84.

Groschke, A. C., and H. R. Bird. 1941. *Maryland Agr. Expt. Sta. Bull.* A-6: 145–172.

Guymon, J. F., L. A. Underkofler, and E. I. Fulmer. 1941. *Proc. Iowa Acad. Sci.*, **48**:212–223.

Haehn, H. 1938. British Patent 488,464. July 7 (1939. *Chem. Abstr.*, **33**:310).

Hammer, B. W., G. L. Stahly, C. H. Werkman, and M. B. Michaelian. 1935. *Iowa Agr. Expt. Sta. Res. Bull.*, **191**:381–407.

Handren, R. T. 1943. *Chem. Industries*, **53**:350–352.

Hanes, C. S. 1940. *Proc. Roy. Soc. London, B*, **129**:174–208.

Hansen, A. E. 1935. *Food Industries*, **7**:277, 312.

Hanson, F. S. 1942. *Paper Trade J.*, **115**(24):37–40.

Hao, L. C., E. I. Fulmer, and L. A. Underkofler. 1943. *Ind. Eng. Chem.*, **35**: 814–818.

Harden, A. 1932. *Alcoholic Fermentation.* Longmans, Green and Co., New York and London.

Henrici, A. T. 1930. *Molds, Yeasts and Actinomyces.* John Wiley and Sons, Inc., New York.

Henrici, A. T. 1941. *Bact. Rev.*, **5**:97–179.

Hermann, S. 1929. *Biochem. Z.*, **205**:297–305; **214**:357–367.

Hermann, S., and P. Neuschul. 1935. *Centr. Bakt., II Abt.*, **93**:25–31.

Herrick, H. T., and O. E. May. 1928. *J. Biol. Chem.*, **77**:185–195.

Herrick, H. T., R. Hellbach, and O. E. May. 1935. *Ind. Eng. Chem.*, **27**:681–683.

Hildebrandt, F. M., and N. M. Erb. 1939. U. S. Patent 2,169,246. Aug. 15.

Hildebrandt, F. M. 1941. *Food Industries*, **13** (Dec.):62–63.

Hildebrandt, G., and W. Klavehn. 1934. U. S. Patent 1,956,950. May 1.

Hitchner, E. R. 1934. *J. Bact.*, **28**:473–479.

Hoehn, W. M., L. H. Schmidt, and H. B. Hughes. 1944. *J. Biol. Chem.*, **152**: 59–66.

Hsieh, K.-C. 1939. *Hwang-Hai*, **1**(3):1–3 (1940. *Chem. Abstr.*, **34**:2129).

Hughes, H. B., and L. H. Schmidt. 1942. *Proc. Soc. Exptl. Biol. Med.*, **51**:162–163.

Iwanoff, N. N., and E. S. Zwetkoff. 1936. *Ann. Rev. Biochem.*, **5**:585–612.

Jacobs, P. B., and H. P. Newton. 1938. *U. S. Dept. Agr. Misc. Publication* 327. 130 pp.

Janke, A., and S. Kropacsy. 1935. *Biochem. Z.*, **278**:37–59.

Johnson, M. J., W. H. Peterson, and E. B. Fred. 1931. *J. Biol. Chem.*, **91**:569–591.

Johnson, M. J., W. H. Peterson, and E. B. Fred. 1933. *J. Biol. Chem.*, **101**:145–157.

Joslyn, M. A. 1940. *Wallerstein Labs. Commun.*, **3**:30–43.

Joslyn, M. A., and M. A. Amerine. 1941. *Calif. Agr. Expt. Sta.* (*Berkeley*) *Bull.*, **651**:1–186.

Kamlet, J. 1943. U. S. Patent 2,314,831. March 23.

Kane, J. H., A. Finlay, and P. F. Amann. 1943. U. S. Patent 2,327,191. Aug. 17.

Katagiri, H., and K. Kitahara. 1933. *Mem. Coll. Agr. Kyoto Imp. Univ.* 26, pp. 1–29 (1933. *Chem. Abstr.*, **27**:3235).

Kelly, F. C. 1936. *One Thing Leads to Another.* Houghton Mifflin Co., Boston

Keyes, D. B. 1943. *Wallerstein Labs. Commun.*, **6**:134 (abstr.).

Killeffer, D. H. 1927. *Ind. Eng. Chem.*, **19**:46–50.

Kinoshita, K. 1929. *J. Chem. Soc.* (*Japan*), **50**:583–593 (1931. *Chem. Abstr.*, **25**:5664).

Kinoshita, K. 1931. *Acta Phytochim.* (*Japan*), **5**:271–287.

Kluyver, A. J. 1931. *The Chemical Activities of Microorganisms.* University of London Press, London.

Kluyver, A. J., and L. H. C. Perquin. 1933. *Biochem. Z.*, **266**:82–95.

Kluyver, A. J. 1935. *Ergeb. Enzymforsch.*, **4**:230–273.

Kluyver, A. J., and C. Schnellen. 1937. *Enzymologia*, **4**:7–12.

Knobloch, H., and H. Mayer. 1941. *Biochem. Z.*, **307**:285–292.

Knudson, L. 1913. *J. Biol. Chem.*, **14**:159–184, 185–202.

Krebs, H. A., and L. V. Eggleston. 1941. *Biochem. J.*, **35**:676–687.

Kresling, E. K. 1940. Russian Patent 56,741. March 31 (1942. *Chem. Abstr.*, **36**:2994).

Kuo, C.-L. 1939. *Hwang-Hai*, **1**(2):11–19 (1940. *Chem. Abstr.*, **34**:2129).

Langlykke, A. F., W. H. Peterson, and E. McCoy. 1935. *J. Bact.*, **29**:333–347.

Langlykke, A. F., W. H. Peterson, and E. B. Fred. 1937. *J. Bact.*, **34**:443–453.

Lawrie, J. W. 1928. *Glycerol and Glycols. Production, Properties and Analysis.* (Chemical Catalog Co., Inc., New York) Reinhold Publishing Corp., New York.

Lees, T. M. 1944. *Iowa State College J. Sci.*, **19**:38–40.

Liebmann, A. J. 1942. *Wallerstein Labs. Commun.*, **5**:131–137.

Lipmann, F. 1941. *Advances in Enzymol.*, **1**:99–162.

Lockwood, L. B., and A. J. Moyer. 1938. *Botan. Rev.*, **4**:140–164.

Lockwood, L. B., B. Tabenkin, and G. E. Ward. 1941. *J. Bact.*, **42**:51–61.

Lockwood, L. B. 1942. *Mfg. Confectioner*, **22**(9):12–13.

Lockwood, L. B., and G. E. Ward. 1945. *Ind. Eng. Chem.*, **37**:405–406.

Mamoli, L. 1938. *Ber. deut. chem. Ges.*, **71**(2):2701–2703.

Mamoli, L., and G. Schramm. 1938. *Ber. deut. chem. Ges.*, **71**(2):2698–2701.

Mamoli, L., R. Koch, and H. Teschen. 1939. *Naturwissenschaften*, **27**:319.

Marvel, C. S., and A. E. Broderick. 1925. *J. Am. Chem. Soc.*, **47**:3045–3051.

May, O. E., H. T. Herrick, C. Thom, and M. B. Church. 1927. *J. Biol. Chem.*, **75**:417–422.

May, O. E., and H. T. Herrick. 1930. *Ind. Eng. Chem.*, **22**:1172–1176.

May, O. E., A. J. Moyer, P. A. Wells, and H. T. Herrick. 1931. *J. Am. Chem. Soc.*, **53**:774–782.

May, O. E., G. E. Ward, and H. T. Herrick. 1932. *Centr. Bakt., II Abt.*, **86**:129–134.

May, O. E., H. T. Herrick, A. J. Moyer, and P. A. Wells. 1934. *Ind. Eng. Chem.*, **26**:575–578.

McCoy, E., E. B. Fred, W. H. Peterson, and E. G. Hastings. 1926, 1930. *J. Infectious Diseases*, **39**:457–483; **46**:118–137.

Meyerhof, O. 1942. *Wallerstein Labs. Commun.*, **5**:181–186.

Meyerhof, O. 1943. *Wallerstein Labs. Commun.*, **6**:19–25; *Am. Brewer*, **76**:26–29, 74, 76.

Michaelian, M. B., and B. W. Hammer. 1935, 1936. *Iowa Agr. Expt. Sta. Re search Bull.*, **179**:203–227; **205**:203–214.

Mickelson, M. N., and C. H. Werkman. 1940. *J. Bact.*, **39**:709–715.

Morikawa, K. 1927. *Bull. Agr. Chem. Soc. Japan*, **3**:28–32.

Morikawa, K., and S. C. Prescott. 1927. *J. Bact.*, **13**:58.

Moyer, A. J., O. E. May, and H. T. Herrick. 1936. *Centr. Bakt., II Abt.*, **95**: 311–324.

Moyer, A. J., P. A. Wells, J. J. Stubbs, H. T. Herrick, and O. E. May. 1937. *Ind. Eng. Chem.*, **29**:777–781.

Moyer, A. J., E. J. Umberger, and J. J. Stubbs. 1940. *Ind. Eng. Chem.*, **32**:1379–1383.

Moyer, A. J., and R. D. Coghill. 1945. *Arch. Biochem.*, **7**:167–183.

Negelein, E., and H. Brömel. 1939. *Biochem. Z.*, **303**:231–233.

Nelson, M. E., and C. H. Werkman. 1935, 1936. *J. Bact.*, **30**:547–557; **31**:603–610.

Nelson, M. E., and C. H. Werkman. 1940. *Iowa State College J. Sci.*, **14**:359–365.

Neuberg, C., and E. Reinfurth. 1918. *Biochem. Z.*, **89**:365–414; **92**:234–266.

Neuberg, C., and B. Arinstein. 1921. *Biochem. Z.*, **117**:269–314.

Neuberg, C. 1942. *Am. Brewer*, **75**:22–30.

Nisikawa, H. 1940. *Bull. Agr. Chem. Soc. Japan*, **16**:97–99.

Nord, F. F. 1939. *Ergeb. Enzymforsch.*, **8**:149–184.

Nord, F. F. 1940. *Chem. Rev.*, **26**:423–472.

Norman, A. G. 1937. *The Biochemistry of Cellulose, the Polyuronides, Lignin, etc.* Oxford University Press, New York.

Norman, A. G., and W. H. Fuller. 1942. *Advances in Enzymol.*, **2**:239–264.

Northrop, J. H. 1919. U. S. Patent 1,293,172. Feb. 4.

Northrop, J. H., L. H. Ashe, and R. R. Morgan. 1919. *Ind. Eng. Chem.*, **11**:723–727.

Northrop, J. H., L. H. Ashe, and J. K. Senior. 1919. *J. Biol. Chem.*, **39**:1–21.

Olive, T. R. 1936. *Chem. Met. Eng.*, **43**:480–483.

Osburn, O. L. 1935. *Iowa State College J. Sci.*, **10**:97–98.

Osburn, O. L., and C. H. Werkman. 1935. *Ind. Eng. Chem.*, **27**:416–419.

Osburn, O. L., R. W. Brown, and C. H. Werkman. 1937. *J. Biol. Chem.*, **121**: 685–695.

Osburn, O. L., R. W. Brown, and C. H. Werkman. 1938. *Iowa State College J. Sci.*, **12**:275–284.

Oxford, A. E., and H. Raistrick. 1932. *Biochem. J.*, **26**:1902–1906.

Oxford, A. E., H. Raistrick, and P. Simonart. 1935, 1939. *Biochem. J.*, **29**:1102–1115; **33**:240–248.

Pasternack, R., and E. V. Brown. 1940. U. S. Patent 2,197,021. April 16.

Peckham, G. T., Jr. 1944. *Chem. Eng. News*, **22**:440–444.

Perlman, D. 1944. *Ind. Eng. Chem.*, **36**:803–804.

Pervozvanskiĭ, V. V., and M. A. Ivashkevich. 1939. *Microbiology (U.S.S.R.)*, **8**:339–352 (1940. *Chem. Abstr.*, **34**:7321).

Peterson, W. H., E. B. Fred, and J. H. Verhulst. 1921. *Ind. Eng. Chem.*, **13**: 757–759.

Peterson, W. H., and E. B. Fred. 1932. *Ind. Eng. Chem.*, **24**:237–242.

Pitcher, W. H. 1941. *Iowa State College J. Sci.*, **16**:120–121.

Porges, N., T. F. Clark, and E. A. Gastrock. 1940. *Ind. Eng. Chem.*, **32**:107–111.

Porges, N., T. F. Clark, and S. I. Aronovsky. 1941. *Ind. Eng. Chem.*, **33**:1065–1067.

Porges, N., T. F. Clark, and E. A. Gastrock. 1942. *Iowa State College J. Sci.*, **16**:451–469.

Porter, R., C. S. McCleskey, and M. Levine. 1937. *J. Bact.*, **33**:163–183.

Prescott, S. C., and C. G. Dunn. 1940. *Industrial Microbiology.* McGraw-Hill Book Co., New York.
Raistrick, H., and A. B. Clark. 1919. *Biochem. J.*, **13**:329–344.
Raistrick, H., J. H. Birkinshaw, J. H. V. Charles, P. W. Clutterbuck, F. P. Coyne, A. C. Hetherington, C. H. Lilly, M. L. Rintoul, W. Rintoul, R. Robinson, J. A. R. Stoyle, C. Thom, and W. Young. 1931. *Phil. Trans. Roy. Soc. London, B*, **220**:1–367.
Raistrick, H., and P. Simonart. 1933. *Biochem. J.*, **27**:628–633.
Raistrick, H., and G. Smith. 1933. *Biochem. J.*, **27**:1814–1819.
Raistrick, H. 1938. *Ergeb. Enzymforsch.*, **7**:316–349.
Raistrick, H. 1940. *Ann. Rev. Biochem.*, **9**:571–592.
Reichstein, T., and A. Grüssner. 1934. *Helv. Chim. Acta*, **17**:311–328.
Reilly, J., W. J. Hickinbottom, F. R. Henley, and A. C. Thaysen. 1920. *Biochem. J.*, **14**:229–251.
Reynolds, H., C. S. McCleskey, and C. H. Werkman. 1934. *J. Infectious Diseases*, **55**:207–219.
Reynolds, H., B. J. Jacobsson, and C. H. Werkman. 1937. *J. Bact.*, **34**:15–20.
Reynolds, H., and C. H. Werkman. 1937. *J. Bact.*, **33**:603–614.
Roberts, M., S. Laufer, E. D. Stewart, and L. T. Saletan. 1944. *Ind. Eng. Chem.*, **36**:811–812.
Robinson, G. C. 1922. *J. Biol. Chem.*, **53**:125–154.
Rosten, M. 1941. *Pulp Paper Mag. Can.*, **42**:558–562.
Sakaguchi, K., T. Inoue, and S. Tada. 1939. *Centr. Bakt., II Abt.*, **100**:302–307.
Scheffer, M. A. 1928. "De Suikervergisting door Bacterien der Coli-groep." Dissertation, Technische Hoogeschool, Delft, Holland. W. D. Meinema, Publisher, Delft.
Schmidt, L. H., H. B. Hughes, M. H. Green, and E. Cooper. 1942. *J. Biol. Chem.*, **145**:229–236.
Schoen, M. 1928. *The Problem of Fermentation. The Facts and the Hypotheses.* Chapman and Hall, Ltd., London.
Schoene, L., E. I. Fulmer, and L. A. Underkofler. 1940. *Ind. Eng. Chem.*, **32**:544–547.
Schofield, M. 1943. *Food*, **12**:315–316.
Scholler, H. 1936. *Chem.-Ztg.*, **60**:293–296.
Schreder, K., R. Brunner, and R. Hampe. 1934. *Biochem. Z.*, **273**:223–242.
Simon, E. 1943. *Nature*, **152**:626–627.
Singleton, P. A. 1943. *Wallerstein Labs. Commun.*, **6**:133–134 (abstr.).
Sjolander, N. O., A. F. Langlykke, and W. H. Peterson. 1938. *Ind. Eng. Chem.*, **30**:1251–1255.
Smit, J. 1930. *Die Gärungssarcinen.* Gustav Fischer, Jena.
Smith, G. 1942. *An Introduction to Industrial Mycology*, 2nd Ed. Edward Arnold and Co., Ltd., London.
Smith, L. T., and H. V. Claborn. 1939. *Ind. Eng. Chem., News Ed.*, **17**:370–371, 641.
Smyth, H. F., and W. L. Obold. 1930. *Industrial Microbiology. The Utilization of Bacteria, Yeasts and Molds in Industrial Processes.* Williams and Wilkins Co., Baltimore.
Speakman, H. B. 1920. *J. Biol. Chem.*, **41**:319–343.
Speakman, H. B. 1923. *J. Biol. Chem.*, **58**:395–413.
Speakman, H. B. 1925. *J. Biol. Chem.*, **64**:41–52.

Stahly, G. L., and C. H. Werkman. 1942. *Biochem. J.*, **36**:575–581.

Stanier, R. Y., and G. A. Adams. 1944. *J. Bact.*, **47**:411–412.

Stanier, R. Y., and S. Fratkin. 1944. *J. Bact.*, **47**:412; *Can. J. Research*, **22**:140–153.

Stephenson, M. 1939. *Bacterial Metabolism.* Longmans, Green and Co., London and New York.

Stiles, H. R., W. H. Peterson, and E. B. Fred. 1929. *J. Biol. Chem.*, **84**:437–453.

Stiles, H. R., and L. M. Pruess. 1938. *J. Bact.*, **36**:149–153.

Stone, R. W., and C. H. Werkman. 1936. *Iowa State College J. Sci.*, **11**:1–3.

Stubbs, J. J., L. B. Lockwood, E. T. Roe, B. Tabenkin, and G. E. Ward. 1940. *Ind. Eng. Chem.*, **32**:1626–1631.

Stubbs, J. J., L. B. Lockwood, E. T. Roe, and G. E. Ward. 1943. U. S. Patent 2,318,641. May 11.

Sumiki, Y. 1933. *J. Agr. Chem. Soc. Japan*, **9**:714–716.

Swallen, L. C., and J. B. Tindall. 1942. U. S. Patent 2,294,346. Aug. 25.

Szücs, J. 1944. U. S. Patent 2,353,771. July 18.

Takahashi, T., and T. Asai. 1930, 1933. *Centr. Bakt., II Abt.*, **82**:390–405; **87**:385–412.

Takahashi, T., and T. Asai. 1933, 1936. *Centr. Bakt., II Abt.*, **88**:286–295; **93**. 248–252.

Takodoro, T. 1935. *J. Agr. Chem. Soc. Japan*, **11**:365.

Tanner, F. W. 1944. *Microbiology of Foods.* The Garrard Press, Champaign, Illinois.

Tarvin, N. R. 1941. U. S. Patent 2,260,126. Oct. 21.

Tatum, E. L., W. H. Peterson, and E. B. Fred. 1935. *J. Bact.*, **29**:563–572.

Tatum, E. L. 1944. *Ann. Rev. Biochem.*, **13**:667–704.

Tauber, H. 1943. *Enzyme Technology.* John Wiley and Sons, Inc., New York.

Taylor, R. L. 1943. *Chem. Industries*, **53**:53–55.

Thaysen, A. C., and H. J. Bunker. 1927. *The Microbiology of Cellulose, Hemicelluloses, Pectin, and Gums.* Oxford University Press, New York.

Thaysen, A. C. 1939. *Chemistry and Industry*, **1939**:685–689.

Thom, C., and M. B. Church. 1926. *The Aspergilli.* Williams and Wilkins Co., Baltimore.

Thom, C. 1930. *The Penicillia.* Williams and Wilkins Co., Baltimore.

Thom, C., and K. B. Raper. 1932. *Science*, **76**:548–550.

Tikka, J. 1935. *Biochem. Z.*, **279**:264–288.

Tilden, E. B. 1939. *J. Bact.*, **37**:629–637.

Tytell, A. A., and B. S. Gould. 1941. *J. Bact.*, **42**:513–526.

Underkofler, L. A., and E. I. Fulmer. 1937. *J. Am. Chem. Soc.*, **59**:301–302.

Underkofler, L. A., W. K. McPherson, and E. I. Fulmer. 1937. *Ind. Eng. Chem.*, **29**:1160–1164.

Underkofler, L. A., and J. E. Hunter, Jr. 1938. *Ind. Eng. Chem.*, **30**:480–481.

Underkofler, L. A. 1942. *Brewers' Digest*, **17**(12):29–32, 35(T195–198, 201).

Unger E. D., W. H. Stark, R. E. Scalf, and P. J. Kolachov. 1942. *Ind. Eng. Chem.*, **34**:1402–1405.

Unger, E. D. 1943. *Wallerstein Labs. Commun.*, **6**:134 (abstr.).

U. S. Treasury Department, Bureau of Internal Revenue, Alcohol Tax Unit. "Statistics on Alcohol." Fiscal year ending June 30, 1941.

Utter, M. F., and C. H. Werkman. 1941. *J. Bact.*, **42**:665–676.

van der Lek, J. B. 1930. "Onderzoekingen over de Butylalkoholgisting." Dissertation, Technische Hoogeschool, Delft, Holland. W. D. Meinema, Publisher, Delft.

van Niel, C. B. 1928. *The Propionic Acid Bacteria.* J. W. Boissevain and Co., Haarlem.

Vaughn, R. H. 1942. *Wallerstein Labs. Commun.*, **5**:5–26.

Virtanen, A. I., and M. Nordlund. 1933. *Biochem. J.*, **27**:442–444.

Visser't Hooft, F. 1925. "Biochemische onderzoekingen over het geslacht *Acetobacter*." Dissertation, Technische Hoogeschool, Delft, Holland.

von Loesecke, H. W. 1945. *Chem. Eng. News*, **23**:1952-1959.

Waksman, S. A., and D. Kirsh. 1933. *Ind. Eng. Chem.*, **25**:1036–1041.

Waksman, S. A. 1940. *Botan. Rev.*, **6**:637–665.

Waksman, S. A. 1943. U. S. Patent 2,326,986. Aug. 17.

Walmesley, R. A. 1939. U. S. Patent 2,235,056. March 18. British Patent 515,831. Dec. 5 (1941. *Chem. Abstr.*, **35**:6057).

Walsh, J. F., H. C. Needle, and R. E. Daly. 1939. U. S. Patent 2,143,359. Jan. 10.

Warburg, O., and W. Christian. 1941. *Naturwissenschaften*, **29**:589–590.

Ward, G. E., O. G. Pettijohn, L. B. Lockwood, and R. D. Coghill. 1944. *J. Am. Chem. Soc.*, **66**:541–542.

Wei, W.-T. 1939. *Hwang-Hai*, **1**(3):4–5 (1940. *Chem. Abstr.*, **34**:2129).

Weinstein, L., and L. F. Rettger. 1932, 1933. *J. Bact.*, **23**:74–75, **25**:201-238.

Weizmann, Ch., and B. Rosenfeld. 1937. *Biochem. J.*, **31**:619–639.

Weizmann, C. 1938. *Chemistry and Industry*, **1938**:1049–1050.

Wells, P. A., A. J. Moyer, and O. E. May. 1936. *J. Am. Chem. Soc.*, **58**:555–558.

Wells, P. A., A. J. Moyer, J. J. Stubbs, E. T. Roe, H. T. Herrick, and O. E. May. 1937. *Ind. Eng. Chem.*, **29**:653–656.

Wells, P. A., D. F. J. Lynch, H. T. Herrick, and O. E. May. 1937. *Chem. Met. Eng.*, **44**:188–190.

Wells, P. A., J. J. Stubbs, L. B. Lockwood, and E. T. Roe. 1937. *Ind. Eng. Chem.*, **29**:1385–1388.

Wells, P. A., and H. T. Herrick. 1938. *Ind. Eng. Chem.*, **30**:255–262.

Wells, P. A., and G. E. Ward. 1939. *Ind. Eng. Chem.*, **31**:172–177.

Wells, P. A., L. B. Lockwood, J. J. Stubbs, N. Porges, and E. A. Gastrock. 1939. *Ind. Eng. Chem.*, **31**:1518–1521.

Wendland, R. T., E. I. Fulmer, and L. A. Underkofler. 1941. *Ind. Eng. Chem.*, **33**:1078–1081.

Wentworth, T. O., D. F. Othmer, and G. M. Pohler. 1943. *Trans. Am. Inst. Chem. Engrs.*, **39**:565–578.

Werkman, C. H., and R. W. Brown. 1933. *J. Bact.*, **26**:393–417.

Werkman, C. H., R. W. Stone, and H. G. Wood. 1937. *Enzymologia*, **4**:24–30.

Werkman, C. H., and H. G. Wood. 1942. *Botan. Rev.*, **8**:1–68.

Werkman, C. H., and H. G. Wood. 1942. *Advances in Enzymol.*, **2**:135–182.

White, E. C., and J. H. Hill. 1943. *J. Bact.*, **45**:433–442.

Whittier, E. O., and J. M. Sherman. 1923. *Ind. Eng. Chem.*, **15**:729–731.

Whittier, E. O., and L. A. Rogers. 1931. *Ind. Eng. Chem.*, **23**:532–534.

Wiley, A. J., M. J. Johnson, E. McCoy, and W. H. Peterson. 1941. *Ind. Eng. Chem.*, **33**:606–610.

Willkie, H. F., and P. J. Kolachov. 1942. *Food for Thought.* Indiana Farm Bureau, Inc., Indianapolis. 209 pp.
Wise, L. E. 1943. *Paper Ind. and Paper World,* **24**:1223–1227.
Wood, H. G., and C. H. Werkman. 1934. *Proc. Soc. Exptl. Biol. Med.,* **31**:938–940.
Wood, H. G., and C. H. Werkman. 1936. *Biochem. J.,* **30**:48–53, 618–623.
Wood, H. G., C. Erb, and C. H. Werkman. 1937. *Iowa State College J. Sci.,* **11**:287–292.
Wood, H. G., and C. H. Werkman. 1940. *Biochem. J.,* **34**:129–138.
Woodruff, J. C., H. R. Stiles, and D. A. Legg. 1937. U. S. Patent 2,089,522. Aug. 10.
Woolley, D. W., and W. H. Peterson. 1937. *J. Biol. Chem.,* **122**:213–218.
Wünschendorff, M., and C. Killian. 1928. *Compt. rend.,* **187**:572–574.
Wynkoop, R. 1943. *Ind. Eng. Chem.,* **35**:1240–1242.
Yabuta, T. 1924. *J. Chem. Soc. Japan,* **125**:575–587.
Zaĭtsev, A. N. 1939. *Microbiology (U.S.S.R.),* **8**:584–595 (1941. *Chem. Abstr.,* **35**:2553).
Zerban, F. W., and L. Sattler. 1942. *Ind. Eng. Chem.,* **34**:1180–1188.
Zerner, E. 1920. *Ber. deut. chem. Ges.,* **53**:325–334.

MICROORGANISM INDEX

SUBJECT INDEX

HARPER ADAMS AGRICULTURAL
LIBRARY
COLLEGE